SCIENCE FOR THE ELEMENTARY SCHOOL TEACHER

A BLAISDELL BOOK IN SCIENCE AND EDUCATION

SCIENCE FOR YOU

Book One · CRAIG-BRYAN

Book Two · CRAIG-DANIEL

Book Three · CRAIG-HOPMAN-LEMBACH

Book Four · CRAIG-HURLEY

Book Five · CRAIG-HILL

Book Six · CRAIG-SHECKLES

Book Seven · CRAIG-JACKSON

Book Eight · CRAIG-URBAN

A Teacher's Edition of each book is available.
For all Information please write to
GINN AND COMPANY
BOSTON · NEW YORK · CHICAGO
ATLANTA · DALLAS
PALO ALTO · TORONTO

SCIENCE for

GERALD S. CRAIG

PROFESSOR EMERITUS OF NATURAL SCIENCES
TEACHERS COLLEGE, COLUMBIA UNIVERSITY

the Elementary School Teacher

FIFTH EDITION

BLAISDELL PUBLISHING COMPANY

A DIVISION OF GINN AND COMPANY

Waltham, Massachusetts · Toronto · London

Preface to the Fifth Edition

This book has been designed for classroom teachers in the elementary school. It has grown out of a conviction developed in my teaching experience in the elementary school that the basic information required for teaching science in the classroom should be included within the covers of one book.

It has been my purpose throughout the preparation of this edition, as in the case of the earlier ones, to write the kind of book that would enable teachers to learn more about science while teaching children. The book has been designed as a continuous source of information—a volume on a teacher's desk at home and at school to which she can turn for her planning of teaching-learning situations, and as a source which she might utilize during her instruction, even as she works with children in the classroom. Many teachers have been delighted to discover some of the older children spontaneously using the earlier editions in the furtherance of their study of science. Some have found this book useful in encouraging children who have developed special interests and abilities in certain aspects of science.

Many teachers with little or no education in science have taught science successfully in their classrooms by using the earlier editions of this book. I hope that many more teachers will enjoy happy and successful experiences with elementary-school science as a result of using this new edition.

In the preceding edition the consideration of science from the developmental point of view was much enlarged and improved. I attempted to integrate this point of view into all portions of the book and into all considerations of children in relation to science. One result of this attempt was that more attention was given to the education of young children, including the preschool and primary levels. The science for older children, too, was oriented toward child development. I have continued to integrate this point of view into the new material in this edition.

Science is an actve, dynamic field. Almost daily one hears of new scientific discoveries and inventions. With the fine assistance of my associates, I have attempted in this edition to provide classroom teachers with the most modern and authentic information that could be secured for each of the areas of science treated in this book. This applies not only to the experiences and meanings designed for children but also to the scientific hypotheses that are useful for teachers in developing their own conceptions of the universe.

More specifically, Chapters 7 and 11 have

been expanded in keeping with increased interest and knowledge of the universe, space exploration, the structure of matter, and man's use of raw materials. Those chapters dealing with the land, water, and interior of Earth have been revised. New knowledge of Earth's age has made necessary the revision of the material on the geologic timetable, radioactive dating, and the antiquity of fossils. There is additional material on plants, their use of water and nutrients, and the germination of seeds. Also included in this revision is new material on magnetism and electricity and on man's impact on the environment.

The earlier editions of this book found their way into many parts of the world. In this edition I have attempted to improve the original content by considering the teaching problems in various kinds of regions. Attention has been given to experiences with and interpretation of natural phenomena found in deserts, swamps, forests, prairies, and mountains; in northern, southern, and tropical regions. To accomplish this, it has been necessary to develop field centers and to work with teachers in many different places.

The earlier editions have been used extensively as a basal book in professionalized content courses in science, in institutions of teacher education, and in workshops and study groups in in-service education. I believe teachers and students will find this new edition even more useful for their needs in professional education in elementary-school science. Written as this book has been for constant use on the teacher's desk, it is well-designed for service as a basal book in any kind of professional education of classroom teachers in the elementary school in science.

It is impossible to give credit individually to all who have contributed to this book. I am indebted to countless students in my classes, to teachers whom I have visited in their classrooms, and to the many children I have taught, observed, and interviewed.

Research associates to whom special acknowledgment is due for the work in connection with the development of materials for the earlier editions are Katherine E. Hill, Charles K. Arey, John Urban, Elizabeth F. Feeney, Franklyn M. Branley, June E. Lewis, Catharine Bergen, and Eleanor Friend.

Louise Palmer Wilson, Lawrence C. Craig, Charles W. Harp, Etheleen Daniel, Alice M. Williams, Anees Adil, and Beatrice D. Hurley assisted in reading the manuscript of the earlier editions and made valuable suggestions.

In the work on the preceding edition, the research associates were Mary E. Sheckles, Julian Greenlee, John Garone, and Jerome J. Notkin. Alice Craig Erney assisted in the preparation of the manuscript. Alta Miller, and Anne Hopman contributed photographs of classroom situations, and ideas.

In the work on this edition, I am indebted to Wilhelmina P. Abelardo, Quezon City, Philippines, for the results of her careful experiments with static electricity in a tropical climate. Theodore C. Ridout was invaluable as a research associate. My wife, Prudence Bower Craig, participated in all phases of the writing and preparation of the material for this edition as well as of earlier ones.

G. S. C.

Contents

Part I

SCIENCE
AND THE
ELEMENTARY
SCHOOL

CHAPTER 1

Children and Science

Children Are Greater than Science. It has seemed necessary to the author of this book, as he and those associated with him have worked with science in elementary education, that he make certain that his thinking at all times involve a central concern for children. Science has its importance in elementary education *only* as it serves boys and girls and, through them, the democracies of which they are a part.

This stress on children rather than on science is stated here as a standard, or criterion, that we have attempted to live by as we have written this book. And we have constantly reminded ourselves of this standard as we have proceeded with our task, to make certain that we did not forget *children* in our development of the professional subject matter of science for classroom teachers.

It is easy for specialists to become enamored of their own special fields, and to lose sight of the learner. But the elementary school, with its great purpose, is no place for the specialist to "strut" his specialization. Rather, it is an institution in which a specialist must walk in true humility, for he has been permitted to live with, to teach, and to learn with children —the adults of tomorrow.

The question in the study of the curriculum can never be "What is best for science?" Rather the question must be "What is best for children?" The teacher must recognize always that children are *greater* than science.

Frequently we hear science personified in statements such as "science does this," as if science were a being, a personality. But science is inanimate. Science does nothing in and of itself. It is man who does things with science. Science decides nothing; but man makes decisions, although he may utilize the findings and techniques of science in reaching decisions. Science is the product of mankind; mankind is not the product of science, although man's ways of living will in turn be influenced by the science he himself has developed. It is good for us as elementary-school workers to realize that modern science is the result of the work of boys and girls, grown-up boys and girls of the past and present.

This book is written with an abiding faith in the potentialities of children. This faith comes as a result of the privilege of teaching and learning with children, and in living with them at home and at school over a period of many years. It is written in the belief that if we truly help the children in our democracies to become wise, we shall not need to be discouraged concerning the near or distant future. One can think of no vocation or profession (unless it be parenthood) that plays a greater role in the destinies of a nation and the world than that of the profession of elementary-school teaching (Chapter 2).

Elementary teachers work with the most precious material in the universe, the minds and characters of the young of the human race.

Science Learning Starts at Birth

The Developmental Point of View. Science in elementary education should be considered from a *developmental* point of view—a point of view that is sound with regard to both the fundamental nature of children and that of science. The fundamental characteristic that is common to both children and science is that both are actively involved in interpreting the objects and events of the environment, for science may be defined as man's attempt to explore, to interpret, and to operate with the materials and forces of the universe that surrounds him. Modern science grew out of this age-old endeavor of the human race. The individual, whether child or adult, attempts from birth to death to orient himself to his environment.

This indicates that the historic function of science—that of exploring or interpreting the events of the environment—is in keeping with the dynamic drives of children. We shall see from the content and procedures developed in this book that teaching and learning in the field of science can be consistent with the nature of children.

A Child Interprets His World—Science Is Man's Attempt to Interpret the Universe. The word *interpretation* is a more satisfactory and more inclusive term for describing what goes on inside a child, and within the field of science, than the word *explanation* or *understanding*. It will be illustrated at many points within this book that neither children nor scientists have final explanations or understanding of the happenings in the universe. But both children and scientists are involved in the active process of interpreting the physical world. Children use their sensory capacities and intelligence in making such interpretations, as we shall see (p. 7), and science can be characterized by a continual revision of content and techniques (p. 48). "Interpretation" is a dynamic term which allows for growth and development and is in keeping with the nature of active and growing children. It is also a term more in keeping, as we shall see later, with the modern concepts of science, as contrasted with the more traditional classical and absolute view of knowledge.

In this developmental view of science education, children do not come to school for the first time at "zero" in science learning. They have already reacted to gravity, energy, lightning, thunder, darkness, light, weather, and a host of other natural phenomena. They may bring with them misconceptions, superstitions, and fears, and become a liability to society; or they may come to school with a good attitude for learning and ready for the development of intelligent, resourceful behavior. The facts that a child lives in a universe that stimulates him to interact with it and that he is surrounded by other individuals with interpretations which they force upon him causes him to form interpretations in the preschool years.

Science learning, as defined in this book, begins in the cradle. As a child begins to have an awareness of his environment, he begins to develop learnings of various kinds. It will be worth while for us, as teachers and parents, to realize the significance of these early experiences. These learnings are the beginning of science education for a child. From a developmental point of view, therefore, the parent may be thought of as a child's first teacher of science.

By the time a child begins elementary school, it is quite likely that he has gained certain concepts of roughness, smoothness, sharpness, lightness, heaviness, shininess, dullness, brightness, darkness, speed, acceleration, inertia, firmness, stability, instability, transparency, opaqueness, translucency, hardness, softness, and many other characteristics found in his environment. He has the beginnings of an understanding of these concepts—concepts which are, in reality, abstractions. This is not to say he has learned all there is to learn about these abstractions; but what he has learned, associated as these concepts are with his experiences, is most fundamental.

Density is not an easy concept to understand in its total meaning. Yet children may secure a concept of density from their experiences, and it may be a working concept in that the children may recognize through kinesthetic senses that some things are heavy for their size, while others are light. A piece of balsa wood used in building a toy plane will be very light for its size, while a hammer may be heavy for its size.

Early learning in science, according to the developmental concept, is a result of the natural human drive for adjustment (p. 8). Much of the child's learning about his environment may be associated with what the adult usually calls "play." But much of this so-called "play" is a learning process through which a child learns to manage himself in a universe of matter and energy.

Learning through Experiences. We, as adults, are likely to overlook the significant learning about the environment that goes on in the early months of a child's life. Learning from experience that water can be poured from a cup, or that crawling over the edge of the bed will result in a fall, can be learning experiences with our Earth's gravitational field. Or again, attempts to catch the sun's rays or smoke may initiate children into a beginning awareness of the variety of things in his environment. Words for these things may follow weeks or months later, but the words have more meaning if there is already a personal association through the child's own experiences.

A mother in Ohio who kept anecdotal records of her son Jonathan's learnings about his environment relates that at fourteen months he tried to catch smoke and sunlight. He chased soap bubbles about the room and shrieked with anger when they burst and disappeared as he tried to pick them up. The emotion displayed by this fourteen-month-old child reveals there was indeed learning involved.

Jennie, two and one-half years old, fell off the sofa while playing by herself. She was not hurt and crawled back onto the sofa to repeat the experience. She did this a number of times, each time giving a cry of pleasure. She seemed to be enjoying these experiences. She then looked around for another place to fall from and had decided on the arms of the sofa, which were higher than the seat of the sofa, when she was stopped by her mother. Here we have a form of play on the part of a small child which involves an experience with Earth's gravitational field of force. The kind of experience Jennie had is so universal that the reader might almost question its being listed here as involving learning in science.

But had gravity become an erratic force, stronger at one time than at another as Jennie fell from the sofa while playing, a different behavior undoubtedly would have been developed by her. After having fallen down to the floor, had Jennie floated up toward the ceiling, she would have been a surprised little girl. One such experience would have profoundly influenced her outlook upon the physical world and her basic attitudes and fears. If all other boys and girls had had similar experiences with an erratic gravitational field, one would find an entire generation with different attitudes toward the universe about them—a generation with more cautious behavior. The author is not attempting to be absurd in describing Jennie as floating up, but rather to emphasize that there is significant learning in the simple, everyday experiences of young children. The behavior of children is profoundly influenced by the meanings they derive from these experiences.

The school and home should provide a wide choice of experiences for children. It should be kept in mind that children may as easily develop destructive as constructive habits, and behavior that indicates a feeling of responsibility for the environment is in large part the responsibility of both teacher and parent. Behavior patterns formed in the early years of life can become basic patterns for a lifetime.

In the preschool years children have a wide range of rich experiences with physical and biological phenomena. They have a variety of experiences, including those with friction, momentum, inertia, magnetism, static electricity, simple electric circuits, snow, ice, water, steam, melting, boiling, freezing, conditions necessary to certain living things, care of animals, seasonal change, the sun, the moon, stars, clouds, mirrors, magnifying glasses, evaporation, condensation, varieties of kinds of locomotion found in the animal world, animal mouths, ears, noses, coverings, balance with building blocks, wagons and tricycles, heat and cold, effects of seasonal change, different animal habitats in the community, solution of solids in liquids, molds, the large number of seeds produced by some plants, and so on.

We prefer to call the kind of meanings a young child may secure from such experiences "experiential meanings." The development of concepts of the environment may begin with the child's experiences in handling, feeling, holding, and smelling objects, in poking one's finger into them, in trying to grasp them, to pull them apart, and the many other activities observed in babies, young children, and, for that matter, in all of us. The point made here is that the experiential learnings begin before there are words and form a very basic structure for learning concepts at later levels. And we believe it is important in the home and at all levels—especially the nursery-school, kindergarten, and primary-school levels—for the child to have rich experiences with natural phenomena. The learning can be experiential—that is, based on experience—regardless of whether or not words are utilized to express the concept involved in the experience.

A Dynamic Psychology of Science Education

A discussion of the teaching of elementary science, therefore, naturally starts with two elements—a child and the environment. A child lives in the environment. In a sense, his environment begins with his skin, coming so close that it surrounds him continuously from birth to death. In another sense, the environment continually encroaches upon the individual, and there is a constant interchange of material between the two; otherwise death results. The environment has *meaning* for the individual, and the kind of meaning it possesses for him has much to do with the kind of individual he is. If he thinks his environment is filled with hostile spirits of which he is afraid, or if he thinks it operates on a set of freakish principles (such as lucky and unlucky numbers, and other superstitions), then he is likely to be one whose mental potentialities are stunted. If, on the other hand, the individual sees his environment as something that can be studied and intelligently utilized, he will have a more constructive outlook upon life. Man's growth, both individually and socially, is limited by the kind of meaning his environment has for him.

A child interacts with the environment whether he receives a good education or not. A definite task of the school is to guide this interaction in the direction of those meanings which are beneficial to the individual and to society. The most accurate information available is essential to the building of beneficial meanings. The most accurate information is secured from the field of science.

Many teachers of children find it useful to accept the viewpoint of a dynamic psychology for understanding children. Their ideas of children may be stated simply in such words as these: A child lives in a dynamic universe which is new to him. He is challenged by his many experiences. This universe is filled with a great variety of objects. He is impressed by the events (phenomena), small and large, occurring about him—events such as rusting, decay, rain, weathering of rocks, electrical shocks, thunder, wind, falling objects, birth, and death. He finds himself in normal circumstances tremendously stimulated, and turns naturally to exploring and learning.

A young child is naturally egocentric. He is not to be condemned for being so, for his learning must go on inside himself. His egocentricity grows out of his great potentialities for ceaseless drive and for adjustment to his environment and to his own needs and potentialities. His adjustment is a result of his own interpretations. As a result of his great drives and yearnings, he feels inside himself a whole gamut of emotions which are to him discoveries about himself. He may display grief, irritability, anger, restlessness, impatience, disappointment, and so on. Although such expressions are not to be condoned or encouraged in children, they are not to be considered evil in themselves, for out of these emotional drives have come and will come many of the great constructive developments of mankind, such as democracy, better living conditions, religious freedoms, and improved health.

A child is an energy system, and in all the universe we do not find anything more impressive. It is remarkable that out of the use of his energy, a child develops intelligence in a universe filled with such a vast variety of living and nonliving objects, an almost kaleidoscopic array of events and changes. Within his rapidly widening universe, the child attempts through every means available to him to identify himself and his "inheritance."

Viewing children from this dynamic point of view assists parents and teachers to understand that the drives of children, which are so frequently annoying to the adult, are potentially *constructive* traits.

Science Is a Result of Human Drives

In a very real sense, then, we might say that the potentialities of science are inside human beings. To make it more personal, we may think of these potentialities as being in such human beings as ourselves—teachers and children in the classroom. Indeed, science itself has grown out of this tremendous urge—this wonderful potentiality—on the part of mankind through the long centuries to understand the universe.

Man, from the remote past, has sought explanations for the things that happen in the world about him. The rainbow, birth, death, life, lightning, and other events have challenged him. He has frequently used great ingenuity and much fancy to develop explanations for the phenomena about him. In fact, these explanations have had much to do with man's actual adjustment to his environment (p. 81).

According to the developmental point of view, the origin of science is in man's distant past. An implication of this for teachers in the elementary school is that science need not be thought of as something foreign to them or to the children they teach. Science, as we know it today, with its discoveries and inventions, is the result of urges in men and women through the ages. We can see these same urges in children today, as they follow their natural drives and as they attempt to secure adjustment and equilibrium in a dynamic universe. They use the senses of smelling, tasting, feeling, seeing, and hearing, the kinesthetic sense, imagination, curiosity, energy, irritability, restlessness, play, response to external conditions—they use these senses and other partly understood drives deep within their natures to project themselves into the areas of the environment. They depend upon impulse, fancy, creative activities, and logical thinking, just as all of their ancestors did.

From the developmental point of view not all of science is difficult. On the contrary, from this point of view science is part of the earliest learnings of children. Furthermore, the technical, vocational, and specialized aspects of science have no function in elementary education. Elementary science is closely related to the experiences of children and to the kind of thinking they can do, so that teachers need have no fear of science or of teaching science. A teacher can learn the science that is needed while teaching at any level in the elementary school.

The fear of science felt by some adults is not usually found in children. The adult may have been conditioned to a dislike of science in part by previous contacts with science instruction at the high-school and college levels; whereas children, having felt no such conditioning, are still following their natural impulses. Teachers can free themselves from any such negative reactions if they will attempt to see the environment and science through the eyes of children. Encouraging children in a classroom to express themselves freely, without fear of being humiliated about their ideas of natural events, has assisted many teachers to understand children and at the same time to gain a new look at the world for themselves.

Children React Individually to the Environment

Throughout life an individual is being introduced to natural phenomena. Static electrical shocks, color, thunder, snow, running water, rusting, insects, and other phenomena in his surroundings, as well as those of his own body, may arouse his curiosity and demand explanation.

Teachers find that children react to their surroundings in many ways. Some delight at times in using their fancies in the explanation of phenomena, giving way to their imagination and creating their own explanations. While imagination should not be allowed to flourish unrestrained, it can be very helpful when properly guided.

Imagination is needed in the development of scientific hypotheses and theories. Many outstanding scientists have been men of ideas. However, they have rigorously checked their imagination by experiments, observation, and tested facts, and by the observations of other careful observers. Sometimes children in a class will report explanations with flights of imagination that will seem absurd to the adult. Teachers need to be well aware of the total growth of a child in such cases. The ideal is to have a child, as he proceeds through his education, learn to distinguish between the times he uses his imagination and the times he uses reliable information. Usually queries from the teacher or other pupils will suffice: "How much of what you have just said do you know to be true?" "How can we show that your ideas are accurate?" Frequently these questions call for the use of authoritative books, for excursions, or for experiments. In any case, children should not be penalized for displaying imagination, for it is not a trait to be inhibited, but rather one to be developed into a well-rounded total behavior pattern. It would be a dull human race if imagination were extinguished.

One dark day Susan, seven years old, said, "The sun is home in bed." Simple as the interpretation was, it had merit in that Susan attempted to relate her own observations and experiences to a phenomenon which for her needed explanation. It took the human race thousands of years to explain scientifically what Susan was trying to explain at the age of seven. Part of teaching skill involves knowing how and when to challenge the conceptions developed by children, and how to interpret the growth patterns of children as they learn about their environment.

Sometimes a child may rely heavily upon explanations which he has received from adults. Such explanations may not necessarily be reliable, for they may contain the inaccuracies of the adult's information as well as the possible error in the child's understanding of the adult's ideas. As a child progresses through the school, he should become increasingly aware of the importance of relying solely upon accurate sources of information.

What and How, Rather than Who. Of course, all of this calls for tact on the part of teachers, since the accuracy of the parents' knowledge may be involved. It should be remembered that no adult, teacher, parent, or scientist can be expected to have all the most accurate information on all subjects or, for that matter, on more than a few subjects if indeed, on any. Probably nothing will be as helpful in such situations as the teacher's admission that she is still learning, that sometimes she makes mistakes, that she is willing to listen to others' ideas, and that she is willing to use and rely upon the most reliable information available in all matters of vital importance. There is, then, no issue between a parent and a teacher about who knows the more. In science, by its very nature (p. 48), we are more concerned with *what* is the most reliable information, not with "*who* knows the most" or with "*who* is right." Science carries with it a mental hygiene for both children and adults, in that in its study one is concerned with the solution of problems rather than with merely proving people "right" or "wrong."

Variation in Abilities in Science. Many children display a somewhat passive attitude toward any attempt at interpreting the environment. They may show no curiosity or interest in investigation, or they may refuse to participate in group discussion. In some cases an individual child may remain passive because he recognizes that his activity in such directions would not compare favorably with that of his fellows. In other cases a child's home life may serve to repress interest and curiosity.

Sara, eight years old, had been with a group of children for two years. In her class there were a large number of boys and girls who were very much interested in studying science. For over a year and a half Sara participated so little that no one could have told whether she was interested or not. One day she came into the discussion with a naturalness and eagerness which amazed the observers. She continued to participate in this new way at intervals. The teacher wisely made no comment about Sara's long period of silence. Sara, feeling no embarrassment, from either praise of her new efforts or criticism of her previous silence, kept on with her new interest. No pressure had been exerted upon her during the long period of her silence. Those who observed were impressed with the quality of her

thinking. Apparently there had been growth along with the others, although there had been little overt behavior on which this thinking could have been evaluated.

Teachers should expect to find differences in the ways in which children respond to science, and should not strive to make the children's reactions identical. Some children are interested in physical and biological phenomena and can exercise leadership in science activities; others will display little or no leadership. Teachers can utilize the natural leadership in the class to improve creative class discussion and planning, performance of original experiments, and the interpretation of content in reading material. A teacher can also encourage superior children to pursue their special interests. The fact that some children have individual science interests does not indicate that every member of the class must have them. All teachers must expect individual differences in science, for the interplay of inheritance and environment makes for basic differences in the individuals themselves. Variation is a characteristic of life and adds to the richness of the characteristics of human beings and of all living things. The elementary school must respect this fundamental aspect of human beings.[1]

Children having special abilities in certain aspects of science should be guided to share their knowledge and skills with others in a cooperative fashion. The talented child may need to learn how to recognize merits in others. A teacher may cater so much to the superior child that undemocratic behavior is promoted. The elementary school has a contribution to make to all, and we would like to feel that all children are equally important in the elementary school, regardless of their future position in society.

There have been many cases where a child who expressed himself very infrequently

[1] See the treatment of "There Are Great Variations in the Universe . . . Variety," p. 97.

turned out to be the one who was doing the most profound thinking. The spirit of the discussion should be such as to encourage this type of child to share his thinking with his fellows.

A large class of seven- and eight-year-olds showed wide individual differences. Some children would remain in a group discussion for long periods of time (if allowed to do so) and would speculate with the teacher concerning the nature of other planets, the adaptations of animals, and other matters. These children enjoyed such discussion so much that it was more like play to them than work. They intensified their study through their reading and reported back on their own problems. However, for others in the group twenty minutes of this kind of discussion was too much, and these children became restless if they were kept in the discussion for a longer time.

The teacher involved in this instruction allowed, and even encouraged, any who wished to leave the group to do so and to take over other activities, such as art or reading, when the "tempo" and "rhythm" set by the smaller group of eager students was too much for them. It was interesting to note, however, that these children were being observed carefully by the rest of the class—frequently to such an extent that they stopped their new activities to go back to the science discussion, sometimes to listen and sometimes to participate.

Children vary in the length of time they can concentrate on the kind of activities required in science—activities such as investigating, experimenting, discussing, developing explanations, and reading for information. And there is no reason why the teacher should attempt to level off a group. Individual differences should be considered, of course, and certain children should be especially encouraged to pursue the kind of individual activity that seems to be beneficial to them. However, in the interest of democracy, and because of the vital nature of science in modern life, there should be some teaching-learning activities that are common to all the children in a class. The significance of this can be better understood in relation to the purpose of the elementary school in a democracy (p. 34). Individuals who can do more than others through their own individual enterprise should be encouraged to do so; however, these children should report back to the entire group whenever possible.

Variation in a Child's Behavior. Children vary from time to time in kinds of behavior. A six-year-old, on the western slope of the Rocky Mountains, disappeared from his family group one day. From somewhere in the basement came a light hammering. In approximately an hour Jimmy emerged from the basement and exhibited four blocks of wood, fastened together by nails in such a way as to represent a tugboat and three barges. This child had made a brief visit during the previous summer to a busy seacoast harbor. This visit, in addition to a book about boats, seemed to have stimulated a relatively long period (an hour) of concentration. On the preceding afternoon the same child had been most restless about many activities, exhibiting little ability to concentrate on a single project for more than a few minutes at a time. Purpose, energy, imagination, and other drives can alter a child's ability to concentrate from moment to moment.

Children Are Continually Making Interpretations

Virginia, a ten-year-old from the state of Washington, said, "Days are shorter in winter because there is fog in the evening and in the morning."

Henry, a ten-year-old in the same school, said, "Winter comes because Earth is farther away from the sun in the winter."

Here we find proposed explanations which are not satisfactory as accurate explanations, but which have merit if one views a child's study of science as one of growth in interpreting the environment. They also serve to reveal to the teacher some information concerning the kind of thinking Virginia and Henry are capable of, as well as the nature of the ideas they hold. Instruction for any age level of the elementary school must begin at the growth level of the children. It is the teacher's responsibility to find how far each individual child has advanced in his growth toward important goals, and to evaluate his progress.

In their thinking children frequently attempt to relate cause and effect from the sequence of events they observe in the environment (p. 62). Sometimes they see two unrelated phenomena occurring at the same time and, as a result, associate the two in a cause-and-effect relationship. Charles, eleven years old, suggested that the radiator was magnetic because "the heat" attracted the needle. In this case Charles could be led to see the importance of testing his conclusion on a day when the radiator was not warm.

Children's suggestions or proposals can often be used to make instruction more vivid and to relate experience to meanings. Proposals can also provide opportunities to care for individual differences. A child capable of moving at an accelerated pace in science can be helped to do creative work growing out of his own proposals and suggestions, without interfering with the science activities of the entire group.

Lucille, ten years old, asks why it is that one tree grows up to become a maple while nearby another becomes an oak. This question is not to be treated lightly. A simple explanation may satisfy Lucille, such as calling her attention to the difference between oak and maple seeds. Then again, it may be that Lucille has in mind something more profound that would involve the simple elements of evolution, adaptation, inheritance, and the conditions necessary to life and reproduction. Discussion, observation, and guided reading may help this child to a better understanding and intelligent adjustment.

It is not always the wording of an inquiry that reveals a child's quality of thought. For example, children nine years of age engaged in a heated discussion about where cats came from. The teacher said, "From mother cats." But the children said, "Where do mother cats come from?" and "Grandmother cats?" and "Great-grandmother cats?" and so on. It was clearly not a case of facetiousness but rather a desire to push back to its origins an interest frequently displayed by children. This question could have involved the reproduction of a single species; then again, it could have involved tracing the problem back to the origin of cats from their wild forebears.

In teaching it should be kept in mind that the experiences a child has had greatly color his explanations of events. Out of the experiences he builds a working picture which he may use in explaining a new experience. Even his imagination grows out of his experience.

In most cases what may seem fantastic to the adult is drawn out of a child's interpretations of past experiences.

The fourteen-month-old child, Jonathan, expressed anger when the bubbles burst (p. 5). Perhaps to him the bubble seemed like a ball, and he expected to find that the bubbles had the same characteristics as other "balls." Other balls had been handled by Jonathan, so why shouldn't the bubble have been handled in the same way? Navarra, in his study of a three-year-old,[2] calls this attempt of children to postulate on past experiences "expectation." In Jonathan's case—as in many experiences of children, and of adults too—there is a second phenomenon involved. The second phenomenon is inside Jonathan in the form of an emotion. The emotional world inside the child is as much of a world of discovery for him as the world of material and energy that surrounds him. Who hasn't been amazed at some time or other by the world of emotions?

It would be well for the parent of a child like Jonathan to arrange other experiences with bubbles. Perhaps by repetition such a child would learn to accept the fact that not all round objects are like his plastic and rubber balls. Here we would find modification of the original interpretation that Jonathan made. He would soon learn that some things do not burst in his hand but other things do, such as bubbles. The learning is experiential in character; it probably involves almost no words, but does involve his special senses of seeing and feeling.

Children Repeat Experiences. Repetition of an experience is important in learning. Children's tendency to repeat over and over the same thing—filling a bottle with sand, shouting down a hallway, striking an object to

[2] John Navarra, *The Development of Scientific Concepts in a Young Child: A Case Study.* Teachers College, Columbia University, New York, 1955.

make a sound—reinforces learning. Repetition allows time, so important in learning. This allows a fuller penetration of the experience and may reinforce the memory.

Some children, five-year-olds, were playing with various objects at a tank of water. They tossed them in, one by one. Some floated, some sank. Then David tried to make one of the celluloid objects sink but it would not. Sally, watching David's inability to make the object stay under water, pushed the object clear to the bottom. It was as though she expected the depth of the water to sink the object. Both seemed a little puzzled for the moment but soon left the tank for other interests. Later in the day they returned and repeated these experiences, and this seemed to be somewhat in the nature of an experiment for these five-year-olds. Careful observation of children will show that this is a fairly normal pattern of behavior.

A child may repeat an action and get a variation. He may strike an object lightly and get a soft sound, or he may strike it with vigor and get a louder sound. Children may try out their shouting in different rooms and places and note the differences. Children do vary their actions and note the results of their variations.

Since the world is new to children, an adult can sometimes understand children better by studying his own reactions to something which is quite novel to him. The adult may have seen a sight that is entirely novel to him, perhaps in his travels. He looks and looks. He may use some of the other senses such as hearing, smell, and touch. In a day or so, if he is still in the same strange surroundings, he may repeat his observations. If the place or the experience has been especially challenging to him he will seem to drink up its special features. If the novel experience has had unusually pleasant, or even frightening, aspects he may often relive it in his memories.

Children will perform certain activities over

and over. They repeat an action. They repeat it again. Then they go off to some other activity, but they frequently return to the original activity and continue to repeat the experience.

Repetition of an experience with natural phenomena involving a sequence of events has the elements of continuity, suspense, and even some drama (Chapter 5). There is much of the dramatic and challenging in science. By observing children's own spontaneous activities—particularly the kind of thing they tend to repeat or talk over while studying some facet of science—a teacher can learn much about what has challenge for children.

In this type of repetition a child is employing spontaneously some of the principles of good concept formation. Repetition of experience reinforces the learning. Repetition may provide a child with opportunity to build a better mental image or working picture of a sequence of events. (See Experiences described in Parts II to IV.)

Children forcing an egg into a bottle, in the experiment described on page 438, usually call for a repetition of this experience. Observing it a number of times, they may have a better image of the sequence of events—the bouncing of the egg up and down on the top of the bottle, the extinguishing of the fire, the movement of the egg down into the bottle, the sound accompaniments, and so on. Since the sequence of events holds the key to the interpretation, repetition of the experience provides opportunity for children and teacher to think through an explanation.

Repetition may provide opportunities for a child to utilize additional senses more fully. The entire experience may utilize one or more of the special senses, such as seeing, smelling, tasting, hearing, and feeling, as well as the kinesthetic senses (p. 63).

The Role of the Emotions in Interpreting Experiences. Children may feel some emo-

tion in the process of repetition. In some cases children, and adults as well, may explore their own emotional capacity more or less subconsciously in the course of a repetition of an experience or in the prolongation of an experience.

The emotional aspect of science learning has been neglected in education. Science, although objective and realistic within itself, causes many-angled emotional impacts on society and on the individual. The emotions engendered by science are generally constructive and positive. As a matter of fact, science as an activity of man has had a most wholesome effect on his emotions and his ideals. One could turn to almost any subject matter found in this book and see ways in which it has impact on man's basic patterns of thinking and on his emotions (p. 45).

Children frequently respond with fine feeling during a discussion in science. It may be in response to such profound and universal ideas as time, space, change, adaptation, and so on (Chapter 4). Such feeling may be indicated in facial expressions. Children in stating hypotheses of their own are sometimes quite exultant. They also enjoy testing their hypotheses.

There is a constructive emotion which might be expressed as "a feeling of adequacy in being able to operate a toy or an appliance, or to control a situation." This emotion is often tied up in a feeling of belongingness, in a feeling of co-operative enterprise with one's classmates.

There may be a feeling of fear toward certain types of things. Some children pass through a period when they are afraid of very loud noises, such as train whistles, although they themselves may be quite a source of noise themselves. There is the emotion of anger when something breaks, as in Jonathan's case, or when something doesn't work. There may be the feeling of inadequacy when a child finds himself inferior to other children in his manipulations. There may be the fear of animals, of machinery, of thunderstorms. Teachers and parents need to be aware of the kind of emotions that are found in children in such learning situations.

It may be that the emotional aspects of some learnings in science are due to the physiological meaning of the learning to the learner. A study of the abstractions listed on page 5 as experiential learnings indicates that these abstractions of children grow out of experiences with their own bodies. For instance, gravity, balance, equilibrium, speed, inertia, and heat may have definite meanings in terms of experiences in the past. We might say these ideas are based on memories of bodily impressions. As a result, science learning uniquely involves both the body and the mind as an integrated unit. It is only natural under such an arrangement that there should be an emotional aspect to science education.

There are many ways in which science is related to emotions. There are emotional feelings of appreciation of what one finds to be profound or beautiful in the universe. There are emotions that grow out of the discoveries and applications of science. These emotions may be positive and constructive, filling one with feelings of poise, purpose, stability, optimism, and fulfillment. At times, however, the emotions may be negative and destructive, in that the progress of science has unleashed energies with which man may not be able to cope. There are emotions in the face of uncertainty that can be quite negative. A task of the school today is to help children to face uncertainty with intelligent resourcefulness (p. 74).

We see from this that emotions are of necessity a part of one's reactions to life. There is a need of recognizing the constructive role they can play in the education of children in science in a democracy. The role of emotions in the development of behavior patterns is discussed in Chapter 3, "The Nature of Science and Its Implications for the Education of Children."

Children Reconstruct Their Ideas of Their Physical Environment

Children, by their very nature, must revise their ideas as they have new experiences. They reconstruct their ideas of the universe and of their relation to it even as they go forward to meet new experiences. In a sense, their behavior corresponds to an industry, a home, or a new school building in which the normal activities are continued even as the building, including the foundation, is being rebuilt. There are many instances in which children reconstruct for themselves in a short span, even in a few minutes, what seem to be very fundamental ideas of the world about them. They continue on to new experiences even though the old foundation of their understanding is abandoned and a new one proposed. A study of children's ideas reveals children in a wholesome learning situation much of the time or in the continued process of reconstruction of their ideas.

One may even say that children abandon and reconstruct their ideas of the environment more readily than the average adult. Indeed, children make much more *profound* changes in their interpretations than adults do, and they make such changes in basic ideas almost continuously. A child may accept fairies one week and begin to abandon them as possibilities the next week. In fact, the younger the child, the more basic the interpretations that are involved, because the young child is building the framework of his ideas of the nature of the universe.

This ability of children to reconstruct their ideas is an important ability to preserve in education. The progress made by the human race would never have resulted without this ability. The last three or four generations, especially, have been forced, frequently by necessity, to change their ideas as a result of new discoveries and inventions. A generation is needed which is educated to expect change and to direct the change to the welfare of all.

Children Develop Hypotheses. Sammy, a boy of five, living in the western United States, was playing with a top to which had been fastened a long, glittering ribbon. When Sammy threw the top into the air, the ribbon would make a beautiful streamer which followed the top as it fell. So Sammy was enjoying his own newly created plaything. An eighteen-year-old friend happening by became interested in Sammy's new plaything, too, so he threw the object into the air. Unfortunately, it landed on the roof of Sammy's house. Sammy was dismayed and began to cry at what he thought was the permanent loss of his new toy.

Jess, a five-year-old living next door, heard Sammy cry and rushed over to find what was causing his friend such distress. When he learned about the difficulty from Sammy, he gave him this advice: "Don't cry, Sam. The wind will blow it down."

Jess stated a hypothesis. Furthermore, it had the ingredients of a good hypothesis because it was based on experience. Sammy and Jess lived in a region where the wind can blow at times with considerable force.

Children Use Their Imaginations. The ability of children to use their imaginations helps them in the development of hypotheses

(p. 58). Observations of children in normal, spontaneous activities will reveal that they frequently weave their imagination into the real, everyday experiences of life. Yet an examination of that imagination will reveal a basis in experiences they have had, a basis in their own sensory experiences or in experiences from stories they have heard or read.

Many adults find children willing to think in terms of the very small, such as the particles of an atom, or in terms of the very large, such as the vastness of space, with its galaxies of stars. Frequently an adult is less willing to tear himself from the world of normal reality.

Children Anticipate Happenings (Phenomena). Navarra has indicated[3] that the beginning of the process of developing hypotheses may begin in the element of anticipation, or expectation, of the early experiences of small children (p. 5).

The fourteen-month-old child, Jonathan, was previously described as displaying anger when bubbles which he tried to pick up burst in his hands. Perhaps if we could analyze what went on inside him we might find there was something in the nature of a hypothesis that determined his behavior. He treated the bubbles as he did the balls. His anger grew out of disappointment when his expectations or anticipations were shattered. His expectation that bubbles can be handled is in the nature of a hypothesis.

The ability to develop hypotheses begins in the early months of life. The genesis of hypothesis-making was well advanced for Jennie, repeatedly falling off the sofa in Colorado (p. 5), for she anticipated, or expected, the process of gravitation to be the same on all her repetitions of the experiment. Children early develop expectations.

Children crying for attention at night stop when they hear the parent approaching. Here learning is a sequence of events; that is,

[3] John Navarra, op. cit.

the sound of the parent getting nearer, then the parent, then the kind words, the personal attention, and the drink of water.

Later we shall discuss how a parent and a teacher can use this drive in children—this power of expectation—to encourage them to use their intellectual powers in solving problems (pp. 112–119) and in developing resourceful behavior patterns (pp. 74–77). By providing opportunities for children to state their own ideas, the adult also provides himself with avenues for evaluating children's thinking.

Concept Development in Children Is a Dynamic Process.[4] Frequently adults disparage children's recollections of past events because the concepts of time expressed by the children do not conform to the adult's standard of time. They point to the confusion young children have with ideas of "yesterday," "today," and "tomorrow," and to their difficulty in realizing there is a year between Christmases and birthdays (pp. 93–94). Adults should consider children's concepts of time from a developmental point of view, for this will help them to understand that children's ideas of time require time for development, through experience. Such a point of view will also give the adult a better appreciation of children's memories. A sympathetic adult can greatly stimulate the growth of a child's concept of time, by beginning with the child's own concept, helping the child to enlarge it, and thus assisting him to a better perspective for his own memories.

Time is a large element in learning, and the concept of time is never fully mastered by any

[4]Mary Sheckles, *Building Children's Science Concepts: Experiences with Rocks, Soil, Air, and Water.* Teachers College, Columbia University, New York, 1958.

individual. Adults must be understanding and must try to provide children with opportunities to gain improved concepts of time.

Jean, a three-year-old on an all-day trip to visit her grandparents, began after half an hour to ask, "When will we get to Grandma's?" This question was repeated at frequent intervals. By late afternoon, the comment was, "My! Won't we ever get to Grandma's?" This was said with considerable feeling.

One can look at Jean's experience with impatience and say that Jean had little concept of time or distance. Such an explanation would not be one based on a dynamic view of the child, or of the universe, but would be a negative approach.

A better interpretation is the positive, dynamic one. Jean was having learning experiences. She was making associations of time with distance. She was learning about the extent of time, the length of day. She still had more to learn about time—she always will have. Jean's learning, like much learning in science about the phenomena of time, was accompanied by the development of emotion.

Children do remember many experiences of the past. Mary, five and a half years old, said, "I remember your house, because we could run around and around in it." She was recalling the arrangement of rooms, which provided the children with ample space to play games indoors, although it had been over a year, or a fifth of her lifetime, since she had been in this particular home.

As we shall see later, experience is a large factor in learning science. A teacher can utilize the experiences of children in teaching science by encouraging them to draw on their past experiences through discussion and creative activities of all kinds.

Interpretations Differ with the Maturity of Children

Adults are apt to overlook the most elementary learning in young children. A mother was watering a plant potted in dry soil. Her two-year-old daughter, who was observing, exclaimed in surprise, "Oh, Mother, the water goes down!" This child's statement might seem, on the surface, so obvious as to warrant scarcely any attention; yet the child was undoubtedly making important associations between this and past experiences. She was taking an intelligent and active interest in her environment.

As the child matures, he profits from past experiences and utilizes old learnings in interpreting new situations. More complex concepts emerge under the expert guidance of the teacher. It is not a simple concept, that water goes down when the plant is watered; at later levels of development it involves an awareness of gravity, the absorption of water in the soil, the escape of air bubbles, the realization of water as a condition necessary to life, and so on. As the child matures, he can weave in more relationships and build up new concepts. Water and its relation to living things, for example, may be seen as an important element in determining habitats and in understanding geography.

Thus we see simple learning elements added one to another to form new concepts, which in turn are added to other concepts. In this way the maturing child grows toward an understanding of the basic principles of science which explain a wide range of the phenomena of living and nonliving things. Such principles of science as space, time, change, adaptation, interrelationships, balance, and variation may become, in turn, fundamental to the development of vital attitudes on social problems.

As the child grows in science, his ability to think in terms of space and time enlarges, and he begins to associate natural phenomena and other events over longer periods of time and over larger stretches of space. In this sense the pattern of science learning is continually one of growth. Thus, since the basic principles of the universe are never fully mastered, individuals can continue to develop more accurate and more profound meanings about science principles throughout life.

Children can supplement their observation and experimentation by utilizing authoritative science books in developing meanings. Interests may flow out of reading, and the teacher has the task of associating the reading with suitable experiences.

Children Have a Sense of Humor. Frequently children's proposals have a fine quality of humor. The moments in teaching can be very rich when there has been a warm flow of laughter through the classroom, when both children and teacher have joined in the fun. Such a thing occurred in a discussion in a rural classroom in North Carolina in which there were children of much farm experience. An attempt had been made to draw some meanings about the word "animals." Upon questions being raised about mules—a thirteen-year-old, rather large for his age, spoke with a whimsical voice and a smile on his face, "Mules? Why, mules are mules." The class, children from the farm who had ample experience with mules, rocked with wonderful laughter that was refreshing to adult and children alike. To a farm boy who thought there was no need of looking for any further classification for a mule, it was not a refusal to learn but a fine bit of humor which could only be appreciated by those who know mules. There is no better tonic for good relationships in the classroom than a good laugh (but never to humiliate an individual) in which the teacher participates.

Humor can be a part of science instruction.

It can grow out of the science instruction and lead back into it. Interpretations about the universe will frequently appear to children as humorous. Douglas, eleven years old, at the close of a group discussion asked the instructor very seriously, "Are we animals?" The instructor gave an affirmative answer, whereupon Douglas went chuckling out of the room. He accepted the fact, but he found it humorous.

Adults Affect Children's Interpretations

In a midwestern village a gardener named Dave Cheney called across a street to an eight-year-old, "Hey, boy, do you want a cat?" The eight-year-old sprinted gleefully across the street, only to have a spitting, scratching kitten thrust into his hands. This kitten was not like any the eight-year-old had experienced. It was a frightened kitten, snatched cruelly from its mother by Dave who was annoyed to find a litter of kittens on his premises.

There was no fear of the kitten—only surprise—on the part of the child, in spite of the scratches. He held the kitten firmly but with a feeling of kindness, although this fighting, living, furry mass was anything but pleasant. The eight-year-old, quite carefree a few minutes before, found himself suddenly responsible for a helpless but frightened small animal.

The boy began to plan for this kitten as he trudged home. He dreamed about gentling this little kitty so it might become a sleek, handsome, dignified cat like some of the cats he knew in the village. But his dreams were soon shattered as he reached home. The adults manifested fear and alarm at the sight of the defensive little kitten and questioned the child's intelligence at being such an easy mark for old Dave's cunning. The behavior

of the adults changed his attitude from benevolence to that of fear. The change was so great that the emotion of disappointment and grief for the loss of his dream affected his appetite for several days.

Adults very frequently fail to consider the effect of their own behavior upon children. Adults can be so blind to the ideals and dreams of children! How many times adults enter and trample down the altars of the inner shrines of children!

Five-year-old James, playing in the yard, was attracted by the movements of a garter snake. It was his first encounter with a reptile. Fascinated by this creature which gracefully glided out of his way, he had no feeling of fear. He ran into the house to tell of his discovery. He knew no name for the animal, so he got down on the floor and imitated the snake. The older members of the family indicated their concern and ran into the yard to kill the snake. The child, observing the adults, changed his attitude from curiosity to fear, and the new attitude toward snakes was so strongly embedded that it remained into adulthood.

We encounter another illustration of the way adults influence children's interpretations of their environment when we consider the feelings engendered between racial or religious groups. Small children of different groups will play together with little or no sense of discrimination unless some adult introduces his prejudices. The new attitude thus introduced may become fixed and may exert a strong, intolerant influence on the emotions and the quality of citizenship.

A six-year-old white girl was visiting with her parents at a home on an Indian reservation in Arizona. She was playing with a group of Indian children and was overheard to suggest "Now, let's play Indian, shall we?" "Playing Indian" was a game, and she saw no relation between these Indian children and the game.

Sometimes explanations given by adults are mixtures of fact, superstition, and misinformation. For the child, the result is unwholesome attitudes and maladjustments. It is not so much the lack of reliable information that is to be regretted as it is the maladjustment that comes about because the child does not know what is reliable information, nor how and where it is to be secured.

In one family the mother was very much frightened by electrical storms. At such times she would gather the children about her in a dark closet, deep in the interior of the house. One of the daughters, since grown to adulthood, tells of her compelling desire now to rush outside during an electrical storm. Sometimes, as in this case, an adult's behavior will have exactly the opposite effect, and the behavior of the children, when they are free to choose for themselves, will be the reverse of that recommended by their parents.

The School and Home Should Help Children to Orient Themselves to Their Environment. Kenneth, a child of kindergarten age, looked from a window down upon the street. He pointed to the scene below. "There's Broad Street. There's the five-year-old playground. There's the court. There's where Daddy goes to work. Grandpa and Grandma live over there." The teacher stood by, an interested listener, as this child oriented himself with his world.

This aspect of orientation to the world should be a continuous process, involving orientation not only to space but also to social groups and issues. In this work the teacher and the parent should be sympathetic listeners and guides.

The individual's environment or world should be continuously expanded. Children may be taken to places which give them a view over the community, such as a hilltop or a roof. They may point out the things they recognize—mountains and hills, lakes and rivers, railroads, factories, farms, and the activities of people. The teacher can then enlarge on their environment, adding details as the children seem able to understand them. Later, points beyond the horizon can be mentioned—towns and cities to which the highways and railroads lead, the county seat, the capital city of the state, some great neighboring industrial center. Much of this orientation can come about naturally.

With this kind of work there should be a large globe in each schoolroom. To small children it can soon become a familiar object in their environment. A small lump of modeling clay can be placed on the globe to represent their town or city.

As the child grows, his environment or world should be enlarged to include the state or province, the country, the nation, other nations, the solar system, the Milky Way, the other galaxies. These should not be considered discrete units, to be mastered once for all time; for one can be learning something about several or all of them at a given level. Free discussion of the children's observations and interpretations will help to develop meanings (pp. 124–126).

In the later years of the elementary school the expansion of the child's world should include the idea of different kinds of living conditions found in the world. This type of development can be greatly enriched by a study of the conditions necessary to life, by experimentation with growing plants and taking care of animals at school and at home, observation on field excursions, and reading in authoritative books for children.

As a child orients himself to the environment, it is only natural that there should be some margin for error in his thinking and that misconceptions should develop occasionally. We must not expect the young learner necessarily to be able easily to draw valid conclusions. Frequently misconceptions are indications of active minds, of attempts to associate scraps of information from various sources and to mix it all with fancy. The following is a bit of conversation overheard in the kindergarten:

Mildred to Henry: "How far away is the sun?"

Henry: "It is away up in heaven."

Mildred: "It isn't in heaven at night, 'cause I saw it come down."

James to Mildred: "Well, God can't sleep with the sun in his eyes, so he sends it down."

In this anecdotal record, we see a fleeting picture of children attempting to explain something. There has been an association of information, gained from adults, with experience and observation, altogether a wholesome process. Too frequently adults in their own evaluation of children's thinking are inclined to emphasize the error in the child's thinking because they disregard the elements that differentiate good and bad thinking. The *total* growth of the child is the most important factor to be considered.

Perhaps in the teaching of elementary science there has been more misunderstanding about this issue of learning patterns than about any other. There are some who think of science in terms of distinct units, with a number of content items to be memorized quite exactly. There are others, fortunately, who think of a child as growing continuously toward an intelligent adjustment to his environment. Such a teacher offers a child guidance in accordance with the values she holds worth while.

This does not indicate the abolishment of written curriculum materials and children's books in science. Quite the contrary. The teacher will need the assistance of what has been determined, by careful curriculum studies, to be the kind of interpretations that children require for individual growth and social progress. These goals cannot be attained by hit-or-miss methods (Part V).

Providing Young Children with Opportunities for Safe Exploration. The nursery school, kindergarten, and early primary years should provide a wide scope of rich experiences with physical and biological phenomena (Parts II, III, and IV).

A teacher in a nursery school was greatly annoyed by one youngster who at almost every opportunity pushed blocks down an incline. When a student teacher indicated the kind of elementary knowledge the child was securing from those experiences, the classroom teacher viewed the child's activities in a new light and the conflict between teacher and child was ended.

The nursery-school teacher who provides opportunities for the child to explore his environment in a safe and sane way is giving the child assistance toward building constructive attitudes. The child's curiosity about his environment can be utilized to effect a wholesome adjustment. If, on the contrary, this curiosity is repressed, the child's normal orientation to his environment is stifled and maladjustments may result. The teacher of a young child needs to be expert in making provision for safe exploration, manipulation, and experimentation. This is no small order and no job for a novice.

Let us look at some further illustrations of how young children can be helped to orient themselves to their environment:

A group of eight-year-olds was confused by the difference between smoke and steam. The teacher helped by showing how each was produced.

Kindergarten children, playing in the school yard, learned that the sun did not shine on the same place all of the day.

Children digging in the ground learned of a great variety of living and nonliving things in the soil.

Children's Play Activities May Have Investigative Trends. Helen, Elizabeth, and Mary went about the nursery hitting all available objects with a small stick. After striking each, they would comment upon the similarity or the difference of sound. They asked the teacher why there was a difference in sound.

Helen and Willie were playing "horsie" in the nursery school yard when Willie, pausing for breath, discovered his shadow. After calling Helen's attention to it, they both ran about the yard and, in different places, would stop to look for their shadows. Once when they could not find their shadows, Willie declared, "We left them over by the steps."

Patricia brought a small horseshoe magnet to her kindergarten class, and in opening the door to the locker room brought the magnet into contact with the key. The key was attracted to the magnet. The children wanted an explanation. Under the teacher's guidance, various kinds of objects were brought near the magnet.

In the nursery school, Henry was riding a tricycle when he encountered an obstacle. First he was baffled. Later he tried to get over the obstacle by backing up and approaching it with greater velocity.

Play should be considered as one avenue to the study of science. It required skill to know just how much instruction should follow the situations described. With small children the particular interest may be fleeting but may return unexpectedly a week or a month later. In all cases the teacher will do well to watch the children's reactions, both as individuals and as a group, to all activities. The wise teacher is one who knows how to add enough but not too much information. Many adults tend to swamp a child with mature information at the least signs of inquiry. The primary concern should be to stimulate the child to further inquiry.

When considering how to respond to young children's interest in science stemming from play, many teachers have found it desirable to ask themselves, "How may the child be challenged in useful directions?" With small children it may often be done by providing manipulation with materials that direct the experience toward the correct explanation, as in the illustration with the magnet given above. All investigation growing out of play should be viewed as a part of the whole pattern of growth for the child, rather than as a complete unit in itself. The teacher should realize that the child will have other opportunities in his life to continue with the lines of thought introduced in these simple activities. Always the teacher should be an interested and attentive observer, and, best of all, a participant in the activity.

Play is useful in creating interest and in developing functional observations and basic knowledge. However, even when inquiring about phenomena around them, children usually do not care to have their play stopped for a serious discussion.

The play tendency with physical phenomena is not outgrown after early childhood. It is found in later childhood—even in adulthood—and quite properly so.

Strictly speaking, an experiment is not play; it is a serious way of solving problems. Nevertheless, many children consider experimenting an enjoyable experience. The materials for experiments should, in general, be simple; they should be such as are usually available in the community. The materials should be those which have meaning to children. The use, in the elementary school, of the traditional equipment used in the high-school sciences cannot be defended in terms of a developmental point of view in science.

Children's Interest in Natural Phenomena. Children may be interested in a wide variety of scientific phenomena—living things, mechanics, Earth forces, movement, energy, balance, and so on.

The interest of children can be broadened and deepened through a stimulating environment. Books, experiments, excursions, and discussion can be used to good advantage in opening up new fields for study.

If a subject in science does not prove to be interesting to a class, the teacher can afford to question her own teaching methods or the appropriateness of the subject for that particular level of the child's growth. Usually the teacher can rely upon the natural challenge that resides within the area of science that she is teaching.

The child is studying about an active universe—a universe which is still new to him. It is a universe of big and little forces—a universe of big and little living things, a universe of materials of varying color, hardness, and other qualities. It is an intriguing universe; it has intrigued man for thousands of years.

Teachers should expect a wide span of differing interest in science. Some children will like to study animals; others, electricity; and still others, the stars. But by careful planning the teacher can cause a child who had shown an almost exclusive interest in animals to become interested in electricity, and so on. A teacher can help children develop an interest and a challenging attitude toward almost any subject in science, if the subject is properly ad-justed to their abilities and experiences. The development of challenge may depend as much on the teacher's knowledge of the children as on his knowledge of the subject itself. For if the right situations are set up, ordinarily children will take a large share of the responsibility for the study of science.

It is generally assumed that boys are more interested in electricity, mechanics, and other physical science subjects than are girls. What usually is not recognized is that the home and the school normally tend to condition girls from early childhood away from those interests which have been traditionally considered masculine. Girls are given dolls rather than electric trains or other mechanical toys; girls in some classrooms are seldom invited by teachers to take leadership in classroom tasks which involve manipulation, such as wiring electric bells or lights for a toy house.

But the modern housewife is one who operates a wide variety of electrical and mechanical equipment in her daily work, and it is likely that the home of the future will contain even more extensive mechanical and electrical improvements. The average woman has as much need to know about the proper use of electricity as the average man, if not more. Furthermore, women are proving to be successful research workers in the field of physical science.

Teachers have found that they can overcome much of this conditioning by encouraging the girls to participate in such experiments as wiring electric bells, playing with magnets, and similar activities. Grace, twelve years old, took pleasure in asking her father where the fuse box was in her home and telling him what she knew about fuses. Helen, seven years old, took her place with a group of boys and asked them to show her how to wire a bell; soon she was able to do it just as well as the boys.

As an observer of children over a period of more than thirty years, the author is strongly inclined to conclude, on the basis of anecdotal observations, that the western culture is much less inclined today to deny little girls the opportunities of mechanical experiences. Children see their mothers operating modern contrivances in the home. Two world wars, a Korean conflict and a "cold" war frequently growing hot have shown that a democracy needs resourceful women. Much can be done to make democracies strong, in peace and in war, if teachers and parents of young children encourage girls as well as boys to perform the practical and useful mechanical operations encountered in our daily living. There should be no discriminations in science on the basis of sex.

Studying Children While Teaching Science

What Kind of Boys and Girls Are We Developing? Teachers will find their teaching enriched if they will study children while they teach them. Science with its challenging content and its rich contribution to the attitudes and behavior of both adults and children offers unique opportunities for the study of children.

The greatest concern in studying children is not how much information children have secured, important as that may be. Rather, the main emphasis should be on what kind of boys and girls we have. What kind of thinking do they do? What are their outlooks upon the world? Are these outlooks constructive and democratic? Do the children think for themselves? Are they developing good ways of thinking? Are they learning to be resourceful? Are they developing responsibleness?

At all times teachers should be alert to the kind of behavior changes that occur in the children in their classes. The teacher may ask, "Are the children developing dogmatic attitudes, or are they willing to consider new ideas? Do they tend to accept every idea they hear without hesitation or discrimination? Do they look for further evidence before drawing conclusions? Are they learning to use and appreciate authoritative books? Do they report on out-of-school experiences in a whole-some way? Do they propose thoughtful explanations? Are they learning to plan? Can they work co-operatively with others? Do they have constructive outlooks? Are they realistic? Are they resourceful and responsible?"

In this kind of study it must be recognized that behavior may reflect the home and the general background of the children. A dogmatic parent may cause a child to lose initiative and independence, to become gullible and incurious.

Studying Spontaneous Behavior. It should be kept in mind that it is the behavior in which a child has been allowed considerable freedom of choice that is the most useful for evaluation. The closely worded or directed question of the quiz program and the rigid recitation have little significance in evaluating behavior. In a sense it is the *spontaneous behavior* of children which is useful for evaluation —the proposal of something to do, the inquiry, the choice of language which indicates open-mindedness, the critical-mindedness, poise, resourcefulness, the challenge of a statement, the willingness to consider new ideas and to take on new duties, the use of old learning in new situations. All of this seems to favor a type of discussion in science instruction which allows for freedom of expression and thinking.

A comment, reply, question, or some other proposal by children can have qualities of spontaneity and can arise naturally from instruction, particularly if it is developmental (Chapter 5). Anything a child or adult does in which there has been some freedom of choice is to that extent spontaneous. We frequently use the word "proposal" as a term to indicate any comment from children, whether it be a fact, a question, a problem, a bit of content, a tale of the imagination, or a hypothesis. The proposal, as we describe it, is something which comes out of the intelligence of the child and serves, to a degree, to reveal where he is in his thinking.

The developmental procedures in elementary science described in Chapter 5 leave a large opportunity for spontaneity. The question-and-answer procedure of the traditional recitation, however, where "correctness" depended upon a definite wording, left little freedom of choice and not much opportunity for spontaneity.

It is recognized in this that teachers need to study children as individuals and as groups and from a total, rounded-out viewpoint of education. Science, with its profound meanings, offers unique potentialities in studying children from this developmental point of view. Children should not be evaluated as if the development in behavior relating to science were isolated from all other aspects of their lives. Science, as an interpretation of the environment, should be thought of as an intrinsic part of the life of children in the modern world, a part that may be a very important factor in building desirable behavior.

Are the Children Developing Responsibleness and Resourcefulness? The human being, whether young or old, is an exquisite and complex being which has in it possibilities for a great variety of behavior. The human being can rise to heights of unselfish service to others, and at other times be petty and self-centered, a demon who appears to care little or nothing for others and snaps at anyone who would dare say "good morning" to him. Perhaps nowhere is the pattern "variety" (pp. (97–98) better exhibited than within a single human being. A child may be happy, tearful, sad, pugnacious or vindictive, depending upon the forces inside him and outside him. Like a great organ, a child has rich overtones and can be a melody of delight: yet at other times, when the environment and his own nature have reacted unfavorably upon him, he may seem like a "fury." There are so many forces within and without, inherited and environmental, which can play on children and to which they can react, that the human organism is never exactly the same from minute to minute.

A child is learning to operate with these forces in his early years. He can be conquered by those forces and become defeated, a timid or an overaggressive soul for his entire life, or he can learn to operate with and through these forces so that he becomes a resourceful and responsible individual in a democratic way of life. The understanding parent or teacher can do much toward determining the direction of a child's behavior patterns.

Many of a child's behavior patterns grow out of his experiences with the materials of the environment. The meanings he accepts from these experiences have much to do with the kind of individual he becomes. He may move through these experiences with the materials about him and tend to develop irresponsibility, which we might term a negative pattern, or he may tend to develop resourcefulness and responsibleness, which we might term positive patterns. The terms *resourcefulness* and *responsibleness,* because they constitute behavior patterns of great importance in a democracy, are evaluated in Chapter 2 and the development of such positive patterns in Chapter 3.

Developing a Concept of Ownership. One of the things a small child has to learn concerning the materials of his environment is the concept of ownership. This is not a simple concept. A child needs time to develop the idea that some things belong to him and some things belong to other people. He must learn early that some objects around him are not for his immediate use. The concept of ownership can be traced further, for he must learn that some things belong to his family and some things belong to the neighbors. One adult in midwestern United States can well remember the day when, as a very small girl, she extended the play space by opening the gate to the property next door. She only got as far as opening the gate, and the action of her parents at that point has lingered in her memory to this day. The concept "this is our yard, that is someone else's; you are not to go beyond that gate" was all too quickly learned. The teaching was powerfully motivated by the parents, but perhaps not too wisely, because this and similar incidents caused the child to develop an overly cautious and timid behavior that endured into adulthood.

A young child may take what belongs to someone else without any knowledge of wrongdoing, for he has not developed the concept of ownership. This attitude as it pertains to certain parts of the environment, has been carried into adulthood by some. Sometimes schools by encouraging children to bring things to school and build up collections unintentionally set up conflicting standards. More will be said about this when we discuss conservation as a pattern of behavior (p. 62).

It should be noted that ownership is a concept growing out of a culture. For instance, the concepts of ownership among the American Indians were very different from those brought to the Western Hemisphere by the European cultures. It is not our purpose here to develop in any detail the concept of ownership as it applies to behavior patterns; but it is necessary to recognize the concept if we are to study children's behavior patterns intelligently.

With this concept in mind, let us ask ourselves some questions about the children in our care: Do the children exhibit an awareness of property ownership? Do they borrow from each other? Do they return articles to the right owner? Do they recognize public property? How do they treat property? How do they react to "lost" materials they have found? Are they as careful of other people's property as they are of their own? Do they have a healthy respect for and understanding of the concept of ownership?

Studying How Children Interact with the Physical Universe. In the early months of a child's life, definite patterns of behavior begin to emerge in regard to the materials found about him. These patterns grow out of the interpretations a young child develops for himself through first-hand experience with these materials and through what he accepts from all that adults tell him. Emotions, as well as behavior patterns, are quite likely to be developed from these interpretations (pp. 51–77).

We should study children in reference to the way they work with materials. Do they tear the materials apart? Do they examine a toy with care? Are they afraid of the toy? Do they exhibit behavior in keeping with the rules of safety, or do they rush in to grab materials without thought? Do they push their hands about impulsively, or do they think through their behavior and act with poise? Do they assume responsibility for their actions? Do they exhibit care for a toy? Where do they leave it—in a safe place, or on the floor for others to kick about, break, or fall over? Are they curious about the toy's source of energy? Do they succeed in operating the toy? Do they use their imaginations as they play with the toy?

Of course all these appraisals of children's behavior must be made in terms of each child's growth and development, and such development is usually determined in large part by the child's present and past experiences.

A child tends naturally, as an active organism, to utilize the materials about him. He may use them for different purposes than those for which the materials were designed. He may use a delicate toy as a hammer or as a teething ring. Sometimes a child seems ruthless and destructive because he has toys placed in his path which have purposes he little understands.

James' father purchased an electric train for his five-year-old son. The father was quite disappointed with his son on Christmas morning because the boy was not willing to spend the entire morning playing with the electric train. James found other aspects of the environment equally interesting, as for instance the stuffed bear, the big colored ball, and some metal objects with which he could make a wide variety of interesting noises. This behavior of the five-year-old was not to be interpreted as a lack of interest in the electric train, but rather that this child had a wide variety of interests. The adult cannot impose his interests on children, but he can provide children with a wide variety of experiences.

A child's attempts to pull things apart are not necessarily associated with any bad motives. A child is a learning organism. His learning, to a very large degree, is learning about *objects,* both animate and inanimate. That things pulled apart or dropped may be broken and rendered useless are to be learned. How else is a child to learn such things except through observation and experience?

Overly Cautious Behavior. Donald, five years old, had his first experience with a bal-

loon. While blowing air into the balloon, it burst. The adults about him enjoyed the situation because Donald was greatly puzzled by the phenomenon. However, a lot of emotion was locked in Donald's question "Where is it?" How could anything as big as that balloon seemed to be when filled with air become reduced to but a fragment of rubber? In many ways it was a big experience in learning for a boy of five. It took him some time to adjust fully to the situation.

For a while Donald was overly cautious with all materials as a result of his experience with the balloon. Here was something easily destroyed. He became fearful that other toys would be easily destroyed. Had the adults treated this experience less as a joke and more as a thing which could be explained and predicted, Donald would have developed a less cautious attitude towards all other materials. Donald needed to learn that while some things are easily destroyed, other things wear out slowly and are not easily destroyed.

Impulsive Behavior. Like most behavior patterns, ideal behavior may be regarded as a balance between two extremes. It is not desirable for a child to grow up in life overly cautious, nor does one want him to develop reckless behavior.

Marie, nine years old, was irresponsible and careless with materials. In observing Marie at school and at home, one could not but be concerned about her own safety as well as that of her friends. The most innocent looking object seemed to become a lethal weapon as soon as it became a part of Marie's immediate environment.

In a classroom in New York state, a duck was given the freedom of the room. Walter, a ten-year-old, impulsively picked up the duck and placed it on his own shoulder. Of course the duck, not being equipped to maintain his footing on such a resting place, fell off the child's shoulder and hobbled off across the floor, leaving pools of blood behind it. The observer had reason to believe that in this particular behavior there were no sadistic tendencies. After studying the boy, it was apparent that he had not been taught at home or at school to think through his behavior nor to consider the sequence of events. But if this child were allowed to continue these impulsive behavior patterns sadistic trends might result.

The meanings to be derived from such a situation—meanings which are implicit in the actual subject matter—could be of great assistance in developing more thoughtful behavior on the part of Walter. For instance, he should be asked to examine the duck's feet. Are they adapted to maintaining a balance on his shoulder? Can the duck hold on? Can he fly well enough to prevent a hard fall? To what kinds of places are duck's feet adapted? Also, along with this development, there should be a consideration of values and purposes. Do we want the duck to be hurt? Do we want other living things to suffer needlessly? Are we responsible for the duck in our classroom? There should be a lifting of children's values, and sometimes even of the teacher's values, through a give-and-take discussion of this kind.

Neither the overly cautious behavior of Donald nor the impulsive behavior of Marie or Walter is to be desired. In a democracy we need resourcefulness and responsibleness with materials, as we shall see in connection with our discussion of purposes of science in childhood education (pp. 62–77). Intelligent resourcefulness and responsibleness may grow out of thinking through to possible consequences of behavior. This involves consideration of the safety of others as well as oneself. To run with an opened knife or scissors is to invite disaster. To throw burning matches about is to invite fire. Resourcefulness should never be confused with mere impulsiveness. Intelligent resourcefulness is a great goal for all democratic peoples and has always been a great source of strength in the democratic way of life.

But intelligent resourcefulness and responsibleness must be learned. Even at birth the human organism, with its dynamic drives has the capacity for this learning. The parent and the teacher must make certain that children use these great dynamic drives in such a way as to develop desirable behavior patterns.

Children are never too young to be encouraged in this kind of planning. If I do this, what may happen? How may accidents arise? How can I safely cross the street? How can I play safely? In all planning it is important to think through to the consequences of behavior. If we keep walking across the lawn at this place, a path will be worn. If we dig up these plants, we may start erosion. If we throw paper around, our park will no longer be a beautiful place. If we build a campfire here, we may set the forest on fire.

Adults' Behavior Influences Children. Children, too frequently, are surrounded by adults who display impulsive behavior. Adults may litter the landscape with paper, empty bottles, tin cans, and other refuse. They may be careless with burning matches and lighted cigarettes. They may deface the walls in public places by scribbling their names. Adults may overload electric circuits with appliances. They may leave a picnic site looking much worse than when they arrived—carving on trees, pulling up shrubs, or breaking off the branches of trees. They may neglect pets, drive cars recklessly, and fail to lubricate and otherwise care for the machines for which they are responsible. There is probably no single factor which influences the behavior of children for good citizenship more than the attitudes and behavior of the adults in their environment, particularly of those adults to whom they look for leadership.

The Industrial Revolution and Behavior Patterns. As a traveler moves about in the world today, he finds peoples of different cultures, and these cultures may vary enormously. Many diverse influences mold and leave their mark upon cultures. But perhaps no force has had a stronger influence upon cultures than has the Industrial Revolution—the forces of pure and applied science.

Peoples in various cultures differ greatly in the way they behave in reference to the materials of the environment. It seems that people care for that which has meaning for them. A machine to an industrial people is something to be cared for and operated carefully. The same machine might be neglected and soon ruined by an individual or people with little or no understanding of the possibilities and limitations of the materials of which machines are made or of their use and care.

In some countries the development of machines has been a part of the culture for many generations. The people of these cultures have participated in one way or another in the invention, installation, improvement, and care of machines. In other cultures the machines have been introduced from the outside in a finished form. In these latter cultures, unfortunately, the machines are exotic to the majority of population. A person from an industrial society traveling in such countries will observe differences in attitudes toward machines and should be sympathetic and understanding in evaluating the behavior he encounters. The fact that an inanimate object needs care requires instruction. A traveler from a country possessing an advanced technology will often be amazed at the great learning taking place in one short generation in a country where modern technology has been but recently introduced.

James lives in a culture which has been enriched by the Industrial Revolution. At the age of ten months he very much enjoyed sitting behind the steering wheel of the family car and (with the engine turned off and under his parent's supervision) moving the wheel as much as possible. There was no difficulty to get him to agree to ride in the front seat while his father drove the car. Under these circumstances he remained quietly absorbed for relatively long periods of time. It would be difficult to say how early he began to learn how the car was started and driven, for every movement his father made in driving was observed by James at an early age and from a very personal point of view—that is, as if he, James, were doing the driving. As James grew older, it was almost impossible to have anything done to the car in which he did not participate. If the hood was up, he was peering at the engine. Soon James' father found himself leaning upon his son for such information as when the car was last lubricated or when the filter was last changed. James felt a real concern for the care of the car. He realized through observation of his father's behavior and through observation of the performance of the car itself that there were certain limitations and possibilities in the machine. When the time came to learn to drive, James almost knew how to drive and to drive well, for all he needed was to feel in his hands, legs, and muscles the actual manipulations.

James, however, was a child whose ancestors had for at least four generations participated in the Industrial Revolution. His grandfather, as a farmer in the Dakotas and later in Texas, had participated early in this revolution through the introduction of various types of farm machinery on his own land. From earliest infancy, machines formed a part of James' environment. He had no difficulty in adapting to machines, because machines were accepted as a part of his life, as were the responsibilities for the proper use of machines. For him the problems were quite different than they are for the child in a culture where the machines have been introduced from the outside world and whose parents have not yet learned to accept the machines for what they are.

Perhaps an interesting aspect of James' environment was that adults about him at times discussed problems of life in terms of machines that might be invented in the future. So there was ever the horizon ahead of better ways— not exotic, "foreign" ways, or of a culture built by strange men from "overseas," but of an industrial world built by people who were like his own grandfather. This industrial world was James' world. It was part of his heritage, and he would grow up to help share it with people. He had no difficulty in adjusting to it because he was a part of it from his earliest memories.

Mildred, now a mature woman, lived as a child on a farm in midwestern Canada. She comes from a family which has participated in the Industrial Revolution for four generations. As a small girl she frequently accompanied her father in his work on the farm. She noted his care for the farm animals and for the farm machinery. While she was quite young the new dairy buildings were constructed. Listening, she learned while her father learned as the new machinery was installed. She heard her father and mother discuss problems connected with the new equipment and saw them in learning situations day after day. Of course she did not understand all she heard, but her learning was great. She gained important attitudes. In addition to using and caring for such appliances as a washing machine, vacuum cleaner, and cream separator, Mildred had a feeling that her mother could, if necessary, operate the other farm machinery as well.

Mildred, now a wife and mother, feels at home in an industrialized society. She has concern for the equipment of her home and she makes sure that it is well serviced. When purchasing any appliance for her home she asks intelligent questions. She is resourceful,

although she recognizes that it is good policy to have difficult repairs done by service people especially trained.

The above is not given as exceptional for it has occurred in millions of families. These anecdotal records are given in order to indicate the tremendous value of this kind of experience, for it has fine, rich overtones—the relation of one generation to another and the kind of learning which makes democracies strong. We need to reappraise this kind of education, for no nation can be strong which does not utilize wisely its materials and its heritage.

A ten-year-old boy in New Jersey was so deeply concentrated on a task at a table in a schoolroom that he seemed oblivious to all his surroundings. When the boy was questioned, it was found he was working with a toy motor of his own construction. The observer was impressed by the fact that this child worked with his motor in a skillful fashion. He exhibited a fine feeling for the bit of mechanism.

In this activity the child was displaying behavior which when common to other children and adults can be priceless in the cause of democracy. In the first place it was highly constructive behavior, for he had a feeling for the proper use of materials. Here, in a real way, was behavior in keeping with conservation, since he was spontaneously making wise use of materials. It was also apparent that the child felt responsible for the motor.

It occurred to the observer that here was a kind of behavior that he, as a teacher, had observed many times in classrooms—the concentration of a child upon getting something to operate, a concern with making something run, a desire to repair something, a feeling of responsibility, a creative development, a thoughtful application of one's energy to a constructive task.

On the other hand, almost everyone has had experience with children who for one reason or another have built up an irresponsible and destructive pattern of behavior.

Toys may have been strewn about and broken by negligence. It is not our intention to go into this kind of behavior or to try to explain it entirely. Rather, we should examine it from a developmental point of view—in this case, the developmental viewpoint of science in elementary education.

Manipulative Abilities. Children will show a considerable amount of variation in their manipulative abilities. In a certain upper-grade classroom a boy known as Harold had a great deal of difficulty in reading. One day it was necessary to place small electric lights, attached to dry cells, over certain pictures. Harold blossomed forth, took the leadership, secured the necessary materials, and wired up the lights with the help of his classmates. Throughout this work he was both in word and deed the foreman of the group. He followed this by installing an interroom telegraphic communication between a cloakroom and his classroom.

Upon investigation it was found that Harold had developed a position of considerable importance in a local garage. He was not only tolerated in the garage but encouraged, and at times paid, for his voluntary services. He was superior to his fellow classmates in manipulating tools. Thereupon, the teacher used this incident to vitalize Harold's interest in reading, indicating to him that he should have an authoritative basis for what he was telling the class about electricity. Harold's reading ability improved as a result of this motivation. He also developed a position of greatly increased status in the class because of his mechanical abilities and confidence in himself. His presentations of electrical circuits to the other children showed a knowledge of human relationships as well as of electricity.

We need to recognize that education to use one's hands constructively is of basic importance in the survival of our democracy. One reason for the static condition of certain cultures has been what we might call class distinction on the basis of work. If a man used his hands in manual work he was considered to be of inferior class. The scholar or the member of the ruling class was expected to have soft, clean hands at all times.

There is power in the use of science, and the human hand as well as the brain has played a part in the development of science. It could be said quite truthfully that the human hand is a vital part of human intelligence. A nation which cannot use its hands is weak. A nation which can use its hands constructively is strong, and can exert leadership for the benefit of all.

The hand has not been sufficiently recognized in elementary education. Too frequently children are rated solely on their ability in the "three R's." Such a tendency holds much in common with the philosophy of keeping the hands of the scholar clean and soft. It is time we gave proper recognition to mechanical abilities. Harold was made to feel that his achievements in wiring circuits were not inferior to achievements in reading. If a democracy is to be preserved there must be recognition of the great value of being resourceful with one's hands.

The Sensitive Child. Teachers will need to be aware of the sensitive child and to provide him with opportunities with which he can cope. The timid child, called upon to perform a manipulative task before others, such as lighting a candle or fastening a wire to a dry cell, may become quite conscious of his own lack of co-ordination and "know-how." Such a child may be encouraged to use a work table where he can do these manipulations in a more relaxed atmosphere; later, having secured the confidence in himself he needed, the timid child may be eager to repeat it for others. It should be kept in mind that many people with poise and splendid co-ordination find themselves nervous when asked to do a simple manipulation with their hands with onlookers present. It might be well to assume that perhaps everyone, young and old, is sensitive, to a degree, even if it is not manifested in overt behavior.

Each Child Possesses Individuality. Carey, an eleven-year-old, had become very conscious of his awkwardness. This self-consciousness grew out of the fact that he had little opportunity to play with the other children. Whenever he did any manipulation of materials, some other child or adult would take it away from him with the words, "Here, let me show you," or, "Here, let me do it." Although he was liked by his fellows, disparaging comments were made about his awkwardness from time to time. He became very self-conscious, and his awkwardness increased. But when alone he was quite skillful with his hands. He took clocks apart and put them together again. He had a very fine intelligence and quickly grasped problems and developed his own ideas.

A teacher interested in Carey helped him to gain control of his co-ordination in the presence of others by indicating to him his achievements when he was alone. He developed a calm, wholesome, social outlook for his participation in the science experiences, particularly those experiments in the classroom with others. He proved later to be a person of unusual mechanical ability.

In a class of seven-year-olds there was a study being made which involved the lighting of a candle. The teacher, who was an excellent student of children's behavior, called on Priscilla, a quiet and sensitive girl, to strike the match and light the candle. Before Priscilla did this, the teacher held a short discussion of safety precautions, which revealed the presence of sand and other necessary materials for fire prevention.

Priscilla had never before struck a match. As the match flared into flame, she dropped it to the floor. The teacher stepped on the match and with a calm, reassuring voice said, "See, Priscilla, you need not be afraid. Don't you want to try again." Priscilla did, and was successful. She beamed with satisfaction as the candle burned as a result of her action.

This is an illustration of how significant may be the interaction of the behavior of the adult with that of a child in the development of children and, for that matter, in the development of teachers, too. A calm, reassuring voice, and an invitation to try again, gave a timid child a feeling of confidence and resourcefulness. This may have been one event, along with other events, which gave this timid child a definite boost in a desirable direction. A disapproving voice, on the other hand, might have been, along with other events, enough to cause the child to become even more timid and withdrawn. But the teacher was aware of Priscilla's timidity and knew that it was important for Priscilla to be successful with this experience. To this teacher, studying children was a necessary part of her teaching.

Much harm has been done to boys and girls by calling special attention to their strength and weaknesses. Each child is an individual and possesses individuality. He differs from his fellows. He has a biological as well as a democratic right to be different. He has a right to keep his own sense of self-respect. No greater injustice can be done a child than to have to hear himself described unjustly or unkindly in the presence of his peers and to have developed within him a lack of faith in himself.

Children Have Potentialities for Science

In this chapter we have observed the tremendous potentialities of children. We may well come to the conclusion that the main organic purposes and drives of children from birth are those which may be considered conducive to the study of science. Considering these inherited potentialities of children, it is well for teachers to realize that they can learn science *with* children as they teach.

But the mere utilization of the drives of children does not, in itself, constitute an adequate definition of the purpose of science in childhood education. In the next chapter we will discuss the basic purposes of science in the public elementary schools of a democracy. We shall see that an understanding of these basic purposes is essential to any consideration of content and method.

CHAPTER 2

Science in the Education for Democracy

The Concern of Society with Behavior. The education of children in almost any society is maintained for the preservation and advancement of that society. The survival of any society is largely dependent upon the conduct and the activities of the members of the society; hence there is a concern in practically all kinds of society for the education of children and youth in what that society considers to be desirable social behavior.

Under an absolute government children and youth are educated along those lines which develop the kind of behavior that is desired by the group in power; what the children may learn and even the methods of teaching and learning are controlled by the dictators.

Democracy's Basic School

But in a democracy the public elementary school must be maintained by the people for the preservation and the advancement of the democracy. In the United States it has at times been called "the great common school," in that it is the school for all the people. The school was established and dedicated by the early forefathers as the one institution that was to be common to everyone, regardless of race, religion, or economic status. It was a unique institution in that it was to be controlled by all the people for the education of all the people for citizenship in a democracy. The elementary school is to be considered as one of democracy's great resources and there-fore, like all resources, to be used wisely and guarded faithfully. Each subject that is taught in our schools, therefore, if it is to win a permanent place in the curriculum, must be a subject that is consistent with the development of well-rounded and responsible citizenship in a democracy.

The Elementary School—An Institution under High Pressure. The nature of the elementary school in a democracy is one that contributes to the development of an institution working under tremendous pressures. Freedom of communication and the abundance of ideas, old and new, are among the

34

factors contributing to this situation. There are many groups and many individuals in every nation that are anxious to have the attention of boys and girls. These groups, most of them with democratic goals, attempt to create for themselves a place in the elementary-school program. Other groups with selfish and undemocratic goals would be willing to attempt to control the minds of children at the first opportunity. Any pressure is undesirable which is used to create within the school program a position of special privilege or disloyalty. Constant vigilance—a sifting and weighing of pressures—by those responsible for the welfare of children is necessary.

Because of pressures exerted by our society upon the elementary school, a new category does not gain acceptance in the curriculum quickly. There isn't enough time or energy available on the part of children and teachers to cope with all the demands of all the pressure groups. Many proposed subject-matter categories have not succeeded in becoming established as a permanent part of the curriculum, often in spite of well-financed publicity. Pressures of different kinds will come and go, but only those areas which can be most satisfactorily supported in terms of the purpose and nature of the elementary school will become accepted permanently as a part of the curriculum on a wide geographical basis.

If science is to become a permanent part of the curriculum it must be designed to meet the purpose of the elementary school, otherwise it will fail and pass into extinction as have other proposed curriculum categories. It is most important that we think through to a sound point of view the place of science in the public elementary school. However, we must not do this for the sake of science but always for the sake of the children and of democracy.

In a democracy the program in the elementary school must be one that is acceptable or can be made acceptable to the people of that democracy. This means that any subject which remains in the curriculum remains there only if the people are willing for it to do so. Hence, the teaching and the learning designed for the elementary school must rest upon a foundation of thought sound enough to withstand the test of public discussion or controversy. If science remains in the elementary-school curriculum in a democracy, it is because it has been accepted by the people and remains acceptable to them.

It is apparent to the public that every child needs to be able to read, write, and use numbers. Reading, writing, and arithmetic stand as established through acceptance over many centuries, until today there is no questioning their importance as categories in the curriculum. Reading and writing of a kind have been taught since the time of the earliest beginnings of picture writing, and arithmetic has been taught since a consciousness of numbers first dawned upon man. Thus in some cultures there has been a teaching of the "three R's" for three or four thousand years.

But our modern science—science as we know it today—is so very recent in its development that we must regard it as a mere youth among the other hoary, seasoned fields of study. Naturally, therefore, the *teaching* of modern science to children is of even more recent origin. Such teaching has been practiced for little more than two decades at most, and in some regions for a much shorter time. Yet the teaching of modern science has made progress in our time.

During the last thirty years, science has grown steadily in the elementary schools of the United States, Canada, the Philippines, and various countries of Latin America, Europe, Asia, and Africa. This growth of science indicates that the movement of elementary-school science has passed the exacting tests of the elementary school.

Science Education for All Children

Since the elementary school is designed for all the children, *science for the elementary school must also be designed for all the boys and girls*. Enrolled in the elementary schools today are not only the future scientists of our country but the laymen as well (and everyone is a layman outside his own field of specialization). The task of science instruction is a much larger one than discovering children of exceptional ability in science and starting them on their way to becoming scientists. Primarily, the task involves education for all children for their own and for society's benefit, and only secondarily involves concern for the welfare or future of science itself. This pattern for science in public elementary education is being adopted by a number of democratic countries.

Science in childhood education should be an area which is fundamental for children. It should be freed from the paraphernalia of specialized science. In fact, in all our thinking we must consider how science fits into a program of elementary education and not how children can be made to fit into a program of science. We should describe science as a part of the whole program of childhood education, rather than thinking of science as a separate program.

It is well for the specialists in elementary science to be cognizant at all times that the elementary school is dedicated to the preservation and development of democracy and not merely to the preservation and development of science. But how can science be used to contribute through the elementary school to the preservation and development of democracy? Let us consider this question in the following section.

Using Science to Make Democracies Strong

There has grown up a conviction that the free nations must remain strong if they are to remain free. There is also a realization that there is power in science, and therefore that science is an essential element in maintaining strength and in improving the democratic way of life. It will not be enough to have a small portion of the population educated as scientists; to be truly strong, an entire nation must be made conversant with science, a task uniquely suited to the elementary school, since this is the institution of all the people. To realize this goal, science must be placed in the curriculum as one of the fundamentals.

Strength for free peoples is secured not only through military defense but, even more important, through the development of good living conditions. Through the use of science man can do much to shape his own future, since science has tremendous potentialities for the improvement of living conditions for all.

The children now in our elementary schools will live as adults in a world of tomorrow. Our boys and girls will live in a time of great decisions. They will need to make certain that science will be used for good and not for evil purposes. They will need to determine how democracies can be kept secure. There will be great problems concerning the use of new and old sources of energy. Theirs will be the problems of wise utilization of natural resources, the distribution of new synthetics, medicines, and drugs, provision for health and well-being, development of materials from new sources, establishment and maintenance of research agencies dedicated to public welfare, the establishment of a balance of nature that will provide ample food and recreation for all, and the development of a stable economy based on the natural resources and other problems to be solved, all within a democratic framework. Implicit in all of this will be the need to consider problems connected with international or world co-operation.

What we can be certain of is that boys and girls will need to be resourceful and democratic in the decades ahead if our way of life, and theirs, is to survive. Therefore, we are concerned with the development of resourceful and democratic behavior. If we succeed, we shall not need to be unduly concerned for the future, for with the development of resourceful behavior in accordance with the high purpose of democracy, our boys and girls can use science to shape the future with complete confidence.

It is to be noted in this discussion that science is considered as a tool for humanity. There is no intent in the education of children to develop science for its own sake or to defend science as a vested interest. Only as science serves in the development of children and in the welfare of humanity can it be defended as essential in the education of elementary-school children.

It is most important that we recognize that boys and girls need to do much more than talk about science. If democracies are to preserve their way of life, there must be developed in their populations the ability to operate intelligently and resourcefully with the materials and energy of the universe to the best interest of mankind.

Social studies, however valuable they may be, are not sufficient in themselves to enable children to meet and solve the problems of today and tomorrow. Teachers and school systems are likely to miss the great contributions of science to children, and through the children to the larger goals of democracy, when they place science in the curriculum merely as a segment of the social studies. Science grows out of the tremendous urges of the human organism and does not have to be motivated through social studies.

Content and Methods in Elementary-School Science Should Conform to Democracy. Since the elementary school is an institution of democracy, the content and methods utilized in elementary-school science should conform to democracy. Every child should have an opportunity to participate in teaching and learning activities in science in a democratic fashion. A child should not be given special status in a group except through those democratic procedures by which any individual rightfully gains status.

Sammy's father is a scientist in New Mexico. In Sammy's classroom there is much reference to Sammy's father, not only by Sammy but by Miss Scone, the teacher. The children frequently hear comments about him. Miss Scone will say, "You know Sammy's father is a scientist"; or "What did your father say, Sammy?" Or Sammy will say, "My father works in a laboratory"; or "No, that isn't right; my father said so"; or "My father knows all about it." Sammy is becoming dogmatic, undemocratic, and unscientific. He quotes his father as an authority for almost everything, and he isn't always too careful in his quotation of his father's statements. The mention of Sammy's father frequently stops democratic processes in the classroom. Sammy is becoming egotistical. He uses his father's name to bolster his own status.

But Susan, in the same classroom, has a

father who is an excellent farmer. Her father is constantly reading and studying about soil, crops, conservation, politics, and other subjects. He is a civic-minded leader and has done much to improve the economics of the community. Susan's father is never mentioned in the classroom.

The other children in Sammy's class seldom have their fathers' names mentioned in the class, and they feel a little chagrined, if not apologetic, for being the sons and daughters of parents who are not scientists. Mary's father is a policeman who had recently risked his life to keep law and order. In fact, he was in a hospital for several months as a result of a bullet wound. Tom's father is no scientist, but he is a fireman and recently in a destructive fire he had been overcome by the fumes and had been hospitalized. John's father is a barber, and a good one who keeps his shop in good hygienic and sanitary condition in accordance with the best information of modern science. Mildred's father is a fine cabinetmaker. Jane's father is dead and her mother works as a domestic servant. Jane is silent much of the time when science is being studied. She seems overawed by Sammy's father, who has never visited the classroom but who seems to be a ghost parading through the classroom whenever science is discussed. To Jane, Sammy and his father seem to have some kind of an ownership of science. Whenever the class studies science, Jane feels like some trespasser on the grassy plot in a park near the school where there is a sign reading KEEP OFF THE GRASS.

One reason Jane is silent is that one day in a discussion she dared to question Sammy's logic by saying, "How could that be when . . .?" But Sammy's reply, "My father said . . ." (plus the tacit approval of Miss Scone of Sammy's reply) silenced Jane for good in science. Yet Jane's thinking on this occasion, and at many other times, is superior to Sammy's.

Miss Scone recognizes that Sammy is developing unscientific and undemocratic behavior. She also knows that Sammy has an absolute idea, and therefore a false idea, of knowledge, in spite of his father being a scientist. But Miss Scone is overawed by scientists because of the enormous amount of publicity about science which has appeared in the press in recent years. Scientists seem to her to be supermen. But Miss Scone need not have been ill-at-ease, for she is an excellent teacher of children in spite of this one weakness. Her specialization is the education of children, and she is just as specialized in her field as Sammy's father is in his. She need not be afraid of Sammy's father. In fact, she is doing Sammy no kindness at all in allowing such a situation to develop.

Sammy needs to be treated like other children. Actually, Sammy feels inferior, and he relies upon his father's name to give himself security. Jane, on the other hand, has learned to stand on her own feet. She is quite self-reliant, and even though she is silent during most of the discussions of science, her silence is thoughtful and her attitude both poised and co-operative. Sammy seeks security in his father's reputation, but Jane has adequacy for the problems at her level.

There is no aristocracy in a true democracy. Jefferson, among the early leaders of democracy, was aware of the value of science and the common schools. He recognized the need for people with ability, but he also recognized the need and worked for widespread educational opportunity. We must not make the scientists or any other group into priests of a new order. In a democracy it may be Jane who will become the skilled scientist and Sammy may perform work that requires much less specialized knowledge.

Some have suggested that the primary purpose of science in the education of children is to develop "little scientists." Such an idea is not consistent with the fundamental purpose of the elementary school or with the nature of science in society. There should be no hero worship of scientists except insofar as an individual scientist may deserve such recognition. Democracy would be weakened if society allowed to be created within itself a distinct scientific class, or caste. Scientists serve mankind well, but so do carpenters, barbers, farmers, soldiers, senators, artists, doctors, teachers, truck drivers, and everyone else. Scientists, outside their own special fields, are at times somewhat naïve, and at times exhibit traits of gullibility and dogmatism, thus failing to apply some of the fundamental tenets of science. Scientists are human beings like other people.

We have already discussed the dynamic potentialities of children, as revealed in their behavior. These potentialities represent the greatest resources of the human race. We do these qualities a great injustice by describing children as "little scientists." There is no need that they should be. Children are children, the young of the human race: we are very proud of them, and they can be very proud of themselves, as such. We need look for no greater appellation for them.

Traditionally, in education at all levels, the content fields have been organized for the purpose of developing specialists. For instance, teachers of a special field such as botany were concerned with discovering students who might become botanists and cared little for the instruction of the rank and file of students who might have abilities in other fields than botany. These specialists preserved the logical order of content within the specialized fields and neglected the needs of the majority, who would never become experts in the specialists' own particular fields. In recent years the secondary schools and colleges have made an attempt to break from this traditional practice, and from this attempt has come the "general-education" movement.

The history of elementary education reveals the remains of subject-matter categories that have resulted from the refusal of specialists to adjust their field to the purposes of the elementary school. Nature study, a category proposed for the elementary school at the close of the last century, was dominated largely by specialists in agriculture, botany, zoology, and other specialized fields of science, with little regard for the fundamental purpose of the elementary school. An exception to this may be found in the writings of Wilbur S. Jackman (1855–1907) of the University of Chicago, who did pioneer work in developing a constructive point of view for nature study and science in elementary education.[1]

A Resourceful Population Is Needed at All Times. The preservation and improvement of democracies must rest on a sounder basis than that of educating future scientists. Both in time of peace and in time of war, an intelligent and resourceful population is needed. For a nation to be free, it is not enough that scientists make discoveries in the laboratories, for there are decisions to be made, the complex life of the community must go on, industry and agriculture must maintain their momentum and find ways to improve their operation, and behavior in every walk of life should reflect courage, creativity, and responsibility in dealing with the resources of a country. No nation is any stronger than the combined wisdom of its people. If attention is given to the development of science in a way which is in keeping with the purposes of the elementary school tomorrow's scientists will be integrated into a population conversant with the attitudes and content of science in a democracy.

Democracy can only benefit by having its future scientists and laymen in the same classroom in the elementary school. It is most important that children who are to be future scientists come through the experiences in the elementary schools along with children who

[1] W. S. Jackman, *Nature Study*, Third Yearbook of the National Society for the Study of Education, Part VI, 1904.

will pursue other vocations. It is most important in a democracy that science be the product of the democracy and be used as a tool of its people. Science has great potentialities for both good and evil. Any tool as vital as science must be in the ultimate control of all the people.

Any design for elementary education that calls for the complete separation of children with ability in science from other children is a step toward a totalitarian form of government. We must at all hazards avoid letting any group which has lost contact with the majority of the people gain control of our government.

Power Should Be in the Hands of All People. There is power in the knowledge of science. People living in a democracy should realize this and keep the control of that power in their own hands. This means that science is fundamental in the education of boys and girls for they must become intelligent as citizens in order to make decisions necessary to manage a democracy that uses science as one of its tools.

Children with exceptional abilities in the field of science can be given opportunities for leadership and creative activities in the classroom and in the community without being separated from those who are less gifted along these lines. Some scientists have had an unnecessary degree of difficulty in communicating their ideas to people who are not specialists in their special fields. Children with special abilities in science can begin to learn to communicate with their fellow classmates through discussions, as well as through writing, art, and the use of dramatics in the classroom. Therefore, even if one should look at science education as being a means of developing future scientists for a democracy, one would still have no justification for completely separating the more gifted from the rest of the children.

What of the Future?

Education for Uncertainty. For what kind of a future are we to prepare our children? Will the next few decades bring peace or war? Will it be a world of waste or a world of resourcefulness? Will the people living during the next decades be characterized by hysteria and gullibility or will they be calm, confident, and realistic? What new inventions and discoveries will be made during the lifetime of the children now in our classrooms? What will be the impact of these discoveries and inventions on these boys and girls during their lifetime? Will they be able to preserve and strengthen the democratic way of life? How are we to answer these questions?

It is impossible to know now what the future will be. Our grandfathers could not have foreseen the conditions of today. For in any facet of life at which we look—whether it is transportation, communication, entertainment, food, family life, housing, or whatever —the change has been almost beyond description. The impact of new developments has been kaleidoscopic and overwhelming, and the adjustment of mankind to such a new world has been both good and bad. Horrible wars, depressions, poverty, waste, dust bowls, increased erosion, extinction of valuable plant and animal species, air, soil, and water pollution, and introduction of pests have resulted along with increased length of life, new medicines, greater comfort, and new hope for a peaceful, democratic world. As the population increases, problems of health and sanitation, recreation, the use of space, and the pollution and conservation of resources grow. Man is slowly learning that in the world of scientific discovery and invention no one individual or nation can live in isolation. Man is being taught by necessity that he must assume responsibility for his behavior if he is to survive.

In a way we are living in a period of paradoxical conditions. Everyone knows that through science man has made discoveries about the nature of the universe which can be useful in developing a higher standard of living, better health, more conveniences, finer recreations, and yet many of these discoveries provide man with new means for human destruction. We may be on the threshold of a new era. Will it be an era of progress toward a better civilization or a plunge backward into a new Dark Age? The boys and girls in the elementary-school classrooms will live in a time of important decisions—decisions as to whether science is to be used predominantly for good or for evil. It is essential to the very survival of our civilization that the next generation have the abilities to secure the potentialities of science for the welfare of all people.

Traditionally schools have been designed for an era of certainty, with a tendency toward fixed intellectual goals and a more or less absolute and authoritarian view of subject matter. But we do not know what the future will be for the children in our classrooms today. Furthermore, we are learning through science that what we know today may need revision tomorrow. Man's conception of truth changes. Our children will need the ability to reconstruct their ideas throughout their lives.

The preservation and advancement of democracy depends to no small extent on the behavior patterns developed in children. Since we do not know what the future will be, we need to educate children for uncertainty. This does not imply that we need be pessimistic about the problems these children will face in the future. Rather, we can be confident that if we assist them to develop democratic and resourceful behavior, they will make their own future, and make it a good one.

Developing Adequacy for the Present and Future. A great deal has been accomplished in the development of security for individuals, for nations and groups of nations. The ability to provide security rests upon the wise strength of peoples. No government or group of governments can guarantee security of any kind to an individual or to a people except as the governments involved have the "wherewithal" to support that security.

We know we cannot guarantee children security for the future. It could even be an injustice to them if we were to encourage them to develop a feeling that our generation is building for them a completely secure future. We cannot know today what is the exact content they will need tomorrow, for we do not know for certain the nature of tomorrow's discoveries. We cannot know for a certainty the problems of tomorrow that our children will face.

The behavior patterns of "guaranteed security" given to children should be replaced by the behavior patterns of "adequacy to meet challenge." We need to assist children to become adequate to the problems of today and whatever they may face tomorrow. We need to help children learn how they can assist themselves by working together. The best security our children can have is in being adequate to the problems of tomorrow through democracy, intelligence, and resourcefulness.

The place of science in a program of adequacy is indicated in the following statement by the physicist, Rogers D. Rusk,[2] "It is not a government committee or a government fund of gold in Washington that can guaran-

[2]Rogers D. Rusk, *Forward with Science.* Alfred A. Knopf, New York, 1943, p. 11.

tee security in old age and sickness, and financial depression; it is science with its potentialities for the production of comforts and luxuries, medicines and means of curing disease and so on."

Children Need a Dynamic Education for the Preservation and Advancement of Democracy. It is our contention that children's attitudes toward their environment and universe are the very core of the development of a resourceful adjustment to the future.

Children need a positive and dynamic program, one which develops a feeling on the part of children of being *needed* by our democracy in a world which must continually strive for peace. Children are needed not alone to assume responsibility for their own nation but also to work toward a better world for all nations. There are many opportunities for children and teachers to work to improve conditions in the classroom, the school, and the community. (Chapter 6.)

In a final sense, the real capital of a nation is not its wealth in terms of money in circulation or stored in vaults, for the test of strength in either peace or war rests on the resources possessed by a nation's people and by their resourcefulness. A democracy is only as strong as the resources available to it, only as resilient as its ability to meet situations with challenge, responsibility, and intelligence. Science is directly related to resources and resourcefulness. When properly applied, science and resourcefulness have so much in common that we might think of them as being synonymous; in fact we might say quite truthfully that science is the result of man's resourcefulness through the ages. Our emphasis in elementary education will need to be on the development of this kind of democratic and resourceful behavior.

It is most important to the success of our way of life that children have a favorable attitude toward science. Science should not seem foreign or exotic to them. Science viewed as the result of the age-old drive of mankind to adjust himself to his environment and to maintain his own equilibrium in the welter of biological and physical forces carries with it a larger point of view than a purely vocational one. Science is the result of man's experience and logical thinking through the centuries. Science, like democracy or the mother tongue, belongs to all who wish to make use of it. Children should be made to feel that science belongs to everyone.

Science Must Be Designed for Classroom Teachers as Well as for Children in the Elementary School. It should be borne in mind that the success that science has had in the elementary school is to no small extent the result of the work of classroom teachers. They have experimented with new activities, new content, and new methods. Many of them have constructed curriculum materials and developed reading material in science. The interest with which children take hold of science delights many teachers and, according to their testimony, has paid large dividends in the co-operative attitude secured from the children, not only toward science but toward other school activities.

In looking to the future, it is most important that science be maintained as a feasible and possible program for classroom teachers. Specialists in subject matter and other fields are prone to make excessive demands upon classroom teachers. Such requirements as expecting teachers to know by name all objects in the environment, animate or inanimate, to be a field naturalist, a laboratory technician, and a general bureau of information are impossible as well as impracticable. Elementary-school science must continue to be structured along lines realistic both for classroom teachers and children. It must be recognized that the classroom teacher has many professional duties; teaching science is but one of her tasks. She is a specialist in the *education* of children and not necessarily a specialist in science. Any co-operation between classroom teachers and science specialists should be based on the idea that *both* are specialists.

Elementary-school science must not be high-school science brought down to the elementary-school level. Traditional demonstrations and equipment of high-school or college physics, chemistry, and biology can provide no adequate basis for instruction in the elementary school. Very few high-school teachers, however well qualified they may be at their own levels, are competent in elementary-school science. Assignment of high-school science teachers to supervisory duties in the elementary school is a wise practice only where the high-school teacher has not only real understanding of the elementary school but also ample experience in teaching young children. The material used in the classroom should be, in general, the kind of material already familiar to children in their own community.

Science, as a newcomer in the elementary-school curriculum, has created a need for the reconstruction of teacher education. Much progress has been made through new curricula in many teachers colleges and schools of education, as well as through workshops and field centers set up by local school systems. Professional subject-matter courses in many different branches of science for classroom teachers have been developed in many teacher-education institutions.

In institutions responsible for the education of elementary-school teachers, science courses of the traditional type based on an absolute and mechanistic concept of science can have little value for teaching children. Instead, the content of such courses should be dynamic and based on an understanding of children. The total offering in science for classroom teachers should be of a professional character, suitable for the significant role of teaching children.

The Role of "Purpose"

Perhaps no one factor will do more to improve instruction in a classroom than that the teacher have sound *purposes* for the education of children. These purposes should be thought through very carefully. They should be so well thought through and established in a teacher's mind that she can see these purposes guiding her continually, moment by moment, in her work with children. The purposes of instruction should play a fundamental role in education. Without careful consideration of such purposes, or objectives, elementary science can become a matter of mere object lessons and "busy work."

Any consideration of content, method, and evaluation must be made in terms of purpose. Even contacts with parents and the community should be motivated and guided by the purposes a teacher and a school hold for the education of children. The purposes presented here will be further elaborated in terms of *behavior* in Chapter 3, in terms of *meanings and content* in Chapter 4, in terms of *techniques and procedures* in Chapter 5, and in terms of the *community* in Chapter 6. All of these will be integrated in the professionalized subject matter for teachers presented in Parts II, III, and IV.

In this discussion we have stressed that the public elementary school in a democracy is an institution that is unique. It is a school maintained by the people of a community for the education of all the boys and girls. The personnel of the public elementary school is responsible to the democracy for its curriculum. The public elementary-school teacher is therefore in a position of responsibility in a democratic community. It is well that it is so, for if democracies are to be preserved each must have an institution which is responsible to its people for the education of its young citizens.

The role of the classroom teacher as an official responsible to the community might seem to some people to degrade the position of such a teacher. We think not. We believe that this role of responsibility in the preservation and improvement of democracy is a role that has vastly contributed to the continuation of democracies. One hesitates even to think of the weakened condition in which we would find democracies today if there had been no public schools and no public-school teachers.

It is most important that every democracy should have teachers who are answerable to the democratic processes in positions of responsibility for the education of its children. But it is to indicate that democracy can not survive long if that democracy loses control of the education of its children. It is unpleasant to think of what would happen to a democracy if the education of any large segment of its children passed out of the control of its people.

We have not discussed the purposes of science in the elementary school with any thought of being dictatorial. Rather we have attempted to state for classroom teachers what we believe to be valid purposes, with the hope that the purposes presented may be of some value in the work of the classroom. We have attempted to establish the purposes of science in childhood education in terms of the fundamental purposes of the elementary school.

These purposes have been presented also in the belief that a classroom teacher can be a potent agent in the education not only of children but also of parents and citizens in general. We believe such teachers can assist in constructing in the minds of all the people an understanding of the role of science in the education of children. The public needs to become aware of the place of science in elementary schools.

Each teacher in a democracy is free to develop her own ideas. The discussion used in this book may be of some value to her in constructing them.

CHAPTER 3

The Nature of Science and Its Implications for the Education of Children

What Is Science? One hears so much about science in daily life that it seems important that we know something about its nature before proceeding further. Science, like many important things, can be described in many ways. In this book we are concerned with describing science in ways that will be useful to teachers and parents.

What is science? How can science be described developmentally? What are the possible contributions which science can make to the behavior of today's boys and girls in the life of tomorrow? What are the implications of science for the present and future? Can our boys and girls be equipped to utilize science in making the world better?

Man Has Demanded Explanations in His Attempts at Adjustment

The Beginnings of Science. To understand the place of science in the education of children in a democracy it is necessary that we learn something about the nature of modern science. Yet to appreciate the characteristics of modern science, we will do well to look back to the *beginnings* of science.

As we have said earlier (pp. 8–24), science considered from the developmental point of view is the result of human drives. It originated far back in the dim past of mankind, as man began to develop his first tools and to make his first explanations for the happenings in nature. Some of the achievements in man's distant past that were very important milestones in his progress may seem to us today to be very simple. One can see a similarity between the progress of mankind and the learnings of a child. Early in life a child can make fundamental learnings about the things around him and about social relationships that are so simple to the adults looking on that such adults often fail to regard them as fundamental to a child's development.

Man found himself surrounded by phenomena, or events, that he did not understand. There were the ordinary events, such as sunrise and sunset, and the weather. There were the terrifying and extraordinary events of earthquakes, electrical storms, prolonged droughts, and floods. Quite early in his history man may well have been attracted by the beauty of the phenomena about him—the ocean waves, the clouds, waterfalls, mountains, rainbows, plant and animal life. Then there were the events upon which he was so dependent, such as those of seasonal change, weather, and reproductiveness. All of these phenomena were mysteries to man in that distant past. The environment was so much a part of the life of man that both the ordinary and the extraordinary events demanded explanations.

But not only the environment demanded explanations, for man was a mystery to himself. Where did he come from? Why was he able to do what he did? What was his relationship to the living and nonliving things in his environment?

On all sides and within himself were things and events to be explained. His adjustment to the environment, his search for food, clothing, and shelter called for an attempt to understand his environment. So he made interpretations for himself of the things about him.

Early in many cultures man developed myths which were often childlike in nature. Very frequently these myths had to do with "good" and "evil" beings which he imagined to exist about him. Thus, early, his explanations became an integral part of his primitive religions, creating supersitions and taboos, and thereby profoundly limiting his further study of the environment.

The Traditional Absolute View of Knowledge. In most cultures, unfortunately, these early interpretations of man become fixed and static for relatively long periods because, as a part of tribal religions, they were considered true for all time and not subject to modification. The individual who expressed doubt concerning these primitive interpretations frequently was punished and ostracized. Only the very strong dared rise above them, because the interpretations were deeply imbedded in tribal beliefs. In this way many explanations advanced by "medicine men," high priests, and other myth-makers became crystallized in the culture.

Man, as a result, developed and passed on to posterity highly imaginative explanations of his environment. The constellations became heroes in the sky, the volcano became the abode of an angry god, the rainbow a bridge between Earth and heaven, the desert a place scorched by the "sun chariot," and the long, dry period was attributed to the curse of the wrathful harvest god. Man asserted that he had perceived the truth about his natural environment when he had little or no understanding of the truth. His desire for explanations led him into a wilderness of misconceptions. Nevertheless, it was a meaningful environment to him, filled as it was with "good" and "evil" spirits. He had to turn to the environment for food, clothing, and shelter. But his *methods* of procuring subsistence were modified greatly by the meanings the environment held for him. If certain animals were declared sacred, he dare not use them for food or even defend himself against them. If certain taboos were established they had to be observed unquestioningly.

However, we should not approach a consideration of primitive people, whether they were the primitive people of the past or those living somewhere on our Earth today, without a feeling of respect. Many of the mores of a tribe of people were tremendous factors in their ability to adapt to the environment in which they lived. The fact that a given culture is in existence today indicates that it contains within it some strong elements which have favored adaptation for survival within the existing environment; otherwise the culture would have been destroyed in the welter of natural forces and social conflicts.

Some of the ideas developed by the men in primitive cultures had merit. Plants which helped in the treatment of certain illnesses were found by various primitive cultures. Many simple machines were developed in these cultures (pp. 749–751). The contributions of certain early cultures to our modern life through improvement of various plants and animals for food, and through the domestication of certain animals for work, is very large indeed.

The Absolute View of Knowledge and the Failure of Some Civilizations. Often cultures have become extinct, and sometimes valuable inventions and discoveries have been lost with such cultures. Sometimes these cultures became extinct because important information had been guarded as the peculiar property of a special class of individuals, such as medicine men or priests who were protected by their established religious customs. Should this special class be destroyed, then the information is almost certain to be lost. Possibly this was true of the Inca civilization of South America, a civilization which had excellent ideas of conservation and much other information of a scientific nature. But once the Spanish exterminated the Inca leaders, this information was largely lost.

The Mayan Indians in Central America built probably the first astronomical observatory in the Western Hemisphere, and developed a new type of architecture and an excellent calendar. But this advance in man's knowledge was secret information, known only to the superior group of priests of the Mayan religion. Of this valuable information there was not a sufficient knowledge among all the people to prevent the loss of their culture. The exact cause of the decay and extinction of their culture is not known, although there is evidence for thinking that it may have been caused by the inability of the population to solve the problems of soil depletion and of the depletion of their main source of energy, which came from the trees which they used as fuel. The culture was so completely lost that the descendants of the Mayans were finally discovered living among the ruins of their temples, ball courts, convents, and other magnificent structures with no real knowledge of the origin of the ruins or of the extinct culture. The experience of a number of extinct cultures indicates the hazards of restricting important knowledge of any kind to a class of people set aside from the general population.

The absolute outlook on knowledge was favorable to a form of government which was absolute. Through this absolute outlook, the rulers could be arbitrary and dictatorial, the people themselves having few rights. The absolute view of knowledge goes hand in hand with absolute forms of government.

The Inca civilization of South America was rather easily overcome by the invading Spanish. Some students of this culture have pointed out that the Incas would not have been so easily subdued by the Spanish if the Inca population had been taught to think for themselves. It would have required little more than the destruction of a few of their bridges in the high valleys of the Andes mountains to have prevented Pizarro's small band from conquering the country. The absolute outlook of the Inca rulers did not permit the people to be resourceful and to think for themselves.

The meanings that anyone accepts as explanations of the objects and events in his environment have much to do with the kind of adjustment that one develops. If he develops unfounded and absolute ideas he will be likely to become maladjusted to the world about him and may develop timid, impulsive, and irresponsible behavior.

Primitive superstitions are still harbored by many people living today. This is true even in regions of advanced technology. There are many who are found fettered by fear of ill omens, by astrology, numerology, fortune-telling, and other unscientific practices. Such people are adjusted very poorly to modern life. There are many who are bound by absolute ideas passed down from the past. Such people will have difficulty in adapting themselves intelligently to modern progress in a democracy. Carrying a rabbit's foot in one's pocket for good luck, belief in the reading of tea leaves in a cup, fear of a black cat crossing one's path or the fear of the number thirteen, and other unfounded beliefs can cause individuals to develop maladjustments that make them liabilities in a democracy.

Not all of the present-day superstitions and unfounded beliefs have come down out of the past. An examination of the thinking in many modern communities will reveal superstitions, unfounded beliefs, and dogmatic fictions in the very process of being created and accepted.

Modern science is a relatively recent development. It has grown out of man's long attempt to work out his adjustment to the environment (pp. 82–83). Let us now examine the nature of modern science, and learn from our examination some of the ways in which science may contribute toward developing the kind of behavior that is needed by citizens in a democracy.

The Nature of Modern Science

Through modern science man strives always for a better understanding of the universe. Unfounded prejudices, false opinions, gossip, rumor, astrology, myths, and superstition cannot be considered reliable sources.

Science is an active, dynamic field, constantly demanding willingness to make new observations, to repeat experiments, to consider new facts, and to challenge earlier conclusions. Science is far from a finished subject; in fact, it is likely that science is only in its beginnings. All the areas of science are undergoing change as a result of continuous study. New ideas are being added and old ideas revised. There is constant development of our ideas about such varied subjects of scientific inquiry, as stars, ventilation, weather, the oceans, living things, diseases, nutrition, rocks, and metals.

Man learns through experiences, by means of his senses. New instruments such as telescopes, microscopes, and others, have extended man's range of observation and experience. By means of such new instruments man is able to push his study into areas new to him—the distant galaxies of stars, the interior of Earth. He is learning about ultra-microscopic particles and the nucleus of the atom. His study has not been confined to the present, for he has been able to learn about events that occurred in the distant past of Earth and of the universe.

In spite of our many new technical tools, it is exceedingly difficult to explain many happenings in nature, even everyday occurrences. So scientists have been forced to develop provisional explanations, or hypotheses, to guide them in their further study of many things. But scientists must abandon any hypothesis as soon as it is found to be unsatisfactory. There is much that scientists have not explained satisfactorily. Many times a scientist must say he does not know about problems within his own field of specialization, even though he may rightly be considered the world's leading authority on the problem involved.

However, hypotheses, although tentative in character, have been very helpful in making new discoveries and inventions. Hypotheses of science have played an important part in the recent history of mankind. Many important modern inventions and discoveries have been made possible only by the use of hypotheses.

Democracy, Science, and Religious Freedom. There is considerable evidence that three great achievements of mankind—democracy, scientific techniques, and religious freedom—developed contemporaneously and out of the same human struggles. An examination of these achievements will indicate that these three have much in common in basic meanings. In the opinion of many students,

real science cannot exist outside a democracy.

Democracy can exist only where there is freedom of investigation. In other words freedom is necessary both to science and to democracy. Then, too, there can be no real democracy, nor real science, where there is no freedom of religious belief. And there can be no freedom of religion when there is no political or scientific freedom. When there is true democracy, there is freedom of religion and of science.

Of course, there has been some excellent scientific research in totalitarian states in certain fields. However, if the dictatorship sets up absolute rules or absolute facts for research, which most dictatorships have been inclined to do from the very dawn of history, there can be little reliability to the research carried on under such conditions.

The implications of the absolute point of view of knowledge and of the concept of modern science are indicated in the following chart.

Science and Behavior

The Implications of Science for Human Relations. This condensed description of the nature of science and the interrelationships of science, democracy, and religious freedom has been provided because it has many implications for a teacher and can provide her with a sense of security and adequacy in teaching children. Every teacher has the right according to the modern concept of science to play an honest role in the classroom. She has a right to admit that she is learning; that she

makes mistakes sometimes; that sometimes a child with a special interest may be learning faster than she is in that particular area. In a very real sense, the techniques of science require honesty, and neither teacher nor child should be penalized in any way for being honest. The learner should never be humiliated or made to feel apologetic for the admission of ignorance. The implications of science for mental hygiene and human relations are profound.

Concepts of Knowledge and Ways of Thinking

CHARACTERISTICS OF A SOCIETY	BASED ON AN ABSOLUTE POINT OF VIEW OF KNOWLEDGE	BASED ON THE CONCEPT OF MODERN SCIENCE
1. Nature of truth	Fixed concept of truth	Development and testing of hypotheses
2. Nature of knowledge	Knowledge absolute	Knowledge subject to revision
3. Nature of thought	Thought control: ideas passed down from above	Thought development: individual has right to develop own hypotheses
4. Nature of interpretation	All interpretation of the events of the environment must conform to prescribed thought	Interpretation of events based on observation and logical thought subject to revision
5. Nature of education	Education based on propaganda	Education based on freedom of thought
6. The curriculum	Rigid body of content for learning	Flexible content for learning
7. Nature of learning	Superstition	Learning through experience
8. Nature of teaching	Dictatorial teaching	Developmental teaching
9. Teaching-learning	Stress on recitation and memorization	Developmental procedures
10. Personal attitude	Dogmatism	Open-mindedness
11. Outlook on the universe	Fixed outlook: prejudiced: preconceived	Objective, realistic outlook on universe
12. Values	Values fixed by absolutes	Constant consideration of values
13. Goals of learning	Knowledge can be mastered	Concept of continuous learning
14. Attitudes	Fixed status of attitudes	Attitudes continuously subject to revision
15. Attitudes toward religion	Religious dogmatism: imposition of religious ideas	Religious freedom and tolerance
16. Attitudes toward future	Predetermination of events	Discovery, invention, creativeness
17. Outlook on the future	Certainty	Uncertainty but with intelligent resourcefulness
18. Place of the individual	State or group control of individual	Right of the individual to choose
19. Adjustment	Adjustment to prescribed order	Resourcefulness, adequacy to problems of future
20. Discipline	Obedience to commands	Democratic discipline
21. Acceptance of ideas	Gullibility: acceptance of dictated ideas	Call for evidence, logical thinking, independent thought
22. Means of governing	Autocratic	Democratic processes
23. Meaning of "authority"	Authority is a dictator	Authority is a consultant
24. Method of making decisions	By dictation or revolution	Democratic processes

Stating the Source of Information. In science it is important to state the source of our comment in explaining a phenomenon, such as evaporation of water, hibernation of animals, erosion of soils, and so on. For instance, we might say, "I read an explanation in . . ."; or "My father said . . ."; or "On my way to school I saw . . ."; or "I think it might have been . . ."; or "I used my imagination"; or "I have an idea . . ." or "I think I am right"; or "I can do something to show. . . ." This is preferable to giving such information as if the statements were unquestioned facts. We have sometimes called this identifying the source of a comment. Teachers and children should develop the behavior pattern of identifying the source of comments they may make in discussions in science and all important matters. Either child or teacher might ask such questions as "Where did you get the information?" "Why should I accept the information as being reliable?" "How do you know that it is reliable (or accurate)?"

Both teachers and children have a right to use their imagination, to speculate, and to repeat information as long as they distinguish between reliable and unreliable information. By such behavior we assume *responsibility* for our speech. It is quite different from the behavior of gossip, loose talk, and rumor spreading.

This type of development should not be allowed to harm the good human relationships of children. Frequently children use parents' opinions as reliable information. It would be well for the teacher to handle such comments in a manner that will in no way decrease the child's respect for his parents. The attitude of the teacher may be that we are glad to hear what the parent has said, and indicate at some suitable time that further development of the statement is given in authoritative books.

Perhaps the comment might be, "What do persons who spend their lives studying this kind of thing have to say?" Science instruction should be utilized to improve the human relationships of children—those of children with other children, children with teachers, and children with parents.

It is obvious that the great behavior patterns growing out of science are not built in a finished manner in a day, in a year, or even in a decade. For instance, critical-mindedness and open-mindedness, responsibleness, and resourcefulness require time for development. Development of these patterns of behavior should be considered a continuous program throughout the elementary school and on throughout life.

It would be well for the teacher to consider the relations of the content and techniques of science in the development of such behavior patterns as open-mindedness, critical-mindedness, and responsibleness. The instruction for these behavior patterns should not be isolated from other instruction, nor from life itself. Teaching-learning activities in any aspect or content area of science in childhood education can be utilized in developing desirable behavior for democratic citizenship.

Developing Open-Mindedness

Willingness to Consider New Information. A scientist must be willing to examine everything which will help him secure the right conclusions. The great contributions of Darwin grew out of his willingness to investigate anything and everything which related to his problem. This characteristic of the scientist has significance for childhood education.

As children proceed through school, they should learn to examine everything related to a given issue. Children should be eager to listen to the comments, proposals, conceptions, objections of others. On the other hand, a child who is reluctant to accept a given conclusion because of certain observations he has made should feel free to state the reasons for his reluctance. It is the teacher's task to build up a spirit of tolerance in the classroom. However, this spirit of tolerance should not be utilized as an excuse for inaction. One can still be willing to listen to suggestions from his fellows, to recognize the importance of looking at many aspects of the problem, and yet follow through with desirable action. We can be tolerant and yet be active in improving conditions in our classroom, playground, and community.

Remedying Dogmatic Traits in Children. It is not uncommon to discover in a class children with a tendency to be dogmatic. Children who are successful in certain fields, and therefore frequently correct in their information as compared with their fellow classmates, may assume an attitude of always being right. Such children may display an unwillingness to consider other explanations. They become quite intolerant of suggestions from their fellow students, and disdain further investigation or the suggestion that they "look it up" in an authoritative source. Experiences in the study of science can be used to indicate the importance of a willingness to consider new evidence. The teacher may relate this attitude to specific illustrations affecting social behavior, such as group planning, where an open-mindedness to suggestions from others should be apparent.

In a classroom of ten-year-olds, a teacher wrote the word "grateful" on the blackboard. Henry, a child of superior intelligence, told her she had the *e* in the wrong place, assuming that the word was spelled "greatful." She asked him to look up the word in the dictionary. The child was so certain of his own spelling that he replied, after using the dictionary, "The word isn't in the dictionary." This experience of Henry's was used to make a comparison with their learnings in science. One child pointed out, "In science you don't call another person wrong until you are sure of your facts."

Avoiding Gullibility. Open-mindedness should in no way be confused with gullibility. While we want to teach children to be open-minded, we must at the same time avoid developing gullibility. Although we strive for a willingness to consider new ideas, we accept

ideas as right only when they have been proved to be so, or proved to be the most reliable we can secure at that special time.

We may have convictions on matters and still be open-minded. For instance, we can believe in democracy, in education, and in improvement of living conditions for all people, but our convictions should not prevent us from examining weaknesses in our beliefs and injustices in conditions about us.

Gullibility is illustrated in the following incident. A group of adults in a large city accepted the explanation that modern children are wild because children are no longer being nursed by their mothers, but instead are being raised on cows' milk. The wildness of the children, it was said, was caused by the milk of the cows. This idea that the wildness of the children was due to "wild" milk from "wild" cows was advanced by someone who had attached the title of "doctor" to his name in order to lend authority to his ideas. The reasoning of this "doctor" was that (1) we have more wild children today (which we can not accept as fact), (2) we have more children nourished by cow's milk, and therefore (3) cows' milk is the root of our evil. The people who had accepted this idea had little or no education to help them evaluate the reliableness of the source of the statement. (In this case the source was the "doctor".)

Our education should assist children to look through the trappings of propaganda, dogmatic assumptions, and unreliable sources of information and to think logically and realistically about all important matters. Citizens in a democracy must not be gullible. In fact, we might say they must ever be alert against gullibility.

Changing the Attitudes of Children. A teacher of a one-room rural school relates how fearful the children in her building were during electrical storms. She immediately made plans for a study of electrical storms, including lightning and thunder. From this study the children considered what they should do during such a storm to secure the greatest possible safety. Here we have the consideration of new ideas in the face of community superstitions and the change of behavior as a result of learning in science. We have an illustration, also, of the relation between knowledge and the change of attitudes and behavior.

Many children have encountered the need for changes as a result of new information about food, vitamins, sanitation, and the like. In the later elementary grades, and even to some extent in the earlier years, children may gain some comprehension of the changes that have been brought about by new discoveries or by the introduction of new objects, ideas or methods into the community—for example, rural electrification, synthetics, plastics, or improvements of water supply and sanitation.

The Attitudes and Behavior of Teachers. In her own behavior a teacher, too, must display the ability to learn. She should be willing to have her own statements investigated by the group. Teachers usually gain the children's respect by such a procedure. Another way of stating this is that a teacher should welcome an opportunity of learning with the children.

A group of children asked a teacher whether a certain experience would "work" under different conditions. The teacher quickly said, "No." The children asked whether they might try it under those conditions. He said, "Yes." The experiment worked under the new conditions. All laughed, including the teacher, as he said, "Well, you see I learned something." The class continued their investigation with a spirit which indicated that the teacher had actually cemented a bond between himself and the children by this experience of "give-and-take."

We have in this incident an experience in connection with instruction becoming the setting for an experiment as a result of the inquiries of the children (p. 126).

Perhaps no factor has greater potentialities for developing behavior patterns in the education of children than the behavior children observe in the adults with whom they are associated. Teachers and parents may teach a great deal through a little behavior. The behavior of small children very frequently reflects the attitudes and behavior of parents.

Attitudes such as open-mindedness may be displayed by adults by the way the adults approach the interests of children. For instance, a small child may bring an object to an adult. Usually in such cases the child will watch the adult's behavior with tremendous concentration. Such situations have potentialities as teaching-learning situations.

The adult can brush aside the interest of the child by making a comment of no relevance to the object in question, such as "Your face is dirty." By such a comment as this the adult gives the impression that he, the parent, sees no importance in giving direct attention to the real concerns of the child.

On the other hand, the adult can display open-mindedness by manifesting interest in the object that the child brings to him. He can look at the object. If the object is something to be operated the adult can take his turn in operating it. He can learn not only about the object but about the child, his interests, his ideas, and his kind of thinking.

Perhaps the adult can introduce the child to a new phenomenon by means of the object. If it is a bright object, such as a pan, he may reflect the light in different directions and allow the child to take his turn at producing this new phenomenon.

Susan, one year old, found her parents interested in looking at things she brought them. The parents displayed a behavior of learning, even with simple toys which interested her. Their attitude seemed to suggest that they could learn more. From a very young age

Susan observed the open-minded behavior toward learning which her parents displayed.

The parents took Susan with them to visit many places, sometimes on short trips and sometimes on long trips. When Susan was eight years old she went on a long automobile trip with her parents. They visited some of the national parks. Susan sat at the campfire with her parents one evening, while they listened to the Ranger-naturalist talk. She didn't understand all of the talk, but she did understand part of it. After the talk people asked questions. Susan's mother asked a question of the Ranger. Susan was proud of her mother—it wasn't surprising to Susan to see her mother learning.

As they walked back to their tent after the campfire, she listened to her parents and sometimes she talked. She didn't understand fully all of their talk, but there were many expressions she heard that summer which reflected open minds on the part of her parents and helped to build up a behavior pattern of open-mindedness.

For instance, she heard her father say, "You know I thought bears . . . , but I was wrong, according to the Ranger-naturalist, and he knows more about bears than I do." Father seemed to be learning a great deal on the trip. He wasn't ashamed of learning.

But Susan was learning, too. They gave Susan opportunities to talk about her experiences and to be a part of the family study group. They listened to Susan's ideas. Furthermore, sometimes the parents changed their minds about some things as a result of suggestions made by Susan. One day Father made a statement. Susan said, "But Daddy, I saw the bird and it was red," and Father said, "Well Susan, if you say it was red, I am inclined to believe it was. But suppose we watch for some others." The parents exhibited learning tendencies along with teaching-learning situations.

It didn't seem to make so much difference who knew the most, or who was right or wrong, correct or incorrect. The question was not *who* had the best information, but rather *what* was the best information. Their discussions were never debates.

Susan was not allowed to monopolize the conversation on the trip, even though she showed a tendency to do so at times. One reason for her eagerness to allow Father and Mother to participate in the conversation was that Father and Mother listened to her and talked right to her—not above her, not below her. There was a give-and-take which developed respect all around. Her parents accepted her as a companion as well as a daughter.

Susan's father and mother recognized there was much they did not know, and that there was much knowledge for mankind to discover. This meant that they had one thing in common with Susan, that there was much to learn.

Susan is older now. But she still gets into teaching-learning situations with her parents. She often has something to share with her parents, something she has read, something she has learned, a new human relationship, and so on. She knows her parents will listen to her experiences and her imaginings and her learnings.

Open-Mindedness Revealed in Behavior. Indications of open-mindedness often prove disappointing or annoying to someone who is dogmatic or to someone who wishes the feeling of security which may come from a final and certain answer. Scientists are often disappointing to other people because they are cautious in their statements. For instance, a scientist in his field may say, "Well, it isn't fully known. Dr. Brown, who spent some time studying it, proposed that the explanation may be . . ." A scientist will consider all the evidence he can find, even if the evidence causes him to abandon some of his original ideas.

The open-minded individual is usually a good citizen. He looks at all sides of an issue. He is willing to listen to others. He can take suggestions. He is interested in good ways of doing things. He is willing to change his mind. He is democratic.

One can frequently evaluate attitudes of dogmatism or open-mindedness through listening to comments.

Dogmatism is frequently indicated by remarks such as "There is only one way to answer that." "I know what causes that." "You listen to me." "Why, of course, it has to be." "I have the answer." Dogmatism is indicated in an individual by his failure to listen to another's idea or, having heard the idea, to consider it. Dogmatism is also indicated by persons who are unable to recognize that there may be specialists in the area under consideration. Dogmatism is sometimes indicated by the individual who starts talking before another individual is through. Sometimes dogmatic statements are made with unnecessary show of emphasis or emotion.

Sidney grew up in a home in which the father was dominating. The mother gave in to the father's opinions constantly. Once the father gave an opinion on anything, he expected everyone to accept it without question. He took personal offense at the least questioning of his ideas.

Sidney learned that the home was more peaceful if he never indicated any disagreement on any subject with his father. In fact, he adopted the policy from early childhood of waiting to learn his father's ideas on a new subject before expressing his own views. However, much of Sidney's thinking on subjects was never revealed to the family during the period before he started out on his own. On some subjects on which Sidney's father was especially vehement, Sidney didn't seem to think at all. Sidney's attitude seemed to be, "Why even bother to think about it, for Father won't let me talk about it in my own way."

After he started on his own career, Sidney found himself in rebellion against all of his father's ideas: he seemed to enjoy rushing to the opposite extreme. He belonged to a different political party from that of his father. He joined a different church, and supported measures in the community which his father opposed. During this period the criterion he used for decisions was, "Do the opposite from what my father did." He became just as dogmatic in his rebellion against his father as his father had been in making decisions for his family.

As Sidney reached the maturity of middle age, he finally established his mental and emotional equilibrium, and he became a stable, well-adjusted individual. He began to realize he was deciding issues for himself and his family on the basis of irrational emotions established in him in childhood. He began to consider matters on an objective basis and gradually began to encourage democratic procedures in family discussions. In turn, his feeling mellowed towards his father, for he came to understand the errors he himself had made with his own family.

Meanings Contributing to Open-Mindedness. In their experiences in science and other fields children should come to accept such ideas as the following:

There are many things which scientists are not able to explain in any final way.

Scientists try to learn more about the universe.

People who have specialized in a given area are the most reliable sources of information.

Scientists in a given area must be willing to consider the ideas of other scientists in the same field.

Scientists find it desirable to check their thinking by performing experiments, making observations, and checking with authoritative information whenever possible.

There is much for all of us to learn.

To make sure that we have the right explanations, we must think very carefully.

On all important matters, people should make certain they have the most reliable information before making important decisions.

We should be willing to listen to the ideas of other people.

We need not accept such ideas in a final way unless they prove to be reliable.

We must be willing for others to challenge our ideas.

Many people jump to conclusions without doing good thinking or searching for evidence. Sometimes these conclusions do harm.

Some things which seem to be facts today may not be true tomorrow.

We should expect new discoveries and inventions.

New discoveries and inventions may make great changes in the way we live. We should expect and strive to make these changes for the better.

New discoveries and inventions may make it necessary for us to change our thinking about many things.

We should be willing to change our thinking whenever necessary.

We should not decide what to do on a basis of anger, fear, prejudice, hatred, or ignorance.

We should listen to good suggestions or ideas, even if these suggestions and ideas come from people of some other region, another race, or another religion.

Developing Critical-Mindedness

Through science man strives for better understanding of the world. This characteristic, too, has wide implications for the procedures of teaching in the elementary school, because it presents a clear demand for critical-mindedness. Unfounded beliefs, prejudices, opinions, gossip, rumor, astrology, myths, intuition, and superstition cannot be considered sources upon which reliance can be placed. A scientist must always be willing to abandon a theory he has developed if that theory no longer is satisfactory. He must make certain that he has done all the work that is necessary before he can ask others to accept his findings. He must be willing to consult anyone regardless of race, religion, or nationality, who may be able to assist him in his problem. He must be willing to consider the careful findings of others competent in his field or in related fields. Discoveries in science call for careful planning and thinking. A scientist must distinguish in his writings and speech between statements that he finds are reliable and those in which he is merely expressing a possibility or supposition. It is only through such steps as these that a person can be considered an authority in a given field.

Furthermore, a scientist is considered an authority only in the field of science in which he specializes. An astronomer may be an authority on variable stars but not on birds and mammals. A modern scientist works within a limited field; even then he finds many problems to work on throughout his life. He never learns all about the field in which he specializes, for there is always more to discover.

In the far-reaching sense, the best idea is one secured from an authoritative source. Education must indicate, then, the place of men who are authorities. It is also incumbent upon a government to be guided by the best available information about its problems; for instance, it is important for a nation to secure the best informaion it can from experts on weather in all problems relating to the weather. The people of a nation must be certain that such agencies are staffed by a personnel that will be competent in the subjects involved. Children should be initiated into the function and place of scientific authorities and governmental scientific agencies. Among the latter may be listed departments of agriculture, weather bureaus, and geological surveys, of state, province, or nation.

Scientists should not be presented to children as supermen. The lives of such scientists as Louis Pasteur, Benjamin Franklin, Michael Faraday, George Washington Carver, and Michael Pupin can be used to present the humble surroundings into which some of the most important scientists were born. Many great scientists remain humble throughout their lives. In fact, the heritage of science is not that of the supernatural, but rather that of diligent and courageous effort and willingness to co-operate with others.

Much of the foregoing has a direct application to the method of securing facts and the application of facts to problems. Children bring to the classroom an assortment of ideas, some based on prejudices, opinions, gossip, astrology, superstitions, and other unscientific sources—ideas secured largely from adults. These, in turn, will be mixed with some ideas that are reliable. The teacher will find it an impossible task to weed out all the false ideas, but she can direct a child's growth to a method of determining what seems to be reliable and what seems to be unreliable. This is an important element in the establishment of good citizenship.

Making the Distinction Between Fact and Fiction. The teacher will find a wide variety of experiences which can be utilized to direct a child toward the importance of reliable information. Early in his school life he should know that there is a difference between fairy tales and reliable explanations. There can be little doubt that many children are given too steady a diet of fairy tales, comic pages, and other fictional materials, with the result that they become escapists from the world of realities. It is quite clear that a teacher should avoid combining fiction with science. Good fiction has its proper place in a child's life, but it should never be utilized to explain natural phenomena. It has been proved that children find scientific explanations, when properly presented, just as challenging as "make-believe" accounts. Alice Williams,[1] in her study, found that if a story got in the way of scientific factual material children were irritated. Books for children which combine science with fiction cannot in any real sense be considered authentic science books.

Young children frequently strive to distinguish between fiction and fact through such questions as "Is this make-believe?' and "Is this true?" Later on the child has many opportunities to question the reliability of material covering a broader scope of living. He lives in a world which will try to tell him what to eat, what products to buy, how to dress, what to read, how to vote, and how to think and act on a wide variety of matters. The discipline of science, with its demands for honesty of thought and speech, with its constant challenge for reliability of statement, should be so thoroughly a part of the curriculum that the generation now in the elementary schools will be better able to distinguish between propaganda and reliable information than any generation that has preceded it.

Some children tend to jump to hasty conclusions and snap judgments without examining the facts essential to those conclusions. Unfortunately, education, too frequently

[1] Alice Williams, *Children's Choice of Science Books.* Teachers College, Columbia University, New York, 1939, p. 153.

geared to rewarding the individual for speed through the traditional recitation and achievement tests, often encourages the development of superficial thinking. In science we must call for thorough thinking, for a consideration of all the evidence, for a willingness to check conclusions further, for an attempt to relate conclusions to observations and experience, for an emphasis upon accuracy rather than upon speed and superficiality. There is much to support the idea that science in the elementary school should be freed from the pressure and haste that do not accord with the natural rhythm and tempo of children.

In science children at all levels should be directed toward the importance of making their own thinking reliable. This is not meant to imply that there cannot be a place for imagination or speculation in science; but teachers should strive to develop in the children an awareness of the times when they are utilizing imagination and speculation and of the times when they are dealing with reliable facts. As a child proceeds through the elementary school, he should be taught the importance of telling his comrades when he is merely speculating, and should recognize the importance of avoiding the presentation of mere speculations as facts. This type of procedure can easily become a part of the education of young children. The teacher can challenge a child kindly with such queries as "Where did you get this information?" "Why do you think this information is correct?" and "Do you want us to believe (or accept) this explanation?"

Seeking Reliable Information. Through experiences and experiments with phenomena, discussions, excursions, or thoughtful reading of authoritative books, a child may have an opportunity to develop his ideas and attempt to find out whether they are correct. In the later elementary years and in the sec-

ondary school his attention should be turned definitely toward the consideration of propaganda.

It is also apparent that young children can develop hypotheses as tentative explanations, submitting these explanations to tests which they themselves propose. A group of nine-year-olds was attempting to explain why a candle flame went out when a bottle was inverted over it. One proposed that the candle flame had not had time to adjust itself to the bottle. (They had used the term *adjust* in their social studies.) A number of the group accepted this explanation. The teacher encouraged them to question the explanation. All agreed that, if this explanation were true, the flame would adjust itself if the bottle were brought down slowly enough. Considerable time was spent in bringing the bottle down slowly over the flame, and there was much repetition of the experiment. Finally they agreed that this explanation (hypothesis) was unsatisfactory and that they must look for another.

Frequently observations will cause children to disagree about their conclusions. Such instances can be utilized to indicate that one should draw conclusions only from observations which have been carefully made. It is a well-known fact that observers of an incident, such as a highway accident, may vary greatly in their reporting of the way in which the accident occurred.

It is true that many conclusions accepted by science teachers and scientists, and explanations gained from actual observations of experiments, have later proved to be inaccurate. This indicates that doing an experiment once is not a foolproof way of getting accurate information.

Children should realize that they must be willing to check the conclusions secured from observations against the conclusions of scientific authorities who have made a study of the matter under consideration. Many erroneous conclusions can result from superficial observation. In the final analysis, the best conclusion is obtained by consulting an authority; for children, this means that in almost all cases the best authority for them is an authoritative book of science designed for children.

In one's own community there are often scientific authorities who will be willing to co-operate with the children. In some communities there are scientific institutions such as universities, experimental agricultural farms, industrial laboratories, or weather stations which can be utilized. However, in almost no locality will the teacher be able to find in all fields scientific authorities who are available at the times when they are most needed or who are able to give the proper guidance to children.

Recently a group of eleven-year-olds revealed an almost complete lack of understanding of the place of real scientific authority in their work. One youngster thought the dictionary had the final and most reliable information on all subjects. The teacher utilized this situation to build constructive attitudes about securing the most reliable information. They concluded, quite rightly, that the dictionary was not an authoritative book for scientific knowledge.

Accuracy a Direction Rather than a Status at All Levels

Since man is continuously in the process of making new discoveries and revising his information, accuracy is not an exact status. This means that in the school we do not teach a fact as though it would be true for all time. It indicates, also that we cannot teach all the truth about any single subject. What we can do, however, is to make certain that what a child learns is consistent with the best interpretation available at any given moment and indicate that the interpretation may be changed at some future time.

Accuracy is a direction toward which man in his best efforts must always strive. It is also a goal toward which teachers, parents, and children can move in teaching and learning; it calls for growth for teachers and children alike. The child's ideas which are gained from study can be accurate insofar as they go, but as the child proceeds through the school, his knowledge about any one subject increases in scope and in detail.

In other words, we may not be able to teach children all the reliable information in science about a given subject, but what we do teach can be consistent with what is reliable. Authoritative books can be most useful to both children and teachers in maintaining a high standard of accuracy and a sound development of attitudes.

We cannot hastily call an item correct or incorrect. Instead, it is essential that in all our discussion, thoughtful reading, experiments, and so on we determine what is the most reliable information at a given time. It may not be as serious to be mistaken in the information we may have at any time, as it is to assume that there may be no need to secure new information on important matters throughout our lives. It is also a serious matter to pass along information as if there were no question about its accuracy when we are not sure of its reliability. The nature of modern science is thus entirely consistent with the idea that learning takes place through the continuous growth and development of large concepts. It also indicates how necessary it is to view education as a process which takes place from the cradle to the grave.

The teacher should note that the vogue in education for developing the curriculum in terms of exhaustive isolated units of work is not in keeping with the modern concept of knowledge.

Fortunately, this latter idea of truth does not prove disturbing to children when it is built into their early instruction. Children frequently respond very favorably to the idea that there is much for them to discover in adult life. The adult, on the other hand, sometimes has difficulties when he learns that he must be willing to consider new ideas. The transition of an adult's thought patterns to a realization of the need for constantly revising his knowledge is frequently a period of conflict and frustration. Many teachers have found that when children are introduced to science as an active, dynamic field early in their experience, they avoid this period of frustration in adult life.

As one considers what has been written above, one may well become convinced that the methods and techniques used should be in accordance with honest, intelligent behavior. Science has called for honesty in investigation. In science one must not issue a statement as a reliable statement unless he is certain it is. One must be willing to make certain his data are correct. He must label a statement for what it is, that is, an opinion, a hypothesis, an observation, a fact. A scientist must be honest in his work, for the techniques of science require honesty. The implications of this for behavior will be considered on pages 61–62, to procedures of the classroom on pages 108–111, and to mental hygiene on pages 103–144.

Accuracy is a guide line in learning not only through childhood but throughout life.

New developments in science may bring new discoveries and have profound influence upon decisions in vast areas of personal, national, and international life. In a democracy, individuals must desire to pass judgment on important issues only on the basis of the most reliable information available. The training to weigh evidence and to consider what is and what is not the most reliable information should begin in the early education of children. It should begin in the home before the children start to school. Every citizen in a democracy will need to revise his ideas on many things from time to time if he is to assume the full responsibilities of citizenship.

Being Honest with Children of All Ages. Frequently the statement is made "Well, these are little children; we do not have to be so accurate with them." In statements of this kind, one finds a failure to understand science from the developmental point of view.

Many of the concepts of science require time before they can be understood by an individual. As might be expected, a person at any level may require additional experience before an idea can be understood or even, when it has been understood, be completely acceptable.

Children are naturally more limited in experience than adults. But limitation of experience on the part of the learner is no excuse for condoning error. As has been indicated above, what children learn can be in keeping with accuracy as far as the learning goes. We can not teach or learn at any age short of specialization all the known facts on any subject of science.

The teacher need have no hesitation in having any statement modified by doubt if she feels uncertain about any proposal or tentative suggestion coming from herself or from her children. In any discussion which is developmental in nature a teacher may set the stage favorably for the proper evaluation of all comments and proposals made by children.

There may be misconceptions on the part of the learner. This is also true for the teacher, in a good teaching-learning situation. The learner may have a misconception one day, to be remedied by a more accurate conception the next. The teacher is not to be condemned for lack of knowledge, provided she continues to teach in a spirit of honesty consistent with science.

Science Is Not Fiction. Science is not fiction, nor is fiction science. There is no opposition here to the reading of any kind of desirable fiction so long as it is recognized that it is fiction. In a discussion in science, fiction can not be considered as authentic material, regardless of how much it may be dressed up with pseudo-science.

This is especially true, for example, of space-travel. Fiction writers frequently use some reliable information with their fiction. This seems to provide enough realism to carry the story.

When children quote science fiction, the challenge isn't one for the teacher solely. It would be well to ask children who quote such fiction, "Does your information come from a book, from a movie, or from television?" "Who wrote the story?" "Is he an authority?" "Was he writing a story or was he writing reliable science?" "Have you checked the story?" "How much do you think is reliable?" "Do you want us to believe it?"

In this type of questioning the teacher need not discourage reading of fiction, so long as the children will recognize it for what it is.

Meanings Contributing to Critical-Mindedness. In the development of critical-mindedness it is important that the child be directed at all times toward authoritative material in science. The following are suggestive of the type of meanings which children may derive from instruction directed toward critical thinking in the classroom:

Fairy tales and myths can have no part in reliable explanations.

Many superstitions, prejudices, and myths that have no foundation in fact are passed down from generation to generation. We cannot depend upon them.

Astrologers and fortune-tellers are unable to see or predict the future for anyone.

We do not secure correct explanations of anything by guessing or by uncontrolled use of the imagination.

Many people are not careful about the opinions they give. They do not check them to see whether they are correct.

We cannot depend upon the opinions of people who have not made a careful study of what they are talking about.

Opinions should never be presented as if they were facts.

We must be willing to change our ideas whenever it is necessary to do so.

Where important matters are concerned, we should rely only upon what we know to be the very best information.

We should place confidence in the techniques which are used by scientists.

When we want to secure the best information, we must turn to reliable authorities.

It is desirable to check our thinking by performing experiments, making observations, and consulting reliable people and books.

We should never strive to influence others unless we are certain that we have reliable information.

Advances in science make it necessary to change our ideas about many things from time to time.

Matters that affect the welfare of people should be thought through very carefully.

It is important for us to get the best information we can whenever we are performing any civic duties, such as voting or holding office.

People filling important positions in the government and in the community should be well trained for the positions they hold.

Not everything that is printed is correct. It is important that our government should publish only reliable information.

On matters of importance, we should use only material written by authorities.

As scientists make new discoveries, it becomes necessary to revise books of science.

Modern science is the product of human minds.

Scientists are not supermen. The discoveries of science result only from careful study.

The discoveries of the present and future are dependent upon the discoveries of the past.

Developing Intelligent Responsibleness in Children: Conservation As a Pattern for Behavior

Learning to Think through to Consequences. In the study of science we have an unusual opportunity to improve the behavior of children in the direction of assuming responsibility. A toy that is thrown about and carelessly treated is not likely to operate successfully very long. The domestic plant or pet animal at home or school that is well cared for proves to be more useful than if it is neglected and treated irresponsibly. The electric train operated carefully and thoughtfully may provide great satisfaction for years and may even be passed on from one generation to another. The roller skates left to rust outdoors may soon prove to be useless. In these incidents we have illustrations of the "consequences of events" which indicate the importance of assuming responsibility for the materials of our environment. Instruction in science can assist in providing explanations and in developing intelligent responsibleness for the materials of our physical universe.

Thinking through to the possible consequences of our behavior is associated with learning from experiences and with an understanding of the natural *sequence* of events that children encounter in their daily life. A few illustrations of such sequences are: Earth rotates, causing the sun to "rise" in the east, bringing day, and to "set" in the west, bring-

ing night; spring arrives after winter, and we have renewed growth; fuels burning cause smoke; smoke gets into the air, and we have a dirty city; in most places in the northern middle latitudes (temperate zone) a wind from the north brings colder weather; the cover is left off the paste jar, and the paste dries out; the water in mud puddles evaporates in dry weather, and the mud becomes dust. Children can experience many sequences of events. These sequences are determined by the energy and forces of the universe, including, of course, human energy.

In the main, these sequences of events roll over our lives every day and we are none the worse for them. But when we behave without considering the consequences of the sequence that follows the behavior, we may do harm to someone, perhaps to ourselves. If we run around a corner we may knock someone down. If we make a path across the yard, we may have mud puddles there in a rainy period. If we are careless with a campfire, we may cause a forest fire. These consequences and many others can be explained in terms of energy, evaporation, combustion, and other phenomena. Therefore, there are many experiences and meanings (content) in science which can be utilized to make the idea of a sequence of events acceptable.

We use the term *sequence of events* here rather than the traditional term *cause and effect* because it is more consistent with what children, and for that matter adults, observe. The use of the term is consistent with the concept of causality as presented by modern science.

However, it is true that children very frequently press back to origins and causes. It seems as if one of the drives of children and of mankind is to get back to the reason for, and cause of, events. But even the most highly specialized scientist can scarcely contend he has found the ultimate cause with all finality for events or phenomena. For there may be a cause back of the cause he suggests. The "cause" the scientist discovers may be an effect of a more basic "cause" which he has not yet fully interpreted. In science we do develop working explanations; however, few would contend that we have found final explanations. Most of our explanations are hypotheses. This discussion illustrates again the characteristic of honesty in scientific techniques. This treatment of causality should be considered along with the nature of science (pp. 45–51).

There is no objection to a child or teacher using the word *cause,* however, provided he is developing toward an understanding of the real meaning of the term. Progress of children should be evaluated in terms of improvement in behavior (Part V).

In a sense, children gain some experiential meaning of the sequences of events very early in their lives. One could illustrate this in many ways. "What goes up must come down" is an old saying describing Earth's force of gravitation: a child may learn about this force by experience, perceiving the sequence of events involved even before he can talk. Such a child learns to anticipate the "coming down." He is involved in the use of gravity when he drinks from a cup; he experiences water flowing down in a very per-

sonal way. Later he may attempt to use a straw, thus drinking upwards. This he must learn to do, for it is a different experience involving the use of gravity. His early experiences with the sequence of events involved in eating, drinking and playing may cause him to need many a bath and change of clothing before he learns to anticipate such common sequences of events.

His experience with a ball, drinking from a cup, floating objects in a tank, the water fountain, the washing of his hair, the seesaw, and the swing may be experiential learnings about gravity. It is interesting to note, however, that *gravity* is only a *word* for gravity as a force pulling objects to the center of our Earth (pp. 716–722), but the word does not explain what that force is and why it acts as it does. In this way we have evidence of young children having experiential learnings about something at the age of a few months which cannot be completely explained by the most specialized scientists.

Working with materials in the classroom and at home may be used to illustrate, over and over again, the sequences of events and how certain conditions and certain behavior produce certain events. Experiences with the sky, water, soil, rust, evaporation, air currents and other phenomena as described in Parts II, III, and IV of this volume can be utilized to illustrate the sequence of events.

EXPERIENCE. *We can feel air move when we fan.* Have someone we might call Mary move a fan back and forth through the air. Have another person we might call John stand a few feet away from the fanning object. Does John feel it? If not, have him gradually move closer to Mary.

The fan *moves* the air. The motion of the air is *felt* by the other person, even though the air cannot be seen.

The experiment could be repeated. Have

John blindfolded. Have Mary fan with the object noiselessly. Can John tell when Mary fans and when she stops fanning?

If John has dampened his face with water, he can feel the moving air more easily. Water evaporates more rapidly in moving air. Water, when it is evaporating, has a cooling effect which may be felt on the skin.

Here we have a common sequence of events: Mary fans, air is moved by the fan, John feels the moving air although he is several feet away, John is cooled by the more rapid evaporation of the moisture.

Excursions outside the classroom, including the short ones, will be useful in indicating sequences of events. On the playground plants may have difficulty in getting started to grow because the germinating seeds are apt to be trampled underfoot and because the soil is hard-packed by the activities of the children. At the margin of the playground, however, where there is not so much tramping of shoes on plants and soil, there may be a few scattered plants. A path through the thicket or weed patch at the side of the school playground or across a vacant lot will be almost devoid of plants, while on each side there may be many plants. This kind of thing can be noticed in both humid and dry areas, in the city and in the country. The lush vegetation close to the border of an irrigation ditch, even though it may be weeds, represents a sequence of events following the introduction of water in the ditch, while at a short distance from the ditch where land is dry there may be very few plants. The term "sequence of events" need not be used with children while developing growth toward a behavior of responsibleness. We are concerned with developing an appreciation of the *idea* "sequence of events" and an ability to recognize and cope with the "sequence of events" in life rather than with the teaching of the term.

Impulsive and Random Behavior. Impulsiveness is a trait which is not confined to children. An adult who realized he was lost on the prairie on a dark night testifies to recalling the impulse to move at random in any direction. The same adult noted the same tendency on the part of a group of surveyors when they realized they were unable to recognize their location in a sand-dune region on a dark night while attempting to locate their camp. In the face of emotional stress persons who are ordinarily quite calm and intelligent will feel a tendency to give way to impulsive action, and may indulge in energetic though pointless activity.

A factor creating impulsiveness may be the driving energy of the human being demanding action. When the next step of a situation is not clearly indicated, there is an impulse to expend energy in behavior, even though it may result in little more than nervous tension.

Children have so much energy to expend! If they are healthy and alert they are active almost continually. When a child is awake and quiet, a parent looks for an explanation, and this reaction on the part of the parent is in a sense a recognition of the ceaseless drive of a child's energy. Actions that appear impulsive grow out of this tremendous drive. One adult remembers well the physical and mental strain forced on her one day when she was a small child by being made to stay quiet for an hour. As she recalled this experience she suffered physically, although there was no emotional strain between parent and child. She had merely been told, "If you want to go to the party, you must be perfectly quiet now for an hour. You must not get out of bed. Go to sleep."

It should be recalled that the random activity of children is a way in which children learn. The exploration of an environment involves looking here, there, and anywhere, at any time there is an opportunity. Such explorations may appear to be purposeless, but from the point of view of dynamic individual growth and development they hold great potentialities in intelligent orientation to the environment.

In very young children behavior cannot always be evaluated as to purpose in terms of what it seems to be. James, three years old, had been successful in catching a house fly. As he held it he looked it over with great concentration. Then he pulled off its head and its wings. He threw away the insect with its amputated parts and went on about his other activities. There was no expression of regret or pity, nor did he reason that this animal was a pest.

Was James sadistic? Perhaps James had not yet distinguished between living things and his nonliving toys. Death had not entered into his experience, and very little suffering. However, it might be well to see that James has experiences and is encouraged to draw interpretations which set the stage for developing a consideration for living things.

In itself, impulsiveness, or random behavior, in children is not so much something to be condemned as it is an indication of a need to direct the development toward "responsibleness." To the teacher, impulsive behavior in children indicates a need for directing their activities toward assuming responsibility. The responsbilities the children assume should be within their abilities. Responsibleness requires growth, and growth requires time: this requires patience on the part of the onlooking parent or teacher.

Walter, the ten-year-old described on page 27, whose impulsive behavior caused injury to a duck, may need to assume responsibilities that accord with his abilities and provide growth for him. This may require Walter to learn meanings about the adaptations of living things and the conditions necessary to life. It will also mean the development of a suitable emotional basis for behavior built up on the basis of scientific meanings.

Too frequently adults find humor in the impulsive behavior of children. This can prove both frustrating and confusing to children, for one minute they are rewarded by a smile and a laugh for impulsive behavior and another time impulsive behavior results in punishment.

None of this is intended as an argument against spontaneous play or recreation. For, as described in Chapter 1, play is recognized as one of a number of avenues for learning science. In play, however, children should learn early the importance of responsible behavior and of considering the safety of others as well as themselves.

The Place of Content and Meaning in Developing Responsibleness. It seems necessary for us to point out in this discussion that we are not concerned more with ducks, turtles, or other animals than we are with boys and girls. For we are primarily concerned with the best interests of boys and girls. These boys and girls do not live in a vacuum, however; they live in a universe of adaptations, interrelationships, and great variety. Clearly, children must learn to face responsibilities if democracy is to survive.

The need for responsible behavior is caused not only by the possible physical injury a child may sustain in the form of a bite, a scratch, or kick from an animal, but also by the possible intellectual and emotional injury caused by ruthless, selfish behavior toward another living thing. It seems inconceivable that a child can grow toward responsibleness through experiences in which animals have been mistreated, however innocently.

In a kindergarten in New Jersey an observer was impressed by the dignified calm of the room. The children were seated around Anthony, one of their classmates, who was being tutored by an older, nine-year-old child from another classroom. This older child was teaching Anthony and his classmates how a guinea pig should be handled for the best interests of the guinea pig. There was rapt attention as Anthony held the animal, under the supervision of the older child.

Later, there was the problem of passing this experience on to another child, and finally to all the children in turn. There was no impulsiveness. How to pass the guinea pig from Anthony to Martha was discussed, and then Martha took her turn. Here was planning for responsible behavior.

There was no carelessness, or squeezing of the animal. One had the feeling of growth in responsibleness in this experience, but the responsibleness was based on content which dealt with information about the conditions necessary to living things—in this case, guinea pigs. There was an absence of tension, and there was no pressuring of a child into an experience for which he was not prepared.

Contrast this with the case of another classroom in which hamsters were kept. From time to time children carelessly picked up the hamsters, squeezing them, and in some cases giving the hamsters rough treatment. Caresses form a poor recompense for maltreatment of a living thing. The teacher and parent must be concerned with more than the welfare of animals, for the most important factor is what is happening to boys and girls when they are unthinkingly cruel to other living things. In fact, patterns of sadistic behavior may develop in the child who one minute caresses an animal and the next minute is inadvertently choking it.

EXPERIENCE. *Animals may be expected to use their means of protection if they are mistreated.* An animal naturally uses its inherited weapons when it is hurt. It is only natural for an animal to respond to ruthlessness with biting, clawing, kicking, or whatever means has been successful in the survival of its species. Many an animal has been needlessly condemned to death when in reality it was doing only what was natural for it to do.

A mother dog should not be teased. The instinctive need to protect the young puppies on the part of the mother is a kind of inheritance and has helped in the survival of dogs.

It is easy for children and adults to judge animals by human standards of behavior. We must keep in mind that other animals have a different inheritance than man. Man has different sensory capacities, and he has greater intelligence. Therefore, we should not judge the "rightness" and "wrongness" of an animal's conduct by our own standards.

In providing children with experiences with animals, it is well to make it possible for children to grow toward a reliable perspective of living things. Such growth, regardless of age level, beginning in the preschool years, should be in terms of meanings of the basic patterns of the universe. It would be well to consider these universal patterns in relation to establishing responsible behavior.

If we have some understanding of adaptation or of the interrelationships involved in life, we may be prepared to give other living things greater consideration. Life in any form is entitled to consideration. Living things require conditions for their healthy existence. Space for exercise, the proper environment for living things in terms of water, light, temperature, and nutrition can all become factors for consideration on the part of young children. This should be part of the education of children in the home during the preschool years (pp. 4–8).

In a school in a large city, Fannie proudly brought a rabbit to her kindergarten room. Fannie, an only child whose family lived in an apartment, seemed to need a pet. However, Fannie was most possessive of the rabbit and was unwilling to share it with the other boys and girls. Instead, she kept the rabbit within her own clothing. Her teacher, knowing Fannie's concern about the rabbit, directed the discussion about what the rabbit needed. There was the matter of space for play and moving about. This had meaning to Fannie for she, too, liked to play and have room to move about, rather than to be cooped up in a small space. Fannie began to enter into making plans for a proper place for the rabbit, where there would be the conditions necessary to living for the rabbit. Fannie with the other children took responsibility for the rabbit, but took the responsibility on the basis of information gained. The information was directed toward conditions necessary to life (in this case the life of the rabbit) and to the kind of environment to which the animal was adapted, although the terms "adaptation" and "conditions necessary to life" were not used in the discussion.

We can usually assume that children are ready to take responsibility when they have the necessary information and when the responsibility is within their abilities. If not, it is time to make a study of the child and of the factors in his life that cause irresponsibility. The factors may lie outside the school, but the school may be a determining agency in changing a child's negative, irresponsible behavior. Classroom teachers in public elementary schools have made great and lasting contributions to this development of responsible behavior in the young people of democratic countries.

To consider the development of responsibleness, a teacher should also consider children's co-ordination and physical maturity. A child should not be permitted to enter into an experience with another living thing when the child lacks the co-ordination or ability to do it without injury to the living thing involved. To develop intelligent behavior patterns, the teacher or parent must make a continuous study of the children.

In a school in North Carolina, a boy had brought a turtle to the classroom. The only available container for the turtle was a small aquarium jar scarcely providing enough space for a small goldfish. The turtle attempted to escape from the jar but would constantly slip back along the sloping sides of the jar. In the classroom there was the constant sound of the turtle's attempt to escape, as it struggled up the sides of the jar and slid back to the bottom. The children in this classroom were disturbed by the arrangement and asked a visitor present if he thought the turtle was happy. The visitor replied (without being facetious, but rather to promote thinking) that he had never been a turtle and so didn't know whether turtles were ever happy or not. The discussion then turned to the kind of environment needed by this turtle in order to be *healthy;* children are almost invariably concerned with the welfare of other living things.

It developed, however, that the boy who had brought him in knew where he had found the turtle and described the place. Animals are usually found in places where they are more or less well adapted. Could the children supply suitable conditions for this turtle in the classroom—conditions like those in the place from which he had come? They decided such conditions could not be provided and that the turtle should be returned to the place where it had been found. They did this the very same afternoon. Here they exhibited behavior which showed both responsibleness and a feeling for conservation.

In a school on the Gulf Coast of the United States, a visitor had been asked to lead the children on an excursion around their beautiful school grounds. As the visitor arrived, the children were at the door waiting. Apparently an instructional excursion was considered to be a wild romp over the meadow and into the adjoining wood to see what they could catch. This they did, before the visitor had a chance to get their attention, and soon the children were back, their fists holding their finds. The human fist, be it a child's or an adult's, forms a humid environment on a hot summer day. As these children opened their fists to reveal the living things enclosed, it became clear that they had not supplied suitable containers for the living things involved.

The children were not to be condemned. After a brief discussion, in which the question of the purpose of an excursion was considered, it was decided to take a walk and look for a purpose. These children had no desire to see living things die in their hands. Children, if normal, like life and like living things. They returned empty handed, but they had observed living things in their natural environment. They also had developed purposes for future work. Here was analysis of behavior as evaluation of instruction.

Another group in the same school was quite intent on building an aquarium. In a walk they discovered a place where they could look down on a natural pool of clear water which was teeming with living things of considerable variety. They decided this pool would be their aquarium, which they could observe daily, and they did not remove any of the living things from it.

Growth in Responsibleness. Developing any behavior pattern is not isolated from other instruction, nor from life itself. The teaching-learning activities in any area of science can be basic to developing responsibleness.

Boys and girls grow into situations of citizenship in which they will be responsible for keeping the air clean, the soil fertile, streams free from pollution, farms productive, cities healthy, the country beautiful, and the world peaceful. The responsibility of citizenship should not be something thrust upon them suddenly as they come of age. Responsibleness should be a pattern for growth, begin-

ning in the cradle. Responsibility should be the birthright of every child.

In a rural school in the Appalachian Mountain region the children assumed responsibility for an adjoining woods as a game preserve. They proudly exhibited an authorization from the state in which the school was located. These children took the visitor through the woods and indicated what they had already accomplished and what they planned for the future. Their plans indicated a fine maturity of thought. They planned for the natural forces to operate without disturbance. Places set aside for outdoor reading, discussion, observation, and recreation were designed so as to interfere very little with the natural growth and distribution of plants and animals. As a visitor accompanied these children he felt that here were boys and girls developing adequacy for the problems of the future. They had developed a wholesome attitude toward the beautiful natural climax flora and fauna of that region which was taking over and controlling their game preserve. As the visitor walked with these children, he became the student and the children the teachers. Here were children confident of a birthright in their native land and a place in society. They were developing responsibleness and resourcefulness. The visitor wished all children everywhere could have this birthright.

One adult testifies to the abiding influence of a naturalist friend who was never satisfied with leaving a camp site as good as when he arrived at the spot, but always found some way to leave it in better condition than before he camped there. In this accomplishment the naturalist considered not only the next camper but all the other living things of the area. Here was conservation as behavior.

The children of a certain school made an unnecessary path across the grounds with their bicycles. Later these children complained about the mud puddles that had formed during a rainy period. The puddles had resulted from the erosion started by the bicycles forming a path. Here was a sequence of events and the consequence of thoughtless behavior. Here, though on a minor scale, was impulsive and random behavior, followed by unfortunate events.

In one school a visitor found that there had been established a planning committee for the entire school. The committee was composed of representatives elected from each of the classrooms in the school. It was an inspiring experience to attend this committee meeting, which was conducted outdoors where the children, as they planned, could view the grounds. The older children assumed the greater responsibility for planning and execution, but the younger children felt themselves a part of the democratic situation. Often the interests of children are neglected completely by those concerned with planning school grounds. For example, there may be less erosion on a school ground completely landscaped by engineers than if the children had a hand in the planning. But erosion in the behavior of children is of more vital concern than the disappointments of a landscape engineer.

A group of children in one school in the Atlantic Coastal area planned a picnic area for their school grounds. Naturally, and perhaps we could say impulsively, the children decided to rake the leaves off the area. This they did with great thoroughness. The area was a hillside—a place where during a heavy rain water would flow from a nearby highway.

Here was energy and enthusiasm at work. It became the task of an adult to indicate the consequence of their planning. The adult asked by the teacher and children to serve as advisor or consultant was taken for a tour of the new picnic spot. The consultant did not tell them what to do. He merely observed with them the erosion which was starting and how on other areas the carpet of leaves was protecting the soil. The children saw the significance of the learning and hurried to return the leaves to the area. However, they were unable to place the leaves on the spot as adequately as it had been done by natural processes over many years. No great damage was done and special care was taken to prevent the children from feeling guilty. In fact, everyone, including the children, thought it was a good learning experience.

The Problem of Vandalism. Much has been written about the problem of vandalism. There is no contention that what is written here will automatically solve this great problem. Our concern here is not merely the destruction of property but the loss, individually and collectively, which occurs when a democracy loses the responsibleness and resourcefulness of the individual citizens. The latter is the greatest resource a democracy can have.

In a democracy it is vital to develop in children a feeling that in a real sense the environment belongs to all of us. There is no reason why this feeling of responsibility should not be associated with such a desirable emotion as patriotism. Such a feeling could be expressed in such words as: "This is our country. Let us make it a good place in which to live."

The prevention of vandalism lies in the development of instruction. Let us examine more fully the place of emotions in the teaching of science.

Development of Desirable Emotions through Science. In science education there has been a strong tendency, over the years, to ignore the emotional aspects of science learnings. It has been customary (and not without logic) to think an individual could and should learn science without emotion. The logic was that science was a discipline of realism and objectivity, and therefore far removed from any emotion.

But science is associated with emotions. The great patterns of the universe are profound. Anecdotal records of children's discussions about science indicate spontaneous expressions of profound wonder, amazement, curiosity, hope, enjoyment, appreciation, satisfaction, and bafflement.

During a discussion in an Arizona school there had been a real desire on the part of several children to secure some hope that there was evidence of life on other planets. It was suggested by some of the children that life, such as human life, was dependent upon a rather narrow range of temperatures, as compared with the great range found throughout in the universe. "But," said Florence, "that doesn't mean that some kind of life couldn't have gotten used to other kinds of worlds. Maybe some kind of life might have developed in an air in which there was no oxygen." Here we have a profound thought on the part of eleven-year-old Florence. The flash of her eyes, the smile on her face, the enthusiasm of her voice all indicated a girl profoundly stirred by her growing knowledge of the universe.

There are many anecdotal records which might be quoted to show children's spontaneous expressions of great appreciation of aspects of the universe. One can scarcely study science without being profoundly moved by the concepts of space, time, change, energy, adaptations, interrelationships, variety, and balance.

One adult visited the Grand Canyon of the Colorado River with some children. It was the first time that any of them had seen this place—a place which cannot be adequately described. The adult had expected to give quite a bit of instruction when they first came upon the canyon, perhaps even dwelling on the beauty of the place. But as they reached the rim of the canyon and looked across, many miles, to the opposite rim he sensed the quiet of the children. No one had spoken to them

about being silent. It occurred to the adult that this was no time for him to force his knowledge and feeling about the canyon on the children. Instruction could follow in its time. The children were too busy perceiving the sight through all their sensory avenues. The adult recalled then how many times he had wished he could enjoy a beautiful scene without having to try to express to some friend or guide how beautiful it was.

We should not force our own sentiments and emotions on children. The meanings of a situation speak louder than any eulogy we may wish to make. If children are allowed to face problems and situations with the best meanings available to them we need have no distrust of them.

Emotions, in themselves, are not to be condemned, of course. The human race would be dull if its individuals had no emotions. There have been constructive emotions in human history—love, devotion, affection, admiration, curiosity. Emotions have aided in the development of freedom of thought, speech, religion, justice, and investigation. These freedoms have been based on enlightenment. History reveals a long list of martyrs for these causes. But man's emotions have been destructive when they have been based on ignorance, arrogance, bias, intolerance, cruelty, and tyranny.

Perhaps in a democracy we need to study more fully the place of emotions. We must guide children to develop their emotions around a sound core of democratic values. It is the contention here that emotions can be based on meanings that are in keeping both with the best information in science and with democratic values.

This means in large part that in teaching there should be a great deal of stress upon the constructive, happy emotions, such as the feelings of pleasure in the fine achievements of the human race. Perhaps too much is said about the faults of mankind. The record of mankind is in general a splendid one, for man has developed the arts, the sciences, democracy, tolerance, justice, and has hungered for understanding of the infinite. We need to develop in children the pride of knowing that he is a member of the human race. Children should come to have pride in the achievements of all mankind. Our children should have confidence in the great potentialities of mankind.

Children should learn to feel enthusiasm and confidence when they come to realize that problems can be solved through the means of democracy and science. There can be joy in fair decisions, in good sportsmanship, in high democratic ideals. There can be pleasure in honesty, intelligence, and well-trained ability.

But there are desirable emotions in a democracy that may cause sadness, regret, and disappointment. We desire children who dislike sham, intolerance, injustice, bias, and undemocratic procedure. Children should dislike the weaknesses of thoughtlessness, cruelty, dishonesty, gullibility, and dogmatism—both in themselves and in other people.

Children are needed who deplore waste of resources, including, of course, human resources. We need children who, when they grow up, want to eradicate slums and to improve standards of living and practices which bring on accidents and poor sanitation. Children should feel sad when they see forest fires, rivers flooding villages, or streams cutting into fertile countrysides. We want them to detest the erosional scars on the hillsides, the pollution of the atmosphere and waters of the earth. We want them to be unhappy about any landscape, whether rural or urban, which is littered with papers, tin cans, and refuse, and by the destruction of beauty wherever it exists. They should learn to resent the needless destruction of wild life, including both plants and animals. We want children to have a vision of a better world and a feeling that

they are responsible for making it so. Children need to have emotions which spring from a knowledge of what can be done to make the world a better place in which to live. We need to develop in children an awareness that the resources of their country, and of all countries, are to be cherished and used wisely. The soil, the air, the mineral resources, the human resources are as much to be respected as a nation's flag. In fact, the flag is only a symbol of a nation and its resources. Any patriot would be shocked to see his country's flag, or that of any other country, hauled down to the ground and trampled upon; we should be equally shocked by the wasting of a country's resources.

At the peak of a mountain, in a beautiful national park in the United States there is a lone tree growing 8500 feet above sea level. This tree is several centuries old. It has managed to survive at this altitude, under severe conditions. In some ways it isn't much of a tree, for it isn't very large or very high. But when one contemplates the long round of seasons, of blizzards, and of drying winds, one can't help but feel an appreciation for this old tree which has survived so long and so persistently. It serves as an example of the toughness, resiliency, and insurgency of life. It is impossible to comprehend, much less describe, the factors which have operated in the survival of this individual plant.

Recently a highway has been built through this park so that tourists might enjoy the valley below from this peak. Tourists, with their knives, have done more damage to this old tree than all of the storms of the past. We need to develop a respect—indeed, a positive pleasure—on the part of children in leaving things unmolested.

Donald had lived in a region of rolling land, in midwestern United States, for a number of years. He was fond of the region, but in a sense he never really looked at it. While he was still young, his parents moved to a region of high plains in a southwestern state. Later he returned to his birthplace. He looked at his native state with new eyes. He saw the beauty of the rolling hills for the first time. He had appreciated the beauty of the vast prairie, which seemed to him to sweep on and on forever, and he had belittled his own birthplace; but not now, for both regions were beautiful, each in its way.

We need to help children to orient themselves to their region. Children should have an opportunity to look at a region. This view may be from a hilltop, a high building, or an open space. The occasion may be a picnic, or it may be in connection with instruction. The purpose of such occasions may vary from time to time, and from age level to age level. But a continuing purpose might well be to teach children to see the community as part of their own lives, so that they develop a feeling of responsibility for their environment.

The children in a rural school in the Berkshire Hills took great pride in their school ground. They had made it a beautiful place and visitors to the school often lingered there. In front of the school there was a lovely stream. The children kept the immediate bank of the stream and the stream itself free from refuse. The stream was shallow and clear, so that children could work safely near the stream under the teacher's supervision. One day at an outdoor conference an appraisal of the school ground was made by the children and the teacher. Their eyes strayed beyond the grounds, across the stream to an eyesore in the community scene—the rear of a gas station. The front of the station, where the customers drove in, was immaculately clean; but the rear, which the customers never saw but which was in plain sight from the school, was cluttered with rusting parts of cars, decaying tires, and general refuse and disorder.

Robert, one of the children, commented about the ugliness of the filling station as seen

from the school ground. Miss Fitzgerald, the teacher, quite wisely hesitated to open up the question too widely, because Mildred, one of the children in the school, was the daughter of the manager of the filling station and she wished to do nothing that would cause Mildred unnecessary distress. However, Robert's comment was apparently enough when Mildred carried it home and repeated it to her father to cause him to walk back and take a real look at the ugliness of the back yard of his station. He realized for the first time how grim the refuse from his station must appear to the school children and to the teachers. Mildred's own feelings seemed quite wholesome and stable during this episode. In fact, if anything, she seemed to show evidence of spirit and self-confidence, possibly because she went home with a statement which was taken so seriously by her father. Children like nothing better than to be accepted at face value. Miss Fitzgerald was a student of children. She evaluated the behavior of the children. She was particularly alert to any changes in Mildred's behavior during this episode.

This is no plea for blind emotions; rather, we need emotions built upon scientific and democratic information. Conservation is a body of content, like all content in science, which will change with new discoveries. The emotions to be established should be those which are based on the best interests of democracy.

Children should be encouraged early in life to enjoy the activities that grow out of operating with sources of energy. David, fourteen months old, was very much interested in the Christmas-tree lights. He looked at them again and again. He found where they were turned on and off by observing the behavior of adults. He wanted to turn them on and off himself. The switch was too stiff for his little fingers, but his parents helped him, so he might have the satisfaction of turning them on and off. The adults hesitated to give him so much time for this kind of experience. But it was important. He was having the experience of operating a device which controlled energy. He was developing resourcefulness and responsibility. Electricity was no longer something outside his environment, a strange phenomenon, but rather a part of his everyday experience. A few months later, he wanted to turn on the lights in the house. This he was allowed to do on the same basis as he had the Christmas-tree lights.

The fact that the adults did not deny him some of these experiences created a positive feeling in David toward the adults. Instead of concealing any of his behavior, he sought the adults out to join with him in his purposes. Furthermore, these experiences were satisfying to David, for he had not only a feeling of accomplishment but a feeling of power in pressing buttons which turned on the lights. He had a positive and constructive emotional feeling. Although David is older now, his resourcefulness has continued; his emotional development growing from these and other experiences has been good.

Conservation As a Pattern of Behavior; Developing Responsibility for Our Environment. Conservation in the education of children must be much more than teaching a body of content, for it appears now that conservation must set a pattern for behavior if the democratic way of life is to be preserved,

strengthened, and improved. As children develop better understanding of the basic patterns of the universe, they also may acquire more intelligent behavior in reference to natural resources (including human resources). Therefore, behavior and content, or perhaps a better term, meanings, are not two different things. The best meanings available about conservation and the patterns of the universe, along with high human values, should set the stage for the behavior patterns.

We need to develop in children a feeling of responsibility for the environment. Before removing objects, animate or inanimate, from the environment and bringing them into the classroom, there are many major considerations which the children may consider. To whom does the object belong? Do I have the right to take it to school? Do I disturb the environment if I remove this object? Am I destroying the natural beauty of the environment by removing this? Is the study I am going to make of the object one which merits its removal from the environment? Should I plan to return the object to the environment as soon as the study is completed? Can this object be studied properly if it is removed from the environment? Can I care for it properly in the classroom? Am I prepared to give it the care it needs to survive? One should keep in mind that living things are usually found in an environment to which they are more or less well adapted.

The Development of Resourcefulness

Responsibleness and resourcefulness, as patterns of behavior, are clearly related, as we have seen. One can scarcely think of one pattern without thinking of the other. Both must be considered as desirable patterns of behavior if democracy is to survive. Nowhere is this illustrated better than in intelligent planning.

The Contribution of Science to Intelligent Planning. It is essential for man to plan intelligently. Science must be utilized in this planning.

An example of growth in planning may be given. Philip, eight years old, was drawing a ship with two funnels from which smoke was streaming in opposite directions. Andrew, eight years old, stopped to look at the drawing and indicated to Philip that the smoke from the two funnels should be moving in the same direction. Philip observed his drawing. Andrew continued to explain the reasons for his statement. Philip said, "That's right," and changed the drawing. Here we have Philip making a drawing to suit his fancy but willing to consider suggestions involving scientific meanings and to make the necessary changes. Both Philip and Andrew displayed resourceful behavior. Philip modified his impulsive action by his willingness to follow an analysis of what he had done.

Recently, when a visitor was introduced to a group of twelve-year-olds as a scientist, the other children began to ask how a scientist worked. They had an idea that a scientist went about in rather an impulsive way, striking matches to this and that, and drawing conclusions from a host of haphazard experiments. That a scientist spent long periods of time in careful study, in reading and planning

before performing experiments, was a new idea to them. Science seemed to lose no appeal for these children as a result of this new conception.

A teacher in preservice education, encountering an electrical plug which did not release easily from an electrical outlet, jammed the blade of a screwdriver impatiently between the outlet and the plug, thus causing a short-circuit and blowing a fuse. She had illustrated the importance of meeting situations with thoughtful planning rather than with impulsive behavior and superficial thinking.

In science there will be many opportunities for pupils at all levels to participate in planning. The children themselves may on various occasions propose one or more of the following: the *challenge,* in the form of a problem they want to solve; the *procedures* by which they think the problem might be solved; the *plans* which they make to put these procedures into effect; *evaluation* of their own planning, particularly as to its worth-whileness and of their own safety in carrying it out; *drawing conclusions; checking the conclusions* for accuracy; and suggestions for the *improvement* of future planning.

Children can participate in planning the solutions of many types of problems. It may be deciding what food to have for a picnic, what methods would stop erosion on the school grounds, what adjustments would improve ways of passing through the halls, or what steps to take to secure correct information about some problem on which they are working. The teacher should be well aware of the children's pattern of work and have them consciously move toward a better pattern. Such inquiries as "How may we find out?" "Is this the best information?" or "How may we plan our work?" place on the child considerable responsibility for planning.

In the teaching of science it is frequently necessary to extend some problems over a considerable period of time in order to secure materials from homes or community, to find more information necessary to satisfactory planning, or to allow sufficient time for changes to go on in whatever is being investigated. It is wise to repeat experiments, recheck observations, reread a passage in a science book, think over what the pupils are trying to do. The growth of the group should be toward improvement in ability to meet situations by planning. The failure of an experiment may be utilized to emphasize the need of better planning.

Teachers should be cognizant of the manner in which children attack problems. Sometimes children are unable to participate in planning because their earlier home and school life has provided them with no suitable opportunities for expression. Occasionally there are groups which substitute random thinking for planning. One group observed tended to flit from subject to subject with great interest, never staying long enough with anything to have much feeling of success. A little such exploration or orientation is a fine thing, but it should never become the sole pattern of study. A happy medium between narrow concentration and breadth appropriate to the child's level of development should be sought.

Usually a variety of teaching procedures should be employed. It is an error to follow in a routine way any one procedure, regardless of how modern or how good it may be. The same holds true of instruction which calls for an emphasis on pupil-participation in planning. How monotonous it would become, for both teacher and children, if at every turn the teacher called for planning! There is a place for many different kinds of procedure in the field of science.

It is especially important to plan for safety on excursions and to encourage children to participate in this planning. Street crossings, the possibility of encountering poisonous snakes or poison ivy, and other possible hazards should be considered. If private or public property is concerned, the responsibility of teacher and children for the property should be thought of. Leaning on the glass of a museum case might break it, with possible injury to those in the vicinity.

Also, one can consider what safety precautions should be observed in the course of experiences and experiments in science. If a candle or a match is used, sand or water should be present. If machines are used they should be operated so that no one is injured. This kind of planning involves forethought and thinking through to consequences. The teacher can employ such questions as "What do you expect will happen?" instead of using the word *consequences*.

Meanings Contributing to Responsible and Resourceful Behavior. The following statements suggest the type of meanings which children may derive from instruction directed toward the development of responsibleness and resourcefulness:

We are not able to secure reliable explanations by guessing.

To make sure that we have the right explanation, we must do very careful thinking.

Sometimes it is desirable to check our thinking by performing experiments.

Scientists carefully plan for their experiments and studies.

Men can discover many things by performing experiments.

Frequently, however, people who are not scientists do not get the right explanations by performing experiments. They make mistakes and get the wrong answers. A true scientist is willing to check his explanation at any time.

The most reliable information can be secured from scientists who spend their lives working in those fields in which they are authorities. We should place confidence in the techniques used by scientists.

When we want to secure the best explanation, we can turn to reliable books.

It sometimes is necessary for a scientist to try to give explanations of matters related to his field of study about which he is not certain. Such explanations are not guesses but hypotheses: a scientist may spend years in the process of developing an explanation, or in checking a theory or a hypothesis, which he puts to the test whenever he can do so.

Should his explanations be found unsatisfactory, the scientist no longer holds to them.

It is well to note that some decisions can be made by voting, as in the election of officers. However, information about Earth and the universe is never secured by voting. The best way to secure reliable information about Earth and about the universe is through study by specialists who have done careful research, who have read what has been written on their subjects, who confer with other specialists, who examine information they secure, and who experiment whenever necessary.

We may find it convenient to develop an explanation or a plan for something. Such an explanation is a tool to use, but as soon as our explanation or plan is found to be unsatisfactory, we should leave it and attempt to find a better explanation.

We should never depend upon mere hearsay, gossip, or rumor as a source of information. We should never have unwarranted prejudices against other people, whatever may be their nationality or race. We should be willing to cooperate with other people.

Government agencies, such as those giving information on weather or agriculture, should be kept thoroughly scientific, so that we may have confidence in their studies and conclusions.

It is well to have times when a group such as a class can talk over their plans together. In making plans we should be willing to consider the suggestions of others.

All citizens should give their full co-operation to a democratic government, regardless of whether the men and women that hold office are those for whom they themselves voted.

Man is learning that he can avoid many difficulties and much unhappiness if he plans carefully for the future.

Scientific discoveries indicate that it may not be impossible for people all over the world to have sufficient food, comfortable living conditions, and healthful surroundings.

It is important that we realize that everyone can help to improve conditions in our classrooms, in our communities, in our country, and in the world. We should be willing to talk over the kind of changes we want and to discuss how we may secure such changes.

The records to be found in Earth's rocks indicate that large portions of Earth have been more or less favorable for life for millions of years. Man can expect Earth to remain a favorable place for the existence of life far into the future, and should try to make conditions better for all people.

By study man is improving his ability to predict the weather, earthquakes, floods, and volcanic eruptions, thus preventing needless loss of life and destruction of property.

By study and planning, man is able to prevent floods, control soil erosion, improve soil fertility, develop better kinds of plants and animals for his needs, construct buildings which do not topple over in earthquakes, control sanitary conditions, wipe out disease, develop more energy to operate his machines, make new substances for his needs, and make old substances more plentiful.

By proper planning for the use of lands, for example, it is possible to eliminate many floods.

The soil is a part of a country. It is a resource. It should be improved whenever possible.

Water, too, is a great resource. It should be used wisely and not wasted.

When flowing water looks muddy, it shows that erosion is taking place. Vegetation should be planted to help resist this erosion, and perhaps dams should be built to slow up the flow of the water to the ocean.

Conservation is a wise utilization of resources. Conservation is the responsibility of everyone. Conservation is dependent on the way people act or behave. We should waste nothing.

We should never destroy things, either living or nonliving, unless there is a sound reason for doing so.

A plant or animal should be removed from its natural environment only when there is good reason for doing so.

Rare plants and animals should be protected unless there are good reasons for doing otherwise.

We should not destroy the beauty of things about us by carelessness.

We should never be cruel to any living thing.

We should give good care to our pets and domestic animals.

We should leave places of natural beauty which we visit as beautiful, or even more beautiful, when we leave.

We should not remove anything from property that does not belong to us unless we have secured permission.

Machines, toys, tools, and other materials give more satisfaction to us if they are given good care.

It is important to plan our experiments, excursions, and other activities in such a way as to avoid accidents.

We should plan for the safety of others and for our own safety.

We should feel responsible for our behavior.

We need to educate children to appraise their surroundings. It is too easy to accept what is familiar in the environment. People can grow accustomed to the muddy water of streams, to litter, to pollution, and to waste until such things are not recognized as undesirable. In these appraisals of one's surroundings there can flow a feeling of poise and confidence that community and world problems can be faced and solved through intelligent behavior. Children should be educated so that they spontaneously approach problems and plan a course of action in keeping with democratic and scientific attitudes.

Democracy and Behavior

In summary, we may say that the success or failure of democracy depends upon the character of the behavior of its citizens. The study of science opens new avenues, and may profoundly influence the behavior of the individuals that are exposed to it. Science, in its dynamic aspects, has therefore a very important contribution to make to the behavior of boys and girls, and can be one of the determining factors in their development. Scientific habits of thought and action lead to the development of resourcefulness, responsibleness, critical-mindedness, and open-mindedness. These qualities are needed in an intelligent citizenry, and are essential if democracy is to survive and to advance. Progress toward a better life calls for a better understanding of the world on the part of its citizens.

An examination of science in the elementary-school curriculum (Chapters 4 and 5) will further reveal the potentialities of science in the education of children.

CHAPTER 4

The Content of Science in the Education of Children

What Shall Be the Content of Science in the Elementary School? The desirable behaviors described as "purposes" in the preceding chapter cannot be constructed by children in a vacuum. For each individual child there must be a background of meanings or content.

The content of the curriculum of the public schools, including that part devoted to science, must be designed to guarantee leadership to the people of the democracies, in the community of nations. This leadership must be more than a leadership "at the top," for it must be a leadership which has its source and resources deep within the wisdom of intelligent peoples.

The content of elementary science must be selected or considered on a basis of sound principles. It must be challenging and meaningful. For instance, the content must be designed with the abilities, the drives, and the capacities of children in mind. In a very real sense, the meanings and content proposed in this volume have been, in large part, designed *by* children as well as for children, since so much of the content and procedures are the result of teaching-learning experiences in the classroom.

The meanings and content of elementary science which are built into the curriculum by children, by teachers, and by other curriculum-makers must be in keeping with the great purposes for which the public elementary school is designed. The content must have social value.

The content of elementary science must be suitable for use in the program of the elementary school, where the classroom teacher responsible for the total program can *learn while teaching* children.

The Subject Matter of Experience

In our modern times, when man is making new discoveries and continuously revising his knowledge, one might think that the content of science would play a very minor role in the education of children. With knowledge being changed and revised there are some who would say, "Why teach content if it may not be the same tomorrow?" But such is not the case.

"Content" is the meaning gained from experience. There is no education without meaning, for meaning is the substance of life experiences. The active human being is continuously securing meanings about his physical and social environment, as well as about himself. Some of the meanings he learns are profound and may change his whole life, while others are insignificant and may be soon forgotten. Content is basic to the development of attitudes, outlooks and behaviors. Content is the substance we accept to direct and guide our lives.

Harry, five years of age, had been listening to stories about bears. At this time he was greatly puzzled by the difference between fact and fiction. He asked frequently about what was true and what was make-believe.

Harry had traveled only a few times beyond the edge of the village in which he lived. He had observed no bears in the village, so he began to wonder whether bears would be found in the woods that he could see on the horizon beyond the edge of the village. These woods seemed to him to be the very edge of the world, and in a sense this was true, for the woods *were* at the edge of "his world."

He asked if bears lived in the woods. When he was assured there were no bears about the village anywhere or in the woods, the world seemed a little safer to him. After this he went outside and played in the yard without fear. A more wholesome basis for future learning was at least partially established.

Here we have content that is meaningful to Harry. Bears, in fact, became so meaningful that he modified his behavior as a result of content. This comparatively simple situation is illustrative of the role of content in develop-

ing meanings essential to intelligent adjustment to the environment.

Content As Meanings Basic to Behavior. The traditional conception of subject matter was that it was something quite fixed and static in character. As a result, the teaching-learning procedures involved memorizing of content, with frequent examinations to test one's ability to recall facts. Subject matter was something that could be "mastered." When one had learned certain bodies of subject matter, one was considered educated.

The traditional concept of science as a body of absolute and fixed subject matter has been supplanted by the *modern* concept of science, with its constant demand for honesty and willingness to revise content whenever necessary. This has revolutionized our concept of the nature and place of subject matter in education.

Content, as we use the term, is more than merely the body of experience possessed by an individual; it also represents the learning of the human race. Therefore content, or subject matter, is far from absolute and fixed, but rather is flexible and continuously changing. The process of learning—for a people, as well as an individual—must be an active and dynamic one in our modern times.

This is particularly well illustrated in the field of science, in which man has made many discoveries that have been revolutionary in character. In the past two generations an individual has had to reorganize his thinking a number of times if he was to remain well adjusted to the flow of modern events. Perhaps one of the best indications of a good education is the ability to reorganize one's thinking, attitudes, and behavior on the basis of new discoveries and the resulting new content. In keeping with this characteristic, modern science is sometimes called "relativistic," in that its interpretations are relative to the knowledge of a given period.

The demands of modern life call for a continual willingness to reorganize one's thinking and to consider other hypotheses or other frameworks for behavior. One might think of this as an "alertness for change."

A good illustration of this is indicated in the changing aspects of behavior after the Second World War. Whole peoples have undergone changes of attitude—the "cold war" has had profound effects on the thinking and behavior of many peoples. Difficulties in international relations have demanded new attitudes on the part of democratic peoples, and new developments of nuclear energy have completely reversed many age-old concepts, making new attitudes necessary if civilization is to survive. There is being developed today a new kind of versatility—a versatility toward revision of content and patterns of behavior. In a world in which there can be no isolation, there must be willingness to examine behavior in a local community against a world backdrop of international relations.

Subject matter in the modern curriculum plays a more important role in education than ever. However, learning subject matter is not an end in itself. Instead, it is a necessary means to the development of behavior essential for the preservation and advancement of democracy.

Content-Learning As an Ongoing Process of Emerging Intelligence.

Content or subject matter as the sum of ideas in science should be viewed as the result of an ongoing, or growth, process. For the individual it should be a continual process from birth to death. The individual is continually gaining new content ideas, attitudes, habits, and outlooks in science as a result of living through new experiences. The individual is also casting doubt in regard to some ideas previously learned—and modifying some and actively abandoning others that have not been found functional.

Content-learning is not unlike the physio-logical processes of life. Cells are worn out, abandoned, and eliminated, while new cells are being made and the processes of life go on within the living organism.

The Role of Content in Human Adjustments.

The intelligence of an individual defies complete description. We may be sure that it involves memories of interpretations of experiences in the past. These interpretations constitute the content an individual knows. Some of these interpretations are reliable, others are unreliable. Some new concepts are being formed. Some concepts held by the individual have been found by the individual to be unsatisfactory, and often he discovers this while he is actually in the process of constructing new ideas to take the place of the old ones. The individual may be quite reluctant to discard an idea that has proved to be erroneous, and he may have some difficulty in adjusting to new ideas. If this is true, the individual may suffer from imbalance and feel a sense of frustration in the process of learning. If the new content item is replacing a content item that the individual considered basic to his way of thinking, he may suffer considerable maladjustment. This happens many times. It has happened among scientists themselves. The work of Galileo, Copernicus, Newton, Darwin, Pasteur, Einstein, and many others was so revolutionary in character that whole segments of knowledge had to be reconstructed. New hypotheses resulted and a new line of experimentation had to be planned.

It has become customary to speak of periods in history characterized by great human adjustment as revolutions or as ages. Illustrations of this are the Copernican revolution, the Industrial Revolution, the steam revolution, the revolution of transportation, the age of speed, the air age, the chemical age, the atomic age, the age of automation, the age of plastics, the space age, and so on. So many important discoveries have been made in recent times that the present period is known by a variety of terms.

The content, or knowledge, in any individual's total experience is more than a series of isolated "items" known by the individual. We will see that this is particularly true as we begin to examine what is involved in concept formation (p. 107).

Not all of an individual's ideas are necessarily reliable ideas, be he either child or adult. For all of us may have some misconceptions and unreliable ideas. So the content anyone has learned on any subject will contain items that will need revision and reconstruction. It is important for a teacher to see that children are moving toward more reliable content and that they are learning to determine what are the best sources of information.

Intelligent Adjustment through Interpretation. The environment, with its dynamic display of change, has challenged man from the very beginning. Long before the day of modern science, men in their various cultures were developing bodies of subject matter about the universe. This subject matter about the universe was the result of mankind's drive for adjustment to his environment. This drive was so great that it could well be described as constituting a great central purpose of humanity. Man sought for his own security and stability in the welter of events (phenomena) that he witnessed. So we can see that the subject matter of any civilization grew out of deep human drives and concern for adjustment and equilibrium. What was the meaning of things about him? How did he fit into the picture? What was his origin? Was this his ancestral home? Did he come out of the sky or out of Earth? What were the causes of the events that occurred about him?

Not having reliable information at hand, almost all early peoples invented supernatural stories, which became the subject matter to be passed on from generation to generation.

These stories of the environment frequently were considered to be a part of the religious beliefs. The kind of adjustment made by a people depended upon the kind of content they accepted. A tribe could be courageous and strong, or fearful and weak, depending on its ideas. If a tribe had strong beliefs in omens and superstitions its conduct might be quite fickle, depending greatly upon casual happenings. Instead of considering the basic factors of a problem, a tribe might make important decisions on the basis of casual signs and omens.

Furthermore, the disposition of a people was dependent upon the kind of interpretations that the people accepted. Some cultures have been morbid because the people accepted an outlook upon the universe that might be termed a defeatist or fatalistic outlook.

In some societies behavior was limited greatly by taboos and superstitions. The individual in such a society had little opportunity to be independent and resourceful. The outlook of the individual in such a culture might well be essentially pessimistic.

In some cultures a defeatist attitude was prevalent in the accepted interpretations. In some cases the leaders or other medicine men predicted eventual catastrophes and defeat. This kind of attitude can be found in our modern times, for we have many prophets of doom today. Throughout the history of man there has been a tendency to predict a gloomy future for mankind and disaster for all of his adventures. With this concept that man's ultimate destruction was destined, there was little tendency to make constructive plans for the future. Why should there be planning when "what would be" could not be changed?

Around such basic ideas of the universe was built a catastrophic or cataclysmic outlook upon man's future in many cultures. In some cases such an outlook was promoted with the thought of forcing whole populations into subservience to absolute government and absolute religious ideas. People accepting such ideas were easily subdued and offered little resistance to the loss of independence. To this end, the population's patterns of behavior were deliberately confined within the structure of ceremonials, rituals, observances, and taboos. Many of these patterns have remained to the present day and are inconsistent with the concept of democracy.

Man's primitive concepts about himself and his environment were nearly always absolute and fixed concepts. He asserted that he had secured the truth about his natural environment when actually he had secured little or no truth. Such concepts hindered the development of science, education, and democracy, because such a man thought there was nothing new to learn or to discover.

Nevertheless, the environment was a meaningful environment to man, filled as it was with good and evil spirits. To the environment he must turn for food, clothing, and shelter, and the method of procuring subsistence was modified greatly by the meaning the environment held for him.

The environment still has meaning for man today, in spite of the changes science has made in his interpretations. Man observes and studies, he weighs and analyzes, he examines and re-examines, he checks his conclusions. He develops explanations (hypotheses) for the events (phenomena) of his environment. He has learned more about how the natural forces operate in producing the weather, the rainbow, the growth of plants and animals, diseases, floods, earthquakes, and volcanoes than ever before. One by one superstitions have been indicated as unreliable. His explanations of weather, lightning, migration, and other phenomena of life have been altered many times and are still undergoing alteration. He has become less dogmatic and more open-minded; he realizes that much remains to be discovered. In other words, his outlook

on life has become more truly experimental. In fact, modern man in spite of the vast accumulation of his knowledge, may be more aware of his ignorance than were his primitive ancestors.

The scientific interpretation of natural phenomena calls for ability to revise or discard old knowledge as new truth is discovered. It calls for realistic adjustment to the universe, and for willingness to plan our lives in terms of the most reliable information available. It calls for an acceptance of critical analysis of all private and public questions, and for freedom from gullibility.

Superstitions and other primitive beliefs are still harbored by many people who have had little contact with the field of science. There are many who are bound and fettered, even in modern industrial society, by fear of ill omens, fetishes, taboos; by astrology, fortune-telling, and other unscientific ideas and practices. Such people are adjusted very poorly to modern life. They represent a decided liability in times of decisions. They are the victims of ideas and patterns of thinking inherited from the past; their adjustment to life, being based upon an absolute concept of knowledge and of science, is not subject to revision.

The Evolution of the Concept of Catastrophe. The relation of meanings to adjustment is possibly best indicated in the changing ideas man has learned to accept about catastrophes. From a concept of catastrophes as a punishment inflicted upon him and upon his kind by hostile beings, man has moved to the idea that many great catastrophes and cataclysms can be prevented.

Man watched the eruption of the volcano, felt the earthquake, witnessed the violence of the hurricane, tornado, flood, or pestilence. It was easy for him to people his universe with beings unfriendly to man. Fear was the natural emotion created by the disasters that he encountered. With his limited knowledge he had little chance to be resourceful and avoid the havoc of disaster when it did come. Most of the interpretations that were invented in the earlier cultures caused man to be a cowering, fearful creature facing the unknown with an outlook of defeatism. Such interpretations also made him savage and cruel.

But over the long centuries man has developed resourcefulness. He began to study the catastrophes. There is much that is still unknown. But he finds nothing to support the idea that inside Earth or around Earth there are unfriendly beings. Instead, catastrophes seem frequently to be the results of forces returning to equilibrium after they have been in unbalance. And in some cases man, who has become a great agent of physical change, may have been the cause of unbalance.

Today, for example, man studies the inside of Earth. Now, instead of reaping destruction and death from earthquakes, he is learning to build his structures so that they are earthquake-proof, and he is learning accident-prevention procedures of behavior during earthquake shocks (pp. 290–292).

He is learning how to prevent much of the destruction from hurricanes and other storms through advance warnings, proper precautions, and timely preparation. Radio, television, telephones, newspapers, and other media of communication play a vital role in turning what might be a catastrophe into a mere news item. It seems now that we may be able to predict the tornado, the violent twister of North America, in the not too distant future. In fact, some success has already been attained in this direction.

Man is learning to prevent floods by conservation practices, discussed in Chapter 6. One by one the diseases that have caused plagues and widespread suffering in the past are being conquered.

Even the volcano is yielding to study, and scientists who study volcanoes are gaining considerable success in predicting eruptions and in preventing loss of life during eruptions.

Man looks out in space and sees no large object with which Earth is likely to collide for eons of time. He studies Earth and finds that it has been a fit place for life for long geologic periods of time. Slowly man has learned that there is no reason for believing that Earth is peopled by unfriendly spirits. He finds that he can assume that Earth is likely to remain a fit place for life for vast eras of the future. He has discovered that often his worst enemy is himself. The catastrophes of today—war, fire, exploitation of natural resources, tenements, introduction of pests, economic depressions, pollution, famine—are in most cases man-made, and preventable.

As long as man adhered to the conception that catastrophes were caused by actions of unfriendly beings, he did little planning for future generations. He could not conceive of man as a species existing long on Earth. Naturally enough, he was interested originally in the immediate needs of his own generation; exploitation without regard to further needs was the rule. However, the realization that Earth is very old has given many people the anticipation that it is necessary for man to do away with all forms of waste and exploitation. A concern about wise utilization of resources, and a feeling of responsibility for the generations not yet born who will live in the far distant future, are conceptions which point to an advanced state of development.

The evolution of the concept of "catastrophe" has been submitted here not only for its own importance but also to indicate how the meanings or content of science may have tremendous implications for the outlooks, attitudes and behavior of mankind.

The Content of Elementary Science

Almost everyone is impressed with the extensive nature of science. It has indeed grown tremendously in scope. No one can learn all known science in an entire lifetime. It is also obvious that a teacher cannot teach it all. Only a very small portion of known science will be taught to children, but that portion can be most important in the development of citizenship. The question of how much of the content of science is taught is not of nearly so great importance as is the question of *what* science content is taught, *how* it is taught, and the *purpose for which* it is taught. With the world situation as it is today, it is important that the content and procedures of science used in the education of children be those designed for the preservation and advancement of democracy.

Because of the extensiveness of science, there has been a tendency to develop what might be called encyclopedic instruction. Under this method students have been required to learn wide areas of content. Comprehensive instruction has been developed about animate and inanimate objects, and about topics in the environment, with little sensitivity on the part of curriculum-makers as to the value of the content of the teacher and children involved. In the encyclopedic type of instruction the purposes of science in elementary education became lost in content of little value and in busy work.

In the content fields it has been a traditional practice to organize instruction around object lessons. In science the instruction was arranged about such objects as turtles, frogs, raccoons, leaves, rocks, goldfish, flowers. This approach encouraged a type of casual nature study and busy work which lacked vigor, challenge, and fundamental human values. If a child brought in an object, or if he related an interesting experience, there was instruction about the object or incident. If there were no objects and no incidents there was no science instruction in classrooms. No sequence was followed. No developmental program was presented.

The nature and scope of the learning secured was dependent upon such incidents as the blooming of a flower, the bringing to school of an object, the appearance of an animal, the whim of an individual, the element of chance. The teacher usually kept the animate and inanimate objects on a table and from time to time utilized them as material for discussion. Many teachers expected children to feel a sentimental interest in these objects, an attitude which could scarcely be defended as a basic one for science or for child development. When one considers that science is far from incidental in the life of the child or in contemporary society, he can scarcely justify a science program dependent on a collection of rocks, feathers, shells, and other bits of material, all of which are largely shorn of meaning and isolated from their natural context in the environment when they are brought into a schoolroom.

The incidental approach has led to undue emphasis upon the naming of objects (identification). The classroom teacher need not hold herself responsible for knowing the names of the birds, insects, rocks, snakes, plants, and so on; her expertness lies in the education of children, rather than in the field of taxonomy.

Very few individuals are competent to identify objects accurately in more than one or two fields. The traditional requirement that teachers have the ability to identify and relate bits of interesting information about any object in the environment, and possess as well the other kinds of skills that go with classroom teaching, was never based on a realistic conception of either science or elementary education, and has seldom if ever been satisfactorily attained in the entire history of the elementary school. It is interesting to note that this impractical demand for taxonomy was a demand that came from specialists in the various fields of specialization in science, and who conceived of the purpose of education in terms of developing a relatively few specialists like themselves. It is important that teachers have no hesitation in admitting that they are unable to identify many kinds of animate and inanimate objects.

If objects need to be identified, they can often be identified in terms that have meaning to the children; designations such as the soft rock in Harry's yard, the big boulder in the meadow, and a round, smooth pebble from the school grounds may be names given to the rocks by children.

Older children may have occasion to use books designed to help them make the identification of an animate or inanimate object. Unless the children can actually participate in the identification, there is usually no point in making it. A teacher may feel free to admit she is no authority in identification, and she should feel no embarrassment in recognizing that someone in the community knows more about rocks, animals, or plants than she. However, she need have no hesitation in using such a specialist in her classroom if the specialist is a person who is willing to assist her. But in any case, successful teaching of science does not rest upon the identification of all the miscellaneous specimens that may be brought into the classroom.

Science Is Not Incidental or Accidental in the Lives of Children. Science is no mere incident in the lives of children. In fact, it is and probably will continue to be one of the most dominating and decisive factors in the lives of children. Schools developing science on an incidental basis will not provide boys and girls with the education they need for the great decisions they must make for themselves, their country, and the world.

This incidental approach was based on an underestimation of children. In fact, it could be stated quite accurately that the point of view of the incidental approach was developed by scientists who were experts in specialized fields of science and knew little about children. They felt science necessarily involved techniques which could not be utilized by children. They tended to minimize the value of the natural drives we find in children.

This is not to say such incidents have no place in teaching-learning situations. Natural incidents can be used as experiences for concept-formation and for the development of understanding of phenomena. This book is planned to provide teachers with rich suggestions as to procedures by which observations from school windows, happenings on the school ground, events at school, at home, or in current news can be utilized in science in a program for the education of children for democracy.

Children Have Problems about Themselves and Their Environment. The function of science in the elementary school is much more fundamental than that of merely acquainting children with the names of rocks or securing interesting information about individual species of plant and animal life. In an elementary-school program which emphasizes the development of desirable social behavior science should be organized around problems that have social value and are challenging and worth-while to children. A teacher, therefore, must look back of the objects in the universe to the meanings that children will need to understand in order to participate intelligently in life. Incidents and objects may serve to illustrate and develop the meanings of science and to assist in the solution of problems; but in a functional curriculum they are not ends in themselves. They are means to a greater end, the development of resourceful and democratic behavior.

It is most important that the problems considered in the classroom be those that are challenging to children. This does not mean that the teacher should wait for the children to express an interest in a problem before initiating the instruction, nor that priority is placed on the child's curiosity. Instead, the school, with all of its facilities and resources, focuses its attention upon the *total* development of children. A teacher, through the curricular and professional materials available to her, has a knowledge of the types of problems that are likely to be stimulating and worthwhile to children. She utilizes continuously the incidents and resources in the child's environment, community problems, the natural drives of children, authoritative children's books and motion-picture films, and anything else available that will give the problems the challenge which they deserve.

It should be kept in mind that problems cannot always be completely solved or mastered in a given time or classroom situation. Scientists as well as children find that, even after extensive work on a certain problem or subject, there remains much to be learned. Teachers frequently are so concerned with the details of a study that the work becomes more exhaustive than is good for a child's own development. The extent to which a problem is pursued should be determined by the teacher's judgment of its value to the children and by their response to it. In most cases a problem should be abandoned if, after it has been given a fair trial, the problem seems unimportant to the group, or if they cannot or do not participate in the planning for its solution.

Problems vary greatly in extent. There are those which are properly short, requiring perhaps only a few minutes. For instance, the question, "Where did the water go that was in the saucer?" On the other hand, there are problems which may extend over a longer period of time, perhaps coming into the discussion and study at intervals throughout the year. For example, there are problems demanding considerable observation, collection of data, reading, and other kinds of activity. Many teachers prefer to have a number of problems under consideration at one time.

Content Is Essential to the Solution of Problems. As has already been implied, the problems considered in science instruction are those which come as a result of the child's orientation to his environment. Problems must have meaning or content before they can be solved. As a child becomes oriented and adjusted, he has need for meanings implied in the objects and incidents of his surroundings. The school should, therefore, utilize the kind of problem which introduces the child to the meanings which are essential to the development of desirable social behavior.

Science is a large subject. Thousands of scientific books have been written, yet man has only begun to make an acquaintance with his universe. Elementary science should be that which has a legitimate place in the elementary school. Therefore, a teacher need not be appalled by the extent and complexity of science as a whole, for she is responsible for imparting only a small portion of the sum total of scientific knowledge; namely, that portion which is pertinent to a group of children at a given age level.

We must see the values of science for an individual child and for society. Science has value only in so far as it contributes to the welfare of mankind. Content and attitudes cannot be divorced in an educational program.

Content may have profound influence on one's ideas about many matters beginning in childhood and extending through life. A child may establish an attitude of fear or courage toward the dark, depending on the kind of meanings which the darkness has for him. Throughout life he will establish attitudes which are based on the meanings he derives from his experiences. Attitudes toward play, co-operation, methods of performing scientific experiments, health, sanitation, the foreign policy of his own nation, and the utilization of natural resources—all these depend to a very great extent upon the kind of information one has come to accept.

Content, or the meaning attached to experience, is, then, more important than mere facts. As the human race developed content, it developed new attitudes. That Earth was round was more than a fact; it became a revolutionary idea which influenced man's attitudes and behavior in reference to commerce, colonial power, and internationalism.

In a classroom where there is little awareness of its social value, content is apt to become mere bits of colorless information for the children to learn by rote. On the other hand, if we see its value in changing children's lives, content has a new significance and is much more likely to have challenge and meaning. The social and developmental values of science give direction to the meanings which children derive from their own experience.

The teaching of science is not alone a matter of what content is taught, but how the content is utilized. The setting through which content is taught and learned is probably as important as the content itself. Ideally, a child has a feeling for the value of the content even as he learns it. This value lies in its challenge to him.

Basic Patterns of the Universe. We have indicated that a child learns through the solution of problems, and we have discussed the relation of meanings, or content, to the solution of problems. Content may become more meaningful to a child if he is given a *continuous* orientation toward the basic principles of science. For instance, the clouds which a child observes passing between himself and the moon may seem to be near the moon; but when he learns that the clouds are probably less than a mile above the surface of Earth and that the moon is as much as 250,000 miles away, he understands that the universe is larger than it seems to be. Here we see that the teacher's guiding principle was the creation of a challenge to learn more about the largeness of the universe. Later the child learns of other objects which are much farther away. In this way emphasis is placed, not on memorizing distances, but on a child's growth toward a rather basic consideration (which is never completed nor mastered)— that of adjusting himself to the universe in which he lives and of developing intelligent attitudes and patterns of behavior.

Similarly, a child may learn about some of the simple interrelationships of the living things with which he is acquainted. The emphasis should not be on memorizing the specific content involved but on the idea of interrelationships. Later his conception of interrelationships may develop to the extent that it involves an appreciation of the effect of introducing new species into an environment, the extinction of native species, the dependence of man on various living things, the balance of nature, and the interdependence of nations.

A realization of the immensity of the universe and an understanding of the interrelationships of living things are so fundamental in character that they may be thought of as basic conceptions, since they assist in interpreting a wide range of phenomena and in solving many problems. A recognition of these basic principles on the part of a teacher, and in the printed material available for the children, tends to give to learning a social value which is not present if content items are taught as more or less isolated or as related only to the problems under consideration. Therefore, as the attention of teachers and children is focused on solution of problems, content is found to be essential; the content itself can serve a child in his growth toward the acceptance and utilization of the basic principles of science in his own life experiences.

Learning to Operate Intelligently with Natural Forces. Man's difficulties very frequently arise because he fails to give enough consideration to basic physical and biological principles. Sometimes he rushes into his problems without completely visualizing the events that will follow his actions, and as a result he often reaps a whirlwind of disasters. Deforestation, overgrazing, introducing pests, or building a city on a natural flood plain are illustrations of man's failure to take physical and biological principles into his planning.

In a sense man can never control nature. What he can do is to operate and co-operate with nature in a way that will secure what he thinks is most beneficial to his welfare. This means, of course, that he must be acquainted with the ways (or patterns) in which natural forces operate. A program of education which stimulates awareness of these patterns does not involve making every boy and girl a scientist. Instead, it places emphasis on the guidance of all individuals toward a realistic and objective outlook.

It should be kept in mind that man himself is subject to these basic patterns, for he is one of many species of living things which exist on this minor planet, in a vast universe of matter and energy. Yet, it is only through the use of his intelligence that man, in his endeavor to cope with his environment, gains superiority over other living things. Therefore, an understanding of the patterns of the universe is essential to an understanding of society.

Basic Patterns of the Universe As Fundamental Conceptions for Growth

The ideas that have been developed about the basic patterns of the universe are utilized in this book as basic, working *conceptions* of science relating to space, time, energy, motion, change, adaptation, interrelationship, variety, and balance. Thus, we may think of such conceptions as our ideas of these patterns, and hence as patterns of growth and development.

Such conceptions cannot be listed as mere content, but rather as interpretative ideas which serve to orient the individual to the natural and social events in the universe about him.

The race has been thousands of years developing an understanding of these patterns and abandoning the old superstitions. Superstitions are still with us and represent the shackles of an old order. The new conceptions represent a growing heritage that has been passed on to us as a result of man's search for truth. Such conceptions should not be treasured merely by specialists, but rather should be shared with the entire population, so that they too may profit from such knowledge and experience.

The modern conception of space has proved

revolutionary in its effect upon man's thinking. It has helped man to develop from an individual who thought that Earth upon which he lived was the center of the universe, with all other bodies swinging about it, to an individual who has learned that he lives on a minor planet in a vast space. The modern scientific ideas of time, energy, motion, change, and interrelationships likewise have been revolutionary to man's thinking and have changed his entire outlook upon himself, other living things and his physical environment. They have been basic working conceptions in the development of new educational values.

The statements of the conceptions are not in themselves the goals of the instruction. They are not aphorisms or proverbs to be written on the blackboard or in a book to be memorized. Rather they are expressions of ideas that have been of great significance in man's past and undoubtedly will be in man's future. They should be in the mind of the teacher or the curriculum-maker and should assist in giving a perspective of values. Children should be allowed to live through experiences which will help them to gain increasing understanding of, and control over, these conceptions. In a sense such conceptions are never mastered or completed at any level of childhood or adulthood; for example, as the student progresses from primary-school to research levels he can always continue to learn more and more about the great age of Earth. This conception, as it emerges for a child, will become of increasing value to him in interpreting events. In early childhood he may realize that Earth is a little older than his grandfather. A little later on he may discover that it was here before George Washington, Columbus, the Vikings, and the American Indians. He may observe the action of weathering in the local region, and in some small measure he may recognize the time involved. He may see how weathering has been instrumental in developing soil. Later in the course of his education he may gain some appreciation of the long processes of change in other regions, the changes which have taken place in the shape of the continents, the making and wearing down of great mountain systems, the great changes in the climates of the various regions of Earth, the story of the succession of life on Earth, and the continuous operation of natural forces. He may come to realize that the forces which have operated in the past are much the same as those that are operating today.

This description may serve to indicate that it is not the statement of the conception that should be considered the objective, but rather the building up of a background of ideas and experiences which are involved in the conception and which, in turn, make the conception understandable, acceptable, and useful to the learner in interpreting new experiences. It is not memorization of facts that should be considered the goal, but the growth of the individual along lines of the profound truths of science. Experiences in discussion, excursions, laboratory experiments, and reading may be utilized in securing this growth. Emphasis in this point of view shifts from the learning of small content to interpretative experiences contributing to growth along the lines of these larger conceptions which have had such profound influence upon modern thought and activities and upon the development of a finer type of citizenship. As a consequence of this, stress is placed upon action, especially upon intellectual action, rather than upon considering the learner as being merely a receptacle for facts.

The Profound Scope and Nature of the Conceptions of Science. The learner's reaction to a large number of events in the universe, both past and present, should have changed as a result of growth in the direction of the conceptions of science. An individual who has attained some understanding of the modern concept of time may find that his ideas about the formation of Earth have been revolutionized: from a primitive interpretation that Earth, as we see it today, is the result of a series of cataclysms covering a period of only a few thousand years he will come to accept the modern way of considering it as the work of natural forces acting through eons of time.

It is evident that an understanding of this conception may change the scope and nature of a man's thought reactions to questions and problems in several fields; even those of social phenomena may be involved. He may change, as a result of his study, from an individual who anticipates that a catastrophe will destroy the entire Earth, and who is therefore pessimistic concerning the future of society, to an individual who sees no reason for not expecting the conditions necessary to life to continue for many ages to come.

Hitherto man has developed his society as if it were a transitory thing, because he anticipated the end of the world at almost any time. This anticipation was based upon his primitive and superstitious conceptions of Earth, acquired through inaccurate interpretations of volcanic eruptions, earthquakes, hurricanes, floods, and like events. The modern concept of time has encouraged man to plan for the future of mankind, with the thought that Earth will be a home for mankind for thousands, perhaps millions, of generations to come. Man's awareness of the problem of the conservation of natural resources, and his planning for generations yet unborn, are dependent upon his acceptance of the modern scientific concept of time. Thus we have an illustration of how a basic working conception of natural science has had significance in a wide area of human affairs, even contributing to the development of new social attitudes and values and to the solution of current problems.

Likewise, the modern scientific conceptions, like those of adaptation, interrelationship, change, motion and energy, have had profound influence on thinking in wide areas of human affairs. Teachers at all levels should be aware of these conceptions and provide opportunities for children to grow intellectually in the directions pointed out by such conceptions. Effort has been made to indicate to teachers, through curricular source materials and children's literature in science, some of the ways in which these conceptions may be utilized to help children interpret experiences with natural phenomena.

It should be borne in mind that these conceptions are comparatively new in terms of the long history of mankind. If one could line up all one's forefathers, going back through the Dark Ages, through the Bronze Age and the Stone Age, one would have a sizable regiment of men. But in this long line it is probable that only one's own father, grandfather, and possibly great-grandfather could have had much more than a primitive conception of space, time, and change. Yet the child in the elementary school today can know more about some of these things than the scientists did a century or so ago. This indicates the recency of some of our modern scientific ideas.

Although a conception is never mastered, in any final sense, still it can become a part of the whole learning process, entering into and directing it even in the primary grades. Under the guidance of the cultured teacher such a concept can enrich experiences, both within and outside the classroom, and integrate them into a total picture, or pattern. This pattern is not a temporary or artificial one; it is based on the very nature of the universe—Earth, interstellar space, living things, matter, and energy. Thus a child may continue through life to integrate learning about these general patterns and configurations and to use them to interpret experiences.

For instance, the modern scientific ideas of time and change can make a teacher conscious of indications of how natural forces operate on Earth, both in the past and at present. This awareness assists a child in integrating around these basic ideas a whole series of natural phenomena, such as the washout after a rain, the rocks that have been worn smooth, the evidence of folded rocks, the glacial scratches on rocks, the rocks that have been made from smaller particles, the prehistoric animals, the earthquake, the landslide, and the havoc produced by flood. Each of these becomes a part of a larger configuration—a pattern, a perspective, and a key to the interpretation of man's problem of utilizing natural forces for his own welfare. That a bit of soft rock crumbles in the

hand may contribute to the larger concept that it must have taken a long time for the forces of weathering to have produced the soil of Earth. This explains the fact that space, time, energy, motion, change, adaptation, interrelationships, balance and variety are sometimes called *integrating themes*. These themes are not to be thought of alone, for they overlap. It also explains the fact that mere subject-matter mastery can no longer be justified as an aim in science in childhood education.

Instruction, therefore, becomes a two-way process, an interplay between an educational value and the experiences of the children.

The Large Patterns of the Universe As Guide Lines for Teaching-Learning

The Universe Is Very Large—Space. As man has studied the universe that surrounds Earth, he has become impressed by the immensity of space. Earth, which he once thought was very large and the center of everything, is very small compared with many other objects in the universe. This Earth is one of several bodies which revolve about a star known as the sun. This sun is one of millions of stars which compose a vast galaxy of bodies which is called the Milky Way. Man has learned that there are many other galaxies within range of the modern telescope.

While a complete understanding of the immensity of space is undoubtedly beyond the mental capacities of any one individual, it can become a guiding factor in the interpretation of the experiences of children at all levels. A young child may begin his growth in the understanding of space as he begins to associate with himself the rooms in his home, the yard, or the immediate vicinity about his home. Later he learns the location of the nursery

school or kindergarten when he is taken there by adults. Still later he goes to school by himself and learns where the homes of his relatives and friends are in relation to his own home. As he travels to neighboring communities, his world becomes larger. He may be intrigued by the observation that the sun and moon seem to follow him as he moves about.

A child's early contact with this pattern may merely teach him that Earth is a very big place compared with his familiar neighborhood. He may become acquainted with the appearances of the day and night sky. Later, his learning will reveal that Earth is very small in comparison with the stars and space. About the same time he will also learn that the stars are suns which are very, very far away. In later years he increases his understanding of the vastness of space by learning about the extent of the solar system, the Milky Way galaxy, other galaxies, radio stars, cosmic rays, the light year, and so on.

Any adult who has read modern astronomy,

has attended lectures in this field, visited an observatory or planetarium, or considered the possibilities of space travel knows that his conception of space has been greatly extended since childhood. There are new, challenging thoughts for boys and girls of all levels—the junior high school, senior high school, and college levels—and, for that matter, many new discoveries are still to be made by the astronomer. Some comprehension of this conception is essential to an appreciation of the significance of science in its revolutionary effect on modern thought. It is important that children should be started properly along this path, rather than allowed to absorb inaccurate and unscientific ideas of the universe and astronomical bodies and to grow up with Earth-centered conceptions in an age of modern science.

Earth Is Very Old—Time. The conception of the great age of Earth and of the universe has come to mankind as a revolutionary idea. Not only has it profoundly influenced scientific understanding but it has altered man's attitude toward his own place and function in the universe. It was natural for primitive man to think that Earth had been formed just a short time before the advent of his people. Some of this primitive belief persists into modern times, and where it does, it still controls thought in scattered areas. Children in their early years may learn that soil is formed from rocks, and through activities, observations, and experiences discover that the process of soil formation took a long time. They may also learn something about the forces which operate upon Earth to produce changes; that it was a long time before Earth became a suitable place for plants and animals; that many kinds of animals have lived on Earth and have become extinct. These ideas furnish children with useful content in constructing their understanding of the great age of Earth.

Children may have a variety of interesting experiences with Earth forces. For example, they may examine pavements broken by water freezing in winter; feel rocks softened by the action of weathering; observe erosion after a rainstorm; note how plants keep soil from eroding; examine different kinds of soil with a magnifying glass.

Time is something to be learned. Children must learn the concepts of "yesterday," "today," and "tomorrow"; the meaning of a "second," a "minute," an "hour," a "week," a "month," a "season," and a "year"; the sequence of seasons; the varied life spans of living things. A tree may be several hundred years old; on the other hand, a mouse may be in old age when he has lived only a few months.

Time is relative to both children and adults. A half hour may be a long time if we are waiting for a plane or train, but very short if we are playing. A year between birthdays can seem a long time, but it is short in terms of the centuries the American Indians have lived in the Western Hemisphere. A teacher and a parent can greatly enlarge children's concept of time.

In later work children may learn something about what has happened to Earth, the causes of natural features in various localities, the long ages of prehistoric life, the struggle of life for existence, the forces operating on Earth, and some of the changes that have taken place on the surface of Earth. This comprehension of the great age of Earth is essential to an appreciation of the antiquity of man and of man's attempts to build social institutions for his own welfare.

The goal is not the memorizing of a chronological sequence of events, but rather an approach to the modern conception of time. This idea reveals to man the importance of building his social and political structure with the thought that he may live on this planet for some time to come, provided he uses his intelligence to assure survival. This concept is fundamental to building an understanding of what is intelligent utilization of natural and human resources. This understanding is a necessary part of man's planning for his own future.

Such a background to an appreciation of the modern concept of time should tend to inhibit chauvinism; it should teach each pupil that all life existing on Earth today is the result of a long succession of living things—a development involving a vast number of individuals and extending back to the beginning of life on Earth.

The mountains, rivers, valleys, plains, seas, and other physical features that we think of in connection with a given nation and that often come to be revered by the people of that nation have not always been there as they are now. The surface of Earth has changed its appearance many times in the past and is constantly changing today.

As the result of a long series of experiments in the art of living, man has become a dominant force in nature, and we have a right to feel a sense of pride in the achievement of all mankind. It must be emphasized in our instruction that this achievement is restricted to no one race or nationality.

Energy Is Involved in All Motion and Change—Energy. Everything in the Universe Is in Motion—Motion. The Universe Is Constantly Changing—Change. Although energy, motion, and change can be thought of as separate patterns, they are so closely related that one can rarely be thought of without the others. There is no motion without change and a display of energy. Every physical and chemical change involves some form of energy (p. 373). Energy either promotes changes or results from them. When heat, a form of energy, is applied to water, the water boils; when heat is withdrawn (when the water is cooled), it changes to ice. The energy of the small particles of matter keeps them in a state of constant motion and change. Electrons constantly spin and revolve within an atom (p. 378).

The conception of change permeates all fields of knowledge, and man must consider these changes if he is to operate intelligently with natural forces. Modern geology reveals that our physical environment does not remain constant, that the history of Earth is a story of change—change in climate, in topography, and in the succession of living things. Energy and motion are involved.

The conception of change is manifest not only in geological history but in living things, as, for example, the changes produced by birth, growth, age, and death. There are also changes produced by the biological principles involved in the struggle for existence; and these cannot be ignored by man in his striving to adapt the world to his needs. Then there are the changes produced by energy and motion. Astronomical bodies are seen to have changed position and character through cycles of time. The scientist learns to look for energy and change in his explanation of phenomena; the layman must expect change as a condition of everyday life; the student of social studies and the citizen must anticipate change in the political, social, and economic structure. Information concerning changes produced by physical and chemical phenomena developed in terms of children's own experiences can be introduced during early school years and continued through later levels.

Children see water disappear from a dish by evaporation. They pick up rocks which have weathered so much that the rock disintegrates into small pieces in their hands. They see changes in the sky, in the weather, and in the seasons. They see and feel the manifestations of energy daily.

Illustrations of change include such phenomena as rusting of iron, melting of ice, boiling of water, weathering of rocks, variations of weather and of seasons, and innovations produced by man's discoveries and inventions.

School windows should be utilized more fully for the study of the succession of changes due to weather, to the seasons, to the time of day, and man's activities in relation to these changes. Brief excursions around the school grounds will provide varied experiences, depending on the region. The children may see frozen, muddy, and dry soil; the growth of plants; and a variety of plant structure, such as roots, stems, flowers, and seeds. An outdoor thermometer may reveal temperature changes. Art work can be utilized in the study of changes.

A community of living things never remains in a strictly static condition. Children can observe the changes in a weed patch near the school, in a thicket, or in a garden. There is a continual shifting caused by weather, seasonal change, and just ordinary life and growth within the cycle of new life, maturing, and death. Children can see evidences of energy, motion and change all around them.

There is no exception to the inevitability of change, even when man is involved. Natural forces are always present and working in an environment. Perhaps man can never control the natural forces. Rather, he must learn to work intelligently with these natural forces to bring about changes which are advantageous and in his best interest.

In addition, are great changes brought about by man's inventions and man's discoveries. Of course, children are not so aware of the significance of these changes as are adults. However, the school must prepare children to meet change, for the next generation may need to be prepared for even greater changes than those the present generation of adults has seen.

Man has lived through revolutionary changes in his social living because of the introduction of new forms of energy and of ways to utilize that energy. The discovery of fire, the introduction of animals to carry man's burdens, the steam engine, the electric generator, the internal combustion engine, the television greatly changed man's social and economic conditions. The utilization of nuclear and solar energy is bringing, and will continue to bring, tremendous changes. Children should gain a feeling of confidence from the fact that they are not the first of the human race to witness revolutionary changes in the use of energy. Furthermore, it might be well for us to know how man's discoveries of new forms of energy have brought about great potential supplies of energy for everyone. The advances in the field of agriculture and soil culture may have significant impacts on the future course of world events by increasing the supplies of food-energy for mankind.

Changes brought about in a community also may be significant. What did the country look like before the earliest settlers came in? What changes have been brought about by man? For example, discussions following observation of the changes being made in a community by men working with a bulldozer or power shovel may be useful in developing an awareness of modern changes.

There are approximately a hundred elements which enter into combinations and thus form the multitude of substances about us. Chemists find that some of these elements combine in so many different ways that to date they have been able to make but a small proportion of all the possible combinations. Chemists are learning to build out of cheap sources substances which in their natural states have been very rare. They have also learned how to make new substances, such as new drugs, insecticides, medicines, plastics, synthetics, and so on. In this way science contributes greatly to improved health, finer recreation, and a higher standard of living.

Life Is Adapted to the Environment—Adaptation. Adaptation is a pattern which permeates the entire realm of living things, for wherever there is life there is adaptation. This is a conception of great significance in the modern world. Indeed, man's problem today is to adapt his social, economic, and political structure to the conditions of the environment and to his own needs. In the primary years children can learn something about the homes of some animals and their adaptation to life in various places. They can be introduced to the idea that animals' body structures have become modified to fit their environment. Later they can learn how plants and animals, including man, are adapted to seasonal changes. The study of prehistoric life is a story of adaptation, and can be supplemented by a study of how animals are protected from harm, how animals take care of their young, and how plants continue to live on Earth. Man adapts himself through community life. The advantages and disadvantages of this form of adaptation, along with a study of solitary animals, may be considered on intermediate levels. As the child matures, the scope of his concept of adaptation is further broadened through a study of prehistoric modifications, of the weapons which animals use, and of the struggle for existence.

The conception of this pattern, like the conceptions previously outlined, may influence an individual at all levels of his development. It may modify the child's interpretation of simple observations of the effect of seasonal change on plants and animals. It may give substance to the youth's understanding of the structural variations of living things, and to his consideration of problems of public welfare. It may determine the adult's participation in politics and in community life. While the scientist finds much that remains to be discovered concerning adaptation, the significance of this conception in the social studies can scarcely be overemphasized.

Some of the more general facts involved in understanding the concept of adaptation are the relationships of living things to temperature, water, food, light, gravity, and certain gases found in the atmosphere; the effect of some of the limitations of these conditions upon life; the narrow range in those conditions on Earth, as compared with those found in the universe as a whole; the adaptations imposed upon plants and animals that live under these conditions; the prolificness of life; the interchange of energy and substance between plants and animals, and between the physical environment and living things. Through experimentation, discussion, and reading, children learn that living organisms need light, oxygen, nitrogen, carbon dioxide, heat, water, and other things in order to exist and to produce young. When some of these things are scarce, or too abundant, life may suffer.

Man may find in all this an implication for international understanding; man frequently is limited by the physical conditions of the environment to which he adjusts himself. Some people must live in inhospitable places such as swamps, deserts, and arctic regions. These people must utilize the materials that are available for shelter, food, and clothing. It is not surprising, therefore, to find among the peoples of Earth a wide variety of customs. Many of these customs may seem foolish to others, yet they are the result of the experiences of many generations in a given environment and may well be necessary to the very survival of that people.

International co-operation has become a necessary adjustment on the part of mankind if our culture is to survive.

Through science in the elementary school, children have an opportunity to realize that man is only one of a multitude of living things, and that, like these other things, he has survived because he has made adjustments and adaptations to the environment.

There Are Great Variations in the Universe —Variety. On Earth there are wide varieties of climate, exhibiting differences in the range of temperature, in the length of the growing season, in the amount of rainfall and its seasonal distribution, as well as differences in exposure, in slope, in drainage, in elevation, and in soil. These factors create many kinds of environments and require adaptations to these environments. All around us we see in nature a variety of forms, differences in structure, size, habits, and life histories of plants and animals. They range from the ultramicroscopic organisms to the gigantic forms of the redwoods and whales. The life span of some living things is very short, while that of others in some instances covers several hundred years.

When we see how many different kinds of living things there are, it is not surprising to find that there are also many different kinds of people. Man has wandered about the world for thousands of years, living in many widely separated habitats. We should expect, therefore, to find different races, languages, and customs. But an important concept that science may teach is the basic similarities of peoples everywhere and their interdependence despite their differences. No two living things are exactly alike, although they may be of the same species. We cannot, therefore, judge all people of any nation on the basis of one or two we may have known.

Variation is manifested in the physical as well as in the biological world. There are many systems of organization in the physical world—the atom, the element, the molecule, the compound, the substance, the planet, the solar system, the galaxy. There are many kinds of minerals, soils, and rocks. Though there are approximately one hundred elements, there are many thousands of different compounds. There is variety in the manifestation of energy. Man, too, tends to develop variety of forms in his inventions, discoveries, engineering, and arts.

Children should become acquainted with this theme by being introduced to the range and scope of certain obvious characteristics in the physical and biological aspects of nature. Instruction should be chiefly concerned with the *theme,* rather than with mere identification of animate and inanimate objects.

Each child has two parents. Each parent brings to the child a diverse inherited background. When we consider that this means for each child four grandparents, eight great-grandparents, and so on, the potentialities working for variation in the human race become apparent. When to this observation we add the fact that each child has a different environment, the tremendous variations found in children in any classroom are understandable. Every individual is a result of successful adaptation through a long span of generations, for each of his ancestors is in turn the result of two parents reaching maturity in spite of sometimes hazardous conditions.

The concept of individuality, that each individual is unique and different from all other individuals, is a part of the larger pattern of variety. Williams,[1] a biochemist, has recommended that children should learn in the kindergarten that they possess individuality. His recommendations merit serious consideration by elementary-school workers. They point to one way in which science can contribute to mental hygiene. Each individual has a right to be different. He should not be amazed to learn he is superior to some of his classmates in some ways and inferior to others in other abilities. This pattern can be used to develop a feeling for the dignity of the individual, a feeling extremely important in a democracy.

[1] Rogers J. Williams, *Free and Unequal: The Biological Basis of Individual Liberty.* University of Texas Press, Austin, 1953, p. 177.

Following are some of the variations that are found in the environment of children:

Changes that take place in the out-of-doors

The many different kinds of animals

The variety of animal noses, eyes, tails, mouths, coverings, legs

The variety in prehistoric animals

The different ways in which animals move about

The difference in animals' homes—such as those on desert, in the arctic, in swamps, underground, in fresh water, on the seashore, in the ocean depths, in the forest, in the meadow, in trees

The variety in locomotion, food-getting, breathing, and protection of animals

Different ways in which animals grow up

The many different kinds of plants, such as those that develop from spores, those that develop from seeds, those that are annuals, those that are biennials, those that are perennials

The animals that are social, and those that are solitary

The animals that are cold-blooded, and those that are warm-blooded.

The Interdependence of Living Things— Interrelationship. This is a theme which is practically universal in character. We see the significance of interrelationships as an integrating theme in many of the forces operating on Earth; for example, in the description of astronomical bodies, weather, and other physical phenomena; in the interdependence and interrelation of living things to each other and, in turn, to their physical environment; in the causes of ill health; and in the relation of pests and parasites to economic loss in the agricultural world.

Space does not permit a full discussion of how the idea of interrelationships in physical and biological phenomena may be developed. In the early years children gain experiences which lead to an understanding that some plants and animals in the garden are harmful. In later work they learn the value of certain other plants and animals and what people are doing to protect them. In later elementary school work attention should be focused on the problem of conservation and on preparing pupils for a more comprehensive study of the biological principles involved in the struggle for existence, in the balance of nature, and in the interdependence of life. Some of the relationships of scientific discoveries and inventions to man's progress and welfare should be considered. Man does not live by and for himself alone. He lives in a world of interdependencies and interrelationships. He is dependent upon earthworms and plants for the fertility of the soil. He is dependent upon the birds to keep the insects in check. He needs snakes, owls, hawks, and other animals to keep rats and mice in check. Spiders serve to control the number of insects. An animal which seems rather insignificant to us may play an important role in the development of conditions suitable to man.

The interdependence and interrelationships of living things to other living things, and of living things to the physical environment, is basic to the understanding of social issues. Physical and biological forces do not recognize national borders. A wind blowing in one country may be due to world-wide atmospheric conditions and to the pressure of air in regions within the borders of other nations. Animals do not necessarily stop at national borders unless those borders are also natural barriers, and even then certain animals are known to cross many such barriers.

In science Earth must be considered commonly as an entity; a disturbance in the physical or biological environment in one part of Earth may have significance for many other parts, just as a fire in one section of a community is of concern to the entire community.

A disease or a pest in one section of the world may become the concern of all peoples. Nations, therefore, should learn to work together in an intelligent way for the welfare of all peoples of Earth.

The natural resources of a country such as soil, oil, coal, gas, forests, and pastures are the result of natural forces operating through millions of years. People have not created these resources, but they frequently waste them through carelessness and mismanagement. Man can waste in a generation or two what has been the result of titanic natural forces operating over very long periods of time.

Man, if he is to remain civilized, must disturb the original balance of nature, for only savagery can exist where man does not attempt to make changes. It is man's task to use the natural processes and resources in such a way that he secures what he needs for a high standard of living *without* hazarding the welfare of future generations. Man need neither return to savagery nor disregard natural resources; he now has science to use in planning for the years ahead. It is incumbent upon the public schools to develop a generation with ability to meet its problems, both personal and social, with intelligence, co-operation, and resourcefulness. This calls for an appreciation of the interdependence of living things, and of the interrelations of living things with physical forces and materials.

The Interaction of Forces—Equilibrium and Balance. As one observes the many events or phenomena in his environment, one is impressed by the dynamic flow of events and the energy involved in them. If one could be an observer over centuries and eons of time, one would be aware of the titanic forces in operation on Earth; but seen one day at a time, over the short span of a human lifetime, these forces often pass unrecognized. Some, such as evaporation, seem small; yet scattered over the face of Earth, the force involved in evaporation is tremendous, and results finally in rain, snow, dew, frost, weathering, erosion, floods, blizzards and other events.

There seem to be tendencies toward equilibrium and balance in the operation of forces. In a normal atom it is thought that the positive electrical charges balance the negative electrical charges. It is thought that a static electrical charge is the result of unbalance in these electrical charges. The shock we feel or the lightning flash we see is the resulting establishment of equilibrium between these charges. Even the thunder can be thought of as a clap caused by air rushing in to fill a space where air was expanded by the heat of lightning.

We have already spoken about the balance of nature. At times man has been heedless of it and has experienced economic loss resulting from dust bowls, soil erosion, waste of resources, epidemics, plagues, and pests.

There are forces operating in the structure of Earth. It is thought by some geologists that in maintaining balance these forces have caused the formation of mountains, continents, and oceans. We regard earthquakes and volcanic eruptions as a result of the balancing which takes place between the forces operating in Earth's structure.

It should be kept in mind that the sun is a great source of energy and that it shines on Earth all the time. It shines on the other side of Earth while we are having night. It shines when it is cloudy, although there are clouds between us and the sun. The sun, then, is like a great solar engine which furnishes energy for green plants to grow and make food, for water to evaporate, and for the movements of winds and ocean waves. These movements are modified by Earth's gravity, by its rotation, and by friction. There is a tremendous interplay of forces in the universe.

Wherever we look, we witness the operation of forces and the many evidences of balance.

We also have experience with the operation of natural forces in and on our own bodies and with our own efforts to maintain balance and equilibrium. Many psychologists explain learning at all levels as a process of attempting to gain intellectual balance in the face of a new situation, a problem, or a challenge. They explain that when we are faced by a challenge or a problem, we gain an initial intellectual imbalance. The attempt to come back to equilibrium brings learning. This point of view is in keeping with the dynamic psychology of science in childhood education as supported in this book.

The Areas of Social Needs

In addition to the development of the basic patterns of the universe, the curriculum-maker and the teacher should consider the areas growing out of living and social needs such as health, safety, conservation, and economics. It is evident that these areas will utilize content described in other parts of this publication and will form a basis for the development of desirable behavior. (See "Patterns of the Universe," pp. 81–100, and Chapter 6.)

Developing Behavior Consistent with Health. Science in the elementary-school program should develop a large background for the teaching of health. Many schools are now integrating health instruction entirely with science. Science provides the necessary background for the teaching of health information and the development of good health habits. Therefore, science in the elementary school should offer opportunity for the integration of science and health. Moreover, in the study of science children should gain a vision of the potentialities of science in the improvement of the health of their nation and of the world.

Developing Behavior Consistent with Economy. The relation between science and economy has too long been neglected. Because of his own ignorance of the operation of biological and physical science principles and pat-terns, man is at present beset by a host of problems concerning national and international economy. Recent projects in a number of countries are helping to solve these economic problems in local environments by reestablishing in the natural forces a balance in favor of man's interests and welfare. The place of science in bringing about the wise utilization of natural resources for the welfare of mankind is an important aspect of the science areas related to social needs.

The relation of science to the economic problems of man is well exemplified in his struggle with pests. Man has carelessly introduced exotic plants and animals into almost all regions of the world. Many of these transplanted plants and animals, unchecked by their natural predators and competitors, have multiplied so rapidly that they have brought havoc to the economic life of the nation. Control comes not alone from the work of fact-finding public or private scientific agencies, but also from the intelligent co-operation of the entire population. Much can be done to secure this intelligent co-operation through an integrated program of education in the public schools. Mankind cannot afford to have another generation ignorant of the elementary biological principles of nature.

Another similar problem is that of finding ways to prevent loss of soil through erosion. In almost any section of the world we can find examples of the loss of natural resources resulting from the lack of soil conservation. Creating an awareness of this problem, in order to bring about intelligent individual and community action concerning it, is no small part of the science program in the elementary school.

Many species of our indigenous plants and animals have become extinct because of man's ruthlessness and ignorance. Still other species are in danger of being destroyed. Man cannot continue to be ignorant of the web of life in which he is by nature involved. The elementary school, as the tool of the people, should work toward developing a generation concerned with the wise utilization of natural beauty and resources.

Few areas undergo greater revision than this area. New discoveries in the field of chemistry, such as insecticides, weed-killing substances, and other, may make new outlooks possible. New outlooks upon the plants known for centuries as weeds create a need to reappraise some of man's habits. Controversies between those favoring big dams and those who advocate stopping the water where it falls and "walking" it down to the ocean, rather than allowing it to "run" down, washing the good soil with it, will re-echo again and again in the years to come. New information in reference to handling industrial waste and sewage will create needs for the re-

construction of thinking. Only a wise, educated people should decide these questions. The task of the elementary school is to develop children who want reliable information and who are willing to make decisions in terms of what is important for the welfare of all. (Chapter 6.)

Developing Behavior Consistent with Safety. We cannot fully anticipate the environment of the future. New inventions may eliminate many present hazards and create new ones, making it impossible for use to develop a fixed code of conduct in safety instruction; instead, we must place more emphasis upon scientific principles which are basic to safe conduct. Children at all levels should be encouraged to enter into planning with the teacher for safety on all excursions, even though only to the edge of the school ground.

Consideration should be given to what one should do in case of fire or other disaster, so that the behavior is automatic. Classroom teachers and parents can have a powerful influence over the destiny of whole regions and nations by developing in children a willingness and ability to base their conduct and behavior upon sound information. Safety education, as one aspect of the goals of conservation, can well be integrated into the development of responsibility for one's own behavior and for the environment.

Teaching Content Is Not an End in Itself

In this chapter we have presented the larger ideas that may guide the role of the content of science in a program of instruction for the elementary school. It has been indicated that it is difficult to conceive of education without content. The meaning attached to experience is content, and much of the content of science

has brought new visions, hopes, attitudes, and behavior to the human race.

But teaching content is not the final purpose for the teacher. It is most important that a child or a teacher should *not get lost in small content*. For a teacher the product of her teaching must be thought of in terms of boys and girls. It isn't a matter so much of what content they have learned, but what kind of boys and girls have been developed. Are they developing into responsible and resourceful people? Are they willing and able to think for themselves? Can they meet the challenges of today and tomorrow as citizens?

A classroom teacher in a public school will realize that her work does not stand alone—it is not final. There are many agencies educating the children in a teacher's classroom— parents, radio, television, newspapers, and comics—and some of these may be conducive to good behavior and some to bad behavior. It is the teacher's great task, inso far as it is possible, to help children integrate all of the constructive elements of education and to give it direction and meaning toward the great goals that are in keeping with democracy. It will console her to recall that other classroom teachers may have taught the children and many others may follow her and her brief year with them. But there is no one else during this year that plays this great role in the lives of the boys and girls in her classroom.

Evaluation of teaching and learning content should be in terms of behavior and should be an integral part of the instruction.

In this chapter we have not attempted to indicate the specific small items to be taught; instead, we have focused on the larger patterns. We have held to the idea that content should be organized about large patterns of the universe, about problems of children, and about meanings and themes of social and developmental value.

CHAPTER 5

Procedures in Teaching and Learning Science

The Vital Role of Purpose in Teaching-Learning Procedures. Content, important as it is, does not in itself offer a complete solution of the problem of achieving the educational purposes of science in the education of children. Techniques and content cannot be divorced in a discussion of teaching science. The organization of content, regardless of how vital the particular content may be to children and to society, does not in itself solve the problems encountered in teaching. We now must consider the *techniques* by which we may achieve the purposes and values that we have set up as worth while for the elementary school.

We have already observed that the purposes a teacher holds as important for science in the education of children play a very important role in the selection of content. This same thing is true in the consideration of what is good procedure for teaching and learning.

Purposes should be of such a character as to be operative moment by moment in the all-round experiences of teaching and learning.

We shall not review the purposes that have been proposed in this book (Chapters 2 and 3) except to indicate that the purposes have been stated in terms of *children* rather than in terms of either content or techniques. However, desirable purposes for children in a democracy cannot be accomplished without consideration of content and techniques.

Evaluation of children's growth and development in science should be an integral part of instruction. The best evaluation of education is determined in terms of purposes and values that are sound. In a democracy, this means the purposes and values must be sound for democracy.

No factor will do more to improve the instruction of any teacher than for her to establish clearly in her own mind the purposes for her work with children. These purposes will serve to guide her through the problems relating to content, techniques, and evaluation. These purposes should be purposes she believes in strongly and which she feels she can support in a discussion with members of the community.

Instruction through Interaction

The values or purposes which a classroom teacher recognizes for her instruction should spring from a broad, cultured outlook upon society and a deep social consciousness. The task of the curriculum-maker, then, is to render available to the teacher the kinds of curriculum materials (content, attitudes, and skills), based on research, that will assist the teacher in creating her own values, in envisioning the contribution of these values to the child's growth, and in devising the ways and means of securing these values for the children through her instruction. Perhaps this volume will assist the classroom teacher in the elementary school in creating her own values.

An important element in good teaching is a teacher's continuous study of the potentialities of education in terms of the individual activities of children. A child's growth in the understanding and appreciation of interstellar space or any other portion of the environment may be influenced by a teacher's conception of the possible significant implications of the content to children and, through children, to the welfare of society. The values a teacher recognizes have much to do with the type of problem utilized, how the problem arises and is solved, and the setting, or context, of both the problem and the content.

If a teacher lacks vision, the instruction is likely to be dull, uninteresting, and vague. If a teacher thinks deeply about educational values, the instruction in science is more likely to be well-poised, balanced, and challenging. To illustrate, let us examine the records of the activities of a group of children in a school in Alabama. We find that these children had built a concrete pool in their school grounds and desired to have some living things in it.

Some teachers might have allowed them to fulfill their purpose without attempting to lift that purpose to a higher level in the direction of values which the teachers held worth-while. Let us examine the role of the teacher in this instruction.

A functional understanding of the interrelationship of living things to other living things and of living things to their physical environment constituted basic working patterns significant in establishing proper social values in the mind of the teacher. She would not expect her children to come to a complete understanding (for that would be impossible even for the scientist specializing in the field), but would expect that they could *grow toward* such an understanding, if guided properly. She saw an opportunity in this simple problem for the children to gain some small conception of the relation of the physical environment to living things. Instead, therefore, of allowing the children to fill the pool with fish bought from a local store, she raised the question as to what kind of life would be fitted to live in the pool, pointing out that they would not want to place anything there that had little chance to survive.

Soon these children were aware of the importance of studying the conditions that existed in the pool, such as the temperature throughout the day, the light, and the depth of the water. They searched the environment for places that had conditions of a kind which they could establish in their pool. They found in the vicinity of their school several different kinds of habitats supporting life, such as pond, field, meadow, woods, and even places where conditions approached those of the desert.

They discovered on field excursions that

habitats might be different in different places. In and about the pond they found living things in the mud, in the shallow water, in the deeper water, and along the shore. On an excursion to a pond in which they planned to catch minnows the teacher led them to see these different habitats. The classroom became a laboratory with jars containing living things established in various kinds of habitats for study, collected with conservation in mind. In the study of the various habitats in their vicinity they were challenged constantly to determine if that kind of habitat could be established in their pool.

And so we see that the instruction was characterized by a lifting of the children's purpose to a higher level because they had a teacher who thought deeply about educational values. The activity which might have consisted largely of buying goldfish from a local store became a well-poised, balanced, and challenging study of the conditions that were necessary to life in the various habitats of the local environment.

It is apparent that *teaching science is more than* a matter of presenting the content of science as something which must be accepted by a child. Teaching is a two-way process between the educational purposes and values in the mind of a teacher on the one hand and the experiences and purposes of the children on the other. This means that a teacher thoroughly aware of the values toward which she would like the children to grow begins with their ideas, regardless of the imperfection and inaccuracies of these ideas. Growth must start from where the children are.

It is well to recognize that a teacher and a child both have values for every learning situation. A teacher's values can be in terms of her high purposes for children. A child's values rest in what he brings to the situation in the way of purposes, experiences, drives, interests, concepts, imaginations, challenges, proposals and so on.

For instance, in the development of the concept of time it is important to provide an opportunity for children to express freely their ideas of time. A teacher, having a more mature awareness of the concept of time, may have an opportunity to refine these ideas. Mabel, a nine-year-old girl, expressed the idea that the mountains in the eastern part of the United States were formed about the time of the arrival of the Puritans at Plymouth. This expression, added to other expressions of ideas from the class, provided an opportunity to extend the child's concept of the age of our Earth.

In considering the comments of children a teacher needs to evaluate what children say in terms of their own development rather than in terms of a strictly adult interpretation of their words. In the case above, Mabel had been impressed with the fact that the Puritans arrived in Plymouth a long time ago. Therefore, she placed the formation of the mountains in a category she had just recently learned as a "long time ago."

In other words, finding out where children are in their learning is accomplished in terms of the meanings they have established through their experiences. To Mabel it was a long time ago that the Puritans arrived; to a geologist, thinking in terms of the great age of our Earth, their arrival was quite recent. We need to view children's concepts from a positive rather than from a negative point of view, in keeping with dynamic psychology.

Too much emphasis is placed on evaluating children's concepts in terms of what is wrong with their ideas. While this is important to know, it should be balanced by what they bring to the thinking that has potentialities for growth. This latter is a dynamic and positive outlook and one that corresponds to the nature of children. Teachers working with this point of view will develop good human relations with children.

In another group, composed of six-year-olds, the children expressed the thoughts that a dry cell contained electricity, that electricity could be seen, and that the liquid that could be seen leaking out of the worn-out dry cell was electricity. These expressions gave the teacher some idea of their concepts of electricity and provided an opportunity for teacher and children to co-operate in problem situations demanding experiments, in which the children set the problem, proposed the method of procedure, applied the techniques, and finally formulated the conclusions. Here we have the teacher's conceptions of energy changes interacting with the ideas and experiences of the children in such a way that both teacher and children co-operate in directing the teaching and learning. The children participated in the teaching as well as in the learning. The teaching and learning were integrated. The thinking of the children at the beginning was erroneous in large part but offered tremendous challenges for learning.

Some children in a rural-school group thought that the sun was as large as a nearby building, while others thought it might be as large as a mountain. These expressions led to the development of a more adequate conception of space.

Some seven-year-old children, discussing means of putting out a fire, said that a blanket, a rug, or sand smothered the fire. The teacher used the word *smothered* to interpret experiments in which children extinguished very small fires on an asbestos pad with these materials. The concept of "smother" was broadened to include the necessity of air in burning. This fundamental meaning was used in drawing conclusions concerning desirable behavior in case of fire—for example, not running in case our clothing catches fire, so that we do not pass the fire through more air. Here we have the clarification of a term used by children through the interaction of their experiences and the purposes, or values, of a teacher. The instruction was directed

toward intelligent behavior as is related to possible experiences at home and at school.

Sometimes a child's ideas may be stated in the form of doubts about conclusions developed in previous instruction. For instance, Fred, eleven years old, made the following statement in a class discussion in a rural school: "I was swimming down at the beach last summer. I swallowed a lot of water. My, but it was salty! I don't see how the oceans of the world could have got so much salt from the land. Our brook beside the school isn't salty." Here was a challenge in the classroom in the form of a doubt of an explanation that had been presented in class. The teacher had in mind the value of the modern concept of time in recognizing the educational possibilities in Fred's doubt. When Fred realized that Earth has been here a long time—long enough to allow enough salt to accumulate in the oceans to make them as salty as they are—he had progressed intellectually toward the modern concept of time.

Or again, the idea of a child may be a misconception in the form of a question such as "Where does the sun go when it goes down?" The teacher can be guided by the modern scientific concept of space. Through co-operative discussion and demonstration the children may be helped to move intellectually from the misconception of an Earth-centered universe to a conception more in keeping with the modern scientific idea of space. They may move intellectually in a year, or even in a few minutes, far enough to realize that there are other parts of Earth than the part in which they live; on these parts of the world the sun also shines.

It should be observed that in the statement of the problem to be solved there are two factors: a teacher's values, or purposes, and a child's ideas, or conceptions, and experiences. A teacher's purposes assist in determining the direction of the instruction; a child's idea gives the starting point of attack. The resulting curriculum is not dependent upon the whims of children, nor is it dependent upon mere incidents and accidents, because a teacher's purposes are the result of her study of the needs of children and of society. Nevertheless, because she does have sound purposes, she can utilize more wisely the challenging experiences of children.

Too frequently a teacher fails to determine the difficulty or misconception that obstructs the way of learning because she inhibits the free expression of children. In the study of science no child should be penalized or humiliated for expressing an erroneous idea; a misconception may be useful in the formulation of problems. Once scolded or penalized for the statement of a misconception, a child may become reticent, and a teacher may lose one of the best means for the evaluation of growth. Misconceptions should be brought out into the open so that they may be corrected through instruction—this is the constructive and normal thing to do.

In carrying out this interaction of teacher and children, the teacher plays as significant a role in teaching as ever; in fact, the new role calls for greater skill, since a teacher uses not only her own thinking but the child's as well. A teacher should be aware of the directions determined by her purposes for education and should make certain that the children are growing in those directions. Therefore, she must evaluate the progress of a child in terms of her well-thought-out purposes. She can do this to a considerable extent through consideration of the kind and quality of thinking employed by the child in his participation in learning situations.

Provisions for Interaction. Sometimes the instruction in the elementary school is characterized by haste, which inhibits critical thinking. From one content item to another we hurry on, creating a false pressure upon both teacher and children. This pressure is alien to the child's natural tempo and rhythm. Many teachers would do well to relax more with the children and remove some of the restraints which inhibit thinking. We should provide opportunities for the learner to react to the learning, for a learning element to be absorbed, to be thought over, to become acceptable in a real sense. We might think of this process as "internalizing"; that is, the process in which the learner takes the learning and works it over in his mind, combining it with material that he has already learned.

Many teachers have learned the importance of providing opportunity for an idea to be tossed about in the thinking of the group, to be tested through simple experimentation or through observation on excursions, and to be checked against authentic sources. The children participate with the teacher in the group thinking and in guiding teaching and learning. Teaching science in the elementary school is not a mere matter of presenting the content of science.

Giving children full opportunity for internalizing is an important factor in the formation of concepts in science. Learning with children will assist teachers to provide more adequately for internalizing.

This learning with children does not imply that a teacher need be ignorant of the content. Learning can occur for a teacher, as well as for children, when she is learning *how* they are learning.

A consultant working with a classroom teacher and a group of eight-year-olds was surprised to hear the teacher say, "The children think you don't know . . . " It so happened in this case that the consultant knew the information required. The emphasis in this particular instruction had been placed on how the required information might be secured, in order to explore the children's thought structure.

The statement of the classroom teacher at first disturbed the consultant because it raised the question in his mind as to whether he was in any way deceiving the children in the process of exploring their thinking. Yet as he analyzed the situation in his mind he could feel no tinge of deceit. It occurred to him that these were different children, although very similar to other groups he had taught. Therefore, the situation was new to him and in a real sense the information they needed was novel to him. It also became evident that every group is different from all other groups and that the same group may vary from time to time. It is true, he had taught this information scores of times. But this time he was approaching the information with a new group of children, a group with different experiences and concepts from any group he had taught before. He was attempting to survey their thinking as well as their needs. Therefore, the information he needed was more than the scientific content, for it involved the background of the children, their ideas, their methods of thinking, and their experiences.

There can be learning about children in every teaching situation. There can still be learning for the classroom teacher about a group of children even though she has been with them for an entire school year.

Some of the phases of instruction that may be shared with children are sensing problems; proposing problems; defining problems; proposing techniques for the solution of problems; relating experiences pertinent to the solution of a problem; proposing observations that may be made; thinking through the problem; proposing an experiment; assisting in drawing conclusions; assisting with experiments; improving experiments; finding flaws in experiments; repeating experiments; questioning the authority of printed material; questioning superstitions, myths, and other unscientific material; discarding faulty opinions; recognizing the difference between the proposals of class members and authentic information; determining the values of the learning.

Developing Critical Thinking

A procedure demanding critical thinking which is employed by some teachers is somewhat as follows:

Certain children advance explanations for a given phenomenon. How do we know whether a particular explanation is reliable? An individual or group of children working together may suggest ways of finding out. Perhaps an experiment is proposed. Does the experiment show evidence for the reliableness of the explanation? This calls for thinking and discussion, with many children participating. It calls for trying the experiment, repeating it to determine whether the same results are secured, and considering the way in which the experiment was performed to see if it was car-

ried out carefully. Perhaps an observation out of doors is needed. If so, opportunity for observation must be sought and the method of observation planned co-operatively. The observation may be one which can be checked again and again to see if the conclusions are the same. A proposed explanation can be considered as a hypothesis on a child's level which must be tested. If the explanation is found to be unreliable, then we must look for another explanation. Reading authentic children's science books will be necessary for the most reliable information.

This reasoning demands accurate explanations or interpretations which should bring forth critical thinking. A teacher must not expect children to have at first all the attitudes and skills essential to doing this type of thinking. It will take time to develop such attitudes and skills. Into the reasoning can flow the attitudes of open-mindedness, objective and impersonal criticism, willingness to accept criticism, freedom from bias, willingness to make contributions to group effort and to check conclusions by authentic sources.

In all such cases a teacher's awareness of an adequate set of values prevents the instruction from becoming bogged down in small content; and on the other hand, her awareness of the place of a child's responses in teaching gives her an opportunity to evaluate the child's growth.

So science in the elementary school is no longer dependent upon rigid courses of study or units of instruction. Rather, it can be the result of the interaction of the interests and experiences of the children on the one hand and the well-thought-out values of a teacher on the other. This does not mean, however, that a child does not have some hand in setting up values. The children who thought that the liquid from the dead dry cell was electricity had a part in setting up values for the class, for they were manifesting some desire for an explanation of electricity. Or again, a child ten years old inquiring about the formation of Earth is setting up values concerning the natural origin of things.

Too frequently in our teaching we have tended to do the thinking for the children— rather than allowing them to do it for themselves—by our insistence that they be good followers and accept the content presented more or less passively. We should do well in the examination of our teaching to consider how difficult it has been for us at many times to work new ideas into our own thinking. We, as adults, may be willing to accept an authority as an authority in economics, art, science, or in games and sports; but new meanings developed by these same authorities do not necessarily become a part of our thinking by the mere repetition of the statements. The content must be worked over, thought over, and brought to bear on previous learnings and experiences by the learner himself. This working of meanings into the fabric of his own knowledge and experience must be done by the child himself, although his classmates and teacher can be of great assistance. A new idea may need to be approached from a number of angles. Group discussion, experimentation, and observation have much to do with the orientation of the individual to a new idea. Teacher "drive" alone will not suffice.

There are degrees of critical thinking, and there are opportunities at all levels to improve the criticalness with which one thinks. The thinking of children in the kindergarten is not so refined a product as the thinking of a scientist within the area of his own specialization in his laboratory or in the field. But the thinking of young children very frequently displays elements of criticalness, and these elements may be reinforced, refined, improved, and given opportunity to function in other situations under the guidance of the skillful teacher.[1]

Certainly one of the important tasks of a teacher is that of assisting children to become aware of the values of careful thinking, not only in the study of science but in all the important issues of life. This means that the techniques of science (pp. 112–122) must be given large implications for all educational procedures; they must be not only something which a teacher applies but also something which the children apply as a standard by which they can check the procedures employed by them in learning.

The following are some of the kinds of behavior which may be the results of critical thinking:

[1] Katherine E. Hill, *Children's Contributions in Science Discussions*. Teachers College, Columbia University, New York, 1947.

Questioning magic as an explanation of events

Searching for an explanation of things which happen (natural phenomena)

Realizing that some natural phenomena have not yet been explained satisfactorily by scientists

Rejecting the personification of natural forces in explanations

Rejecting animistic (those that ascribe spirits to objects) explanations

Realizing that interpretations advanced by scientists today may be corrected and improved by the same or other scientists tomorrow

Changing one's ideas as a result of new evidence

Rejecting guessing as a means of getting at truth

Repeating an experiment in order to check observations

Demanding more evidence

Rejecting faulty thinking

Being willing to check conclusions

Questioning the accuracy of sources of information

Identifying the source of one's comment

Questioning the acceptance of the opinions of those who are not qualified in the field in which the opinions are given

Questioning superstitions, prejudices, astrology, and fortune-telling

Advancing hypotheses in the solution of problems

Advancing ways of testing hypotheses

Applying tests to hypotheses

Realizing the importance of reliable information

Placing confidence in the techniques of science

A teacher should participate with the children in solving problems, and should so focus their attention that they will grow in the application of the techniques of science to ordinary life situations.

We need to focus the attention of children upon the importance of critical thinking and to encourage it to be used spontaneously by children. In the performance of an experiment in a class of ten-year-olds, a tin can was crushed by the pressure of air. Some of the children exclaimed, "That is magic." For a few minutes it seemed that magic as an explanation was entirely acceptable to all the children. The teacher, however, with the value of critical thinking in mind, questioned magic as a cause of the crushing of the can. Soon the children were searching for other explanations. In this case we see the definite direction given the instruction by the teacher's having in mind the value of critical thinking. This casting of doubt on magic as a suitable explanation is of greater social value than the mere explanation of a single happening or phenomenon.

Many times children offer as evidence in a given topic the opinion of some person in the community. On page 146 we have attempted to indicate how opinions which are not reliable may be utilized and at the same time develop good human relations for all concerned. This constant questioning of the sources of information should permeate all phases of the instruction in science. Gradually there should be built up in the mind of a child, through his experiences in the elementary school, the importance of going to reliable sources for information upon vital questions.

In science the question, "What is the most reliable information about a given phenomenon?" is always in order. How can we find out? We can use observation, careful thinking, and experiment, realizing that in the end the final authorities are the scientists who specialize in the particular field. The views of the scientists may be secured by a child by consulting authentic material prepared for children and occasionally by consulting directly an authority who may happen to live in the local community. This indicates that authoritative science books can play a vital role in the development of critical thinking (pp. 132–135).

Science, with its opportunities for objectivity, for the use of experimentation, for the manipulation of forces, for the checking of statements, offers a unique opportunity for teachers and children to employ critical thinking. There should be freedom for discussion, asking questions, proposing tests, testing statements, and consulting information. But in the end we must work for the most reliable information. How do we know that this information is reliable? How can we find out? A teacher should permit a child to bring to bear whatever personal experience, observation, experimentation, and thinking he has to offer on the problem at hand, in order that important meanings may be worked thoroughly into his experience. A teacher should focus the attention of children upon the good elements of thinking so that children become aware of what constitutes good thinking. Either favorable or unfavorable evaluation of an individual child in the presence of other children should be done with awareness of the effect of such comments on the personalities and human relations of children.

The children's thought structure—that is, how they think, what they rely upon for information, their attitudes—should be examined by a teacher frequently if not almost continuously. In this way a teacher can evaluate children's development (pp. 943–945). It should be kept in mind that the kind of thinking children do is more important than what they learn. It is also through examination of children's thinking that a teacher can determine whether children are ready for the learning involved. This illustrates how evaluation is an integral part of teaching.

Teaching and Learning Science Calls for Activity

Because of science man has become a predominant force in nature. He must learn to operate intelligently with the natural forces of the universe. His difficulties very frequently arise because of his failure to give enough consideration to basic natural patterns and principles. Perhaps man should not aspire to the control of natural forces but rather should know how to co-operate with them for his own welfare. At least he must be on his guard lest he upset the equilibrium of the forces to such an extent that he cannot restore a balance that is in his favor.

Sometimes he rushes into his problems without completely anticipating the events that will follow his action, and as a result he often reaps disaster. Mankind must act, but he must learn to act with intelligence.

The influence of science upon life is dynamic. During the last few decades, discoveries have followed discoveries with rapidity in many fields of science, greatly altering the manner of living for millions of the world's people. Boys and girls must realize that through science and democracy they can make their own world better.

It is apparent from this that science in the elementary school is not merely the job of teaching a child subject matter for his passive acceptance. In addition to understanding, science involves doing, reading, working, thinking, planning, co-operating, and intelligently operating with the natural forces in the classroom, on the school ground, in the community, and in experimenting with simple materials. This does not mean that every boy and girl should become an embryonic scientist; instead, it places emphasis on the guidance of all individuals toward a realistic and resourceful outlook upon the problems of life. If a teacher conceives of children as individuals who are in constant interaction with the environment, then she has a suitable basis for making an evaluation of her own instruction and of the children's progress in science. The best means of evaluating progress of children in science is through the observation of behavior.[2]

Such questions as the following may be utilized in this evaluation: Does the individual display interest in the environment, or is he bored with it? Does he believe everything that he hears? Is he willing to consider new information? Does he exhibit changed attitudes? Does he call for distinctions between fact and fiction? Does he relate fiction from books, radio, and television as if it were true? Is he willing to seek and act upon reliable information? Does he reject personification, superstition, prejudice, astrology, fortune-telling? Does he reject guessing and faulty think-

ing? Does he exhibit willingness to experiment? Does he work with others in planning for activities? Does he use meanings previously learned in new situations? Does he see how science can be utilized to improve his home, his school room, his school grounds, and his community? Does he label the source of his comment? Is he developing a wholesome outlook on the universe? Does he develop hypotheses? Is he willing to challenge his own ideas? Is he willing to be realistic? Is he well poised? Is he willing to have others challenge his ideas?

In this consideration of "teaching and learning science as a call for action" the emphasis is upon the idea that science is dynamic in its consequences for human beings. Therefore the procedure, or method, of teaching and learning should be vital, challenging, and active. If for any reason a teacher finds her teaching has become dull and colorless, she has only to study the children and science, and revise her procedure accordingly. For both children and science are active and dynamic and never dull.

The Solution of Problems

It is evident that, while children do not discover new facts for mankind, they do discover new information for themselves, and this they must do day by day if they are to become adequate for the world of today and tomorrow. Fortunately, they have the assistance of the rich scientific heritage which is theirs for the taking and which has been provided for them by the scientists of the past and present.

[2] Katherine E. Hill, *Children's Contributions in Science Discussions.* Contributions to Education, No. 931, Teachers College, Columbia University, New York, 1947. Joe Young West, *Techniques for Appraising Certain Observable Behavior of Children in Science in the Elementary School.* Contributions to Education, No. 728, Teachers College, Columbia University, New York, 1937.

If a teacher will keep in mind the kinds of challenges open to children, she will have a natural approach to the techniques of science. How can we find out? How do we know this is reliable? Are you sure of your facts? The techniques which are described in what follows can be adapted to the level of the children so that they will know what they are doing and why they are doing it, and so that they will have some control over the process.

There has been much discussion in scientific circles concerning the methods of investigations used in the various fields of science.

Naturally there is considerable difference in the exact techniques that are utilized in the various sciences, and even within a single specialized field. However, there has been considerable acceptance of the principal elements involved in these techniques. Children frequently utilize them spontaneously in connection with their own investigation or orientation to the environment. In the following we shall consider these elements in connection with the development of children.

Children Can Sense Problems. Children at all levels orient themselves to problems or questions. This orientation may come through short or long intervals of manipulation of materials (including play), observation, and use of appropriate reading materials and visual aids. The orientation can be observed in most of the small child's activities and is associated with what the adult usually calls curiosity (Chapter 1). Young children may return again and again to an object or to some phenomenon for repetition of the orientation. At this stage there may be a *sensing* of a problem, and therefore it illustrates one of the elements involved in the techniques used in making investigations. A teacher can use discussion to give point to these activities and to cause the problem to emerge more clearly for the children. This does not necessarily indicate that a long discussion is needed, for perhaps only a comment and question is needed (pp. 124–126). A teacher may be able to develop fragmentary experiences into functional channels which are in keeping with sound purposes for elementary education.

Children Can Define Problems. In the application of the techniques to the classroom the problem to be solved should be formed clearly in the minds of the children and the teacher. It should be remembered that in this process a child formulates his own problem, but it is also important to remember that

in such a formulation the other children and the teacher may be of great assistance.

In the elementary school the problem (what is to be discovered) may need to be stated and restated. This is true even though the problem has been well stated on a printed page. A teacher should find out what the children have in mind when they use words in the statement of the problem. Perhaps the children have a different meaning or concept of the problem from the teacher's or from that stated in the book. A discussion which provides for children an opportunity to state ideas freely assists in making relatively certain that the teacher and children have the same problem in mind.

In the process of defining a problem it is most important that the problem should become one which the children accept as theirs. In good teaching the problem becomes one that is meaningful to them in the real sense of the word; it should become a problem which they *want* to solve, not a mere hurdle set up by a teacher.

Children's participation in stating problems does not necessarily leave the selection of curriculum materials to children. The emphasis intended in this discussion is that a child be fully aware of the problem and be ready to attack it before the group moves on to formulate a method of solution.

Frequently teachers find that children can express a difficulty in a manner challenging to other children. In a group discussion a teacher was having difficulty clarifying a certain idea. Douglas, a boy of twelve, in a few brief sentences placed the difficulty before the group in terms of their own understanding. The ideas and the problem apparently became theirs, and they expressed enthusiasm for continuing along the lines set up by the teacher with the assistance of Douglas.

A problem often needs redefinition for various reasons; refinements may be necessary as a result of certain experiences of the children, or there may be unforeseen difficulties in the problem itself. In all cases of redefinition the children must participate.

Very frequently a problem will be found to need further analysis. A study of the weather may call for a study of atmospheric pressure, the cause of winds, or evaporation. This breaking down of a problem into its component parts is an activity for children as well as teachers. Too frequently this step is performed for children rather than by children. *Free discussion* becomes an important function in breaking up a problem or topic into its component parts.

This analysis of a problem into its constituent elements is most important in good thinking. It has been our observation that poor instruction is often caused by considering too many learning elements at a time. Learning moves only as rapidly as the learner changes his ideas.

The problem may grow out of a practical situation. In New England some children were attempting to beautify the grounds of their rural school. They transplanted various plants from a meadow and deep forest to their school grounds. Those from the meadow did well in a sunny place on the school grounds; those from the forest did not do so well. Why? How could they use this knowledge in continuing their work in beautifying the school grounds? Here was a situation which involved conditions necessary to life, such as light and water.

Sometimes the problem comes from a discussion, a current event, or a basal book. Regardless of its origin, the problem should be one that is meaningful to children and can be related to their experiences. Freedom of discussion will guide a teacher in making certain that both she and the children have the same problem in mind. Discussion, then, by its very nature, must play an important part in the study of science.

Children Can Suggest Techniques for Solving Problems. Having defined our problem, the next step is to find a way of getting the solution. Children should have a voice in this. Frequently a problem suggests the method of solution. Mary, six years old, says, "A magnet attracts paper clips because it is sticky." Alice proposes a method of solution. Since by feeling it the children find that the magnet is not sticky, they must look for another explanation for the attraction of the paper clips. Too many times the question is answered by an overzealous teacher or parent, without giving children an opportunity to suggest the techniques for solution.

It should be noted that Mary proposed a hypothesis when she said that the magnet was sticky. The hypothesis did not stand the test, and the children abandoned it. Frequently children propose and test hypotheses. A hypothesis in the classroom may be checked by observation, experimentation, and information gained from authoritative books, although in reality the last is the final criterion.

Marvin, seven years old, asks if a magnet will attract iron through water. June, six years old, says, "Let me put some paper clips in the water and see if the magnet will pick them up." Here, again, we have the children proposing a problem and a technique for its solution.

Another illustration of how the problem suggests the method of solution comes from the kindergarten. A child asks, "If I stand on a chair, can I touch the moon?" The problem is solved by trying what it suggests. A teacher, guided by the modern conception of space, can guide children as far as she thinks they are prepared to go. They can discover that other high places such as the tops of buildings or hills with which they are familiar are not high enough to permit them to touch the moon. Even an airplane does not go high enough. How far beyond the initial problem shall the discussion go? This can be answered only in terms of how far the responses of the children pursue the line of thought set up by the original problem. A teacher should be guided by the responses of the children in reacting to new situations that occur.

A problem, whether it comes from a teacher or from children, placed squarely before the group in their own vocabulary, demands group action in deciding how the solution is to be secured. Discussion helps the group to clarify the problem and to get at the method of solution. Perhaps experimentation will prove to be the best technique for solution, as in the case of whether a magnet will attract paper clips in water, or whether a magnet attracts paper clips because it is sticky, or whether we can touch the moon by standing on a chair. Sometimes an excursion out of doors will help in the solution. But always the conclusion secured must be in agreement with the statements of the authorities (scientists) who spend their lives in working in the particular field of science involved in the problem. Frequently the answer can be secured only by resorting to books, as for instance, in the case of problems involving the relationships of sun, moon, and stars, where the untrained may make false interpretations based on observation. So reading authoritative science books must play an important part in the solution of problems.

A problem should be abandoned only when it seems wise to do so. Sometimes class discussion flits from point to point, and little is accomplished. Persistence of purpose should be a characteristic of the study of elementary science. There are times when a problem or question may be abandoned for good reason, but action leading to abandonment or postponement should be intelligent and purposeful.

Democracy in a classroom frequently resorts to the practice of voting in the solution of problems. Sometimes this is carried too far by teachers, so that almost all answers are arrived at by a class vote. Children should understand when it is fitting to answer questions by a vote and when it is not. For instance, no amount of voting will decide questions about the pressure of the air or the rotation of our Earth on its axis. The truth about natural phenomena cannot be learned by the group's expressing a choice.

One cannot exaggerate the importance of the education that children in democracies secure in their games and in school by being good sports in abiding by the results democratically arrived at. It is interesting to observe how quickly the minority accept the will of the majority in a democracy. In elementary schools, however, we should have more discussion about what questions can properly be determined by voting and what cannot; and having decided when to use the ballot, we should use it intelligently.

For instance, adults are frequently asked to vote on questions such as that of conservation (Chapter 6). We must approach questions of this type with all the reliable information we can muster. The attitudes built up in the classroom may have considerable bearing upon more intelligent preparation for casting a ballot.

Children should think through the various suggestions of ways to solve a problem. Will any of these ways give us an accurate answer? Many methods will not. For instance, sheer guessing will not give us an accurate answer. Or again, voting will not give us accurate explanations of natural phenomena. Neither can we place any dependence on explanations that presuppose magic. As children pass through the elementary school their understanding of the relation between the technique used in solving a problem and the accuracy of the solution should grow.

In the elementary school children should learn the function of the hypothesis in science.

They should come to realize that a hypothesis is much more than a guess, that it is proposed only after much careful study, that it is abandoned as soon as it has been proved unreliable, and that it has been a necessary step in the eventual solution of many scientific problems. In fact, the elementary-school program should provide opportunity for children to advance, test, and test again hypotheses of their own making. The fact that children will propose hypotheses for the solution of problems if given opportunity is frequently overlooked by elementary-school workers.

Such a question as "How may we find the explanation?" may cause children to propose a hypothesis. In fact, teachers should condition the learning situation in a classroom in such a way that children naturally propose hypotheses. In such conditioning of the learning situations a teacher is making use of some of the tremendous drives of children which lead them to anticipate or expect happenings (phenomena), to manipulate materials, to use their imaginations, and to reconstruct their ideas of their physical environment (Chapter 1).

There should be the kind of discussion which allows children to give expression to speculation, to suggest techniques for solution, to deliberate in planning, and to evaluate the whole process at many points in instruction. In other words, there should be provision for initiative on the part of both teacher and children.

EXPERIENCE. *To understand the nature of a hypothesis.* The value of hypotheses can be brought to the attention of children. The word may be new to them but the experience is not. It is a part of problem solving and they may use it frequently. The question of what we do when we lose something, a coat for instance, may be brought up. How do we attack the problem of getting it back? We at once wonder where we could have left the coat. Could we have

laid it down? We try to remember where we were after four o'clock, perhaps. Did we leave it on the playground or was it on the fence at Jimmy's house when we tried to ride his new bicycle? We look at both places and it isn't there. Then we remember that we didn't stop at either place that day. So we set up the new hypothesis that we must have forgotten and left it at school, perhaps because it was so hot and we didn't feel cold when we started home. Next morning this hypothesis proves to be true. In the same way, large and more complicated hypotheses become part of our efforts to answer questions about the unknown. Children will be able to think of many questions they have answered in this way.

Children Can Arrive at a Solution. At the end of the procedure a tentative conclusion may be reached. In the final analysis, the conclusion must be in agreement with the statements of scientific authorities. Therefore, the conclusion reached by the group must be checked through the use of accurate reading material prepared for children. Children should come to realize through their experiences that authorities have to change their ideas every now and then. Children should become accustomed to the acceptance of new ideas when they seem reliable, although such acceptance may mean the revision of information gained previously. Sometimes children find two authorities in disagreement. Such occasions can be utilized to introduce the children to the fact that man has much to learn and as a result has not come to an acceptable explanation of many things; hence the disagreement.

We often fail to grasp the natural opportunities arising in the classroom for developing some of the scientific attitudes. This was illustrated in an instance in which a teacher was discouraged almost to the point of refusing to teach science because the children found that two books, apparently equally authoritative, disagreed in their explanation of a common phenomenon. She commented with a show of dejection to the visitor in whom she had confided, "The worst of it is that the children have discovered it (that the books don't agree)." This teacher manifested in her sincerity and her concern for good relations with children, real potentialities for becoming a successful teacher of children. She saw new values in the situation when she realized later that in this predicament she had an opportunity to face a situation with her children which would give them some impression of the conception that much knowledge remains to be discovered. She then led the children to see that scientists frequently developed explanations about things for which they did not have a satisfactory answer. The more significant value to be secured by the children was growth in open-mindedness and not the determination of the best explanation of the phenomenon under consideration, important as that might have been.

A letter was received recently from Harry, a ten-year-old, who was writing as a representative for his class, to find out why the encyclopedias they were using disagreed as to the number of moons for one of the planets in the solar system. To answer this question there may be an interesting array of possibilities: the copyright date of the publication, the sources used by the editors, the revision of previous observations made by astronomers, and possible errors of astronomers. The answers to such questions as Harry's clearly show that man is still gathering information about his universe and help to indicate that scientists are not the supermen of science fiction, but people; and, like other people, are subject to error as well as open to learning.

Children Can Check Conclusions with Authentic Materials. We cannot rely on our own thinking alone. We must be willing to check our conclusions with the conclusions of others who have specialized in the subjects involved. The great findings of science have been produced by people who have been willing to examine anything which related to their problems. Children should learn the value of depending upon the information provided by scientists. They must learn that they cannot gain reliable information through discussion alone; nor can they be certain that the conclusions they themselves draw from experiments or observations are infallible. They must be willing to check conclusions against the contributions of men who have spent their lives studying and investigating in the fields involved. Since in most cases children cannot consult scientific authorities, they must turn to authentic material developed for them at their own level of comprehension, such as books or visual aids, but with the recognition that such material needs revision from time to time.

Throughout the study of science in the elementary school, children will encounter the fact that many phenomena have not been completely explained by scientists. Children should have an opportunity to gain some comprehension of the evolution of various explanations from their early primitive origin to the modern scientific ideas. Comparisons may be made between the way primitive ideas were developed and the techniques now employed by scientists. Comprehension can be secured through a variety of subjects such as stars, relations of Earth and sun, migration of birds, development of new forms of energy, lightning, ventilation, causes of diseases, and the formation of Earth. Many times a teacher will become so mired in the details of the study of ancient myths that she loses sight of the development of the conception that man still has much to discover. Many children welcome the idea that there is something left for them to discover during their lifetime. They, like their parents and their grandparents, will live in an era of great discoveries; some of the children in our classrooms today will be society's discoverers tomorrow.

Throughout this procedure teachers should see that children develop appreciation of the contribution of the past to the knowledge of the present. Newton well expressed the indebtedness of the present to the past when he said, "If I have seen farther, it was by standing on the shoulders of giants." The indebtedness of those living today to the people of the past is something that needs to be taught. Without the discoveries which have taken place through the ages we would all be primitive aborigines. The techniques are tools man can use to improve his health and general well being.

Children Can Focus Attention upon the Nature of Science. The recitation method, a traditional procedure in teaching, may be described as a ferreting of answers from children. In this procedure a teacher asks a question, expecting the children to give a correct response. This response is followed by another question from the teacher, to which another correct response is sought. Such teaching gives little opportunity for children to participate in the guidance of their learning. It also provides little opportunity for a teacher to learn about the children's experiences, their ideas, their questions, or their planning for the solution of problems. Such a procedure makes little use of the techniques used in various fields of science.

There is more to instruction in science than eliciting pat answers to questions and problems. Attention should be focused upon the techniques used in discovering and the attitudes of children. This statement does not imply that a teacher should assume an arbitrary position as a judge, to hand down decisions as to whether a given child has exhibited a right or a wrong attitude. Rather, the attention is upon the procedure of how we may secure reliable information. Good teaching involves

evaluation of the procedures employed by teachers and children alike. It should also tend to develop an appreciation of reliable information and of the processes through which it was secured.

This discussion of techniques should not be interpreted to indicate that they should monopolize instruction. It might be uninteresting if children were forced to utilize, in all their work in science, the techniques involved in making discoveries. Children should at many different times in the elementary school be led to the realization that statements found in an accurate source of science material are reliable and that they can begin, and pursue, their study of many subjects through the use of such sources.

The procedure of utilizing scientific techniques can become fatiguing for children, so that they cannot employ them for any length of time. In some groups there are certain individuals who can pursue a technique for rather long periods each day. But others are soon fatigued and ready to leave the group and play. A wise teacher will know how long it is profitable to the children to be held to the rigor and discipline of any technique. There must be times when children may go directly from a problem to reading material. There will be times, and quite properly so, when problems will arise *from* authentic reading material. With many groups the techniques would be utilized only at intervals.

Each child should be given opportunity to grow in the use of the techniques. This would seem to indicate that not all the children should be held in the group discussion for the full time that a discussion period lasts. Some teachers in primary grades require all children to be a part of the group for a certain length of time, but also see to it that those who are able and willing to pursue this type of activity longer can do so after others have gone about other activities which seem more interesting.

It should be kept in mind that we, in our adult life, cannot discover all the information we need in daily life through our own individual employment of the scientific techniques. As adults, we may encounter many problems —the paint on a house, a new rug for the floor, questions about capital or labor, or about the problems caused by communism in distant parts of the world—problems upon which we, as members of a democracy, are asked to have an opinion. We cannot possibly solve these questions individually by using scientific techniques. However, we can apply the *attitudes* gained from them (pp. 49–78) to our thinking on these questions. Our purpose in using these in the classroom is for its influence on the *behavior* of children.

The Attitude of the Teacher. An important aspect in the teaching of the scientific attitudes is the attitude of the teacher herself. In her behavior a teacher must indicate her willingness to solve problems. There must be willingness to have statements challenged and investigated by the group. The teacher must display critical-mindedness and willingness to participate in intelligent planning (pp. 53, 60).

The Place of Science in a Democracy

Techniques Are Tools. Through motion pictures, fiction, radio, and television the public frequently secures a distorted idea of the function of science in society. With many who have not thought the matter through, science has become a field of activity producing wars and depressions. Others see it as a sinister and satanic force in civilization, as exemplified by the villain-scientists in fiction. Many think of science largely in terms of new horror inventions, new methods of war such as atomic bombs, hydrogen bombs, poison gas, germ warfare, and other devices. Still others associate it with those unfamiliar things that are beyond their own comprehension, and "science" and "scientific" have become words to be utilized by advertisers to foist wares on a gullible public. Undoubtedly, only a portion of the population at the present time has come to an adequate interpretation of the nature of science as a tool of society, the value of which transcends that of all man's previous inventions and discoveries. Scientific attitudes remain alien to many people in an era of scientific discovery.

There will be many who would contend that the scientist is the only one who needs education in the techniques of science. However, although the scientist is the only one who needs specialized training in the use of the techniques of science in making new discoveries for society, it is evident that all citizens in a democracy need some acquaintance with the nature of these techniques, a vision of their place in society, and some skill in their use as a way of thinking on all vital matters. If scientific techniques and scientific attitudes are to prevail in a democracy, the voters must become intelligent concerning the elementary tenets of the nature of science. The preservation of a democracy in this scientific era is dependent upon the perspective of all the people. When the public has come to a realization of the true place of critical thinking in public and private life, there will be no danger of its inhibiting the work of the scientist because some demagogue arises to poison the public mind against science. A broader vision of the function of science will help to prevent it from becoming a tool of war and destruction.

We need as never before to have a vision of the function of science in a democracy. Science in many ways might be compared to the stone ax or to dynamite; for it can be utilized in constructive work in developing the health, safety, recreation, increased comforts, and intellectual outlook of a people, or it can be utilized in destructive work, such as war, and in the restraint of freedom and opportunity.

Are the techniques of science to be allowed to become the tool of the citizens of a democracy, a tool by which man can control his environment for his own welfare and advancement? If so, it seems evident that the members of a democracy need to have a first-hand acquaintance with scientific techniques and attitudes. To teach some of the content of science is not enough. We must do more—we must impart to the individual a vision of the definite potentialities of science in the progress of mankind. We need to develop scientific techniques and attitudes as a line of action in a democracy. Science, then, has a contribution to make, not only to the vitalization of the content of the elementary school, but to the procedures of instruction.

Freedom of speech, freedom of religion, and freedom of research are important elements in the democratic way of life and should be preserved at all costs. But along with them we need to develop on the part of the public a thorough awareness of the importance of basing conduct upon critical thinking and the most reliable information. On all sides there is evidence of credulity, of willingness to accept hearsay, opinion, gossip, omens, and myths as truths. The members of a democracy should be trained to recognize the importance of reliable methods and information if a democracy is to prevail. The elementary school should develop a critical attitude—a continuous evaluation of conduct upon the best expression of truth available.

Too frequently the approach to the education of children in the use of scientific attitudes and techniques are based on the false assumption that the majority of children in our classrooms are expected to become producers of scientific research. Only a small proportion will make discoveries in the field of science. But intelligent operation of the environment by man in a democracy surely can succeed only if that democracy is ultimately willing to follow the most reliable information available. Man must be permitted to work in freedom for the benefit of all.

A democracy must make certain that the means by which it is to secure its scientific information are kept reliable. Too frequently pressure groups of one kind or another gain control of the laboratory in order to use the name of science to promote what may not be the truth. The method by which the truth is to be obtained must be preserved free and untrammelled. The method is more important than the content it produces, for the latter cannot be produced without the former. Preserving the freedom of man to inquire in a democracy depends upon at least an elementary, general knowledge of the techniques of science on the part of the people.

It is important that the people of a democracy have enough training in the scientific attitudes and techniques to realize the importance of securing information from authentic sources on all crucial matters, instead of being swayed by emotions, superstitions, sentimentality, unfounded opinions, and gossip. An education to this end offers a real challenge to the schools.

There are probably research workers in the field of science who think that any advocacy of the techniques of science as a method of study for children is preposterous. Such persons usually have had little experience with children who are studying scientific phenomena. They may conceive of the highly technical work that they do as involving techniques that should be kept sacred to the scientific cloister. Our contention is that these techniques have their contribution to make to the thinking of all people in a society, once we really set about educating them in some of the fundamental aspects, or elements, of these techniques.

These techniques are confined too frequently to the research laboratory, whereas it should become part of the mental equipment of all persons in a democracy. We do not contend that it is desirable or possible for any large proportion of the population to discover new truths for society, but rather that thinking and action in a democracy would be more effective if these techniques were more generally understood and used. Group decisions then could be made objectively, with a minimum of uncontrolled prejudice or emotion and with a constant striving to secure the best information available and a willingness to base action upon that information to the best interest of all concerned. It is contended here that we should reconstruct our methods in education so as to develop an appreciation of the place of the scientific techniques in a democracy and an ability to think critically and effectively. The elementary school, as the school of democracy, should play a significant part in such a program. No other institution is so well equipped to do this task.

The Discipline of Science and Democracy. Science and democracy both require discipline, and the discipline must be inside the individual to be effective. This means that the basic concepts of science and democracy must be internalized because the learner must find these concepts acceptable. To be a citizen in a democracy demands discipline and responsibility. To seek reliable information, to act on it, and to change one's behavior when more reliable information is produced calls for internal discipline of high quality.

Perhaps the most effective, simple description of the techniques of science is that they involve honesty. The implications of this are indeed tremendous, for it means that teachers and children can be honest with each other (Chapter 2). It calls for the disciplines associated with the abolishment of prejudice and bias in thinking, with suspension of judgment until reliable information has been reached, with a willingness to examine all pertinent data and an avoidance of gullibility and dogmatism.

This may indicate that, while science is not to be separated sharply from other subjects in the curriculum, there is a "shift of gears" in our activity whenever we employ scientific procedures. For instance, we may go to fiction for enjoyment, but we do not go to fiction for truth about natural phenomena. The idea of science in the mind of a child should not be so much that science is a separate subject in the curriculum but that it is a way by which man learns.

Science, democracy, and freedom of religious belief are the great achievements of the human race (pp. 48–51). However, democracy could be lost if science were to be utilized to "lock-step" the thinking of children. Science must operate in a spirit of freedom if it is to be understood by children. Any attempt to force it on children through workbooks, laboratory manuals, and through other enforced procedures will only serve to defeat the purposes of democracy and of science. The tempo, spontaneity, and creativity of children must not be destroyed in our attempts to educate them.

Man's Conception of Truth Changes; Much Knowledge Remains to Be Discovered. If we think of ways by which mankind has been learning, and is still learning, about the nature of his universe, then we need not be surprised to learn that our concept of knowledge has been greatly modified. When we modify our concept of knowledge, we may expect to find profound changes in classroom methods. Consider the bearing of "Man's conception of truth changes" and "Much knowledge remains to be discovered" upon the attitude of a teacher. She no longer needs to act as though the words she speaks or the statements in books are the utterings of infallible truth for all time. The teacher has become a more human individual, one who admits that she finds something to learn. A teacher is no longer the all-wise person who rushes in with an answer for all the problems which arise in the classroom. In keeping with these ideas there is an opportunity for the children to internalize the information for themselves, and there is occasion for children to propose ways for the solution for their own problems.

Once man believed that a fact was a fact for all time; but now, if he is intelligent, he must recognize that today's facts must be modified by the discoveries of tomorrow. It is most important that man does not become bound and shackled to content, to methods, and to principles which have been proved un-satisfactory. Man's continued success must be dependent upon his willingness to base his conduct on the most reliable information available at the time and upon the realization that this information is far from absolute, since it may need to undergo revision in the light of new discoveries. In terms of the classroom this means that we must see that children learn the importance of revising their conclusions whenever necessary; in terms of the problems of life it means that children must be open-minded.

Science should be considered from a developmental point of view. A consideration of the natural drives of children (Chapter 1) will indicate that children have inherited the means—the intelligence and the basic drives—to make adjustment to their environment. By using the natural drives of children and by refining them a teacher can build an intelligence about science.

A Variety of Procedures

A teacher should look to a variety of procedures in her teaching and learning situations. There will be no attempt in this book to recommend an exact method of teaching. It has been our experience that providing children with a change of procedure is pleasing to them. A change of method may bring new children into positions of leadership. It is well to avoid routine methods. Science with its broad fields of the environment, from stars to flakes of dust in the garden, demands variation by the very nature of the interpretations and the fields involved. Then, too, a current interest such as the report of a volcanic eruption, of a new vaccine, or of some unusual weather condition may influence procedures greatly in a classroom.

In a sense, all suggestions in this chapter can play a part in the classroom. Discussions, instructional excursions, observations, experiments, reading, use of visual aids, group work and planning can be utilized in teaching science. A teacher should refrain from allowing any one of these to monopolize the instruction.

A teacher should consider her own interests, tempo, and rhythm along with those of children. We believe that it is important for a teacher to be happy and comfortable with procedures. We believe that it is important that teachers be happy with children in teaching and learning science. It would be well for a teacher to study herself as well as the children, and to experiment with different procedures from time to time.

A teacher should be present as a participant in all the procedures. This rules out the use of unpleasant tasks as home assignments. A teacher should be a learner, for good teaching in science involves learning.

Developmental Procedures. If there is one term that can describe the kind of instruction that is appropriate to all phases of science teaching in the elementary school, it is *developmental*. Such teaching is developmental for both children and teacher, since both are learners. As has been indicated in Chapter 3, this point of view is consistent with the nature of science. In the developmental procedures the instruction *develops,* using the experiences and knowledge children may have or that can be provided for them. It is *developmental* in that children may participate in the development of the planning for the use of experiences, experiments, discussion, and authoritative reading materials to provide the solution of problems. The new learning is made acceptable to the children by the nature of its development in instruction. Children are given time to internalize new learning, integrating it with their experiences and ideas.

In any consideration of teaching methods, the primary concern in elementary education is what kind of boys and girls are being developed. All of us need to be cautious that our procedures do not become devices or ends in themselves. Therefore, evaluation should be an integral part of instruction rather than something done at the end of a period of instruction.

At all times in teaching it is well for a teacher to know what point the children have reached in their development. In this chapter and at other places in this volume suggestions are given as to ways in which teachers can secure this information. It is also well to find out how the children think; that is, the type of thought structure they have. Such questions as "What do you think?" "Why do you say that?" "How would you get the information?" "Do you think that is information we

should accept?" will give teachers evidence as to how children think and where they are in their development.

Regardless of how instruction is initiated, vital teaching recognizes the concepts children may have on a subject or problem. So it is well for teachers to provide opportunity for children to express their ideas, however incomplete or inaccurate, in order that misconceptions may be brought into the open. It is most important that they be allowed to express themselves without the fear of censure or ridicule, although at times there can be enjoyment of children's humor and fun without hurting personal feelings (pp. 18–19).

Through developmental procedures the teacher can determine the natural development of a concept from the children's point of view. Sometimes in the development of a concept it is found that a more elementary concept has not been established in the thinking of a group. Authentic basic books are planned with a sequence in mind that has resulted from the study of children and of the science involved.

Very frequently children's concepts have originality and show imagination. Their concepts also provide opportunities for evaluation of preceding work and reveal the kind of instruction needed for the clarification of ideas. Working with children with developmental procedures will develop profound respect for the natural ideas developed by children. Every child needs an adult who will sympathetically and intelligently listen to him. If more children could have such a person to talk to, then fewer corrective institutions would be needed.

In a consideration of any procedure of teaching it is well for the teacher to think of the procedure in terms of the development of children. In this publication we are attempting to integrate the developmental point of view with teaching procedures.

Developmental procedure may flow out of

the use of authoritative children's science books, especially if the books have been designed by someone who has the development of children in mind. In fact, books are essential to science in a program of elementary-school education.

Types of Activities Employed in Teaching and Learning Science

It will be noted that in the preceding presentation there are a number of types of *activities* that play an important part in the study of science; the discussion, the experiment, the excursion, and reading. It is our purpose to discuss each as it functions in science in the elementary school.

The Discussion. Discussion plays a vital part in the study of science, for it serves to clarify the problem, the phenomenon to be explained, or whatever is to be studied. It can provide an opportunity for the teacher to understand the children, for the children to understand the teacher and each other. It serves to make the children's experiences with the phenomenon more meaningful to the children.

Discussion plays a necessary role in intelligent planning in a democracy. Discussion for the purposes of planning can be utilized in many kinds of situations in the elementary school, so that children become thoroughly conversant with planning, and come to realize its value for them. Discussion is vital to the development of intelligent behavior in a democracy. Therefore, it is most important for a teacher to strive to improve the ability of children to participate in democratic discussion.

Such a procedure aids in planning the ways of studying science and the techniques of solving problems. It serves to evaluate the techniques before and after they have been used. "How shall we find out?" is a clear call for discussion and brings to every child in a group the benefits of the thinking of others.

Classroom teachers have found that the instruction fairly bristles with "leads" in science when children are permitted to express themselves freely and when teachers themselves have become aware of the larger values of science in the lives of children. Discussion can be utilized by teachers to develop new interests for study. Discussion is used frequently by many teachers to vitalize a problem or a new topic for children.

Discussion can be used by the teacher to learn what kind of ideas children have about things. Since instruction should start where children are in their development, discussion plays a vital part in helping the teacher to find out what kind of ideas the children have. In a sense, discussion in a classroom can serve as a sort of interview in which the teacher interviews the children and the children interview the teacher and each other. Such questions as "What are your ideas?" "How would you find out?" "Where did you secure your ideas?" "How would you explain it?" are *leading* questions.

The ability to discuss may be considered as developmental. Young children are often described as displaying little ability to participate in discussion. However, when observed from a developmental point of view, young children display potentialities for the development of group discussion. For instance, young children like to have other people near them;

they are usually unhappy when they are alone. Young children frequently bring objects to adults for observation. This kind of behavior could be viewed as a beginning of discussion for the young child. He may look at something *with* the adult, although the episode may be very brief in nature and although the child may use no words. Even before a child can use words, he enjoys hearing the words of the adult. The repetition of important words such as *hot* and *cold,* along with appropriate experiences and the manner in which they are repeated, are most important elements in a child's early concepts.

Even though much of the time a young child seems to flit from one object to another, he may stop long enough at any object or event to form a sensory impression. He may seek approval of adults for his activities. The parent or teacher can lengthen the child's period of concentration by indicating his own willingness to study or observe the point of challenge.

A young child's ideas can be solicited by the adult. While such conversations may be brief, the opportunity to develop a child's *abilities* for discussion is enormous.

Discussion should be free; that is, children should feel a freedom to bring their problems, their thinking, their challenges, their hopes and fears to teachers and to parents without fear of humiliation. Once a child is humiliated by anyone, he is not likely to express his real inner thoughts to the same individual again.

Discussion is also a means by which the teacher can evaluate her own instruction. What kind of ideas do the children have? How have their ideas changed? What do they say spontaneously? What do their comments reveal about their behavior? What are their ideals? Are they democratic? Are they open-minded? Critical-minded? Do they feel responsible? Are they resourceful? Do they share ideas? Do they plan? Are they developing good purposes?

The attitude that many teachers have is that answers to problems and questions must be stated quickly, with little or no discussion. This frequently interferes with the best learning. That children will solve their own problems and thus develop their own techniques for attacking problems was illustrated in one school where the administration favored the use of special consultants in science. But generally there was so much demand for such a consultant that she could not get to the classroom at the first call. To the pleasure of everyone, it was found in many cases that before the consultant arrived the children had progressed toward the solution of their problems by such techniques as securing pertinent information, suggesting experiments, and bringing in materials. The delay in these cases had not interfered with responses; rather it had sharpened them. It also had served to focus the attention of all the children upon the problems. A problem became a group problem, not just the teacher's or that of one child. In this way, the classroom teachers had opportunity through discussion to develop what they thought were better techniques and critical attitudes in reference to sources of information, techniques for securing information, techniques for problem solution, and other values which are usually neglected in the formal approach of handing out content to be learned. In this school, discussion was utilized in planning.

The comments of a free discussion are of greater value in evaluating children's growth than are the closely herded responses of the recitation. Free discussion is much more in keeping with the nature of modern science than is the recitation (pp. 48–50). Teachers can utilize discussion to develop improvement in the quality of thinking of the boys and girls in their classrooms. Discussion is a type of activity that can be profitably used in conjunction with all other types of activity. We shall see that discussion plays a vital role in the experiment, in the excursion, and in using authentic science books.

Let no one assume that the art of discussion is something that is to be completely mastered. To participate in a discussion in a manner in keeping with democracy and modern science requires education of the finest quality. However, this kind of education is not secured through education of the traditional, formal nature. Many feel that science in childhood education can play a part in the development of citizens with ability to participate intelligently in discussion of matters of public consideration.

Reliable information is not secured by discussion alone. Talking will not produce a new discovery (see "The Solution of Problems," pp. 112–119). Through discussion we can employ other types of activities. But in all important matters we must depend on the information supplied by a specialist in the field involved. This information can be secured through the use of authentic science books.

Discussion is useful in the development of concepts in such ways as the following: orienting to the question or problem; developing the setting of a problem or of a concept; focusing attention on the problem or question and upon a means of solving the problem; developing a challenge for study (readiness); discovering the difficulties in children's thinking; focusing the children's attention upon the meaning involved; making a rich association between the problem and the children's own experiences; establishing a worth for the learning; encouraging the internalizing and personalizing of the learning; recalling learning spontaneously in connection with new learning situations. Without discussion, concept formation would probably be most meager in a classroom.

The Experiment. One might think of experimentation as a development through the centuries, growing out of the primitive trial-and-error procedures and the random, impulsive behavior used by primitive man. The development of any human culture from the trial-and-error procedures to the development of scientific experimentation required centuries.

A teacher should also have some realization of the place of experimentation in the development of children. Experiments in science can play a significant role in developing intelligent behavior patterns of critical-mindedness (p. 56), open-mindedness (p. 51), responsibleness (p. 62), and resourcefulness (p. 74).

The experiment has certain characteristics. In the experiment there is a *purpose*. The purpose usually would be to secure information. To make certain that the procedures are good (or adequate) in accomplishing the purpose, those performing the experiment must do careful thinking.

In a very real sense an experiment would not be an experiment if one merely set out to obtain evidence or demonstrate something, for in an experiment there is open-mindedness concerning the outcome. In an experiment one is finding out; therefore one must not be biased or prejudiced ahead of time about the final results. In other words, in an experiment one must suspend judgment as to the outcome until the experiment is completed.

We may well think of experimentation as demanding discipline. Frequently an experience which is called an experiment may in reality be a demonstration of a natural event or phenomenon. (We shall see later that such an experience with a phenomenon may have high value at times in formation of concepts for the individual.)

It is well to have a *control* in an experiment; that is, a duplicate experiment set up under conditions which vary only in the conditions to be tested. For instance, if one wanted to find out if wet clothing dried faster or more slowly (if the water evaporated more rapidly) in warm places, one would want to use two sets of materials under conditions that were identical except that one would be warmer than the other one. One would need to have the same kind of clothing, with the same "wetness," spread out in the same way, and with the same conditions of the air such as quiet or windy air in the room (p. 477).

Another illustration might be the experiment to find out what would happen if a glass or plastic tumbler would extinguish a burning candle. In this case it might be well to have two candles; one, which we might call the "control candle," would be left to burn in the open air, while the other candle, which we might call the "experimental candle," would be covered by a tumbler.

Teachers and children may think of a number of experiences where one set of material can be placed under control situations and another identical set under experimental conditions.

One performance of an experiment may not always give reliable information. Often it is advisable to repeat an experiment to determine whether the same results are observed in the repetition. The children should understand the reason for the repetition. Frequently learning can be reinforced by performing an experiment more than once. Many times children may wish to repeat the experiment. Teachers will recall many times in their experience when children have said, "Let's try it again."

It is well for the experiments to be accompanied by much discussion, to make certain that the purpose, techniques, and conclusion are integrated in the thinking of the group, thus strengthening the concept formation. Discussion should play a large part in every experiment and can be used by both children and teacher in thinking through the experiments.

It is desirable to go to authentic science books for children which have been designed for children. The experiment from a book can become the children's own experiment through a free discussion and planning for the experiment. The purpose and how the procedures accomplish the purpose should become clear and acceptable to the children. It is well to have discussion of the experiment at the various stages of experimentation; for instance, before the experiment is initiated, after the experiment has been completed, and, if the experiment is one that requires sufficient time, there might be discussion during the experiment.

Frequently children will raise problems for which they will themselves suggest experiments. This is most gratifying when it occurs. Sometimes problems are created by an experiment which has been performed, causing them to vary the conditions of the experiment (see the anecdotal records, pp. 52–55). Children frequently propose variations to experiments found in books. This is to be encouraged, provided they stay within safety regulations.

Experiments should only be used that can be handled and manipulated with safety by the children. For example, the recommendation of strong acids for use in the elementary school cannot be defended. The tendency to push the use of high-school and college apparatus down into the elementary school cannot be justified. Materials already familiar to children are more useful in concept formation than specialized equipment, regardless of how efficient the latter equipment may be. An experiment is not usually something to be used for only a few minutes in a classroom and then forgotten, nor is it an experience to be hurried to completion. Sometimes considerable planning is necessary in evolving and designing an experiment, collecting materials, and checking to determine if the experiment will give the information. Children may participate in all these phases. An experiment is one of the kind of experiences to be "lived through." A few experiments so performed are worth more than a large number performed in routine fashion with little discussion.

When an experiment is first encountered in a book or proposed by the children, it isn't necessary to do it the next minute. Talking it over to see who will get the materials and how it is to be done may make for a richer performance of the experiment on the next day or some other later time. However, it shouldn't be postponed too long. It is well to vitalize the experience by sufficient preparation and then do it.

In most cases, it is not practical or desirable to have all children perform the experiment at the same time. Instead, all children can enter into the consideration and even into the designing of an experiment and watch certain designated children perform the experiment. If possible, the experiment should be repeated with different children in the role of experimenters. All observers can "live through" the experiences of the experiment with those performing the experiment.

If possible, all material utilized in the experiment should be left in the room on a table or counter, or in other available space, where all children may have an opportunity to get thoroughly acquainted with it and perhaps even at free moments perform the experiment for themselves. At free times during the school day, the children can have opportunity to manipulate the materials in a relaxed fashion.

Every classroom, from the kindergarten on through the elementary school, may be thought of as a laboratory where investigations may be made. The materials for such purposes are very simple. Most of the materials needed can be found in any community. Children can bring many of the materials needed for experiments from their own homes.

Usually the next day, after a planning conference, the classroom is adequately supplied for one or more experiments.

While children should have rich experiences with experiments, it isn't necessary for every use of material in the elementary school to be an experiment. Experience with a phenomenon, as frequently indicated in this book, is important in teaching and learning at the elementary-school level. For mankind has built up science through his *observations* (experiences) and logical thinking. Experience is basic to the development of concepts at all levels, beginning at birth.

For some time the word *demonstration*, as a device in teaching science, has been in bad repute. While we do not seek to revive the word, we would nevertheless recommend that elementary education involve rich experiences with the physical environment. In reality, however, it is most important that we realize fully the place of experiences in teaching and learning science. Experiences with the phenomena of the environment, including experiences which can be set up in a classroom, can do much to help children progress in science toward the larger purposes as set forth in this book.

In any teaching and learning experience it is well for a teacher to keep in mind the aspects of concept formation. In addition to making certain that the relation of the procedures to purpose is clearly understood, it is well to make certain that all children can be in a position for good observation. Sometimes children (and adults) performing any kind of work with materials will stand between the children observing and the materials. It is well to have the children working with the materials back of the table or counter; that is, on the opposite side from those observing. The place for observation should be at a height suitable for all observers. Repetition of the experience may assist in the observation of some features missed on the first performance, thus giving a better experience with whatever special senses—sight, hearing, feeling, smelling—that are involved in the experiment.

In experiences in the classroom where one or more children are performing with materials while others are watching, it should be recognized that each group is having different experiences. Those performing would have feeling and manipulating experiences, along with sight, smelling, and hearing; those who are watching would lack the feeling and manipulating experiences but must make greater use of their imagination in order to participate in the experience vicariously. All children should have opportunity to participate in the manipulation of materials and performing experiments at times.

It should be kept in mind that in the learning in science we have a number of sensory gateways. We are quite likely to forget that the full impact of some concepts is more than a matter of seeing. For instance, in the study of forces and energy such as magnetism (including electromagnetism), static electricity, and gravitation the sense of touch and the kinesthetic senses (or feeling from body muscles) are involved. A child can feel the attraction or repulsion of magnetic forces if he holds the magnets in his hand. He may feel the force of the gravitation of Earth on his body. He may feel the shock of static electricity.

All avenues of concept formation are important—touch, smell, taste, hearing, sight, and the kinesthetic senses. All appropriate avenues should be used that can be used with safety.

Teachers of special education should remember that there are all these avenues to concept formation. A child who is blind can still feel the attraction and repulsion of the magnets, the shocks from static electricity, and so on. Teachers of special education will find in science that important concepts can be made quite real and challenging through more than one sensory gateway.

One way of evaluating the success of any activity involving materials and observation is for the teacher to be aware of the children's spontaneous references to the conclusions of an experiment or to the procedures of the experiment—through discussion, art, or written expression at a later time.

Sometimes an experiment serves to clarify the problem, for it aids the children to visualize certain natural forces in operation. Sometimes these forces are of such a nature that children can themselves direct their operation, as, for instance, the magnetic force in a magnet. The experiment may also be used by a teacher to free children from superstition.

The experiment may be of great assistance in finding the solutions to problems. Many times, however, inaccurate or totally wrong answers are secured from experiments by those who are not trained to experiment is a given field. Too much confidence should not be placed in experiments in the classroom. Conclusions secured from such experiments should, in the end, be checked by authentic sources. Experiments should be accompanied by discussion and reading.

The traditional science laboratory notebook has little or no place in elementary science. *Record-making* should be approached entirely from the point of view of child development. What kind of experiences in record-making do children *need*? Record-making should never become busy work for children or hurdles to be passed. Frequently, however, group record-making of experiments is highly successful, when all participate in the making of one record.

The Excursion. There is an advantage in taking children outside the classroom to study a phenomenon in its natural habitat. In an education for participation in democracy it is important that learning be placed in a setting that is real. Children need an education that treats with real phenomena in a real world. Observations in the out-of-doors and in the community can play a vital part in instruction.

Excursions need not be lengthy, either in time or distance. There are many interesting observations that can be made at the edge of the school ground, by walking around a block, by visiting a place where there is a view over the landscape, such as the top of a hill, by observing a weed patch, a thicket, the school furnace, nearby construction work, and so on. Some excursions may take no more than fifteen minutes. Occasionally there may be long trips to a museum, a place of historic interest, a farm, a forest, or a public building. It should be kept in mind that the commonplace may contribute to learnings as rich as those to be found in the unusual and spectacular.

In considering desirable excursions for children it is well for a teacher to make a careful study of the children. The environment of children should be enlarged, broadened, and enriched with meanings wherever possible. For instance, city children may need to visit a farm. Children with careless habits may need to see the contrast between areas which are not strewn with papers and rubbish and areas that have been frequented by careless persons. Sometimes an excursion can be utilized to clear up misconceptions of children. The excursion should be viewed in terms of its value in the development of individual children rather than as an end in itself.

It is well to know the children in a group quite well before making a long excursion. Every teacher knows it is important to develop some degree of responsibleness on the part of the children before making a trip that may involve crossing traffic centers. *Safety* is the *first* factor to be considered in all excursions. It might be well to attempt short excursions first with a new group of children. It is also well to encourage children to participate in the planning of the safety during excursions, even though the excursion may involve only a five minute walk. After an excursion children can participate in a discussion of how to improve their excursions. Many teachers invite parents to accompany them on an excursion.

On an excursion it isn't necessary to point out everything. In fact, it would be well to keep the actual instructional time quite brief while children are standing. Important features can be pointed out on the excursion, to be discussed more fully at some convenient place where children can be seated. Important features for discussion may be described by some of the children in convenient forms of art work. Keeping the instructional talk, whether it be a talk by the teacher, by some of the children, or by a special guide, within the ability and concentration span of children will pay big dividends. Sometimes after a discussion there may be a return excursion to a spot, to clear up certain details.

It is well to utilize the excursion as a means for developing leadership in the group. As far as it is possible, every child should have an opportunity to be a leader, even if the leadership is used in a minor capacity at times. This leadership can be exerted in ways involving safety planning, as well as instruction.

An excursion should have a purpose, and the purpose should be clear to the children. However, there can be exploratory trips when the purpose is exploration, from which more specific purposes may evolve for later study. Excursions can vitalize classroom teaching and learning situations, and, on the other hand, classroom instruction can create desirable purposes and planning for excursions. When weather and climate permit, discussions can be conducted with the teachers and children seated outdoors.

When a stop is made for observation, it is well for teachers to give attention to good concept formation. Are the children grouped about in such a way that each can observe well? Observation in science is not limited to using the eyes, for there may be sounds to be heard and odors to be smelled, as in a forest or meadow, or in some industrial or municipal development.

It isn't our purpose in this chapter to point out all of the purposes for which excursions may be made. By making use of Parts Two, Three, and Four, a teacher will find many appropriate purposes for excursions. Chapter 6 can be utilized in planning excursions into the community, in connection with studies of health and conservation.

The effect of seasonal change upon plants and animals can be frequently observed out of doors. Most regions have some seasonal change. In some regions the variations may be in terms of "wet" and "dry" seasons. In regions of the four seasons, teachers should realize there are more than four variations, for there is a variation within an individual season as for instance early, middle, and late winter. In observing seasons, it is well to use the ears as well as the eyes. Are there sounds of insects, birds, and other animals? The absence of sound may be significant. In considering the effect of seasonal change upon living things it is well to consider the adaptations that living things have made to seasonal change (pp. 645–684). Short walks taken frequently over the same places will permit the teacher and the children to note the changes that have taken place between excursions.

The observation of the results of a rainstorm, of sleet, of a wind storm, of freezing weather, or of dry weather may be purposes for some excursions. Perhaps there are faults or folds in rocks on a hillside which may be observed. Sometimes, because of construction work, a profile of the soil is available for observation. Many times there are persons in a community who may be able to point out interesting features in some nearby place.

Many elementary-school rooms are well situated for some observation of the out of doors directly from the classroom windows. Windows in a school provide opportunity for observations of the seasons, weather, and other phenomena. These observations can be expressed through art and language in making records.

A power plant with power lines, or even a furnace room in the school, may be used to clarify some concepts of energy. A trip to a water-purification plant can serve to indicate some of the problems the community has in regard to water. The custodian of the school, the supervisor, or the superintendent in charge of school buildings may assist in tracing for the group the service conduits for electricity, fuel, and water which lead in and out of the buildings. Perhaps blueprints are available at the offices of the Board of Education and might be shown to children. The means a community uses for sewage and waste disposal can be observed in many communities. The effect of the atmospheric conditions on structures can be observed by comparing surfaces of new buildings, or those recently cleaned or painted, with those that have been exposed for long periods. These observations may serve to develop an awareness of atmospheric pollution, if such exists in a community.

Children should not be encouraged to build up collections in connection with excursions or any other activity. Excursions can be utilized in developing an awareness of the importance of the kind of behavior that is in keeping with conservation (pp. 100–102). In fact, it might be well to take children to places where areas have been despoiled by careless collectors in order to indicate how collectors have destroyed the resources of beauty (pp. 62–73).

Places which have been altered by man can be rich places for study. An abandoned farm or garden, an excavation, a quarry, or a gravel pit are interesting places—although, as on all trips, safety education should be an important part of the instruction. It is interesting in such places to observe the increasing vegetation, and, with older children, the succession of plants moving into the area. Even a disturbed place in a desert or dry area (pp. 154–173) will reveal information concerning natural forces at work.

Different types of environments can be compared. The contrast of plant and animal life to be found within a short walk from many schools is enormous. Perhaps there is a lawn, a meadow, a swamp, a sand pile, a refuse pile, an irrigation ditch, a lake, a stream, a forest, a field, a playground, a thicket, a bayou, a sand dune, tundra, a mountain or hill, or some other feature of the environment nearby. Sometimes the margin of an environment, for instance the border between a pasture and a wood, is very instructive.

In all of this work it is not necessary for a teacher to know the names of the species of plants and animals, nor to identify the rocks and soils. The approach should be one of observing the area with the children, with a direction toward some meanings or themes. There is no need of a teacher assuming the role of a naturalist or scientist. The role of a teacher is a role of honesty with children.

However, a teacher should assist children to *interpret* the environment. Both children and teachers have a right to attempt explanations. They may not be certain their explanations are right, but they have a right to say, "This is my idea." The important thing is to label a comment for what it is (pp. 49–51).

There can be many social implications growing out of study in connection with excursions. These are too numerous to be pointed out in this chapter. (See Chapter 6, and Parts II, III, and IV.)

School programs should be made flexible enough to permit the children to spend considerable periods outside the classroom. Administrators need to abandon policies which discourage teachers from conducting excursions; furthermore, teachers can influence the community in developing sentiment favorable to environmental studies.

A teacher can encourage children to link experiences they have outside the school with the instruction in science. If for any reason it is impossible to take children on excursions, teachers can guide children's discussions of their outside experiences and cause these experiences to enrich the learning in the classroom.

Experimentation should be developed with field work. Some things need close study and observation. The classroom considered as a laboratory will enrich greatly the study of the out-of-doors.

Some observations can be made more satisfactorily indoors than out of doors. An illustration of this can be found in such matters as the germination of seeds, the construction and operation of an electric magnet, the metamorphosis of an insect, emergence of young from an egg sac, or the opening of buds. Strict conservation practices should be observed in the use of materials from the natural environment; one cocoon, for instance, may be sufficient for observation (p. 73).

As a means of getting information about phenomena, an excursion has limitations. Unless a person is truly expert in a subject, he may observe a phenomenon and yet come to a wrong conclusion. In the end, conclusions arrived at through excursions should be considered as thoroughly reliable only when they have been checked with authentic material. This means that excursions and other instruction need to be integrated with authentic science material designed for children.

Reading and Study of Authentic Information. The nature of science in our modern age (Chapter 3) makes the use of science books a necessity in a classroom. Learning to use science books wisely as a resource in the development of children will pay a teacher dividends in the way of personal satisfaction and professional improvement. Too frequently books are abused rather than used.

Science books which have been planned to furnish integration from level to level and to present a well-balanced instruction in science for each year can assist teachers and children in accomplishing the purposes of science in the elementary school. Science books can serve to open up new areas for study and to vitalize or motivate the instruction at all phases. In fact, if science books are utilized properly many of the problems of vitalizing science instruction will be solved for a teacher. Science books can help to associate learning with the experiences children have had in the past. They can be utilized in planning experiments, excursions, discussions, and other experiences for the teacher and the children. Science books, with the accompanying teachers' manuals, can assist the teacher to be adequate for the problems of teaching science. In fact, a teacher can feel quite secure in that children can turn to the *books* for content rather than using her as an information bureau. Books properly used can greatly lighten the teaching load for teachers.

Reading in science and other content fields should not be rapid reading. Science reading material should be used in such a way as to encourage children to think for themselves. Reading should be accompanied by discussions, experiments, looking out the windows, excursions, art work, written expression, recording of information from observations, and other activities. Continuous reading for long intervals, without stopping for some other type of activity, should be very rare.

For the most part, science books should be used at times when teachers and children are studying together. Using science books for home assignments is quite likely to defeat the purpose of science in a democracy. Using science books should be a pleasant and stimulating experience for both teachers and children.

Teachers are not only studying science, for they are also studying the children and how they are thinking and learning. So there should be much thinking on the part of both teachers and children while reading, and such thinking can come out in discussion and other activities. We prefer to use the term *thoughtful reading* for the kind of reading involved. This means there should be free discussion with reading science. The nature of this discussion will have much to contribute to the success with books and with instruction in science.

Children should be encouraged to internalize as they read. There should be frequent stops for the consideration of what has been read. Children should be encouraged to discuss and challenge what they have read. Books cannot do the thinking for the children, for the children must do that for themselves.

Attention should be given to the development of a vocabulary of the science words that are used in the books. A concept of the new words can be developed through discussion, experiments, relating of experiences, or excursions. It is well to encourage the use of the science words in later experiences, so that the words become a part of the vocabulary. Such terms as gravity, hibernation, migration, energy, electrical current, heat, weather, and many others can come into use at frequent intervals.

Because a book is written according to the best scientific information available does not mean that the statements contained in the books should be accepted as learning without thinking. It is one thing to accept a statement as reliable, but it is another thing to accept a statement as a part of one's thinking. In the latter case, the statement is absorbed by a child in his own language and with his own meanings. The statement then becomes something more than one in a book; it is as if he has discovered the meaning for himself.

The content read should be taken into the individual's intelligence and related to his own experiences and his own imagery. This time for internalizing is an important factor in developing reading in content areas. The process of internalizing might be thought of as "personalizing"; that is, making the learning personal. Science reading material should be designed by the authors to help the child to do this personalizing spontaneously. Since the personalizing of learning is an important factor in concept formation, reading science content should not be a hurried process. A little reading of this kind, integrated with discussion, experiences, experiments, and excursions, is worth a great deal more in developing resourceful boys and girls than hours of the rapid reading of words.

In using science books, a teacher need not pose as a specialist in science (pp. 49–54). She and the children can seek information from books together. On the other hand, she should have no hesitation in adding information if she has any to offer and if she feels it would be helpful. One of the greatest skills of a teacher is to know how much information she should give in a learning situation. Again and again adults are tempted to give a child more information than he wants and more than he can internalize and personalize at the time. This may be one reason that science specialists are sometimes poor teachers of young children.

To understand the full meanings of science books in elementary education, it is important to have some understanding of the nature of science as it is today. To go into all phases of this subject one would need to consider many aspects of scientific content found in Parts II, III, and IV of this volume. But for our purpose here it is enough to point out that modern scientific interpretations are the result of centuries of progress. Some of our modern interpretations do not conform to what we seem to observe from day to day. For instance, we may see a relatively flat landscape, yet Earth is approximately a sphere. The stars look small, but most of them are very large, very many times larger than Earth. The sun doesn't look like a star, but through astronomy we find that the sun is a star. The sun seems to move around Earth, but in reality Earth turns on its axis, moving around the sun (Chapter 7).

We find that no one individual by himself can build up any great amount of the information of modern science through his own experience, in his lifetime. Every individual is indebted to the past of the human race for the knowledge of today. If teachers or children are to be adequate as individuals today and tomorrow they must have access to the learning of the past. This heritage is best expressed in books.

Reading science books will serve to furnish the content of experiences basic to modern life. Such books can serve to make the work of the classroom easier. In using books it is well to keep the growth and development of the children in mind. It is not necessary at each study period to come to a sharp close of a development. Some of the best teaching that has been observed has been where children have come to the close of a period with many challenges still unanswered and unsolved. In these cases they left their activity but continued to think about it and came back the next day eager to relate experiences they had had at home or elsewhere. In some cases, toys or something the children had built were brought in to illustrate their ideas. Real learning has no benediction at the close of a period, for real learning is growth toward other purposes.

In recent years new, powerful media have come into our lives in the form of radio and television. Many good programs can be found and undoubtedly children are learning much from them. However, interviewing children in many schools in widely different regions has demonstrated that science instruction in the elementary school is needed more by children having access to many media than those that are served by a few. There has been fiction mixed with science in many programs, and children viewing them have distorted interpretations of the world about them. However, this is not an argument against television or even a recommendation for programs to be changed.

It seems likely that instead of new media such as television supplanting the public-school teacher they are making the work of the teacher more important than ever. The public-school teacher is the official of democracy who must be ever alert to see that the development of children is moving in proper directions and developing desirable and resourceful behavior. The more numerous are the sources of information, and the more numerous are the media for dispensing it to children, the more important becomes the role of the teacher in the public elementary schools of a democracy. There is nothing that can take the place of the classroom teacher. She can fulfill this role, as thousands of teachers are doing, when fortified by well-balanced and authentic reading material for children.

Planning Instruction in Science

Flexible Planning. There are some who would contend that there should be no planning in the modern elementary school, the program being one of extreme opportunism, in which the instruction is dependent entirely upon the demands of children. Some who follow this extreme, opportunistic philosophy would base science upon an "incidental" basis. There are others who would specify in detail the program in advance and follow that specified program rigidly. The position taken in this book is one which favors neither of these extremes, but rather advocates the development of the science instruction on a basis of flexible planning.

Flexible planning requires that a teacher have a broad knowledge of the larger purposes which she believes are essential for democratic living and a knowledge of the possible steps by which these purposes are to be achieved. She cannot know where the instruction is to begin until she has learned where the children are in their growth with respect to these larger values. To find where they are in this growth she must live with them and encourage them to be natural with her and to feel free to express themselves. She learns about the children as she proceeds with them through teaching-learning experiences.

A teacher knows the areas of the environment in which she particularly desires the children to gain increased understanding during the year. Therefore, there must be planning with reference to the larger values, or purposes, toward which progress is to be made; but that planning must be flexible, depending entirely upon her growing understanding of the children and their ability to think in the particular areas. A teacher must plan her instruction with a view to adapting the learning to the learner. Furthermore, she must plan her instruction so that the learner may help to define problems and to suggest how the problems are to be solved. A teacher must not expect all groups at a given level, or all children in a given class, to reach the same level of development in the same length of time.

The planning of the teacher should make full allowance for special interests, current events, and local happenings in the classroom or immediate vicinity. These usually will be of such a nature as to fit into a broad interpretation of educational purposes and values of science in childhood education, such as that presented in Chapters 1, 2, and 3. An earthquake anywhere in the world may be used in the study of Earth changes. Some astronomical event, such as a shower of meteors, an eclipse, or an astronomical discovery may be utilized to develop an increased understanding of space and the interrelationships of astronomical bodies. A discussion of soil erosion in a newspaper or the occurrence of erosion in the local community may be used to illustrate changes on Earth's surface and man's influence upon the rate of erosion. One child's special interest in electricity may change the character of the instruction concerning the nature of electricity and the way in which man uses it. Or the rusting of an iron object in the immediate environment may be used to illustrate chemical change.

In this way of looking at planning, we note that less attention is paid to the children's initiation of a given study than in some other modern interpretations of elementary-school procedure. It is held here that it is feasible for a teacher to have given areas in mind and plan to have the children study in those areas. She must, however, secure and use the children's interests and drives; and she is dependent in large part on the wholeheartedness of their responses and spontaneous proposals for the tempo of the study.

In planning it is wise to be able to have some knowledge of developmental patterns in relation to larger purposes. In preceding chapters such patterns have been set forth in terms of meanings and behavior.

The experience of a teacher described in the following is an illustration of adjusting the instruction to a group of children. This teacher was urged to teach science to a group of children as a demonstration for a workshop. She was given no opportunity to meet the children or to know them before she met them in class. She limited the area in which she planned to teach, since science, without such limitation, is so large a field as to make the prediction of materials needed for a given demonstration impossible. The area selected was the relation of astronomical bodies to Earth, with the children's mental growth in the conception of space as the objective. This teacher had in mind the relationships of the Earth, sun, moon, and stars. Not knowing the children, and having no records of them for guidance, she could not know where they were in their thinking or what kind of working pictures they had of the universe.

She had to rely upon her ability to get them to respond, and the only way she could do this was to live with them during the period and not hurry. Therefore, her plan did not call for definite subject-matter goals in the period. She brought to the room a globe to represent Earth, an electric light for the sun, and some small flashlights for the other stars. After a little talking on her part (these children were not accustomed to participate in a discussion), they began to respond with their ideas of the size of Earth. Then the response became genuine, with the teacher and children both participating. Growth on the children's part concerning the enormous size of the sun as compared with that of Earth, and the size of Earth as compared with that of the local vicinity, and with the distances on Earth which each child had traveled, was accomplished in the period. Definite growth and interest could be noticed in their responses and questions.

In this study, artificially limited as it was, a number of things should be noted. There was planning. The teacher had a purpose in mind—a universal value needed by everyone and therefore by these children—namely, growth toward a scientific conception of space.

This group was composed of children from a rural area, with many age levels represented, so that there was a great variety in the background of experience represented. There was an exchange of ideas through discussion and an improvement of the ideas of every member of the group before the instruction had closed.

She had chosen a large area, the universe, with special emphasis on Earth, sun, and stars. She was prepared to adapt the instruction to the pupils' needs, stepping the learning out to the larger concepts of space if the group manifested ability for more-advanced learning elements, or stepping the action back to more elementary and basic concepts if the response indicated misconceptions and more immature thinking. She knew that every individual must be somewhere in his mental growth with reference to this universal conception. She was dependent upon the co-operation of the children. It was necessary, therefore, for her to feel that she had all the time she needed, and so she refused to set definite subject-matter attainments for the period.

Her first objective was to arouse thinking in the group and get an expression of that thinking. Therefore, she was careful that no child should feel harsh disapproval because of any wrong ideas which he might advance. The teacher wanted their ideas. To this end, it was necessary that the children feel free to express their ideas of sun-earth relationships, whether right or wrong. It was her aim to clear up as many inaccurate ideas as time permitted and to help the children to develop an interest in this field if they had none before. She also wished to show them how they might gain increased understanding, or, in other words, study by themselves. At later periods these children used books to assist them in further development of space concepts.

Scope of Learning in Science. Scope of learning in science should be considered in terms of a child's growth and development. Here we find that as a child encounters a dynamic universe—one still new to him—he interacts with what is all around him—above, below, and on all sides of him. He seeks an interpretation of objects in the sky, of phenomena in the atmosphere, of Earth beneath him, of other living things, of evidences of energy and movement, of the works of human beings, and of social phenomena. A school should, therefore, provide a child with an opportunity to secure meanings about many aspects of the environment, including those above, below, and all around him. The curriculum must be broad in scope and universal in character, rather than lopsided and provincial, as it has been so many times in traditional practice. A child must be allowed, and even encouraged, to explore all aspects of his environment from which he can secure meanings of social value.

Survey of the Environment

CONDITIONS NECESSARY TO LIFE

What life needs

How plants and animals make use of gravity, warmth, light, water, food, and air

What happens when these conditions are changed

How some kinds of life are fitted to deserts, swamps, polar regions, etc.

The interrelationships of living things and the physical environment

Weather changes

Past climatic changes

Struggle for existence

Balance of nature

Relation to health and safety

How man changes living conditions

How man can improve living conditions

LIVING THINGS

Effect of seasonal change

Animal homes

Vast variety of living things

Prehistoric animals

How animals are protected

Plant and animal dispersal

Social life of animals

Animals of today

How animals are being exterminated today

How animals have become extinct in the past

Struggle for existence

How living things get their food

How living things grow up (life cycles)

Metamorphosis

Tendencies toward balance and interdependence in nature

Economic value

Conservation

Relation to health

The interrelationships of living things including man

Wise utilization of other living things

Wise development of human resources

Importance of intelligent planning

BEYOND EARTH

Earth in relation to the universe

Movements of Earth

Effect of the sun on Earth

Explanation of day and night

Explanation of seasonal change

Relation of Earth and moon

Variety of matter and energy in the universe

Explanations of tides, eclipses, phases

Earth a part of solar system

Our own Milky Way galaxy

Other galaxies

Stars, comets, meteors

Gravitation

The vastness of space

Space exploration

The great age of the universe

The vast number and variety of objects in the universe

EARTH

Weathering of rocks

Erosion

How rocks are made

How soil is made

How mountains are made

Earthquakes, volcanoes, geysers, caves

Structures of Earth

History of Earth

Prehistoric life

How continents, oceans, and atmosphere of Earth came to be as they are

Forces operating on Earth

Changes in appearance, climates, elevations, plants, and animals

Changes in the local vicinity

Changes wrought by man

Gravity and weight

Variety of Earth materials

The great age of Earth

PHYSICAL AND CHEMICAL FORCES

Heat:
  Changing solids to gases and gases to solids

Light

Sound

Gravitation

Magnetism

Electricity

Atmosphere and weather

Energy and its different forms

Sun a source of energy

Chemical changes:
  Rusting, breathing, etc.

Where we get our energy

Relation to health and safety

Wise utilization of energy

Elements, compounds, and mixtures

Man makes new substances

Using new sources for materials

Prevention of pollution of air and water

Solution of materials

Relation of matter and energy

MAN'S ATTEMPT TO UTILIZE HIS ENVIRONMENT

Man's inventions and discoveries

Man's use of energy

Man's use of minerals

How man measures things

Wise utilization of human resources

Man's dominance over other living things

Man lives in a vast web of interrelationships of plants and animals

Man's frequent destruction of other living things as a result of his ignorance

Man's errors and successes

Attempts to control pests

Conservation: A feeling of responsibility for the environment

Importance of scientific content and procedures to society

Relation to health and safety

Wise operation of the forces and objects of the environment for the sake of man's welfare, comfort, and happiness

Discoveries in science create changes in man's way of living

Man can make his own future with science and democracy

The vogue for centering the work about one dominating unit has led sometimes to unnatural and forced correlation, and has not been congenial to the well-rounded development of a child. Science instruction need not be focused upon one large center of interest for any long period of time. There may be many interests in the course of the year or even at the same time. Some of these may focus on a relatively small problem which can be quickly solved, whereas others may lead to an entire series of related problems involving content and procedures from a number of subject matter fields. We must make certain that we do not restrict a child to a narrow segment of the environment, but rather provide him with opportunities to adjust himself intellectually to the entire environment. In this way, we may secure a balanced and well-rounded instruction in science at each level of the elementary school.

We should be cognizant of the fact that the environment of children is not to be confined to the immediate locality of the school. It is extended to include everything to which children react. An earthquake in Japan, a hurricane or tornado, a new discovery, the center of Earth, the moon, Mars, an expedition to the Antarctic, a distant star—all may become aspects of children's environment.

The chart, "Survey of the Environment" (p. 138), will serve to give teachers a balanced view of the environment—from the point of view of science in the elementary school. This chart provides for the "up, the down, and the sideways" of a child's environment. The topics listed here are not titles for "units" in science. They should be considered as aspects, or phases, of science in the environment. The survey presented by the chart is a comprehensive one for science in the program of childhood education. It is scarcely necessary to indicate that this survey is not to be thought of as an outline for any one level of the elementary school.

Continuity of Learning in Science. The teacher and the school should have clearly in mind a desirable curriculum which suggests the continuity of learning, in terms of the needs of children and of democracy. Such a program has the advantages that come from planning in advance. In turn, the curriculum can be revised, abbreviated, or even set aside, in keeping with the apparent needs of individual children, groups of children, and the community. The curriculum, therefore, should be flexible in character.

Continuity in the curriculum should be planned in terms of the child's growth and development. The young child is naturally egocentric (Chapter 1). His growing up naturally means continual adaptation to his world and an increase in his participation in the happenings of his neighborhood. As he reacts to his environment, he encounters new problems and new meanings. It is apparent that this reaction may produce an unsatisfactory member of society, or again it may produce desirable social behavior. It is the school's task to provide an interaction that will produce the kinds of boys and girls that are needed by the democracies (and we may be certain that such interaction must involve science). Therefore, sequence and continuity in the curriculum must be in terms of problems and meanings. As a child extends his environment and develops more adequate meanings, he becomes ready for new problems and new meanings, resulting in a continuity of learning. Prepared continuity of meanings should be thought of in terms of possibilities, or potentialities, of growth toward educational purposes, rather than as rigid patterns.

To consider continuity of learning for children properly, a teacher must conceive of it in terms of long periods of time. For instance, the learning about any one area, such as conservation, that a child does in one year will be but a small segment of his total contacts with conservation in his lifetime. Nevertheless, under a teacher's guidance that segment can be all-important. A teacher must realize there will be learning about conservation, or some other subject (including negative learning involving misconceptions) after the child leaves her. In this sense, continuity is part of the growth and development of children.

Frequently growth is hampered by a zeal for the exhaustion of topics. Teachers often feel a need for pushing a given study, thus sometimes destroying the challenge that the subject may hold for the children. It is important that the children have a good feeling toward the content and the problems of a given area as they move on to a consideration of new needs. In science a subject can never be mastered or finished, for there is always something more to be learned. The children should not feel that the subject has been exhausted, and that they will never have any further problems in the area studied. Rather, they should have an active realization that there is a wide range of problems remaining for study in their later education, and that many of these problems can be studied as problems having social significance, or may develop into hobbies to be pursued in their leisure time. The interest engendered in the problems should remain active for some time, possibly a lifetime, reviving with current events and new developments in the classroom or in the community.

Frequently high-school teachers complain that children come to the high school feeling that they have already completed the study of some subject, such as living things, air, weather, or electricity, and therefore have nothing more to learn in these areas. It must be recognized that this type of complaint has a tradition probably as old as education itself, for it has been most natural for teachers at any level to blame earlier teachers for any assumed defects found in the learner. However, as elementary teachers we may well assume a responsibility, beginning with the

nursery school, of impregnating our whole elementary-school instruction with the attitude that there is much more to learn about everything. In fact, we can say that men who spend their lives studying any subject will find there is much yet to be discovered. This can be illustrated in terms of weather, electricity, living things, stars, ventilation, health, or any other subject. We can also make children realize they will witness new discoveries, and that some of them may help to discover new things. We should develop a readiness for more learning at higher levels and keep alive the children's ability to reconstruct their environments in terms of new learning.

Integrating Science with Other Areas. Science as an area is closely integrated into all phases of our modern life. There is scarcely a problem that we face today, either as individuals or as a community, that we do not find involves science. Science has brought new problems to society, but it is at the same time contributing to making mankind adequate to such problems as they arise.

It is practically impossible to teach science successfully in the elementary school without integrating it at many points with other categories of the curriculum. The meanings of science are not isolated, but have impact upon the development of children and upon the problems of society.

A desirable integration results from a thorough consideration of the basic purposes of the elementary school. For instance, a purpose of the elementary school, as presented in Chapters 2 and 3, is the development of desirable social behavior. It is apparent that the content and procedures in the instruction of science have contributions to make to this basic purpose of a democracy. Other areas of the curriculum also contribute to this purpose. Integration in the curriculum, then, should emanate from problems which naturally draw upon the materials of two or more areas and which contribute to the fundamental function of the elementary school in a democracy. If a problem of value to children lies solely in one subject-matter field, there is no need to seek content from another area. In other words, integration should not be confused with forced correlation. Integration should not be a "device" to be employed in instruction; it should be utilized when it contributes to sound educational purposes.

There are close relations between science and other areas of the curriculum. Sometimes these relationships can only be observed on an adult level and have little meaning, if any, to children. At such times it would be a mistake to force integration on children. To do so would be to employ integration as a device, and, as a result, one would have only a forced correlation of little value. Interpretation, when it occurs, should be an integration on the level of growth of the children and within their understanding.

Young children on the primary levels are interested in adjusting to the environment. They are challenged by their physical environment, and the interpretations they seek are more developmental in character than social. As teachers, we need to view both the developmental purposes (which are social in part, since they bear on the individual's development in society) and the social purposes. We must not force social values upon children before there is a readiness for them.

There can be rich integration of science with other fields. Mathematics is frequently needed in the course of study of problems in science, particularly the problems which develop conceptions of time, space, and distance (Chapter 4). Mathematics is also valuable in developing such concepts as the prolificness of living things (Chapter 15). Art frequently provides children with the best expression of their conceptions of things. Social studies and science are so closely related that problems in one of these fields frequently invade the other. Science has come out of the stream of human history and from its very beginning has influenced human history. Out of an integration of these fields can dawn a hopeful picture of the future. Industrial and household arts give application to many of the elements learned in science. Health and science are closely related, for they have the same scientific origins (p. 100).

Unfortunately, too many attempts at integration arise from no higher motives than combining subject-matter areas—for example, the correlation of social studies and science. In such a correlation the teacher asks, "How can I add some science to my social studies?" or "How can I get some art into my science instruction?" Such practice, although very common, can scarcely be commended.

Many schools are arranging in the daily program of each classroom a relatively long period, free from outside interference, to be devoted to what has been termed the basal core program. On some days this time may be spent completely within one field, such as science; on other days the time may profitably be devoted to a variety of other areas, such as art, social studies, and science. Such integration helps to widen the child's view of his world.

Too frequently in relating science to the other subjects the values are lost through a kind of instruction which could be described as a "mere talking about science," with little or no real study of science. This should not be the case. For merely "talking about" the social values of science will not serve to prepare boys and girls for great challenges, and for decisions which they must make as a part of a democracy in a world continuously undergoing change. In any type of program there should be an adequate provision for utilizing the tremendous potentialities of science instruction for human welfare in the modern age. It is inconceivable that these potentialities can be realized in childhood education without any actual working with science. A teacher and a school should make certain that there is a genuine growth on the part of the children in interpreting their phys-ical environment. This must not be lost in any reshuffling of categories. An integration should be meaningful and should preserve the values of science in the development of boys and girls.

Considering the Development of Individuals

In approaching a consideration of individual differences it should be kept in mind that every child is an individual and that he possesses individuality. He has a human right to that individuality and should never be humiliated because of it (pp. 97–98).

As an individual, whether he is considered gifted or not, he is entitled to his self-respect. For a child to be herded off into a group and branded by some title to indicate that he is a special class of individual, seems to the author to be undemocratic. One is distressed to go into schoolrooms and hear children classified in whispers loud enough for the children's sensitive ears to hear—that these children are among the blessed, they are gifted, or that these children are retarded and a problem to society. In such schools one feels there is being developed a two-class citizenship, an enterprise unworthy of democracy's basic institution. Every child is entitled to a respect for himself. The public elementary school as an institution of democracy should develop poise, resourcefulness, and the confidence of all children in themselves.

It is altogether possible that gifted children are injured as much by being so classified as are retarded children in being classified as retarded. And can a school always be certain who is gifted and who is retarded? Sometimes those branded as "gifted" are the ones who easily comply with what the school or some test-giver wants, while progress may be produced by the child who has possibilities of thinking for himself. One might well doubt whether the genius of Thomas Edison or Charles Darwin would have been discovered in an elementary classroom by our present pencil-and-paper tests. But there are future Edisons and future Darwins in our classrooms today.

Should these children be separated from the rest of democracy? Is it wise to place them in a cloister for the gifted?

This author views with considerable alarm any widespread tendency to separate future leaders, even if they can be found at the elementary-school age, from the other children. It would be much better for a child to establish his leadership in democratic living with his fellows because of his good character and his qualities of leadership, than to have the school educate these possible leaders as a separate group. This is particularly important in science, since in knowledge of science is power and power must be in the hands of *all* the people.

It is the author's firm belief (p. 36) that the education of all the people for the utilization of science in the democracies and for the welfare of all people is of fundamental importance in the preservation and improvement of our way of living. The separation of future leaders, including scientists, at an early age from the rest of the population could lead to a fascistic or communistic dictatorship.

Thomas Jefferson said, "I know of no safe depository of the ultimate powers of society but the people themselves; and if we think them not enlightened enough to exercise their control with a wholesome discretion, the remedy is not to take it from them, but to inform their discretion by education."

Adapting Science to Individual Differences. There are many factors supporting the need for a common instruction for all members of the group, with provision for the care of individual differences, through special interests for those developing such interests, and through opportunities for free activities for those who either have difficulty in keeping up with the group pace or for those who go beyond the group pace.

Group work, where all children in a class study together, has many values. It develops the free exchange of ideas after the manner of democratic practice. It permits those who have contributions to make to group activities to do so in a democratic fashion. In the study of problems connected with electricity certain children may develop leadership, while in the study of another area such as that of living things other children will make the greatest contribution. Activities furnish opportunities for focusing attention upon the elements of good thinking and the scientific attitudes. Group activities give the teacher an opportunity to use the teaching-learning as a means of refining the methods employed by the children. Group work provides opportunities for creating and developing individual interests. In the main, the interests of individuals should be brought into the group work so that all members of the group may gain something from the special studies of individual members.

Not all members of the group should be held down in their work to the group average. Some can without any difficulty go beyond the group at certain points in science work, while others may not be able to maintain the pace or keep up with the group. A flexible classroom situation will provide ample opportunity for free-activity periods of one kind or another. A selection of suitable equipment and materials of science may be placed on tables or wall counters so that children will feel free to work with these materials at various times, as opportunity offers. Sometimes certain children may be inclined to hesitate or hold back because they are afraid to handle the simple electrical equipment that is needed for a class in elementary science. When the group is large, the teacher may not be able to provide opportunities for all these children to become familiar enough with the materials so that they begin to lose their fears, during the periods when the entire class is working as a unit. However, through activity periods these children may be encouraged to manipulate the equipment.

Sometimes children who have been successful with the equipment may be assigned to assist those who have been less successful. In this way, a child who might otherwise find himself completely out of step with the science in the group work soon becomes convinced that he can enter freely into the group activity. In the relaxed informality of a small group, consisting of perhaps only two or three, he can more easily overcome shyness or timidity, and make advances in his own way.

Science seems to operate best in a flexible type of classroom. The furnishings of the classroom should be planned for flexibility and movability. A room in which seats are nailed to the floor, with little or no work-table space, hampers the instruction in science and hinders any attempt to provide for individual differences.

Teachers should be prepared for the contingency that a few children may grow very rapidly in some aspects of science. It is not uncommon for some children to outstrip the other children and the teacher as well. This need not indicate superior ability on the part of these children to that of a teacher, for there can be many factors operating in such a situation. For example, the interest of one or more children in a certain development or problem may become so absorbing that they direct all of their excess mental effort into that problem. With their efforts thus focused on their problem they may be in a much better position for learning than the teacher who is fully occupied with a multitude of classroom duties. A teacher need not feel chagrined at this kind of a situation. Rather, she can feel she has been instrumental in the development of leadership in children.

Of course she should do all she can in such situations to make certain that these children have regard for accuracy and are checking their conclusions as carefully as possible by consulting authentic sources. She should plan to give these children an opportunity to share their knowledge with other children. In this way we may assist in developing leadership through classroom activities. This leadership grows out of democratic situations.

CHAPTER 6

Utilizing a Community Wisely in Teaching and Learning Science

The Role of the Classroom Teacher As a Student of Children in a Community. In Chapter 1 it was indicated that, as they teach, classroom teachers can enrich their teaching through the study of children. Since boys and girls are changing from day to day, as a result of the interplay of the factors of heredity and of the environment, they cannot be studied once and for all time and given evaluations that are filed on cards. When we speak here of "studying children," we are thinking of the kind of study which hundreds of elementary-school teachers are doing today with children. These teachers are so successful in living in the classroom with children that the children think of the teachers as their friends. The knowledge these teachers accumulate in their study of children can be gathered because the children feel free to express themselves about their ideas, disappointments, fears, hopes, and ambitions.

Boys and girls are located in time and space —the time is the present, the place is the community. Boys and girls are a vital part of the community, and the community and its environment has a great influence on their development. Like all other living things, children cannot be properly studied without considering the environment in which they live. A growing understanding of the community is essential to the understanding of the boys and girls.

The teacher's specialization is the education of boys and girls. In her guidance of teaching and learning experiences she will need to utilize the environment and the community as resources. She can learn much about the community and the environment as she teaches boys and girls. But since the community is so intimately integrated with the lives of the boys and girls, she will need to build up a sensitivity to the impacts of the community upon the attitudes, feelings, and behavior of boys and girls. Utilizing the community and its environment as a resource should strengthen democratic behavior in the children.

A teacher need not pose as an expert in any one of the fields presented by any of the problems of the community. For the most part, the factors creating these problems are intricate and the best recommendations for their solution come from men who are duly qualified to be authorities in the fields represented. With many community problems, experts are required from several fields, and even then many problems remain controversial for a decade or more.

A teacher's task is to draw the information from reliable sources and to guide children toward a realization of the importance of utilizing authentic sources. The teacher, then, is a connecting link between the scientific agencies of the community, state, and nation and the children in her classroom. As such, a teacher will need to be alert so that she may detect the difference between propaganda and reliable scientific information, for propaganda is frequently given the artificial appearance of sci-entific fact. A teacher can learn science with children; she can also study community problems with the people of the community.

The classroom teacher has a program of heavy responsibility. This publication is written with sincere appreciation for the tremendous contributions that classroom teachers have made to boys and girls, and through them to the democracies of which they are a part. It is hoped that this chapter will serve to make the work of the classroom teacher an easier and more pleasant task by assisting teachers and parents to study the present and future of boys and girls in terms of the community.

The Community As a Resource for Learning

The community is a resource in the teaching of science in the elementary school. It should be considered along with authentic science books, visual aids, experiments, and other instructional materials in the all-round education of children.

This chapter is designed as source material from which individual teachers may draw the information they find suitable for their own classroom teaching situations. This can best be determined by a teacher who studies this material with the children in her classroom in mind. No teacher can utilize all the suggestions offered in this chapter in one year. However, there will be many ideas that teachers will find adaptable to the needs of the children at the various levels of the elementary school.

This chapter is designed also for the consideration of teachers in a school or in a school system working collectively in developing a professional study of the community. By such a study an articulation of the community problems which have a basis in the fields of science can be considered in connection with a study of the curriculum. Through such a study the personnel of a school or a school system can determine the kind of teaching and learning which is pertinent at the various age levels. Such a study could be made with all teachers of a system participating, so that all levels of the elementary school are represented.

In many public-school systems members of the teaching and administrative staffs are undertaking a co-operative study of the community and its problems as a part of the in-service educational program, and in this way all school people share in the information secured. In some public-school systems booklets of regional information have been developed by individuals, teachers, or groups of teachers, sometimes working with parents and community leaders. These booklets have been made available to the staff and to interested citizens. Science field centers for elementary-school teachers have become increasingly popular in connection with programs of in-service education.

In many school systems a camp or field center has been established where teachers may go with their classes for a period of a week or longer. This is a most wholesome trend and one to be encouraged. It is believed that the material in this chapter will prove useful to the teachers planning for the period of study in such a camp. The learning experiences in such a center can be very rich indeed if there is suitable planning for all the aspects involved, such as health, safety, and instruction.

In using this chapter, it is well to keep in mind that the classroom teacher is employed by the community to teach its children, rather than to lead in social and economic reforms as some have advocated. Her task is therefore always to be oriented toward her specialty—the education of children.

The attitude of children and youth to the community, to the nation, and to the world is a vital resource in itself. The very continuity of democracy is dependent upon the perspective children develop. When this perspective is unintelligent, irresponsible, or undemocratic we have delinquency. A pattern of honesty, resourcefulness, and democracy toward the community needs to be developed in children, beginning in the cradle (Chapter 3). This task is so vital that the cooperation of the entire community is needed, including all of the teachers, parents, and citizens, and all agencies.

The content of this chapter has resulted from experiences in connection with field centers and workshop conferences for elementary school teachers in Alabama, Arizona, Colorado, Connecticut, Maryland, Missouri, New Hampshire, New York, Puerto Rico, South Carolina, Texas, Washington, and elsewhere.

In studying this chapter, classroom teachers should consult "Basic Patterns of the Universe as Fundamental Conceptions for Growth" (pp. 93–100). These patterns will serve to vitalize the study of the community and provide integration. Studied with the content of this chapter, "Science and Behavior" (pp. 49–77) will assist teachers in relating the development of children's behavior to the problems of the community. For content supporting the various problems listed in this chapter see Parts II, III, and IV.

Orienting All Children to the Community. Teachers can utilize in their teaching the first-hand experiences that children have had in the community by encouraging conversation about such experiences. These experiences may very often be small observations about things the children do or cannot do; what they have seen from the windows at home or at school; some experience out-of-doors; something that happened on an instructional excursion; what they have seen from hilltops and other high places; or something learned through thoughtful reading. Quite frequently teachers will find in the community individual citizens who are able to supply reliable information about some phase of the environment. Teachers should feel no embarrassment in asking for information from any competent member of the community.

Every community has an environment that is rich for study. The suggestions in this book will provide teachers with possibilities, whether the school is located in the city or in the country, on the prairies or in the mountains, in the far north or in the south, in a desert or in a rich farming region.

As rich as a community may be for study, it should never be utilized as a curriculum in itself. The community is best understood in terms of the fundamental natural and social forces which have operated to make it what it is. The local community is but a minute portion of a larger, world community. The local community is subject to disturbances which come from outside, such as hurricanes, floods, cold fronts, economic depressions, the causes of war, the spread of contagious disease, the migration of peoples. It is hoped, therefore, that teachers utilizing the material of this chapter will see the community as a portion of the world and will think of it as illustrative of much that has been presented in the preceding chapters.

A school system should develop an understanding of the problems of a community, in terms of the fundamental principles which are operating to create the problems as well as those which could operate to correct undesirable situations. Soil erosion, as an illustration, is a result of the action of the energy which grows out of the interaction of wind, water, sun, gravity, and so on. Prevention of erosion is a matter of making certain that this energy operates to man's advantage.

There is no contention here that children can solve any of the community's problems, nor is there any desire to force adult problems upon children. Rather, the community and its environment is a laboratory for teaching and learning science. Experience indicates there are problems to which children can apply scientific principles to improve situations. It is well for a community to provide opportunities which allow children to take a hand in making changes for the better (Chapter 3). But such opportunities should be of such a nature that children can cope with the factors involved and secure community support. The main concern of the public schools is the development of the kind of boys and girls that are needed in society today. We must then consider how the environment and the community can best be used in the development of adequacy for the present and the future (pp. 41–42).

The Community and Behavior Patterns in Children

The environment can be utilized in the development of behavior patterns of great importance to democracy. Let us see how these patterns are related to the community.

The Feeling of Belongingness. One of these patterns grows out of the feeling of "belongingness" to the community. Belongingness may grow out of feelings which reflect such ideas as "This is my region." "I belong to this community." "This is my town, my state, my province, my country." "This land is a part of my country." "Here is one of my country's rivers."

The Feeling of Being Needed. Related to this feeling of belongingness is the feeling of "being needed" by the family, the community, the country, and the world. Intelligent and democratic boys and girls are needed today more than ever. This feeling of being needed is reflected in such ideas as "Here is something that someone should do." "I can do this." "I can help." "Other people need me." "There is a need that all of us plan for the safety and health of others as well as for ourselves." "There are improvements to be made in the community and in the world." "There are new discoveries in science to be made, and I may have a part in making them."

The Feeling of Responsibleness. Some behavior patterns grow out of a feeling of responsibleness for the environment (pp. 62–73). This feeling of responsibleness is reflected in such ideas as "I want this region to be beautiful, healthful, and safe for people." "I can help to make it so." "Every little thing done helps, even if it is no more than avoiding littering the out-of-doors." "I want to avoid waste of resources." "I want to help my community and the world to avoid waste of resources." "I have a responsibility for the resources of my community in that I belong to the community." Sometimes little behaviors can become destructive, for example, tearing up vegetation, picking wild flowers, making a path across a hillside where erosion can be started, failure to extinguish a fire in camping.

The Study of Natural Resources in a Community

In developing behavior patterns and the meanings of science in the elementary school (Chapters 2, 3, and 4), classroom teachers will find it necessary to associate these purposes with what is meaningful. Children establish meanings during their experiences in the immediate environment. The community, because it is near and real to children, affords a rich opportunity for the development of concepts. It is important that children establish intelligent attitudes about the resources of their community, their nation, and the world.

There are more suggestions about community resources made on the following pages than should be utilized at any age level. A teacher can choose from these suggestions those that are most pertinent to the children in her classroom.

The natural resources of a community are an important key to an understanding of that community. One may think of the resources of a region as located in the solid, liquid, and gaseous (atmospheric) parts of Earth. These three parts are so intermingled and interrelated that the story of resources is somewhat involved. A community resource may be found in the land (the solid part of Earth) in the form of deposits of minerals and nonminerals or in the form of a rich soil for agriculture. A resource of the community may be a system of waterways which contribute to the development of a transportation network. In some cases important products are derived from the waters found in the region. Some regions de-

pend upon climate and beautiful scenery, which make delightful settings for popular resort areas. In recent years deserts or regions of heavy snows which were at one time considered undesirable for community life have been changed into vacation and recreation areas. Therefore we must conclude that almost no area is devoid of resources.

Air travel has made it possible for man to reach quickly and easily areas which previously had been almost completely inaccessible. It is likely that in the future there will be an expansion of comfortable and even luxurious resorts in polar regions (even on the Antarctic continent), on deserts, and in tropical jungles, thus making it possible for the traveler to enjoy the varied scenery of the planet. Some of the children in our classrooms may range quite far in their travels as they grow older. Some may become pilots or stewardesses in commercial planes which travel to areas which now seem strange to us. Some may take part in the exploration of space or of the oceans' depth. There is no reason why a teacher cannot discuss these possibilities with children. It would stimulate their imaginations, and children need a hopeful view of the future.

However, it might be well to balance any description of the attractiveness of a career in a distant land by an understanding of some of the great accomplishments and possibilities in the immediate vicinity. There have been thrilling achievements in the home community. One of the great achievements in many regions of the western hemisphere has been in the field of agriculture, which makes use of specialized knowledge and its practical applications from many scientific fields. The agricultural developments which have taken place within one generation constitute a successful record of almost unbelievable proportions. Comparable changes have occurred in lumbering and forestry, mining, stock raising, and many other industries.

In the story of some of the developments in a local community along with the history of the region, we frequently find material which might serve to balance off the diet of fiction and comic books. Children should hear of some of the achievements of the community. Local incidents connected with the sources of energy, perhaps the story of the old mill and its water wheel, the coming of steam power, the electric power plant, the local development of transportation from the earliest forms to the present, the coming of the first railroad in the region, or the first steamboat travel may be retold or portrayed, as may be the old pony express. The first development of a mine, the first industries, the change from old industries to new ones, and why such industries have changed, how new sources of energy came to be used—in all these developments there is drama as well as occasional comedy in the intimate story of the community and its people. Certain older members of the community could be invaluable at this point, for they might remember other ways of living, and when and how changes took place.

Considering the transportation, the communication, and the limited sources of energy and materials available, many people lived very well indeed in the early days of settlement. They were resourceful and ingenious. How many of us would be able to make bread, weave the clothing for large families, or find our way through a wilderness of trees?

We should help children to enjoy this drama and to appreciate the achievements of the community. Then, if attention is called to the mistakes in a community—the waste of resources, say, or unsanitary conditions—a school staff has already built up an honest and friendly background of attitudes among the children.

The welfare of mankind rests as much on his ability to utilize resources wisely as on the resources themselves. Coal and petroleum were to be found in the Western Hemisphere before Columbus made his way across the Atlantic Ocean. However, the American Indians never developed these resources, and as a result coal and petroleum contributed little or nothing to the Indian culture or ways of living, while the European culture which was transported to American soil learned in time to adapt its ways to the use of these great resources. So we see that the knowledge man discovers about his resources has much to do with the kind of culture developed. To a large extent, the environment of man is determined by the use that he makes of the materials available.

The knowledge and methods man is accumulating in science has much to do with the use of resources. In Chapter 11 will be found an account of how through chemistry man can have new substances which will contribute to his health, recreation, and standards of living. Man is learning to make, on a very large scale, substances which have been very rare and costly. Thus, because of a discovery made in the laboratory and in the field, man may find resources of great value in a clay bed, in a coal deposit, in sea water, in natural gas, in sawdust, in industrial waste, in a refuse pile, and even in sewage. From the point of view of community study it means that what is an important resource in a community at one period may not be so important in a later decade, while another resource totally overlooked at one time may become vital in the economy of a region at a later time because of advances of science. Certain rock formations located in isolated parts of the world, which were formerly considered to be of little or no importance, have become of great strategic value because of the development of nuclear energy. In other words, what may be a natural resource depends very much on the discoveries of science. Boys and girls must look to the future of science with open minds. They should waste nothing, for they cannot be sure what may be a valuable resource tomorrow. Throughout the text there are illustrations of conservation as behavior.

The Soil As a Community Resource

Our Earth is a vast storehouse of materials important to man's welfare. In many communities the greatest resource is the rich farming land. In such communities the elementary school has at hand a resource which may touch the lives of children at many points.

Is the soil farmed by tenants or landowners? If tenants, where are the landowners? On the average, how long do the tenants remain with a given piece of land? What is the nature of the tenant-landowner relationship? In rural communities the management of farms is important. A nation is more successful with its agriculture when the soil is managed by those who have a real interest in it.

Recently a teacher found that two children felt no responsibility for the school property. Upon investigating she found that their parents were certain tenant farmers who felt no responsibility for farm property and indirectly caused the children to develop the same feeling. In this case the teacher was deeply concerned with the development of wholesome behavior on the part of the children (see "Developing Responsibleness as a Behavior Pattern," pp. 62–73).

Have science and invention, through modern agricultural methods, encouraged individuals to consolidate small farms into larger farms? What are the trends in your community? Are these trends beneficial to the people living in the community?

Soils Need Good Management. Is the soil in your region considered as good now as when the region was first farmed? In many regions the first farmers found a soil so rich with valuable soil materials that the fertility seemed inexhaustible. It was the practice in many of these regions to plant a single crop year after year without using rotation or other methods of soil improvement. Sometimes this practice of farming has been called "mining the soil," since it tended to remove soil materials with little thought of the soil as a resource. Eventually such a process will deplete any soil. Thus, in a region that originally had rich soil we may now find some of the farms poor, as a result of years of mismanagement, and right alongside these poor farms may be farms which reflect careful soil management. If conditions of this kind exist in your community, note the conditions of the houses and barns. If you have occasion to visit any of the families, observe if you can the standards of living. Is the soil related to social conditions?

Soils Have a History. Many regions have never had good soil. Under normal circumstances physical and biological forces require a long time to make good soil. Many things can happen to soil. The ice sheet which formed in northern North America and Europe during the last Ice Age scraped the soil off some sections and deposited it in others. Good soil may be covered by worthless rock material and lava flows, or it may be eroded away and deposited in swamps or in the oceans. It can be blown about and deposited where it cannot be used. Beneath lava flows, glacial drift, or water deposits have been found old soils that were formed when the conditions in that region were quite unlike those existing there today.

Some soils are too young, geologically speaking, to be of much value as farm land. Sometimes soils fail to become good because of extreme leaching of the soil, in which the food elements are washed out by hard rains, carried down through the surface soils, and finally deposited below the reach of plant roots. Some soils need water in order to develop into richer soils. Some regions are too mountainous for farming, some are too dry, while still others have poor soil. As one travels about over Earth, he is impressed by the fact there is so much of Earth that apparently is not tillable, in spite of man's continual effort to push and plow into new areas. Children, both urban and rural, need to develop an appreciation of the soil as a resource. The teacher might keep two thoughts in mind in this study: first, a long, long time is required to make soil from rock; second, much of the land surface is unsuitable for agriculture. Soil, as one of a nation's great resources, should become identified in children's minds as a part of the nation.

Soils reflect a geological history. What geological factors have operated in the past to make your neighborhood what it is (Chapter 10)? Much nontechnical information is available concerning the geological history of various regions of the world. This information can usually be secured if inquiry is made of the proper agency. Children are usually interested in a simple account of the prehistoric story of their region.

Developing an Appreciation for Soil. The way soil is formed may be considered at various age levels. Small children may become acquainted with some of the simple aspects of soil formation. They can examine rock in different stages of weathering. Have them rub rock with rock to see whether particles are worn off. Older children can gain impressions of the long time involved in soil formation. The relationship of good soil to chemical elements may be discussed in the later elementary years. Have children feel different kinds of soil. Sometimes one can find several kinds about a school ground, especially if materials have been transported from other places. Rub the soil in your hand. Do you feel sand? Do you feel clay? Is it sticky?

Have them smell the soil. Good farmers like the smell of good soil. In a sense, the smell of the soil is one of the true smells of the country. This activity may be linked with the study of the westward migration. As the pioneer pushed westward in North America, he ran his own soil tests with his eyes, his nose, and his fingers. When it was good soil the pioneer was happy and settled down, usually, to cultivate the soil.

There are usually many types of soil in a community. Have children indicate the wide variety of soils by bringing samples in small bottles. Samples may be obtained from the banks of streams, from a meadow, forest, garden, gravel bed, sandhill, or beach. School grounds often have different kinds of soils. Frequently there are places on the school ground where soil has been brought in to fill up a low place or where the topsoil has been levelled off. A teaspoonful of soil from each place may be sufficient for study. These samples can be examined under the hand lens. Perhaps the children may be interested in speculating on the causes of the differences in soils. A map may be used in the study of the samples. Children may like to make a mural map of the school ground or the community and indicate thereon the different kinds of soil that have been found. If possible, go with the children to the localities from which the samples have come. Fill planting boxes with different kinds of soil. Introduce the children to the terms *sand, loam, silt, clay,* and *humus.*

In collecting any soil the children should be advised how to secure the soil without injuring the environment. See "Developing Intelligent Responsibleness in Children" (pp. 62–73).

When the class is studying the soils of a community, a teacher should avoid causing any child to feel depressed because he comes from a region of poor soil. It should be remembered that wherever one may look, the soil will be different from that at another place although, in some cases, the differences may be slight. The science of agriculture can show how a soil can best be used and improved. Some soils are good for one use; others for quite different purposes. Agriculture applies the knowledge gained from many scientific fields. Through the science of agriculture, it is apparent that man can do much more about improving the soil than was formerly thought possible.

Are there places in your community in which the soil is so poor that the natural vegetative covering should not have been removed? In this connection, it is interesting to note that many regions are attempting to restore the land to its original condition. Many sections which were originally forested will yield greater financial profits if they are scientifically reforested. Similarly, many prairie lands should be returned to grass. Do you see any such trends in sections of your community?

What was the region like when it was first settled? Consult old records or talk with old residents. What changes have taken place? Which ones have been beneficial? Which ones have been detrimental? Are there any abandoned farms? Why were they abandoned? What kind of vegetation is growing now on the farms? Where do you think the seeds which started the new vegetation came from? Perhaps you can make an excursion with your class to an abandoned farm.

EXPERIENCE. *To ask land owners for permission to take a sample of soil.* It is well for children to secure permission from the owners before they collect any soil. Even though the soil taken is no more than a teaspoonful, it is well for children to develop a feeling for "ownership."

EXPERIENCE. *To develop an appreciation for soil.* Children frequently call soil "dirt." In turn, dirt has been given a meaning that implies that it is something to avoid. But soil is the rich resource of a country. Soil has a use and has great value. It is not something to be disliked, but rather something to be appreciated as a great resource of a people.

Small children like to dig in the soil. It is the home of many living things. It protects germinating seeds. It furnishes fertility for seeds and eventually, with the use of the energy of sunlight, with water and warmth, provides us with food. Soil is not just "dirty" dirt, but it is a part of the land of the children's country.

Your region has had an interesting history. In some schools teachers have assumed the responsibility for obtaining such information. They consider such problems as these: Are there evidences of prehistoric cultures, such as cliff dwellers, mound builders, or other early people in your region? What Indian tribes inhabited your region? How did they use the land? What was the nature of their culture? What was the nature of the early settlements of European peoples in your area? What was the nature of later settlements? Which land was utilized first? Have there been large migrations away from the region? How was the soil responsible for these migrations?

To what extent do the farmers in your community secure good agricultural advice? Is such advice readily accessible? Have the farmers been educated to the need of scientific practice in agriculture? The attitude of farmers toward agriculture may be a reflection upon the effectiveness of instruction in the schools of the past. Is there a farm agent or other representative of a national, state, or provincial agricultural bureau in your region? Farm agents or other agricultural agents are usually pleased to attend conferences of teachers and parents and to discuss the agricultural problems of the vicinity and the relation of the school to agriculture. The farm agent may have many suggestions for planning the instruction, but the final judgment of what should be taught must rest in the hands of teachers who know the children.

The Interrelationships of Plants and Soil. Some plants tend to make soil acidic, while others may make it alkaline. Some plants increase the general fertility, while others tend to rob the soil of fertility. Plants influence the soil, and soils determine the kind of vegetation to be found in a locality. This reciprocity indicates one of the links in the vast web of interrelationships.

The soil is in reality the meeting place between the atmosphere above and the mineral products of the subsoil. In a sense, the soil is dynamic in character. The soil is not, therefore, a static substance; it continuously exchanges water and gases from the atmosphere and soil materials from the subsoils below. As a result, it can lose valuable material, or it can gain in fertility. One important task of the farmer is to make certain that he is assisting the soil to make those exchanges which are increasing its fertility. This is one of many illustrations of the importance of man learning how to operate with natural forces for his own long-range welfare. These forces can operate to increase or decrease the fertility of the soil. Man is usually the deciding factor. The methods of his cultivation and harvesting, as

well as the kinds of plants he grows, depend upon the nature of the changes made in the soil. And what he grows in the soil may in turn greatly influence the soil itself. (See "The Interaction of Forces," pp. 98–99). One could continue the study of interrelationships to demonstrate that the animals in a region are directly or indirectly dependent upon the plants (pp. 545–546). In many cases, particularly for animals living underground, the nature of the soil may directly be a determining factor in making the regions suitable or unsuitable for certain animals.

The Nature of the Soil Determines Man's Health. When we realize the quantities of different kinds of minerals which enter into the composition of the bodies of human beings and other animals, (pp. 549–553), and the dependence of animals upon the products of the soil, we gain an appreciation of the importance of good soil. The full development of the body and the maintenance of general good health are dependent upon good nutrition. Frequently soil is so deficient in some important elements that food products grown there are likewise deficient in the elements vital to health.

Many diseases have been traced directly to a lack of certain food elements, such as phosphorus, calcium, iodine, and cobalt. When these elements are deficient in the soil, the plants grown there will be deficient. Much research must be done so that we may know more about the relationship of soil to health. It is clear, however, that there is a vital relationship between soil and health, and that when this relationship is studied carefully it may have much to do with the improvement of the health of the human race.

The problem may be studied by asking these questions: From what geographical regions is the food for your locality secured? (This kind of information can be obtained from local markets or food stores.) Are there any nutritional deficiencies reported for the vegetables raised in your immediate region? How can the school help to see that children have a proper diet? Are there signs of malnutrition in your region? Are there found in your immediate region any diseases which are related to malnutrition? What are the causes of malnutrition, if any, in your community? How can the situation be changed? There is no reason for malnutrition existing in the Western Hemisphere, and, with study, malnutrition could probably be completely eliminated from the world. How can the school assist in improving the nutrition of your community? What is being done by the United Nations to improve the nutrition of the undeveloped areas?

Erosion Can Be a Destructive Force in a Community. Teachers should remember that erosion is a geological process which has been in operation for millions of years (Chapter 9). From the long-time view of Earth, erosion has been beneficial for much of Earth's surface. Erosion, working away on the surface of Earth, has probably prevented, under changing conditions, the development of undesirable areas of flat land with claypan subsoil, watersoaked plains, and severely leached soil. It is likely that normal or geological erosion for Earth as a whole over the ages proceeded no faster than soil was being formed. Erosion has been detrimental to man's welfare when, through his carelessness, he has removed the natural protective covering and thus speeded up the process, to his own great loss in health and well-being.

Some erosion is the result of wind. Children in almost any region can be made aware of dust in the air. It might be well to provide children at all school ages, and even at later preschool ages, with some responsibilities for keeping furniture at home and at school clean.

Such activities may assist them to realize that there is dust in the air (pp. 433–435). Of course, not all of this dust is caused by erosion as we usually think of it, for some of the dirt may come from industrial activities. This kind of study can be used to make children aware of the importance of air being free from unnecessary dirt. It would be well for teachers to be optimistic about the possibilities for the future, for much progress has been made in many localities in recent years. Accounts of cities and regions which have eliminated smog, smoke, and other problems of air pollution may give children a feeling of how problems have been solved successfully through co-operative effort. When today's children grow up they may always live in air which is free from smog and other forms of injurious air pollution. The air in cities can probably be made as clean as that of rural regions.

Children in many regions will be aware of dust storms. In almost any region there are times when dirt will be blown about, stinging one's face, getting into one's eyes, and sometimes ruining freshly painted surfaces. Recently, in a visit to an elementary-school system, there were to be seen little piles of dust in every breezeway as a result of a heavy wind storm. As the visitor entered each school in the system he encountered almost immediately after the greeting an apology for the condition of the breezeways. Such storms can be used to indicate to children that wind transports soil. This is an observation which can be made through the sensory experience of feeling as well as through that of sight.

The total concept should be developed; that is, one spot loses soil and other spots gain some soil. Too frequently in teaching this subject the fact that material that is taken from one place must be deposited somewhere is ignored. The place receiving the material is not always fortunate. Wind sorts soil by the size and weight of the particles, which results in piles of material that is often of little value for growing plants.

EXPERIENCE. *To see that soil is removed from one place by the wind, to be deposited in another.* In a wind storm school windows can be used for observations of soil on the march. It may be swept off the school ground by the wind and deposited in a breezeway. Why is it moved from one place and deposited in another? This latter is a matter of wind velocity. Wind or air at high velocity moves more soil than when it is slowed up, as it is in breezeways.

There are regions which have been called "dust bowls." Such regions are those in which the vegetative covering has been recently removed, leaving the soil free for transportation by the wind (see "Forest Lands as a Community Resource," pp. 164–166 and "Grasslands as a Community Resource," pp. 162–164). Frequently the blown material may be piled up, sometimes caught against some obstruction, to form a sand dune. In some localities sand dunes may be observed. However, little deposits, higher on one side than on the opposite, can be found around relatively small objects such as a weed, a bunch of grass, a small piece of wood, or a rock. Children may be able to locate such places. Does this indicate the direction of a prevailing wind? Sometimes in dry, windy regions one may find the soil built up all around the base of a bush or shrub. A short excursion, perhaps only to the edge of a school ground, may be helpful in finding evidence of wind erosion. The importance of vegetation for holding soil can sometimes be taught just as well with a small obstruction and little deposit as with a large sand dune.

Winds sometimes carry soil great distances. Soil particles from the famous dust-bowl storms which took place in Texas and Oklahoma in 1936 were carried to the eastern United States, to the eastern provinces of Canada, and even far out in the Atlantic Ocean. Dust storms such as these have been called "black blizzards."

Evidences of water erosion can be found in all parts of the world. The types of water erosion are conveniently named by the kind of scar they make on the land. Sometimes the scar is like a sheet, that is, soil is removed in a relatively thin sheet from a surface. This kind of erosion is aptly called *sheet erosion*. Unfortunately, sheet erosion once used to occur without farmers being aware of it. Now, of course, farmers in many regions of the world are very much more alert to erosion than formerly.

Another type of erosion has been called *rill erosion*. It is more severe than sheet erosion, in that there are many small streams, or rills, created which follow some depression or slope on the eroded surface. A great amount of soil can be removed in one storm by such erosion.

When most people think of erosion, they think of *gully erosion*. Gullies are like great gashes on the land.

Riverbank erosion is another type of erosion. In this case, the river washes against and cuts into its banks, often carrying away enormous quantities of rich farm land. It is important that we get children to have a feeling of loss for their country and world when they see erosion or any other form of waste of resources. It is important that, with this emotion of regret or sadness, they also realize that erosion and other forms of waste can be prevented. It is well for them to gain an impression of the importance of vegetative covering on the land. In each of the four types of erosion, a covering of plants can play a large role in retardation, and in some cases can completely prevent erosion.

Erosion can continue so far that all the good topsoil of a large area disappears. After that, the subsoil may start to move. In this case the damage can be great. The topsoil on the side of a hill or mountain may be carried down to the valley below. This might seem a fine thing for the people living in the valley and detrimental to the people living on the hill or mountain, but in reality it can be very detrimental to both groups. The subsoil from the mountain may be carried down and deposited on the good topsoil of the valley. The farmers living in the valley can then no longer farm the good valley soil because it has been covered over by the poor subsoil from the mountain. Thus, both those living on the sides of the valley and those living on the valley bottom are likely to lose greatly when such a region is plowed carelessly.

Are there illustrations of soil erosion in your immediate locality? Do you find gully erosion? Sheet erosion? Riverbank erosion? Rill erosion? What methods are being used to combat erosion in your vicinity? The introduction of vegetative covering in a gully may be one method used in your community. Perhaps kudzu vines are used. If your region is badly gullied, investigate kudzu vines as a means of healing erosional scars. To what extent are the people in your region aware of ways of preventing erosion?

Find examples of contour plowing and terracing. Children of upper elementary years will learn much by visiting areas in which methods of combating erosion are being used. Remarkable progress has been made in many areas in the prevention of erosion.

The gravitation of Earth can be related to erosion. It is gravity that causes water to run downhill. Terraces and contour farming tend to hold the water, thus giving it more opportunity to sink into the ground where it is wanted and less opportunity to rush down the slope.

Some literature of the past has given the impression that farmers were quite ignorant people in that they did not realize earlier that good soil was washing away. This kind of an impression is false. Many farmers long ago recognized the economic loss of erosion.

George Washington and Thomas Jefferson were among the farmers who preached soil conservation. Ideas of the importance of conservation in the Western Hemisphere were not confined to the post-Columbian period. As indicated on pages 47 to 48, the Inca Indians of South America had advanced ideas about conservation many centuries ago; they were in this regard far in advance of the Spanish who conquered them.

Many modern reservoirs have been filled up with sediment and rendered useless because there was no longer sufficient storage space for water. Some authorities think dams should not be placed on streams until the valley sides have secured a good vegetative cover (see "Water as a Community Resource," pp. 167–173). Local newspapers may give information from time to time about the condition of the reservoirs in the region. Some authorities on conservation point out that once the reservoirs behind dams become filled with silt, floods will be more disastrous than ever.

Discuss with the children the color of the water in streams. Is it clear or is it muddy? If possible take children along a small brook or rill.

What is the color of water as it runs off after a hard rain? In many regions the water running down a field after a heavy rain will be colored yellow, red, or black by the soil the water is carrying away. Have children observed the color of such water in the rain? This is an observation they can carry out in the course of their usual activities outside of school, or on the school bus on the way to school; and, in some schools, the run-off can be observed from school windows.

Frequently one can find evidences of erosion on school grounds. These evidences may be miniature gullies or miniature areas of sheet erosion. Note the changes after a heavy rain. Where does the soil that was washed away go? Perhaps it was washed up onto a sidewalk or against a fence or post. Even in a city one can find evidence of erosion on sidewalks and streets, by the little piles of dirt and other loose material one sees there.

These small evidences of erosion may be called (and quite properly) by young children, "the washing of the rain." Teachers might well start with the children's vocabulary. The meaning of "washing" could be enriched by comparison with their own experiences in washing, in observing other evidences of washing on the playground, or in observing a rainstorm from windows and watching what happens on the playground during the storm. Does the water stand at any place on the school ground for any length of time? How does it flow? Where does the water finally go? Is the soil wet after the rain? Examine soil several days after the rain, perhaps to a depth of several inches. Do the same after a dry period. Do the same on the playground and in a garden. Make sure each time that the children take responsibility for smoothing the ground as much as possible before leaving the place.

Build the concept of "washing" into the concept of "erosion" when children are ready for it.

Keep in mind that words or terms can play a vital part in concept formation if introduced at the proper moment—a moment of readiness.

Soil Is Related to Living Conditions. In regions where man is attempting to farm poor soil, one usually finds poor housing, scanty food supplies, and generally poor living conditions. As you travel about, note the living conditions of various localities in your village, township, county, province, or state. To what extent are these conditions related to the soil? In some cases the land should have been utilized for other purposes; for instance, for forest lands and game preserves. At present authorities on land planning are attempting to discourage people from growing crops on land which cannot be profitably cultivated. However, a major discovery in the chemistry or physics of the soil might cause some of the submarginal land to become profitable for farming. There is a considerable possibility that farms in eastern United States and Canada that were abandoned several generations ago as a result of the westward migration may become profitable again for agriculture because of the development of ways of increasing the fertility of soil. If this happens it will be an illustration of how the discoveries of science can be utilized to contribute to the welfare of people.

It is possible through planning to develop in a region a permanent income for the entire population. Through education of the generation now in our schools, land planning can come as a result of democratic processes. This is one of the most important problems for peoples of all nations.

Children should be given an opportunity to plan for their own school grounds. Too frequently professional landscape experts work out the landscape problems of the school grounds so completely that the school property seems an inappropriate place for the activities of growing children. There should be ground left where children can carry out plans and active experimentation; in some localities children actually plan for the beautification of the school grounds (see "Developing Intelligent Responsibleness in Children," pp. 62–73). Education should give opportunity for children to plan, to experiment, and to have the satisfaction of achievement in the direction of something of social significance.

If the community furnishes, as some communities do, a relatively large tract of land for the school, it would be well to provide areas for a number of habitats, or ecological areas, for study—woods, meadows, gardens, pools, and so on—in order to have different habitats nearby when needed. These separate areas need not be large, and paths can be made through them for convenience.

It would be well to have at least one place in every community where the natural forces of living things are operating without interference from man. An abandoned spot such as an old garden may be a place for children to observe the succession of plants. To observe the final taking-over of the place by the climax vegetation may take years, but children may be able to find places in the area, such as an abandoned garden, field, pasture, or vacant lot, where they can see the different stages in the progress toward a climax vegetation. From these observations they can see that a climax vegetation will eventually take over if the area is left undisturbed. What is the climax vegetation in your area?

Near a school in Alabama there was a small wood. On the forest floor there was a fine accumulation of forest litter. Also nearby was a piece of ground almost completely devoid of vegetative covering. Both spots, forest floor and bare ground, could be reached in a minute's walk. The children examined these almost daily during the spring. They noted how the forest litter acted like a blotter, while most of the water from a rain shower ran off the bare spot. They saw how clear the water was in the little stream near the woods, but the water from the bare spot was red with the soil of the land. The water in the stream was red at the point where the water from the bare spot flowed into it after a rain. A few days after the rain the bare spot would be baked and dry, but beneath the leaves on the forest floor it would still be wet. The leaves on the very bottom were decaying and turning into soil.

The Crust on the Desert. In most places on a desert one will find a crust. Some authorities contend that this is caused by the force of raindrops falling on the bare land of the desert.

EXPERIENCE. *Finding the crust on a desert.* If one teaches in a very dry region, children may be taken on a trip to examine this crust. Find a small spot which is bare of vegetation and has not been trampled upon or interfered with by man or other animals. In some parts of western United States and northern Mexico such places may be found near the school grounds. This crust is scaly, and a slight movement of a thumb over the ground will remove a scalelike flake of soil. If you do not find it at the first place examined, walk a few yards and look again at the ground. A hand lens or reading glass may help in examining the crust.

This crust forms a kind of packed covering, and as a result the wind does not reach parts that are beneath so readily. In desert areas where there are new developments such as housing developments serious dust storms can occur as soon as this crust has been removed. Teachers in desert regions may have opportunities for observing such developments with children in their own regions.

There Is Much Activity Going On in Soil. A handful of soil may seem an inert, lifeless, uninteresting thing, but if we study it we will find it is far from static. In fact, there is so much going on in soil that one could study it for a lifetime and not be able to learn about all the changes going on.

Some of these are simple and can be readily observed. Air gets into soil. This is of importance to us, for soil well supplied with air is necessary to the growth of many kinds of plants and for the germination of many kinds of seeds.

When water enters soil, air may be pushed out. This can happen when it rains or when snow melts. As the water soaks down into the soil, air is pushed out.

EXPERIENCE. *To show there is air in soil.* Pour water into a flowerpot in which the soil has not been watered for some time. Watch the bubbles as the air escapes and water takes up the spaces between the soil particles. In almost any region during a drought the same results can be secured by pouring water onto the ground. Escaping air will bubble up through the descending water.

Water entering the soil accelerates chemical action: much of this chemical action improves the soil. Water is instrumental in leaching the soil. Through leaching, material can be carried down to levels below the topsoil. Some of the material, such as salt, may be detrimental to plants, and in this way *leaching* is beneficial. However, when there is excessive rainfall, some valuable soil materials can be carried down below the place where plant roots can reach them. Some weeds have been found valuable because the roots are tough enough to get down through hard subsoil. They help to loosen the hard soil, and this in turn helps crop plants to grow well where otherwise they might not survive.

Heat, as well as water, increases many kinds of chemical activity in the soil. This is one reason that chemical activity is greater in moist, warm regions than in cool, dry regions.

Children should have opportunities to see how water dissolves various things (pp. 413–414). This can be related to the problems of leaching in the soil.

EXPERIENCE. *To examine soil with a reading glass.* Much can be learned by examining soil with a hand lens or reading glass. A small portion of soil (a teaspoonful) spread thinly on a piece of white paper will bring results. Notice that some pieces are like little rocks. They may constitute the sand in the soil. Other bits may be much smaller. Some of these particles may be clay. There should be some evidence of decayed parts of plants and animals.

EXPERIENCE. *To examine soil in water.* Place a cupful or two of soil in a large glass jar, such as a cookie or fruit jar. Add water so that the jar is nearly full and stir the material. Set it aside for a few minutes. Examine it. The heavier particles will go to the bottom first. These particles will be pebbles and sand. This should form a layer if there is enough of it. Above this layer there will be a layer of very fine material which will be the silt and clay. The silt is composed of small particles like flour and the clay particles are even smaller. Above this layer will be muddy water and humus (decayed plant and animal material). Examine the jar over a period of a week. The humus material will settle down on top of the silt and clay. Good soil contains sand, silt, clay, humus.

EXPERIENCE. *To study the soil layers (horizons).* Frequently, places about the community can be found where the soil layers are exposed. It may be an excavation, a trench, or gully. If so, an excursion will be valuable.

Such an exposure of layers of soil is quite appropriately called a *soil profile*. Note the *topsoil*, or surface layer. It might be well to encourage the use of the term *topsoil*, since it is a good descriptive term for the concept. It is called *horizon A* by soil students. (The words "soil horizons" are of no great importance in most instruction in the elementary school.) Note the color of the topsoil. The color is caused in part by the decay of plants and animals. This topsoil may be only an inch or so in depth in some regions, while in other regions it may extend down from the surface to a depth of several feet.

A bit of grass sod often reveals a network of roots which you can see extending down along the profile. Grass plants become thoroughly anchored in the soil by the roots, which grow out in all directions, tying the plants into the soil. "Another set (of roots) starts downward, and soon many hundred root ends of main and side branches have the plant so tied to the soil that the natural elements will not easily tear it loose."[1]

The topsoil, or horizon A, is the layer of soil which is usually cultivated for crops; below the topsoil one may find the soil of horizon B. This horizon, or layer, receives the material which is leached from the topsoil. In regions of heavy rainfall considerable material may be carried down into horizon B. As a result, one may see by the coloration that horizon B has been receiving material from the topsoil. Soil development is definitely in progress in both horizons.

Below horizon B may be found horizon C, which contains weathered rock particles (Chapter 9). Sometimes horizon C is spoken of as the parent material from which the soil of the region has been formed. Horizon C is not considered as a part of the true soil.

Sometimes the bedrock of the region is so close to the surface that it may be difficult to find all three horizons. In some places the topsoil may have been carried off by erosion.

Living things produce many changes in soil (pp. 638–640)—plant roots push down into soil, burrowing animals are active, and so on. Earthworms feed on organic matter in the soil and thus thoroughly mix the soil. There are myriads of small animals that spend part or all of their lives in the soil (pp. 392–396).

There are great numbers of micro-organisms of many kinds which play a most significant role in making soil. These organisms are at work continuously. A study of their habits and of their relationship to soil, air, and water, to each other, to climate, and to the plant covering, living and dead, on the soil has opened up new fields for scientific investigation and has been richly rewarding to the farmers and others concerned.

The soil population of micro-organisms may consist of bacteria and such plants as molds and algae, and of such animals as protozoa, of which there are many different kinds. There may be other micro-organisms as well (pp. 510–518). There may be only a very few, or there may be billions to an ounce of soil. Their range of activities is phenomenal, for they change complex mineral substances, organic materials, and gases in their life processes. The structure of the soil (pp. 301–303) may even be determined to some extent by them.

Some micro-organisms are dependent on others for nutrients, and these may form associations; among others there is keen competition for food, and these cannot live together. As a result, in a long-established environment, such as a mature grassland or forest, these organisms finally achieve a balanced population. When the soil is disturbed and other plants are introduced, the soil population changes. Each horizon or layer of soil has a characteristic population.

The soil is a world in itself, and without this complex multitude of minute organisms it would scarcely be possible for the larger plants and animals to exist.

EXPERIENCE. *To study leaching in your region.* In some regions examples of leaching may be found where there is an exposed bank. This exposure may be on a road cut, or in a building excavation. The leaching may be indicated by the coloration that has been carried downward by the water seeping through the layers. One may be able to detect the black coloration that has come from humus, leaf mold, and other decaying vegetation above. Brilliant hues of red, yellow, and even blue come from chemical compounds leaching downward. The colors can usually be traced back to their origin in the top layers.

Leaching might be compared with percolation, for it is the water percolating down through the layers of the soil which produces leaching.

[1]H. W. Staten, *Grasses and Grassland Farming.* The Devin-Adair Company, New York, 1954, p. 138.

We Can Improve Soil. Gains are being made in the knowledge of how to improve soil. Ideas of soil fertilization have been ancient knowledge among many peoples. Now with increasing knowledge gained in many fields of science there are many authorities who feel that in the future we can manage our soils much better than we have in the past, and thus make it possible to raise more food. This is especially important when one considers that the population of Earth is increasing greatly and that a large percentage of today's populations never have enough to eat.

One of the great potentialities of modern science is that through it man is constantly opening up new vistas of better living. There is no better illustration of this than in the tremendous advances made through agriculture. In a generation farming has improved to an extent that seems almost miraculous. Whether or not the advances of agriculture, if spread to all the tillable soils of the world, can eventually furnish enough food for all peoples is at present a controversial subject. Children should be alerted to the possibilities of great developments in agriculture in the future. This is as important for children living in the cities as for those living in the rural regions.

EXPERIENCE. *To visit a farm.* A visit to a farm is good experience for children at any age level. What does the farmer raise on his farm? How does he prevent erosion? Does he terrace? Does he practice contour plowing? Does he keep the soil covered so water and wind cannot erode it? Does he add fertilizer to his soil?

There are many kinds of farms. It would be well for children to have the experience of visiting different kinds of farms, such as a poultry farm, a fruit or vegetable farm, a cattle ranch, a dairy farm, a grain farm, a fur-animal farm, an irrigated and a nonirrigated farm.

These trips should not all be made in one year. It is best to distribute them through several years of elementary education. In these trips a teacher can display good learning attitudes by showing her interest in what the farmers say.

Grasslands As a Community Resource

Grassland is an important resource in many communities. Rural teachers will usually have some knowledge of the status of the grasslands in their locality. In urban regions teachers should have some knowledge and appreciation of the great value of grasslands in the country as a whole and in the agricultural territory near their own cities.

A teacher may think of grasslands as anything from pasture lots or small meadows to the vast prairies of central North America. Pastures, even though very small, are interesting places for study and for excursions with children. Is the pasture in good condition? Is it covered with grass or weeds? Sometimes old pastures have been neglected. Cattle do not eat plants they do not like, such as those having a bitter taste, hard stems, or thorns. These plants, being relatively unmolested through several years, may have reproduced themselves so effectively as to crowd out grasses. Sometimes pastures have been ruined by overgrazing or early grazing. Valuable native grasses have been almost exterminated in many regions as a result of burning, plowing, or overgrazing. In recent years it has been found that these native grasses are so well adapted to resisting drought and adverse weather conditions that many communities in the prairie states and provinces of the United States and Canada have tried to bring back the native grasses of the region.

The scientists who study the soil have learned that the best soils were built on the grasslands. It is no accident that the great food-producing states are those which were our great grasslands. Grasslands are similar to forests in that they are renewable if left undisturbed or if managed scientifically. This is possible today if the farmer or ranchman makes certain that the land is given a chance to maintain itself in good condition. Grasslands once seriously injured may require a long time for complete recovery. On the other hand, proper management can constantly improve their fertility.

Grass protects the soil from erosion. The heavier the covering of grass, the greater the protection. Sometimes one will find rolling topography with fairly steep surfaces which show little or no gully action because the farmer has kept a good covering of grass. You may watch for places of this kind in your locality. Once the grass is destroyed, the soil is subject to the action of water and wind. One can run water from a hose over two sloping surfaces—one with soil exposed, the other with a thick mat of grass covering—and demonstrate the value of grass in the conservation of soil.

After 1865 the great grasslands of the prairies of North America were opened for agriculture and grazing. Before long, too many cattle had been introduced and the grass was cropped close to the ground. Then sheep were brought in to many areas, since they can eat grass more closely than can cattle. As a result, little or no protective covering was left on the soil. The hoofs of the animals destroyed the stems of the grass and finally even the roots. Strong winds, blowing across the prairies, whipped the soil far and wide. In some regions sand dunes were developed because there was no longer a vegetative covering. Under careful supervision many similarly devastated areas have been returned to grazing land and even to cultivation.

Perhaps you can observe soil being blown about in areas where the grass has been cropped too closely.

Ranchmen and farmers declared war upon such predatory animals as wolves and coyotes. These beasts, however, had kept such destructive animals as prairie dogs and jack rabbits in check. Now the latter were free to multiply in great numbers because their natural predators had been locally exterminated. Prairie dog villages grew in size until the natural range for cattle was greatly reduced in many localities and jack rabbits competed with livestock for food. In many areas it was necessary to resort to poisoning the prairie dogs and jack rabbits. At present, many localities are more kindly disposed toward the predatory animals, and are even permitting them to return, in order that the smaller destructive animals may be held in check. How does this relate to the balance of nature (pp. 568–585)?

Grasses seeded into slopes will hinder the erosion of the soil, since grass tends to bind the soil into place. Farmers frequently seed drainage slopes in grass, thus furnishing feed for cattle, homes for game birds and other animals, and protection for the soil. Such places will make suitable sites for excursions with your class. Perhaps children will describe places they have passed in buses or cars where the highway department has planted vegetation on the steep slopes of road cuts, thus preventing the slipping of the land, as well as beautifying the locality.

Learn something of the conditions of the pastures and other grasslands in your locality. This problem of reseeding will vary greatly with the region represented. In some of the prairie regions the grass is the greatest natural resource. In some localities it is related to the dairy industry, while in others it represents only one phase of diversified farming.

The grasslands may be studied by finding the answers to such questions as these: What is the attitude of the people toward pastures and grasslands? What kinds of animals in your locality are raised on grasslands? Consult the local farm agent or some other agricultural authority. Perhaps you can observe farms or ranches and see the condition of the pastures. How much understanding should urban people have of the problems of the dairy industry and of the cattlemen?

In some regions much land which should have been left to grass has been cultivated. What disposition should have been made of the land in your region? Is there any public domain in your region? Does the management of it seem satisfactory? Perhaps the farm agent or a representative from an agricultural college will be willing to speak at a conference of teachers about the local problems of the grasslands and their relation to the welfare of the people of your community.

There is a great body of evidence to show that overstocking the grazing lands may cause a financial loss. Overgrazing leads to the eventual destruction of the grasslands. Furthermore, more young cattle can be brought to maturity if the grass is ample. There is no advantage in overstocking if the cows cannot secure enough grass to produce an ample supply of milk to bring the calves to maturity.

In general, one must conclude that there has been a very great improvement in the public's attitude toward grasslands within the last decade. The continual growth of this attitude will contribute greatly to restoring this great resource.

Forest Lands As a Community Resource

The attitude of people toward the place of trees in the national economy has undergone a profound change. During the period of early settlement of the North American continent, trees were frequently considered nuisances to be destroyed, much as a farmer would destroy weeds. In spite of the fact that trees furnished useful building material, the great forest lands seemed to the early settlers to be barriers to the development of a civlization. Frequently the forests were burned in order to expedite the settling of the land.

Today we are learning that forests, like grasslands, can be maintained in such a way that the landowners will have a permanent source of income. The traditional method of lumbering consisted of cutting down all the trees from a tract of land. This left the land exposed to erosion, and the rich topsoil was washed from the steep slopes. Frequently the accumulated soil of centuries of soil formation has been washed away in a few weeks after trees have been removed from a hillside, in some cases causing the fertile valley below to be covered by the subsoil which also was washed down from hillsides.

It has been found that cut-over land is more subject to fires than a growing forest because the waste materials from the lumbering are scattered about carelessly, a condition which encourages the rapid spread of fire. As a result, fires often follow after an area has been logged in a destructive manner. Repeated fires in an area will tend to destroy the ability of the land to support tree growth. This condition represents a great economic loss of timber and the productiveness of the soil. Are there tracts of this kind in your region?

The attitudes of the people of a region toward forests may be reflected in large part by the kinds of forests, windbreaks, and wood lots that are maintained in that region. If possible, teachers should make excursions to some of the nearby woodlands and note the general conditions prevailing there. Is fire protection maintained? Is the forest or wood lot congenial to wild life? Are the forest lands contributing to the welfare of the community? Are suitable recreation facilities maintained in the forest lands? Is an entire tract of land completely lumbered at one time, or is there a program of continuous lumbering in which trees are left to protect the soil and to insure a supply of lumber for the future?

There has been a vast improvement in the methods of lumbering in many parts of the world. Trees are harvested in a scientific way, with opportunity for the continuous seeding of an area. This kind of lumbering is called scientific lumbering. In this way the forest in a region is never completely lumbered; in fact the forest vegetation is disturbed very little at any one time. One advantage of scientific lumbering is that those involved have continuous employment. It is important that the community should have a permanent source of income. Too frequently in schools the traditional wasteful methods of lumbering are emphasized without sufficient mention of modern lumbering practices.

Forests have a much greater value than most people realize. They contribute greatly to the water resources of a region. Forests planted on watersheds will increase the supply of water for power and irrigation projects. Rain falling on a thick carpet of leaves and needles is more likely to soak into the ground than that falling on the barren ground where there is no vegetative covering. A rich vegetative covering tends to regulate the flow of water into streams and to increase the underground water supply. The canopy of leaves forms a layer which protects the soil from the damaging effects of the rain, sun, and wind. Water falling on the bare ground may run off into streams and cause floods.

Note the nature of the litter on the floor of a forest. Examine it carefully. Lift up a few leaves and examine what is underneath. Observe that the decaying vegetation forms natural pockets for the storage of water. Such a covering is instrumental in producing a steady supply of water for human needs.

Water which does not get beneath the top surface of the soil is subject to evaporation. Soil which has plants growing in it absorbs more water than does soil which is barren. Water from a rain flowing over a field without a good vegetative covering will be colored by the soil it is carrying, whereas water in a stream in a deep forest usually will be clear. Perhaps children can report on such observations.

Forests in a distant locality may play an important part in the economic life of a region that is not wooded. Sometimes the slopes of the watersheds above a dam are covered with forest, conserving the water for regions below, where the water is used for irrigation. This illustrates the interrelations of regions.

Trees are important in preventing the soil on drainage slopes from pouring into the reservoirs of a community's water supply. Evergreen trees which form carpets of needles are particularly helpful in protecting the soil from washing into the reservoir, thus assisting greatly in insuring communities water that is clear and in continual supply. Clear water in turn is an asset in producing pure water. Are trees planted on the drainage slope of the water supply of your community?

It is a well-known fact that forest lands have definite value in flood prevention, because forests retard the passage of water from the point where the rain touches the ground to the place where it is flowing in a stream. This action of the forest land tends to regulate the water in the stream.

A teacher may become acquainted with the methods of fire prevention in forests, and relate this to the study of oxygen and the nature of fire. Are the people co-operating in fire prevention? What can the school do to help build a constructive attitude toward fire prevention?

Many products useful to a civilized community come from trees—paper, rayon, some of the plastics, turpentine, rosin, tannin, maple sugar and syrup, alcohol, dye substances, and cellulose. Out of cellulose a large number of useful articles are made. How will forests in the future serve to remedy shortages in metals? What is the relation of forests to national wealth? What are the special commercial products that come from the trees in your region?

Windbreaks and Shelter Belts

In some regions the wind may do great damage to farm land by drying the moisture in the soil and by eroding the land. For many years windbreaks have been used about farmhouses in parts of the prairie regions. There has been an interest in building shelter belts in Canadian prairie provinces, and from North Dakota down through the Great Plains states and into Texas and Mexico. The wind is forced upward by one farmer's windbreak and encounters another farmer's windbreak before it reaches the ground.

Shelter belts serve to beautify the country and furnish protected places for valuable wild life, in addition to the conservation of moisture and soil. Farmers in many regions have used the shelter belt as a source of firewood.

Many people derided the attempts of the United States government to establish shelter belts in the western prairie states. They felt the trees would not be able to grow because of the small amount of rainfall. However, botanists and other scientists who have studied trees selected those plants which were well adapted to dry climates. They have also studied the best methods of planting; for instance, shrubs and low-growth trees are placed at the edges; while the tall trees grow in the center of the windbreak. They have also studied methods of keeping the shelter belt in good condition.

Are you in a region in which windbreaks are important? What purpose can they serve in your locality? Are the windbreaks well cared for? Do they give cover to wild life? What kinds of wild life should be encouraged to live in shelter belts? Would a windbreak near the school grounds be advisable?

An excursion with the children to a shelter belt may reveal the contrast of living things in the belt and on the surrounding prairie. Are the windbreaks a source of firewood for farmers? Are the farmers securing any economic profit from the windbreaks? What is the attitude of the people toward windbreaks and shelter belts? Is there any information on this subject from accurate sources that is available to farmers?

Water As a Community Resource

The Demand for More Water. Modern man demands a large supply of clean, pure water. It might be well to have someone who knows about the history of the community tell the children about how water was secured in their region in the past. Perhaps such a person can tell about an old well or an old spring; how people carried water, and how they used it. This could serve to contrast the present and past in the way water was used in bathing, cooking, washing clothes, cleaning floors, watering stock, and so on. The contrast of modern kitchens and bathrooms, with their running hot and cold water, with those of a generation or more ago could be discussed. Is more water used now, or less? Old photographs of the community might help. Some children might be interested in making up a story about what it would have been like to have carried water into the house from a well or spring for the needs of a large family. In some communities there may be evidences of an old "spring house."

Perhaps a period when there is great scarcity of water in a community, or even a temporary period when water is not available in the school or at home on account of repairs, can be used to illustrate how much our daily activities are dependent upon a supply of water.

Various ways in which water is used in the community might be listed. Perhaps flower beds, the lawn, or gardens are watered by the children. In some communities it may be necessary to supply water for these purposes only during dry periods, while in others it is necessary to water plants throughout the year.

Perhaps there is some irrigation in the vicinity. There has been an increase in the use of irrigation in many parts of the world. Usually we think of irrigation in connection with desert regions, but in recent years it has been introduced into other areas, such as parts of the eastern and southern United States.

Water for irrigation is secured in various ways. Many streams have been dammed to make reservoirs for irrigation projects. Sometimes this water may come from melting snow in the mountains, or from rain; in some regions the water is pumped up from underground water supplies.

Another use of water may be in air-conditioning. With the increasing use of air-conditioning, there is an increasing use of water.

Many industries are heavy users of water. In fact, it would be impossible to operate some industries at the present time without great supplies of water. As a community becomes more industrialized, the greater is the demand for water. Farms, and especially dairy farms, must have a generous supply of water for cleaning the cows, the stalls, the milking machines, the milk cans and tanks.

The supply of water has a tremendous effect upon the distribution of plants and animals. As one travels across any continent, he becomes aware of how the vegetation varies in both kind and quantity with changes in the amount of water available for growing plants. Frequently within the local region the plants and animals found in a moist valley will differ from those found on the drier surrounding hilltops.

Are there parts of your community where the ground conditions are moister than at others? Is there an observable difference in the kinds and numbers of plants in such places? These questions can be related to experiments performed in the classroom. How does the pattern of adaptation explain different habitats (pp. 95–96)?

Many persons are surprised to discover that there may be limited desert spots in a region of heavy rainfall. The desert spot may be dry most of the time because the water drains away so rapidly. For instance, the top of a hill which is not covered with vegetation may be quite dry a short time after it has rained.

The number of inches of precipitation (Chapter 12) does not always reveal all the information about the conditions of moisture available for growing plants. In some regions heavy rains may not be very beneficial. The water may not have a chance to be absorbed by the soil before it runs off. Water may also seal up the top pores of the soil, particularly if there is no vegetative covering, and thus prevent the absorption of water. The water may flow off quickly, creating a flash flood which can do considerable damage. In some regions rains of this kind are called "lake-fillers" because the water flows into the natural depressions. It is well in such regions to use vegetation, terraces, and small spreader dams to hold the water long enough so that some of it will soak into the soil.

In warm regions the water from a rain may evaporate very rapidly. Water that is exposed to air is subject to evaporation. This is an important concept to teach children, and can be easily shown or observed (pp. 475–487). We can place money in a bank and go back later and get it, but such is not the case with water left in storage in surface reservoirs. It evaporates from reservoirs and tanks, and even from jars unless tightly closed. In Australia experiments have shown that if a thin layer of cetyl alcohol, derived from whales, is spread on the surface of a reservoir, it helps to retard evaporation and thus conserve valuable water supplies.

Rain or snow can come too early or too late for crops. Reading the current events in a newspaper or listening to farmers talk will inform one as to the importance of rain or snow at the right time. Sometimes there is so much rain that the soil cannot be worked; at other times the soil can become so wet that the crops cannot mature properly; and at other times the crops may spoil in the fields.

From all this it can be shown that water plays an important part in man's story. He has lived near water most of the time throughout his history. He has fought for his rights to use water holes and streams. He had to learn how to carry water with him if he went on long journeys into dry regions. If his home region became too dry, man had to move to an area where more water was available.

Among many tribes, water holes or other watering places were favorite places for hunting. By concealing themselves near a watering place, hunters could kill the animals that came to drink or bathe in the water hole. Children know how camp sites were usually located near a stream or spring long ago when the early settlers were making their way westward to find new homes.

Few problems have greater political significance than those relating to the control of water supply. Do you know of any political struggle for the control of water in your region? In your country?

The Pollution of Water. It is important that water which is to be used for domestic purposes should be clean and pure. Many communities have great difficulty in securing a supply of suitable water. Some get it from lakes and rivers into which other communities have dumped their sewage. Where does your community get its water supply? Is it an adequate supply? Is the water satisfactory on the basis of health standards? Is the water tested frequently? Is the water hard or soft? Is the water chlorinated? Is it fluorinated? Perhaps the children would profit from a visit to the water-supply system.

Water plays an important role in the disposal of sewage. Communities bordering on oceans frequently empty sewage into them. This sewage in turn contaminates bathing beaches and surrounding areas. What is the condition of bathing beaches in your community? Where do people go for swimming and water sports? The contamination of lakes and rivers has been mentioned.

Careless sewage disposal can injure the fishing industry and fishing as a recreation. It has been claimed that an acre of water could be made to produce as much food as an acre of land. Whether this is true or not, it is indicated that people must be on their guard lest they destroy the great fisheries. Perhaps the pollution of water has partially or completely destroyed the fishing in your locality. Every step should be taken to make all waterways into fishing grounds where fish can live and grow.

Frequently waste from industries is dumped into drainage systems, polluting streams and lakes. As communities have become more industrial in character, the problem of pollution has become greater. How should this problem be corrected?

Traditionally man has used the natural drainage of a region for the disposal of wastes. As long as a region was sparsely settled, there was little likelihood that the drinking water would become polluted. But in our modern industrial regions the disposal of waste materials has become a great problem in many cases. Even burying waste material in the ground will usually not keep it from polluting streams or the underground water supply, because percolating rain water will carry it into the natural drainage of the region.

The problem has become so great that many industries have found it necessary to employ chemists to propose ways of disposing of their waste materials. This has often helped the industries because chemists have found new products to make out of the wastes. Such products are called by-products (Chapter 11).

Sawmills frequently have had difficulty in disposing of sawdust. Usually it was left in great piles, and often it would get into lakes, where the chemical action set up would kill the fish. But now lumbering industries have found many uses for sawdust, and it is no longer wasted or permitted to become a menace. A great variety of useful products, such as bowling balls, phonograph records, wallpaper, dishes, and many other things are made from it.

Lakes, rivers, and ocean shores are usually considered places of natural beauty. Are such places kept beautiful for recreational purposes in your neighborhood? Can the school help in improving the situation? One city almost completely surrounded by water was forced to prohibit bathing at its beaches because the water was contaminated.

Perhaps you live in a community where the water is obtained from individual wells and the sewage disposal is primitive. If such is the case the school should consult the Department of Health for possible direction of instruction.

In recent years it has been necessary for many regulations in reference to the conservation of water to be made into law. On account of the growing shortage of water, it has been necessary to prevent the pollution of water sources. Therefore, in some industries the water used must be purified and used again. Are individuals in the community reasonably careful in their use of water? A leaky faucet can waste gallons of water in a short time.

The Prevention of Floods. Sometimes one would get the impression from news items that floods are something which have developed in recent history and are the results of modern civilization. Such is not the case, for there is much evidence that there were floods long before the historic period. However, there are many authorities who are of the opinion that civilization has increased the size of floods and has also caused them to occur more frequently.

It should be kept in mind that man has settled frequently on the flood plains of rivers. In a real sense, when man does this, he is encroaching on land that belongs to the river, since the river has been flooding at intervals over these plains for long stretches of time. Many cities have been built on these plains; railroads and highways are often built along the river valleys to avoid the steep grades of the hills and mountains on each side. If a river was navigable, it was thought necessary to build warehouses, docks, trade centers, and industries beside the riverbanks. Man has tended to restrict the river into smaller channels as a result. But when the river was flooded, the flood plain became covered by water, with consequent loss of life and property.

There has been a great deal of controversy about the problem of how to prevent floods. There are some who feel that the only way to secure protection from floods is through measures directed at the lower courses of the rivers. They would build levees and spillways, straighten and deepen the channels, and arrange for diversion channels and reservoirs. In some places they would build dams, but in most cases they would do all they could to speed the water along on its way to the ocean.

There are others who would favor better planning for the use of the land along the upper parts of such streams. This group believes that land management would do much to give protection in the lower valleys. This group would build few big dams on the lower parts of the rivers; rather, they would plan the use of the land of the river basin in such a way that water would be retarded as soon as it reached the ground. They would do this by keeping a good vegetative covering—in the form of forests, grasslands, and good field

cover—on all parts of the basin. In this way, they contend, much of the water would soak into the ground rather than flowing off rapidly to the ocean. These people speak of the "soil blotting up the water." They point out that soil can act much like a blotter if it has a good vegetative covering.

These people would have land terraced if necessary, and the fields would be plowed on the contour instead of up and down the hills. In this way, water would be stopped during a rain, and there would be time for much of it to go into the ground. Small spreader dams would be placed in the upper parts of the river basin to spread out the water and to slow it up in its course to the ocean.

Progress has been made in the development of forests along the headwaters and sides of rivers. Fire towers and equipment for fighting fires in forests have been built in many forests. Lumbering interests are co-operating through the use of selective lumbering, thus leaving a forest intact to protect the sides and tops of hills at all times.

More attention needs to be given to overgrazing in many localities. Stockmen are learning that when the grass has been destroyed, they no longer can remain in business as stockmen. As a result, more and more stockmen are aware of the importance of building up good grazing land. This is especially important on the land surrounding the headwaters of streams.

Some successful farmers very carefully watch the water that flows over their land. If it is muddy at any place on the farm they take steps immediately to slow up the water at that place. They see that something is planted which can retard the water, or they make a terrace, or they build small spreader dams.

Many contend that water planning should start with land planning. They feel that if we properly plan the use of land along the sides and at the headwaters of a river—as to crops, recreation, lumbering, and grazing—we shall e able to control the flow of water. They oint out that through land planning water an be kept longer where it is needed. Those ollowing this line of thought would encourage armers to develop farm ponds.

In many communities farm ponds have een developed, and often, in addition to the apply of water for livestock and seepage into ne ground, they furnish fresh fish for the able. Rural people also utilize these small orage basins for fire protection. A view from n airplane or a high place will provide one ith an opportunity to see how widespread ne development of farm ponds has been.

Many authorities who encourage land planning of river basins view with dismay the tendncy to build dams in many parts of the world. hey point out that the reservoirs back of the ams will become filled with sediment if the uilding of a dam is not accompanied by land lanning and erosional controls on the higher opes. They have predicted that once the eservoirs become nearly filled with sediment, ne floods will be more disastrous than ever bere. They view dam building on the lower arts of a river as only a temporary device. o support their argument, these people call ttention to the many reservoirs which have lready been filled with sediment.

Another criticism of building dams on the wer parts of a stream is that almost always ne water in the reservoir will cover some of ne best valley land in the region. It is usully true that farmers are forced to sell fine alley farms before such dams can be built. n some cases entire villages have been forced) move to a new location.

Those favoring dams as a means of preventng floods argue that the water can be stored ehind dams and used for other purposes, such s irrigation, generation of power, recreational urposes, and in some cases for navigation. Iany who favor land planning admit that ome dams are justifiable for purposes of water torage, but they feel that there is a tendency

to build too many dams instead of meeting the problem through land management.

Many industries have been forced to move on account of the shortage of water. In many ways this is a good thing, since it will help to avoid the problems of heavy concentration of industries in certain areas. Some industries have moved from the United States to Canada where there are great resources of water and water power.

The Storage of Water. It is probable that the boys and girls in classrooms today will, as adult citizens, have many problems to decide that relate to water and its use. It is well known that in the United States and Canada today there is tremendous competition between various regions for water rights. Perhaps few questions at the present time are more disturbing than that of providing enough water for growing communities.

In a way this seems surprising, for most people have thought of water as something which ought always to be plentiful and cheap. That water, which is too plentiful at times of flood, should ever be scarce enough to create a problem, may seem to many children hard to believe, particularly if they live in regions of considerable rainfall. It should be kept in mind, however, that securing an ample supply of water is a problem in many regions of considerable rainfall, such as portions of northeastern and southeastern United States.

It was nothing new for man to turn to underground supplies of water, for he had long used wells. Recently man has been able to drill wells much deeper than before, and he can pump the water out of these underground supplies much faster than he ever did before. From many of these aquifers (described, p. 271) man is drawing water out faster than it can be replenished. It now seems that many regions may face in the near future a "water famine" unless some solution to the water problem is developed for these regions.

Children should gain an appreciation of the importance of underground water supplies. There may be events in the community that make this problem quite real. In many places the water table (the top of the ground-water reservoirs) is being lowered. In some places it has been necessary to drill the wells deeper in order to reach the water. Sometimes the aquifer has been emptied and there is no way for it to be recharged, either due to lack of rainfall or to rock layers so compact that water cannot penetrate them. If the water level drops low enough, springs and wells, marshes, lakes, and rivers may dry up.

In some cases, the water table near oceans has been lowered so much that salt water from the ocean has come into underground sources, rendering the water unsatisfactory. Has the water table dropped in your community? Has anything been done about it? Are there great natural aquifers in your region?

There is a hopeful indication for the future. Man is learning the importance of replenishing the great aquifers of Earth. He is learning where water can enter the aquifers from the surface, through porous layers of soil and rock. During rainy periods and general flood conditions, he can cause the water to be spread over these porous layers. Sometimes the places where the water is spread out are called "catchment basins."

The underground storage of water has an advantage over the reservoirs of water on the surface because underground water does not evaporate. In all reservoirs of water behind dams there is much loss through evaporation. Our boys and girls will hear more about this subject as the problems of the water supply are considered in public discussions in the future. One of the great achievements of the future may be the increased conservation water through replenishing the undergroun reservoirs.

The Oceans As a Resource. The oceans a the largest source of the fresh water that falls rain or snow (p. 475). Because increasing more fresh water is needed in many regior man is learning how to make ocean wat "fresh" on a large scale and economic enough for use by cities and for irrigatio When this is accomplished, deserts may l made into great agricultural regions. Perha this will come about during the lifetime of tl children now in the elementary schools. Ma has been making use of the oceans for purpos of shipping and recreation, the hunting of ar mals for food and such products as oil and fu for a long time. His recovery and use of tl minerals in the ocean has been small.

New knowledge about the living resourc of the oceans and how to protect yet use the may provide food for millions of people. A increased knowledge of tides, currents, wave pressure, temperature, and light; the gas and minerals dissolved in ocean water; an the habits and movements of ocean life wi contribute to this. Better management alon coastlines can reduce pollution and improv growing conditions for shellfish. Hatcheri may help to maintain a supply of ocean li and water farming, or aquaculture in shallo and deep waters may be improved and e tended (pp. 263, 413, 532, 681).

Scientists and farsighted planners are takin a great interest in the study of the oceans an their resources and how they may be used benefit mankind. Children should look fo ward with hope and confidence to a futu they can help to fashion. It is a frontier abou which relatively little is known.

Wild Life As a Resource of the Community

Perhaps no resource has suffered more from neglect than has wild life. This neglect is due largely to lack of awareness of the real values of this great resource. Many people are inclined to look upon wild life as a kind of luxury for humanity—something which has to do merely with how hunters are to spend their week ends. What are the attitudes toward wild life in your community?

The value of wild plants and animals to man is enormous. They add to the attractiveness of the out-of-doors and assist greatly in recreation. Many kinds of wild plants and animals are important items of food in man's diet today, and others, under intelligent management, might become important items of food in the future. Some species such as the fur-bearing animals supply man with warm clothing.

Wild Life in the Balance of Nature. Wild life has so great a significance in man's ability to establish a balance of nature favorable to himself that many authorities question whether, without vast reserves of wild plant and animal life, man can long hold his own with the array of biological and physical forces. Wild life should be studied in relation to the concept of interrelationships (Chapter 14).

There are many ways in which wild life becomes *exterminated* in a region. Frequently, this is because the animal is hunted for its value to man as food and clothing. Sometimes wild animals are nearly brought to extermination because their natural homes are destroyed. Forest birds and other animals lose their homes when the forests are removed; swamp animals lose their homes when the swamp is drained; those measures that change the environment make a change in the wild life of the area. Large metropolitan areas of North America are all built on land where wild life once lived. Another way in which man destroys wild life is by aiding animals whose nature it is to prey upon any species of wild animals. Domestic dogs and cats, which have the protection of man, destroy vast numbers of wild animals.

Discourage the Collecting of Wild Life. Teachers can do much to develop a desire to preserve the natural beauty of the out-of-doors. Work should not be planned about collections of wild flowers and other objects, for this negates the best principles of conservation. Man destroys many wild plants because of his collecting tendency. A good educational program takes children into the out-of-doors, where they can see objects in their natural settings and habitats, and leaves the habitats undisturbed (see "Conservation as a Pattern for Behavior," pp. 62–73).

Study your own community. What wild life was there before the country was settled? What species have been exterminated in your region? Which of the original species are left? What are the conditions of streams and lakes for fishing? Have any wild animals moved into your region? (The coyote is an animal which has extended its range in North America during the past century.) What wild life is left in the forests or on the prairies? Is there a wild-life refuge in your vicinity? What wild plants are near extinction in your community? Is there a comprehensive program of wild-life conservation in your community?

Wild life played an important part in the

settlement of North America because the early settlers were dependent upon game for food and clothing. As the land was cleared of the natural covering and plowed and swamps were drained, many animals had no place to go for refuge. Useless slaughter followed in some cases, with the result that many animals were exterminated, while others became so rare that the future of the species was held in doubt.

Children need to appreciate the full meaning of the extermination of a species. Such an appreciation should not rest upon sentiment but upon an understanding of the balance of nature. An individual species of plant or animal exists because of the operation of natural forces for millions of years. Man cannot make these species. Once a species is destroyed, it is improbable that it will ever again be evolved in nature. We can never tell when, in the course of events, we may be in serious need of the kind of plant or animal that we may have destroyed.

Assisting Wild Life. There is in evidence a change of attitude toward wild life. Many people prefer to spend their vacations in regions where they can have glimpses of living things they cannot see at other times. Areas such as national parks, where wild life has been given a degree of protection, have become popular places for recreation. Today we find many people concerned with the protection of wild life. Through their organizations, hunters are increasingly appealing for good sportsmanship. What are the attitudes of the hunters in your area? Are these attitudes satisfactory? This is a topic which children might discuss.

Farmers who wish to encourage wild life must have places on their farms for the growth of natural vegetation. Many farmers have found that they can encourage some forms of wild life without this interfering with their own agricultural pursuits. Wild animals need

a cover of plants for protection, especial when there are young present. Windbreal and shelter belts serve this purpose, and man farmers find it well to allow for some natur growth at the edges of pastures and fields an along borders between the fields.

Such combinations of plant cover have n always been considered sightly. The trad tional tendency in farming has been to kee the borders of fields, pastures, and woods clea of all vegetation. However, when one realiz that this vegetation not only furnishes all-yea round cover and protection for wild life as we as protection against erosion, one can build u a sense of appreciation for the natural vegeta tion.

Thick cover provides protection against th chilly and drying winds of winter. Cover als furnishes protection for young plants, which i turn may be utilized as food by some animal When the countryside is covered by sleet, ic and snow, the animals, including birds, ma find sufficient food under this cover to tid them over until the weather is again suitabl for searching for food elsewhere.

Land which is submarginal—that is, lan that should not be cultivated for variou reasons—can be left for the natural develop ment of the climax vegetation. Wild life ma thus be provided with a plant cover in suc places, to take the place of its natural habita Many farmers permit hunters to hunt gam on their land, but only on condition that th hunter pays a fee to the farmer. This er courages the farmer to develop a good plac for wild life.

Children are quite likely to think that a re gion such as a thicket, weed patch, or brus should be destroyed and cleaned out (pp. 532 546). The fact that such places have economi significance in the preservation of wild lif may be a concept to be learned. We need t develop in children a feeling for the beauty the natural processes. A weed patch or thicket are not in themselves ugly sights, unles

ey are made so by man's carelessness, as
hen he uses the spot as a dumping ground
r refuse.

Small farm ponds (pp. 167–172) may be-
ome places for fish and other water life.
o you see any such ponds in your commu-
ty? Take the children on an excursion to a
ortion of an unspoiled region such as a wood-
nd to see what kinds of life they can find.
leally, a portion of the school ground should
e left to develop naturally so that children
n have an out-of-doors laboratory close at
and.

What part can wild life play in the balance
nature in your community? Does the local
titude toward wild life need changing?
hat part can wild life play in making your
cality more interesting? What economic
lue can wild life have in your community?
hat animals migrate through your locality?
ow can they be helped and protected during
is migration period? Are there any agencies
your community devoted to the conserva-
on of wild life?

In many communities careless methods of
arbage and refuse disposal result in the mul-
plication of cockroaches, rats, mosquitoes,
nd flies. These animals may seriously com-
ete with wild life and may injuriously affect
e health of man as well. The school may
eed to consult with the local board of health
r information on this subject.

What plants and animals in your commu-
ty may rightfully be considered pests?
ometimes animals considered to be pests
ter turn out to have real value. Snakes,
arthworms, birds, spiders, and many other
rms of animal life have a very important
lace in establishing world conditions suitable
r man's welfare. Plants which we call *weeds*
ay have great value at times, as a result of
eir ability to cover such places as fallow
elds, grading beside new roads, or some other
te from which the natural vegetative cover-
g has been removed.

Certain kinds of plants, or combinations of
plants, are so well suited to a certain soil, climate, and set of growing conditions that they
tend to crowd out other plants. These plants
will dominate the region if man does not interfere. Biologists call such plants the *climax
vegetation*. In some regions the climax vegetation is pine trees; in others, it is bunch grass
or short grass; in others, mesquite and cactus.
Because weeds may be the first plants to grow
in a disturbed area such as a road cut they
are sometimes called *pioneer plants*. Later
comes the climax vegetation, which can hold
and dominate the region unless man decides
otherwise. Sometimes the climax vegetation
has real economic value. Each kind of vegetation has its characteristic animal life. On
an abandoned farm or garden the succession
of plants and animals can be observed (Chapter 14).

Plant and Animal Pests. For various reasons,
both good and bad, species of plants and animals from one region may be introduced into
new regions. Man has carried plant and animal species from one continent to another.
Some of these imported species have become
pests and place the native wild life at a disadvantage. The list of such pests found in North
America is long. What species have been
introduced into your region? What steps
have been taken to control pests in your region (pp. 698–706)?

Then, too, there are certain forms of wild
life that follow man about on the surface of
Earth and exist at his very doorstep, even entering his home. Such animal life is not welcome; nevertheless, it exists because man does
not combat it with sufficient aggressiveness.
Rats, mice, cockroaches, bedbugs, and body
lice are illustrations of this type. On the one
hand, man destroys many forms of native
wild life that he admires; on the other hand,
by his carelessness he creates conditions which
assist forms of wild life to become pests. Man's

method of disposing of waste and sewage has much to do with the multiplication of rats and cockroaches. It might be well for a teacher or a committee of teachers to visit the community dumping grounds. Do you see evidences of rats, mice, or cockroaches? Such a place can be a vast breeding ground for these animals.

Conservation of Wild Life and Behavior. The study of wild life can be associated with the development of responsibleness (Chapter 3). Children can do much to discourage the collecting of wild plants and animals. They can assume responsibility for their own animal pets to see that they do not destroy young wild animals. Children can develop good sportsmanship in relation to hunting, fishing, and other outdoor sports connected with wild life.

They can learn to take responsibility for re reation places (p. 68). The study in the cla room should at all times illustrate conservati as a line of behavior.

More attention needs to be given to the e termination of rats. In almost any city o can find rats in large numbers. They cons tute a menace to health and property. Ch dren need to be alerted to these pests so th they can help to eliminate them. Cleanlin is one of the important aspects of the ca paign: rats feed on man's refuse and sewaξ

In these problems the children should re ize the importance of a sound balance of n ture favorable to man. At the same tin they need to see that man does not live in vacuum; rather, he lives in a web of interi lationships and interdependencies of livi things (pp. 685–709).

Industrial Development As a Resource in the Community

Possibly there are industrial developments in your community. These may vary from small industries involving one or two workers to vast ones employing thousands of people. Why is such industry located in your community? What form of energy is used to operate these industries? From where does the energy come? Trace the energy to its source, possibly to coal mines or water power, and thence to the sun (Chapter 22).

How long have the industries been in your community? What changes have accompanied their development? Have these changes created problems in your school? Are the employees well paid? What are their living standards? Is the management of the industries concerned with the welfare of their employees?

Are industrial wastes dumped into the

streams? What part have the industri played in the development of canals, hig ways, and railroads? Have they affected t natural beauty of the region? How can tl condition be improved? How have industri affected the housing of the community? I the industries pollute the atmosphere?

It is easy to recognize the value of an i dividual's work in an industry and the vit part that industries play as a valuable resour in a community; but often the value of sm: tasks is overlooked. Therefore, it is well for teacher to learn about useful work that ch dren have performed at home, on the farm, in other parts of the community. They can encouraged to talk about what they did a how they did it. How did they learn to do Were any machines used? What source energy was used? It is well to help childr

ace a value on the constructive tasks. It is
ell to have them contribute to the improve-
ent of the classroom and to give them credit
r it. It is well for them to take pride in
cleanliness in the school and pride in work
that contributes to the community. It is well,
too, for them to realize the value of small tasks
in the life of the community and the nation.

Valuable Deposits As Resources in the Community

Man benefits from such fuel deposits as
al, oil, and natural gas; such metals as zinc,
ad, and iron; such nonmetals as building
aterials, fertilizers, and valuable chemicals.
In the past there has been much wasteful-
ss in the way in which deposits have been
ilized. In some cases, the higher-grade ores
ve been taken and the low-grade ore has
en left in such a condition that its full re-
very is impossible or highly expensive.

The forests, grasslands, wild life, and, to
me extent, soil and water can be renewed
th proper care. The deposits of mineral
d nonmineral materials are not renewable.
atural processes required a long time for
ilding these deposits. Man is using them
ore rapidly than they are being made by
atural processes (Chapter 11). We must de-
lop ways of utilizing these deposits so that
r civilization will have a sufficient supply
r thousands of years to come.

Are there valuable deposits in your region?
re they being worked today? Do you have
your classes children from homes in which
ere are workers in the industries dependent
on these deposits? What seems to be the
ture of the industry involved? Such de-
sits may vary from a small quarry of build-
g rock or a small gravel pit to large deposits
coal, iron, or copper. To what extent is the
elfare of the community dependent upon the
dustry which has grown out of the deposits?
re the owners of the industry residents in
ur community? Are there indications that
the deposit may be giving out? Are there
"ghost towns" in your region? If so, why were
the towns abandoned?

Some mineral deposits are fuels such as bituminous coal, lignite, anthracite, petroleum,
and natural gas. Children should learn to
recognize these as sources of energy. Into this
picture have come uranium ores which offer
great potentialities in the development of
peaceful uses of nuclear energy (Chapter 22).

Eventually man will learn to use solar energy more effectively and in this way will save
the mineral fuels. Already there has been
success with a solar battery. Coal offers great
potentialities in the making of plastics. As
man learns to use solar energy, he can afford
to use coal and petroleum in the manufacture
of these new substances rather than burning
it for fuel (Chapter 11).

The story of energy is an interesting story
for children. The relationship of coal to the
development of the steam engine, transportation, and industry always proves interesting
to children. The evolution of man's use of energy can be utilized in murals and other art
work. As man has developed more energy, he
has been able to avoid much of the back-
breaking toil of life (pp. 722–741).

One bright prospect in the look at the future
is that man is learning to make substitutes for
some of the things which he has made from
metal in the past. Sometimes he uses sawdust
and other waste materials for such purposes,
and frequently he finds he can improve on the

quality of objects that have been made from metal in the past. In this way he is learning how to conserve valuable ore deposits.

He is also learning to turn to ocean water for some valuable materials. He is learning how to dig his mines deeper and thus make available more deposits.

Some useful materials such as aluminum and silicon ores are plentiful near the surface, and man is learning how to extract the materials from different kinds of ore deposits. For more information concerning how man is learning to use the materials of Earth for his own welfare see Chapter 11.

An important item in the conservation of materials is the salvaging of old and worn-out articles. In many countries salvaging of such materials has not been recognized for its true value. It needs to be viewed as a means of conservation. Those people involved in the wise salvaging of materials are rendering their nation and the world a real service. Too frequently, places where such salvaging is done are unattractive, and while it is not easy to make salvaging depots attractive, every mean should be used by the operators to improv the appearance of their places of business.

Disposal of wastes has been a problem of man for a long time. It has been increase greatly in recent decades by the increase i population. As we have learned in connection with water, we can no longer afford to dispose of sewage, garbage, and other waste through our waterways.

Recently great progress has been made i the development of sewage-disposal plant Through these plants, many useful materia are being made from the waste material whic has in the past polluted rivers, lakes, an ocean beaches. Our children may live in a period when the disposal of raw sewage int waterways will be a very rare occurrence This would not only conserve useful materia in the sewage, but it would contribute to th conservation of water and improve the recre tional facilities and health of the people.

The Human Resources of a Community

Resources have value only as they contribute to the welfare of man. It is one thing to find resources and to build up industries; it is another to improve the living conditions of the people. It is important that boys and girls learn about ways in which resources can be used for the welfare of mankind.

Resources belong in two large categories. One would include those which give man forms of energy for doing his work, such as sunlight, water power, coal, and petroleum. The second category would be materials, both living and nonliving, which supply construction materials, such as forests, wild life, and minerals.

The indications are that man has sufficient resources to establish higher living standard the world over than are found anywhere to day. To solve this problem, communitie need to co-operate with communities, an nations with nations.

There seems to be an ample supply of er ergy for mankind for a long time to come. our petroleum supplies are exhausted at som time in the future, it is entirely likely that ou chemists will be able to produce adequate sur plies of suitable fuel for the heating of ou homes, the operation of our automobiles, an for our other needs for energy. In the futur we shall probably make greater use of wate power for the development of electrical powe than we do now. Some valuable metals ar rare, but scientists are producing substitutes that will amply care for our needs. There is disagreement as to whether a sufficient supply of food can be produced for all the people of the world. The fact that people have starved in the past and others have suffered from malnutrition indicates the unwillingness of people to co-operate on a world-wide basis and to apply the modern developments of agriculture and transportation of agricultural products. We need greater expansion of scientific agriculture in many parts of the world.

Unemployment has been one of the great fears which have beset mankind. But now almost every discovery and invention of science opens up many new vocations. We need to develop methods by which people can be educated to new vocations. Unemployment no longer need be a necessary characteristic of civilization.

We see from this the importance of remedying many of society's ills through the active utilization of science. No longer need conservation imply saving; rather, it should mean wise utilization. When recognized that wise utilization is international in scope, conservation might become a factor for peace. Plants and animals do not recognize national boundaries as natural barriers.

In this chapter we have emphasized the community. A child, however, in the process of his education should gain a vision of a larger, world community. Much that has been treated here can be discussed at later elementary and early secondary-school levels from the aspect of the world community. The welfare of other peoples may have fundamental importance to the peoples of the Western Hemisphere. It would be well for teachers to allow children to develop pride in the cooperation that exists between people of their country and the people of other countries on such problems.

However, the local community can be a "theater" of active study. The resources in the community in the form of scientific and welfare agencies should be more thoroughly utilized by the school. What are the community's resources for recreation? Has it utilized the natural beauty of the region to develop suitable places for recreation of many different kinds? Frequently highly industrialized communities have allowed the industries to make the community an ugly place. The natural beauty of a region is a resource to be utilized wisely. Make children aware of the natural beauty of the physical features of the community.

What is the attitude of the people in your community toward the resources of beauty in the region? Do they mark and carve public buildings? What is the attitude of the children in your classroom in this matter? How do they respond to responsibility for the care of the washrooms, classrooms, auditoriums, and corridors? Can their attitude be improved? What is their attitude toward the parks and playgrounds? How may education be used to produce better attitudes?

What are the health resources of the community? Is there sufficient co-operation between the school and the health authorities? What improvements need to be made? What are the health needs? What are the health habits of the children? What are the washing facilities in the washroom? Too frequently the child is taught health habits in the classroom, only to find that the school has ignored them in the provisions made for soap, water, and towels in the washroom. What sources of information do the parents of the children rely upon? A conference of teachers and parents with physicians might be useful. How can the health resources be improved?

Man is interested in securing for himself the best he can from the universe. In doing so, he must realize that he needs to work with the natural forces of Earth. He must also learn to co-operate with other people in his own community, state, or province, nation, and the world. The potentialities of science are frequently lost through lack of co-operation.

One often hears of the "balance of nature." The real balance of nature as it is found to exist is not the exact relationship that the sentimentalists would have us believe. Man, if he is to remain civilized, must disturb the original balance of nature, for only savagery can exist where man does not attempt to make changes. It is man's task to use the natural processes and resources in such a way that he secures what he needs for a very high standard of living without jeopardizing the welfare of future generations. Man cannot return to savagery, nor can he disregard natural resources; he now has science and democracy to help him plan for the years ahead. It is incumbent upon the schools, both elementary and secondary, to develop a generation that has the ability to meet its problems, both personal and social, with intelligence, co-operation, and resourcefulness.

Shaping the Future through Science

For thousands of years man struggled for the bare necessities of life; what he got he usually paid for with hard, back-breaking toil. He grew old while he was still young in years because of the severity of his daily work. Only those who were the favored of despotic rulers escaped this back-breaking toil.

As long as there was a lack of energy to do work for man, a few people attempted to exploit the many to get the work of the world done. But with the development of technology at the beginning of the Industrial Revolution, there arose an increased demand for skilled trades and for engineering. Another consequence was the development of the labor movement, with its demands for improvement in the status and the living conditions of industrial workers. Along with these trends came demands for free education for all.

Agriculture, like industry, has been profoundly affected. Farming has become a scientific vocation featuring tractors, selective breeding, soil improvement, scientific marketing, refrigerated transportation for products, and so on. Efficient modern farming has moved a long way from primitive agriculture.

Thus we find there is a direct relationship between advance in science and development in industry and agriculture. Without the progress in science and technology, it is questionable whether the majority of the people would have had an opportunity to attain living conditions and democratic standards much higher than those of peasants and serfs.

Slowly the majority of people of many races and nations are beginning to realize that want and disease are no longer necessary. Any careful observer today can easily detect a swelling tide of demand for better living conditions. Fundamentally, this demand has arisen because more people of the world are beginning to realize that science can be utilized to improve living conditions.

Here are the challenge and crucial issues for democracy, on which no teacher in a public school can remain neutral. It is her clearly defined task to reveal to children the possibilities for an improved era. The great test of democracy will be finally determined not only in terms of its armed strength but also in terms of its ability to make adjustment to the impact of science and to co-operate in the promotion of the welfare of all the people on Earth. It is from an unintelligent world adjustment to the potentialities of science that the future causes of war are most likely to arise.

A community of living things never remains in a strictly static condition. There is no exception to this, even when man is involved. Natural forces are always present in an environment. Man must work intelligently with these natural forces to bring about changes which are in his best interest.

The community is a laboratory for the study of natural and social forces. The teacher must be continuously a student of children who are living in this community. There must come a realization of how the local community and the larger, world community may, through the potentialities of science, develop improved living conditions for everyone.

The classroom teacher in the elementary school should consider herself an agent of both education and science in the community, and be willing to co-operate with reliable health, welfare, recreational, and scientific agencies—local and national—which serve her community. With it all, she must realize that her teaching should be active and dynamic, in keeping with active children and a dynamic universe. In her study of children, she must view them through a dynamic psychology (pp. 4–34). Therefore, her teaching with the material indicated in this chapter should not be so much academic as practical in character, for it should lead children to an understanding of how, through their own activities, they may participate intelligently and resourcefully in the world of the present and of the future. Children's outlooks upon the present and the future should be realistic, but should be based upon the hopeful realism of the tremendous potentialities of science and democracy.

EARTH
AND THE
UNIVERSE

CHAPTER 7

The Universe

Children Learn about Space. A fundamental purpose of instruction (pp. 92–93) in this area of children's environment is to develop a concept that the universe is very large. From birth children may be thought of as having experiences with space. The experiences involved in becoming aware of objects in the environment are beginning space concepts. When a child learns that his fingers are a part of himself, he is learning an early space concept. In this experience he is locating his fingers relative to himself and he is thus orienting himself in space. His space concepts are developed through much of his experience, exploring the rooms of a house, the yard, and areas immediately around his home. Instruction relating to immensity of space can begin with very young children.

Although children are being introduced to ideas of astronomical space almost from birth, it is important for teachers and parents to be aware of a child's natural pattern of growth in concepts of space.

In assisting children to gain some appreciation of space, it is well to bear in mind that the whole is made meaningful through experiences with the parts. Distances experienced on Earth assist in building up an idea that Earth is very large as compared with local areas. In the elementary school, it is learned that Earth is only a small body in the solar system; possibly in the later years of the elementary school, it is learned that the solar system is a minute portion of the Milky Way; and finally the idea is grasped that there are many galactic systems besides the Milky Way. The memorization of small content, therefore, is not the goal of the work. The goal is the orientation of the child to the universe in which he lives, which, in turn, surely is constructive in developing an intelligent adjustment of the individual to his daily life. We may be certain that all children do not come out at the same place or with the same meanings. Some even may be bored by the idea of vast space, some may be quite indifferent, but some will be challenged and will be desirous of pursuing the study. Each, however, should be given an opportunity to grow, according to his ability, in this conception of space and in an appreciation of the place of scientific thought in modern life. The individual who has some appreciation, imperfect as it may be, of the universe of galaxies is surely more likely to be a useful citizen than one who through ignorance holds to a geocentric and anthropomorphic universe. The former is one who is more likely to conceive of man as directing his future by his intelligence. The latter is one who sees man's future as limited by mystical forces.

History reveals that the ideas held and interpretations made of these ideas about the universe by people have had much to do with the kind of individuals they became and the development of their culture.

EXPERIENCE. *Distant views orient children to space.* Children may be taken to a place where there is a good open view; one which will allow distant observation. They may be taken to this same place a number of times during the year. As discussions relating to their experience develop, a globe may be used to indicate what a little bit of the total Earth they have looked at. This is an experience which can be repeated many times during the year with the same group, as well as with groups at various age levels.

Man has always been extremely curious about the objects in the sky. Often they have seemed to him to be portents of good and of evil. Even today we find many people who hire astrologers (those who tell fortunes by the stars) and other fakers to predict future events. A study of modern astronomy tells us that the stars have no influence over our lives. The teacher in the classroom can do more than anyone else to destroy astrology and other forms of superstition by making certain that children develop ideas in keeping with modern science.

Teachers have little difficulty in securing interest in the sun, moon, and stars. The questions vary from the type asked by nursery and kindergarten children, "Where does the sun go when it goes down?" to the questions of older children concerning the distant stars and galaxies. Many of these questions have been asked by men as far back as history can take us.

Authentic information plays a unique part in this development. This is indicated by the fact that children are able to secure comparatively few correct ideas concerning the universe by their own observation or by empirical reasoning.

Through the medium of art the teacher may learn something about the children's concepts of the world about them. Children look about. They see what seems to be a big Earth. The sun looks smaller, very much smaller, than houses, trees, and other objects on Earth. From their own observation they would conclude, as all men did until a few centuries ago, that the sun and stars move about Earth. They may even think that the sky is a hard-shelled dome moving around Earth, and, as one little girl stated, that the stars are holes in the sky. These are natural conclusions from observations. As they express these and similar ideas through art work and discussion, care should be taken that no child feels that he has been criticized if his ideas are wrong. The child, through his art, has given expression to the way these phenomena appear to him. It should be a learning situation for all.

But objects in the sky are not what they seem to be to the unlearned. Only the moon moves around Earth. Earth moves around the sun. The stars are suns, some of them much larger than our own sun. It is imperative, therefore, that the teacher place in the children's hands reliable information concerning the universe. This field, like others in science, is one in which we must rely upon the authorities in the field. We must turn to the astronomers for the most reasonable ideas of the universe.

Astrology Is Not a Science. There are a great many instances in history of the use of the stars to predict some disaster, such as the end of the world, the destruction of a nation, or a deluge. This use of the sky to foretell disaster for the world has interfered with the progress of mankind, since it has tended to make a weakling of man and to discourage him from planning his future.

In 1524, for instance, the civilized people of Earth expected a flood similar to Noah's flood because the planets Saturn, Jupiter, and Mars were in conjunction in the Sign of Fishes. Many built arks similar to Noah's and refused to go about their usual work. Even in recent years there have been predictions of an early end to the world in addition to other catastrophes.

This is only one of many instances that can be found in history which indicate how gullible man has been in believing astrologers, soothsayers, crystal-gazers, mind-readers, fortune-tellers, and voodoos. Many people still continue to believe in astrology, in spite of the advances of modern astronomy.

EXPERIENCE. *Should we place confidence in horoscopes and astrology?* Older children could examine astrological materials in newspapers and magazines. An examination will show that there is much ambiguity in the statements. They can be compared with the old joke about flipping coins, "Heads I win, tails you lose!" Have children consider whether or not people are wise to base their lives on such materials. Teachers would use this type of experience only if there were a need for it.

It will be recognized in the content that follows that we are somewhat handicapped in our every-day life by a vocabulary which has come down to us from the past. We say the sun rises and sets, but it does not; Earth rotates on its axis. We speak of shooting stars, but we find that they are not stars—in fact, that they are not at all like stars. These shooting stars are meteors. But actually as the meteors pass through the air they *look like* "shooting stars."

Earth Is an Astronomical Body. Many people do not recognize that Earth, too, is an object in the universe. Naturally we are more interested in Earth than in any other body in the universe.[1] Earth has many characteristics which are like those of other celestial bodies. Children are always interested in comparing other objects in the solar system and in other parts of the universe with our Earth. In fact, it has been the author's experience that in free discussion with children the topic tends in this direction frequently.

Gravity—The Gravitation of Earth. One of the most popular topics with children is gravity. It is interesting to note that children, and all of us, live our entire lives in the field of Earth's gravitational force. All through the day the child is experiencing gravity, although he may not identify it as such. In fact, gravity is such a prevailing force that it could be considered in the explanation of almost everything that happens, in some way or another. Gravity is essential to the full explanation of weather, movements of animals, operation of machines, and a host of other phenomena.

Scientists have not explained satisfactorily what gravity is. Children like to speculate concerning the nature of gravity and they often compare magnetism with gravity. At other times they may confuse gravitation with shocks from static electricity.[2]

[1] For a more complete description of Earth, see Chapters 8, 9, and 10.

[2] See Chapter 23 for a fuller treatment.

The reader may be confused by the fact that there are two terms used in this connection: one is gravitation and the other is gravity. *Gravitation* refers to the force that draws any two bodies together. This force applies throughout the universe. *Gravity* is a more specific term, used to express the gravitation or pull of Earth. It is often used loosely to mean "gravitation."

Children may use the word *pull* in relation to the gravity concept. But it might be appropriate to move on to the word *attract* when they are ready for it.

Very frequently children become involved with gravity in their games. For example, examine the activity in which a three-year-old child, Jennie, engaged (p. 5). This child was securing experiential learnings with gravity through play. The parent and the teacher should recognize that this is true learning and that it is also basic to further learning about gravity. One could trace early experiences with gravity back to the cradle. One could well recall that learning to walk is learning to operate in Earth's gravitational field. There must be a great deal of learning about gravity when a child learns that an object falls to the bottom of the pan of water and that water poured out of the cup falls down and not up; and so with a score of other early experiences.

EXPERIENCE. *What is up and what is down?* Children sometimes ask, "What holds up Earth?" and frequently invent curious tales as answers to this question. Such explanations are interesting. Ask children to draw the universe as they think it is. Sometimes they think there are a bottom and a ceiling to the universe. It is natural that they should think so, since they live on Earth, where there is always a bottom, the ground. They can scarcely refrain from thinking of a bottom out in the universe. The teacher must remember that the ancients did the very same thing when they believed that Earth rested on something, such

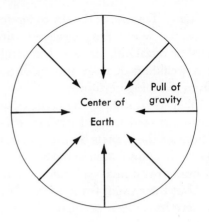

Earth's gravitational attraction is toward the center of Earth.

as the shoulders of Atlas or the back of a turtle.

Earth is a ball moving in space. Children often ask and are interested in why Earth keeps moving. It keeps on moving because there is nothing to stop it. There is no bottom or top to the universe. We shall see later that the sun and its family are a part of a great universe of stars.

Down, for us, is always toward the center of Earth, and up is away from the center of Earth. Draw an Earth on the blackboard. Show what is up and what is down for a boy or girl in North America, Asia, Australia, and South America. Notice that in each case down is toward the center. You might have the boys and girls make figures to represent the children of the different continents. Place these figures of boys and girls on the globe on the different continents. These figures can be stuck on the globe with modeling clay. Note that the figures all point to the center. Let them see the directions in which balls would go up if they were thrown by the children on the different continents. The ball going up in North America would travel in the same direction as the ball coming down in Australia.

Children who are old enough to have studied many maps know that the north part of a map is usually near the top and the south part near the bottom. This often leads them to think of anything south as down and anything north as up. It may help them to know that the north part of a map is placed at the top of the paper because of an arbitrary custom, not because the north is any higher than the south; on the contrary, the opposite condition is frequently the case.

Children seem to think that something must be holding Earth up; but, as a result of this study, they will come to realize that Earth is a ball in motion. As one child expressed the latter thought, "There is no floor or ceiling to the solar system," or, we might add, to the universe.

EXPERIENCE. *Encourage free discussion on the topic, "What is gravity?"* It is the author's experience that children like to discuss the nature of gravity. It is well to let them use their imaginations in developing possible explanations. Keep in mind that scientists haven't explained gravity satisfactorily as yet.

You might ask children to describe an imagined day in which gravity didn't work. This might be co-ordinated with both written and oral expression by asking them to write about what might happen on such a day and later discuss it orally. This same activity might also be co-ordinated with the art work. Scenes may be depicted in which gravity doesn't work. These can be contrasted with the same scene in which gravity does operate.

It seems altogether appropriate that the gravitation of Earth and other objects in the universe might come up for brief consideration many times every year. The purpose of such free discussion would be to have children relate their concept of gravity and to clarify some of their concepts through discussion. This kind of free discussion should not be hurried. Give time for speculation on the part of the children. It would be well to give consideration to their tempo in this matter. Let them return to the subject at later times if they wish.

A teacher can find more information about gravity and its effects on plants and animals in Chapter 14.

The Sun

The sun is the most conspicuous object in the sky. It is conspicuous by its presence in the daytime and by its absence at night. Small children are apt to think of the sun as a rather accommodating body which shines for us in the day and does nothing in particular at night. Teachers, in their teaching throughout the elementary school, beginning with the kindergarten, should be guided by the larger interpreting conception of the vastness of space, regardless of their own ideas of educational method. The children should come to realize early that the sun is not an accommodating body which exists for our convenience and which is turned on in the daytime and off at night. It shines all the time, giving out its light in all directions. It shines on other parts of Earth when it is not shining on us. It shines when it is cloudy, although we usually speak of it as not shining on a cloudy day. It is shining far out beyond the clouds; the clouds merely cast their shadows on the ground. At night we are essentially in the shadow of Earth.

EXPERIENCE. *Young children observe the sky.* Children may be encouraged to watch the sky. They can note changes in the sky even during short intervals. Make them aware that the statement "The sun is not shining when it is cloudy" is not true. Supporting evidence to refute this statement may be gained from observation of the sky.

Some children may have had the experience of having flown in an airplane. They may be able to describe going up in the airplane and finding the sun shining above the clouds.

EXPERIENCE. *How shadows are made.* Show the children how shadows are made. Place various objects between the sunlight or an electric light and the children to show how shadows are made. Let the children form shadows. Show them that shadows are made by clouds. On foggy days let them examine the fog, which is a cloud near Earth. The fog casts a shadow on Earth and makes it darker.

EXPERIENCE. *Shadows change during the day and during the seasons.* A shadow stick may be placed in the schoolroom or on the school grounds. Note how the shadow moves during the day. Note the position of the sun for each position of the shadow. Note the size of the shadow. When is it longest? When is it shortest? Watch the shadows of trees, fence posts, and other objects. Many people use the shadows instead of watches to tell the time of day.

This and other experiences with shadows can be used with young children to make them

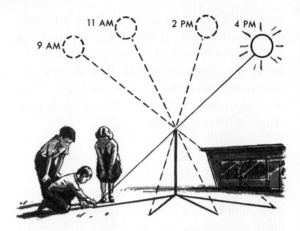

conscious of directions. Let them watch for the North Star at night. A knowledge of directions may be useful later in observations of weather.

Note the change of shadows during the different seasons and at definite times each day.

Are there shadows at night? Are there shadows due to moonlight?

The Sun Is an Enormous Body. The concept of the sun in relation to its effect upon the life of Earth is one to be developed through several years, perhaps even a lifetime, rather than one to be developed on just one age level. In the earlier years it may be merely a matter of the child's realizing that the sun is a larger body than Earth. Later, as the child matures, the concept will come to have more meaning as more information is gained about the sun.

The diameter of the sun is about 109 times the diameter of Earth, or approximately 865,-000 miles. Our sun is, therefore, 109 times as big in all directions as Earth. Over a million balls the size of Earth could be packed inside the sun.

If a railroad tunnel could be built through the sun, a train going 60 miles an hour would require 600 days, or over a year and a half, to pass through this tunnel.

The sun is so large that if it were a hollow ball and we could put Earth inside it, we should find plenty of room for the moon to re-

volve about Earth inside the sun, with almost enough space left over to allow a second moon to revolve about Earth twice as far from Earth as our moon is.

The diameter of Earth is about four times that of the moon. Therefore the diameter of the sun is about 400 times that of the moon. Why, then, does the moon appear to be about the same size as the sun? It will be made evident in the later discussion that the sun is much farther away from Earth than the moon. The farther away an object is, the smaller it appears.

In spite of its great size as compared with Earth, the weight of the sun is estimated to be only about 330,000 times the weight of Earth. The reason for this is that the material of which the sun is composed is not so crowded together as the material which makes up Earth. We say it has a lower *density*.

From this we see that Earth is very small as compared with the sun. What a tremendous globe the sun is!

How Far Away Is the Sun? The distance from Earth to the sun is about 93 million miles. This is a tremendous distance. An automobile going 60 miles an hour would travel a distance equal to this in 177 years.

EXPERIENCE. *Using speed to build an appreciation for distance.* Older children might be encouraged to estimate how long it would take to travel the 93 million miles by various methods of transportation. The speeds will, of course, vary. For example, a passenger plane may have a speed of 300 miles an hour, but some planes equipped with jet engines have speeds in excess of 700 miles per hour. Once the means of transportation is specified, the older children may do the long division themselves.

It requires eight minutes for light to travel the distance of 93 million miles from the sun to Earth, although a ray of light travels in a second a distance about equal to seven times the distance around Earth at the equator. (The velocity of light is approximately 186,000 miles per second.)

On account of the eccentricity of Earth's orbit (deviation from a perfect circle), the sun is 3 million miles closer to Earth on January 1 than on July 1.

Although Earth travels in an elliptical orbit, its orbit differs so little from a circle that we cannot tell it from a circle in a small diagram or in classroom demonstrations. The sun is not exactly at the center of the orbit, but in a small diagram it is off center by such a short distance that we cannot detect it. Children may ask why Earth is nearer to the sun in the cold season of the north middle latitudes (North Temperate Zone). Their attention should be called to the fact that not all of Earth is having winter at the same time. See the explanation of the cause of the change of seasons on page 202.

EXPERIENCE. *Why the sun and moon seem to follow us as we travel on Earth.* We often watch the moon as we walk or as we ride in an automobile. We leave trees and houses behind us, but the moon seems to remain in about the same place all the way. Children sometimes think that the moon is going along with them. The reason for this is that the moon is so far away. As we ride in a railroad train, we pass wayside objects near the track so quickly that we can scarcely see them, but we pass the farm-

house or clump of trees in the distance more slowly. Children can go out on the playground and have a similar experience. They should select a distant and also a nearby object; have them point a finger in the direction of these objects and walk parallel to them. The direction will change more rapidly for the closer object than the one farther away. The moon is so distant that it seems not to change direction at all as a result of our movement on Earth. We cannot pass the moon by walking or riding about on Earth.

The distance between Earth and the moon is equal approximately to ten times the distance around Earth; the distance between Earth and the sun is over 400 times the distance between Earth and the moon.

Approximately twelve thousand globes the size of Earth, placed side by side, could easily fit between us and the sun.

EXPERIENCE. *To show why Earth receives so little of the sun's total heat.* Place at one end of a large blackboard a small arc of a great circle to represent the sun. Place at the opposite end a small circle not over an inch in diameter to represent Earth. From the arc that represents the sun trace some rays out across the blackboard in different directions; make clear that the sun is not a circle but a huge ball giving out heat in all directions. Only a minute part of the total heat reaches Earth; the rest goes out into space in all directions.

The emphasis at this point need not be on the relative sizes of Earth and sun, but on demonstrating that a small body, such as Earth, at a great distance from another body which gives off heat, actually receives but a minute part of the total heat.

The idea might be further demonstrated by placing a small ball in one corner of the room and a light, such as an electric light, in the opposite corner. Show how the light gives off light and heat in all directions but that only a small part of the light and heat is received by the ball.

EXPERIENCE. *To show the cause of day and night.* To demonstrate the cause of day and night, darken the room as much as possible. Use a flash-light, an electric light, or even a candle to represent the sun. Place a globe of Earth so that one half of it will be lighted clearly by the light. Ask the children to explain the cause of day and night. As far as you can, draw the explanation from them. If wrong or inaccurate ideas are given, attempt to have the children see wherein they are wrong or inaccurate. Secure as much response from them as possible. Be patient in encouraging all possible suggestions, making clear which ideas are wrong and which are right. Some of the children may attempt to carry the sun (the light) around the globe. If you cannot get the right explanation from them, ask them to rotate the globe on its axis. In dealing with young children who are not familiar with the globe, let them stick a pin in it at the place where they live. A piece of paper or cloth may be fastened to the pin to make a sort of flag so that the pin can be easily seen. If the globe is a metal one, use a small quantity of modeling clay or some sticky substance with which to fasten a marker to the globe.

The children may demonstrate how rotating Earth causes day and night. How long does it take Earth to rotate once on its axis?

In this work it is well to keep just one learning element before the children, that of the cause of day and night. When good questions arise which are not pertinent to the study of the cause of day and night, write them down for future study. This can be done without discouraging individual interests.

Older children may be able to determine that looking down on the north pole Earth rotates in a counterclockwise manner, that is, opposite to the way in which the hands of a clock move. Two methods help to demonstrate this, both based on experience. First, the sun rises in the east and sets in the west. This provides a good opportunity to teach the directions on a globe if the children are not

already familiar with them. Show them, on the globe, places east and places west of where they live. How will they rotate the globe so that the sun rises in the east and sets in the west with reference to the pin which marks the place where they live? The other method is based on their experience with television programs. They know that there is still day on the west coast of North America after the sun has set on the east coast. Children in Hawaii and the Philippines can know that the sun may have set on the west coast of North America while it is still day with them. If they follow both these Experiences with globe study, they will find that Earth rotates on its axis in a counterclockwise manner when they look down upon the north pole and in a clockwise direction when they look down on the south pole.

The children may rotate the globe with reference to the light representing the sun so that the time of day at the place marked by the pin is approximately the same as the actual time of day. They may do the same for sunrise and sunset, for noon, midnight, the time of going to school, of going home, and of going to bed.

An understanding of day and night is fundamental to much of the study of astronomical bodies which follows. On it depends an understanding of how the sun rises and sets and of how the moon and stars rise and set. It helps in the understanding of tides.

One might even place medium-sized flash-lights in different parts of the room at some distance from the globe to represent stars, and a medium-sized electric light near the globe to represent the sun. Why cannot the stars be seen in the daytime? It is because the sun, being so much nearer than the stars and therefore seeming so much brighter, blinds us to their light. Show the children that an electric light seems bright at night, but that on a bright day in the sunlight, out of doors, it seems very feeble.

This problem of the stars in relation to the sun may be introduced through an interest that the children manifest or through one initiated by the teacher with such a question as "Where shall we place candles or small flashlights to represent the stars?"

This demonstration may be used to show how stars rise and set. Rotating the globe causes the lights about the room to seem to rise and set at the place on the globe marked by the pin.

In all this work it is important to attempt to get the children to visualize the real Earth and the real sun instead of their thinking too much of the small demonstration material in the room. Have them find out all they can that is wrong with the apparatus. It is possible to find many things that are wrong. The light representing the sun is much too small for the globe representing Earth. It would be impossible to get into the room a light large enough to represent the sun faithfully in relation to the globe that represents Earth. The sun is a million times larger than Earth. The globe and the light are too close together, considering the size of the globe. Earth's diameter is 8000 miles, while the distance from Earth to the sun is 93,000,000 miles, which means that if our globe is a foot in diameter, we should be forced to place the light 11,000 feet, or over two miles, away to have the two at the correct relative distance from each other. Perhaps the children know some house about two miles from the school. This will give them some comprehension of the distance from Earth to the sun and of how great that is as compared with distances on Earth.

Earth Revolves about the Sun. Earth not only rotates on its axis but also revolves about the sun. With the younger children it is not necessary to develop the cause of the change of seasons at this point. Let the children revolve a globe about a light. They might rotate the globe as they revolve it. Introduce the difference between rotation and revolution. Rotation is the same as turning. It takes Earth a year to revolve about the sun.

If we look down at the north pole of Earth,

Although the Earth-child revolves about the sun-child, he does not pass over any place on the floor more than once. Earth does not return to any point where it has been before.

Earth appears to revolve about the sun in a counterclockwise movement. The children should realize that it takes Earth a year to make a revolution. It might be well to have them think of what has taken place in a year of their own lives.

The children are likely to think from this demonstration that the sun is stationary. Encourage the children to question their demonstrations. They should endeavor to compare the demonstrations with the actual phenomena. It is difficult to have any demonstration of the universe in a schoolroom or on the school ground completely accurate. This need not discourage one in teaching; rather, it can be used at many levels of the elementary school to indicate the tremendous size of the universe. This can be shown in developing the idea that the sun moves while Earth is revolving. The children may like to act this out. One child should represent the sun, another Earth. Ask the sun-child to walk slowly across the room, allowing time for the Earth-child to move around him. The Earth-child should make a complete revolution about the sun-child. If someone were to mark the path of the Earth-child on the floor with chalk, we should have not a circle but a figure composed of waves. Many figures in books are drawn as if the sun were stationary; but actually it moves at a tremendous speed, taking Earth and the other planets with it.

Another child might represent the moon and revolve about the Earth-child at the same time that the latter revolves about the sun-child.

EXPERIENCE. *Why we do not feel Earth moving.* Sometimes children ask why it is that we cannot tell that Earth is moving, since we are really passengers on it, in the same way that we can tell we are moving when we are riding on a railroad train or in an automobile. A number of things suggest themselves to help the child in thinking through this situation.

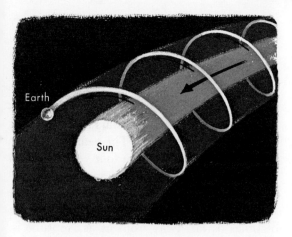

and night. Therefore we cannot notice any movement by looking about us on Earth. Moreover, Earth moves very smoothly. It has no sharp corners to turn. It does not slow down for red lights. It does not run on rails with little spaces between them, as a train does. It does not run over a bumpy highway or a highway with hills and hollows. It does not have an engine inside to vibrate it, as an automobile has. It does not start and stop.

It has been estimated that the sun is moving in the general direction of the bright star Vega at approximately 13 miles per second. This speed is so great that it cannot be compared to the speed of even the fastest transportation on Earth. However, the children in late intermediate grades should gain an impression that the sun moves in space at a speed that far transcends the speed of the fastest automobile or airplane.

In riding about in automobiles we pass nearby objects, such as trees, telephone poles, and houses. The objects out in space are so far away that Earth does not pass them as it moves. However, we see them rise and set because of rotation. Then, too, all the objects on Earth rotate with us. We can depend on finding the school in the same old place each morning. It rotates with our home and everything else that is on Earth during the day

Relative Motion. Children are likely to have noticed the deceptive effects of relative motion in automobiles. Suppose two cars are waiting

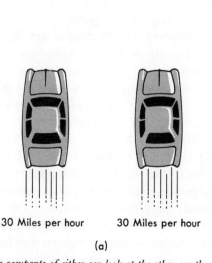

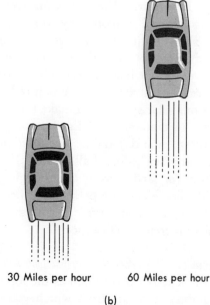

30 Miles per hour   30 Miles per hour

(a)

(a) *If the occupants of either car look at the other car they will seem to be standing still.*

30 Miles per hour   60 Miles per hour

(b)

(b) *To the occupants of either car, one car will be moving much faster than the other.*

side by side at a stop light, and both cars start to roll backward at the same speed. If we are riders and look at the ground, we know we are rolling backward, but if we look from our car to the other, we may think we are standing still. We are moving in relation to the ground, but in relation to the other car we are not moving. If something is said to be in motion, it is important to ask the question "relative to what?"

If the cars are headed east, they are carried swiftly eastward by the rotation of Earth, even though they may roll westward in relation to Earth. If they start forward at 10 miles an hour, their speed is added to that of the rotating Earth, so that they are moving faster than Earth itself.

In relation to the sun, Earth moves in an ellipse. But in relation to Vega or the other "fixed" stars Earth moves in a spiral path that carries it forward as well as around the sun. Of course, a man standing on Earth also rotates about the axis of Earth, so that in relation to the stars he traces an even more complicated spiral.

The Sun Is a Star. The sun is an average star. It is average in more ways than one—in color, size, brightness, and age. Children ask why it does not look like the other stars. The answer is that it is so very much closer. If we were to construct a very much reduced model of our solar system and make the sun a ball 2 feet in diameter and Earth a pea 213 feet away, we should find that we should have to place another 2-foot ball nearly 10,000 miles away (or farther away than the length of Earth's diameter) to represent the nearest star outside our solar system. Things may look quite different at a distance.

EXPERIENCE. *Why does the sun not look like the other stars?* Go to a point, such as the top of a high building or a hill, from which you can look out over a wide area. How do different objects look? Do you see houses, cars, people, fences? If you never saw them any closer, do you think you could describe them very clearly? The sun is much closer than the stars. This explains why the sun does not look like the stars.

The sun is a star, and stars are suns. This means, of course, that the stars are very great distances away from us. The nearest one is so far away that it takes light four years to reach us from it. If this star were darkened tomorrow, we probably should not know it for four years. The nearest star is tens of thousands of times as far away from us as Neptune is. Still other stars are so far away from us that it takes their light millions of years to reach us.

The Energy of the Sun.   (Pp. 375, 735–738). People often refer to the sun as a ball of "burning" gases. Photographs of the sun show flamelike projections, and we instinctively think of anything that is very hot and shoots out tongues of flame as being "on fire." An ordinary fire, however (pp. 400–405) is caused by oxygen combining with other substances. The process is called *combustion*. When the material in a stick of carbon unites rapidly with oxygen, it forms carbon dioxide gas and gives off heat. We say that the carbon *burns*. When hydrogen burns, it forms an oxide of hydrogen that we call water.

Both carbon and hydrogen are known to exist in the sun and the stars, but the stars are not burning in the ordinary sense. They would soon be used up, and could not possibly produce such vast quantities of energy over periods of billions of years.

What, then, is the source of the sun's energy? Physicists have worked out several possible answers. The most common source is believed to be what is known as the carbon cycle. Although the surface of the sun is a relatively cool 6000°C. (over 10,000°F.), temperatures in the interior would be expected to increase to many millions of degrees. The temperature at the center of the sun is believed to be about 20 million degrees centigrade (over 35 million on the Fahrenheit scale). Enormous pressures would exist there, reaching several million tons to the square inch.

Under such conditions chemical compounds such as those formed by ordinary combustion cannot form. All molecules are separated into their atoms (p. 375). Atoms are stripped of their electrons, so that their nuclei are exposed, and frequently collide at high speeds. The same thing happens on a smaller scale in our cyclotrons and other man-made particle accelerators. Under such conditions one element can be changed into another. In particular, nuclei of hydrogen can unite to form helium in a series of steps. In the first step, a proton (hydrogen nucleus) collides with a nucleus of carbon, forming nitrogen 13, and releasing a unit of energy in the form of a gamma ray. In another step the nitrogen 13 decays, giving off an electron. At the end of the sixth step in this chain a nucleus of helium is formed, and the original carbon nucleus reappears, when it may be involved in a new cycle.

Quantities of energy have been released, just as in a hydrogen bomb, and only hydrogen has been used. Of this element there are vast quantities, not only in the sun and the stars but floating in space in the form of clouds between the stars. It is the most common of the elements, and is in fact the basic building block of the universe. The transformation of hydrogen to helium in the *carbon cycle* is regarded as the principle source from which the sun and most of the stars draw their energy.

A second likely source of energy is the *proton-proton reaction*. In this process hydrogen nuclei combine directly to form helium, at somewhat lower temperatures than those necessary for the carbon cycle. This process also occurs in the sun, in all probability, in cooler layers that are farther from the center, and may be the chief source of energy of some of the stars that are cooler than the sun.

The sun, the stars, and the H bomb alike depend for their energy on reactions of this type. They are called *thermonuclear* reactions, because they involve reactions between nuclei at very high thermal conditions. Such reactions tend to be self-sustaining, but high temperatures are needed to start them.

Observing the Sun. Although the sun is a star of only average size, it radiates vast amounts of energy into space every second. We have learned only a little bit, here and there, of how this occurs, partly from direct observation, partly from experiments and calculations. Much yet remains shrouded in mystery.

When we look at the sun we see the surface of a glowing ball, the *photosphere,* from which most of the sun's light comes. It is a relatively thin, opaque layer of gas, which completely conceals the interior of the sun. This is surrounded by a reddish atmosphere several thousand miles thick, the *chromosphere.* Outside this layer lies the *corona,* which formerly could be seen only at times of total eclipse, when the moon shut off the blinding glare of

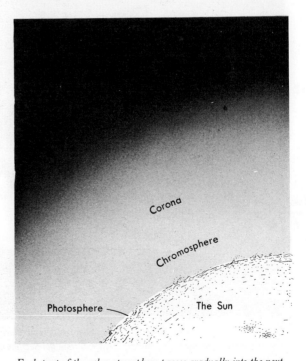

Each part of the solar atmosphere passes gradually into the next.

the sun's light. Today it can be studied at any time by means of a specially designed "eclipsing telescope," the coronagraph. The corona surrounds the sun with a pearly glow that extends outward for a million miles into space. It is shot through with myriads of rays pointing outward from the sun.

Instruments show that the temperature of the photosphere is about 6000°C. (10,000°F). The temperature of the corona appears to be at least half a million degrees centigrade, but the reason for this is uncertan.

Visible markings include bright flares, or prominences, and dark spots that move across the face of the sun. The same markings often reappear at regular intervals, indicating that the sun rotates in a period of about 27 days at the equator. The sun is not a solid ball, however, and different parts rotate at different speeds. Markings nearer the poles take longer to reappear, up to 35 days.

Prominences. Solar prominences or flares take a variety of forms. Sometimes shadowy filaments drift across the sun, appearing a little darker than the sun. When they reach the edge of the sun they are seen to be towering masses of red gases, only slightly less bright than the chromosphere. They are often like sheets of glowing gas, sometimes arching around in loops to meet the sun again. Some remain stationary for long periods; others show gases moving upward at great speeds, or descending with equal speed, or fluctuating, or occasionally exploding off into space. One recorded prominence extended more than a million miles outward. Some are like tornadoes, twisting upward in a narrow column that may bend its top back toward the sun. Another, less active type is the "haystack," which remains perched in a moundlike form for long periods of time.

Motion pictures are used to photograph the

This giant flare occurred during intense disturbances on the sun which bombarded Earth with more than the normal amount of cosmic rays. The photograph was made on February 27, 1956 from the Sacramento Peak Observatory, New Mexico. (Wide World Photos.)

changing shapes of prominences. Photographs also show uncounted multitudes of smaller projections, or spicules, along the edge of the sun. These appear to be caused by smaller jets of escaping gases.

EXPERIENCE. *To compare the rotation of Earth and the rotation of the sun.* What a strange world it would be if different parts of Earth's surface rotated at different rates! What strange things might happen! Africa might move over and take the place of South America, while South America moved to another place. It is good that Earth has solid surfaces for us to live on.

We have already learned of the tremendous temperatures of the sun. We know that heat turns solids into liquids and liquids into gases. It is not surprising, therefore, to find that the sun is gaseous.

Gases are not "solid," hence different parts of the sun, or any gaseous body, may rotate at different speeds. Even solids may slip a little, and it is thought by many scientists that the inner parts of Earth may rotate at speeds different from the surface, like an armature inside a generator (p. 771), thus producing electrical and magnetic effects.

EXPERIENCE. *To compare the sun and Earth.* Children should gain an impression of the variety of astronomical bodies. We have now described only one, the sun. How does it differ from Earth? What are the other kinds of bodies in the universe like?

The Sun Is Very Old. The sun is very old. The fossils in the rocks indicate that hundreds of millions of years ago plants used the energy of the sun (Chapter 10). Long before the time when life began to appear on Earth, Earth itself must have been formed from the sun, or its birth must have been in part due to the sun. The sun and the solar system may have existed for about five billion years. Astronomers tell us, however, that the entire period of existence of a star such as the sun, from birth to death, is but a minute part of the period of existence of the universe. We should expect the universe to be much older than our sun.

Sunspots. The Chinese observed large dark spots on the sun as long ago as A.D. 300. Early observers thought they might be objects between Earth and the sun. Galileo trained his new telescope on them and found that they were part of the sun. We have since learned something of their nature, but there is still much that we do not understand about them.

Sunspots appear dark in color against the intense brightness of the sun. However, they are usually brighter than strong artificial lights.

Sunspots appear in increasing number and size over a period of years, then diminish again, in a fairly regular cycle of about 11 years. The length of time from a period of largest number—a *sunspot maximum*—to a period of smallest number—a *sunspot minimum*—is known as a *sunspot period*. They often appear in pairs, or paired groups, at about 30° north or south of the sun's equator, one group preceding the other as the rotation of the sun carries them across its face. They move somewhat the way our storms move across the surface of Earth. A pair will often show magnetic polarity, the leading spot being a north pole and the following one a south, as in any magnet (p. 785). A child who plays with a small magnet on his desk is playing with the same force that exists in the sunspots. The sunspots are much, much larger and more powerful than the small magnet. Succeeding pairs of spots will show the same arrangement, and will keep drawing closer to the equator as the cycle approaches sunspot minimum. Presently a new series will start, away from the equator, as before, and with reversed polarity, the leading spot in each pair being a south pole throughout the series.

The reasons behind this behavior are quite unknown, but it is evident that many complex operations occur in the interior of the sun. Large masses of free electrons (p. 448) moving in great circular currents would generate intense magnetic fields, and vice versa. These electric and magnetic fields would have strong effects on the ionized gases, both in the interior and in the atmosphere of the sun. This would account for some of the movements and strange distortions of the gaseous prominences, as matter, electricity, magnetism, and gravitation react with each other.

Sunspots Affect Earth. The influence of the sun is felt on Earth in many ways. When the sunspot cycle advances toward a maximum, shortwave radio reception tends in general to improve, but violent magnetic disturbances might occur that may completely disrupt radio communications, and even blow the circuit fuses of electric power lines. Brilliant displays of the aurora are seen. The needles of magnetic compasses swing wildly.

Such a "magnetic storm" occurred on July 26, 1946. At 11:15 A.M., E.S.T., astronomers saw a large solar flare erupt over an active sunspot. A complete radio blackout occurred at the same moment, probably indicating that the visible light from the flare was accompanied by strong ultraviolet radiations, which disturbed the ionosphere.

The ordinary citizen who is not using electrical instruments may not be aware of these "magnetic storms." What we usually think of as fine weather may continue unchanged during the "storm."

It requires about 8 minutes for radiation from the sun to reach Earth. This includes not only visible light but also shorter waves of ultraviolet and X rays, and longer waves of infrared. It may also include radio waves, bringing us audible evidence of an active sunspot.

In addition to radiation, the sun is believed to pour out streams of *corpuscles* (a word commonly used to mean "small particles"), chiefly protons and electrons from dissociated atoms of hydrogen. These are particles of matter, and cannot travel as fast as radiation. When they are discharged from a very powerful sunspot, they are observed to require about a day to reach Earth. Still other streams of corpuscles are thought to be released by the *spicules*—fine, irregular streaks shooting out from the chromosphere—and to be concentrated by the large magnetic field that surrounds the sun. These do not travel as fast as the more violent eruptions. They require about 3 days to reach Earth, and seem to follow a 27-day cycle that corresponds to the rotation of the sun.

When charged corpuscles reach Earth, they strike Earth's magnetic field and are deflected toward the poles. Their impact excites atoms in the atmosphere, producing the luminescent

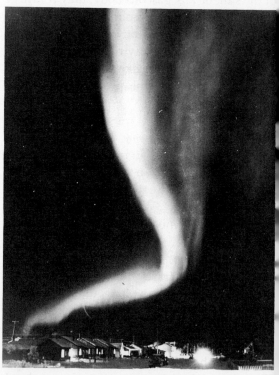

Aurora over Yellowknife. (Gerhard Reimann, Yellowknife, N.W.T.)

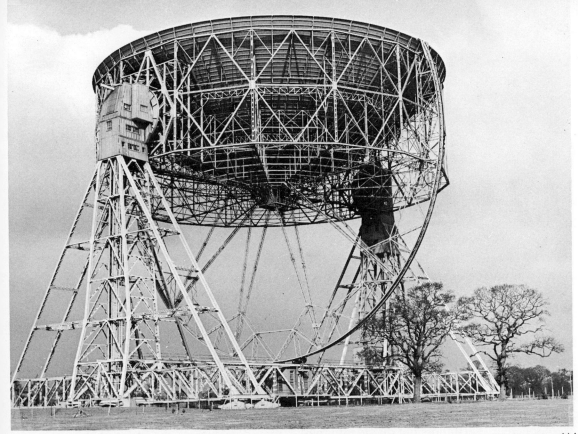

The 250-foot-diameter radio telescope at Jodrell Bank, Cheshire, England. Stars and other bodies in space give off radio waves which can be received with this dish-shaped antenna. It has also been used in tracking deep space probes and satellites. (Three Lions, N.Y.C.)

glow that we see as the *aurora*, often with very beautiful effects. Ribbons of white or colored light ripple outward from the poles in different patterns. Auroral displays appear to be associated with unusual activity on the sun.

Airglow, sometimes called the permanent aurora, is a glow in the sky that is too faint for the eye to notice, but is always present. It is bright enough to interfere with the attempts of astronomers to photograph some of the faintest stars. It is thought that energy from the sun produces the airglow in a manner similar to the way it produces the aurora.

Radio Astronomy. There are really only two "windows" by means of which we can study the universe. Astronomers since Galileo have used one of them, the "seeing window," to study the stars with optical telescopes. More recently we have been using the other, receiv-

ing radio waves by means of radio telescopes. With such equipment radio astronomers can use the "listening window" to study the universe (Chapter 24).

Balloon and Rocket Astronomy. The difficulty of obtaining information from outside Earth except through the "light window" and the "radio window" has led astronomers to take an active interest in space exploration. By means of balloons and rockets they are able to hoist telescopes and other instruments to high altitudes, where better observations can be made. They find, for example, that Earth is bathed in very strong ultraviolet light, particularly in the shorter wavelengths that are stopped by the atmosphere. Useful records of X rays from sunspots are also made in this way. Satellites such as Pioneer V, now orbiting the sun, can report conditions many

millions of miles from Earth, if the instruments continue to operate.

Why Do the Seasons Change? Why do we have different seasons during the year? Sometimes children say it is because the sun is nearer Earth at certain times than at others. But this, of course, is not true. While Earth is having summer in the Northern Hemisphere, it is having winter in the Southern Hemisphere.[3] Earth does not divide into two halves, with the summer half nearer the sun than the winter half. Actually Earth is about 3,000,000 miles nearer the sun in January than it is at other times of the year, but this is such a small distance as compared with the total distance from Earth to the sun that it makes little difference. Besides, as has been said, the sun is nearest during the wintertime of the Northern Hemisphere.

Almost everyone has noticed that the globes of Earth found in almost every schoolroom are tipped, or inclined. That is, the north and south poles are not straight up and down; they are inclined at an angle of 23.5°. The reason for this is that Earth is tipped this much with reference to the plane (level) of its orbit about the sun.

We have demonstrated the rotation of Earth on its axis, which causes day and night.

<hr/>

[3]There are other kinds of seasons too—such seasonal changes as wet and dry seasons. For a study of the effect of seasonal change upon plants and animals see Chapters 19 and 20.

We have demonstrated also the revolution of Earth about the sun. The children in most cases should have an opportunity to live with these ideas awhile before proceeding to the cause of the change of seasons. In fact, the entire growth leading to the latter might well be distributed throughout their progress through the elementary school.

EXPERIENCE. *Cause of change of seasons.* We may demonstrate the cause of the change of seasons with the same apparatus used in demonstrating the cause of day and night. Darken the room as much as possible, or choose a dark day. Place a light in the center of the floor. An ordinary electric lamp will do. A more accurate effect could be had by not using a shade, because without a shade the lamp throws its light out in all directions, just as the sun does. In order to conserve the children's sight, however, it is necessary to place a shade over the lamp so that it will shine only in the direction needed. A flashlight, if strong enough, is excellent, or a projection lantern will do. Have the children realize that the sun shines in all directions, and not in just one direction, as a flashlight or a projection lantern does.

Having placed the light, which represents the sun, in the center of the floor, draw a circle with chalk around the light. (Strictly speaking, Earth does not go around in an exact circle; see p. 191). Place the globe of Earth on this circle. Keep the feet of the tripod or base on the floor at all times. Have the north pole pointed toward an imaginary North Star away up in the sky. It is well to have children rotate the globe on its axis to bring out again the cause of day and night. Stop a fourth of the way around the circle for a discussion. Do this for each season.

At the position where the inclined north pole is toward the light, we can observe a number of things. First, the Northern Hemisphere is having summer and the Southern Hemisphere is having winter. The Arctic Circle is having its long summer day. The Antarctic Circle is having its long winter night. This represents June 21. Rotate the globe in this position. Note that the days are longer than the nights for the United States but that the nights are longer than the days for Argentina.

A string can be used to measure these lengths. Notice that the sun would be low in the sky at the north pole.

What season comes next? We move the globe counterclockwise another fourth of the way around the circle, making sure to keep the north pole inclined in the same direction, that is, toward the imaginary North Star. We now have about September 22. Notice that the light has now reached the south pole. It is also shining at the north pole. If we were at either pole, the sun would seem to move around the horizon. This can be demonstrated by rotating the globe. The days and nights are now equal. The day is shorter in the United States, Canada, Europe, and almost all of Asia in this position than on June 21.

What are the seasons during September for the various parts of Earth?

Now move the globe to the third position, another fourth of the way around the circle, making certain that the axis is pointed in the same direction. We now have conditions which are the reverse of those of the first position. It is now about December 21. The Antarctic Circle is having its long day. The Arctic Circle is having its long night. The days in the Northern Hemisphere are much shorter than the nights.

By moving the globe another fourth of the way around we have March 21. Here, again, the sun is shining at both north and south poles, but it is low on the horizon. We have equal days and nights. This is known as the vernal, or spring, equinox. September 22 is known as the autumnal equinox.

If this demonstration is repeated, with the globe held so that its axis is straight up and down, that is, at right angles to its orbit, it can be shown that the change of seasons is caused in part by the inclination of Earth's axis. This is not recommended, however, until children thoroughly understand the first demonstration.

It is well to have the children repeat the demonstration a number of times. New facts may be discovered. It is important that in

each position the axis of Earth be tilted in exactly the same direction.

We all know the sun does not give so much heat to us when it is low on the horizon as when it is high overhead. A ray of sunlight coming to us from a point low on the horizon strikes Earth's surface obliquely. Hence a given area of Earth will receive less sunlight. Take a flashlight and throw the light straight down on the floor. Notice how bright the floor is at this point, but notice also that not much of the floor is lighted. Now throw the light at an angle. Notice that more floor space is lighted but none of it is lighted so well.

So it is with sunlight. Going back over the demonstration, we see that places having summer receive rays that are more nearly vertical than places having winter. The vertical rays strike directly, heating less surface but heating it more intensely than the oblique rays. Then, too, the oblique rays shine through more atmosphere; that is, the sun shines through more atmosphere when it is low on the horizon (p. 425).

One must not forget that the length of the day and of the night has a great deal to do with determining the temperature of a particular place on Earth's surface.

A teacher should not hurry this demonstration. It should not be crowded into a single period. It is important to give the children considerable freedom to move about at the different positions of the globe of Earth, so that they can see it from all angles.

The Stars

In spite of the conspicuousness of the stars at night, man has been ignorant of what they are until comparatively recent times. Early he invented stories about his heroes and his deities to explain the presence of the stars. The ancients thought the stars to be immovable lights on some sort of dome or vault in the heavens. The dome was supposed to move about Earth. Earth was thought by all the ancients to be the largest body in the universe. Man early developed theories of how these stars mysteriously influenced human lives. These ideas have come down to us in the form of astrology. It is impossible to believe in astrology after one has gained some exact knowledge of astronomy.

Stars Are Suns. It might be well for the teacher, before approaching the subject of stars, to interview the children through a class discussion as to what they think stars are like. The children may have some ideas which resemble the ideas of the ancients. Very frequently children are confused by the stories of science fiction and by inaccurate reporting of space exploration and need assistance in gaining a sound perspective.

We have learned that the sun is a star. It appears to be different from the other stars merely because it is so very much nearer to us. We have already learned that the sun is an average star. It is average in many different ways, such as brightness, size, and color. There are many stars which are much larger. There are many stars which are much smaller. There are many which are much hotter, and many which are cooler.

The ancients called the stars "fixed" because the star groups and constellations remain unchanged for long periods of time. They distinguished the stars from the planets, which seemed to wander about among the stars, although they knew comparatively little about the nature of either. Now we know that the stars do move. In fact, astronomers have found nothing in space which is not moving. All bodies in the universe seem to be in motion. The stars merely seem to us to be "fixed" because they are so far away from us that their motions have little effect upon their positions. This explains why the constellations have much the same shape today as they did in the days of the ancient Greeks.

Studying the Stars. The stars are so unbelievably far away from us that it is difficult for us to learn about them. Not even the nearest stars look like tiny disks through the most powerful telescope. They are all just points of light, each pouring out energy into space.

In spite of the handicap of extreme distance, scientists have been able to establish many facts, and to develop reasonable theories that are helpful in guiding their further study. Children should be encouraged to feel that the study of the stars is on the outer frontiers of science, and that learning more about them is interesting and challenging. We have much to learn about the nature of the universe, but great strides are being made, and great discoveries may be expected in the near future.

Distance to the Stars. Astronomers can measure distances to the nearer stars by a method known as *parallax*. The position of a nearby star against the background of very distant stars is carefully photographed. Six months later the same star is photographed again. It will appear to have changed its position in relation to the background, because in six months Earth has moved to the opposite side of its orbit. Since Earth is more than 90 million miles from the sun, the observer on Earth will then be more than 180 million miles from where he was before. The star will be seen from a different direction and will appear to have moved. By making precise measurements of the distance the star has

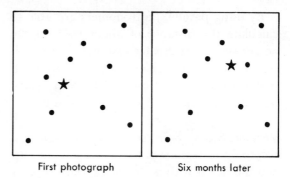

First photograph   Six months later

Parallax is usually determined by photographing a near star against the background of distant stars, and photographing it again six months later. (Adapted from Robert H. Baker, Astronomy, *7th edition, D. Van Nostrand, Princeton, New Jersey, 1959.)*

shifted position against its background, it is possible to calculate the distance to the star by trigonometry. The nearer the star is, the more it will appear to shift its position.

We judge distance every day in much the same way. A man in the middle of the street looks larger than the same man on the far side of the street. Our eyes judge his distance by his apparent size. We are able to judge distances more easily with two eyes than with one, because we automatically make use of the principle of parallax.

EXPERIENCE. *Children may try the "winking" test of parallax.* Close one eye and hold up a pencil at arm's length. Move the pencil directly into line with a distant object, such as a doorknob. Now open that eye and close the other one, without moving the pencil. Notice how the pencil appears to jump to one side. Hold the pencil nearer the face and repeat the test. The nearer the pencil is to the observer, the more it appears to shift its position against the background.

Try looking at objects outdoors, one nearby and another far away, in the same way. The size of the parallax of any object depends on how far away it is.

By using parallax, astronomers are able to calculate the distance of about 6000 of the nearer stars. At greater distances the parallax, or apparent shift of position, is so small that it ceases to be accurate. Other ways have been found to calculate distances, however.

Variable Stars. Some stars vary in brightness according to regular patterns. They flare up and die down with a steady rhythm, so that their changes in brightness are easily measured. The north star, Polaris, is one of these. It varies through bright and dim stages in a period of about 4 days. An important variable star is Delta Cephei, in the constellation of Cepheus. This star was the first of its type to be studied. It varies in brightness with clocklike regularity, one complete cycle requiring 5 days, 8 hours, and 37 minutes. Stars of this type are known as Cepheid variables.

Astronomers have determined that the greater the *true brightness,* or luminosity, of one of these stars, the longer is its period of variation. Also, it is evident that the closer a star is, the greater is its *apparent brightness*. A comparison of the true brightness of a star with its apparent brightness makes it possible to determine its distance.

Double Stars. Many stars are double stars, although it is rarely possible to see two with the unaided eye. Often two stars revolve about each other in a common gravitational system. If one of the stars passes in front of the other, it will partially or wholly eclipse it, reducing the amount of light. Thus a double star may be a variable star. Sometimes a third companion exists not far away. Castor was discovered to be such a triple system. Then it was found that each of the three members is itself a double star. Castor is thus a multiple star composed of six units.

Composition of a Star. The sun is the star we know the most about. Its composition is found to be about 92 per cent hydrogen and about 7 per cent helium. Other elements are present in very small amounts. It is thought that most of the stars have approximately the same make-up. In the sun and similar stars, the hydrogen is changed to helium (p. 197) at a moderate rate, and can probably continue to change at that rate for billions of years. In some of the hotter stars, such as Rigel and Deneb, the hydrogen appears to be changing much more rapidly. It may last only the relatively short time of a few millions of years. Some, the white dwarfs, seem to have already used up their hydrogen and shrunk down to a very dense mass of closely packed atomic nuclei. The material in these stars is calculated to weigh more than 150 tons per cubic inch. They may ultimately cool off completely and become invisible black dwarfs.

Sirius is the brightest star in the sky because it is fairly close to us. Its hydrogen is also used very rapidly. It has a small companion star, known as Sirius B, which is a white dwarf.

Children often ask about the formation of stars and the various stages through which they pass. According to one theory, the vast clouds of hydrogen that exist in space begin to contract and grow hot, forming helium, as in the sun. The hydrogen is finally all converted to helium, which in turn is converted to carbon and to heavier elements up to atomic number 60 (p. 376). Beyond this point the star ceases to give off heat. It grows cooler and collapses to form a very dense star. The next step may be a violent explosion, a supernova, in which most of the matter of the star returns to gaseous hydrogen again. The cycle could then begin to repeat itself.

Color and Temperature of Stars. Stars have different colors, as anyone can see. The differences are believed to be largely due to difference in surface temperature. There are seven principal types of stars, known by the

THE SEVEN CLASSES OF STARS

Class	O	B	A	F	G	K	M
Approximate temperature	50,000°C. (90,000°F.)	25,000°C. (45,000°F.)	10,000°C. (18,000°F.)	7000°C. (12,000°F.)	6000°C. (10,000°F.)	5000°C. (9000°F.)	3000°C. (5000°F.)
Color	blue	blue	blue	yellow	yellow	orange	red
Typical stars	(rare)	Spica Rigel	Sirius Vega	Canopus Procyon	Sun Capella	Arcturus Aldebaran	Betelgeuse Antares

seven letters O, B, A, F, G, K, and M (see chart). Stars of Class O are the hottest, but are relatively rare. Their temperatures range above 50,000°C. (90,000°F.).

More common hot stars are those like Spica and Rigel, of Class B. Their surface temperatures are around 25,000°C. (45,000°F.). They are blue. Their spectra show prominent helium lines. Typical of Class A are Sirius and Vega, which are also blue stars. Their temperatures are around 10,000°C. (18,000°F.). Many stars of this class show strong hydrogen lines in the spectra. These very hot stars are believed to be consuming their hydrogen at a prodigal rate, so that they are not expected to last as long as some of the cooler stars.

Somewhat cooler stars belong to classes F, G, and K. Our sun and Capella are Class G stars. They are yellow or orange, and have a surface temperature of about 6000°C. (10,000°F.). Metals show prominently in their spectra, particularly calcium and iron. Coolest of all are the red stars, with temperatures as low as 3000°C. (5000°F.). Strangely, this type is represented by the supergiant stars, Betelgeuse and Antares. These stars are masses of extremely thin gases, and are among the largest we know.

The Size of Stars. The sizes of some stars can be calculated approximately from their color, brightness, and distance. In the case of double stars that eclipse one another the motions can sometimes be figured out rather well, and sizes can be roughly determined. The diameters of a few stars that are near enough or large enough can be found with a system of mirrors from the interferences of light waves reflected from opposite edges of the star. Stars ranging from one to three times the diameter of our sun (which is nearly a million miles) are Procyon, Altair, Sirius, and Vega. Giant stars are larger. Arcturus has a diameter of 30 suns, and Aldebaran may have a diameter equal to 60 suns.

Still larger stars are the supergiants. Antares has a diameter figured to be about 450 times the diameter of the sun. Betelgeuse is a variable, pulsating star of approximately the same size. The diameters of these stars are greater than the diameter of Earth's orbit. It would therefore be possible to place the sun and Earth, in fact all the planets out as far as Mars, inside one of these stars. The planets would have plenty of room to move in their usual orbits about the sun.

The white dwarfs, on the other hand, are much smaller than the sun. The dwarf companion of Sirius has a diameter of about 30,000 miles. Other stars of this type are about the same size as Earth.

Cosmic Rays. Almost daily one reads or hears about cosmic rays. Children, too, hear the words and will ask questions about them.

At the turn of the century experiments were being conducted on radium and other radioactive elements. Researchers found that even in the absence of such elements some radiation existed. When electroscopes for indicating the rays were placed on mountains or carried up in balloons the radiation was found to be stronger at high altitudes than at the surface of Earth. It was apparent that the radiations came from space, and they were therefore called *cosmic rays*. Because the rays had even more penetrating power than ordinary gamma rays (short X rays), they were thought to be gamma rays of very short wave length. They were regarded as part of the electromagnetic spectrum (p. 870), and were tentatively placed at the short end of the spectrum diagrams, beyond X rays. Such diagrams may still be seen, although we now know that they are not correct. Like many scientific theories, this one has had to be altered in the light of new information.

Cosmic rays are not electromagnetic waves. This fact was clearly established in the 1930's, when it was found that the radiations were stronger in higher latitudes, toward the poles, than at the equator. This indicated that they consisted of charged particles that were being deflected toward the poles by Earth's magnetic field. They are composed chiefly of hydrogen nuclei, or protons (p. 376), together with some helium nuclei and a few nuclei of heavier atoms. Such particles strike the upper atmosphere with tremendous force, smashing atoms to bits, and often reaching the surface of Earth. The sources of such rays are the subject of important studies.

One source may be the sun. Another source is believed to be certain stars that are larger and more active than our sun and that eject large amounts of their substance into space. The most likely source of all is considered to be the *supernovae*, those exploding stars that virtually destroy themselves in one gigantic burst.

Particles thus forced out into space may encounter whirling clouds of electrified gas and great magnetic fields in which they are accelerated to faster and faster speeds, like particles in a cyclotron (p. 734). In some such way the protons and other particles may reach their extremely high energies.

There is a close relationship between the study of these naturally accelerated particles and experiments conducted in a laboratory with man-made particle accelerators, such as the synchrotron. In either case charged particles are accelerated to high energies (speeds), and when they strike the nuclei of target atoms the nuclei are broken down into protons, neutrons, and various smaller particles. In the case of cosmic rays these particles produced by the collision are known as *secondary cosmic rays*. They strike other atoms and cause further break-ups, in a kind of cascade, or chain reaction. The end products finally reach the surface of Earth as a "cosmic shower" of atomic particles. Throughout our lives we are bombarded by these particles.

The composition of primary cosmic rays is of particular interest. In order to study the rays balloons are sent up to altitudes of 100,000 feet or more, carrying instruments for recording, such as scintillation counters or thick stacks of photographic plates that record the tracks of the particles passing through them. Sounding rockets are used to obtain information from regions still farther out in space. Further knowledge of these phenomena should greatly increase our understanding of the nature of the universe.

Sources of Light. The moon and the planets are seen by reflected light. The stars, however, are at great distances from us, and shine by their own light. The sun, which is our star, produces light by which we observe other objects, including moon and planets.

EXPERIENCE. *Light helps us to see things about us.* In looking about us we see that there are two kinds of objects: those that are sources of light, such as electric lights, the sun and other stars, and flames, and those that are seen by reflected light, such as chairs, pencils, the blackboard, the sidewalk, and the moon.

A teacher can discuss with young children the objects about them. The children may say, "Some objects shine and some make light." In this discussion utilize the children's natural expressions in the development of ideas. Perhaps you can take them to a dark place such as a closet or projection room in a school. Can they see anything? One can also discuss experiences they might have had at night when the lights were out. Use these experiences to show that some things can be seen only when there is light present. Develop the sun as our biggest and most important source of light. As the discussion with older children progresses, a list of the two kinds of objects—objects which give off light and objects which reflect light—might be developed.

One of the brightest stars known is Rigel, which blazes with the brightness of 18,000 of our suns. On the other hand, a whole class of small, apparently dying stars, the white dwarfs, are believed to have used up most of their hydrogen and now glow rather feebly. The companion of Sirius is one of them. More than three hundred such stars would be required to equal the luminosity of our sun.

The fact that the stars are suns can have a very important meaning in developing a more adequate conception of space. Our sun is very large. Yet our sun is only one of billions of stars. The stars are so far away that they seem to us not to be suns at all. In other words, space is so great, the universe is so large, that there are suns so far away as to seem mere specks in our sky. And some are so far away that we cannot see them without the use of a telescope. Astronomers are constantly having better telescopes built in order that they may make more stars visible for study.

The Number of Stars. There are over four thousand stars that are visible to the naked eye from Earth. Of course not all these are visible at one time; in fact, not more than two thousand are visible at one time. With a telescope we increase the number of stars that we can see by many billions.

Atmospheric conditions have much to do with the number of stars that are visible. Smoke, moisture in the air, and city lights interfere with observations in astronomy. Many observatories are built at high altitudes in dry climates and away from city lights.

Rising and Setting of Stars. It should be recalled that the rising of the stars in the east and their setting in the west are not caused by true motions of the stars, but rather by the rotation of Earth on its axis. The situation might be compared to riding on a merry-go-round. On one side as you go around, you pass certain objects, possibly a Ferris wheel. On the other side you pass some of your friends. So it is with our day's journey on Earth. On the day ride we see the sun and sometimes the moon. On the night ride we see the stars and sometimes the moon and certain planets.

Stars Are on All Sides of Earth. There are stars in the sky during the day. We cannot see these stars, because the sun is so bright. Sometimes a star is so bright that it can be seen during the day; however, such a phenomenon is not common. During a total eclipse many stars can be seen. Stars are all around Earth. This concept of stars being in the day sky has many elements of dramatic learning for young children. They can be challenged by the fact that there are stars in the sky in the daytime. It has been found that a good stimulant to discussion is to look at the sky through the window and raise the question, "Are there stars in the sky now? Where are they? Why don't we see them?" (of course recognizing there is one star, our sun, which we can see in the day sky when it isn't too cloudy). Earth is a small body in a vast universe of stars and other bodies. They are not just accommodating lights on the night ride of Earth, as children sometimes think they are.

Stars Seem to Twinkle. Most people are familiar with the twinkling of stars. This twinkling probably accounts for the way in which stars are commonly represented, with five or six points. Sometimes children make five-pointed stars. It might be well to see that the question is raised in discussion as to whether stars have points. Of course a star does not have five points. A star is an immense globe of heated material. The rapid fluctuation in the brightness of a star, which we know as *twinkling,* is caused by the motions or turbulence of the air above us. In other words, twinkling is caused by atmospheric phenomena rather than by the nature of the stars. The stars are so far away from us that they appear to be specks to our eyes. Any movement of atmospheric layers of different densities produced by different water content and temperature (p. 856) changes a little the course of so thin a ray of light.

Scientists are seeking further explanations about this phenomenon as space exploration adds to our knowledge of Earth's atmosphere and space.

Children will ask why a planet does not twinkle. The beam of light from a planet is thicker. Movements of the air and irregularities in the atmosphere do not, from moment to moment, noticeably affect the course of large rays of light.

Observing the Stars. Astronomers naturally have some difficulty in observing or photo-graphing the stars under conditions like this. They are also hampered, even in clear weather, by smoke and dust in the air and by the glow of light from cities. During World War II the nightly blackout in Los Angeles enabled astronomers at nearby Mount Wilson to make many valuable observations that had previously been impossible. When a location for a new observatory was chosen at Mount Palomar, its distance of fifty miles from the nearest city, San Diego, was an important advantage.

Very delicate observations are best made from a position quite outside Earth's atmosphere. For this reason, telescopic cameras are shot up in rockets to heights of a hundred miles or more, where they can take clear pictures of the stars and return them to Earth. The Tiros satellites, orbiting Earth at still greater heights, send back thousands of pictures of weather conditions on Earth, and open the way to photographing other regions in the universe.

Brightness of the Stars. The early astronomers Hipparchus and Ptolemy used the term *magnitude* to describe the brightness of stars. They divided the stars that they could see with the naked eye into six groups, describing the brightest as first-magnitude stars and those that were barely visible as sixth-magnitude.

After the invention of the telescope this system was extended to include much fainter stars. The 100-inch telescope at Mount Wilson can photograph stars as faint as the twenty-first magnitude. With the 200-inch at Mount Palomar we can reach even farther into the depths of space; but presently we reach a limit.

The sky is everywhere suffused with a faint glow known as the *night sky glow.* It is caused by certain chemical reactions in the upper atmosphere. Astronomers at Palomar find that they can photograph stars as faint as the twenty-fourth magnitude with the 200-inch

telescope, but these stars are barely percepti-
ble against the background of the night sky
glow. Stars that are fainter than this cannot
be photographed, because they are not as
bright as the glow. It is hoped, however, that
electronic attachments may be able to overcome this difficulty.

The Constellations. We might ask whether
stars are grouped together. The ancients combined the stars into constellations and named
these constellations after mythological person-
ages, animals, or inanimate objects which the
configuration of the stars was supposed to resemble. In most cases, they grouped stars together into constellations which do not belong
together at all. Some stars within some constellations do belong together. The stars of a
constellation seem to belong together because
they appear in the sky in the same general direction.

Constellations are useful in observing a
comet or some other astronomical event in the
night sky, just as streets in a city are useful in
locating a house. They are useful also in telling directions at night.

Sometimes teachers stress learning the constellations to the extent that the children get
little or nothing else out of the study of the sky.
If the teacher is guided by the conception of
space, she will find that the study of constellations is only a minor objective. She must bear
in mind that the constellations are entirely arbitrary divisions of the sky. Forty-eight constellations were named by the ancients. In the
past three centuries the total number has been
increased to eighty-eight.

Teachers who desire to assist children in
knowing a few constellations should secure sky
maps for study. A roof or hilltop or open
space away from artificial lights may be used
for field trips. Flashlights may be used in
pointing out the stars on the map. Some children in upper elementary grades are interested in learning the constellations from their
own study of the sky maps. Identification of
constellations should not be an end in itself
but rather a means to the development of a
better conception of space.

**Why There Are Different Constellations in
the Sky at Different Times of the Year.** The
night sky changes during the year. The stars
in the sky in June are not the same as those
in December. The explanation for this lies
in the fact that Earth revolves about the sun.
The night sky is changing constantly as a result. Knowing a number of constellations
when we see them can be quite important and
useful for finding one's way at night in strange
places, in navigation, hiking, and other outdoor activities.

EXPERIENCE. *To show why different stars and
groups of stars are seen at different times of the year.*
Place the globe of Earth near the center of the
room. Let one child represent the sun and
stand near the globe. This child may hold a
flashlight so as to light the globe. Now have
other children stand about the room to represent stars and constellations of stars. Have
the children imagine that some of them are
suspended from the ceiling to represent constellations above the Arctic Circle.

Rotate the globe and revolve it about the
sun-child. Note the difference between rotation and revolution. Revolving in this case
means moving the globe completely around
the sun-child. Observe that the night side of
the globe is turned toward different children
representing different stars and groups of stars.
The stars in the June sky are not the same as
those in December.

However, the constellations directly over
the polar regions remain in the sky for those
regions during the entire year. This also explains why we can see the Big Dipper and
other polar constellations at all seasons of the
year on clear nights. This can be demonstrated through repeating the revolution of the

globe around the sun-child again and noting that the imaginary constellations far, far above the ceiling (over the polar regions) are visible at all seasons of the year. The Big Dipper constellation would be one of these constellations. The North Star, also known as Polaris, the pole star, is usually located by means of the Big Dipper constellation. At the end of the bowl of the Big Dipper are two bright stars. They point toward the North Star.

The same idea can be demonstrated for the south polar constellations by imaginary constellations located far below the floor of the room. These constellations would remain in the sky in the Southern Hemisphere throughout the year. The Southern Cross would be one of these constellations.

The ideas gained from the study of "What is up and what is down?" (p. 188) can be used with this activity.

The Solar System

Our Sun Is the Star of the Solar System. Your county is part of your state. Our Earth in turn is part of a system called the solar system, which, in ordinary language, means the sun's system. Our sun is the star which completely dominates this system, composed of planets and their moons, as well as minor planets, comets, and meteors. In a geometrical sense the sun is in the approximate center of the solar system; but in the sense of influence and gravitational control we can say that the sun is the center of the system, since the other bodies revolve about it.

Many people have wondered if there are other solar systems in the universe. This we cannot know at the present time. We have no telescopes or other instruments that can reveal the presence of planets about stars other than our sun. Some authorities say that whatever happened to produce our own solar system must have happened many times, and that there are many other such systems. Other authorities say that whatever it was that happened was an exceedingly rare event and that there may be few or possibly no other solar systems in the vast universe. In any case, we do not know exactly how the solar system was formed, although scientists have advanced

hypotheses to explain the formation of Earth and other members of the solar system. We do know enough at the present time not to have complete confidence in any conjectures made concerning the presence of other solar systems. Perhaps there are thousands of them in the universe; perhaps there are only a few; perhaps our own solar system is the only one.

Formation of the Solar System. Many theories have been advanced to explain the origin of the solar system. One that has been much discussed recently, the dust cloud theory, holds that it started with a large cloud of dust and gas that began to condense and revolve. Gravitation would tend to make the mass contract and grow hot; rotation would tend to spin the cloud out into the shape of a wheel or disk. The greater portion of the material would condense at the center to form the sun. Local clumps of material might spin independently within the main cloud, finally forming planets, and still smaller eddies would develop into satellites of these planets. The whole system would continue to operate as a unit, each part held in place by a balance between gravitational forces pulling inward and the inertial tendency to fly outward (p. 245)

EXPERIENCE. *Showing how Earth may have been formed.* Diagrams may be made by children to show their ideas of how Earth was formed. The children may like to show the planets in the process of formation. As there is not agreement among scientists about the exact method of formation, the children may use their imagination to some extent in this. It would be interesting to have more than one idea shown in drawings by different children.

EXPERIENCE. *New ideas about the formation of Earth.* Ideas about the formation of Earth are always changing. Watch newspapers and magazines for reports of newly advanced opinions.

Size of the Solar System. If the sun were a globe 600 feet in diameter, placed on the international bridge at Detroit-Windsor, the diameters of the planets, on the same scale,

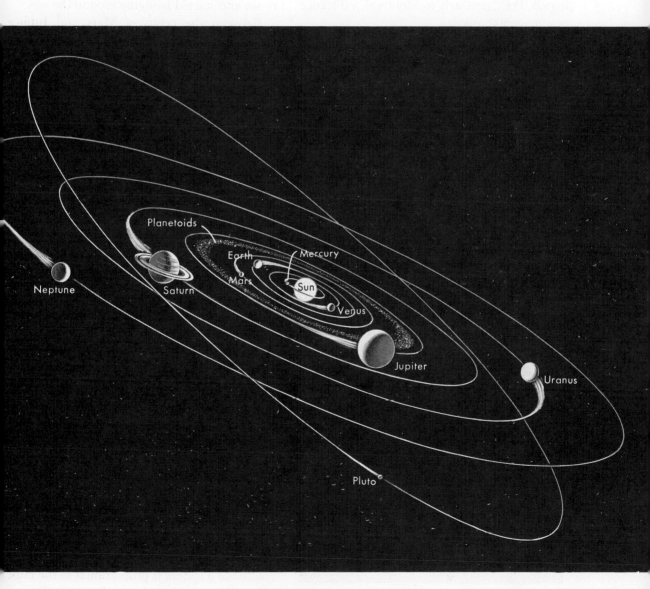

The Solar System

would range from 2 to 60 feet. The orbits of the inner planets would extend as follows: Mercury, to Riverside; Venus, to Tecumseh, Ontario; Earth, to Dearborn; and Mars to Plymouth, Michigan, over 18 miles away. The orbits of the outer planets still on the same scale, and would extend as follows: Jupiter, to London, Ontario; Saturn, to Ft. Wayne; Uranus, to Chicago; Neptune, to St. Louis; and the orbit of Pluto would reach to Washington, D.C., or nearly to Montreal, a distance of almost 500 miles.

The Planets of the Solar System. The ancients, who had no telescopes, were aware of the six planets that can be seen with the naked eye. These are, beginning with the one nearest the sun, Mercury, Venus, Earth, Mars, Jupiter, and Saturn. With the aid of the telescope three more have been added: Uranus, Neptune, and Pluto. They all move in the same direction about the sun, in orbits that are not quite circular but *elliptical.*

EXPERIENCE. *To draw an ellipse.* Older children may enjoy showing how an ellipse may be drawn by driving two nails into a board and passing a loose circlet of string around them. If a pencil is moved along inside the string, keeping it tight, it will trace an ellipse on the board.

The orbits of the planets lie very nearly in

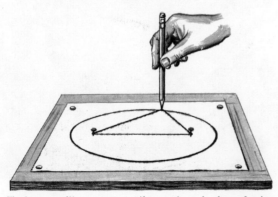

To draw an ellipse, use two nails or tacks and a loop of string.

the same plane as the orbit of Earth and are only slightly elliptical, with two exceptions. The orbit of Mercury is tipped at an angle of 7° to that of Earth, and the orbit of Pluto at 17°. Both orbits are more elliptical than the other orbits, and the orbit of Pluto is unusual in that one end of it dips *inside* the orbit of Neptune. This has led to speculation that Pluto may at one time have been a moon of Neptune that was torn loose by some unusual occurrence and started swinging around the sun.

Between the orbits of Mars and Jupiter there is a group of several thousand small bodies known as asteroids, which will be described later. They are sometimes referred to as planetoids, or minor planets.

No one knows exactly how many planets there are in the solar system. There may be other planets beyond both Neptune and Pluto which have not been discovered. The problem of how many planets there are in the solar system provides an opportunity for developing the idea that man has much to learn, and therefore he must be open-minded.

Children are intensely interested in knowing what the other planets are like. A favorite question among both children and adults is whether there is any life on these planets. We shall see from the discussion which follows that we do not know for certain whether there is life on some of these planets or not. On most of them the conditions are such that we should not expect to find there the kinds of living things that are found on our Earth.

Size of the Planets. In size the planets fall roughly into pairs. The diameter of Earth is nearly 8000 miles; that of Venus is a couple of hundred miles less. Mercury, the smallest planet, and Mars each have approximately half the diameter of Earth. The two giants, Jupiter and Saturn, have diameters that are ten times the diameter of Earth. Because the volume of a sphere is proportional to the cube of its diameter, these huge planets each have about a thousand times the volume of Earth. The outermost pair, Uranus and Neptune, have diameters that are about four times that of Earth. Pluto is so far away and so newly discovered that we do not know much about it, but it appears to be a little larger than Mercury.

Distances of the Planets from the Sun. The distances of the planets from the sun are difficult to realize. The average distance of Earth is about 93 million miles from the sun. The distance of Mars is 142 million; of Jupiter, 483 million; and of Saturn, 886 million miles. Even these large distances are surpassed by the outermost planets. Uranus is nearly 2 billion miles from the sun, Neptune nearly 3 billion, and Pluto about 3.7 billion miles.

A ray of light from the sun, traveling at 186,000 miles per second, goes more than 11 million miles in a minute. Sunlight requires about 8 minutes to reach Earth, and over an hour to get to Saturn. The feeble ray that finally penetrates as far as Pluto spends more than 5 hours in its journey.

These distances that seem so enormous are again dwarfed when we stop to think that light from the nearest star, Proxima Centauri, requires more than 4 years to reach us.

In the study of the solar system it is important that the teacher keep in mind the larger conceptions of science. The solar system offers meaning for the development of the conception of space, in that Earth is one of the minor planets in a system which is but a minute part of a vast universe. In other words, comparing the solar system with Earth, we think of it as large; but comparing it with the universe, we see that it is very small. It can be used also for the development of the conception of inter-relationships, as, for instance, the relationship of the planets to the sun and of the moon to the planets. It can be used to assist in the development of the conception of time, in that the solar system is very old. It can aid also in

the development of the conception of variety, in that there are so many different kinds of bodies in the universe. *The teacher should avoid, at all risk, getting herself and the children lost in small details about individual planets. There is no need of requiring memorization of information about the planets.*

EXPERIENCE. *The out-of-doors is needed to demonstrate the solar system.* In any demonstration of the relative sizes of the planets and their distances from the sun, it is impossible to put size and distance together and keep it in a classroom. As a suggestion, the teacher and the class might use the playground and space children at various distances to represent the relative distances of the planets from the sun. A child can be designated as the sun-child, another as the planet Mercury, another as Venus, and so forth. Only a few planets could be placed on the school ground, but the activity could be used to develop an appreciation of space.

The planets appear in different parts of the sky at different times because they move around the sun at different speeds and in different orbits from that of Earth, and consequently keep getting into different positions.

Mercury. Mercury is the planet nearest the sun. Because there appeared to be irregularities in its behavior, for some years it was thought that there might be a planet between it and the sun. Some astronomers even suggested the name "Vulcan" for such a planet. In spite of much painstaking observation, no planet was found. Einstein's theory accounts for the irregularities in Mercury's course, so that it is usually assumed now that there is no planet between Mercury and the sun.

Mercury's diameter is only about 3000 miles. Mercury has no moons of its own. The planet completes its revolution about the sun in 88 days. Thus we see that its year is less than three of our months. If a person lived on Mercury, he would be four of Mercury's years old when an Earth-child would be but one year old. The planet is only about 36,-000,000 miles from the sun.

Mercury is so near the sun that it is always seen near it as a so-called morning or evening star. It is seen near the horizon just before sunrise or shortly after sunset. Of course it is not a star at all but a planet. It was called a star long before much was known about planets.

We know very little about the surface of Mercury. It is thought that it has little or no atmosphere. There is some evidence that the same side of Mercury always faces the sun, just as the same side of the moon always faces Earth. One can easily understand that, if this is true, the face toward the sun is extremely hot, because of continuous day at such a short distance from so hot a body, and the face away from the sun is very cold.

It may be interesting to the children to learn that this planet, which is hidden by the sun at intervals and moves from one side of the sun to the other in so short a time, was called Mercury after the swift and mischievous messenger of the Greek gods.

Venus. Venus, next to the sun and moon, is the brightest body in the sky. It is about 67,-000,000 miles from the sun. It takes Venus about 225 days to complete a revolution; hence its year is shorter than Earth's. It has no moons.

One would expect that much could be learned about Venus, because at times it comes very near Earth. This has proved to be impossible, because the surface of the planet is completely obscured by a thick layer of clouds. The spectroscope shows that the atmosphere contains carbon dioxide, which may be present in huge amounts. The brightly reflecting clouds, however, are not gaseous; they reflect sunlight in a form that shows they must be composed of solid or liquid particles.

They may be dust clouds, carried up from a desert beneath.

Markings on the clouds move very slowly, suggesting that the planet requires more than a month to rotate once on its axis. This contrasts sharply with the rapid rotation of Jupiter, another cloud-covered planet, on which cloud markings may be seen to reappear every 10 hours.

Scientists do not know whether there is life on Venus, but it seems most unlikely. It is believed that below the clouds the atmosphere is filled with dust to a depth of 20 miles, swirling in a temperature of 500°F., and totally obscuring the sun. It seems improbable that any kind of life could exist under these difficult conditions.

Venus, like Mercury, because it is nearer the sun than we, has been called the "morning star" or the "evening star," depending on whether it is seen in the morning or the evening sky. Venus never sets later than four hours after sunset. This planet, one of the most beautiful of celestial bodies observed from Earth, was named Venus after the goddess of beauty and love. Of course, it is not a star but a planet.

Information from Mariner II spacecraft, which passed within less than 22,000 miles of Venus in December, 1962, tends to confirm the belief that the planet rotates very slowly. Signals from Mariner indicated that Venus has a very weak magnetic field, and therefore probably lacks the counterpart of the intense Van Allen radiation belts near Earth.

Venus is an object of great interest in current events. It would be well to encourage children to watch for discoveries concerning it.

Earth. Mercury and Venus are sometimes called the inner planets, since they revolve inside Earth's orbit. We will describe Earth elsewhere in the book (Chapters 8–21).

Mars. Mars was named after the god of war

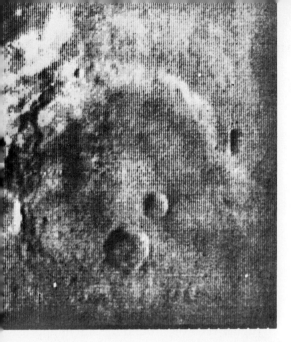

because of its reddish hue. It revolves about the sun in about 687 days. It has therefore a much longer year than we have. It takes over 37 minutes longer to rotate on its axis than Earth, so that it has a slightly longer day than we have.

Mars is a much smaller planet than Earth, its diameter being only 4215 miles. In some respects it resembles Earth. Its axis is inclined to the plane of its orbit, and as a result, it has seasonal change.

As studied by modern observers Mars has mostly a reddish color, which may indicate rocks or deserts, broken by darker regions of bluish-gray, with white polar caps in winter. In summer the northern cap melts completely away, and the dark regions seem to grow larger. This may be caused by a type of life similar to our lichens, which are able to survive under the most unfavorable conditions, and spread with increase of moisture.

At one time it was thought that certain markings on Mars indicated canals that the supposed inhabitants had constructed to ir-rigate the deserts. These ideas have been very popular, but are now discredited as having no foundation.

The Martian atmosphere is filled with a blue haze. Nitrogen and carbon dioxide appear to be present but there is very little oxygen. Such an atmosphere would be a grave hazard for men attempting to land on this planet. Scanty amounts of water vapor are present in the atmosphere, which would condense as hoarfrost during the icy Martian night ($-60°$F.). This moisture could be used by plants in the quick morning thaw, before it all evaporated again in the daytime heat ($90°$F.).

Teachers need to be on their guard against the florid Sunday supplement and other fiction picturing strange beings living on Mars. This type of thing is merely entertainment and entirely unscientific. Allow children to bring such printed material into class, but use it to train them to be critical of it and not to confuse fiction with accurate information.

Is there, or has there ever been, life on Mars? We do not know. Life of the kind we have on Earth is dependent on very definite conditions, such as the presence of oxygen, favorable temperature, and water. The temperature fluctuates a great deal on Mars, far more so than on Earth. Oxygen and water are scarce; there is no evidence of oceans. It is most unlikely that a higher type of life could exist there.

Mars has two moons, Deimos and Phobos. They are both very small, probably less than ten miles in diameter. What small bodies these are! Phobos is the fastest-moving moon in the solar system. It revolves about Mars more than three times while Mars is turning only once, so that an observer on Mars would see this moon rise twice every night. It is quite close to Mars, less than 4000 miles from the surface of the planet. Deimos revolves at a distance of about 15,000 miles from the center of the planet in a period of a little over thirty hours. After we have studied the giant stars, these moons seem like toy worlds. What a great contrast there is in the kind of bodies found in the astronomical world!

Minor planets. As we proceed in our study of the solar system, we find that between the orbit of Mars and that of Jupiter there is not just one planet but a number of small bodies or little planets called *planetoids* or *asteroids*. Several thousand planetoids have been recorded, and the orbits of about 1600 plotted. The largest, Ceres, is about 480 miles in diameter; Vesta, though smaller, is the brightest; Pallas is reddish, like Mars. Hidalgo has a huge orbit that swings, somewhat like a comet, nearer the sun than the rest, then far out beyond the orbit of Jupiter. Icarus has the smallest orbit known; it passes wholly inside the orbit of Mercury.

The majority of planetoids are 10 to 50 miles in diameter. They are generally not spherical in shape, but more like irregular masses of rock rotating in their orbits. Eros has been studied carefully, and appears to be a body with dimensions about 20 × 10 × 5 miles, rotating about its shortest axis. Many others are much smaller, mere chunks of rock hurtling through space.

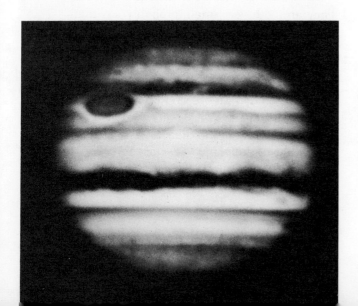

Jupiter, in blue light, showing large red spot. Photographed with 200-inch telescope. Astronomers have found the markings on Jupiter difficult to explain to their entire satisfaction. (Three Lions, N.Y.C.)

The origin of the planetoids is not known. It has been assumed by some scientists that they are the result of some great catastrophe which happened to a planet that revolved between Mars and Jupiter.

Jupiter. Jupiter is the largest of the planets, and therefore was named after the most powerful of the Greek gods. It is, with the exception of Venus, the brightest of the planets, and is a handsome object in the night sky. Although its diameter is 87,000 miles—more than ten times that of Earth—it has only about a quarter the density of Earth, because it contains a larger proportion of gases.

Jupiter revolves around the sun in approximately 12 years. It has a very short day and night, for it rotates on its axis in a little less than 10 hours.

Jupiter is famous for its moons, of which twelve have been discovered. The four largest were discovered and named by Galileo: Io, Europa, Ganymede, and Callisto. The others have not been named. This was one of the great discoveries of science. Galileo, using a telescope, observed that these bodies, which appeared to be stars near Jupiter, were in reality satellites, or moons, of Jupiter. At that time most people believed that all bodies revolved about Earth. To find that certain bodies revolved around some other body, such as Jupiter, was a revolutionary discovery, which shattered man's geocentric (Earth-centered) ideas. The four large moons are larger than our moon; the other eight are very small. The twelfth was not discovered until 1951.

One way in which satellites are thought to have formed might be as follows: As a whirling body of dust and gaseous matter shrinks by gravitation, it spins ever more rapidly, then becomes stretched out at the equator, and finally throws off part of its matter into space. It is natural that this part should revolve about the parent body in the same direction, and also spin in that direction. All the planets show this type of motion, and most of their satellites do. The eight moons nearest Jupiter follow this pattern.

The other four moons, however, revolve about Jupiter in the opposite direction. It is possible that they are planetoids that passed near enough to Jupiter to be attracted by that powerful body. The gravitational pull of this largest of planets may have been strong enough to draw them out of orbit around the sun and into new orbits around itself.

Jupiter has a number of markings, bands of orange, red, brown, and sometimes green, parallel to the equator, that revolve at somewhat different speeds. This startling fact shows clearly that they are caused by clouds rather than by solid features.

An unusual feature is the Great Red Spot. This persistent spot appears to rotate with the planet, and may be the top of a huge column of gas, forming a reddish patch of cloud 30,000 miles long, or it may be a solid body drifting back and forth.

It is believed that the core of Jupiter is a relatively rocky mass, surrounded by ice, which in turn is covered by a large atmosphere. The spectrograph shows that the atmosphere contains large quantities of ammonia and methane. Both of these gases are well known on Earth.

The temperature of the surface is calculated to be around $-200°$F.; but this is not surprising in view of the great distance from the sun, which is about 483,000,000 miles away.

The four planets Jupiter, Saturn, Uranus, and Neptune, which are beyond the planetoids are sometimes called the giant planets or major planets. They are much larger than Mercury, Venus, Earth, and Mars, which are between the sun and the planetoids, and they all share the low temperatures and general make-up of Jupiter.

Saturn. The second largest planet, Saturn, is one of the most interesting and beautiful ob-

Saturn is famous for its ring system. Photographed with a 100-inch telescope. (Three Lions, N.Y.C.)

jects to be seen in the sky. The central ball has a diameter of about 70,000 miles, and is surrounded at its equator by a ring which is 40,000 miles wide. When it is seen broadside, this ring greatly adds to the size and beauty of the planet. When it is edge on, however, the ring is practically invisible from Earth, for it is hardly 10 miles thick.

Saturn has nine moons, the nearest of which is supposed to have a strong gravitational effect that separates the ring into three principal sections. Whatever the cause, there are three distinct rings separated by clear spaces. The middle ring is the brightest. The innermost ring is somewhat transparent, so that the central ball or even distant stars may be seen through it. The rings are sometimes seen to cast their shadows on the planet. Infrared spectra (p. 870) indicate that the tiny particles that make up the rings are coated with ice.

Fine calculations have shown that Saturn has just the right mass to form rings. In the formative period of the solar system it is believed that clouds of cosmic material might have been attracted toward the planets. In falling toward a larger planet, such as Jupiter, they would have been more likely to form moons. Such clouds would plunge headlong to a smaller planet, such as Uranus. In the case of Saturn, they are thought to have been checked by ionizing (p. 379) forces at the right point to coalesce into small particles and form a stable ring.

The planet Saturn revolves around the sun in 29½ of our years. However, its day and night are nearly as short as Jupiter's.

Uranus. Uranus is barely visible, and therefore was mistaken for centuries for a star. It was recognized as a planet by William Herschel in 1781. Uranus is much larger than Earth, having a diameter of about 29,000 miles. About 84 of our years are needed for it to make one revolution about the sun. It rotates on its axis in a little less than eleven hours. It has five moons, the last of which was discovered in 1948.

Uranus has an unusual feature. It "lies down on its side"; that is, its axis is nearly parallel to the plane of its orbit. This means that the planet cannot have seasons as Earth does. When the equator is toward the sun, rotation of the planet produces day and night. When one pole is toward the sun, the other pole remains in darkness and winter for approximately half of the planet's 84-year revolution around the sun.

This motion is in contrast with that of Jupiter, which "stands upright" in its orbit. Jupiter's axis is nearly perpendicular to the plane of its orbit. The rapid whirling of Jupiter produces a 5-hour day followed by a 5-hour night, but no seasonal variations can occur.

Discussing the different types of planetary motion may help children to appreciate the advantages of the seasons we have on Earth, as a result of the planet's axis being tilted at an angle of 23° to its orbit.

Children with special interests in this subject may relate it to the study of space exploration (p. 235).

Neptune. Neptune is also larger than Earth, having a diameter of about 28,000 miles. It rotates on its axis in about 16 hours, and has two moons, the second of which was discovered in 1949. It requires approximately 165 of our years to revolve about the sun.

The discovery of Neptune is one of the famous incidents in astronomical history. It was noted by astronomers that Uranus was pulled aside from its regular course by the attraction of some planet. Two young mathematicians, Adams in England and Leverrier in France, undertook to find the position of this planet by mathematics. Adams secured his results but was unable to interest the English astronomers. The planet was discovered by Galle, a German astronomer, to whom Leverrier wrote concerning his findings. Galle discovered it by means of his telescope at almost the exact spot where Leverrier had found by mathematics that it should be.

Pluto. For a long time it was thought that Neptune was the outermost planet of the solar system. In 1930 Pluto was discovered, and as yet not a great deal is known about it. It is small, perhaps about the size of Mars. It requires about 247 of our years to complete its revolution around the sun.

Are there other planets beyond Pluto? This question cannot be answered finally, but the chances are considered to be small.

As far out as Pluto the sun still wields its influence. The sun remains the nearest star to Pluto. In fact, it is very much nearer than the other stars. Yet, to an observer on Pluto, the sun would not look very much as it does to us on Earth.

In the orbit of Pluto we are within our family system of planets, near our own home fires. In our own solar system we have one star, which is our sun. The nearest star beyond the solar system is a tremendous distance away, far beyond the orbit of Pluto.

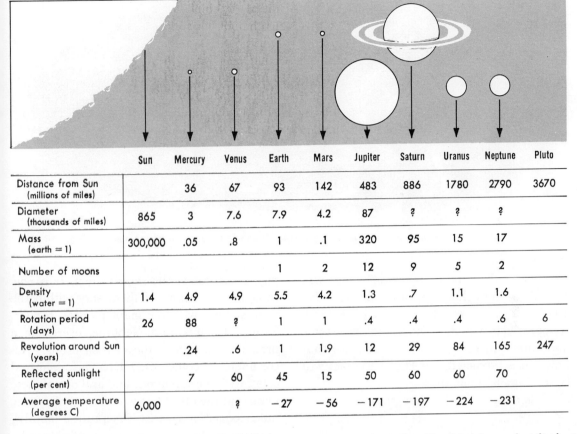

	Sun	Mercury	Venus	Earth	Mars	Jupiter	Saturn	Uranus	Neptune	Pluto
Distance from Sun (millions of miles)		36	67	93	142	483	886	1780	2790	3670
Diameter (thousands of miles)	865	3	7.6	7.9	4.2	87	?	?	?	
Mass (earth = 1)	300,000	.05	.8	1	.1	320	95	15	17	
Number of moons				1	2	12	9	5	2	
Density (water = 1)	1.4	4.9	4.9	5.5	4.2	1.3	.7	1.1	1.6	
Rotation period (days)	26	88	?	1	1	.4	.4	.4	.6	6
Revolution around Sun (years)		.24	.6	1	1.9	12	29	84	165	247
Reflected sunlight (per cent)		7	60	45	15	50	60	60	70	
Average temperature (degrees C)	6,000		?	−27	−56	−171	−197	−224	−231	

The Solar System includes the sun, nine known planets and an enormous number of smaller bodies. Very little is known about the planet Pluto. Note that all figures have been rounded off. These figures are subject to change as more is learned about the Solar System. (After F. O. Rice, Catholic University of America, Washington, D.C., "The Chemistry of Jupiter" in Scientific American, *June 1956).*

EXPERIENCE. *What does life need?* What does life, as we know it on Earth, need? In later elementary years such a study may help to bring together elements from a number of different areas of science. Considerable use of the imagination should be permitted to the child in the discussion. For instance, how must distance from the sun affect the temperature of Earth? From this point of view contrast the possible conditions on Mercury and Pluto. What are the possible effects of rotation upon the conditions on the planets? What are the effects of Earth's atmosphere? What substances are needed for life?

COMETS. It is little wonder that people were superstitious about comets before the development of modern astronomy. Comets seemed to appear suddenly in the sky. More than a thousand comets have been recorded. The word *comet* comes from a Greek word that means "long-haired"; and this, indeed, describes very well the appearance of many comets, for often the tail spreads across the sky like long flowing hair. Sometimes people thought a comet announced divine wrath and the coming of a terrible catastrophe.

The astronomer Edmund Halley did much to cause people to lose their fear of comets.

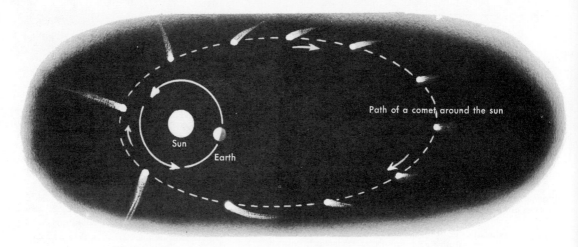

The head of a comet is always toward the sun.   The tail is always away from the sun.

He showed that one comet, which later was named for him, had appeared before. He predicted that it would return in 1758–1759. It appeared in March, 1759, several years after his death. It has appeared twice since that time. It is predicted that Halley's comet will be seen again about 1984.

At one time it was thought that comets

Mrkos Comet was discovered in 1957. The tails of comets differ in length. (Three Lions, N.Y.C.)

passed far out of the solar system. It is now thought that many of them stay within the solar system, with the giant planets, Jupiter, Saturn, Uranus, and Neptune, exercising a predominant influence over their orbits. Accordingly, a comet may have an elongated orbit, with the sun at one end and one of these planets at the other. It would take, of course, much longer for a comet of Neptune's "family" to return to the sun than for one influenced by Jupiter. Sometimes comets seem to be lost to the solar system. Comets have no appreciable gravitational effect upon planets.

The head of a comet is thought to be composed of very fine particles of rock dust and frozen gases. During its icy journey through space the gases remain frozen; but as the comet approaches the sun the gases thaw and expand. Streams of fast particles and radiation from the sun are believed to strike the comet, forcing out part of its substance to form a tail. Some of this material is gradually lost, and comets show a tendency to diminish in size or disintegrate completely. The debris that they leave behind may reach Earth in the form of meteors (p. 223).

It is known that minute particles of matter are pushed away from the sun by the pressure of its light more strongly than they are attracted by the sun's gravitational field, just as currents of wind may blow particles of dust upward in spite of the pull of Earth's gravity.

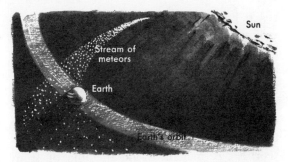

When Earth passes through a stream of meteors, a meteor shower occurs on Earth.

The substance of the comet is almost unbelievably thin. The tail and even the head are quite transparent, and stars may be seen through them. In 1910 the head of Halley's comet passed across the sun without casting a noticeable shadow on Earth. And Earth, in turn, passed through the tail of the comet without most people being aware of the fact.

It is estimated that the density of a comet is about the same as that of a cubic inch of ordinary air that has expanded until it fills a cube 50 miles high. A comet is almost a vacuum.

The tails of comets may be 50,000,000 miles long. Some tails are straight, others curved, and some comets have both kinds. As the comet approaches the sun, the tail is formed and grows longer. As it passes around the sun, its tail continues to point away from the sun. As it recedes from the sun, it goes tail first, like a courtier bowing out backward from the presence of royalty.

Comets waste away. A comet coming near a large body, such as the sun or a large planet, may lose material or even be completely broken up. On the other hand, it may secure new material in its journey. Certain comets, such as Halley's comet, have been in existence for many centuries.

It is interesting to note that although the comets and the planets are members of the solar system, and are under the control of the sun's gravitational attraction, they are different in almost all other respects.

EXPERIENCE. *To compare comets with planets.* How do comets and planets differ with respect to the courses in which they move? In what ways are they alike? in size? in weight? Could we live on a comet?

Meteors, or Shooting Stars. A person looking at the stars frequently sees a shooting star, or meteor. It may look as if one of the stars had bolted across the sky in a flash of light, disappearing almost immediately. True stars, of course, are huge suns trillions of miles away; meteors are usually very small bits of metallic or stony material, most of them no larger than the head of a pin, which Earth encounters in its orbit. Most of them seem to belong to the solar system, and they often travel in large numbers, sometimes as the debris left by a comet that has partly or wholly disintegrated. It will be remembered that the material of comets is very small and fragmentary.

When a meteor plunges into Earth's atmosphere it may be traveling at the rate of 30 miles per second. There it collides with atoms of air, becomes vaporized by the intense heat of friction, leaves a trail of hot, electrified gas behind it, and in a moment disappears from sight. It is the glow of the incandescent gas trail that is seen by the eye; and because the gas is electrified, or ionized, it reflects radio signals in the same way as does the ionosphere (p. 448).

Meteor "showers" occur when Earth passes through a thick swarm of meteors. Some of these appear with great regularity. The Perseid meteors are seen every year, around August 11. The Leonids in 1833 put on a brilliant display that attracted wide attention. Meteor showers associated with Halley's comet occur in May and October.

It has been estimated that a billion meteors

reach Earth every day. Many of them are microscopic and go unnoticed. Some are large enough to be seen as shooting stars that are quickly vaporized. A few are large enough to reach the surface of Earth before they are wholly vaporized. These are known as *meteorites*. Children may need help in clarifying the difference between a meteor and a meteorite. A meteor is the metallic or stony material *before* it has fallen; it is called a meteorite *after* it has fallen. Once in perhaps a million years a meteorite appears that is large enough to form a huge crater where it lands, such as Meteor Crater in Arizona or the Chubb Crater in Quebec. The Arizona crater is three quarters of a mile in diameter, with walls 600 feet high. The one in Quebec is even larger. Other large craters are in Siberia and South Africa.

Large fragments that reach Earth may have a different origin from the small ones that are consumed. They have a close similarity to the planetoids, and like them may be parts of a shattered planet.

There is little damage done by meteors to man. Comparatively few actually get through the atmosphere to the surface of Earth. Moreover, so much of Earth is uninhabited that there is plenty of space for meteors to strike without doing damage. The dust from meteors settles slowly to the surface of Earth, adding to its weight.

We are riding on a rotating Earth. Part of the time we are on the forward side, part of the time on the backward side. We should expect the forward side of Earth to encounter more meteors than the backward side. This seems to be the case. We are on the forward side after midnight. At that time we observe more meteors.

This can be made more realistic to children if they act it out. One child may carry a globe across the room while another rotates it. The forward and the backward sides may be pointed out.

This crater in Arizona was made by a meteor between 5000 and 75,0 years ago. (Josef Muench.)

Many meteorites are preserved in museums. The largest meteorite exhibited is composed of iron weighing 36 tons and was brought from Greenland by the explorer Peary.

All the substances found in meteorites are known to exist on Earth, so that meteorites do not introduce new substances to Earth. Some studies would indicate that meteors are about as old as Earth.

In closing our discussion of the solar system, we may say that we have found a great variety of objects in this system, just as in the universe at large. The solar system is composed of a sun, planets, moons, planetoids, comets, and meteors, rather an interesting family of astronomical bodies moving together in space at a terrific pace.

Earth's Moon

When we say "moon," we mean, of course, Earth's moon—the body which, next to the sun, is the most conspicuous object in our sky. We must remember, however, that some of the other planets have moons. Our Earth has only one moon, as far as we know.

The Moon Revolves about Earth. The moon appears to rise and set because of the rotation of Earth. We have observed that the sun and stars do the same. The moon, however, is the only one of all these bodies which revolves about Earth. It moves about Earth in a little less than a month (27½ days). The word *month* is related to the word *moon*. As a result of its revolution about Earth, the moon rises and sets, on an average, fifty-one minutes later each day. It varies in the time of its rising and setting at some parts of Earth from ten minutes later than on the preceding day to an hour and a half later.

The moon is the nearest body to Earth. The distance from Earth to the moon varies from 222,000 miles to 253,000 miles. The average distance to the moon from Earth is about 238,000 miles. Of course this seems like a great distance to us, who live on a globe which is only about 25,000 miles in circumference. Yet when we study the distant planets and the still more distant stars, the distance to the moon seems like a mere step.

EXPERIENCE. *The distance to the moon as compared with the distance around Earth.* How many times would an airplane have to go around Earth to go as far as the distance from Earth to the moon?

How Large Is the Moon? Earth has a large moon for such a little planet. The distance through the moon is a little over 2000 miles. This is about one fourth the diameter of Earth. In volume the moon is about one fiftieth the size of Earth.

Earth weighs over eighty times as much as the moon. The force of gravitation of Earth is much greater than that of the moon. The surface gravity on the moon is one-sixth that on Earth. The moon does not have sufficient gravitation to hold an atmosphere. It is probable that if the moon did have any gases surrounding it in the past, they escaped a long time ago. Earth has sufficient gravitation to hold an atmosphere. This is, of course, most fortunate for all life on Earth, including ourselves.

One could jump and move about more easily on the moon because there is less gravitation to resist.

The Moon Keeps the Same Side Turned toward Earth. No one has ever seen more than one side of the moon from Earth, for the moon always presents the same side to us as it revolves around Earth. The reason for this may be tidal friction (see p. 231). The moon rotates in the same time in which it revolves. That is to say, the moon rotates only once during a revolution around Earth. Many people have difficulty in understanding that the moon rotates at all.

For as long a time as history gives any information on the subject, the moon has kept the same side toward Earth. However, man has seen as much as 59 per cent of the surface of the moon, because of the way in which it moves.

EXPERIENCE. *We see only one side of the moon.* The way in which the moon moves may be illustrated by a person's walking around some object and keeping his face always toward the object. When the starting point is reached, the person will have made one rotation as well as one revolution. He has rotated, for he has faced in all directions; he rotated so gradually that he was scarcely aware of it.

Each child should have the opportunity of performing this demonstration. To show that he rotated, have him repeat the experiment but this time face continuously in the same direction, such as north. At one time his face is toward the object, at another time his side, at still another his back, and finally his other side. In this case he did not rotate. He faced in the same direction all the time. The concept to emphasize is that the object rotates once as it revolves once. This takes a little time to visualize, and the learner may have to be given a chance to work it out for himself.

To make this demonstration more vivid to children, one can take a ball and mark a face on it to represent the side of the moon turned

Two views of the new moon. The age of the moon at the right is 3 days; the age of the one at the left is 5 days. (Mount Wilson and Palomar Observatories.)

toward Earth. Then certain children in the center of the room may be used for Earth.

EXPERIENCE. *Observation of the moon.* This is an experience which parents might profitably engage in with the children. Go outdoors with the children some night when the moon is visible. Observe it carefully. Use field glasses if possible. The repetition of this trip will show that the same side is turned toward Earth at the different times.

EXPERIENCE. *The lighted portion of the moon which is seen from Earth changes in shape.* We may continue the preceding demonstration with a ball (preferably white) with marks on one side to represent the face of the moon turned toward Earth, and with a child to represent Earth itself. On one side of a darkened room place a light, such as a strong flashlight or a projection lantern, to represent the sun. Revolve the ball about the child, keeping the face marked on it turned toward the child. Throw the light on the ball as it moves about the child, recalling that the sun is a much more powerful light which throws its light in all directions and therefore does not need to be turned to follow the moon. Stop at different positions and have the child representing Earth describe what he sees. Recall the proportions of the distances involved, especially the fact that the sun is very much farther from Earth than the moon; it should be added that this great distance cannot be represented in the room. In moving the moon about Earth be careful not to get moon, Earth, and sun in the same straight line (unless you want to demonstrate eclipses).

Only one half of the moon's surface is turned toward the sun and illuminated at one time. It is obvious, then, that the illuminated side of the moon is not always turned toward Earth. Therefore the side turned toward Earth, with which we are familiar, is not always illuminated, as is shown in the demonstration. Sometimes the moon is approximately between Earth and the sun (not in the same straight line, for at that time we may have a solar eclipse). This is new moon, and the dark side is then directly toward us. (This can be shown in the demonstration.) The moon continues to revolve about Earth, and a week later, at the time of first quarter, half of the illuminated part, or hemisphere, is visible, or, in other words, half of the side turned toward Earth is illuminated. At the time of full moon the part turned toward Earth is entirely illuminated. Earth is at this time between the moon and the sun. The moon continues its revolution, and at the time of last quarter only one half of the illuminated surface is visible. The illuminated part of the moon is constantly shifting because the moon rotates on its axis in a little less than a month, and therefore, by turning, gradually changes the part turned toward the sun. The length of time between the appearance of the new moon and the complete disappearance of the full moon is twenty-nine and a half days.

Children sometimes ask why they can see the outline of the entire moon when, a few days after the date of the new moon, the first slender lunar crescent is visible. That is, the crescent is very bright, but the remainder of the moon is illuminated very faintly. The bright crescent is illuminated by sunlight; the remainder of the moon is illuminated by earthlight, just as Earth is illuminated at times by moonlight. Since Earth is much larger than the moon, it is quite probable that the moon is illuminated much more by earthlight than Earth is by moonlight. The light which we see slightly illuminating the dark part of the moon has traveled a devious path. It started from the sun, traveled to Earth, then to the moon and then back to Earth, where some of it enters our eyes.

The Moon Probably Has No Atmosphere.
What should we find if we were to make a journey to the moon? In the first place, we should have to carry our own oxygen supply, because there is little or no atmosphere on the moon. We should also need to protect our bodies against the fierce blast of ultraviolet rays from the sun, which on Earth are largely filtered out by the ozone layer of the upper atmosphere (p. 449). Without proper protection we should soon be cooked to a crisp.

If one of our companions were an astronomer, he would be anxious to make observations of the sun and the stars, because "good seeing" would be unhampered by the atmospheric disturbances that so severely handicapped his work on Earth.

The fact that there is little or no atmosphere on the moon makes the moon's surface very different from that of Earth. If there is no air, there is no wind to blow the dust about. There can be no clouds on the moon. The clouds we see coming between us and the moon are very near to us, perhaps less than a mile high, and are in Earth's atmosphere. It nevers rains on the moon, and as a consequence there are no brooks, rivers, lakes, or oceans. There is no water to move the rock particles about. With no air, there would be no sound reaching our ears, and we could not talk to one another.

The Moon's Surface. The part of the moon turned toward Earth has been studied carefully. The surface of the moon appears to be rough and brownish. It reflects light poorly since it only reflects about 7 per cent of the sunlight that falls on it. Outstanding features of the moon's surface are it mountains, craters, and maria, or "seas." There are many lesser features.

The mountains are found most frequently in chains, or groups. The higher ones may be about the height of the Andes. Ancient volcanic activity is thought to appear in some of the mountains and possibly in the comparatively level areas called maria.

The surface of the moon is quite different from that of Earth. It has large craters and many steep mountain sides.

At least a million craters are visible from Earth, of all sizes, ranging downward from the largest, which is more than 140 miles in diameter. Each crater is circular, with a mountainous rim that is steep on the inside but slopes off gently on the outside. Early observers speculated that the craters might be of volcanic origin, but volcanic craters are perched on mountaintops, whereas the floors of the lunar craters are depressions that are lower than the surrounding landscape.

Recent studies have shown that the craters were formed by meteorites. It is believed that in past ages Earth and the moon alike encountered or "swept up" large numbers of meteoric fragments. Earth, being larger, would have possessed an atmosphere in which many of them were vaporized, as they are today. Craters formed by larger meteorites would in many cases have been destroyed by erosion.

The moon, however, lacking an atmosphere, would have been exposed to a pelting rain of large and small bodies that struck it with explosive force. The high speed of the meteorites is important, for as they struck the rocky surface their energy of motion would be converted into heat sufficiently intense to vaporize the rock. The gases thus formed would blast a hole estimated to be about 60,000 times the volume of the meteorite, throwing up the debris in a circular rim.

Comparison with meteorite craters on Earth, and with bomb craters formed in the wars, shows close similarities. Estimates have been made of the volume of material in the surrounding rim, and they agree closely.

It would not be entirely accurate to say that there is no erosion or weathering on the moon. We shall soon learn that there are great extremes of temperature on the moon's surface, which may cause expansion and contraction, thus breaking up the surface rocks. The moon has gravitation, which may cause landslides. However, no changes have been discovered since the moon was first accurately mapped after the invention of the telescope.

The Temperature of the Moon. Since the moon rotates on its axis but once in a little less than a month, any given portion of its surface is turned toward the sun for about two weeks and away from the sun for an equal period. In other words, its day and night are each two weeks long. There are no clouds to moderate the heat during the long lunar day. It gets very hot; the temperature during this period is a little above the boiling point of water on Earth, which is normally 212°. In discussions with children this relationship may aid them in developing a concept of the tremendous temperature changes on the moon. At night the moon quickly cools off and probably reaches a temperature as low as $-250°$F. The moon would not be a comfortable place for us to live on.

Eclipses. A total eclipse of the sun is one in which the entire sun is hidden by the moon, which occasionally gets between Earth and the sun in the same straight line. The moon then throws a shadow on Earth. During a

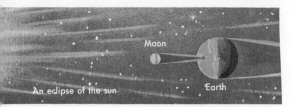

An eclipse of the sun   Moon   Earth

total eclipse the sun's corona, which consists of white streamers around the outside of the sun, is seen. This is always present, but is visible only during a total eclipse, since at other times the bright surface of the sun obscures it.

In a partial eclipse of the sun the moon is a little too high or too low to get directly in front of the sun. A partial eclipse may take place without our noticing it, unless we happen to look at the sun. In looking at an eclipse of the sun, we should use a piece or two of over-exposed camera film to protect our eyes.

When a total eclipse is taking place, it is visible only to people in a fairly narrow strip of Earth's surface. This is because the moon's shadow covers only a few square miles of Earth's surface at a time. People along the edge of the strip will see a partial eclipse. The area covered by a partial eclipse is much larger than the path of a total eclipse.

A lunar eclipse is caused by Earth's throwing a shadow on the moon. At this time Earth gets between the sun and the moon in the same straight line. Lunar eclipses can take place only when the moon and the sun are on opposite sides of Earth, or, in other words, at the time of full moon.

The explanation of the cause of eclipses just given may leave the impression that we should

An eclipse of the moon   Earth   Moon

have an eclipse of the sun and of the moon every month. The reason eclipses are so rare is that the moon's orbit around Earth makes an angle with Earth's orbit around the sun, so that the moon usually passes too low or too high to cause an eclipse. It is only rarely that the moon is at exactly the right height at the moment when it passes between Earth and the sun to cause a solar eclipse or to get in Earth's shadow and thus give us a lunar eclipse.

EXPERIENCE. *To demonstrate solar and lunar eclipses.* In a darkened room use a flashlight to represent the sun and two balls to represent Earth and the moon. Let the moon-ball pass between the sun and Earth to demonstrate a solar eclipse. Let the Earth-ball pass between the moon and the sun to represent a lunar eclipse.

Tides Are Caused by the Moon and the Sun.
Children who live near an ocean or one of its inlets have become familiar with tides, since their swimming may depend on the tides. It is usually rather difficult for them to see how such a remote object as the moon can be responsible for moving large quantities of water on Earth, as it does in producing the tides. It is also difficult for those who specialize in the study of tides to fully understand all of the factors that operate in their formation. Tides are not as simple as they seem.

Not only does Earth attract the moon by its gravitation, but the moon pulls Earth with its gravitation. The moon's gravitation pulls all parts of Earth, the solid part as well as the liquid. However, the liquid part moves more easily than the solid part.

The moon causes the liquid part to bulge on the side nearest to it. The extra water needed to make this bulge is pulled away from other regions on Earth, causing low tides there. It may seem surprising at first that the water on the far side of Earth directly opposite the moon, also bulges. This is because the moon

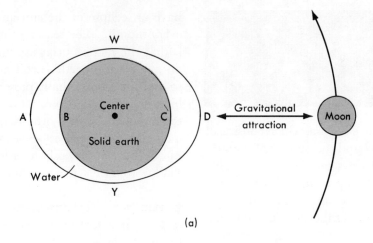

(a)

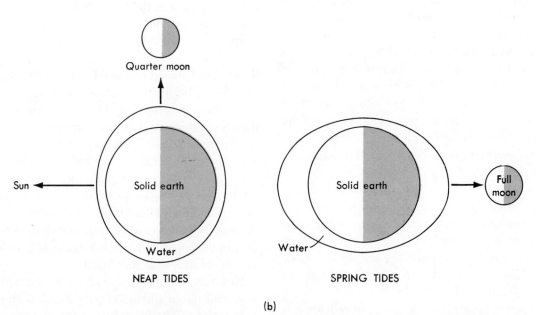

NEAP TIDES   SPRING TIDES

(b)

(a) *High tides occur at* A *and* D; *low tides at* W *and* Y.

(b) *Neap tides occur at the quarter phases of the moon when the sun and moon are not attracting from the same or opposite directions. Spring tides occur at full and new moon when the sun and moon are attracting from the same or opposite directions.*

pulls the whole Earth toward it slightly. The water in front, being nearest the moon, is pulled most and raised in a tide, but the water on the opposite side of Earth is pulled less than the solid part of Earth because it is farther away from the moon. It is "left behind," which means that it, too, is heaped up in a tide.

There may be another force involved in producing tides on the opposite side of Earth. Some scientists think that inertia due to Earth's orbital motion causes water to draw away from Earth on that side, something like water flying from a moving bicycle wheel.

Since it takes Earth twenty-four hours to

rotate once on its axis, it takes approximately a quarter of this time, or six hours, for any place to go from a high-tide section to a low-tide section. It does not take exactly six hours, because the moon is moving all the time. In simple theoretical situations there are approximately twelve hours between two high tides or two low tides. The speed of tidal waves at any one place depends upon a number of other factors such as the shape of shore lines and the depth of the oceans and inlets. Since Earth rotates from west to east, the tides progress in a westerly direction.

Although the moon is chiefly responsible for the tides, the sun also helps to cause them. When the sun and moon are both in the same direction or both in opposite directions, they are both pulling the water toward the same places or away from the same places on Earth, and the tides are unusually high or unusually low. These unusually high or low tides are called *spring tides*. Sometimes the sun is in a direction at right angles to that of the moon. In this case the moon causes high tides in different places from the sun. Such high tides are not so high as usual, and the corresponding low tides are not so low. These are known as *neap tides*. At such times the sun and moon are not pulling together.

EXPERIENCE. *Observations of tides.* Some children may live where tides can be observed or they may have visited a seashore. They may tell the other children about their observa-tions. Pictures can supplement this information.

Tidal Friction Slows Down Earth and Moon. The constant friction and pressure of tides against the western shores of the oceans tends to slow down the eastward rotation of Earth. Added to this is the effect of the pull of the moon and sun on the solid part of Earth. It is estimated that in a hundred thousand years tidal forces have lengthened our day by a little less than one second.

Tides also occur in a solid body like the moon, the nearest part of which is pulled most strongly by Earth. Like that of Earth, its rotation has been slowed down over a long period of time. If one particular area were more strongly attracted than the rest, that portion might continue to face Earth indefinitely. Some scientists think this may explain why the same side of the moon is always turned toward Earth.

The Moon As a Radio Relay Station. Pulsed radar signals beamed at the moon have been received back on Earth about three seconds later. Radio telephone signals carrying the human voice have been transmitted from Earth to the moon and received back on Earth by way of "moon bounce." Artificial satellites may be used in the same way, to reflect radio waves around the curve of Earth. They may prove more reliable reflectors than the ionosphere (p. 448).

Beyond the Solar System

Most of us live in a region known by such a title as a town, city, township, parish, district, borough, county, territory, province, or state. Our region, in turn, is a part of a nation. We have seen that Earth is a planet in the solar system. Is the solar system a part of a larger stellar system, or organization?

Our Own System of Stars—The Galaxy, or Milky Way. The ancients thought that they had the answer to the organization of the stars in their groupings of the constellations. Modern astronomy shows us that the constellations do not represent a true organization of the stars, for the stars that make up the constella-

Our solar system is a part of the Milky Way galaxy.

tions do not always belong together (p. 211). We must look farther for a solution to our problem of finding the system of stars to which our solar system belongs.

Our solar system belongs to a vast system of stars called the galaxy, or Milky Way. All of us have observed the Milky Way. It stretches across the sky and forms one of the most beautiful things to be observed. The Milky Way appears to be a great band that circles the sky. It seems to cut the sky into two nearly equal parts. The exact nature of the Milky Way was not known to the ancients. They invented many legends to explain its nature and cause. Astronomers investigating it have found that it is composed of billions of stars. It is to this system that we belong. The entire solar system is but a faint point in this vast system.

The Milky Way galaxy has been compared to a gigantic pin wheel; the stars of which it is composed are moving about a center that cannot be seen from Earth, because of dark material between us and this center. The center of our galaxy lies in the direction of the constellation Sagittarius.

In the Milky Way we find many *star clusters*. Many of these to the naked eye appear as but a single star, but when studied with a telescope they prove to be composed of thousands of stars.

We also find nebulae. There are several different kinds. Some are called *planetary*

nebulae, which are really mantles of gas surrounding a star. Then there are places in the Milky Way in which there are very thin gas clouds, known as *gaseous nebulae*. The gas in these nebulae is very thin, thinner, in fact, than the air in any partial vacuum that man has made. But if you add up all the gas in these nebulae—what a lot of material it would make! Then there are dark spots in the Milky Way. At first thought, these might seem to be holes in the sky or places where there are no stars. Recently astronomers have been coming to the conclusion that these dark areas are caused by masses of material which are located between us and the stars in that region. They call this material *dark nebulae*. It has the same effect as smoke when it comes between us and a distant view. These nebulae are not totally dark, because they scatter starlight.

One of the most famous of the dark nebulae is the Southern Coalsack. This dark nebula appears as an intensely black cloud to an observer viewing it with his unaided eye, but observation with a large telescope reveals the presence of many faint stars. It is really not so black; it only appears black when viewed against the apparent brightness of the rest of the Milky Way.

We get some idea of how vast the Milky Way is when we learn that it is composed of gas, dust, and 100 billion stars. These stars are moving about its center, the inner stars moving more rapidly than the outer ones. It has been estimated that in the neighborhood of the solar system the stars require about 200 million years to complete a revolution—in other words, that it takes the sun and its family that length of time to pass completely around the Milky Way. From what you know of the story of Earth, try to imagine what Earth was like and what kind of life lived on it 200 million years ago, when it may have been in about the same position in the Milky Way as it is today.

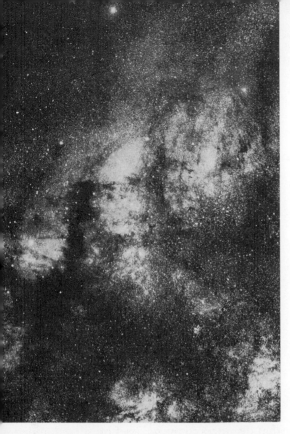

...iew of the Milky Way. Our own galaxy is named for this vast ...n of stars. We can look out at the Milky Way realizing that we ...a part of the same great galaxy. (Courtesy of The American Mu-...a of Natural History.)

Light-Years. The distances are so great out in space that the ordinary units of linear measurement which we use on Earth, such as inches, feet, and miles, cannot be used by astronomers. They use a unit called the *light-year*, which is the distance that light travels in one year. Light travels at approximately 186,000 miles per second. By arithmetic children can see what a great distance that rate of travel covers in a year. The sun is only about eight minutes away by light; that is, the light of the sun reaches us in about eight minutes after it leaves the sun. The nearest star, called Proxima, is over four light-years away. If something were to happen to Proxima so that it stopped shining, we should not know it for over four years.

We gain an impression of the tremendous

233

size of the Milky Way when we learn that it has been estimated to be more than 100,000 light-years in diameter. We are about 33,000 light-years from the center of the system.

EXPERIENCE. *To express in miles some of the great distances in the universe.* Many of the older children in the elementary school enjoy large numbers. It might be well to have those with special ability in arithmetic calculate the estimated distance across the Milky Way galaxy in terms of miles. They can do this by multiplying the estimate given in light years by 365¼ days, by 24 hours, by 60 minutes and then by 60 seconds. They may enjoy the large number which will stretch across the blackboard or their papers. This may help all of the children to gain an improved impression

Spiral Nebula in the Constellation of Ursa Major N G C 3031, Messier 81. The arms in this spiral nebula extend far out from the nucleus. Near the center, stars are so numerous that they blend together and cannot be separated. Farther out in the arms, multitudes of stars begin to appear as individual points. On the photograph they are extremely faint, but actually they correspond in brightness to the brighter stars in our own stellar Milky Way system. They appear faint because NGC 3031 is at a distance of 2,500,000 light years. (1 light year—6 million million miles.) (Photograph from 200-inch Hale Telescope Mount Wilson and Palomar Observatories.)

of space. The older children may be able to find some known distance within their own community that is a mile long and compare it with the distance across the Milky Way.

Once man thought that Earth was the center of the universe, and that everything, including moon, planets, and sun and other stars, revolved around it. Then he found that it was not the center of the solar system, and now he knows that the solar system is not the center of his system of stars. He knows now, too, that there are other systems of stars.

EXPERIENCE. *There is gravitation throughout the universe.* Gravitation is considered to be all throughout space. Earth, moon, and sun are each part of the general gravitational field. This is a little hard to conceive of, but here is a universal force. Encourage children to discuss gravitation as a force that probably exists throughout space.

There Are Systems of Stars Other than Our Own. It is only in recent decades that we have begun to penetrate beyond our galaxy, the Milky Way, into what is sometimes called *extragalactic space.* As better telescopes were made, astronomers observed great numbers of fuzzy spirals, or "pinwheels." These were thought to be clouds of gas, or nebulae, and are still sometimes referred to as spiral nebulae. However, they were soon found to be complete "island universes," similar to our own galaxy, at vast distances beyond the Milky Way, each composed of billions of individual stars. They are ordinarily called galaxies. There are about 100 billion galaxies within the range of our largest optical telescopes, which is over 1 billion light-years, and we have no means of knowing how many may lie beyond. Such distances are almost incomprehensible, but astronomers deal with them continually.

If we consider the motion of a man on Earth

(p. 195) relative to the universe, we must include the fact that the sun and the solar system are revolving about the center of the galaxy, and this motion must be added to the other motions. Astronomers have to allow for it in calculating the motions and distances of other galaxies.

Measuring Distance to the Galaxies. Distances in the solar system and the Milky Way can be calculated by parallax (p. 205). The distances to about 6000 of the nearest stars in the Milky Way have been determined by parallax.

Outside the Milky Way, however, the parallax method will not work. Astronomers have learned much about these extragalactic distances from the study of variable stars, but are still forced from time to time to make corrections in their figures. In 1954 they announced that distances to the galaxies must be doubled. For example, the distance to the galaxy in Andromeda, formerly thought to be about 1 million light-years, is now believed to be twice as great, or about 2 million light-years.

Relativity—A Newer Concept of Space-Time. The following is presented as an exceedingly brief summary of the theory of relativity. No one need be disturbed if he does not readily understand this theory, for there is much evidence that it is not completely understood by specialists. The theory of relativity, developed by Albert Einstein, concerns the physical meaning of space and time. It has two parts. (1) The special theory (1905) explains why the laws of nature appear the same to all observers moving with constant velocity relative to one another. (2) The general theory (1916) has to do with gravitation. Relativity involves much mathematics, and is important in astronomy and atomic physics. A few simple illustrations may be mentioned.

Space is thought of as curved, and closely related to time—the *space-time continuum.* Objects appear different to an observer whose speed is accelerating. A ray of light from a distant star passing close to the sun may be observed during an eclipse to be deflected toward the sun by the sun's gravitational field. As the speed of a particle having mass approaches the speed of light, its mass increases. Nothing can move faster than light, the speed of which is about 186,000 miles per second. Mass is a form of energy, according to the formula

$$E = mc^2$$

where E stands for energy, m for mass, and c for the speed of light.

The Exploration of Space

Children Learn about Exploring Space. The development of powerful rockets and other instruments since World War II has enabled mankind to make serious plans to explore and study the universe beyond the confines of the planet Earth.

Children at all levels are interested in following the progress of the latest balloon ascension, rocket or satellite launching, or the latest expedition into any unexplored region. They are interested in the people concerned with this work, in their equipment, and in the information sought.

It would be well to arrange for periods of discussion and study of such events. This should be a time when children can express their thoughts freely and a teacher gain a knowledge of the quality of their thinking. This would assist the teacher in knowing the points at which a child can be helped to a better understanding of his environment.

Encourage children to express their conceptions of whatever region or exploit is being studied. They could discuss the purpose of such explorations, how information is secured, how information can benefit mankind, and other pertinent questions. For instance, pictures of cloud formations help in weather forecasting; knowledge of radiation may help to explain auroras or the behavior of devices used in communication; knowing more about the atmosphere may help chemists to produce materials that resist heat or corrosion. Photographs of Earth made from high altitudes are of value in preparing maps that will tell more about Earth and be of use to navigators; special instruments may add new knowledge of Earth's shape and interior; the launching of rockets may add to a knowledge of fuels and the ways they are handled. These are only samples of the many aspects of exploration. The purposes of exploration should not be lost sight of in the excitement of the spectacular launchings and preparations necessary to secure information.

Teachers need not be chagrined if children appear to know more about some aspects of the subject than they. A child may be especially interested in some area of exploration and he may have accumulated a body of information. Or a child may have acquired a vocabulary relating to space exploration without much conception of the meaning of the words. A teacher might well encourage such a child to gain a broader perspective or assist him toward a more basic understanding of the vocabulary and the principles involved.

It is evident that learning about aspects of science, such as conditions necessary to life, adaptation, the nature of the atmosphere, and man's use of energy, magnetism, electricity, machines, and communication, provides the fundamental experiences for an understanding of or participation in such programs of exploration.

Sounding Rockets and Satellites. A useful means of gathering information from space is by means of rockets and man-made, or artificial, satellites.

Sounding rockets are unmanned vehicles that are sent different distances from Earth and may either send data to Earth by telemetry (radio signals) or be returned to Earth. Some may go into orbit, although they are not intended to do so. When sounding rockets are sent beyond 4000 miles from Earth they are called *space probes.*

Satellites are thought of as vehicles revolving

The Mariner II spacecraft was started on its flight toward the planet Venus on the morning of August 27, 1962. An hour after launch, a tracking station at Woomera, Australia, picked up signals that indicated the spacecraft had unfolded properly and that the solar panels were supplying power to the craft's batteries. (Wide World Photos.)

around a body in the solar system. If they revolve around a planet, they may be thought of as artificial moons. If they revolve around the sun they are artificial planetoids. Some are placed in orbit around Earth and then returned. Others are launched into an orbit about 22,000 miles above the equator. If these are made to rotate in the same direction as Earth, they will seem to remain in the same place, because they will take about the same time to circle Earth as it takes Earth to rotate once. These are sometimes called "fixed" or stationary satellites.

Each spacecraft is designed and launched for a specific purpose and carries instruments designed to gather and record information and relay it to Earth. This information will have many practical applications as knowledge accumulates and relationships are observed. For example, longer-range weather prediction is becoming a certainty, and communication is being improved. Certain satellites may prove to be an aid to navigators as well.

The instruments that constitute the "payload" of either manned or unmanned vehicles may be of many different kinds, because there are many different things we need to know. For instance, we need to learn much more about the density of the upper atmosphere and its composition; the nature of the ionosphere and how it is influenced by the sun (p. 447); the temperature at different altitudes; the intensity of ultraviolet rays, X rays, and cosmic rays; the number and size of meteors in space; the exact size and shape of the planet Earth; the strength and direction of magnetic fields; the hazards to life that may exist beyond Earth's surface; and many other matters that are difficult or impossible to explore from ground level.

Instruments are often able to operate efficiently under conditions in which man could not survive. Yet a man, by using his knowledge and judgment, may be able to secure information that cannot be secured by instruments alone.

A bulletin board can be of great use in the study of space exploration. Clippings and illustrations of current events can be posted. Older children may wish to make and keep a record of the various space vehicles, their purposes, the heights to which they go, and what becomes of them. This would help to emphasize the great variety of purposes for which these explorations are made.

Orbits. If an object revolves about Earth at a certain speed, the outward movement prevents it from falling to Earth. Gravity causes the object to fall just enough to prevent its flying off into space at a tangent. The object is then said to be *in orbit,* and if nothing interferes, it will remain in orbit indefinitely.

Such forces operate throughout the solar system and, so far as is known, throughout the rest of the universe. They keep planets and moons as well as artificial satellites in their orbits. An astronaut aboard a satellite is himself a living satellite, for the same forces act upon his body.

Orbits in space are regularly elliptical (p. 214), because a perfectly circular orbit seems impossible to achieve.

The point in an orbit nearest Earth (or whatever body provides the gravitational pull) is called the *perigee;* the outermost point, the *apogee.*

Overcoming Gravity. In order to place an object in orbit around Earth or to send it farther into space, it is necessary to learn as much as possible about gravity and about inertia (pp. 187, 716).

If a child stands quietly on scales, they may show that he weighs 100 pounds. Suppose the scales are placed in an elevator and the child stands on them while the elevator starts to rise rapidly. For a moment the scales may indicate twice the normal weight of the child, or 200 pounds. A space expert would say he has "experienced an acceleration of 2 *g*," or twice the normal pull of gravity. If the elevator should descend rapidly enough, the child's apparent weight might drop to zero. He would then be said to be in a state of *free fall,* or "zero gravity." He would feel "weightless."

The test pilot of a fast plane frequently experiences changing *g* forces. When he pulls his plane out of a power dive into level flight, he may experience a force of several *g*. While in the dive, the pilot is like the passenger in the rapidly descending elevator; he tends to feel lighter than usual, because his plane, like the descending elevator, is pulling away from him. The heavy stress comes when he changes to level flight and his plane begins to slow him down.

An astronaut will experience many *g* forces when his capsule is being forced rapidly into space.

In order to raise the child in the elevator, against inertia and the pull of gravity, a force was needed that registered on the scales. A force is also needed to overcome inertia and the pull of gravity on an object when sending it into space. It is necessary to use rockets that can exert tremendous force or *thrust* (p. 769).

EXPERIENCE. *Children may feel the force needed to throw balls.* If there is room on the playground, children may feel and compare the amount of force or thrust needed to throw balls of different weights to different heights. Observe measures to safeguard persons and property. Children may wish to speculate on the reasons why they cannot send a ball into orbit or off into space.

Inertia. When a vehicle has been accelerated to the correct speed for orbiting or for escape from Earth, no further motive power is needed. The resistance of the atmosphere is negligible at such heights, and any object mov-

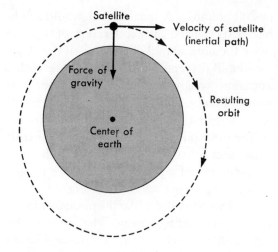

In this diagram the satellite has a velocity to the right, and at the same time, because of the force of gravity it falls toward the center of Earth. As a result it makes an (elliptical) orbit about Earth. (Adapted from Convair's Space Primer, *Convair, San Diego, 1959.)*

Orbital Velocity.

Because the pull of gravity diminishes with distance from Earth, and because the atmosphere becomes less dense with distance, the greatest thrust must be exerted at or near ground level in order to achieve the speed necessary to launch an object into space.

A vehicle such as the manned spacecraft Mercury, which is to orbit Earth, is likely to be boosted vertically, first by a large and powerful rocket, then at an angle by one or more stages of smaller rockets, until an altitude of about 200 miles has been reached and the correct speed has been attained. As it speeds upward, it is turned until it is in a horizontal position. At this point the final stage has burned out and has been detached, and the payload or capsule is moving on a course that will circle Earth in about 90 minutes. The speed needed to make such an orbit, about 18,000 miles per hour, is called the *orbital velocity.*

ing there will continue to move almost indefinitely by its own momentum. This tendency of a moving body to continue to move in a straight line unless something interferes to change its motion is due to *inertia* (p. 741).

When a vehicle attains orbital velocity, the gravitational attraction of Earth changes the motion into a more or less circular one around Earth. Without this pull, the vehicle would follow a straight course (inertial path in illustration), tending away from Earth.

EXPERIENCE. *To observe water as it is thrown from a wheel.* Notice how water or mud is thrown off the wheels of a passing automobile. Or stand a bicycle upside down and have one child turn one of the wheels while another pours a few drops of water onto the tire. If the wheel spins fast enough, drops of water will fly off the wheel at a *tangent,* or parallel to the wheel. They move away from the wheel along the inertial path due to inertia, the tendency of a moving body to continue to move in a straight line.

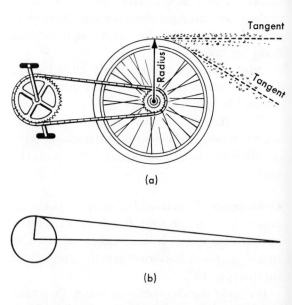

(a) *When the bicycle wheel is turned slowly, drops of water go around with it. When it is turned more rapidly, they tend to fly off in a straight line, along a tangent.*

(b) *At a distance, tangent motion is less noticeable. It is hard to tell whether or not drops come from the center or the rim of the wheel.*

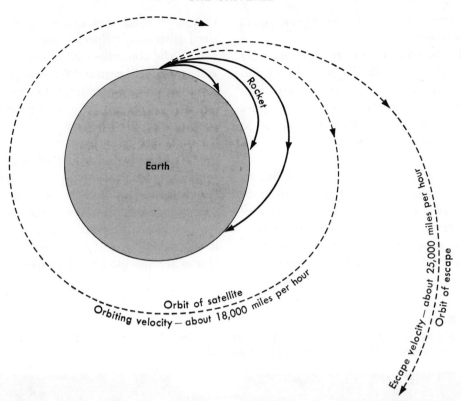

The speed with which an object is projected into space determines its orbit. (*Adapted from Lloyd Motz,* This Is Astronomy, *Archer House, New York, 1958.*)

Children will ask what makes a satellite stay "up." It is the speed at which it travels that enables it to remain aloft. To understand this, consider using different speeds in launching an object from a high tower. With a small speed, the object will soon fall to Earth. With a greater speed, it will go farther before falling. With still greater speed, if it is about 18,000 miles per hour, the object will follow a somewhat circular course as it falls toward Earth. This is its orbital velocity. At still greater speeds, the object will follow more elliptical paths or even escape from Earth.

Tracking. Contact with spacecraft can be maintained by tracking stations. They are usually equipped with powerful and sensitive radio and radar transmitters and receivers for making contact with specific craft. For example, on a particular command signal beamed to it by a radio telescope, a satellite's transmitter can be turned on and can transmit data that has been recorded. This information is recorded as received at the telescope and then relayed by teletype to a processing center. On another signal the transmitter can be turned off, in order to save its batteries.

One network of tracking stations is equipped to track and receive data from unmanned scientific satellites. Another network is equipped to receive from and transmit to craft going to the moon and beyond. Still another network of tracking stations is equipped to keep track of and maintain communication with such manned flights as the Mercury.

The orbits of a satellite such as the Mercury do not pass over the same places on Earth because Earth rotates. Satellites are launched in an easterly direction to take advantage of Earth's rotation.

A flight direction is chosen over relatively uninhabited regions where parts of two and three stage rocket systems will do no harm when they fall. Early American satellites were launched into orbits inclined about 35 degrees to Earth's equator.

Controlling Space Vehicles. It is, of course, impossible to steer or guide a vehicle in space by means of a rudder because of the lack of atmosphere for a rudder to push against. Control is accomplished by means of small rockets or jets set in such a way in the vehicle

that when fired, they can nudge it in the desired direction. Special control equipment will also be aboard as well as a communication system that will permit the sending of messages for automatic control from a distance. If an astronaut is aboard, he may fire the necessary rockets, if he so wishes.

Re-entry. How is a spacecraft orbiting Earth returned to Earth? Simply by reducing its speed. Braking rockets, known as retro-rockets, are fired in a forward direction. The reaction slows the craft, and thus counteracts its inertial movement away from Earth. Parachutes are also used at the proper time to slow

Mercury Control room at Cape Kennedy; Florida. The orbits of the Friendship 7 spacecraft around Earth were followed by numerous tracking and data acquisition stations. (Three Lions, N.Y.C.)

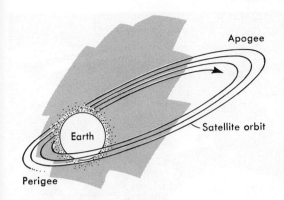

The atmosphere slows down a satellite until it finally plunges toward Earth. (Adapted from the IGY Bulletin, February 1960.)

the gravitational field of Earth. This speed is about 25,000 miles per hour, and is known as the *escape velocity*. For example, a moon spacecraft that has reached this speed and has been aimed correctly will be able to spiral outward from Earth and head for the moon. Because gravitational forces are felt everywhere in the universe, the craft cannot truly escape from the pull of Earth; but at some point in its journey the forward pull of the moon's gravitational field will become stronger than the backward pull exerted by Earth, and the craft, even without power, will start to fall toward the moon.

the descent. The craft gradually falls downward toward Earth in a long arc of several thousand miles. As the craft passes through denser air, it glows red hot from friction and compression of the atmosphere. To prevent its destruction, its forward end is fitted with a large curved *heat shield*, forming a blunt nose that helps to reduce speed. The shield is so designed that its outer surface can gradually melt and drop away, thus carrying away excess heat and protecting the cabin and its passenger. At a suitable height parachutes open, and the craft is lowered to the surface of Earth.

In addition to the problem of radiation if a spacecraft were manned, re-entry from farther out in space would likewise present problems related to heat and lowering the speed of the craft as it approached Earth. For example, if returning from the moon, it might involve making many orbits of Earth, each orbit becoming smaller than the last, due to the slowing effect of the atmosphere as the craft passed through a portion of it on each orbit.

Escape Velocity. In order to carry men or instruments to the moon or to any other distant body or region in space, a craft must reach a speed great enough to "escape" from

Exploring the Moon. Earth's moon is the nearest of the astronomical bodies, and should be the easiest to explore. It may be possible to use it as a base from which to launch other projects, such as the exploration of Mars or Venus. Scientists are anxious to study the moon for many reasons.

It is believed that the moon is airless and dry (p. 227) and therefore not subject to weathering and erosion. As it hurtles through space it may sweep up billions of tiny meteors each day, and at times much larger ones. Earth does this too, but most of them are vaporized as they pass through the atmosphere. If the moon has no atmosphere, the material will not be vaporized, but will be held to it by gravitational attraction. Larger meteors are believed to have produced most of the huge craters on the moon. Tiny meteors are believed to have accumulated to an unknown depth, perhaps forming a layer of dust.

The moon is regarded as a great storehouse, a cosmic museum containing materials that have collected through the ages, records that may be billions of years old and possible clues to the origin of the universe and of life itself. Scientists wish to avoid destroying any part of this record or contaminating the moon with bacteria from Earth until they have had a chance to study it.

Gemini V astronauts L. Gordon Cooper, Jr., Command Pilot, and Charles Conrad, Jr., Pilot, were launched in the Gemini V spacecraft, August 21, 1965.

Exploring the Planets. A spacecraft to one of the planets must travel many millions of miles to reach its destination. It must follow a curved path that has been carefully calculated to intersect the planet's path. The calculations for launching such a spacecraft include the consideration of the orbit and rotation or spin of Earth and of the other astronomical bodies concerned, including gravitational forces and the pressure of sunlight. For example, in calculating the rotation of Earth, let us think of Earth's circumference at the equator as being about 24,000 miles. Earth makes one complete rotation eastward every

24 hours. Thus, a point on the equator moves eastward at about 1000 miles an hour. It is evident that a craft fired eastward will move out into space more rapidly than the same craft aimed in any other direction, because it takes fullest advantage of the speed of rotation of Earth.

Man in Space. Man is naturally bound to an existence in air and to conditions prevailing on Earth. When he seeks to go beyond this environment he must have an understanding of the physical conditions of the particular region he plans to explore, as well as an understanding of his own limitations (Chapter 21), and of the equipment and energy sources (p. 769) needed to transport him and his spacecraft to distant regions.

As he leaves Earth, he will leave terrestrial weather behind but will encounter problems pertaining to a different environment, problems relating to food, air, wastes, radiation, and navigation, as he reaches those regions that are far from Earth.

The rapid acceleration necessary to reach either the speed for orbiting Earth or for escape from Earth puts a crushing pressure on an astronaut, and he experiences this pressure again as the spacecraft is slowed down by the thickening atmosphere on return to Earth. To withstand this crushing pressure, measured in g's, the body is cradled and held on a chair or couch molded to fit the astronaut, which distributes the pressure as evenly as possible. In order to understand why this is necessary, try the following Experience.

EXPERIENCE. *To observe that pressure may change materials.* Make a ball of damp soil or snow, packing it together firmly enough so that it just holds its shape. Toss it up and let it fall on hard ground. What happens? Does the ball flatten out? Astronauts have the same type of experience in take-off and landing, and must avoid being "flattened out." (See other Experiences in Chapter 12.)

After the ascending craft has reached orbiting height, the astronaut will feel light as a feather. He will no longer feel the strong g forces against his body. He does not even feel the normal pull of gravity. He is in a state sometimes called "zero gravity." He feels weightless. The mass of matter that forms his body is unchanged. His weight may be somewhat reduced, perhaps 20 per cent, because he is farther from Earth than is usual for man. He still has weight, however, because he is still subject to the pull of gravity; but his weight has been completely neutralized by a counteracting force. In space flight this condition is referred to as weightlessness.

An astronaut may test some of the interesting effects of weightlessness. Objects in the cabin no longer fall to the floor, but float along with it in orbit. If the astronaut loosens the straps that hold him to his seat, he too can float in mid-air, like a frogman in a tank of water.

The cabin of the spacecraft is pressurized because, as the atmosphere becomes very thin above 60,000 feet, body fluids will boil, a state similar to the "bends." At such times nitrogen bubbles form in the blood vessels and tissues, and in severe cases death may ensue. This condition is brought about by going from regions of higher to lower atmospheric pressure. As further protection, an astronaut is zippered into a flexible suit that can be automatically pressurized, if, by accident, the cabin's pressure system fails, or should a sudden leak occur in the cabin. The suit is coated with aluminum or other material to reflect heat and is, like the cabin, air-conditioned for comfort and survival. Oxygen is provided, and carbon dioxide removed. Humidity and odors are controlled. Food in bite-size pieces and in liquid and strained forms in squeeze bottles is provided and fastened in appropriate places. An instrument panel and devices for communication and outside observation are within reach.

For anyone planning a trip to the moon or farther, involving long periods of time, the problems of a food and water supply and of body wastes are intensified. Added to these, another problem remains for anyone planning such a trip. It is radiation (p. 870). Unless there is adequate protection, an astronaut will be scorched by ultraviolet rays from the sun, from which he is normally protected by the ozone blanket that surrounds Earth. He may also be bombarded by high-energy particles emanating from the sun and from beyond the solar system. By leaving Earth from a region near the north or south pole he may avoid the belts of trapped particles known as the Van Allen belts, or in more general terms, the magnetosphere, as well as radiation left from nuclear explosions that has also become trapped in Earth's magnetic field (p. 448). Consideration will also need to be given to possible collisions with meteors. An astronaut will need protection to preserve his life in this environment.

Sunlight may seem quite different far out beyond the scattering effects of the atmosphere (p. 435). Instead of the diffused daylight that so easily penetrates our dwellings, with clouds or blue sky overhead, an explorer will see a dark sky full of stars, with our own star, the sun, blazing in its place among them. Thus daylight will be replaced by a combination of direct blinding sunlight and darkness. An astronaut may need artificial lights in his cabin. Freed from Earth's atmosphere, the stars will shine with unusual brilliance.

It is readily seen that in leaving his Earth environment man must duplicate it as nearly as possible if he is to survive. Months of training can help him to cope with the problems of entering a space environment.

CHAPTER 8

Earth Is Our Planet

In this chapter there is an emphasis on the fact that there have been titanic forces operating on Earth and that these same forces are thought still to be in operation. "Forces" are not treated here as a separate pattern, but teachers may have an opportunity, in connection with experiences involving time and change, to develop some appreciation on the part of children of the great forces that have operated and are still operating on Earth.

A teacher can gain an appreciation of the value of the content in this chapter to the education of children by studying the section "Large Patterns of the Universe as Guide Lines for Teaching-Learning," Chapter 4, pp. 92–100. Especially pertinent are those units entitled "Earth Is Very Old—Time," pp. 93–94, and, "The Universe Is Constantly Changing—Change," pp. 94–95.

Of course, such large patterns should be viewed developmentally as described in Chapter 4; namely, that a child throughout his life may be gaining a more and more adequate interpretation of his Earth and by means of it is himself becoming more adequate for life as he will find it. In other words, a twelve-year-old should have a more mature conception of these large patterns than he had when he was six.

If children have some recognition of the great age of Earth and its resources they are more apt to respond to conservation as a direction of behavior as well as viewing it as a body of content; if they have some authentic ideas about energy and forces in and around Earth, they will be wiser in tapping and utilizing new sources of energy.

Man Attempts to Explain the Universe. Man has held many curious beliefs about his surroundings. During the infancy of the human race, man's universe probably consisted of only his immediate environment, the valley, desert, plain, or hillside where he sought shelter from the hungry beasts and the terrifying and mysterious thunder, wind, and lightning. With the passing of the centuries, man became more thoughtful; his ideas about his world changed. He learned a new mastery over the savage beasts and discovered that there were other valleys and hillsides than his own. His world was still filled, however, with signs and omens, and he was a prey to the angry or exacting gods with which his imaginings filled Earth and sky. He later discovered that apparently no harm came to him from the stars. They became friendly and guiding lights; the hills

ICE PLATEAU

Yukon R.

Mackenzie R.

Great
Bear
Lake

Great Slave
Lake

ROCKY

COLUMBIA
PLATEAU

MOUNTAINS

GREAT PLAINS

Missouri R.

Lake
Winnipeg

LAURENTIAN UPLAND

Great Lakes

St. Lawrence R.

Great
Salt Lake

GREAT
BASIN

Colorado R.

COLORADO
PLATEAU

CENTRAL PLAINS

Ohio R.

Mississippi R.

APPALACHIAN MTS.

Atlantic Coastal Plain

MEXICAN PLATEAU

Rio Grande

GULF COASTAL PLAIN

*The mountains, plains, and valleys of North America were
formed through long periods of time by the great forces operating on Earth.*

seemed everlasting, and he thought of the physical world as beginning with and existing for man alone. Man and his Earth were the center and the reason for all things. Finally a few scattered individuals had the daring to offer new explanations of physical phenomena and to suggest that man and Earth were indeed but a small part of an immense universe.

Today, through the patient and painstaking efforts of men working in many different fields, we have learned that earthquakes, volcanic eruptions, floods, the formation of mountains and valleys, day and night, and like physical phenomena do not "just happen"; nor are they punishments for waywardness on the part of the human race. There is every reason to think that the forces which operate in the universe today are the same forces which operated in it during the eons of time through which it has already passed.

When people attempt to explain the unknown they try to set up hypotheses which will satisfy known facts and tested laws. Whatever is known about the universe today is the result of building bit by bit on what has been discovered in this way that seems to be true.

Today, with better telescopes, spectroscopes, photographic equipment, photoelectric cells, and better laboratories of all kinds, and with balloons, sounding rockets, and satellites carrying a great variety of recording and broadcasting instruments, many new and surprising facts are being discovered. Therefore, men who now propose hypotheses to explain the magnitude of the universe and the beginning of our solar system have the advantages provided by these instruments for making accurate observations, and their hypotheses must satisfy a much wider range of known facts. There have been many serious modern attempts to explain how the solar system was formed—each attempting to satisfy many complicated principles of physics and mathematics. As yet, none fully satisfies all of these principles, but progress is constantly being made.

That the universe is vast and that there are a great many facts about it that are not yet known may be brought to the attention of children. Children may find out about and compare the ideas of Earth and universe held by the early Indians of the region or by the Eskimos, if they live in the far north. They should be encouraged to have respect for these early peoples and to consider the times in which they lived.

How was Earth made? How did it get started? Where did the material come from that now makes up Earth? These are questions which excite the interest of both children and adults. They are questions typical of those that teachers encounter in the elementary school. But teachers no longer need to be embarrassed by such questions as these; for they should be regarded as motivation, since they may serve to vitalize instruction and suggest topics of study in which both teacher and children may learn together.

Of course no one knows how Earth was made. Yet man has always been curious about it and has attempted to explain how it could have happened. Each primitive people has had its own legends about the beginning of Earth.

Earth—A Dynamic Body

No part of the universe is more challenging to our curiosity than our own planet. Due to its size and because it is extremely difficult to observe its remote parts—the atmosphere and magnetosphere, the deeper parts of the continents and oceans, and the inner parts of

Earth—our knowledge is limited. Time and painstaking effort are necessary to the discovery of new scientific facts. Almost any child asks questions about Earth that the scientist cannot answer.

The fact that Earth is a great ball is already a familiar fact to all. It is not, however, a perfect sphere, since it is flattened at the poles; its diameter at the equator is nearly twenty-seven miles greater than its diameter from pole to pole. This difference is explained by the rotation or turning of Earth on its axis. A spinning object tends to throw off material as it spins. When an automobile wheel spins in mud, bits of mud are thrown off; in the case of Earth, which is much more solid than mud, all parts tend to move outward with the greatest effect at the equator. The effect becomes less and less toward the poles, where it cannot be noticed.

Variations in the orbit of the artificial satellite Vanguard I indicated that the north pole may be about 18 yards less flat and the south pole flatter by about 18 yards than was supposed. The variations also showed the Southern Hemisphere larger by the same amount. The variations in the satellite's orbit are explained by the differences in the mass of Earth at different points and hence the differences in the gravitational pull or force exerted by Earth on the satellite. Later evidence showed that Earth is not perfectly round at the equator. Other variations may be found. Data from satellites will add to our knowledge about the composition and behavior of our planet.

The Formation of Continents and Oceans. No one knows yet how the continents and ocean basins were formed. Nevertheless, many attacks on this problem have been made in the form of hypotheses.

During the nineteenth century the fact that identical or similar organisms, both marine and land plants and animals, were found on or near opposite shores of large bodies of water led some to suggest that these shores had been joined by land, all or parts of which sank beneath the sea. About one hundred years ago James D. Dana suggested that the continents became consolidated early in Earth's formation; hence they were thicker and sank less as the young Earth shrank. The ocean bottoms were of thinner material and hence remained low. Later, Alfred Wegener, the German geophysicist, advocated the hypothesis of continental drift. Briefly, this hypothesis assumed that the granitic mass of the continents could and did easily drift on the basalt lying underneath. Continental masses broke off the original mass and in drifting pushed up many of the mountain chains. Another hypothesis suggests that the continents were built up with the material from volcanic eruptions. Still another hypothesis suggests that Earth was much smaller when newly formed than it is now and has been gradually expanding. Its proponents point to a fissure or rift running at least 40,000 miles across the bottoms of all the oceans. It is an area of great instability, for it is the location of most of the earthquakes occurring in the oceans. Material issuing from the fissure may have built up the mid-Atlantic mountain range as well as other ranges elsewhere. It is claimed that an expanding Earth would account for the gradual breaking of the original light surface rocks into continents, the formation of ocean basins, the undersea mountain ridges, and would change the position of the continents in such a way as to explain the variations in Earth's magnetism through geologic time as found in the rocks (p. 804). Others support the convection-current hypothesis, which suggests that convection currents in Earth rise under the mid-ocean fissure. Their movements, upward and laterally, would force the fissure apart; material would be pushed out, building up the mid-ocean ridges and adding light material to the under parts of the continents. The lateral movements would tend to compress the continents, forming mountains. Each hypothesis has given direction to further study and has served to emphasize the great need for more research on rocks and their behavior and on the ocean bottoms. Newly developed methods and devices for research in these areas are even now bringing many new facts to light.

Geologists have come to the conclusion that the continents and oceans are essentially permanent. To be sure, the continents and oceans have changed their shapes, as portions of the continents were raised above or sank beneath the oceans; but in general there is evidence that the continents never were the deeps of the ocean, nor the deeps ever continents.

Sediments of the deep-sea type are unknown on the land, and the fossils of marine animals which we find on land are those of the inhabitants of comparatively shallow waters. The island of Barbados in the West Indies is an exception. There the land rocks have the appearance of deep-sea deposits. The fact also that the average density of the rocks which form the continents is less that that of those forming the ocean basins supports the conclusion that the continents have been continents for a long period of time, although their shapes have been changed many times by inroads made by the oceans.

Balance in Earth—Isostasy. A hypothesis of balance in Earth, or isostasy, as it is sometimes called, suggests that areas in the outer part of Earth maintain a balance in relation to one another. This means that the continents are higher than the areas under the oceans because they are composed of lighter materials; the heavy, dense rock which underlies the ocean bottoms is balanced by the lighter, less dense continental rock, which thus has to be present in greater volume and hence stands higher. Earthquake waves show that basaltic rock underlying the oceans and the continents is more dense than the granitic rock of the continental masses. Erosion moves vast quan-

tities of material; the denuded areas rise, while the areas of sedimentation sink under the increased load.

There is evidence that areas covered by thousands of feet of ice during the Ice Ages gradually sank during those times (p. 284). The water forming the ice is thought to have come from the oceans, thus making less the burden on the ocean basins and adding to the burden on the continents. As the ice receded, the continental basins became filled with sea water and glacial water. Then, as readjustment took place, the basins were uplifted and the water drained away. Uplift is still going on in Scandinavia and Canada and probably in other places as well. Measurements around the Great Lakes area have been announced that show a rise there in the last century. Parts of the Mediterranean and Indian oceans have been slowly sinking for thousands of years, at about one inch per hundred years. The Caribbean is unstable. Such movements are possible because rock will flow under great pressure. The whole process of restoring balance between loaded and unloaded areas requires immense periods of time and is a continuous process.

EXPERIENCE. *Size of Earth.* Children can be helped to appreciate the enormous size of Earth by discussing the length of time it takes to go from one place on Earth to another; or, by comparing Earth with things in our own community, we can appreciate that Earth is large. Placing a bit of modeling clay on the globe to mark our own town or city or farm, will indicate how much larger Earth is. Also distances individual children have traveled can be indicated. Earth is large. Indicate how air travel has made distances seem smaller. They can be aided in appreciating the relatively small size of Earth by discussing the much greater size of the sun and the enormous distances in the universe (Chapter 7). Through this kind of experience children can

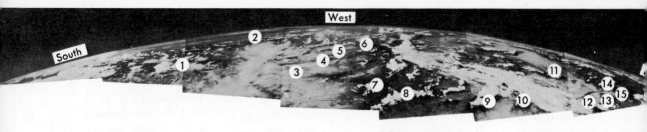

1 Mexico	5 Gila River	9 San Mateo Mts.	13 Sandia Mts.
2 Gulf of California	6 San Carlos Reservoir	10 Magadalena Mts.	14 Valle Grande Mts.
3 Lordsburg, New Mexico	7 Mogollon Mts.	11 Mt. Taylor	15 Rio Grande
4 Peloncillo Mts.	8 Black Range	12 Albuquerque, New Mexico	16 Sangre de Cristo Range

A view from 60 miles up shows that Earth is round. The distance along the horizon is 2700 miles. (Applied Physics Laboratory, Johns Hopkins University.)

learn that Earth may be described as being very large when compared with objects they see around them, but very small when compared with the universe.

EXPERIENCE. *Earth is a planet.* See pages 212–225 for experiences in connection with the planets.

EXPERIENCE. *Earth is nearly round.* Why do you suppose that early peoples thought that Earth was flat? How can it be proved that Earth is round? It casts a round shadow on the moon at the time of a total eclipse of the moon; as a ship sails away, we see the lower part disappear before the upper part; it is possible to travel completely around Earth.

A flashlight may be focused on a globe with a wall in the background, where a round shadow may be observed. Pictures taken from great heights from rockets and satellites show the curved appearance of Earth. Such pictures can be found in papers and magazines.

EXPERIENCE. *To observe land and water areas of the world.* Children may look at a globe to see that there are land masses; some are connected and some are not. Suggest that they notice where the land masses are located. Find some islands. Water surrounds the land. Later, they will find in their work that the shapes of the land areas have not always been exactly the same as they are today.

The Three Parts of Earth

The Gaseous Part of Earth. Earth is made up of three parts: the gaseous, the liquid, and the solid part. Children are more or less familiar with what is meant by a gas, a liquid, and a solid; in fact, regardless of where they may live, they have need of each in their daily experiences. They breathe the air, which is

a gas; they walk upon the solid Earth, and they need water, a liquid, to drink.

The *atmosphere,* or gaseous part of Earth, acts upon the solid part of Earth by assisting in the wearing down of the land and in the transportation of the soil to distant parts. Indeed, it is largely because of the atmosphere that the surface of Earth presents the appearance it does today. (See Chapter 12 for information about the atmosphere.)

The Solid Part of Earth. The solid part of Earth is composed of rocks with a covering of soil of varying depth. It makes up the greater part of Earth by weight and volume and is frequently called the *lithosphere,* which means "rock sphere." We live upon it, travel over it, cultivate it, and drill into it, extracting untold wealth. If we desire to leave it, we must use special contrivances, such as ships, airplanes, or spacecraft, in order to do so.

Our knowledge of the lithosphere derived from seeing or touching it is rather limited, since man has had no contact with it to any great depth. Knowledge of the lithosphere to any considerable depth has been made possible only through the observation of material from wells, mines, and cores obtained by drilling for minerals, and of the rocks which were once deeply buried, and which have been pushed up and then laid bare by erosion. Many hypotheses have been put forward concerning the state of the inner part of Earth, and man's quest for knowledge goes on, being aided by such instruments as the seismograph and by his increasing knowledge of the laws governing solids, liquids, and gases.

The surface of the lithosphere presents in many places an appearance of sharp angles and rugged cliffs, owing to the effects of the atmosphere, running water, ice, and wind. As a result of this action, there is a mantle of soil, finely broken-up rock, covering most of the level areas, below which lies coarser material, the subsoil, and scattered rocks. Below this is solid rock.

Earth Materials: The Chemical Elements. The outer part of Earth is the portion of the lithosphere which is of immediate concern to man. He is in daily contact with it, and his very life depends upon its composition and his understanding of it. We find that this part is made up of rocks and soils (p. 301) having different characterists and formed in different ways through very long periods of time by such Earth-changing processes as the raising and lowering of the land, weathering and erosion, and volcanism. Yet, despite these differences, all these rocks are made up of elements and their combinations.

Four of the known elements make up nearly 90 per cent of Earth's crust. These four are oxygen, silicon, aluminum, and iron. These, with eight others (calcium, sodium, potassium, magnesium, titanium, hydrogen, phosphorus, and carbon) account for 98 per cent of Earth's material.

About one third of the elements are known to occur in a free state; that is, as substances in themselves. They also occur in combination with other elements. The remaining elements are found only in combination with other elements.

Since 1920, new elements have been discovered by laboratory methods. These new elements are sometimes called synthetic elements because they are produced in a laboratory. However, there is no true distinction between "natural" and "synthetic" elements. Plutonium was first produced in a cyclotron; helium was first discovered in the sun. Both of these elements have subsequently been found in Earth (p. 374).

Elements Combine and Form Minerals. The elements that make up Earth's crust combine in a great many different ways, and as they combine, changes take place (p. 380). The minerals that are the result of these combinations may be entirely different in their properties from any of the elements that went into their composition. Although there are a great many different minerals, only about twenty of them compose all the rocks we see. Nearly all of these contain silicon.

The identification of minerals is a whole

Asbestos shows a fibrous structure. This sample came from Quebec, Canada. (Ward's Natural Science Establishment.)

field of study in itself, involving many laboratory techniques. Children, however, can make simple observations as to form, color, and hardness of different common minerals and rocks. It is important that they become increasingly aware that there are great differences in rocks, and that rocks are made up of different minerals. Certain qualities or characteristics of minerals are used in identifying them, such as luster, color, hardness, specific gravity (or density), cleavage, and taste. Thus quartz, which is one of the most common minerals, is formed from silicon and oxygen; it is colorless when pure, forms six-sided crystals, is so hard that it will scratch glass but cannot be scratched with a knife, and, when broken, splinters like glass. The last-named quality indicates that it has no cleavage plane.

The micas are an important group of minerals containing silica (which is the oxide of silicon, or a combination of oxygen and silicon), and varying amounts of aluminum and potassium, plus hydrogen, magnesium, iron, sodium, lithium, and fluorine. Unlike quartz, the micas have one perfect cleavage plane.

They are easily separated into extremely thin sheets which are elastic, springing back into place when bent. The micas are fairly soft, the fingernail being sufficiently hard to scratch them. The colors may vary from transparent to milky white, brown, lavender, or black, but the bases of the six-sided crystals show up with a pearly luster.

When minerals occur with definite geometrical outlines they are called crystals. Perfect crystals of any mineral are formed only under the most favorable conditions. Most often only parts of crystals appear in rocks. A snowflake is an example of a crystal, since it has a symmetrical form with six sides. Most minerals may appear in crystalline form. This aids in identifying even small fragments. Some minerals, however, rarely appear in crystalline form. Some, like asbestos, may be fibrous; pitchblende occurs in small, round, grapelike forms; others may be granular in form, masses of fine or coarse grains. Among the common minerals are the feldspars, quartz, pyroxene, hornblende, mica, olivine, garnet, magnetite, hematite, fluorite, calcite, dolomite, kaolin, pyrite, graphite, talc, serpentine, and gypsum.

Mica is easily separated into thin sheets or flakes. (Ward's N Science Establishment.)

...rtz may form six-sided crystals. This specimen came from Hot ...ings, Arkansas. (Ward's Natural Science Establishment.)

Experience. *Crystals.* Quartz crystals are fairly easy to find. Compare the different kinds of quartz: rose, smoky, rock crystal, etc. Examine other minerals if they are brought in.

Rocks Are Composed of Minerals. Since most rocks are composed of minerals, they take on distinct characteristics of their own. They do not necessarily assume the appearance or qualities of any one of the minerals of which they are composed. Yet, the characteristics displayed by rocks depend mainly upon the materials of which they are composed and the way in which they were formed. If mineral crystals are large enough to see and name, they help in naming the rock. The size and shape of the crystals also tell many things about the history of the rock.

Rarely, a rock is made up of only one mineral; for example, pure white marble is all calcite. Generally, however, rocks are a mixture of many minerals. For example, granite is composed mostly of feldspar and quartz and sometimes contains mica or hornblende.

Rocks may be cemented together loosely or firmly, and some may be extremely compact, while others are very poorly consolidated. They may be relatively soft or easily crumbled, or they may be compact and very hard to break, even with a heavy hammer. The texture—the characteristic produced by the size, shape, and arrangement of the crystal grains—gives a clue to the rock's identity. For instance, a glassy rock would immediately bring to mind the igneous rock, obsidian. On the other hand, the rock might be fine-grained or coarse-grained, and in the latter case might be the igneous rock, granite. In these cases the rate of cooling was the factor which determined the texture. The structure may also tell something about the kind of rock it is. It also tells something about the general class to which the rock belongs. If a rock has layers, it would probably be of sedimentary origin. The color of rocks results from the colors of the materials of which they are composed. The color of the unweathered surface gives the true color of the rock. Many shades of red, brown, yellow, and sometimes green are produced by the presence of iron, but in sedimentary rocks

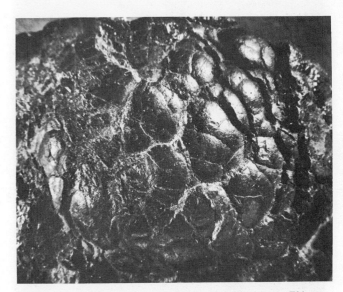

Pitchblende sometimes occurs in this form. This came from the Eldorado Mine, Great Bear Lake, Northwest Territories, Canada. (B.M. Shaub.)

carbonaceous material more often produces the black or gray coloration.

Rocks are thought of as being solid, and people often say, "solid as a rock" when they wish to emphasize the strong, unbending nature of anything. However, under certain conditions of temperature and pressure rocks may become liquid. When this molten rock, or magma, is relieved from such great temperatures and pressures, it becomes solid. A common and easily observed example of this is the rock of which lava flows are composed, and often the rock immediately around volcanoes.

It has been demonstrated in the laboratory that rock, under extreme pressure, can be made to change its shape without becoming liquid. Rocks which have been subjected to these processes in nature are widespread in Earth's crust and may be observed in road cuts or mountainous areas.

This mass of igneous rock is known as Devil's Tower. Some geologists think the tower is all that is left of a dome, formed when molten rock pushed upward between layers of rock. It is a national monument in northeastern Wyoming. (Philip Gendreau.)

EXPERIENCE. *Rocks are made up of minerals.* Try to crack some rocks, such as granite. Be sure to use some precaution against flying splinters from the rocks, and also be careful to avoid mashed fingers. Placing the rocks in a heavy cloth bag before hammering is one way to do this. Do you find little pieces of quartz, mica, and feldspar? Note the different colors of the particles. Can you see that they are not all alike? Rocks are made up of minerals.

EXPERIENCE. *Rocks break differently.* Some rocks break in sheets, some crumble, some break like glass. Break up different rocks, using the precaution of first putting the rock in a bag, and see if you find all of these kinds of rock breakage. Call attention to the great variety in rocks.

The Three Groups of Rocks. The rocks of Earth's crust may be divided into three large groups, according to the way in which they were formed: igneous rocks, sedimentary rocks, and metamorphic rocks.

1. *Igneous rocks.* Igneous rocks are those from which all others are formed. They themselves have been formed from molten rock, and are found either below Earth's surface or on the surface (p. 292). They do not contain fossils, nor do they have the layered appearance of sedimentary rocks. They are recognized by their texture, which depends on their environment while cooling. *Intrusive rocks* far below the surface have cooled very slowly under pressure. The result is a rock composed of large crystals, such as coarse-grained granite. *Extrusive rocks* have cooled rapidly in the atmosphere under low pressure. The result is a rock composed of either very small crystals or none at all, such as basalt or obsidian. Then there are rocks, called porphyries, formed in two environments. These rocks may have begun to cool within Earth, with the crystallization of some minerals, and then may have been poured out where the re-

mainder cooled rapidly. In such rocks are found large crystals embedded in the finer-textured material.

Not all igneous rocks have the same chemical make-up. Some igneous rocks have large amounts of the oxide of silicon, the predominant mineral in sand, and, of course, grade through to those having less silica and a great deal of the ferromagnesian minerals containing iron and magnesium. Even basalt is about 50 per cent silica. This variation complicates their recognition a great deal.

One of the commonest of igneous rocks is granite, with a high content of silica. It is formed far beneath Earth's surface, and because of its slow cooling and retention of gases has many large crystals in it. Erosion exposes it to view. It is found in mountainous regions, where it is often pushed up during mountain-forming movements. Many questions have arisen concerning the formation of granite in such areas. Some think that rocks may become granitized by hot, gaseous emanations from beds of magma. It has many colors and is often used for building purposes. If the molten rock which forms granite cools at the surface, the gases are released and the result is a rock with small crystals, called rhyolite.

Basalt is a dense rock whose crystals are very small. It often presents a columnar structure. It is frequently extrusive and may be the result of a widespread outpouring of molten rock from fissures in Earth's crust; or it may be found as intrusions near the surface. Basalt also occurs as dikes and sills near the surface. It too is a common igneous rock, but with a different chemical make-up from that of granite, having more of the ferromagnesian minerals and decidedly less silica. If the molten rock forming basalt cools slowly within Earth, the gases are retained and a coarse-grained rock called gabbro is the result. There are many other kinds of igneous rock, all showing a varying chemical make-up.

2. *Sedimentary rocks.* Sedimentary rocks are

This is a cliff of sedimentary rocks on the Verde River near Camp Verde, Arizona. Weathering and erosion produced pits and cavelike areas in the rock, and prehistoric tribes used them for shelter and protection. This is Montezuma Castle National Monument. (Philip Gendreau.)

made of sediments which have been consolidated. The sediments may be deposited by wind, water, or ice; or they may be organic deposits or chemically precipitated materials. Some sedimentary rocks are formed by various combinations of these materials and in varying amounts.

Many Earth materials go into solution in water during erosion. This water may then pass into a different environment—for example, a change in temperature or amount of evaporation may take place—and as a result chemical precipitation may occur (p. 316). Certain plants and animals remove chemical compounds that are in solution in water and use them in their life processes. The shells formed by some of these organisms or the whole organism may be deposited and eventually become sedimentary rock. Corals form reefs (p. 618); the shells of clams, snails, and other organisms accumulate and form deposits; diatoms remove silica from solution and their remains form diatomaceous earth. In past ages coal, which is considered a sedimentary rock, was formed from immense numbers of certain plants.

Sediments collect on the land and under water and may become rock. Deposits of soil and rocks moved by wind or by ice—continental or valley glaciers, or lake and river ice —may become sedimentary rock. Fine, ashy volcanic material and the coarser fragments expelled from volcanoes can also become sedimentary rock. When consolidated it is called tuff, volcanic breccia, or volcanic agglomerate. This is an exception to the general saying that sedimentary rocks are derived from older rocks by weathering and erosion, for the volcanic ash and larger fragments may or may not undergo weathering and erosion by the time they have become consolidated into rock.

Rivers and other streams are constantly pouring sand, clay, and mud into lakes and oceans. This material, which we call sediment, settles to the bottom. As years go by, more and more material is deposited, and at a later time, perhaps thousands of years later, this sediment may become consolidated into rock. Such rock as this is called sedimentary rock.

The Changing of Sediments into Rocks. The change of sediments into rocks may be brought about in one or more different ways: by *compaction,* the pressing together of the sediments; by *cementation,* or the cementing together of the particles making up the sediments; and by certain *physical* and *chemical changes,* brought about by heat and pressure.

The pressure exerted by the upper parts of a deposit of sediment upon the lower parts squeezes the relatively loose grains of the sediment together. The more sediment there is, the greater will be the pressure on the lower parts. During this process, there may be a loss of water and some rise in temperature. This sets up new conditions. Grains of the

sediment may interlock and even chemical changes may take place, such as a recrystallization of minerals. Cementation may take place at the same time, or later on. Consolidation may take place without the pressure, through cementation alone. Cementation is brought about by the presence of water with mineral matter in solution. The most common of the minerals that go into solution are the carbonates, silica, iron sulfides, and the iron oxides. Conditions such as evaporation or change of pressure and temperature occur, making it possible for these minerals to crystallize out of the water solution and take their place among the particles making up the sediment. Cementing solutions containing silica make rocks almost as hard as the original igneous rocks from which the silica came. Thus the consolidation of sediments into rocks takes place.

We should expect the sedimentary rock, shale, and its metamorphic equivalents, slate and mica schist, to be very common, since they are made chiefly from the clay which comes from feldspar, a mineral which is abundant in igneous rocks.

Since quartz is a common and very durable mineral, although it is less abundant than feldspar in igneous rocks, we may reasonably expect sandstone to be next in the order of abundance.

Limestone and dolomite come next, because calcium and magnesium carbonates are the most abundant soluble products of weathering.

Limestone, sandstone, shale, and conglomerate are examples of sedimentary rocks. Limestone is composed of chemically precipitated calcium carbonate or the shells of marine animals or a mixture of both. It may be fine-grained or very coarse, with whole shells or fragments of shells plainly visible. Limy sediments represent the chemically precipitated calcium carbonate (p. 391). These limy sediments may exist as beds of limestone, as limy mud, or as a cement holding other material together. Calcium carbonate is apt to be precipitated as a fine mud in beds in warm, shallow marine water.

Many limestones are impure and contain clay, mud, or sand. Thus there is shaly limestone or sandy limestone, with the colors ranging from white, gray, red, and buff to black.

Chalk is one form of limestone. It is made of the shells of tiny animals that lived millions of years ago. Coquina is a very coarse limestone made of larger shells or shell fragments loosely cemented together.

Sandstone is formed of grains of sand cemented together. It is a rock of varying degrees of porousness. This is the quality that makes it a good reservoir for water or petroleum. Occasionally pebbles or fossils are found in sandstone.

Variation in the color and texture of sandstone depends on the size, shape, and kind of the material of which it is formed. The grains of sand may be sharp-cornered or so worn by wind and water that they are round or pitted or have a frosty appearance. The material which cements them together adds color and hardness to the sandstone. A cement of iron oxide gives a yellow, red, or brown color; silica or calcite gives a lighter color. When cemented with silica, sandstone is very hard and makes a good building material. When cemented with other materials, sandstone is not so hard. The cementing material which holds the grains of sand together is generally deposited from a water solution which at some time came in contact with the sand and there hardened.

Shale is formed from beds of mud or clay which have been pressed and cemented together. It can usually be split into thin layers. Shales are very fine and even-grained, though variation in the grain is found, probably owing to variation in the amount of rainfall, to change of season, or to any other change that affected the amount and character of the material deposited. Shales often grade into sandstones. The color of shale may vary from green to gray; even red, blue, and purple are not uncommon. Black shales derive their color from carbon—the remains of plants and animals buried with the mud before decomposition could set in.

Conglomerate is made of gravel or pebbles cemented together. Sometimes the fragments are of different sizes (unassorted), ranging from pebbles only a fraction of an inch in diameter to good-sized rocks. These fragments may be of one or more kinds of rock. Other sedimentary rocks are closely related. Often limestones are found that have streaks of sand and even a few pebbles; and conglomerates sometimes have a fine-grained appearance bordering on that of the sandstones or limestones.

Other deposits that are classed as sedimentary rocks are coal, salt, gypsum, chert, flint, and certain iron ores. Coal and the iron ores are of the greatest economic importance. (For coalmaking see p. 346; for iron as a sedimentary rock see p. 319.)

Salt is considered a sedimentary rock. The two elements sodium and chlorine, which

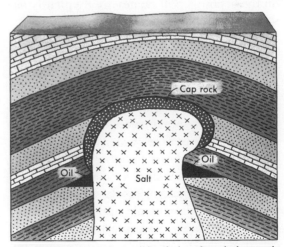

This diagram shows the possible relation of a salt dome to the surrounding rocks. In the process of formation, oil may accumulate.

Marble is a metamorphic rock that is granular in appearance. This is a marble quarry in Vermont. (Courtesy of the Vermont Marble Company.)

form salt, were in the magma. Under certain conditions these elements combined and, being easily dissolved in water, found their way to the ocean. The salt deposits are believed to have been formed when parts of the continents were depressed and shallow seas persisted for thousands of years at a time. Then, as the water evaporated over a very long period of time, the minerals in solution crystallized, resulting in deposits of salt. Since rock salt bends rather easily, deposits frequently occur as salt domes, a shape formed by pressure on the deposit. Salt domes are frequently associated with oil deposits.

Like salt, gypsum has been deposited from the shallow waters of ancient seas or lagoons. Both were deposited under arid conditions. In many places thick beds of gypsum are found as layers in other sedimentary rocks; often gypsum is found under salt beds because it precipitates out of sea water before salt precipitates. Gypsum is a rather soft material and is used in making fertilizer, plaster of Paris, fireproof building blocks and wallboard, porcelain and glass, paints, and for other commercial purposes. Particularly fine deposits, called alabaster, are white and are used for making ornamental lamps and other articles.

Sedimentary rocks have many interesting features which make them good guides to the past. Such things as fossils, old mud cracks, ripple marks, wave marks, raindrop impressions, cross-bedding in sandstone, and layers, or strata show many things about the past.

3. *Metamorphic rocks.* There has been much folding, crushing, bending, and breaking of the rocks that form the crust of Earth. The compressive forces which produced these phenomena, accompanied by heat, changed some of the sedimentary and igneous rocks to such an extent that their original characteristics cannot be determined easily. Also, if rocks become deeply buried under a great load of other rocks or sediment, the temperature and pressure may be so great as to cause a readjustment to a new state of stability under those conditions, and the rock will be changed or metamorphosed as a result. In addition, contact with solidifying masses of hot, molten material and its escaping gases produces the same effect. In such a case the material in contact with the molten rock must readjust to that new situation and the rock is metamorphosed.

The texture may be changed, new minerals may be formed, or both may occur. An entirely new kind of rock may be produced. Such rocks are called metamorphic, which means "changed by heat and pressure." Metamorphic rocks themselves may also be changed by these same processes. In other words, rocks are formed under a certain set of conditions. When any one of these conditions changes—it may be an increase or a decrease of pressure or of temperature—the minerals in the rocks change, or metamorphose, to a state of stability under the new set of conditions.

Some of the important metamorphic rocks are gneiss, schist, quartzite, slate, and marble. The gneisses, quartzites, and mica schists may grade into one another, depending on the amount of quartz, feldspar, and mica present.

Gneiss is a banded, coarse-grained rock composed of the same minerals as granite. The coarse banding may extend in straight parallel lines or be curved and bent. Conglomerates and such igneous rocks as granite may be metamorphosed to become gneiss. Gneisses are widespread over Earth's surface, being frequently found in the older formations.

Schists are thinly banded metamorphic rocks which split readily. They may grade into gneiss, losing their scaly structure, or they may grade into slates.

Quartzite is a very firm, compact rock made of sandstone in which the quartz grains are interlocked with a siliceous cement. The grains are so firmly cemented that, when the rock is fractured, the fracture passes through the grains. This is an example of the change of a sedimentary rock, sandstone, to a metamorphic rock, quartzite.

Slate is a fine-grained rock which breaks in thin, broad sheets. When shale is metamorphosed, it becomes slate. Thus it will be seen that most slate is really derived from clay or mud.

Marble is a metamorphic rock which has been formed from limestone or dolomite.

Igneous rocks, when metamorphosed, may assume a banded, stratified appearance which causes them to resemble sedimentary rocks. On the other hand, some sedimentary rocks, when metamorphosed, lose their marks of stratification, change color, lose any evidence of fossils they may have contained, and assume a highly crystalline texture.

An excellent illustration of the evolution of metamorphic rocks is seen in the formation of anthracite and graphite. As is shown in the story of Earth, coal is formed from plants. The series of changes is somewhat as follows: peat is formed from the woody tissues of plants; later the peat is changed to lignite and then to bituminous coal, and, if a sufficient amount of pressure and heat are applied, the much harder anthracite results. The change may go even further and result in graphite.

The following table lists certain sediments and the sedimentary and metamorphic rocks into which these sediments may be formed. At this point it is well to consider for a moment the long periods of time which are needed for the formation of sedimentary rock from the sediments and again for the formation of metamorphic rock from sedimentary rock.

Both sedimentary and metamorphic rocks may be formed from materials that have been worked and reworked many times by weathering and erosion since they were originally weathered from the parent igneous rocks. The original sediments may have been consolidated and weathered into sediment many times. During those immense periods of time, changes may have been made by oxidation, leaching, carbonation, or by any of the many chemical processes that are possible.

Sediments
1. Sand
2. Pebbles or gravel
3. Lime (calcium carbonate)
4. Mud or clay
5. Peat

Sedimentary Rock
(Formed in Presence of Water)
1. Sandstone
2. Conglomerate
3. Limestone
4. Shale
5. Lignite, bituminous coal

Metamorphic Rock
(Changed by Heat and Pressure)
1. Quartzite
2. Gneiss or conglomerate schists
3. Marble
4. Slate, mica schist
5. Anthracite, graphite

The table below lists two igneous rocks and the metamorphic rocks into which they are formed when they are changed by heat and pressure.

Igneous Rock   *Metamorphic Rock*
1. Granite   1. Granite gneiss
2. Basalt   2. Slate, schists, and serpentine

EXPERIENCE. *Rocks in your community may have been formed in more than one way.* Children may be interested in trying to learn whether such rocks are igneous, sedimentary, or metamorphic. Perhaps the industries in your community may furnish a clue. If there is a cement plant there must be limestone, which is a sedimentary rock. If there is a rock crusher, for what purpose is the rock being crushed? If for surfacing a road, there is a possibility that igneous rock from the neighborhood is being used. If there is a quarry it may be that marble, a metamorphic rock, is being removed for use in buildings.

EXPERIENCE. *Rocks are hard.* Most children form some acquaintance with rocks very early in life. Rocks are often an important part of their environment. They step on them, fall and climb over them, play with them, using them in many ways, and early begin to see differences in the color and size of rocks. They all seem hard and sometimes sharp and sometimes very heavy. The children begin to connect these qualities with words, spoken and then written. Later comparisons of rocks as to these qualities are worth-while as a means of focusing attention on the fact that rocks are not all the same. A magnifying glass is useful in making some observations. Children can be made increasingly aware of the many ways in which rocks are used and of their importance as parent material for soil.

EXPERIENCE. *Giving names to rocks.* Teachers need not feel responsible for classifying rocks or any other object brought into the classroom (pp. 129–132). However, rocks can be located and names can be given to them. For instance, a hard pebble found in Fred's yard on March 15, or a soft piece of red rock found by the sidewalk near Martha's house on January 10, or a piece of coal brought back by John when he visited his grandfather in Pennsylvania. In other words, identifying objects should be undertaken with children from a developmental point of view. In such a procedure, children describe the object in terms that are meaningful to them.

Information about a piece of rock can be placed on the rock: paint a small spot on the rock with white enamel paint, then use India ink to write on the white spot.

EXPERIENCE. *How rocks were formed.* While the teacher should not undertake a specialized identification of rocks, she can, with older children, use the classifications "sedimentary," "igneous," and "metamorphic." The description of how these rocks were formed will help the teacher to an idea of the rock's origin. This type of classification is important because it helps to tell the story of your locality. Was it once covered by a sea? Has it been subjected to great crustal pressure? Have there been intrusions or extrusions of very hot rock?

In this kind of work a teacher can always acknowledge to parents and teachers that she is not a specialist. She may also welcome any assistance that anyone in the community can render in learning about rocks and soil.

EXPERIENCE. *To show why sedimentary rocks form in layers.* Fill a large fruit jar about three-fourths full of water. Put in a few small stones, and about two cups of pebbles and soil from a garden or playground. Now stir well or shake the jar and allow the contents to settle. After several hours examine it. Continue to observe at intervals for a week or more. Note that the material is sorted, the pebbles at the bottom, then the next smaller particles, and so on to the top where the light, strawlike or organic material will be found. This gives an appearance of layers. Note how long the water stays muddy looking. It might be well to leave the water and soil in the jar for several weeks. Does it eventually become clear?

The Continents. Great drainage systems have developed, making a bird's-eye view of any continent look as though it were covered by bare-branched trees with the roots reaching to the oceans. Portions of the continents that are relatively high serve as *divides,* where part of the water flows toward one great river system and the rest flows toward another. The mighty Mississippi rises as a tiny stream in northern Minnesota, flows southward, and finally empties into the Gulf of Mexico, while not far distant from the source of the Mississippi the Red River of the North receives part of the precipitation and flows north into Lake Winnipeg and thence into Hudson Bay.

Certain areas are covered by sediments laid down in ancient seas. Parts of these and other areas, particularly along the borders of continents, have been thrust up into mountains. Of these mountains the highest is Mt. Everest in the Himalaya Mountains in Asia, which rises to a height of 29,028 feet above sea level. This is less than the greatest known ocean depth, which is 36,198 feet; but it gives the lithosphere a relief of over twelve miles. Considering the distance through Earth, however (about 7926 miles through the equator and 7900 miles from pole to pole), the crust is only very slightly irregular.

Sea Level. The water of all the oceans joins, and so the surface of the ocean makes a point from which to measure the heights and depths of our Earth's surface. True sea level would be the surface of the ocean if there were no tides, no winds, no currents, or anything else to disturb the water. But this is far from

reality, and means have been devised to arrive at a figure as near to sea level as possible. Since water is constantly in motion, instruments have been invented which give accurate readings of water level at different times of day. The instruments are called tide gauges and mareographs. Readings from these over a period of time help to establish *mean sea level,* which is the half-way point between average high tide and average low tide, and is also an average, or mean. Mean sea level, commonly called "sea level," then, is the level which is commonly used from which to measure heights of the land and depths of the ocean. Some of the variations in sea level during a year are due to contraction and expansion of water produced by differences in temperature during summer and winter. While there have been many changes in mean sea level during past ages for various reasons, it does remain about the same for long periods of time, and therefore makes a good place from which to measure.

EXPERIENCE. *Not all land is the same height above sea level.* In order that children may grow in their ideas of up and down and of heights of land and depths of the ocean, simple observations of the countryside may be made. Each child may observe what he sees from his own

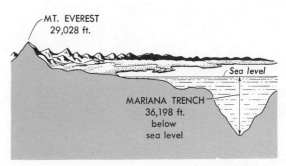

These points are thought to be the highest and the lowest places on Earth. The elevation of all other places is in between.

front door or window, or from some point where he can look off. A view from the school window quite often is satisfactory. Are any hills or mountains nearby? If there is a river or stream of any kind in your neighborhood notice that it is lower than the rest of the land. Attention may be called to the fact that there are hills and valleys, but also that in parts of many countries there are level plains that are several thousand feet above sea level. Is your community at sea level or above sea level? To find the altitude or elevation of your community, very often the road sign at the edge of town gives the elevation. It is nearly always marked up at the airports, or it might be known by someone there. Your Chamber of Commerce might know, or a topographic map of your area would give the figures. Directions for reading the map are on the back. Some road maps give a few elevations.

EXPERIENCE. *Not all land is above sea level.* Bad Water in Death Valley, California, is a little more than 282 feet below sea level. This is the lowest point on the North American continent. It is low because that area sank. It lies between two parallel faults. Not more than eighty miles away in a straight line is Mt. Whitney, with an elevation of 14,495 feet. Part of the Salton Trough in California, in which is located Salton Sea, is below sea level. This trough was once part of the Gulf of Lower California. Have any of the children been in either of these places? What did they see that seemed different to them from higher places?

The Liquid Part of Earth. Oceans, lakes, streams, the water within Earth, and the water in the atmosphere together make up the liquid part of Earth. Geologists often call this part the *hydrosphere,* which means the "sphere of

Ocean currents help to heat or cool the land and distribute nutrients.

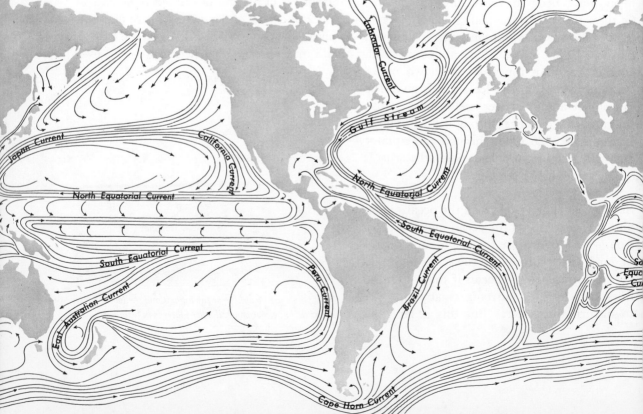

water." By far the greatest part of the water is held within the borders of the oceans, which cover nearly three fourths of the entire surface of Earth. This does not mean, however, that the liquid part of Earth exceeds the solid part in size, or volume; for the greatest depth of the ocean is a little less than seven miles, a very small fraction of the diameter of Earth.

The Oceans. The oceans are the greatest sources of water that we have. In some extremely hot portions of the world it is known that the evaporation from the surface of the ocean is as much as 23 feet of water in a year. In colder or more humid portions, however, the amounts of evaporation are smaller. The process may be described briefly as follows: the water evaporates; winds carrying it meet and override colder masses of air; the water vapor condenses and falls as rain, snow, sleet, or hail, or forms on the ground as dew or frost (486–490).

This sphere of water serves as an equalizer of climate, since the air is neither so hot nor so cold near the larger bodies of water as in regions where they are absent. The oceans and smaller bodies of water, including rivers, provide basins for the deposit of sediments; they may prevent floods in nearby areas, and food and other economic products come from them. They are important for recreation, and by far the larger part of the world's commerce is carried on by way of water.

Drifts and Currents. In addition to the modifying effect that the mere presence of a large body of water has on the climate of a region, there is an equally important effect due to large movements in the water. Large, slow, somewhat circular movements are set up near the surface of the oceans by the unequal heating of the water by the sun in polar and equatorial regions. These *drifts,* as they are called, are intensified and controlled to some degree by the winds and move in a westerly direction

on both sides of the equator with the trade winds. Farther from the equator they move eastward with the westerlies. The movement of water tends to become circular. As the drifts draw near to land, they become more rapid and streamlike, probably owing to the piling up of the water and to the shape of the land. These *currents,* as they are now called, thus are like streams flowing through the ocean.

Not all currents are near the surface. A number of great ocean currents have been found flowing below large surface currents and in an opposite direction.

Little is known about the movement and mixing of ocean water, but it is thought that melting ice in polar regions supplies cold water to the oceans. The cold, dense water sinks, displacing lighter warmer water, which then flows toward the equator. Such things as barometric pressure, tidal forces, friction, and the rotation of Earth may all have something to do with the movement of ocean water.

The Japan Current and the Gulf Stream of the Northern Hemisphere, the Brazil Current and the East Australian Current of the Southern Hemisphere, are examples of currents that carry warmth to many countries that would otherwise be cold. On the other hand, the Labrador Current and the Peru Current sweep south and north respectively from polar regions, cooling warm waters and where they rise, providing nutrients for living things and modifying the climate.

Exploring the Ocean and Its Floor. Limited and imperfect methods of exploration in the past led to the belief that the floor of the ocean was a deep, level plain. In recent years instruments used in exploration have been improved and new ones invented which are making it possible to explore areas of our Earth heretofore out of man's reach (p. 274). Many of these instruments, of diverse and ingenious design, are already available for measuring, sampling, and recording. Ships carrying a variety of special equipment make long voyages, crisscrossing the oceans in systematic patterns. As they do so, radio beams are used to mark locations accurately; echo-sounding instruments record electronically the depth of the water, thus gaining information from which maps of the ocean's bottom can be prepared. Long cores of sediment can be obtained and examined for plant and animal remains, for the time and temperature when the deposits were laid down, and for the composition and possible sources of the sediment. Deep dredging also brings up samples of sediment and rock from the bottom. Magnetometers are used to measure and record the magnetism of the rocks of the ocean floor, and gravity surveys can be made from ships and satellites. The flow of heat from Earth can be measured. Tests at different levels are made to determine the rate of flow of currents and the temperature and salinity of the water. The kinds of plant and animal life at different levels can be surveyed. Photography is used and is being developed as a way of exploring the ocean. Craft of different kinds are being designed for exploration at different depths.

Older children can explore the ocean by bringing in news items about it for the bulletin board, by discussion, and by becoming aware of this part of Earth about which so little is known.

Such devices as these are giving a new impetus to the study of the ocean floor and of the

Manganese nodules are found in many places on the ocean floor. These were photographed in the Atlantic Ocean; field of view, 6 feet, left to right. (Three Lions, N.Y.C.)

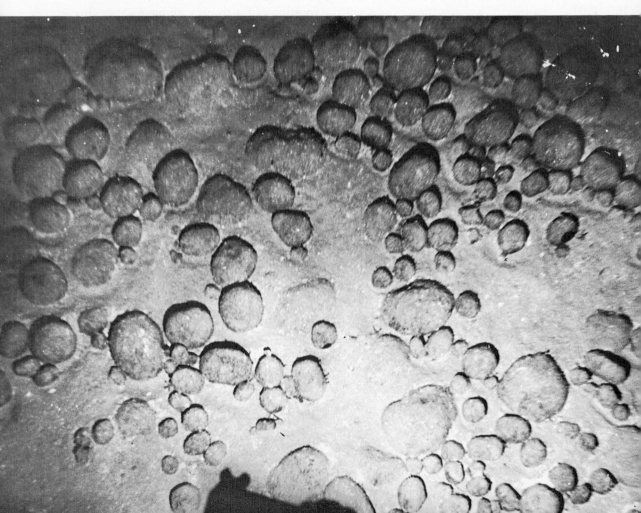

interior of our Earth. The results may shed new light on the formation of Earth and its land masses.

The Ocean Floor. The areas of Earth that lie under ocean water are broken by the continental shelves, mountain ranges, cliffs and ridges; by islands, and by trenches. The *continental shelves,* where they exist, extend out from the present shores of continents for varying distances. The material composing them indicates that they are definitely an integral part of the continental masses, covered with varying amounts of sediment. However, they do not correspond in outline to the present coastlines. For instance, along the eastern coast of the United States the shelf extends under ocean water for over 100 miles and for as much as 500 miles east of Newfoundland, while off parts of the African coast there is either no shelf or an extremely narrow one. In general, the continental shelves slope gradually downward and out into the ocean toward the edge of the shelf. The continental shelves lie under comparatively shallow water which may reach a depth of around 600 feet where the shelf ends and the continental slope begins.

The *continental slopes* are the areas where the continental shelves slope down to meet the deeper areas of the ocean floor. They are generally too steep for thick sediments to accumulate. The shelves and slopes are cut in places by what appear to be deep river *canyons,* in many instances equally as large as the Grand Canyon in Arizona. How the continental shelves and these canyons came to be has brought forth much speculation and many hypotheses. Some geologists believe the evidence points directly to the canyons having been formed while the area was uplifted and free from ocean water, and by the same processes of erosion that are taking place on land today. The submarine canyons are world-wide in occurrence and are found off the coasts of every continent as well as on the underwater slopes of islands such as Hawaii and Bogoslof in the Bering Sea. The underwater area around Bogoslof Island has been carefully mapped, and shows a stream and valley pattern similar to those developed on land. It is said that an 8000-foot rise of that land area or an equal subsidence of the ocean would have made dry land of the area around Bogoslof and permitted normal erosion to form the kind of valleys that exist under water today.

While many very large submarine canyons are found that are totally unrelated to the present-day drainage pattern, yet some of the largest ones are found opposite the mouths of our largest rivers. The canyon off the mouth of the Hudson River extends for some 90 miles across the continental shelf, averaging 300 feet in depth, and then for another 35 miles it becomes deeper, attaining a depth of 6600 feet where it cuts through the rocks of the continental slope. The largest canyon in the Gulf of Mexico is cut into the area off the Mississippi River. The great canyons off the Columbia, the Congo, the Ganges, and the Indus Rivers also might be cited as examples of this phenomenon.

Yet the question remains as to whether the land masses rose as a whole or only in parts; whether the ocean basins became deeper or whether a certain amount of ocean water became transferred to ice in the continental ice sheets during the glacial periods, thus leaving certain areas high and dry. It is a very complicated question, made even more so by the fact that the fossils of land and sometimes those of shallow-water organisms are found in the materials through which these submarine canyons sometimes cut, and by the fact that such fossils have been found on the top parts of many mountains whose summits are now under as much as 3000 feet or more of water. The likeness of plants and animals in certain areas adjacent to each other but now separated by water is also pointed to as evidence that they were not always separated in this manner and that the area had risen or the ocean subsided in bygone times, thus permitting valleys and canyons to form as on land.

Submarine currents, springs, and waves resulting from such submarine Earth movements as faulting, rock slides, or volcanic activity have been suggested as means for the erosion of these canyons; yet none seem entirely satisfactory, nor do they account for the presence of the fossils.

In the 1950's it was found that earthquakes occurred along a 40,000-mile belt running through the mid-Atlantic, Indian, South Pacific, and Arctic oceans. Branches of this belt reach into continents at a number of places and into the western Pacific Ocean. Further investigation may show that this earthquake belt in all these areas coincides with *high ridges* split by a very deep valley or rift, just as it does in the Indian Ocean and in the mid-Atlantic, where these peaks rise from 3000 to 20,000 feet above the ocean floor. Some peaks, therefore, are found to be less than a mile below the surface of the water. They are rugged in outline, and some have sharp peaks, while others have broad, flat tops. The range of mountains in its central part is from 60 to 200 miles wide. On both sides of this range lies a broad, comparatively level basin of true oceanic depth.

Explorations in the Pacific Ocean have disclosed a mountain chain reaching from Wake Island to Necker Island, not far from the Hawaiian Islands. It is an almost continuous range 1100 miles long and 100 miles wide, whose highest point is 14,000 feet high but is covered by about 2700 feet of ocean water. Many of these mountains are flat on top, a phenomenon which some students of the subject think could be a result of erosion by wave action in shallow water. This raises a host of interesting questions as to whether the mountains sank or the level of the sea rose, or just what did happen. Dredging brought up from

their tops fossil remains of such shallow-water life as clams, snails, and certain corals. From the ocean bottom were dredged sediment, layers of volcanic ash of different thicknesses, and, surprisingly, bacteria from a depth of as much as 20 feet below the surface of the ocean bottom.

Single and small groups of peaks are found in many places on the ocean's floor. Some are below water; others reach above water, forming such islands as the Hawaiian, the Canary, and the Cape Verde Islands. These are all of volcanic origin.

While much of the ocean bottom is irregular, with gentle hills and hollows, possibly due to the varying mantle of sediment, there are, in contrast to the mountains, *trenches* which frequently lie near the borders of continents. They sometimes lie parallel to the coastal ranges, and without doubt are due to faulting. They occur in both the Atlantic and Pacific oceans and are the areas near which the greatest number of deep earthquakes occur, although along the trenches the tremors are of shallow origin.

The greatest depth is found in the Pacific, where the Challenger Deep of the Mariana Trench southwest of Guam, reaches a depth of 36,198 feet. In the Altantic the record is held by the Milwaukee Depth, near Puerto Rico, with a depth of about 28,000 feet. In all, there are over fifty of these trenches, some nearly as deep as those mentioned. They may be many miles long.

Steep cliffs of varying heights have been found rising from the ocean floor, indicating zones of weakness similar to faulted areas on the continents.

Ocean Deposits. The deposits of sediment on the floor of the ocean consist of wind-blown dust from the land, materials carried by water, ash from volcanic eruptions, and dust from meteors. To these materials are added the remains of plants and animals. The kinds of sediment found on any area of the ocean floor depend on the distance from shore, the currents, the sediments available, the character of the bottom, the temperature and oxygen content of the water, the depth, and possibly other factors which remain to be discovered. As exploration goes on, ideas concerning the thickness of the ocean deposits are changing. It has been found that there is not a uniform thickness of sediment over the ocean floor. No two areas are alike. On the real ocean floor the sediments may be relatively thin, while on the slopes of the mountain ridges they may be several thousands of feet thick. Near the continents the bottom is covered by material blown and washed from the land as well as by the remains of the myriads of plants and animals that spend their lives in comparatively shallow waters.

On the continental slopes the sediments are in general very fine-grained and are often referred to as mud. Occasionally deep-sea oozes are found. The type of deposit changes as the ocean becomes deeper, and red clay and ooze are found. This material is extremely fine and is derived from the insoluble remains of simple types of plants and animals, wind-blown volcanic ash, and the dust from meteors. The deposit of meteoritic particles on Earth as a whole is estimated to be as much as 5 million tons yearly. However, the evidence taken from cores of ocean sediment shows that the amount has varied through Earth's history.

In the deeper parts of the ocean there are fewer animals and no green plants that live near the bottom. The skeletal deposits in these areas come mainly from the *plankton,* the general name given to the myriads of minute plants and animals that drift along near the surface of the water. Microscopic, one-celled plants called diatoms flourish in the colder water. In tropical water thrive the one-celled animals called radiolaria. The cell walls of the diatoms and the skeletons of the radiolaria are composed of silica and fall to

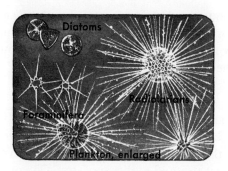

Some of the many one-celled plants and animals making up the plankton.

the bottom when these organisms die. Foraminifera are another type of one-celled animal that form part of the plankton. Their shells are limy, and they are said to have formed the limestone from which the pyramids of Egypt are built. Other minute plants and animals and the young of many larger forms are included among the plankton.

It is an interesting fact that the carbon dioxide content of sea water increases with its depth, thereby increasing the amount of a weak acid which dissolves to a great extent plant and animal remains.

EXPERIENCE. *The ocean varies in depth.* Children may be able to get an idea of the depth of the ocean by comparing it to something they already know, such as, "It is as far to the bottom as it is to the next town and back."

EXPERIENCE. *The location of islands and trenches.* A globe or map may be used to find some of the trenches and chains of islands.

EXPERIENCE. *The ocean rests on rocks.* It is important for children to know that there is a bottom of good, solid rock to the oceans. The ocean bottom is a part of Earth that is lower that the continents. The ocean bottom is one of the great frontiers for exploration. Older children may watch for reports of discoveries in newspapers and magazines.

EXPERIENCE. *Children's ideas of the bottom of the ocean.* Children may wish to write of an imaginary trip in a submarine surveying the bottom of the ocean, or to make pictures of what they think the bottom is like.

EXPERIENCE. *There is salt in ocean water.* If it is possible to obtain sea water, fill a pan with it and then boil to dryness. Or, if time permits, allow it to stand and evaporate. Do you find anything remaining in the pan? This is for the most part salt that has been in solution (dissolved, p. 386) in the sea water.

Lakes. Lakes are relatively small bodies of water scattered over the continents. They range in size from mere ponds to bodies of water covering hundreds of square miles, with, in rare instances, a depth of 5000 feet. Lake basins are natural depressions in the land which occur along seacoasts, on high mountains, or on the prairies. These basins may be formed in many different ways. Stream deposits may accumulate across a valley, thus damming it up. Rivers may cut new beds and sufficient deposits may be made to cut off some section of a winding stream, forming oxbow lakes. These are common in level areas. Debris from landslides and volcanoes may dam up streams, forming lakes, and craters of extinct volcanoes may become lakes. In arid regions the wind may produce basins which fill whenever there is water available. Along coasts the ocean may build up sand enough to form bars which become part of a basin holding water and thus form lagoons or lakes. These are very common along coast lines. Glaciers may either gouge out or deposit material to form basins. These basins are numerous in mountainous regions. The continental ice sheets ground out basins in the rocks and deposited material as they receded, so that thousands of lakes were formed in the northern part of the United States and in Canada. Movements of Earth's crust such

as bending or faulting can produce basins which become filled with water. These are among our deepest lakes. There is great diversity among lakes as to area, depth, and location. The water for these basins may be supplied to some extent by ground water, but mostly by either local or distant rain or snow.

When streams supply the water and drain the lakes, the water is kept fresh, and the lakes are *fresh-water* lakes. The necessary conditions are a source of water and some kind of drainage. In dry regions there is often not enough water to fill the basins and provide drainage. Then the substances dissolved by the water as it runs over and through the rocks and soil are eventually precipitated as salts as evaporation takes place year after year. The common precipitates are sodium chloride, which is common salt, sodium sulfate, sodium and potassium carbonates, and borax. Thus there are *alkali* lakes, *borax* lakes, and *salt* lakes, depending upon the salts deposited. The deposits are sometimes of commercial value.

In temperate and tropical regions lakes provide homes for a great variety of plant and animal life. In the arctic, plant and animal life in lakes and other bodies of water is extremely limited, due to the long periods of great cold and the short growing season, with its very slanting light from the sun. The subarctic with its more benign climate supports a larger variety of plants and animals, both in and out of water.

Since lakes are comparatively small in size and are subject to the local conditions of climate and erosion, they are considered temporary bodies when compared as to age with the oceans or mountains. Lake basins may eventually fill with sediment, or if shallow and if conditions favor the growth of plants, may eventually become filled with plants and their remains. Often lakes will dry up and their basins be returned to land area. Like oceans, lakes also modify the climate, but in a far smaller and more local way, depending on their size. Lakes may also delay erosion by being receptacles for sediment; they regulate the flow of streams, thereby cutting down on floods and the damage they do; and they may be valuable as a source of food and recreation.

EXPERIENCE. *The lake near your school.* If there is a lake near your school, the children may be interested in trying to find out why it is there. Was it formed by deposits which dammed up the water? Did a glacier dig out a basin? If it is a large lake perhaps the children can secure information about it from the State or Province. Is the lake of any value to the community?

Water in the Air. Water is present in the atmosphere in varying amounts and, under certain conditions, condenses and falls in some form of precipitation (p. 486). The distribution of rainfall is exceedingly irregular, and as a result there are areas ranging from withering deserts to steaming jungles. Much of the precipitation, as it evaporates, is gradually and invisibly returned to the atmosphere.

The water in the atmosphere is a powerful and important factor in the formation of soil, since it is able to penetrate, as a part of air, into the minutest openings in rocks and thus attack surfaces which might otherwise escape untouched.

EXPERIENCE. *How can we tell there is water in the air?* Children might name as many as they can of events that might cause them to think there is water in the air. They may name rain, snow, hail, fog, clouds, dew, the dampness on the outside of a glass of cold water or milk in summer, frost or steam on a window, frost on the ground on a cold day, or steamy eyeglasses. Any of these is good evidence that water is in the air. They may be able to name other events.

Underground Water. The water within Earth is largely the water from some form of precipitation that has soaked into and through the porous soil and rocks, although water and steam from magma is present to a certain degree. It is called *subsurface, subterranean,* or *underground* water. There is also *connate* water, usually salty, which may be water caught by sediments as they were deposited ages ago when the area was invaded by the sea. This water is held between beds of rock so compact that water cannot pass through them. It is most often found at depths of 1000 feet or more by people drilling for oil. Therefore it does not affect us to any extent. However, all salty water is not connate. Some may become salty by flowing through a deposit of salt, and in some places salt water seeps into rocks from the ocean and under certain conditions may contaminate wells.

The depth to which this water flows and the amount of it which enters the ground depends upon the character of the rocks and the unconsolidated deposits with which it comes in contact. Some rocks are so fine-grained and solid that water moves through them at the rate of only a few feet in an entire year. Other rocks permit water to enter readily, may hold a vast quantity, and the flow may go on at a far more rapid pace. Hence, sands and gravels and their corresponding rocks are more porous and will permit a faster flow of water through them than will clay and silt and their corresponding rocks.

This slowing down of the flow of water by the rocks serves a most useful purpose. If it were not for that, the water would immediately flow away; more and larger floods would occur, streams would run dry between rains, and regions depending on wells and springs for water would have none.[1] It is an important step in the water cycle.

Water from rain and snow must first thor-

[1]See page 315 for the work of underground water.

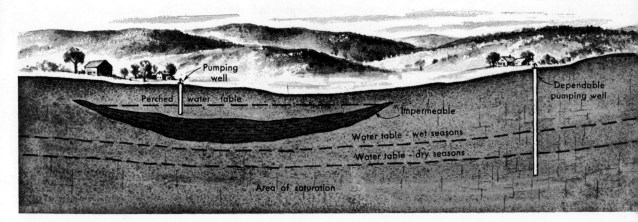

This diagram shows conditions under which water may be obtained from ordinary pumping wells. Note that the location of the regular water table may vary with the amount of precipitation. The "area of saturation" is known as an "aquifer."

oughly moisten the unconsolidated Earth materials upon which it falls before any can flow down to the ground-water reservoirs. The needs of the shallow-rooted plants must also be satisfied before any additional water can move downward. These demands are heavy at times.

In areas where all materials are of the kind that can absorb water the water sinks as far below the surface as the rocks permit, filling up every crevice and pore in the rocks, and any unconsolidated materials. The top surface of this zone of saturation is called the *water table*. It tends to follow the contour of the land surface above, and the water tends to flow in the same direction as the surface run-off, but much more slowly due to friction against the walls of the pores or spaces in the soil or rock through which it passes. Above this level, or water table, which may be very irregular, is a zone where the soil or rocks may be only moist. The water table is sought when ordinary wells are drilled, in order to secure an abundant supply of water. This underground mass of water may be at different depths. In sections having heavy rainfall it is nearer the surface than in arid regions. Also, in some regions where a great deal of

water is used from wells, the water table may be lowered to the point of depletion.

Rocks and unconsolidated materials that are porous enough to receive large amounts of water and to permit its flow in large enough quantities to supply natural springs and pumping wells are commonly called *aquifers* or ground-water reservoirs. It will be noted that the word *reservoir* in this case includes the movement of water and thus is slightly differ-

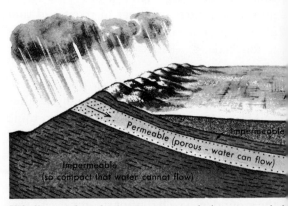

This diagram shows how water may enter sloping porous rocks ly between nonporous rocks, and may flow out at some distant locatio an artesian well or artesian spring, due to the pressure of the conf water. The "permeable" area is the "aquifer."

ent from the ordinary use of the word. Such reservoirs are usually sands, gravels, limestones, and sandstones, as well as dense rocks that have been fractured by movements of Earth. These reservoirs vary in depth and area. However, they are relatively near Earth's surface, because rocks at great depths become extremely compact due to the great pressure of the overlying rocks, and, as a result, water cannot flow through them.

Artesian wells may be developed under certain conditions. Water in the aquifer must be under pressure. This occurs when the water-bearing rock reaches the surface of Earth at some point where it receives water and the rock slopes downward at an angle. It must lie between layers of rock that strongly resist the flow of water through them. Thus the water in the aquifer is confined between these nonporous layers and pressure is built up. Often such artesian systems are made up of water-bearing beds of sandstones or conglomerates between beds of shale or clay. The pressure of water in the aquifer may be great enough to push the water to the surface or beyond when a well is drilled on the downward slope, and a flowing well results. A certain amount of pumping in some wells may be necessary, but a well would still be an artesian well if it was produced from an aquifer with water under pressure.

Perched bodies of water occur when there is a compact bed of rock overlain by porous soil or rock and perched at or above the usual water table. These beds of compact rock may catch and hold water as shown in the diagram. They may provide enough water for a farm or a community. Many relatively small beds of sand and gravel were left by the ice sheets and are useful for holding water.

Experience. *There is water in the ground.* Children may relate and discuss any of their experiences that would lead them to think there is water in the ground. How do they think it got there? Why do they think this? They might be interested in making drawings of their ideas of underground water.

Swamps, Rivers, and Springs. Some of the underground water eventually reaches the sea; some is brought to the surface by means of wells; some evaporates and plants return some to the air by transpiration. Some of it may appear on the surface in the form of swamps, rivers, or springs. When the water table coincides with the surface of the ground over a considerable area, a swamp may result. The swamp may also be fed by streams and runoff.

Swamps or *marshes* are temporary features in humid regions, and may represent one stage in the filling of lakes. Saturation of the ground is a necessary condition. The water table may appear, or the location may be at or near sea level. Swamps eventually become filled with sediment and with plant and animal remains.

Swamps are of importance because they modify the climate to some extent and provide homes for wild life such as birds, fish, frogs, insects, turtles, and other animals, as well as a variety of plants. Plant and animal life inhabiting swamps in colder regions is severely limited as to numbers and variety by the continuous and great cold and, probably, by the lack of sunlight. As conditions become more favorable to life, the plant and animal population is swamps increases until great numbers and a wide variety of plants and animals are to be found in tropical regions.

Swamps may become deposits of peat, marl, or bog iron ore, depending upon the kinds of plants and animals inhabiting them. Hence, climate may play an important part in the changes through which swamps pass. In climates suitable for farming, swamps may in time become fertile farm land when filled.

Tidal or *salt* marshes occur along coast lines. They are the result of the silting up of quiet water such as bays and lagoons. They may receive salt water from the ocean's tides and fresh water from the land. Tidal marshes or swamps support plants and animals that are adapted to living in such an environment. Like fresh-water swamps, salt marshes may eventually become filled with sediment and plant and animal remains. As the filling in is completed, fresh-water and land plants move in and the salt marsh may proceed seaward if conditions permit.

In areas of abundant rainfall the water table may appear at or very near the surface, and there may be a continuous movement of underground water into the rivers. With additional water from rain or snow these streams would flow continuously year after year. In arid regions the reverse is true. Streams which bring water from distant places may add to the supply of underground water in the dry areas through which they flow.

Quicksand is the name given to beds of fine sand that are saturated with water. They may be horizontal beds of sand under shallow water, or their tops may be level with or slightly above the water table; or they may be confined between impervious beds of soil or rock. A bed of quicksand offers no support because of the large amount of water present. Sometimes this condition is found in what seem to be dry stream beds.

Springs are the result of the flow of underground water to the surface, and occur where the land surface cuts across the water table, thus permitting the water to flow out. There may be year-round flow, or the springs may dry up during periods of little rain. This depends on the size and position of the beds of water-bearing material. Springs occur along hillsides, in valleys, and in desert wastes.

Artesian springs are produced by the same conditions that produce artesian wells; namely, water confined and under pressure. The spring occurs at a point lower than the point at which the water enters the aquifer.

Under these conditions the water is forced out.

Some hot and warm springs are believed to receive their flow from ordinary rain water which has seeped down into Earth and which has come into contact with heated rocks or hot gases. The heated water ascends, pushed forth by steam (p. 299).

EXPERIENCE. *Why the swamp is in your neighborhood.* Has it always been a swamp? One of the older citizens of your area might recall whether or not it had changed during his lifetime. Why is it a swamp? Is it part of a lake that is filling up? Was it hollowed out by a glacier in long-past ages?

EXPERIENCE. *Swamps are neither lakes nor dry land.* Observing all safety precautions, children may wish to visit a swamp and observe the plant and animal life. Are there any differences to be seen between these plants and animals and those living on land? Children may find it profitable to make pictures of a swamp, showing its relation to a lake or to land areas.

EXPERIENCE. *Springs are useful features in many regions.* Have the children ever seen a spring? If so, what are some of the things they know about it? Where was it located? Is it of use today? Was it ever used for anything?

The Intermingling of the Gaseous, the Solid, and the Liquid. These three parts of Earth— the gaseous, the solid, and the liquid—are not independent of one another. Bits of the solid part, in the form of dust, mix with the air and also become mixed in water, frequently making muddy the streams and other bodies of water. By dissolving parts of the soil and rocks, the waters of Earth again mingle with the solid part. The salty condition of the oceans, the alkaline or salty condition of many lakes, and the hardness of the well water in many sections of Earth are examples of this.

Water gets into the air through evaporation and returns to the solid part of Earth in rain and other forms of precipitation. Air is dissolved in water; and most of us have grown so accustomed to it that if we drink water which does not have air in it, we say it tastes flat. Water and air get into the soil; in fact, plants will not grow unless they do. So we may say that the solid, liquid, and gaseous parts of Earth are not independent of one another, for the mixing of them goes on continuously. It is most important to living things that it does, for life on the land and in the sea is dependent on the mixing of these three parts of Earth. Much of the discussion which follows in this chapter has to do with the intermingling and interplay of the three parts of Earth.

EXPERIENCE. *There is air in water.* Heat water to see air driven out. The first bubbles are air. The others are steam. Taste water that has been boiled and cooled.

EXPERIENCE. *There is air in soil.* Pour water into dry soil. This is difficult to do because air is in the soil and keeps the water from flowing in readily. Air bubbles escape through the water.

EXPERIENCE. *There is salt in sea water.* Boil to dryness some sea water, or allow it to evaporate. A little solid material will be left. This salt is a solid dissolved in a liquid. Some children may have had the experience of bathing in salt water. They may recall having salt left on their skin when the water evaporated.

EXPERIENCE. *Would Earth have the same amount of air if it had less gravity?* Would Earth have more air or less air if it had less gravity? Is there any connection between the gravitation of the moon and its lack of atmosphere? (The moon's gravitation is about one sixth that of Earth.)

EXPERIENCE. *What if there were no atmosphere?* Children may enjoy thinking of all the things which would be different if Earth had no atmosphere. No animals could breathe; no green plants could manufacture food; probably no rain would fall. There would be much less soil than at present, for some soil is formed by running streams, which would run dry without rain, and some soil is formed by wind; Earth would be warmer during the day and colder at night than it now is; there would be no clouds.

EXPERIENCE. *Air may enter into rocks.* Put several rocks into water one at a time in order to observe carefully. Do tiny bubbles rise from any of them? This is air that is being pushed out by the water.

EXPERIENCE. *Water enters rocks.* Put different rocks into water. Remove and wipe thoroughly. Are they still wet? If so, it shows that water entered the tiny pores in the rocks.

EXPERIENCE. *Where is the water of Earth?* Is it all in the oceans, lakes, or rivers? Some water is in the air, the rocks, and the soil. Plants take in soil water through their roots.

What Is Inside Earth?

The question "Is the interior of Earth solid, liquid, or gaseous?" is one frequently asked by children, and adults as well. One of the greatest achievements of man, confined as he is to the surface of his planet, is what he has learned about the parts of the universe which he cannot approach near enough to touch. Such a part of the universe is the interior of his own planet.

Ways in Which Man Learns about the Inside of Earth. Because man is unable to go far into Earth, his exploration must be confined to work in laboratories or to using instruments. Information about the inside of Earth is gained by observing how different materials behave under extremely great pressures and high temperatures; by direct observation of any materials that can be obtained from within; by observing how earthquake waves act as they pass or do not pass through different parts of Earth (p. 276); and by data recorded by satellites (p. 235). These methods have served to give a certain body of knowledge, to give rise to many hypotheses, and to stimulate a great desire for closer contact with Earth's interior. To this end, holes may be bored through the ocean's fossil sediment and successive layers of crust, through the *Mohorovicic discontinuity,* or Moho, for short, into the mantle. The Moho is the boundary between Earth's mantle and crust. At a site near Guadalupe Island, off the western coast of Lower California, where the water is fairly shallow and the distance is relatively short through the light crust to the mantle, drilling passed through 200 to 300 feet of sediment and almost through the crustal layer beneath.

In such projects the coring drill, with it hollow center, permits bringing up coring tubes from remote regions with samples of sediments and rocks that can be examined carefully in a laboratory. Instruments for measuring magnetism, temperature, density, and porosity are used to secure other information.

Information relating to Earth's interior, the source of its heat, its origin, the concentration of minerals, and many other matters may be gained from such exploration. Even now, the evidence from earthquake waves that there is a layer of basalt below the ocean's sediment has been verified.

Temperature of Earth. No one knows the amount of the original heat of Earth or the extent of the radioactivity in the past. However, the rocks underlying the oceans and the continents are predominantly of igneous

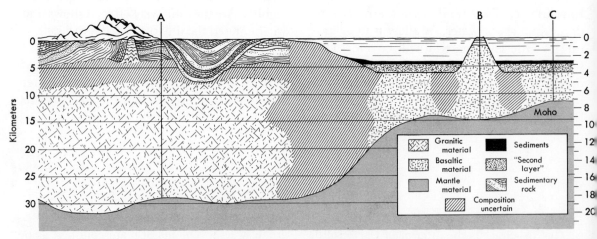

Exploration of the crust and mantle are expected to yield important information about the structure of Earth. Note where the distance to the boundary between crust and mantle (Mohorovicic discontinuity) is least (C). (Adapted from Willard Bascom, "The Mohole," Scientific American, April 1959, pp. 42–43.)

origin. This alone would lead to the conclusion that heat was present in considerable amount at one time. Present-day volcanic activity gives direct evidence that portions of Earth comparatively near the surface are very hot. Intensely hot, molten rock pours down the sides of volcanoes and hot gases burst forth. Hot lava pours from fissures and spreads over thousands of square miles. Temperature measurements of lava as it issues from Earth show that it is about 2000°F. In Iceland, heat from igneous masses below the surface is used for heating buildings. It is said to have a temperature of nearly 200°F. Not far from Florence, Italy, heat from Earth has for years been used to generate electricity.

Even aside from such areas of thermal activity, the temperature of the outer part of Earth varies greatly. The effects of seasonal changes in temperature are seldom noticeable below a depth of 50 feet. The temperature of water from springs and wells in the middle latitudes (temperate zones) may be about 50°–60°F., although it varies.

In the far north, generally north of 60° N, is a region of permanently frozen subsoil due to low atmospheric temperatures. It is an area where the mean annual temperature of the atmosphere near the surface of the ground is below 32°F. The extent of the *permafrost* is influenced not only by temperature but also by the amount of soil drainage and snow, and the kind of terrain and vegetation. In turn it prevents good drainage, and promotes flooding and the formation of a profusion of lakes and swamps. The depth of the permanently frozen ground and the area of permafrost is irregular. Near the southern borders of this region its occurrence is shallow and irregular, but farther north the permafrost becomes deeper. On the Taymyr Peninsula in Siberia the permafrost reaches down to a depth of from 1300 to 2000 feet. It is related to the intensity and duration of low temperatures. Below this outer surface zone of Earth's

crust there is an average increase in temperature of 1°F. for every 60 feet in depth. This average was obtained from temperature readings in hundreds of mines and wells all over the world. In one of the deeper holes bored, 4 miles deep, the temperature was 350°F. Deep gold mines in Africa must be cooled so that men can work in them. The rate of increase in temperature with depth varies greatly from place to place, and may even change abruptly in some bore holes. The possible explanation for this is that some rocks conduct heat more readily than others.

It is not known whether or not the temperature of Earth continues to increase with depth. It is doubtful that it does. But if it does, the temperature at the center would be exceedingly high.

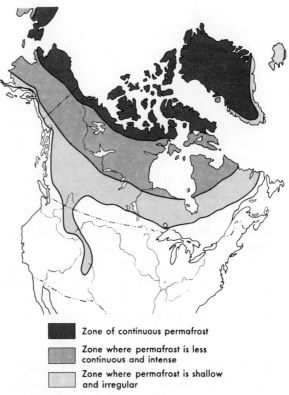

Zone of continuous permafrost

Zone where permafrost is less continuous and intense

Zone where permafrost is shallow and irregular

Permanently frozen subsoil, or permafrost, occurs in the northern part of North America.

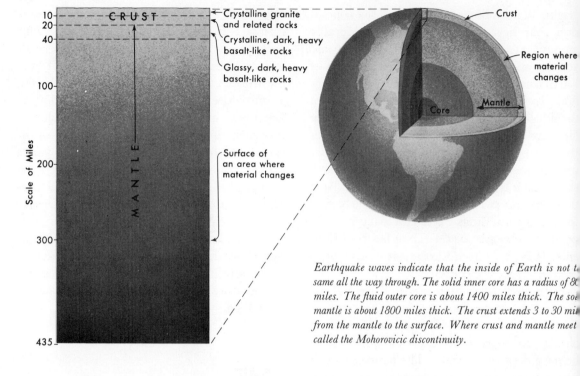

Earthquake waves indicate that the inside of Earth is not the same all the way through. The solid inner core has a radius of 800 miles. The fluid outer core is about 1400 miles thick. The solid mantle is about 1800 miles thick. The crust extends 3 to 30 miles from the mantle to the surface. Where crust and mantle meet is called the Mohorovicic discontinuity.

It is known that heat may result from pressure, and it has been estimated that near the center of Earth there is a pressure of more than 2 million tons on every square foot. Heat produced from friction when rock masses break and slip past each other could also contribute to the sum total. It is known that radioactivity produces heat, but whether or not this continues to Earth's center is not known. However, it is generally thought by geologists and geophysicists that Earth's interior is hot.

A greater knowledge of Earth's heat might solve the questions of the origin of Earth's material and how it came to be Earth as we know it, with its oceans and continents, growing mountains, and volcanic activity.

Earthquake Waves Indicate the Character of Earth's Interior. Other phenomena of which use is made in studying the interior of Earth are the earthquake waves. An earth-

quake sets up a disturbance consisting of series of waves which travel through Earth.

There are two main groups of earthquake waves: the *preliminary,* or body, waves and the *long,* or surface, waves. The preliminary waves go through Earth, and the long waves travel around Earth below the surface.

The preliminary waves are of two kinds: the push-pull, or primary, waves and the shake, or secondary, waves. Their names somewhat describe the direction and rate of speed at which these two kinds of preliminary waves travel through Earth. The following words are often used to describe these waves: *P* or primary, push-pull, compressional, or longitudinal; *S* or secondary, transverse, shake, or shear.

The primary and secondary waves both start out in all directions at the same time from the place where Earth's crust is moving (p. 290). These waves behave differently as they pass through Earth. The primary waves pulse straight ahead like an uncoiling spring; they are the fastest of all earthquake waves, and can travel through any kind of Earth material, whether it is a gas, a liquid, or a solid. Therefore, these waves are the first to be recorded by a seismograph.

The secondary waves proceed out in all directions from the disturbance, as do the primary waves, but they wave from side to side as they progress. This kind of movement slows down the secondary waves, and they are recorded by the seismograph after the primary waves are recorded. These waves are different in another way: they can only exist and move through a solid.

The long, or surface, waves are still slower than the secondary waves. They have a much longer route to travel—around Earth—and they encounter many different kinds of Earth material—soft and hard, and of different chemical composition—on the way. There are several surface waves. One kind, the Rayleigh, resembles surface water waves in its motion, and another kind, the Love, resembles the secondary waves in its motion. There are still other kinds of long waves that move more slowly than the Love and Rayleigh waves. All of these are recorded on seismographs.

EXPERIENCE. *Feeling vibrations.* The general idea of a vibration or wave can be gained by children if they hold a table fork lightly by the handle and strike the other end sharply against some object. The vibrations may be felt in the handle where it is held. Gently strike objects made of other materials. Are vibrations felt or heard? Are the vibrations the same? Sounds are made by waves or vibrations, too (p. 874). Earthquake waves are Earth waves or vibrations, and they, too, change their speed and the way they behave as they come in contact with different Earth materials.

The records made of an earthquake by seismographs at many different locations are compared and studied. The velocity and direction of the waves through the various parts of Earth's interior can be calculated and accurately determined. Scientists can determine the density of the material through which the waves pass by measuring the velocity of the waves. For instance, the waves passing through the bed of the Pacific Ocean behave like similar waves passing through known beds of the igneous rock, basalt. This has been verified by the test drilling near Guadalupe Island. The location, time, and severity of an earthquake can be determined from these data.

This evidence indicates that the center or core of Earth is metallic; that it is very dense and may be composed of such heavy metals as iron and some nickel and possibly cobalt. The core is thought of as being in two parts, the inner and outer core. Because P waves pass through the inner core more quickly than through the outer core, some think it may be solid. The inner core has a radius of about 800 miles. Surrounding it is the less dense outer core, about 1400 miles thick. Since P waves travel through this part more slowly than through the inner core, it is thought to be in a fluid state, but not like water. When these waves reach the outer core they are bent and their speed changes. The S waves do not pass through the outer or inner core.

Around this large core lies the mantle, with a thickness of 1800 miles. Both P and S waves travel through it, and there is evidence that it is solid. It probably consists of iron and magnesium minerals denser than basalt. It is thought to be rigid but capable of changing shape or flowing very slowly under pressure.

The outer 3 to 30 miles of Earth, called the crust, is made up of still lighter materials. Its thickness varies greatly, with an average of 22 miles under the continents and about 4 miles beneath the oceans. The continental crust is thicker under mountains, and the oceanic crust is thickest under ocean ridges and island arcs, and probably thinnest under deep trenches.

Earth, then, has several layers—the crust, mantle, outer core, and inner core, and becomes denser toward the center.

Earthquake waves indicate there may be a distinct border line between the materials at these different levels. The border line between the outer and inner core is not as distinct as the others. The border line where crust and mantle meet is called the Mohorovicic discontinuity. It is not a straight line but one that seems to be related to the way Earth's materials behave and to the balance in their distribution.

The fact that meteorites are either stony or metallic and may be remnants of bodies similar to Earth also gives a basis for the conclusion that Earth is composed of like materials.

The solid Earth, as a whole, can withstand suddenly applied forces twice as great as can steel. However, it is elastic to forces that are slowly and steadily applied, such as the forces exerted by the sun and the moon.

Whether or not earthquakes are related in any way to isostasy or balance in Earth is not known for certain; but it is quite probable that severe strains in the crust accumulate to a point where a readjustment must take place

Earth Is Very Old

There can be no doubt in the mind of any careful student of Earth that it is very old. All evidence points to that fact. The only question about which there can be any doubt is how old it is. No one knows this exactly. Many records are to be found in Earth itself, and additional evidence is being found of its great age from the study of the solar system

and the distant galaxies. Naturally the estimates of Earth's age differ; but they all agree on one very important essential, and that is that Earth was formed millions of years ago

An impulse of early men was to set a definite time for the beginning of Earth, a time bearing some relation to their own traditions and then to contend that all the changes had

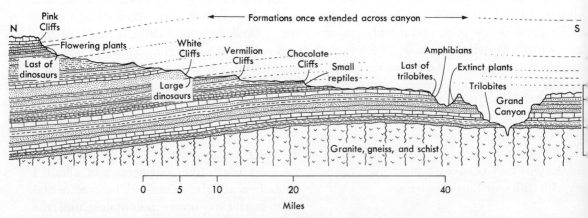

This diagram represents a vertical slice across the Grand Canyon, Arizona, and the cliffs north of it. Only a few of many important fossil locations are shown. An immense period of time was required to weather and erode this region. (Adapted from Introduction to Physical Geology, *2nd edition, C. R. Longwell and R. F. Flint, John Wiley & Sons, N.Y., p. 52.)*

occurred since that time. A common practice of ancient peoples was to set the time for the formation of Earth at a period just previous to the beginnings of their own traditional history. This, naturally, caused many difficulties later, because the evidence in the rocks showed that many tremendous and time-consuming changes had taken place.

Even to the observing eye, very little change seems to take place in Earth itself. Occasionally an earthquake, a volcanic explosion, or a flood occurs; but, on the whole the forces of nature seem to change Earth but slowly. It was natural for the ancient bard to think of the hills as everlasting; they were there when his forefathers were there, and they had seemed to change scarcely at all during many generations; therefore he concluded that Earth had always had its present appearance and would never change. Later, when men noticed that the rocks had been bent, folded, and broken, and that the fossil remains of sea animals were found on the tops of the mountains, they were hard pressed to explain these observations. A theory, which we may call the *cataclysmic* theory, was offered in explanation. This theory, which was not based on a scientific study of Earth but was arrived at speculatively, held that Earth had undergone tremendous cataclysmic changes, when the rocks were tilted, folded, pushed under the seas, and raised again, all in a short time. It was thought by many that the gods must have been angry and spent their madness on Earth by producing devastating changes.

Man has learned that the cataclysmic theory is not reasonable and has introduced the concept of *uniformitarianism*. This concept may be stated simply as follows: The forces of nature have operated in the past much as they are operating at the present time, and therefore we may learn much of the past by studying the changes going on today. There may have been times when certain changes occurred more or less rapidly and other times when changes occurred slowly. The story of Earth, however, is one of the orderly operations of the forces of nature, the same forces which are in operation today. The age of Earth must be measured by hundreds, if not thousands, of millions of years.

The geologist is able to read a remarkable story in the rocks. He reads their story somewhat as one reads a story in an old book: some pages are missing, others are torn, but enough is preserved to enable one to follow the thread of the story.

The evidences of the antiquity of Earth are many. The following are but a few that might be cited:

River Valleys Are Very Old. The erosion of great valleys is evidence that Earth is old. Perhaps there is such a valley near your own home. The erosion, which goes on year after year, can scarcely be measured or even noted by a person who has not been trained to make accurate measurements and observations of such changes. The river in the valley carries away great quantities of mud year after year. Occasionally in a flood it may make changes in its course possibly destroying small islands and forming new ones. But, on the whole, the changes are slow, and in a generation of people the floor of the valley seems to have been lowered scarcely at all, and the valley remains apparently unchanged. And yet the river has been the agent which made the valley, bit by bit, though it may have taken thousands of years. The changes are not noticeable from day to day, but over a long period of time their effect on Earth's surface is tremendous. This is true of the work of erosion and especially of the erosive work of rivers. It has been estimated that it has taken the Colorado River and its tributaries somewhat over a million years to carve the Grand Canyon from the plateau. Not all rivers form valleys at the same rate of speed, owing to the character of the rocks over which they flow; for some rocks are hard and resistant and others are soft and wear away quickly.

Earth contains many river valleys, and we have evidence that there have been rivers in the past which do not exist today. In some cases, these rivers flowed into seas which do not exist today. There is evidence that sometimes rivers have been forced to change their courses by the tilting of the land, by landslides, or by deposition of material transported by rivers or by glaciers.

The Ocean Is Salty. Another evidence of Earth's antiquity is the fact that the ocean is salty. The water in the original ocean must have been fresh or nearly so; yet today ocean water has been found to contain such substances as sulfates and chlorides of magnesium, calcium, and potassium, with sodium chloride, or common salt, present in far greater quantities than any of the other constituents. At least half of the natural chemical elements are represented by these constituents. The rivers, carrying down their loads of material from the land to the ocean, have transported salts, which they dissolved from the land. The water in the ocean is constantly evaporating, leaving behind it the materials washed from the soil. Thus the salts are left in the ocean, and, as more water is brought down by the rivers, the ocean becomes more and more salty. As time goes on, the ocean will become saltier. When salt is used as a measuring stick for the age of Earth, it is done by computing the rate at which rivers carry salt to the oceans. It has been found that the rate varies greatly due to wet and dry years and that salt is carried back to land in ocean spray. This method, although certainly showing a great age for Earth, is not as exact as it was once thought to be.

Rocks Have Been Folded. The folding and bending of the rocks is evidence of the age of Earth. We know that where sediments are laid down in water, they are nearly flat. Many such beds have been tilted and folded and have become, not only dry land, but even parts of mountains. Later they may have sunk below the ocean water, and new layers may have been deposited on them. Fossils of marine animals are frequently found at the tops of mountains.

Sediments Have Been Deposited. Great mountain ranges, one after another, have been built up only to be worn away by the ordinary processes of erosion; and sediments, many thousands of feet in depth, have accumulated by the slow removal of thousands of feet of materials from the land. Estimates of the age of Earth may be made by measuring the thickness of sediments that have been deposited on Earth. This, too, is not an exact measure by any means, because of the varying rates at which sediments are laid down and the length

Upper portion (about 8⅔ inches long) of a sediment core taken in the Gulf of Mexico, on the continental shelf off Texas. The lighter mottlings in the darker, fine-grained sediment were probably caused by burrowing organisms. (Scripps Institute of Oceanography.)

of the intervals between periods of sedimentation, and because the deposits of one period may have been carried away and thus may be missing in the area. A core of rock from a deep drill hole might show the deposits of some periods missing. Unless deformed by folding or faulting, the more recent sediments will lie on top of the older sediments; yet it does prove beyond a doubt that Earth is millions of years old.

Fossils Are Evidences of Ancient Life. The evidence which comes from the records made by the life of the past in one of a long succession of living things. Many limestones, shales, and sandstones are large depositories of fossils. In early geologic time the animals and plants were comparatively simple in their structure, and in later geologic epochs living things became more highly organized. The fossils are in large part the keys by which man has been able to unlock the mysteries of the past. Millions of plants and animals have become extinct. No species, once extinct, has ever reappeared. Some species have lived through many geologic epochs, while others have disappeared after a brief existence. The rocks of Earth plainly bear evidence of millions of years during which there were successes and failures in living forms (p. 333).

Climates Have Changed. There is evidence of great climatic changes during the history of Earth. For instance, salt and gypsum beds indicate an arid climate at the time when they were formed. There is evidence of a subtropical climate in regions which are today temperate or arctic. Coal was formed on the Antarctic Continent, which indicates that at one time there must have been a luxuriant plant growth there, whereas now it is a bleak region of ice and snow. Fossils of tropical plants have been found in Spitsbergen and in Greenland. There is also unmistakable evidence that a large part of northern North America and northwestern Europe was covered with ice several thousand feet thick at one time. In fact, there have been several ice ages and recessions of the ice, accompanied by long periods of warm climate.

Radioactivity Shows Earth to Be Very Old. Another method of estimating the age of Earth and of many substances on it is derived from the study of radioactive elements found in minerals. The discovery of this method was made about 1907, and by 1913 rocks had been dated. This method does not replace other methods of dating; it is another tool to use in this work.

For a long time scientists thought that elements could not be broken down into other substances. Then it was found that some elements, radium, for example, would break down by themselves. Another of the elements that breaks down in this manner is uranium. It breaks down step by step through a series of products. One of these steps produces radium. The last change is to a form of lead. It is called an *end product* of uranium. This lead can be identified, because its atomic weight is different from that of any other lead.

Scientists who have studied uranium and its products have learned how fast uranium changes into this kind of lead and have found nothing that alters the rate of radioactive change. For instance, after 4.5 million years, half of any given amount of uranium 238 (uranium with an atomic weight of 238) will have become lead 206 (lead with an atomic weight of 206). At the end of another 4.5 million years half of the uranium left at the end of the first period will have become lead, and so on, until the uranium is gone. This is what is meant when it is said that uranium 238 has a *half-life* of 4.5 million years.

Another kind of uranium, with an atomic weight of 235, has a different half-life, and its end product is a different kind of lead, lead-207. This is also used for dating. These relationships are often written in this way: U 238 —Pb 206, U 235—Pb 207, and so on. Rubidium 87—strontium 87, potassium 40— argon 40, and thorium 232—lead 208 are also used for dating ancient rocks, because they have very long half-lives. These are all called isotopes of their elements (p. 379). They behave the same chemically but have different atomic weights. Dates obtained in this way are always written with a plus-or-minus sign following the number of years. If a date is written, 600 million $\pm$ 10 million years, it means the date may lie somewhere between 590 million and 610 million years.

When certain amounts of uranium and certain amounts of lead derived from that uranium are found together, scientists can determine when the breaking down process began —in other words, about how old the rocks are. The ratio of lead 207 and lead 206 is sometimes used as a check on figures. These age determinations can also be checked by using a device called a mass spectrometer, which measures the relative amounts of the elements in a sample of rock by sorting streams of electrified particles and recording data about them.

Rocks with enough radioactive elements for study are not available in every locality, but figures are now available for rocks in many parts of the world. The ages of the oldest are 3 to 4 billion years. Some of these igneous rocks containing isotopes of uranium, thorium, and others were intruded or pushed up into sedimentary and other volcanic rocks. These, then, are the oldest rocks that man has ever seen. Four and a half billion years is an estimate for the age of Earth, but when more is known, 5 billion years may be accepted as a more accurate figure. The results obtained from radioactive dating bring the age of Earth closer to the age arrived at by astronomers. An examination of meteorites, that many think may be parts of the mantle or crust of a shattered planet, gives ages of 4.5 billion years

and other ages slightly over that figure. Other means of checking the validity of figures may still be found. There is still much to be learned about dating in this way.

Other radioactive elements with shorter half-lives, with their end products, are used for dating other things. Carbon 14 is useful in dating relatively recent sedimentation, house beams, bones, and other carbonaceous material. Radioactive carbon occurs naturally in the atmosphere, where a constant amount is maintained, some carbon 14 disintegrating, while more is being formed. It becomes a part of plants as they grow, and in turn a part of the animals that eat them and a part of man, who eats both plants and animals. When living things die, and are no longer able to function, the amount of carbon 14 begins to disintegrate, just as uranium does, but with a half-life of 5568 years.

The carbon 14 method of dating has been used on parts of trees, on peat, and on other organic material that is known to have been covered by continental ice sheets, and the ages secured were checked by comparison with the age of pollen deposited in glacial lakes and with annual layers of sediment left by the melting ice. It was found that the last ice sheet receded about 11,000 years ago.

Radiocarbon dating of fossiliferous ocean sediments is considered reliable, and the use of uranium 235 and its short-lived decay product, thorium 230, shows promise of becoming a valuable way to date sediments. Studies of ancient temperatures can be made because different living organisms thrive in either warm or cold waters. The abundance of their shells in ocean sediments, as well as radioactive dating, indicates changes in temperature in ancient waters.

The region in which you are teaching no doubt has changed its appearance many times. It may have been covered by a sea at one geologic epoch, by a desert at another, and by a mountainous region at still another. Earth has not always had its present appearance, for its surface is constantly changing, although most of these changes go on so slowly that we seldom notice them. It is thought by geologists that the forces which operated on Earth in the past are much the same as those which are operating today. It took millions of years to produce many of the features of Earth's surface as we see it.

EXPERIENCE. *How old is Earth?* Children may become more aware of the age of Earth by realizing what few changes take place around their homes in a few years and what great changes have taken place in only a part of Earth's history. We do not usually see mountains formed before our eyes, except in the case of a volcano, such as Paricutin, in Mexico; and yet, to produce mountains, it takes but a small part of the total number of years during which Earth has been in existence.

EXPERIENCE. *Soils and rocks tell Earth's age.* If a visit can be made to some place where a pit is being dug for a building foundation, the children may be able to see different kinds of soil or rocks at different levels. It is partly by means of different rock layers found on top of one another that scientists have learned about Earth's history.

EXPERIENCE. *The story of the place where you live.* Try to find out about the place where you live. Your state department of geology will be able to send you helpful material. Trace the story of what has happened to the place you live in.

CHAPTER 9

The Changing Surface of Earth

Forces That Raise and Lower the Land

Sometimes the surface of Earth shakes and trembles, breaking down structures which have been built by man. It is at such times that people's interest is focused on earthquakes; and children, seeing pictures in the newspapers and hearing adults discuss earthquakes, come to school and ask the question "What causes earthquakes?"

Earth's surface seems to be firm and stable. There is evidence, however, that Earth's crust moves in a far larger way than even earthquake tremors and shocks might indicate. At times parts of Earth's crust have risen very slowly and at other times they have slowly sunk. Sometimes parts have wrinkled like a great blanket pushed together from the sides. At all such times the rocks themselves have moved and their position in relation to each other has changed. All such movements in the outer parts of Earth are included when we use the word "diastrophism." Some of these larger Earth movements have taken place within historic times. Columns that formed a part of an ancient temple found near Naples have been bored by marine organisms, indicating that the temple has been submerged below sea level and raised again. There are old stone landing places built centuries ago

which are now high above sea level. Stone huts built long ago on the southern shores of Greenland have disappeared beneath the water, indicating that parts of that country are sinking; northern Scandinavia, on the other hand, is rising about one foot in forty years. The area north and northeast of the Great Lakes is slowly rising, and uplift is going on around the Baltic Sea. The rate of uplift varies. Parts of Scandinavia are slowly rising at the rate of about three feet in a hundred years.

It is now being considered whether or not a rise in sea level, resulting from the melting of ice between the Ice Ages, might not have been partially responsible for some of the rising water which invaded the low-lying parts of the continents and covered the continental shores during past ages. Some areas which are now under water may be covered for the same reason. It is an interesting possibility and is being studied.

In some places the sinking of land along coasts has caused rivers to be drowned, filling a large part of the valley with salt water. This has happened along the Atlantic seaboard of the North American continent, thus forming deep estuaries, such as Chesapeake Bay, and drowned rivers, such as the Hudson, the St. Lawrence, and the Delaware.

Sedimentary rocks filled with marine fossils are found far inland and high on the sides or tops of mountains, showing that these layers were formed under water. In some places these layers are as much as forty thousand feet thick, indicating that that portion of the continent has sunk to that depth and risen again. Land may move up and down not only along the seacoast but also far in the interior of continents. When the sinking occurs inland, it is far less noticeable than when it occurs along the coast, simply because of the absence of means of measuring, such as those which have been mentioned above.

Some inland regions, such as some of our plains states, have alternated between comparatively short periods of sinking, with accompanying deposits of sediments, and periods of rising, with accompanying erosion. The rocks of these regions, which are nearly devoid of mountains, are characterized by only slight bending and folding. Such broad continental Earth movements are spoken of as *general uplifts*. Earth movements producing mountains are called *local uplifts* and, as the name implies, are confined to smaller areas.

Mountain-making. While this general up-and-down movement of continents goes on somewhat continuously, there have been definite periods when the lateral action was greater than usual and resulted in mountain formation. The crustal movements which produce mountain ranges are spoken of as revolutions. Thus the movements producing the Rocky Mountains are called the Laramide revolution; those producing the Appalachian Mountains, the Appalachian revolution; and the Taconic revolution signifies the crustal disturbance in western New England. Others might be named, but for our purposes these are sufficient. One part of the continent may be rising while another may be sinking.

What causes the land surface to move up and down in this way? The full answer to this question cannot be given at this time. Many students of the problem, however, believe that the movement is a result of the contraction of Earth due to the loss of heat in the interior, or is caused by a rearrangement of molecules and atoms due to pressure or even to the complete change of some atoms, or is caused possibly by a combination of these. The deposition of sediments may cause some areas to sink, and the large-scale removal of material may cause others to rise. Apparently a degree of balance is maintained at all times.

When stresses accumulate in Earth's crust from any or all of these causes and reach the point where they can no longer be withstood, the crust must give way. This means that some portions of the crust may be bent and pushed upward or downward; perhaps a break may occur, and one block may be thrust over another. This relief from pressure takes many different forms. Evidences of great lateral pressure are displayed on all sides. Children living in mountainous regions may be able to see these folds, or steeply inclined strata, on the mountainsides or in road cuts

This is a small syncline (fold downward) and a small anticline (fold upward). Pressure from the sides through a long period of time produced these folds. (Kirtley Mather.)

where they have been exposed. The folds range from tiny wrinkles to great upfolds and downfolds fifty or more miles across. The upfolds are called *anticlines,* and the downfolds are called *synclines.*

Rarely are mountains formed by only one kind of Earth movement, but rather by a combination of several. One process of mountain formation, such as folding or faulting, may predominate in a given region.

Folding Sometimes Produces Mountains. Many mountain ranges have been made by a folding of the rocks in which certain parts of the folds are pushed high above the surrounding land. Many such mountainous regions have similar long histories. An area begins to sink slowly, and as it sinks, eroded material is deposited. A great trough, or *geosyncline,* is thus formed. Then folding, faulting, and uplift destroy the trough and mountains are formed. As they rise, the sedimentary materials deposited in the trough of which they are composed are exposed to weathering and erosion again. This is a cyclic pattern of mountain formation that is duplicated in the histories of mountainous regions in many parts of the world. In some regions it has been repeated several times over an interval of millions of years. Pressure from the side, or lateral pressure, may be important in producing the trough and is certainly involved in the folding, faulting, and uplift of the mountains. No doubt heat, too, is involved. This explains why rocks formed under sea water in a horizontal position are often seen, bent and twisted on the tops and sides of mountains.

What the other forces were that helped to produce these mountains has not been wholly proved. We do know that the folded rocks are among the softer rocks and that the sediments, measuring as much as seven or more miles in thickness, may have encountered varying degrees of heat which doubtless affected them.

These troughlike areas, called geosynclines, were often several hundred miles long and many miles wide. The rocks in such places show that as these areas gradually sank they were covered by sea water. Into these troughs went the material from the adjoining land areas as it weathered and eroded. Thus, the seas remained comparatively shallow, deposition usually keeping up with the sinking, except for occasional periods when the sinking became faster or slower. Certain animals and plants lived in the sea water, and their remains were added to the deposits. The sediments became thick, sometimes as thick as from 20,000 to 40,000 feet, and were pressed together. During the tremendously long time that this took, sediments became consolidated into shales, sandstones, conglomerates, and limestones. Later, many of the shales were metamorphosed to slates, sandstones to schists, and limestone to marble.

It must be remembered that weathering and erosion attacked the rocks and unconsolidated material as soon as they appeared above water. The process continued relentlessly. If no further pressure took place, a rather simple mountain or range of mountains would result. Pressure often continued, however, so long and so severely that one fold was pushed over on top of the adjoining fold. If the rocks did not bend enough to withstand this pressure they broke, forming *faults.* The tops of the folds thus broken were often forced still further over the adjacent rocks. These *thrust faults,* as they are called, were enormous at times. This is true on the east side of Glacier National Park, Montana. Here, a great block of rock at least ten miles long was forced up and over the level land to the east. The mountains formed in this way rise abruptly from the plain. Whatever foothills there are may be what is left of the original block after erosion, or they may be an accumulation of eroded material. Chief Mountain is part of the original block left after erosion, and i

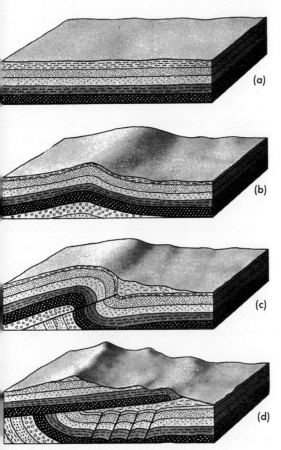

Four stages in the development of a thrust fault which may form mountains. (a) The land before any Earth movement started. (b) Pressure from the side has pushed the horizontal strata into a large upfold, or anticline. (c) Pressure has continued, a break (fault) has developed in the upfold, and a part is being pushed over the nearby surface of Earth (a thrust fault). Eroded material has collected in the depression at the right. (d) With continued pressure the rising mass is pushed far over the nearby land surface. After pressure has stopped the mountains formed will eventually be leveled by erosion.

complicated history over about 400 million years. The greater part of the sediments are thought by some to have come from a part of the continent extending eastward from the Appalachian geosyncline, or trough, called Appalachia. As this area was worn down, additional uplift took place and thus a source for additional sediments was available. With the folding, some parts of the area were shortened or compressed as much as a hundred miles. Others question that an ancient Appalachia was necessary as a source of sediments, and point to our present-day coastal plains as being areas of great sedimentation.

There have been a series of such troughs, or geosynclines, along the western side of the continent, where the same processes went on. The Rocky Mountains rose from a geosyncline which extended from the northern part of North America south to the Gulf of Mexico. Most of the sediments may have come from the most western part of the continent above water at that time, an ancient highland called Cascadia.

Today there are areas where great deposits of sediments are being made. Notable among these in North America is the area around the mouth of the Mississippi River and the northeastern coast of the Gulf of Mexico. Will mountains be pushed up there in some fardistant time?

EXPERIENCE. *Folded rocks.* If there are road cuts through rock in the neighborhood of your school, look for evidence of folded rocks, rocks that have been bent. Take the children to see this evidence. The same general type of thing happened in mountain formation, only in a more complicated manner and on a greater scale.

EXPERIENCE. *To show the effect of lateral pressure.* Use one turkish towel, or several of different colors if you wish to think of each as a separate stratum of rock, laying them on a table. With

sometimes said to be a mountain "without roots," since it rests upon younger sediments and since it did not result from a crustal disturbance at that place.

The area occupied by the Appalachian Mountains and those in eastern Canada is an outstanding example of this whole cyclic pattern in North America. It has a long and

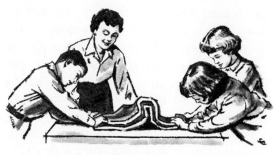

Pressure slowly applied produces folds and wrinkles in the rocks of Earth, just as it does when applied to towels.

a hand at each side or end gently push toward the center, or push in only one direction. Folds will appear and the distance between the sources of pressure will shorten. This may be of help in showing how pressure on Earth's

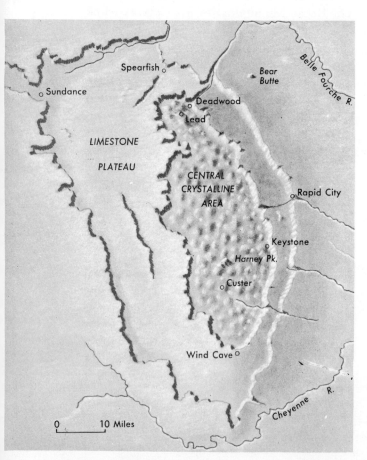

Diagram of the Black Hills, South Dakota, showing ridges and valleys carved from this domelike uplift.

surface bends rock layers, often forming mountains.

Volcanic Mountains. Mountains are sometimes formed by the accumulation of volcanic material on Earth's surface; this material may be lava, ash, or some other product of eruptions. Many volcanic mountains, active and inactive, could be named. Vesuvius in Italy; Mt. Pelée in the West Indies; Krakatoa[1] in Indonesia; Katmai in the Aleutian Islands; Aconcagua in South America; Mt. Lassen, Mt. Rainier, Mt. Baker, Mt. Adams, Mt. Hood, and Mt. Shasta in the Cascade Range in North America; and Parícutin in Mexico. These, large and small, were all built up by material discharged from within Earth. Their shape and size depends upon the amount and kind of material discharged (pp. 295–298).

Dome Mountains. These mountains receive their name from their appearance and from the way they were formed. The domes may be narrow and fairly round, or they may be elongated. They may rise to 7000 or 8000 feet above the surrounding plain. Most dome mountains are the result of an intrusion of molten rock through a narrow, pipelike opening in the rock deep within Earth's crust. Passing through this opening, the molten rock squeezes out over a stratum of rock, as on a floor. Then, as the molten rock accumulates, it pushes the covering rock layers up into a dome. The covering rock strata toward the bottom of these mountains are tilted steeply, while on top the strata may be fairly horizontal, if such strata are still in place.

The Henry Mountains of Utah are classic examples of dome mountains. Many of these domes have been eroded sufficiently so that the intruded igneous rocks are exposed to view. The Black Hills of South Dakota are dome mountains about 100 miles long and 50 miles wide. Much of the top covering of the

[1] Also spelled Krakatao.

rocks has been eroded, and what is left appears as circling series of ridges and troughs. This is due to the differing resistance these rocks offer to erosion.

Faulting Sometimes Produces Mountains. Sometimes the rocks of Earth may be broken along definite lines called *fault lines.* Fault lines vary in length from those extending several hundred miles and reaching deep within Earth to those which are to be observed only with the use of a microscope. They show displacements varying from a fraction of an inch to many thousand feet. Obviously, mountains could only result from faults of large size.

Portions of Earth have many of these long, deep faults breaking the crust into great blocks. These faults are different from the thrust faults in folded rocks because they are vertical, or nearly so, and little or no horizontal pressure was involved in forming them.

Blocks thus formed may either sink or be uplifted. This may result in an elevation that can be classed as a mountain. Tilting of one or more blocks may occur, forming precipitous ridges on one side and long slopes on the other. Their appearance always is modified by weathering and erosion. The Sierra Nevadas of California are *fault-block* mountains, and rise to Mt. Whitney, with a height of 14,495 feet on the east. They are 400 miles long and from 40 to 60 miles wide. The ranges of the Great Basin area to the east are smaller fault-block mountains.

Mountains Left by Erosion. Mountains thus formed are often called *residual* mountains because they are remnants of a once broad, high plateau, eroded by water and wind. Crustal movements in the form of large, vertical uplifts, with almost no tilting or folding of the rocks, have usually occurred in such places one or more times, with the inevitable weathering and erosion going on at the same time.

These areas have often been covered with water for immense periods of time, and many thousands of feet of marine and nonmarine sediments may be present as a result.

Examples of residual mountains are found in Utah's famed Zion National Park. Here the Virgin River has cut down through thousands of feet of sandstone. Such residual peaks as the Great White Throne are over 7000 feet high.

Mesas result from the weathering and erosion of the horizontal sedimentary rocks of plateaus in arid and semiarid regions. The talus slope shows that these processes are continuing to wear away the rock. This mesa is in New Mexico. (Philip Gendreau.)

The Colorado River is cutting its way downward and carrying off numberless tons of sediment from the Colorado Plateau every year. Partly isolated within the canyon stand mountain-sized remnants of the plateau, and, as the river wears back the plateau, they may some day stand alone as mountains. The Colorado Plateau covers parts of Utah, Arizona, New Mexico, and Colorado. It has a long history of deep sedimentation and broad uplift.

In many parts of the west, mesas and buttes are found. These, too, are remnants of a plateau, and they are often called mountains when they are large compared with the surrounding countryside. These forms are typical of arid regions and the way rocks weather and erode in that kind of climate. There is often a harder layer of rock such as sandstone, or possibly lava, which gives protection from weathering and erosion to the softer rocks below. The character of the rocks, the amount of rainfall, and the course of the rivers largely determines the appearance of residual mountains.

The uniform level of the tops of many mountain ranges strongly suggests that they are remnants of an old plateau. An area with a long history of folding and faulting may again be covered with deep sediment, uplift may then take place, and a plateau result. The material composing the plateau may be washed away and the tilted edges of the ancient folds and faults show up.

Mount Monadnock in New Hampshire and Stone Mountain in Georgia are made of such hard resistant rock that they have remained standing while the surrounding area was reduced by erosion to a plain. The name monadnock is given to them, but they, too, are residual mountains, left by erosion.

EXPERIENCE. *To make children aware of mountains and their formation.* (P. 330.) Young children learn from experiences that the ground is not level. Later, they may become aware of hills

and mountains by means of more mature experiences and observations and through stories that are read to them or that they may read. Children may have the opportunity to climb part of the way or to the top of a hill or small mountain. The exertion and time required for this leaves an impression of size and steepness. Some children may see mountains while on a trip and wish to tell about them. They may find that mountains and hills cast long shadows; that they are so high that clouds often cover their tops; that snow may cover the tops of some mountains while adjacent valleys remain snowless; that there may be no trees or other plants on the tops of high mountains. They may find it worth while to draw pictures of any mountains they have seen.

Children may bring pictures of mountains to school and point out the great differences in their size and shape. They may even observe that some mountains are volcanoes. This might be a time to point out that mountains were formed in different ways, without going into a confusing mass of detail. Older children will be more interested in some of the details of mountain formation. Relate this to the place where the children live.

Earthquakes Accompany Mountain-making. There are approximately one million earthquakes each year that are strong enough to be felt somewhere. By far the greater number of earthquakes are caused by sudden slipping between two rock surfaces (a *fault plane*). The rock walls of a fault plane, being pressed tightly together, develop tremendous stresses because one wall may be moving slowly in one direction and the opposite wall in another. The rocks gradually stretch under this stress through the years. When the time comes that they can no longer yield elastically, they slip and come to rest in a new position in which there is little or no stress. This sudden movement sets up vibrations which move outward in all directions. It is the suddenness and the high velocity of the waves, or vibrations, that cause their destructiveness. A sudden slipping of only three quarters of an inch between two great rock surfaces is enough to destroy a city, even though the earthquake tremors last only from a few seconds to a few minutes. Sometimes the displacement occurs near the surface and sometimes deeper down, where, of course, the displacement cannot be seen, though the tremors are felt. Some displacements are known to have occurred as deep within our Earth as 435 miles. Displacements may be vertical or horizontal. Famous among the great faults is the San Andreas fault, extending along the Pacific coast for 600 miles or more. Displacement along this fault line was responsible for the disastrous San Francisco earthquake in 1906.

Earthquakes often originate along those areas where deep ocean trenches meet the high portions of continents. Apparently these are weak spots in Earth's crust. Within these earthquake belts are also found the younger systems of mountains, which is another evidence of crustal unrest. Dramatic examples of this were the severe earthquakes and volcanic eruptions in southern Chile during 1960. Along the length of Peru and Chile lie the Andes, a young and growing mountain system, and not far off the coast lies the 2500-mile long Peru–Chile Trench, with a maximum depth of 26,160 feet.

Volcanoes frequently initiate earthquakes, although such quakes are rarely so vigorous as those which occur along fault lines. Other causes of earthquakes are landslides and the falling in of cavern roofs. Earthquakes due to such causes are naturally much less severe and are considered purely local disturbances.

Man is learning how to protect himself against the destruction caused by earthquakes by building structures such as bridges, buildings, and pipe lines so that they will pass through earthquakes unharmed. Loss of life comes not so much from the shaking of Earth itself as from falling buildings and other structures. Frequently fires may begin during earthquakes and become destructive because the water pipes have been broken, making the usual means of fire-fighting impossible. Careful planning in earthquake regions can prevent undue destruction and loss of life.

Earthquakes frequently cause considerable movement of soil. Landslides frequently accompany earthquakes; faults and fissures may be filled with material, and soil and rocks may be loosened or broken. The flow of spring water may be changed, and various organisms, such as fish, may be killed by the shock. Islands may appear or sink, and seismic sea waves, or *tsunamis,* commonly called "tidal waves," may be produced by these crustal movements. The largest tsunamis are generated by large submarine landslides initiated by earthquakes.

Tsunamis are in no sense "tidal" waves, because the tides have nothing to do with them. The only similarity is that they may ebb and flow like tides, but usually at intervals of less than an hour. A succession of them may sweep across the ocean and cause great damage and loss of life on distant shores. The size and destructiveness of these waves depends mainly on the severity of the disturbance and the nature of the shorelines and nearby underwater contours against which they break. They may reach heights of 40 to 100 feet. Speeds of 475 miles an hour have been reached, yet out at sea the waves may not be noticed.

A warning system has been set up in many places, and children as well as adults should acquaint themselves with safety measures if they live in areas that experience these waves.

Throughout this discussion one should remember that long periods of time may be involved. Children especially are inclined to think that land rises or sinks in short periods of time. Occasionally there is an observable change of the altitude of land as the result of an earthquake, but great changes of altitude over large areas require immensely long periods of time. One need not fear a considerable submergence of any large area during a lifetime or even many generations. It requires long periods of time to produce great changes on Earth's surface.

We have seen that the forces of weathering and erosion cause a wearing down of land surfaces. When one considers how long these forces have been in operation, one may wonder why it is that we still have lofty plateaus and mountains on the continents. The answer is that the continents have been renewed by the processes discussed in this section. To these processes the geologist gives the name *diastrophism;* in the elementary-school classroom they may be called mountain-making processes or forces.

EXPERIENCE. *To feel how two surfaces moving in opposite directions pull on each other.* To experi-

ence this the children may put the palms and fingers of their hands as tightly together as they can. Still pressing them as tightly together as possible, push one over the other. Do they feel the skin pull a little? Do they feel any extra warmth? This, in a minute way, is similar to the slipping along a fault line.

EXPERIENCE. *Value of earthquakes.* Are earthquakes of any value? It will prove enlightening to the class if they try to think of all the ways in which earthquakes are useful and all the ways in which they are harmful. For instance, they give us information about the nature of the interior of Earth (p. 276). They also give us information about forces which cause the movement of rocks. They are harmful in the destruction of life and buildings which they cause, but this can be lessened by man himself through observance of intelligent precautions. Man is learning how to build structures to withstand many earthquakes.

Volcanoes, Geysers, and Hot Springs

Children are interested in volcanoes, although the majority of them have never seen, and probably never will see, an active one. They have seen pictures of them and read about them, and often questions arise as to what causes them. Many ideas have been held in the past about the cause of volcanoes, but after much careful study they have been discarded. We look to improved techniques and wider knowledge for an answer.

It is the movement of molten rock toward and upon the surface of Earth which contributes to changes in Earth's surface. It should be remembered that, like earthquakes, volcanoes are only displays on or comparatively near the surface of more gigantic and intense Earth-changing forces.

Magma Forms within Earth. The heat that causes volcanoes, geysers, and hot springs may arise from the natural heating of the rock, due to shrinking and pressure produced by the force of gravity. It may also possibly arise from the reaction of such radioactive materials as uranium, thorium, and others within Earth, which give off heat in the process of decomposition. Such heat may also result from the action of gases on one another, from the heat associated with movement of Earth's crust, or from other deep-seated forces within Earth which are as yet not understood. Because our knowledge of Earth is still mostly limited to its outer surface, we are still in doubt about all of the causes of the heat which accompanies the formation of magmas.

Magma pockets may be formed at comparatively shallow depths within the mantle, whereas the rest of Earth at those depths remains solid. Probably most magma pockets develop at a depth not exceeding 50 miles, yet some reservoirs are nearer the surface.

Magma contains gases of many kinds. They are held in solution in the magma, and are not present in a gaseous state. It is, therefore, different from the material as it is observed issuing from vents of volcanoes. As magma escapes, gases are lost, and it is then called *lava*. Commonly the word is used to mean molten as well as hardened material, wherever it may be. There are between forty and fifty different kinds of magma, each with a different chemical makeup. No wonder there are so many kinds of igneous rock on Earth's surface! The magma works its way upward toward zones of weaker rock where there may be numerous fissures and vents. Here the magma rapidly loses many of its gases, cools, and finally hardens as it lodges near the surface or erupts upon the surface.

Magma May Cool within Earth's Crust. Not all the liquid rock, or magma, reaches the surface by way of volcanoes or fissures; some of it cools and solidifies in the crust of Earth. At times this liquid rock flows upward through fractures and crevices in the rocks, making vertical or wall-like formations called *dikes*. Dikes may be seen in regions where erosion has uncovered these resistant rock structures. A dike is fairly easy to recognize because it looks like a wall standing up from a mountainside or sometimes from a flat surface of land such as occurs around Shiprock in New Mexico. Shiprock, itself, is what is left of the supply pipe, or neck, of an ancient volcano.

At other times magma may spread out parallel to and between the layers of the rock in sheets. This distinguishes these formations from others, and they are called *sills*. They may be horizontal masses of igneous rock, or they may have been intruded between layers of rock already lying at an angle. After formation, geologic forces may produce tilting of the area so that the sill lies at an angle. A classic example of a sill is the Palisade sill on the lower western bank of the Hudson River. This sill is now greatly eroded. It is believed to have been 100 miles long and at least 1000 feet thick at one time.

Sometimes magma arches up around the opening of a conduit leading from the magma pocket below. Instead of spreading out as in a sill, it stops for some reason and accumulates, producing oval, round, or irregular masses of igneous rocks which push up the overlying layers of rock into domes or arches. Such igneous masses are called *laccoliths*. Like sills they have a floor which is the layer of rock over which the magma spreads. In some places erosion has laid bare this floor; so there is no longer any uncertainty about the formation of laccoliths. Laccoliths vary in size. Some are about a half mile across, and others are much larger.

Batholiths are important forms of igneous rock, for they underlie many mountain ranges. They are vast masses of granite, which is generally believed to have been molten rock at one time. There is a hypothesis that at least some of the material making up the batholiths

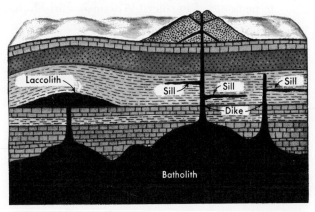

Magma may move through the rocks of Earth's crust and cool there.

may have been changed to a granitelike mass by gases from superheated magma below flowing through it. Much rock that has cooled beneath other rock layers is now exposed to view, owing to the removal of the covering layers by erosion. Many batholiths have been exposed by erosion. Among the large batholiths of North America is that of the Sierra Nevada of California and that of the Coast Range, which runs from British Columbia into Alaska. Geologists speak of rocks which have cooled beneath the surface as intrusive rocks, and of those which have cooled in the air, such as the lava from volcanoes and lava flows, as extrusive rocks. Both kinds are, of course, igneous rocks.

Lava Flows. In a number of places gentle eruptions called *lava flows* have occurred along fissures in Earth's crust. Nearly 225,000 square miles of Washington, Idaho, and Oregon are covered by what is called the Columbia River basalt, which has an average thickness of 500 feet. In places it is much thicker, and shows as many as twelve distinct lava flows. Originally the basalt probably reached a thickness of 5000 feet. The time between flows varied from a short time to a time long enough for soil to form and enormous trees to grow. Their petrified remains are found there now. A somewhat similar area is to be found in northern Wisconsin and Michigan. Other such areas may be found in Iceland and on the Deccan plateau in India, which covers nearly 200,000 square miles and where the basalt averages about 2000 feet in thickness.

The lava which issues from these fissures is unually basalt, a material which is different in content from other lavas and which, being thin and very fluid, flows more readily than other kinds, thus spreading over large areas, one flow on top of another. In many places it cools with a characteristic column-like appearance. Because such enormous quantities of

This is Dry Falls in the state of Washington. The falls were forme in the Columbia River basalt by glacial flood water many thousands o years ago. Molten rock from fissures poured over the land as many a twelve different times and built up the great Columbia Plateau in whic these falls were formed. (G. S. Craig.)

basalt have been poured out on the surface, many students of the problem think that there may be a layer of rigid basalt in Earth which supplies the material for volcanic activity of all kinds when conditions are right.

Experience. *To build a concept that rocks sometimes flow.* Many children have visited Grand Coulee Dam built on the Columbia River lava

Crater Lake and Wizard Island in Oregon were formed as a result volcanic action. It is thought by many that ancient Mount Mazam erupted violently time after time and eventually its center collapse leaving an enormous crater (a caldera) 5 miles across. Wizard Islar is a cone formed by later volcanic activity. (Josef Muench.)

flow. They may also have visited Dry Falls not far away and the old bed of the river, with great cliffs of basalt on each side. They might like to tell what they know about the molten rock that flowed out onto the surface so long ago.

Children are interested in the fact that rock can flow and squeeze into cracks and fissures, or blow out of a volcano.

Volcanoes. What we call volcanoes are only another form of magmatic action. A volcano is the vent, or opening, of the conduit through which volcanic materials are ejected. These materials build up *cones*. Volcanic cones may be small, as shown by the great numbers of widely scattered small cones, or they may be large, as shown by Mauna Loa in the Hawaiian Islands, a volcanic cone 30,000 feet high. This cone has a broad base built up from the ocean floor and rises through 16,000

feet of ocean water to about 14,000 feet above sea level. The shape of a cone naturally depends upon the kind of material from which it is made. A cone built up of lava is apt to be a gently sloping incline, and has a relatively large diameter through its base. The more fluid the lava, the faster and farther it can flow before hardening, and the flatter will be the cone. Such a cone is called a lava cone. A cone made of ashes and other volcanic fragments is apt to be steep, and has a small diameter through its base. This type of cone is called a cinder cone. Most volcanoes are built up by alternate eruptions of lava and explosive activity producing fragmental material. Such volcanoes have moderate slopes. This type of cone is called a composite volcanic cone.

The *crater* of a volcano is the pit at the top. A crater is formed, in the first instance, by the ejection of gases or magma; inside it are one or

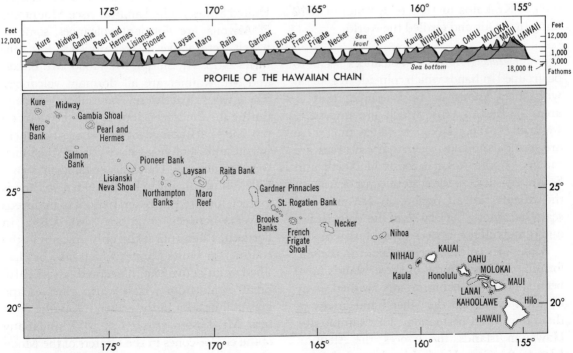

These islands were built by volcanic action. (Adapted from The Hawaiian Chain *by E. H. Bryan, Jr., Bishop Museum Press, Honolulu, Hawaii, 1954.)*

more vents, or outlets, when the volcano is active. During periods of relative inactivity small cones may occupy it. Craters vary in size from very small ones to those several miles across. Each period of activity may change the dimensions of a crater. At present the main crater of Mauna Loa is 3 miles long, 1½ miles wide, and 600 feet deep.

The geologic importance of volcanoes can be readily seen. The transportation of volcanic ash, boulders, and soil in mudflows and the accompanying destruction of plant and animal life are of more consequence than might be supposed at first glance. The same is true of the explosion itself, during which materials of various kinds are distributed over a considerable area. The burial of the ancient Roman city of Pompeii is a striking example of the destructiveness of an enormous ash and lava flow. Mountains and islands may be built up by volcanoes, or great sections may be torn out of them and scattered far and wide. Dust and ash from great volcanic eruptions such as Krakatoa in 1883 or Katmai in 1912 hung in the air and girdled the world.

Where Volcanoes Appear. Volcanoes seem to be grouped in bands which coincide in general with zones known to be fractured, that is, areas in Earth's crust which are unusually weak or broken. It will be noted that these are also earthquake zones. These areas are mainly on the western coasts of North and South America, on the eastern coast of Asia, in the Mediterranean region, in Iceland, and scattered among the islands of the West Indies and islands off the western coast of Africa.

Sometimes volcanoes erupt beneath the sea, forming islands. Some of these islands have been short-lived, being rapidly washed away by the waves. On the other hand, many of them have been permanent; for example, the Hawaiian Islands, the Azores, the Aleutian Islands, the Cape Verde Islands, and the Canary Islands are largely volcanic in origin.

Why and When Volcanoes Erupt. As magma forms at depth it may gradually move upward through a conduit and collect in a basin beneath a volcanic cone until the mounting pressure drives it upward to form an *eruption*. Between periods of violent eruptions a volcano may be only mildly active. At such times there is a minimum of pressure from below. The lava in the fissure leading to magma reservoirs beneath the volcano may become hardened and act as a seal preventing any ejection of gases and magma. It is for these reasons that volcanoes do not erupt continuously. Later the pressure of the gases may again become so great as to blow the seal away with explosive force. Sometimes large sections of the crater or a side of the cone may be blown off by the force of the explosion.

Volcanoes may be active for centuries, erupting from time to time; then they may become dormant, giving off little or no material. There are many such volcanoes in the western United States. The San Francisco Mountains of Arizona are dormant volcanoes, some of which were active as recently as a few centuries ago. Mt. Shasta, Mt. Hood, Mt. Baker, and Mt. Rainier are all dormant volcanoes. These were all active several million years ago during the Pleistocene epoch (see the chart on pp. 338–339) and at other times since then; but hundreds of years have passed since they were last active. They may erupt again sometime. It is difficult to know when a volcano is extinct, for often there are periods of hundreds of years between eruptions. Mt. Lassen in northern California is the only volcano in the continental United States which may be classified as an active one; it erupted last in 1916. Small vents from which warm gases escape may still be seen in the crater. A cinder cone near Mt. Lassen erupted in 1857, and many of the cinder cones in the Craters of the Moon National Monument were active no more than from 300 to 400 years ago.

EXPERIENCE. *To locate some volcanoes.* If any of the children have seen a volcano, they may wish to tell the others what it looked like and where it was. Can any of the class name other volcanoes? If so, they may locate as many as possible on maps or the globe. Younger children may find it profitable to draw pictures of what they think volcanoes are like. Older children may learn about volcanoes from news reports at times.

EXPERIENCE. *To study volcanic islands.* Children may learn that many islands are the very top of old volcanoes that have been built up from the bottom of the ocean. Perhaps they would like to find on a globe where some of these islands are. From pictures they will find that many of them are now pleasant places to live. Perhaps someone will wonder why the ocean waves have not washed them away. This could lead to a question about the qualities of the rock of which they are composed. Igneous rock is very hard, but, even so, probably some of it has been washed away. We know that it has weathered enough so that there is soil on the islands and that plants are able to grow there.

Lava, Gases, and Volcanic Ash Come from Volcanoes. As we have seen, various kinds of material may issue from a volcano, namely, gases, lava, volcanic ash, and dust. The broken lava may vary in size from dust to chunks which weigh tons. Volcanic *ash* is the name given to the quantities of minute rock particles which are thrown out during eruptions. It does not mean that the material is a product of combustion, such as ashes of wood or coal. The broken lava may come from vents which have been sealed with lava from other eruptions; it may come from the rim of the crater or from freshly torn portions of the sides. At times lava is thrown up in spatters; while descending it solidifies and then presents a rounded appearance. When these spatters are several inches in diameter, they are called *bombs;* but if they are the size of a pebble, they are called *lapilli.* The gases, especially steam, are no doubt mainly responsible for the violent explosions which accompany some volcanic eruptions, as well as for the picturesque clouds of dust and water vapor which form above the cone. The gases which commonly accompany eruptions are steam, carbon dioxide, chlorine, carbon monoxide, and sulfur dioxide, and at times nitrogen and hydrogen sulfide. There are occasional traces of other gases, such as fluorine, hydrogen, methane, and argon. It is the combustion of certain of these gases which accounts for the flames which sometimes appear during eruptions. Steam is perhaps the commonest of all the gases, and is responsible for the downpours of rain which often accompany volcanic eruptions. Hydrochloric acid and ammonium chloride may also be given off. Some of the gases which escape from volcanoes are poisonous, although rarely are human beings in such close contact with them that they prove fatal. They often are disastrous, however, to other animal and plant life.

Mudflows. When the high temperatures of lava, which range from about 1000° to 2000°F., are considered, it is no wonder that colossal forces arise from the still hotter magma. In addition to the tremendous pressure produced by steam and the other gases in the magma and the resulting explosion, there is still another important result, namely, the mudflows. Steam, after its release from the magma into the air, condenses and, falling in the form of rain, mixes with any ashes or dust that have been expelled, and thus streams of mud find their way to lower levels, burying all before them. Most of the destruction at Mt. Lassen in 1915 was caused by mudflows. Lava, pouring down a snow-covered mountainside, melts the snow and likewise produces mudflows, with equally disastrous results.

Lava Cools in Different Forms. Beds of lava often show different characteristics, depending on the amount of gas present when they were poured out, the rate of flow, and the rate of cooling. Some may be rough and ropy or light and porous; some may be solid and closely packed; some may display a crystalline texture; some may even be glassy in appearance.

As a lava flow cools, the accompanying gases bubble through it, leaving it filled with openings, or cells, of various sizes, shapes, and numbers, depending on the amount of gas. While the cells are forming, the lava often moves, drawing them out into little strawlike openings which, if the movement of the lava should change slightly in direction, are bent.

Pumice is an excellent example of a rock which takes on an almost spongelike appearance because of the openings made by gas in the lava. To be sure, there are varying degrees of compactness, but some pumice is so light that it will float on water. Cinderlike fragments are called scoria. These are frequently dark, either black or reddish brown.

After the lava issues from Earth, it cools and solidifies. This takes place on the surface first of all, while the still liquid lava underneath continues to move. The crust may be broken and mixed with the hotter mass below; in such a case the lava comes to rest with a very rough surface. Sometimes lava hardens with a smooth surface; sometimes it hardens in a ropy or pillowy form.

The texture of all kinds of lava depends upon the rate of cooling. If the molten rock cools very slowly, perhaps within Earth, there is time for large crystals to form. If it cools less slowly, the crystals will be smaller; or it may cool so quickly that it becomes glasslike in appearance. No finer example of lava which has a glassy appearance as a result of rapid cooling can be found than the obsidian cliff in Yellowstone National Park. This cliff has a general gray appearance because of the

plant life such as lichens and possibly other very small plants growing on it; but closer examination of the broken surfaces reveals that it is a black rock with every appearance of being glass. If that same rock had cooled slowly within Earth, it would have been granite, a highly crystalline rock.

Lava caves or tunnels are interesting phenomena. They are sometimes found in places where the lava was in a very fluid state when it issued from volcanoes or fissures. Such caves or tunnels were formed when the upper-most lava solidified, forming a crust, while the still hot and liquid lava beneath continued to flow. When the supply of lava became exhausted, the hot lava drained out, and tunnel-like openings were left. In some of these caves there are small stalactites on the roof. There is a large lava cave west of Flagstaff, Arizona; others are in the Craters of the Moon National Monument; there is another south of Bend, Oregon, and there are still others in numerous places.

EXPERIENCE. *To observe something about volcanic rocks.* Children will be interested in examining as many pieces of volcanic rock as are available. What do the rocks look like? Notice that none of them have fossils or layers. They may feel quite sharp to the touch. Are they heavy or light? Are they very solid or are there holes in some? Are they dull and grainy or are they glassy? Can the children tell anything of their history from all this?

Regions Supporting Phenomena Associated with Hot Rock. Geysers and hot springs, mud volcanoes, paint pots, fumaroles, and solfataras are phenomena which, with only a few exceptions, are associated with hot igneous rock at various depths below Earth's surface.

Three notable regions where these phenomena occur are Iceland, New Zealand, and Yellowstone National Park. These are all regions of geologically recent fissure flows. In Yellowstone National Park, lava flooded the region, cooled, and solidified, gradually merging below the surface into a great batholith of granite. While this mass has probably solidified, it is still very hot. Gases, among them steam, are still present and are still escaping wherever the opportunity exists. This region, then, is one filled with fumaroles, hot springs, geysers, paint pots, mud volcanoes, and the like.

Fumaroles and Solfataras. Fumaroles and solfataras are vents, or holes, in Earth's crust from which gases issue. Steam is the predominating gas issuing from fumaroles, although many other gases, such as carbon dioxide, hydrogen sulfide, and chlorine, may also be present. It is the water vapor of the condensing steam which is seen coming from fumaroles. Two notable regions which have conditions necessary to support fumaroles are Yellowstone National Park and the region around Katmai volcano in Alaska. Solfataras differ from fumaroles in that they give off large quantities of sulfur gases. From these sulfur is deposited, frequently in such large quantities that it is worked commercially. Solfataras are found near Mt. Lassen in California.

When carbon dioxide is dissolved in ground water, and then passes through limestone on its way to the surface, it dissolves the limestone and deposits travertine, mainly calcium carbonate, on the surface. In quiet weather carbon dioxide often collects in depressions around a vent and smothers animals that get into such places. This happens because carbon dioxide is heavier than air and is without taste, color, or odor.

Hot Springs. Most hot springs are produced by the heating of ground water which has

Deposits from the water issuing from hot springs may form terraces. This is Opal Terrace at Mammoth Hot Springs in Yellowstone National Park. (Josef Muench.)

come in contact with superheated steam from hot igneous rocks below Earth's surface. It is always difficult to tell how much of the water may be ground water and how much may originate in the superheated steam from below. The amount that is ground water probably depends to some extent on precipatation and evaporation, and varies in different regions.

The temperature of the water issuing from hot springs may vary from warm to the boiling point of water. Frequently deposits consisting mainly of carbonates, chlorides, and sulfates are built up around the openings. Spectacular deposits have been built up around the hot springs in Yellowstone National Park, where the water in many instances appears blue, yellow, green, or brown from the minute plants called algae (p. 510) growing in it. Such deposits as those at Mammoth Hot Springs, in the park, are nearly pure calcium carbonate and are called travertine. In other hot springs the deposits may be predominantly silica and are called sinter.

There are a number of factors which determine the rate at which the deposits of sinter and travertine accumulate. It is believed that evaporation, temperature, and algae contribute to the deposition of material. Hence it will be seen that the rate of deposit is exceedingly slow and by no means uniform.

Hot springs are closely related to geysers, mud volcanoes, and paint pots.

Paint Pots and Mud Volcanoes. Sometimes evaporation balances the supply of water in hot springs, and the water becomes thick with disintegrated rock. The resulting mud may be colored yellow, red, black, or even purple by the rock. Such phenomena are called paint pots, or mud pots. Sometimes steam pressure accumulates when the mud becomes too thick for the steam to escape continuously, and suddenly an eruption takes place, spattering mud around for some distance and at times build-ing up tiny cones of mud. These phenomena are called mud volcanoes.

Geysers. Geysers, though far more spectacular than hot springs or even mud volcanoes, are related to them. When steam and hot water are forcibly ejected at intervals, the springs are called geysers. Each geyser is different from others in respect to the length of time between eruptions, the height to which the water is thrown, and the amount of water which is discharged. Some geysers erupt at regular intervals and some at irregular intervals. Many of the geysers in Yellowstone National Park have been erupting for a long time. The water carries silica in solution, and this is deposited in minute amounts. Cones of various shapes are formed around the vents in this manner, and some have been given names in keeping with their shape, such as the Beehive and the Castle.

The eruption of geysers depends on pressure and the boiling point of water. Each geyser has a vent, or tube, through which the water and steam move. The size and shape of the vent help to regulate the time between eruptions. The boiling point of water is raised under pressure; hence it takes the water longer to boil at the bottom of the column of water in the tube than it does at the top. Thus, when the water near the top of the tube boils and spills out, the pressure becomes less on the water near the bottom. Being so very hot, some of it suddenly turns to steam and is violently ejected. When the eruption of some geysers is over, some of the water flows back into the tube, where it meets additional ground water, and the heating process and eruption are repeated. In other geysers little or none of the erupted water flows back into the tube.

It is believed that the conditions which support these many different forms of thermal action have existed for a very long time. In Yellowstone National Park there is widespread

*d Faithful geyser in Yellowstone National Park, Wyoming, has
pted regularly for a long time. Deposits are built up around it.
hree Lions, N.Y.C.)*

evidence of ancient steam vents which are now
extinct. This is due to a change in the flow of
underground water rather than to a cooling

of the igneous rock. In many places in the park glacial boulders are found on top of large deposits of sinter and travertine, which would indicate that those deposits were formed at least several thousand years ago. The drill hole in the basin of Old Faithful shows that eruptions were going on long before the last glaciation in that region. There is no indication that the great batholith underlying Yellowstone National Park will cool suddenly.

EXPERIENCE. *Are volcanoes of any value?* This may be an interesting question for children to think about and discuss. While destructive in many ways, volcanoes give us greater knowledge of the materials making up some areas of Earth and of conditions existing within certain parts of Earth. Volcanic material often contributes to enlarging the land surface of islands and provides new areas for plant growth. This aspect may be observed or discussed. Can the children think of other values?

Weathering Changes Earth's Surface

On all sides we see evidences of the decay of rock. We give the name *weathering* to the breaking down of rocks into smaller bits and finally into soil. Weathering is a process which attacks not only rocks but also the edifices which have been constructed by man. We find it necessary to paint, varnish, and reconstruct our homes because of weathering. No building is immune; eventually the strongest will fall to ruins unless it is continually reconstructed. Weathering is largely due to the atmosphere because it contains the gases and water, which are the agents by which weathering is accomplished. Weathering is an especially appropriate phenomenon for study in

the elementary school because evidences of its action are ever present and its effects important.

Emphasis should be placed on the fact that weathering is a slow process, and that it is a process that has been acting on the outer part of Earth for millions of years just as it is today. It is one of those forces which tend to wear down the surface of Earth.

Gravity as an Earth-Changing Factor. Gravity makes it possible for rocks to fall, thereby being shattered and possibly shattering others. Gravity is important in the large-scale general movement of loose soil and rocks toward a lower level. Gravity does not depend upon rivers or any transporting agent, although it is involved in the fact that water runs down hill. Gravity tends to pull all things toward the center of Earth. Thus it is an important factor in respect to the soil, rocks, and water on Earth's surface (p. 187).

Soil Is Made from Rock. The weathering of rock results in the formation of soil. The process is continuous, and new soil is constantly being formed. Of all the forces that operate to change Earth's surface this is one of the most important to man. Without soil man could not exist. It is necessary for the existence of plants, upon which all animals depend for food either directly or indirectly.

It would be difficult to give a definition of soil that would satisfy everyone. Commonly it is thought of as that part of Earth's crust where plants and animals can live. To a soil scientist it means much more. He thinks of the depth of the soil; of what he calls its structure—which has to do with the sizes, shapes, and resistance to breaking up of the clumps formed by the rock particles; of the texture, which depends on the proportion of small rock particles of different sizes, such as gravel, sand, silt, and clay; of the different layers, or horizons; of the organisms living within the soil and the plant covering. In addition, he is aware of the many factors that, throughout the history of the soil's formation, have made it what it is, and he is much concerned with the factors that are changing it continuously and slowly today.

The formation of soil is a very long, very slow, and very complex process. First, there must be the parent material, the rocks that have been broken into fine bits by weathering, and without which good soil could not be formed. As soon as a fresh surface of rock is exposed, it is acted upon by water, temperature changes, the gases in the atmosphere, and organisms; and so the process of soil building begins. In fact, many of the factors that build soil also are the forces which break down rock into parent material.

Five factors enter into soil formation: (1) the *parent material,* which may come from many different kinds of rock—igneous, sedimentary, or metamorphic—each of which is extremely complex in its chemical composition; (2) *topography,* whether an area is hilly, mountainous, flat, or rolling (upon this depends to a certain extent the amount of water that penetrates the soil and thus is given the opportunity to react with it); (3) *climate,* which controls the temperature, the amount of rainfall, and their interaction on the complex parent material, taking out certain elements and compounds and adding others to the developing soil; (4) *living organisms;* (5) *time,* a most important factor, which allows complex chemical and physical reactions to take place.

The interaction of all these factors is extremely variable, so much so that the same kind of parent material, subjected to different conditions of topography, climate, organisms, and time, produces entirely different kinds of soil.

It is difficult to separate the processes that change Earth's surface because they are constantly interacting. Gravity, water, wind, and the gases in the air do not "take turns" at breaking up, transporting, and depositing rock and soil. For convenience, however, the various phases of weathering will be studied under the headings, "Chemical Weathering of Rock" and "Mechanical Weathering of Rock."

Chemical Weathering of Rock. Many kinds of chemical changes are made in the rocks of Earth's crust. This altering of the chemical composition of rocks may be due either to the process of oxidation, in which oxygen combines with certain other substances in the rocks; to hydration, in which water combines with other substances; or to carbonation, in which carbon dioxide is combined with various other substances. New substances result from these combinations. Some of these new substances are such that they are easily dissolved in water or washed away by it; or they may be easily removed by the wind. In either case a new surface is exposed. As rock breaks up into smaller and smaller particles, more and more surface area becomes available for attack by the forces of weathering. This is especially important in chemical weathering.

Oxidation, Hydration, and Carbonation. The water vapor in the air is of the utmost importance in weathering. It makes possible and hastens the combination of the oxygen and carbon dioxide in the air with substances in the rocks. For instance, oxygen combines with iron much more readily if a little water is present. If iron is in a perfectly dry place, it will keep for years without rusting; but it does not take long for rust to appear if the iron is wet. This is an example of oxidation and hydration, in which hydrous iron oxide, or limonite (which is the same as rust), is formed.

Carbon dioxide forms only a small part of the atmosphere, yet it is highly important when it comes to chemical weathering. Like oxygen, the action of carbon dioxide also is hastened by the presence of water. When carbon dioxide unites with water, a weak acid is formed which dissolves limestone readily. As a weak acid, carbon dioxide also combines with several minerals in the rocks and forms substances some of which are soluble in water. Carbon dioxide is also important because it is necessary for the growth of plants, which in turn contribute to the chemical and mechanical weathering of rocks. In arid regions, therefore, chemical weathering, or decomposition, of rocks goes on at a much slower rate than it does in humid countries, for water increases the activity of these gases in the atmosphere, resulting in the more rapid breaking

up and changing of rocks. Yet, even in arid regions, chemical weathering is important.

When precipitated, water may directly dissolve certain minerals in rocks and aid in the breaking up of rocks by carrying away loose material, thus exposing new surfaces for weathering. Water and air enter into all the fissures and crevices in rock, sometimes deep within Earth, and combine with and dissolve substances in rock, thereby breaking it up.

Plants, Animals, and Chemical Weathering. Chemical action is promoted by the presence of vegetation. Plants take up certain minerals from the rocks in their life processes, and, as they decay, give off acids which hasten the chemical decomposition of the rocks. Plants help to retain moisture and thus again assist in chemical decomposition. Like plants, the remains of animals, as well as their waste products, contribute to the process of chemical weathering.

Foremost among the plants to find a roothold on rocks are the lichens: flat, scaly-looking, gray or brown growths on trees and rocks.

Lichens are among the first plants that grow on rocks. (Courtesy of The American Museum of Natural History.)

Sometimes they seem little more than a colored spot on a rock (p. 560). Later, other plants which require a softer material for their roots may follow. Bacteria, molds, and fungi are always present in large numbers, especially within soils, and also produce chemical changes in the rocks and soil which hasten decomposition.

It is well known that heat will speed up chemical reactions. If a region has both a warm and a moist climate, chemical weathering is speeded up. This no doubt accounts for the deep mantle of soil in some semitropical and tropical regions. If there is moisture accompanied by great cold, the process of chemical weathering is slowed down considerably. This is probably one reason why soil in some parts of the Arctic is poorly developed. There are a great variety of conditions there, just as there are in the middle latitudes, and good soil is also found in these colder latitudes where conditions have been conducive to its formation. Likewise, if a region is very hot but also very dry, chemical weathering will not be so great as in the region where both heat and moisture are present.

Rounded hills and gentle slopes characterize a landscape in moist gions. This is a landscape in Connecticut. (Connecticut Develoment Commission.)

EXPERIENCE. *To show chemical weathering.* Put one piece of iron in a dry place—for example, near a radiator or other source of heat indoors—and another in a damp place. Watch from day to day to see which rusts first. The iron is gradually combining with oxygen and water from the air.

EXPERIENCE. *Plants and chemical weathering.* Examine a rock on which lichens are growing. Scrape off some of the lichens. Notice the bits of rock that flake off with the lichens.

EXPERIENCE. *To note the difference in surface area between one large block and several small ones.* Take two small blocks and place them together to make one large block. Look at the blocks carefully to notice how much surface area

there is. Then take them apart and see that there are now two more sides providing surface area than there were before. It shows that when rock is broken up into smaller pieces there will be more surface area exposed to oxygen, carbon dioxide, and water for weathering.

EXPERIENCE. *To discover the natural color of rock.* Frequently rocks are covered with dirt and other loose material. Young children enjoy washing these rocks in order to discover the real appearance of the rock.

It might be said that the original color of rock is not always exposed by washing. Rocks that are exposed to the air are affected chemically by the substances in the atmosphere and by the weather. Therefore the true color of the rock is not seen on a weathered surface. To show the true color, place a small rock in a bag, for safety from flying splinters, and break the rock exposing an unweathered surface.

Mechanical Weathering of Rock. Mechanical weathering of rock, or the *wedging apart* of particles and blocks of rock, is more widespread in arid regions than chemical weathering; yet almost everywhere the two processes proceed together in varying degrees.

Plants, Animals, and Mechanical Weathering. Plants and animals aid chemical weathering, but they also further mechanical weathering. Plants find roothold on rocks in what may seem to be impossible places. Their roots creep into tiny cracks and fissures, and as they grow, push the rock farther and farther apart. Examples of this are common, and the sum total of the weathering done by them may be underestimated. Animals promote the mechanical breaking up of rocks to a certain extent by crushing soil materials as they move about. Claws and hoofs are no doubt the parts of animals mainly involved in this.

Man has become a tremendous force: his construction and mining activities greatly add to the breaking up of rocks by means of modern machinery.

Alternate Expansion and Contraction. Mechanical weathering may be caused by rapid changes of temperature. Rocks expand when they are heated and contract when cooled. A contributing factor to easy disintegration from this cause is the fact that most rocks are composed of several different minerals, which expand and contract unequally. This alternate

hedral Valley in southern Utah. Sharp angles are characteristic of thered and eroded land forms in some arid and semiarid regions. osef Muench.)

expansion and contraction tends to crack the rocks and eventually shatter them. This goes on rapidly in places where there are great contrasts in temperature during a short period of time, such as on the tops of mountains and in deserts, where the temperature at noon may be high and at night below freezing. Certain laboratory experiments indicate that heating and cooling (but not freezing) alone does not noticeably break up rock. The greatest breakage occurs when water and freezing temperatures are both present.

Water enters into cracks and pores in rocks and expands on freezing, thus pushing the rocks apart. Pieces of rock, small and large, may chip off, and fissures continue to widen through the years. Great slabs of rock may be loosened sufficiently in this way to go crashing down to the valley, shattering other rocks and thus exposing new surfaces for further attacks by the atmosphere and temperature. High mountains are sometimes covered with fields of boulders due to this action.

Fires, principally forest fires, even though confined to relatively small parts of a county, state, or province contribute to the breaking up of rocks by expansion from the intense heat. If water is present in the rock, steam may be created and in expanding shatter the rock.

Other evidences of the weathering of rock thought by some to be caused by alternate expansion and contraction may be found in many places. They sometimes take the form of the peeling off of the outside of rocks in relatively thin sheets, or scales. A fresh surface is thus exposed, and the same process of expansion and contraction is repeated. The presence of water greatly hastens the progress of the peeling. The process of peeling, or exfoliation, may occur in humid regions, where, in a chemical action, water causes minerals to expand. Some scientists argue that expansion and contraction alone, due to changes in temperature, are not enough to produce this type

Half Dome in Yosemite National Park shows the type of weathering called exfoliation. (H. E. Stark, National Park Service.)

of breaking. They think that some rocks which display this kind of leafing off are the kind that have been formed at great depths and that, as the enormous weight of the covering materials is removed, they tend to expand slightly, thus producing the first stages of circular cracks. This, in addition to expansion and contraction, possibly ice wedging, and possibly varying degrees of chemical action, more probably have produced the type of weathering called exfoliation. Under such conditions, any kind of grained or dense rock will finally have a domelike, rounded appearance. Striking examples of exfoliation are found in many parts of the country; notable among them are Stone Mountain in Georgia and the great granite domes in Yosemite National Park; and there are many other examples throughout the Sierra Nevada in California.

Rocks differ in the size of their pore spaces and hence their ability to hold water. Some sedimentary rocks have large pore spaces and therefore are relatively weak. If filled with water which freezes, they break. If not filled with water, there is room within the pore spaces for contraction and expansion. Compact rocks such as basalt provide less pore space and are stronger.

EXPERIENCE. *Crumbling rock.* Frequently one finds bits of rock that can be crumbled easily by a little pressure of the hands. Nearby one may find bedrock of the same kind but hard and resistant. The small piece has been exposed for some time to the action of the atmosphere. It has been softened by weathering.

EXPERIENCE. *Weathered rock at the base of a cliff.* At the foot of a cliff one may find masses of rock debris, called *talus*, which have accumulated as a result of weathering.

EXPERIENCE. *Buildings are subject to weathering.* Dwellings, public buildings, and all other structures undergo weathering. It has been found necessary to treat the outside of buildings, even when built of rock, to prevent weathering. Paint is a common protective covering used on frame houses. Paint, too, is attacked by heat, cold, and the gases in the atmosphere. Children may relate experiences they and their families have had with paint on their houses or cars.

EXPERIENCE. *To show that freezing water can break things.* Completely fill a small bottle with water. Place the bottle inside a paper sack and place in the freezing drawer of the refrigerator. After a few hours, possibly a day, remove the bottle in the sack and examine it carefully. Allow the ice to melt; the bottle should be broken. The reason the bottle breaks is that water requires more space when it turns to ice. When pores and cracks in rock

Some rocks can be crumbled easily; others are very hard and resistant.

become filled with water during cold weather, they are broken apart by the expansion of the freezing water. We prevent this in automobile radiators by mixing the water with special liquids which only freeze at lower than ordinary temperatures.

In colder regions the above experiment can be performed out of doors. The bottle of water can be placed in a place outdoors where the children can examine it at a later time.

Using plaster of Paris, make a block with a crack in it. Pour in water and leave it to freeze. Is the crack wider?

EXPERIENCE. *Rocks can be broken by being struck or rubbed by other rocks.* Take two rocks and rub one against the other. Perhaps they have sharp edges. Show that rock rubbing against rock can make the two rocks smooth. Do the rubbing over a sheet of white paper and note the particles which are rubbed off. Describe the material that comes off the rocks when they are rubbed. Use a reading glass to examine what has accumulated on the white paper. Have the children see that these particles are small bits of rock.

Have the children look for smooth rocks. How did they become smooth? What forces cause rocks to rub against other rocks?

EXPERIENCE. *To show that rocks can absorb water.* Soak some pieces of rock in a pan of water. After they have been in the water about twenty minutes, remove them and attempt to wipe the rock dry. You will notice that, in spite of wiping, they remain moist. This is because the rocks are quite porous, and the water saturates them.

When the water in a rock freezes, the rocks may break apart and thus are weathered. Have children notice how water-soaked some of the rocks may become. If the rain is followed by freezing weather, small particles are quite apt to break off.

Erosion Changes Earth's Surface

Weathering, as applied to rock, has reference only to the decay of rock, not to the transportation of rock or soil particles. *Erosion* is the term that is applied to the transportation of rock and soil particles from one place to another by natural processes.

The important agents of erosion are water, ice, and air. The vast amount of transportation and sorting of rock and soil fragments performed by water and air is due to the fact that both are constantly circulating. The incessant motion of these two agents causes other materials to move with them.

Erosion is probably a speedier process than weathering; for wherever there is wind or water, broken up rock is being moved and moved again. It is carried from one place, leaving fresh rock surfaces for weathering, and deposited in another place. Deep deposits are being made constantly in many places. This fact alone makes it imperative that soil should be cared for, since man depends upon it for the plants, which are necessary to his existence.

The many processes of weathering and erosion interact so closely that it is often hard to say which particular process is responsible for the making and accumulation of a particular soil.

Time after time through the long history of our Earth, regions have been worn down by wind and water to *peneplains,* level or gently rolling plains, with possibly a hill of hard resistant rock, such as Stone Mountain in Georgia or Mt. Monadnock in New Hampshire, left as a reminder of ancient mountains.

Emphasis should be placed on the fact that the erosion of the land has been going on for millions of years and will continue to go on as long as there is soil, and wind and water to move it.

Running Water As an Earth-changing Force. Water is constantly in motion. The combined action of the sun and gravity, causing evaporation and air currents, makes water evaporate into the air and later condense and fall in some form of precipitation, such as rain, snow, or sleet. This movement, or circulation, of water is sometimes spoken of as the *water cycle* (pp. 475–490).

When rain falls, that part of the water which does not immediately evaporate is forced by gravity to flow somewhere. Some of it may sink into the ground, adding to the store of underground water, some of which may later emerge at a spring and flow into the rivers and thence to the ocean; another part of the rainfall may immediately flow into the creeks and rivers, which, directly or indirectly, empty into the ocean.

Running water, then, is a vital force in changing Earth's surface. It is a force that has been operating since an atmosphere existed on our planet and will continue operating as long as there is an atmosphere. Erosion by running water is one of the processes by which highlands are worn down to low plains.

Factors Which Govern Stream Erosion. Of all the agents which change the surface of Earth, running water holds first place in the amount of change accomplished. This varies with the amount of rainfall, the slope, or gradient, of the land, the kind of rocks and soils, and the kind, amount, and distribution of vegetation.

There is probably no region which has absolutely no rainfall, for even in the most arid parts of Earth a little rain falls every few years. In a few places, such as parts of India and South America around the upper Amazon River, there are over 400 inches of rain each year. Between the two extremes are found many regions where the rainfall is from 20 to 60 inches a year. Hence, in varying degrees, all regions are affected by running water.

The slope of the land over which a stream flows determines its swiftness. This in turn determines the amount of material the water erodes by the force of its fall and also the amount of material it carries and where it deposits this material. Slow, quiet streams do not erode so much as swift streams, nor do they carry their load so far.

The character of the soil also retards or accentuates the erosive work done by water. Water can enter or permeate a sandy soil more easily than it can a more solid, compact, fine-grained clay. A loose, coarse soil will also wash away more easily than the more compact clay. The streams which flow over weak rocks, such as limestone, carry more sediment than those which flow over hard, resistant rocks, such as lava.

Generally plants and their roots, living or dead, help to hold the soil in place. The more plants and the denser the mat of roots, the less opportunity water has to wash away the soil.

EXPERIENCE. *To learn about any stream in your area.* Why does this stream run in the direction it does? Is it a slow-running stream or a swift one, and why? Is yours a region with a great deal of rainfall or only a little?

Types of Water Erosion. Water erodes by the force of its fall, much as a stream of water from a garden hose will wash out a path for itself or make a hole in the ground if turned on full force. This process is called *hydraulic action.* The erosion accomplished by this force is greater than at first might be thought. It depends a great deal on the swiftness and the volume of the stream. This type of water erosion is seen most easily when flood conditions exist. In those sections of the country where heavy rainfall or rapidly melting snows cause floods, or in arid sections, where the river beds are usually dry, and infrequent but torrential rains are normal, great sections of riverbanks are washed away and new gullies quickly formed.

A second type of water erosion is erosion by *solution.* Water in its purest state is a good solvent; but as it comes in contact with the air, it takes up varying amounts of carbon dioxide and oxygen, with smaller amounts of other gases, and becomes a still more effective solvent of certain materials. As it runs over and through a soil rich in vegetable and animal remains, it takes up a great variety of substances, among them organic acids, which, again, add to its power to dissolve other substances. As the water soaks deep into the soil, heat and pressure, again, add to its efficiency. As water takes various substances into solution, chemical changes may occur, as a result of which new substances are formed and left behind as deposits.

A third type of water erosion is erosion by *abrasion.* Rocks are worn away by striking and rubbing against other rocks. Water wears down both the rocks embedded in the stream and those that roll and bump along with the stream. Edges are broken off, and finally the rocks become rounded.

These three types of water erosion furnish the material, or load, which is transported by a stream. The load, therefore, is likely to consist of material ranging from good-sized rocks to very fine particles of sand or soil and the substances in solution. The large pieces are not easily carried or rolled along and so are dropped relatively soon. The fine material, being light in weight, is carried for a much longer time and is sometimes deposited as a delta.

Splash and Sheet Erosion and Piping. Water erosion begins as raindrops strike Earth. They may be large or small, but they exert pressure. Their weight and often the added force of the wind against them may produce a marked movement of soil. This is especially true when the soil is unprotected by plants or some other covering. Raindrops beat, move, and sort soil particles not held in place in some way. Often soil may be observed splashed against the lower side of a building, or, if there are small stones scattered about, the soil may be beaten away from the areas surrounding them, leaving the place dotted with tiny pedestals. Raindrops break up hard chunks of soil. The finer grains may be carried off, and with them nutrients for crops. At the same time, there may be a compaction of the soil. Different soils react to this differently. For the most part, fine surface cracks are filled, and the surface may become almost waterproof. This reduces the possibility for water from the next rain to enter the soil. This type of erosion is often called *splash,* or raindrop, erosion.

As soon as rain falls it is forced by gravity to seek a lower level. If more water falls than can evaporate or than the soil can immediately absorb, it runs off in broad sheets. Eventually this water may gather in any depression available and evaporate or soak into the soil, or it may gather into streams, where it may evaporate, soak into the soil, or find its way to the ocean.

When water runs off in broad sheets, it may create tremendous havoc in cultivated fields. This is commonly called *sheet* erosion. The amount of soil movement produced in this way depends upon the type of soil, the plant covering, and the slope of the land.

Note the drainage of this cornfield, and that the furrows run with the slope of the land. A heavy rain has washed away the furrows at this end of the field and carried away considerable quantities of soil. (U.S. Dept. of the Interior.)

Soil loosened and sorted by the pressure of falling raindrops is carried off by the water as it flows over the land. It may either be deposited in some depression or be carried into streams and then be transported by them.

Farmers in many regions find splash and sheet erosion a great problem. Valuable topsoil may be stripped from their fields, gullies formed, their crops destroyed, and their land so damaged that it is no longer productive. A great deal of effort has gone into learning how to control such erosion, and more and more is being learned about the behavior of soils, suitable crops, and methods of control.

In those semiarid regions where the soil is fine-textured and deep, a kind of erosion called *piping* takes place. This kind of soil washes away very easily if water flows over or through it with any force. Piping occurs when water washes out tunnels or pipes under the surface of the soil. The pipes produced in this way may be short or miles long, they may be deep, and there may be one above another. They sometimes begin when water, running swiftly in broad sheets or in a gully, finds an entrance into the soil. Such an entrance might be a crack, an animal burrow, or the deep roots of alfalfa or other plants. Soil, the rainwater, and irrigation water so badly needed in these areas may be lost in this kind of erosion.

EXPERIENCE. *Raindrops have weight.* When one is out in a rain, he will hear and feel the raindrops strike his umbrella or rainhat or sting his face. There is weight in the raindrop. Watch and listen to them as they strike a window or a roof.

EXPERIENCE. *To show that raindrops move soil.* Fill flat pans with soil, pat it down tight, and place several small flat stones on top. Set them in a rain and observe at intervals of half an hour, as long as the rain lasts. A sprinkling-can could be used for rain in case of necessity. What happened to the soil? If this experiment is done inside a schoolroom, the pan of soil should be set in a larger container because of the splash.

EXPERIENCE. *Water helps to sort soil particles.* (P. 160.)

EXPERIENCE. *To show that water dissolves substances from the soil.* Salt is a substance found in the soil. Since it is also a common substance around the house, take a half cup and stir it into a pint of water. It will soon dissolve. Then allow the water to stand until the water evaporates. This may take a week or longer.

Raindrops have weight and can move soil.

The salt will form crystals when the water has evaporated. This is the same thing that happens when salt lakes are formed.

EXPERIENCE. *To note erosional scars.* On excursions and in discussions encourage children to see erosional scars. How has man contributed to this erosion? How do the children think the place looked before the erosion started? Can the children suggest ways to prevent such erosion? It might be profitable to discuss *why* such erosion should be prevented.

EXPERIENCE. *To examine the school playground after a rain.* This may be quite a profitable experience. Frequently on school grounds there may be evidence of small gullies. There may even be evidence of sheet erosion after a hard rain. There will without doubt be deposits of soil and debris in various forms (see Chapter 6). It should be kept in mind that one does not have to have a large gully to show erosion. A small gully formed by a rain storm may be as effective for demonstration purposes as a canyon.

Streams Carve Valleys. That water which does not evaporate or sink into the soil immediately is called the *runoff.* The runoff gathers into tiny streams which run together and form larger streams. These in turn run into larger ones until finally they reach the ocean.

At first some streams carry water only during and after a rain; but as their valleys deepen, they become permanent, being fed by springs or the seepage of underground water from their valley walls.

As soon as streams form, they begin to wear away the soil and rocks and thus begin the process of valley formation. Streams erode in two directions: downward, and outward along their sides. Every curve of a winding stream and every current of air which strikes its surface tends to send the water forcibly against one side or the other, cutting into it and thereby making the stream bed wider. As a stream cuts downward and outward, weathering and the runoff also attack the valley walls, crumbling them and washing the loosened material downward. Thus the walls are widened at the top as well as at the bottom.

As time goes on, the valley becomes wider and the curves in the stream become larger. At the same time deposits are made on the quiet inside section of the curves, and gradually long flat areas, or *flood plains,* are developed in valleys. The long curves, or meanders, swing from side to side across the valley floor, moving down the valley as the stream undercuts the banks. Thus valleys gradually change from steep-sided V-shaped depressions to those whose bottoms have been widened and filled in by deposits until they resemble floors, and whose sides are low and gently sloping.

EXPERIENCE. *To observe a mountain stream.* If there is an opportunity to observe a mountain stream, note the great number of rocks in its bed. Can you explain this? Such streams are different from slow-moving streams on nearly level land. The latter carry few rocks but much soil. Note the shape of the rocks in the bed of the mountain stream. If possible, feel one of these rocks. How would you describe such rocks?

How would you describe the valley in which the stream flows? Is it narrow and steep, or is it broad?

All safety precautions should be taken when children are involved in such a trip.

EXPERIENCE. *To observe any valleys in your region.* Are these valleys deep and narrow or broad and flat? From this you can tell something of the recent history of your area. Was the valley you are observing cut by running water or by a glacier? How can you tell? Verify this by information from some authentic source. Drawing pictures of valleys they have seen will help

Young valleys are steep-sided. This is the part of the Grand Canyon of the Snake River that is popularly known as Hell's Canyon. It is in Oregon. (Oregon State Highway Commission.)

to make children aware of the differences in valleys.

Age of Valleys. The age of a valley is a matter, not of years, but of the degree to which it has developed. We speak of valleys with steep sides and V-shaped as *young* valleys. These valleys are also crooked, shaped by every irregularity of the land. They are also as steep as the slope of the land permits. When streams begin to develop flood plains in their valleys, they are said to be *mature*. This stage continues until the valley walls are gentle slopes except for those parts where the meandering stream is still cutting into the walls. The stage of *old age* extends from the late maturity through the time when the valley can scarcely be recognized as such; the floor is wide and the slopes are so slight as to be barely noticeable.

In the same way a whole region may give evidence of different stages of erosion. The runoff forms gullies and their tributaries, which later become valleys. It should be emphasized that streams dissect the land, carrying it bit by bit to lower levels until it is reduced to a peneplain. Then it may again be uplifted, and the whole process of reducing it to a peneplain may again take place. This has happened time after time in the long history of our planet, and is going on now.

Potholes, Waterfalls, and Rapids. Potholes are a small but interesting feature of stream erosion. They are holes, usually rounded, which have been worn in rocks by the rubbing and scouring action of sand and rocks against one another. They probably begin with a small eddy in the stream; a small rock or sand gets caught in a depression in the bedrock, the water whirls the loose material around, and the hole becomes larger. Other and perhaps larger rocks are caught, the whirling of the water and the scouring of the sand and rocks continue, and the result is potholes. They vary in size from inches to hundreds of feet in diameter. Potholes often mark the course of an ancient river.

Waterfalls and *rapids* are also interesting features of rivers. The former occur wherever

A mature river valley. The Connecticut River winds its way across broad, relatively level valley. (Standard Oil Co., N.J.)

the water falls over a ledge. They cause the water to strike violently against the rocks below, thus increasing the rate of erosion. Waterfalls are objects of beauty, and many of them are numbered among the scenic wonders of the world. They originate in several different ways, among them being the following: (1) Rock is rapidly worn away along joints or cracks in the rock. Of this type Trenton Falls, New York, is a fine example. (2) Soft layers of rock, alternating with hard layers, are worn away. Niagara Falls, New York, is a fine example of this type, with the layers lying horizontally. Niagara Falls are especially interesting because they have a long history. It all began many thousand years ago when the river first flowed across the plateau and fell over the escarpment near Lewiston, New York. As the water continued to fall, it gradually washed away the soft layers of rock below, leaving a table-like layer of hard rock on top with no support. This finally crashed, and the swirling waters continued their work of wearing away the soft rocks. The falls have now retreated seven miles, leaving a deep gorge to tell the story; eventually they may retreat to Lake Erie, the source of the river, and then cease to exist. (3) Waterfalls may be formed when water falls over vertical layers of hard, resistant rock. These may be exposed beds of igneous rock or a hard rock that has been tilted upright. The Lower Falls of the Yellowstone River are formed by the fall of water over a vertical section of lava. (4) The damming of a river often results in waterfalls. Dams are formed in many different ways, such as by landslides, by an accumulation of debris, by a lava flow, or by the work of animals such as beavers. (5) Uplifted fault blocks are sometimes the cause of waterfalls. The land on one side of a fault may be lifted up, thus forming a ledge over which water may fall.

Falls and rapids cease to exist when the rocks which cause them are worn away. They are changing features of Earth's surface.

EXPERIENCE. *To observe potholes and waterfalls.* Children may bring pictures of potholes and waterfalls to school for observation and discussion when it is impossible to observe them firsthand. They may wish to describe any potholes or waterfalls that they have seen. Sometimes potholes may be found in old, dry river beds. They are of all sizes. Can the children imagine how long it would take for them to form? They are usually quite smooth inside. If there is a waterfall in your locality, try to find out if it is moving upstream because of the wearing away of the cliff over which it falls. You may need to consult geological bulletins to find out the answer, unless an old resident of the community can provide authentic information.

Rivers Deposit Material. Many rivers carry vast amounts of material. Part of this is carried in solution, that is, dissolved in the water. Other material is carried downstream by the force of the moving water. Streams may move material mechanically by pushing and rolling it or by carrying it in suspension, as, for example, fine grains of sand, clay, and silt. Many particles fall to the bottom, only to be picked up later and carried farther.

The Mississippi is only one of the great rivers of the world which carry an enormous amount of material downstream. The amount of soil, rocks, and debris transported by rivers depends on the character of the country through which they pass. Many naturally wooded sections have been denuded and the land given over entirely to agriculture. Likewise, many prairie districts have been robbed of the protecting grass roots, and the soil has been left soft and porous by cultivation. Such sections at once become the victims of rainwash and provide the rivers with an abundant supply of rich soil for deposit in other places.

The slope, or gradient, of the land determines to a considerable extent the amount of material carried by a river and the point at which it is deposited. Rivers whose currents are swift leave little material as they flow, until they reach a more level stretch of country, when the deposition of the heavier material at once begins. Sometimes this occurs when the river empties into a larger body of water.

Large *deltas* and fertile flood plains have been built up at the mouths of many rivers. Notable among them are those of the Mississippi and the Nile. However, deposits which form deltas are possible only on shores where lake or ocean currents are not strong enough to wash away the sediment brought down by rivers.

As they near their outlets, these rivers flow through many miles of low, level country. During periods of flood, caused by heavy rains and melting snows in the country through which they flow, their waters spread out over their banks and cover vast areas on each side. As the floods subside and the rivers return to their normal banks, a rich and fertile layer of soil is deposited.

A form of deposition which occurs in areas of moderate to little rainfall is the *alluvial fan*. It may be thought of as a kind of delta. One difference is that the top of a fan slopes, whereas the top of a delta is flat, owing to the effect of the large body of water with which a delta is in contact. Alluvial fans are formed where streams, oftentimes temporary ones, dash down a hillside and suddenly reach level land. The rush of the water is suddenly checked, and much of the material which the water is carrying is deposited.

Thousands and thousands of years ago, the torrents of water issuing from the edge of the melting continental glacier flowed over parts of the Columbia River lava flow. This water gouged out deep canyons and carried the pulverized rock miles away to the southward, where it was deposited. Today the deep, fertile soil derived from these deposits is irrigated by the water from the Columbia River, pumped from the storage reservoir in one of the old canyons by power from the Grand Coulee Dam. This deposit of soil today provides sustenance for thousands of people.

EXPERIENCE. *To study a small stream.* A small stream offers an opportunity for study. Take a walk with the children beside such a stream. Can they point out the places where the stream is cutting its banks? Is the current stronger in some places than in others? Do they see where rocks and pebbles are being deposited; or where fine material is accumulating? Is the water clear? If not, does man have anything to do with its condition? If muddy, what can be done to make the water clear?

In some localities it may be possible to show that the water is not so muddy when it comes from a stream which flows through a woods or a large forest. The leaf mold and the roots of trees and smaller plants should help to hold the soil.

From time to time erosion is indicated as a very destructive process, and of course it is. But when soil is washed away, it must be deposited somewhere else—often in a place where in time it may again support life.

Too frequently in the classroom so much emphasis is placed on the destructive side of erosion that the child fails to see that useful deposition of materials goes on as well.

Water in Soil Near the Surface May Promote Erosion. A slow, large-scale movement of soil occurs on slopes in areas where the soil near the surface is frequently soaked by rain. It is called *creep.* The weight of the soil and water held in the soil tends to drag it downhill. The soil itself slides more easily when wet, especially if it is clay. The weight of the water involved helps to overcome friction and thus furthers downward movement. If the water freezes, it expands, pushing up rocks and loosening soil. This is called frost heaving. It, too, furthers the downward movement of soil. Likewise, the burrowing and trampling of animals, the spaces left by decaying plant roots which become loosely filled with soil, fallen trees pulling up and loosening the soil packed around their roots, and many other things further the process known as soil creep. When fence posts, trees, gravestones, or telephone poles, or occasionally even buildings on a hillside lean toward the bottom, it is almost certain to indicate that soil creep is going on.

A type of creep peculiar to areas where the soil is frozen to considerable depth is known as solifluction. The top may thaw at times, and if the excess water cannot drain downward the area becomes literally a sea of mud. If the thawing occurs on a slope, the whole mass may move downward. In those northern regions where permafrost abounds, surface melting and solifluction at times present great problems. The construction and heating of buildings, the laying of pipes, the construction and maintenance of roads are profoundly affected by this condition.

More rapid movements on a large scale are to be seen in *landslides* and *rockfalls*. Landslides occur on steep slopes when there is sufficient water to loosen large masses of soil and rocks. Often there is an underlying layer of inclined rock or clay which permits the mass to descend, moving slowly or rapidly as circumstances permit. Gravity as well as the lubricating effects of water are involved in this process.

Avalanches occur where snow accumulates along ridges. Melting and its own weight carry the snow down. It often carries with it loose rocks and soil, and its impact may loosen or tear away trees, rock, and soil from the slopes below.

When weathering and erosion loosen and carry away materials supporting a resistant layer of rock, or when cracks have been formed in blocks of rock along cliffs, a rockfall may occur. Sometimes an earthquake, an ex-plosion, or an especially heavy downpour of rain may provide the trigger. Gravity is involved in carrying the material downward. Rockfalls may occur on steep slopes in mountainous regions or on the edges of mesas and buttes in arid regions.

Rock and *dirt glaciers* somewhat resemble glaciers of snow and ice in their form. They may be small or large, and are the result of the lubricating action of water, frost, the presence of certain kinds of soil, and the pull of gravity. An example was the one near Eureka, California, in 1954, which was said to be 6000 feet long, 1200 feet wide in places, and which moved at the rate of 40 to 50 feet each day. It was impossible to stop it, and railroad tracks had to be moved (p. 297).

EXPERIENCE. *To help children become aware of large movements of soil.* Older children may be urged to watch for these movements of rocks, soil, or snow when they go on a trip or on the school bus. What are the conditions that promote these movements, as far as they can observe? Quite often there are reports of landslides, avalanches, or some other form of downward movement of rocks, soil, or snow in the newspapers. Pictures may appear at times, and they may be used on a bulletin board and supply motivation for discussion.

Erosion and Deposits Due to Underground Water. Like surface water, underground water also erodes and deposits materials. The importance of erosion by solution and the transportation of the dissolved substances is very great. Erosion by hydraulic action, or the force exerted by water as it flows, and by abrasion is small in the case of underground water because such water usually moves slowly.

As rain falls, oxygen and carbon dioxide are dissolved; and as the water passes through the fissures and tiny pores in the rocks, minerals are dissolved from them. In regions of plentiful plant growth water also dissolves

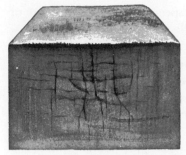 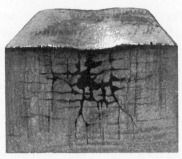 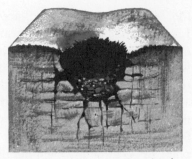

These diagrams show different stages in the formation of sinks. Water dissolves the minerals in the rocks and carries them away in solution. Eventually the roof may fall.

carbon dioxide from plant and animal remains; this too aids in dissolving minerals from rocks. Some rocks, such as limestone and dolomite, are made of minerals which dissolve easily. Rain water, with carbon dioxide from the air dissolved in it, dissolves such rocks readily; and since so much of our Earth's surface is covered by these sedimentary rocks, it is easy to understand the enormous amount of erosion by solution that goes on. Nor are these sedimentary rocks the only ones that are attacked. Even the very hard igneous rocks finally give way to solution.

In regions of considerable rainfall, where limestone and dolomite are abundant, sinks and caves will be found. When water soaks into the ground, it follows any cracks there may be. These cracks, or joints, often run vertically and horizontally. There the water continues its work of dissolving, and at the intersection of the cracks holes form. These may be near the surface, and as time goes on the holes become so large that the roof, or overlying layer of soil and plants, sags and a depression is formed. Eventually the unsupported roof may fall in completely and a surface opening result. Such depressions, called *sinks,* may be formed in rocks that are not jointed. They range in size from small ones to those several hundred feet across. When the bottom of a sink reaches below the water table it may become a lake. If the sink does not reach to the water table, any cracks forming an outlet for water entering the sink may become clogged and a lake form for that reason.

Carlsbad Caverns in New Mexico, Mammoth Cave in Kentucky, the Luray Caverns, Massanutten Caverns, and Endless Caverns of the Shenandoah valley are the result of solution by underground water. In these caverns are large rooms, sometimes on different levels, with smaller rooms and little openings leading off.

Not only does underground water erode by dissolving substances but it also forms deposits from the material which it carries in solution. Deposits are formed because conditions change from those which existed when the material was dissolved. The temperature of the water may be lowered; the water may lose some of

Stalagmites and stalactites are formed by the evaporation of underground water in which minerals have been dissolved. This is a scene in Carlsbad Cavern in New Mexico. (Philip Gendreau.)

its carbon dioxide; evaporation may occur; a chemical reaction may occur between the water, bearing dissolved minerals, and some rock with which it has come in contact; or a reaction caused by tiny plants called algae may take place. There are other causes of precipitation, but these are common ones.

Spectacular deposits accumulate in caves. Underground water bearing dissolved minerals drips or percolates through the roof of a cavern slowly enough so that some of it evaporates; it loses carbon dioxide, and thus a minute amount of calcium carbonate is deposited. Through long ages these deposits are built up and form icicle-like columns, called *stalactites,* which hang from the roof of caverns. On the floor of caverns broader masses rise which are called *stalagmites.* A stalactite and a stalagmite sometimes join and form a huge column. Sheetlike formations of the same material are sometimes found, as well as more grotesque shapes.

Deposits of calcium carbonate form around objects. Such *concretions* are often rounded in appearance and when broken open reveal some object, such as a leaf or an animal skeleton, which is a clue to the history of Earth.

Underground water sometimes dissolves minerals and replaces them with different minerals. In petrified trees we see an example of organic material which has been replaced by minerals, with, in this case, retention of the size, shape, and much of the appearance of the original.

Deposits of calcium carbonate have been made at Mammoth Hot Springs by underground water; and other substances have been deposited, such as silica, sometimes called geyserite, around some geysers, sulfur, and iron carbonate.

In arid regions alkali or salt deposits are formed. In such regions there is not enough rainfall to carry away these substances completely. As the water evaporates from the soil after a rain, these alkali or salt deposits come to the surface with the water and are left there. Frequently this completely unfits land for agriculture or grazing by killing vegetation, since the alkali content is too great. Irrigation sometimes ruins soil in the same way.

Salt and alkali lakes are formed in much the same manner. When, in arid regions, water laden with various substances drains into depressions from which there is no outlet, it evaporates, leaving deposits of salt and alkali.

This power of water to dissolve substances from the air, soil, and rocks explains why water is sometimes hard or why it tastes different in various sections of the country. It also explains why teakettles frequently become lined with lime carbonate.

EXPERIENCE. *Water and caves.* Many caves and caverns are open to the public, and often conducted trips are offered. These are worth while. Things to note are the size of the caves; the stalagmites and stalactites being formed very, very slowly; and whether or not there is a stream in the cave at present. The guide will answer many of your questions and might be able to tell you the age of the cave and whether or not there are plants or animals living in the underground stream. On such trips every safety precaution should be observed.

EXPERIENCE. *To discover whether or not water has substances dissolved in it.* Children will be interested in learning something about the water where they live. Younger children may look in teakettles that have been used for some time to see if there is a deposit from the water. The children already may have dissolved salt in water, allowed the water to evaporate, and found salt crystals left in the dish. This would help them to understand about the deposit in the teakettle (Chapter 11). Older children may take a quart of water in common household use and a quart of water obtained from defrosting the refrigerator, or rainwater, and see how much soap it takes to produce the same amount of suds in each. More soap is needed for hard water. This might lead to finding out where the water for household use comes from; whether it is from wells or from streams. Some may be interested in learning how the water is treated before it is used for drinking purposes and how it is treated in their own homes when used for washing clothes (Chapter 6).

EXPERIENCE. *Action of acid on limestone or marble.* (Chapter 11.) Chemical action in soil and rocks is not as readily observed as physical action. Nevertheless, it goes on continuously. The iron in the soil rusts, for example, giving many shades of red and brown to the soil.

EXPERIENCE. *To find evidences of deposits on our Earth's surface.* Sometimes in drier parts of the country a whitish material may be seen around the edges of a place where water has stood for a while. In other places it is distributed over the soil. In still other places it has accumulated in depressions. Some of this material could be examined. It is a deposit of substances that were dissolved in water as it ran over and through the soil.

Ores May Be Concentrated by Magmatic Water. A form of underground water which is of great importance is that which is believed to originate in molten rock (magma) within our Earth For this reason it is called magmatic water. It it thought to play a large part in the concentration of minerals.

The mining industry and even our civilization as it is today depend on the concentration of minerals for their existence. When minerals are sufficiently concentrated to be of economic importance, they are referred to as *ores*. They are usually mixed with varying amounts of rock called gangue, from which useful by-products may sometimes be obtained.

It has been found that ores appear in beds or veins of diverse shapes and sizes. This concentration permits them to be worked, and thus gives them economic importance. The ways in which ores are concentrated or brought together are what concerns us here.

It was observed that hot gases escaping from certain volcanoes carried copper, lead, and iron and formed such minerals as galena (lead sulfide) and hematite (iron oxide). This led some to think that ores containing metals might be formed from magmas as they solidify. These ores are found in connection with batholiths and other large masses of igneous rocks. The theory of such ore deposits is as follows: The temperature of masses of molten rock, or magma, is exceedingly high. Therefore solutions in the magma occur, not as liquids, but as gases. These gaseous solutions permeate the magma and from it dissolve any metals that it may contain. As the magma mass and the gaseous solutions move upward, they cool; they may become mixed with varying amounts of underground water; they react with the adjoining rocks, and the pressure on them may be reduced. The largest single factor in the forming of precipitates from these solutions may be the decrease in temperature. During this time chemical reactions take place; many of the dissolved materials can no longer remain in solution under the new set of conditions, and they are deposited in fissures. A great many ore deposits give evidence of having been formed at temperatures ranging from somewhat less than 212°F. to more than 1200°F.

Often bodies of ore are formed by replacement. The ore-forming solutions enter fissures, permeate the rock walls, dissolve them, and leave ore in their place. Often, and especially if the rock is limestone, the original appearance of the rock is retained.

The metals are usually deposited in combination with sulfur, oxygen, carbon, chlorine, or silica. Although gold is found as gold, it is nearly always located near the iron sulfide called pyrite.

The world's largest deposits of metals—copper, silver, gold, zinc, lead, chromium, tin, nickel, and tungsten—are formed from the gaseous solutions contained in magma. These are called *primary* deposits.

Secondary deposits are formed when these primary deposits and igneous rocks are at or near the surface, where they are acted upon by water and wind. Erosion and chemical and mechanical weathering wear away the material enclosing such minerals as gold, platinum, and diamonds, and these are left to be blown together by the wind; but more often they are washed into stream beds, where they often form a rich accumulation. These are called *placer deposits*. Even these minerals are worn away to some extent; softer minerals are often worn to a dust and are washed away with the other pulverized rock materials and thus seldom form placer deposits. Placer deposits have been formed throughout Earth's history, and many times have been covered over by sedimentary rocks or by lava flows.

Iron ores have been brought together in more ways than those of any other metal, but the greatest and most extensive bodies of ore have been formed by sedimentation. These are considered to be sedimentary rocks, just as are coal and salt (p. 257). All of these iron deposits have been made in the presence of sea water. Layers of an iron compound are deposited on grains of quartz or tiny fragments of shell, or iron compounds may replace broken parts of fossils, or iron may be removed from solution by iron-secreting bacteria. The Lake Superior iron ores, formed in the Cryptozoic eon (p. 339), are among the largest deposits in North America and are of sedimentary origin. Here layers of iron-bearing material alternate with layers of other sedimentary rocks. In parts of this region this iron-bearing material has been attacked by weathering and erosion, which have worn away everything but the iron. This makes extremely concentrated and valuable ore.

Of the same age and formed in the same way are the great and valuable iron deposits on the Labrador-Quebec border. Methods for mining have been worked out in spite of the greater length and intensity of the cold period. All plants and animals use a number of inorganic substances in their life processes, but some use more of such things as silica or calcium than others, and when they die their remains may be so numerous that a concentration of a mineral results. In addition to iron, deposits of limestone and dolomite, phosphate and silica, are formed in this way, and possibly certain vanadium and copper deposits.

Sedimentation produced beds of coal, petroleum, and clay. Salt, gypsum, and other substances were deposited as sea water evaporated over a long period of time.

EXPERIENCE. *To examine ores.* If someone in your neighborhood has a sample of iron, copper, silver, or some other kind of ore, perhaps he would be pleased to let your class look at it. Use a magnifying glass if you have one. Compare it, if it is iron ore for instance, with some article made of iron that you commonly use. There is usually an observable difference. The metals in the ore are combined with other substances, and man has found ways to separate them and use the pure metal in many ways. He takes the metal after it is separated from the ore and may then combine it with other substances to make articles that he wants.

Perhaps the owner of the sample would like to tell the class what he knows about it.

Some children may have visited a mine at some time and would like to tell about it. Some large mines are above ground and are open and easily viewed.

The Erosive Work of Oceans. Anyone near the seacoast is familiar with the constant movement of ocean water. The waves and currents of the ocean do both constructive and destructive work, building up in one place and tearing down in another. The continuous beating and washing of the waves help to form sea cliffs, terraces, bars, spits, beaches, and sea caves.

Waves are surface movements of ocean water. They are due chiefly to the dragging effect of the winds on the surface of the water, although motions are set up in the ocean by other means. As rivers empty into the ocean, the mixing of their waters with the ocean water causes motion. Heavy rains and the unequal heating of the ocean set up movements in the water. Waves are made up of the vertical, circular movements of individual particles of water, and thus a whirling motion is produced.

The erosive work of waves is due to the fact that in approaching a shore the waves crowd together, and, when they break, a heavy pounding takes place. Any gravel or rocks carried by them act as grinders on the soil or rocks of the shore. Wave erosion takes place in a relatively narrow zone in the area between high and low tides.

Waves may strike the shore at almost any angle, and carry and pile up sand and gravel to form beaches. As they strike the shore, part of the water moves along the shore line as a shore current, and the rest returns in a movement at right angles to the shore called the *undertow*. The undertow is the return of the water to the sea under the incoming waves; it carries sediments, and sometimes one hears that it has taken an unwary bather as well. Sediments are sorted according to size, the coarser material being deposited near shore and the finer material farther out. Can you tell why?

Breakers are a feature of sloping beaches and occur when the top, or crest, of a wave falls over its lower part, which has been retarded by contact with the shore. Ridges or barriers are sometimes built at such places from sediment carried from the sea by the waves and toward the sea by the undertow.

Various forms develop in a shore line. It may be low, flat, and sandy; or high and rocky, perpendicular cliffs may be formed. A zone of weak material in the rock along a shore may become a sea cave or an arch if the land extends out into the ocean. A small portion of this land might even be cut off from the mainland. This would be called a stack. Terraces, benches, and bars are other features of some shore lines.

In some regions there is a constant change of the shore line, owing to the action of waves. This is particularly true during periods of storm, when much damage may be done. Hard, resistant rocks are changed but slightly by wave action, whereas sandy shores shift

Sand accumulates along some shores and may form dunes. Plants tend to hold this sand in place. Small tidal pools can be observed beyond the dunes. (Black Star.)

about at the mercy of the waves. The character of the rock along the shore line and the degree to which it is exposed to ocean currents and wave action determine the amount of erosion that takes place.

EXPERIENCE. *Shore lines are different.* If it is possible, visit a beach and observe what kind of beach it is. Is it sandy or rocky? What else do you observe about it? If shores are not accessible, stories and pictures may be used to show many kinds of shore lines. Perhaps someone in the class has visited a beach at some time. Ask them to tell the others about it.

EXPERIENCE. *Waves have force.* On a windy day children may observe the way in which waves beat against the shore of an ocean, a lake, a river, or even a tiny pond. Pictures of waves created by high winds or hurricanes may be discussed.

Ice As a Geologic Agent in Lakes, Marshes, and Rivers. Ice is an important geologic agent, especially in temperate and arctic regions and in high altitudes. We have already learned how water expands when it freezes, taking up at least 10 per cent more space, and enlarges the pores and cracks in rocks. This process is a very important factor in the disin-

This shore is far up on the western side of the Olympic Peninsula, near Lapush, Washington. Mountains come down to the ocean, and the shore has been eroded in such a way that these sea stacks are left. They may eventually be washed away. (*Joseph Muench.*)

tegration of rocks and the formation of soil.
Ice is an important geologic agent in rivers,
lakes, and other bodies of water during the
winter and spring. When lakes are frozen
over and a further drop in the temperature
occurs, causing the ice to contract, it either
cracks or pulls away from the shore. The exposed water freezes over again, making a new
covering of ice. As the temperature rises and
the ice expands, it must either push up over
the shore line or bulge up in places. If the
former action takes place, sand, clay, or the
rocks composing the shore line are loosened
and pushed up. Upon the melting of the ice
in the spring, this material is quickly and
easily dislodged and added to the lake bed by
the washing of rain and waves.

When marshes freeze over and such changes
of temperature occur, ridges of frozen mud
and plant life are often piled up, with the result that a certain amount of loose material
collects, which can readily be transported elsewhere by rainwash or by the tide if the marsh
is near the seashore.

Rivers in northern latitudes frequently
freeze over during the winter. As spring approaches and water from the melting snow
floods a river, the ice breaks up in chunks,
which become a menace to life and property.
Often bridges are washed out, homes and
places of business are ruined or washed away,
the banks of rivers are dug out, trees are uprooted, and all this material is carried far
downstream.

Erosion due to river ice is likely to be especially great along rivers flowing north. The
mouth of the river remains frozen after the ice
breaks up farther south, thus affording no outlet for the ice-choked stream. Great floods result, and damage to cities and farms alike may
be tremendous.

EXPERIENCE. *Ice takes up more space than water.*
Fill a small container with water and set it in
the freezing unit of the refrigerator, or out-of-

doors if the weather is freezing. Observe that
the ice is higher in the container than the
water was. Or look at a tray of ice cubes
which are thoroughly frozen; they are also
higher than the water was and often have tiny
peaks in the center. (Experience on p. 307.)

**The Formation and Erosive Work of Gla-
ciers.** Glaciers are formed from snow which
turns to ice and which then moves downward
under the pressure of its own weight. Such an
accumulation of snow can only happen where
the amount of snowfall exceeds the amount of
snow that melts or evaporates; there must be
an abundant snowfall in the first place, and
the temperature must be low enough to keep
most of it from melting in the second place.
Therefore the regions where glaciers can exist
are limited to certain latitudes and high altitudes. In other words, glaciers do not originate anywhere below the *snow line*—the lower
limit of snow fields that persist throughout the
year.

The snow from which glaciers are formed
soon loses its characteristic flat, lacy appearance, even in extremely low temperatures,
and becomes granular and icy in appearance.
Evaporation, melting, and recondensation are
among the factors which contribute to this
change. In its granular state it is called *névé*.
Fall after fall of snow presses the lower layers
into beds of ice.

Glaciers Flow over the Land. Although as rigid
as any ice, glaciers, nevertheless, follow the
contours of the land as they flow. This may
seem unnatural; for, when we think of ice, we
think of a material which breaks and chips
rather easily from a quick blow but which certainly does not seem to bend. Under great
and continuous pressure, however, ice does
mold itself to the general form of the land over
which it passes, even though it breaks at times.
These breaks occur when the ice field passes
over mounds or hills, or when it passes over

precipices, thus forming deep cracks called *crevasses*. Crevasses are a great and ever-present danger to mountaineers or arctic explorers.

There are several factors which we know determine to a great extent the movement of glaciers, although there is much about such movement which is still to be proved. It has been found that temperature has a great influence on glacial movements. When the season is warm, rain may fall and penetrate downward. Even slight melting results in the trickling downward of water, which may act in several ways, depending on conditions. For example, as it seeps downward, it may freeze and act as a cement holding the granular ice together; or as it freezes and expands, it may act as a wedge which aids in pushing forward the mass of ice. It is a known fact that water in a glacier does give rise to greater movement.

The thickness of the ice is another contributing factor in glacial movement. The weight of the ice itself tends to push the glacier onward.

The gradient or slope of the land, its smoothness, and the amount of debris which the ice carries also modify the rate of glacial movement. If a valley is steep and smooth, the glacier is likely to move more rapidly than it would otherwise move, even though carrying a heavy load of debris.

It is evident, then, that glaciers move at different rates of speed; some move only a few inches a day and others several feet; sometimes different parts of the same glacier move at different rates of speed.

Kinds of Glaciers. There are two general types of glaciers, namely, the valley type and the ice-sheet, or continental, type. Of the *valley* type are those glaciers which have their beginnings on the tops and sides of many high mountains, following the valleys to lower levels and deriving their name from this fact. Valley glaciers predominate in the middle and tropical latitudes owing mainly to temperature. They do not occur on all high mountains, because many high mountains do not allow snow to accumulate, either because of steep slopes, because of temperature, or for lack of snow. It is interesting to note that the altitude at which snow fields and valley glaciers occur in the tropics is much higher than in other zones. As the polar regions are approached, there is a very noticeable descent toward sea level in the occurrence of these glaciers, some actually flowing into the ocean.

The *continental*, or ice-sheet, type of glacier occurs in regions where the temperature is low enough to allow snow to accumulate on the level as well as on the mountains. When the weight of the accumulated snow and ice becomes great enough, the field begins to spread out. These ice sheets range from small icecaps in high level spots to the fields which now almost entirely cover Greenland and which, it is believed, cover all of Antarctica, except for some of the mountain peaks.

As a result of the movement of glacial ice under great pressure, we find that there have been in the past slow, but great, movements of soil—a leveling off in many places, a gouging out in some, and well-marked deposits in still other places. Such movements are still taking place.

deep grooves in this rock were made by a slowly moving glacier. rock is from Kelley's Island, in Lake Erie. (Courtesy of The erican Museum of Natural History.)

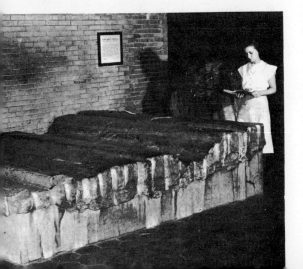

The water from melting glaciers forms streams which scour rocky slopes and carry great quantities of fine and coarse soil and rocks to lower levels. This is Athabasca Peak and Glacier in Jasper National Park, Canada. (Josef Muench.)

The Work of Valley Glaciers. As a valley glacier moves down the mountainside, it gouges out depressions and thus carries material from the mountain, as well as material which has been deposited on it by the wind or has rolled down on it from the mountainside. Then it deposits this material along its sides in long hill-like ridges which are called *lateral moraines,* or carries it along on top. Likewise, as melting proceeds at the lower end, material is deposited in ridges which are called *terminal moraines.* The terminal moraines of valley glaciers may not be at all pronounced in many cases, owing to the steep slope of the valley and the washing effect of the water from the melting glacier.

Many evidences of valley glaciers which disappeared long ago may be seen in the mountains of the western United States, as well as in other places. The gouged-out depressions on mountainsides which mark the beginning of valley glaciers are called *cirques.* A cirque has steep walls on at least one side, which may be several hundred feet high; on another side it leads into the valley down which the glacier passes. Often these cirques are filled with water and, as lakes, become fishing grounds and furnish food and water

for many forms of wild life. Valleys with a rounded, U-shaped appearance are still another evidence of glaciers that have long since disappeared.

EXPERIENCE. *Evidences of valley glaciers.* If you consult publications describing the geological history of your state, you may find that you are living in or near U-shaped valleys which are of glacial origin. There are probably many glacial scratches in the rocks on the floor of these valleys. Some of the features of valley glaciers are easily seen from a road. If children go on a trip with their families, they will probably have some of these features pointed out to them. They are to be found in some national parks.

EXPERIENCE. *The value of glaciers and snow fields.* If any of these can be observed in summer or early fall, streams of water will be seen flowing from them. These are important because they help to fill our rivers with water all year round and are especially valuable during seasons with little rainfall. Great rivers running

This is the southeast face of Mt. Marcus Baker, Alaska. A well-developed cirque is in the central background. Crevasses and medial and lateral moraines are clearly seen on the descending glacier. (Bradford Washburn.)

Valley glaciers carry and deposit soil and rocks in forms called moraines.

through deserts often receive their summer supply of water from just such places, miles away. Children may find out the source of the water in streams in their own neighborhood. Does most of it come from a distant glacier or snow field? The Columbia River, for instance, receives most of its water from the snow and ice sheets in the high mountains of Montana, Idaho, and British Columbia.

The Work of Continental Glaciers. There have been periods during Earth's history when immense ice sheets spread over vast portions of Earth and then receded, only to spread again. Many hypotheses have been proposed to explain the cause of these continental ice sheets, but none have been fully satisfactory.

Evidences have been found of five different ice ages which have occurred during the long history of Earth. There may have been more, but no traces of them have been found. The last Ice Age occurred somewhere between 20,000 and 100,000 years ago, and a large part of northern North America and Europe was covered with an immense sheet of ice. Remnants of this ice sheet are still found in the icecaps of Iceland and the ice sheet which so nearly covers Greenland.

The ice was so deep at that time that it moved large boulders with it, as well as other material of many kinds and sizes. These boulders vary in size from very small ones to some that are larger than houses; some of these latter weigh as much as 500 tons. They may be found scattered about in many parts of New England and Canada. In rare instances a continuous line of them has been found, and they have been traced to the bedrock where they originated; in this way they help to define the direction in which the glacier moved.

As the glacial ice moved southward, rocks which became fastened in it scratched and polished the bedrock over which it passed. The scratches can still be found in many parts of North America and Europe. Geologists can tell by examining them the direction in which the ice sheet was moving in various localities. Some regions were scraped bare down to the bedrock, and their grooved and polished surfaces were left exposed or covered with glacial till, consisting of mixed rocks, sand, gravel, and more finely ground-up rock. Other regions, such as portions of the north-central states, had their soil covered over with varying amounts of glacial till, in some places to a depth of 600 feet. Sometimes an old gravel pit marks the location of one of these

Drumlins are composed of unsorted materials deposited by a slowly moving ice sheet.

deposits, although not all gravel pits are the remains of such deposits.

The deposits of the glacial periods often took the form of mounds of material of different sizes and shapes. They were laid down in different ways. Some of these mounds are called *moraines;* there are terminal moraines and ground moraines. The terminal moraines were laid down in the form of low hills parallel to the end of the glacier. There is often an irregular series of such hills, with depressions between them. When the terminus of the ice sheet remained somewhat stationary for some time, a moraine was formed, the ice, as it melted, carrying forward and dropping its load of debris in a ridge.

Ground moraines consist of material which was dropped from the bottom of the ice sheet as it melted; such material was not necessarily piled up. Occasionally this material was built into small rounded hills, called *drumlins,* by ice that was nearly stagnant but moving just enough to elongate the hills in the direction of its movement. This material consists of anything that was pushed along under the ice or was frozen in it, from the finest clay to immense boulders, and is unsorted.

It is well to remember that material deposited by the ice sheets is a mixed, or unsorted, mass of debris—rocks, gravel, sand, and clay.

Streams flowing through a great ice sheet leave sorted deposits called eskers.

It is called *glacial till,* or drift. Any of the rocks which were scraped along the bedrock as the glacier moved are worn and flat on at least one side. In these ways the material differs from that laid down by the water from the ice sheets.

In a deposit laid down by water, the rocks are rounded, although in the case of deposits made by streams running through and under glaciers, the rocks may retain some of their ice-worn characteristics. In these water-laid deposits the heavy materials fall to the bottom, and the lighter materials remain on top. They are laid down in layers, or strata.

The deposits formed by water when it flows in streams over or through the ice sheets are called eskers and kames. The *eskers* are long ridges, evidently the old beds of streams which flowed through fissures or under glacial ice. In some instances eskers might be mistaken for old railroad beds. The material in them is formed in strata and is usually coarse sand and gravel. Eskers are not so common as might be supposed, for they were often leveled off by movements of the ice. *Kames* are small hills or ridges which somewhat resemble drumlins, except that the material is laid down in strata by streams which issued from the edge of the ice sheet. They may appear as one small hill or as a small group of hills.

Kames are composed of sorted material deposited by water at the edge of an ice sheet.

As the ice melted, a network of little streams formed at the edge of the ice sheet and spread a broad deposit of finer materials over many parts of the country. These deposits are called *outwash plains*.

When the ice sheet followed the valleys, they were often deepened. When the ice movement proceeded across the valleys, a leveling of valley walls and a filling in took place. Depressions were dug out, and mounds of debris were piled up. Often the deposits blocked the course of a stream, forcing it to find a new channel; and sometimes the deposits changed the direction in which the stream flowed. Notable examples of this are the changes made in some of the old tributaries of the St. Lawrence River, which were forced to flow southward instead of north and finally joined the headwaters of the Susquehanna and Mississippi rivers.

Glacial lakes were formed where valleys were blocked with debris or where the ground-moraine deposits were so irregular as to form basins. Glacial lakes formed in the latter way are found in northern Minnesota and Wisconsin. Many of these glacial lakes have disappeared in the United States and in Canada, owing to evaporation or to the lake being filled in by sediments. The largest of these lakes was ancient Lake Agassiz, which covered an area of a hundred thousand square miles southwest of Hudson Bay. It extended through eastern North Dakota, northern Minnesota, into Manitoba, and west into Saskatchewan. All that remains of it is the Lake of the Woods and Lake Winnipeg.

Thus we see the enormous changes which ice has made on Earth's surface through the ages and which are still going on today in a smaller way.

The teacher should bear in mind that, considering the great age of Earth, the work of the last Ice Age is comparatively recent, although it happened many thousands of years ago.

EXPERIENCE. *Evidences of glaciation.* Find out if the place where you live was covered by the last great ice sheet that spread over North America. It it was, you may find evidence of it in scratched rocks, huge boulders in unusual places, or fields covered with rocks which were deposited there as the ice melted. Such rocks were formerly part of the bedrock in some other place. Such deposits may vary a good deal in size and shape.

EXPERIENCE. *Bedrock.* Can you find some rock that appears to be bedrock? It lies under all parts of the land but often is covered with soil, small rocks, and other material. Bedrock that you can see is called an *outcrop.*

Wind as an Earth-changing Force. Like water, air is never still. It is in continuous circulation. This movement of the air plays a part in the changes that have gone on in the past history of Earth and that continue to go on today (p. 278). It should be borne in mind that the energy of the wind is derived from the energy of the sun.

The winds of Earth create most of the ocean waves, which in turn change the shore line of islands and continents (p. 94). Tidal, or seismic, waves, which are an exception, are produced by a disturbance of the ocean floor.

Wind Erodes by Deflation. Winds change the surface of Earth by blowing particles about from one place to another. This is called *deflation*. This goes on more rapidly in dry areas than in moist areas, owing to the absence of the protective covering of vegetation and hence to the greater quantity of dust and other small particles that are exposed to the wind. Depressions, especially on the plains where the climate is dry, may be blown out or enlarged until they reach considerable size. Anything that serves to loosen the soil, such as the trampling of animals or the cracking and scaling of the soil as water dries up, makes

This smooth, almost perpendicular bank of loess south of Vicksburg, Mississippi, shows that it was cut by modern road-building machinery. It also shows that the sharp corners and flat sides of the minute particles of which the loess is composed permit it to resist erosion and retain a perpendicular position. (G.S. Craig.)

it possible for wind to remove it. This soil could be carried to some other place and deposited.

Dust, volcanic ash, and fine sand may be blown great distances. In 1934 a vast cloud of dust from the western United States drifted eastward far beyond the Atlantic coast line. Dust from the Sahara Desert has been dropped in France and Italy and even carried to England. Ships far at sea have experienced falls of dust.

Great deposits of dust may be found on our Earth at places where the winds regularly slacken. This material is called *loess* (pronounced "löss" or "less") and is deposited in places where only the wind could have carried it. Owing to the kinds of material of which loess is composed and to its sharp corners, it is thought that it was produced by mechanical weathering. These sharp corners permit the particles to fit together closely when deposited and enable it to stand in almost vertical walls when cut by streams or roadways.

The use of a powerful microscope shows that loess is a mixture of clay particles and of such minerals as mica, quartz, and feldspar.

It makes exceptionally fertile soil where water is available for crops. This material is sometimes deposited over large areas and in beds several hundred feet thick. In China such beds occur, blown there from the arid lands to the west. They furnish the sediments which give the Hwang Ho (Yellow River) its name. In the Mississippi Valley loess beds occur, but they are not so deep as those in China. In a few cases sedimentary rocks have been found which show the characteristics of loess that has been worked on by water.

Sometimes sand is blown about to form *dunes*, which may migrate, at times overwhelming forests, farms, and even villages. The dunes move in the direction of the prevailing winds. They are rounded, sometimes crescent-shaped, and are marked by ripple marks and cross-bedding. These ripple marks are so called because of their resemblance to the marks made by water in the sand on beaches. The cross-bedding is due to slight changes in the direction of the wind, which cause the sand to be blown in slightly different directions.

Ancient dunes which have been consolidated into rock are found in many places. They have many of the characteristics of our modern dunes.

Man has sought to control the movements of dunes by planting shrubs, grasses, and other plants that are adapted to growing in sandy soils. He has been successful in some localities. The importance of wind as an agent in removing material loosened by other means and thus exposing new surfaces to atmospheric attack should not be overlooked.

EXPERIENCE. *To show that wind carries soil.* Have the children notice the dirt blown about by a wind. Dirt from the playground may accumulate in airways and in protected corners, and visibility may be cut down considerably. Whirlwinds, and the dust they stir up on relatively quiet days, will be of interest.

Sand dunes are of many shapes and sizes, depending on local conditions, such as material avail-able, the wind, and the objects in the area. Ripple marks, a sloping windward side, a crest, and a steep slope on the lee side are features that are often seen. (Bristol, from Three Lions, N.Y.C.)

EXPERIENCE. *There is dust in the air.* On ordinary, quiet days allow children to have duties in connection with keeping the room clean. Permit them to dust some of the furniture or books. Where does the dust come from? How did it get into the room? Is it necessary to dust more than once a day?

EXPERIENCE. *Wind-blown soil does damage.* In areas of great drought, dirt is apt to be blown about, covering up fence posts, roads, ditches, and even low farm buildings. The damage this does to farm land cannot be estimated. A discussion of ways to combat this would be valuable.

EXPERIENCE. *The effect of sand on trees and shrubs.* Have you ever seen shrubs or trees that have been nearly covered by soil or sand and then left uncovered as the sand moved on? Their lower branches were dead and only those above the sand were growing. The lower ones had been cut off from air and sunlight.

EXPERIENCE. *The control of sandy soil.* Notice any area where measures have been taken to keep soil from being blown away. Grass adapted to holding sand in place is often found, and farmers often plant windbreaks, broad belts of trees and grass. They protect the soil from the wind and at the same time conserve moisture. Can any other measures be named to keep sand or soil from being blown about?

EXPERIENCE. *Wind erosion.* Perhaps you live near the coast or elsewhere where you can observe the way in which sand is being drifted over the land by the wind. This should be watched from year to year. Children might select a spot to watch and might place stakes in various places to measure by.

EXPERIENCE. *Features of wind erosion.* If you are near a desert watch for such features as depressions with vegetation among dunes; places from which wind has blown away every particle of loose soil or rock and where the underlying rock has become polished; places were the wind has blown away all the finer particles, leaving a surface covered only with pieces of rock. Can you find any other features that occur only in desert regions?

Wind Abrasion. Wind changes the surface of Earth by blowing rock particles against rock surfaces. This process is called *abrasion.* This has a definite wearing-down effect, regardless of the size of the particles. The cutting power of the sharp-edged particles formed in arid regions, where mechanical weathering predominates, is considerable. Both the grains of sand which are blown about by the wind and whatever they strike are worn. Man applies this principle when he uses the sandblast to clean stone buildings. This action of the wind is especially evident in the desert, where there are few plant roots and little moisture to hold the soil in place, with the result that there is an abundance of loose soil. There cliffs are undercut, and slender columns topped by caps slightly larger are found. In such regions bits of glass may be found that are frosted in appearance because they have been worn by windblown sand. The

same thing often happens near the seashore, except that the glass and sand there are moved, for the most part, by water. Most sand is made of quartz, and it is very hard and sometimes sharp; hence it is an excellent abrasive. Rock surfaces may be polished and grooved by wind-driven sand. Pebbles also are shaped, smoothed, and sometimes highly polished by being blown about.

EXPERIENCE. *Wind-blown sand has a cutting force.* Young children learn a great deal through their senses. They can feel the force of the wind against their faces and stinging particles of sand which pelt their skin when they are playing out of doors. Even the smallest particle can be very painful driven against one's face or hands by a strong wind. The sharpness of some sand particles is attested by the pain they cause if lodged in an eye.

EXPERIENCE. *Wind abrasion around us.* Sometimes one finds glass that has been worn by sand being blown against it. The glass may no longer be transparent—but rather frosty looking. It may also have lost its sharp edges. Such glass can sometimes be found on the desert.

The Orientation of Children to Earth's Landscape

In this chapter we have discussed some of the ways in which the surface of Earth has been changed. The present landscape is the result of such forces as have been described. A teacher can make use of the landscape in the community to orient children to these processes. It would be well for children at various times in their elementary school experience to gain an appreciation that the landscape is changing every day even though the

changes may seem very small. Over a period of time they may be great.

From a developmental point of view there are some experiences that most assuredly have value for young children and others that have value when used with older children. The experiences that follow are illustrative of the kinds of experiences that children and a teacher may have in a community.

EXPERIENCE. *Special features of the landscape.* It would be well for young children to gain an early orientation to the environment. The windows of the school may be used. The teacher may refer to things that happen at different places, as, for instance, "There is a cloud over Old Baldy this morning" or "You can see far today" or "Did any of you notice how muddy the river has become after all this rain? Why is this?" Rivers of the region may be mentioned by name.

Later, map-making may be undertaken. With younger children the maps may only involve the corridors and rooms of the school or the way home, but later maps involving many features of the landscape can be made to include such things as hills, rivers, and so on.

Teachers can help to build up an awareness that features of the landscape have been formed by forces and events by asking children "How would you explain it?" or "How do you think the valley was made?" It is well to get children to think in terms of possible explanations. They should be encouraged to think in terms of long periods of time.

In many parts of the world there are eye-arresting scenic features such as plateaus or fantastic weathering. For such scenic features there is likely to be a local name. Use this name with the children frequently.

The trip between the school and the home should be made instructive for children, whether they walk or ride in the school bus, and even if the classroom teacher is not with them. Have them report on what they observe along the way, and in discussions particularly emphasize changes or variations in the landscape.

With the older children it would be well to go into the origin of special features in the locality. Have them check their own ideas with the ideas of specialists through the use of reliable books.

In considering the locality it would be well to enlarge the region for study to include special features sometimes visited by children with their parents such as caves, petrified forests, lakes, mountains, the seashore, and so on.

EXPERIENCE. *The relation of features of the landscape to the economic development in the region.* If the windows of the classroom should not provide a good view of the locality, arrange to walk with the children to a suitable place for a look over the region. The same place can be used again and again.

Features of the landscape should be considered in connection with the social, historical, and economic events in the neighborhood (Chapter 6); for instance, railroads and highways following the streams, and cities located along natural trade routes.

EXPERIENCE. *Using current events.* Earth's surface is constantly changing. Events are announced over television and radio that indicate changes in various parts of the world. It may be a volcanic eruption, an earthquake, a landslide, a new island formed. These events can be utilized to indicate that there are forces operating on Earth today.

EXPERIENCE. *Making maps or models of the region.* Maps of the region can be made with modeling clay or plaster of Paris. These maps can show the location of mountains and the drainage pattern of the region.

EXPERIENCE. *Using photographs taken from planes, rockets, or satellites.* Through the newspapers and magazines there are available to children photographs taken from high altitudes. Older children are nearly always interested in such photographs. One feature of the high-altitude photographs is that they show Earth as a globe. See if the children can locate their own locality on the map. The bulletin board can be utilized in much of this work.

CHAPTER 10

Earth History As Revealed in the Rocks

This chapter is offered as source material to show that Earth has changed continuously over an extremely long period of time. This material may also provide a basis for a better understanding of the geographical region in which a teacher is working. It is not intended for teachers to memorize the material in this chapter, nor is it necessary to teach it to children in chronological order. The names of the eras and epochs, the names of the mountain-building times, the names of the rock systems and formations, and the names of the plants and animals that have come and gone are not necessary to a child's understanding of geologic history.

The basic working conceptions of science which are especially illustrated in the study of Earth history are *change* and *time*. These vital and universal conceptions should be recognized by the teacher on all levels as patterns or forms about which the instruction should be organized. The child's orientation to his universe should become more intelligent as a result of the teacher's having recognized these conceptions as direction posts for the instruction in this area. Thus, by directing the instruction toward the basic working conceptions of modern science, the teacher will avoid becoming lost in small content and busywork.

The dramatic and challenging aspects of these themes are self-evident. (See Chapter 4 for a development of the concepts of space, time and change, and Chapter 6 for teaching and learning as it relates to the community.)

There is no escape from the indications of Earth's great age and the changes that have taken place on it. Mountains, rivers, ice sheets, and seas have come and gone, and newspapers frequently report the discoveries of remains of ancient man, their handiwork, and their ways of living. Rarely, a report is made of the finding of a plant or animal thought to have become extinct ages ago; but geologic history is still being made. Newspapers may also report that thousands of tons of rock have fallen where the water rushes over the precipice at Niagara Falls. People should be reassured to find that this is a normal wearing away of rock at that place and that all safety precautions were being taken at the time. It is recalled that several such rockfalls have occurred during historic times. It has been possible to reconstruct the history of the falls back to the time when they began. A cone of lava and cinders have been built up in the middle of a field in Mexico within very recent times. This is the volcano, Parícutin. With a little encouragement, older children will be eager to watch for pictures and accounts of such events. Thus they can be made aware of some of the processes that have been going on through the ages. Geologic history is being made today.

It is important that children grow in their understanding that Earth and the living things upon it have not always been as they are today. Many children are challenged by this fact. The size and the many different kinds of dinosaurs fascinate them. The unusual forests that formed the coal we use today are equally interesting to them. There were changes in the elevation of Earth's surface in ages past, with resulting changes in temperature and moisture. There was variety and interdependence among living things; each needing heat, nutrients, and moisture for life—just as organisms are today.

As children develop it is desirable to help them grow in their understanding of the concepts of time and change (pp. 93–95). Even young children can understand that the events of today soon become those of yesterday. Just as things happened yesterday, last week, last month, or last year, so there are events that took place thousands and millions of years ago. As one child said, "Not one of her great-great-great-grandparents as far back as there were any ever saw those mountains, because they had been worn away."

The concept of time may be approached in many ways. Children often like to talk about things they can remember and how long ago it happened. They are often quite conscious of other children being older than they, even if the age difference is slight. Their parents and other adults seem very old to them. The age of their pets, their homes, their trees, and other things may be compared with their own age. A discussion of all the events taking place in just one day, week, or year may help them to realize how long a year is. Recurring events such as breakfast, bedtime, Sunday with its different routine from other days of the week, birthdays, or Christmas may serve as milestones in measuring time which young children will grow to understand. Many young children are familiar with the words "thousands" and "millions," and sense that both words mean a great, great many.

This chapter mentions a few of the more important events or milestones in Earth history. It will help a teacher to understand how Earth became what it was when man found it and as it is today. Man is a comparative newcomer, and yet he too has his place in Earth's history —a very important place. He is unique because he has the ability to learn about his environment and to use it for better or worse, as his knowledge and judgment grow.

How Geologists Learn about the Ancient Earth

The rocks present in any region tell a story of the past—how they were formed, their age, and sometimes even the climate and the kinds of plants and animals living at the time when they were formed. By studying the rocks we can learn a great deal about Earth's past, for in the rocks we find evidence of events which occurred in the distant past. Scratches on bedrock may give us information concern-

ing an ice sheet which covered a great region. Beds of rocks which were formed in horizontal layers, but which were later twisted and bent, show forces that were at work beneath the surface of Earth millions of years ago.

Geologists can tell from the structure and composition of rocks how they were formed. The relative age of rocks may be ascertained by considering (1) the transformation of radioactive materials; (2) the rate of deposition to-day compared with the entire thickness of sedimentary rocks; (3) the kind of fossils found in sedimentary rocks; (4) the position of rocks in Earth's crust. Each of these checked against the others gives fairly reliable conclusions as to the relative age of various beds of rock (pp. 280–283).

The records of plants and animals in the sedimentary rocks give us much information concerning Earth at the time these plants and animals lived. Such records are called *fossils*. There are four different kinds of fossils: (1) preserved bodies or parts of bodies of plants and animals; (2) casts of plants and animals; (3) prints made by parts of plants and animals; (4) petrified remains of plants and animals. We should think of fossils as records of something more than living things, for the very fact that a given plant or animal lived and died constitutes an event in geological history.

Most of the bodies of plants and animals that have lived on Earth have decomposed quickly after death. A few have been preserved by various agencies. Some plants and animals have been preserved by the dry air of deserts and of certain caves. Mammoths and rhinoceroses have been found buried in the ice of Siberia and elsewhere.

Sometimes animals meet with accidents in which they are quickly entombed in a mass of material that protects their bodies from decay. Tar, quicksand, substances which later harden into amber, and other materials may act in this way. Animal bodies are preserved more frequently in shallow seas and swamps than on dry land. They are often quickly covered with mud and sand and thus escape the forces of disintegration present on the land.

Many times in the past, portions of the continents have been worn down and slowly submerged beneath shallow continental seas. At times the marine waters flooded the region now occupied by the Rocky and Appalachian

This is a well-preserved fossil skeleton of a fishlike reptile, ichthyosaur. The shape of the body was outlined by the ca that remained. (The American Museum of Natural History.)

mountain systems and parts of the interior basin of the continents. Into such seas came many forms of marine life, which lived and died in vast multitudes, leaving their shells to be buried in sand and mud and to be cemented and consolidated into rock. The deposits made by all except the earliest continental seas are rich in fossils. These same processes of fossil-making are doubtlessly going on today in lakes, marshes, and along the

The body of this animal, a trilobite, was dissolved by groundw and replaced by minerals (in solution) which hardened. The cast was formed. Sometimes minerals do not replace the b Then only a mold or impression is left. (William Eberly.)

submerged outer parts of the continents, known as the continental shelves.

When covered with sediment, the hard parts of a plant or animal may leave a cast. Groundwater may dissolve the hard parts of the organism, leaving a hollow space, or mold, in the surrounding sediment; and if the space is then filled by minerals which harden, a cast results. The cast will resemble the outside of the organism but not the inner parts.

As might be expected, animals which lack hard parts, such as jellyfish, worms, and plants without hard parts, do not leave such well-made records in the rocks as animals with hard structures, such as skeletons and shells, and plants with woody parts. However, perfect prints of many such organisms have been found. These are produced by a process called carbonization, in which chemical changes take place when the plant or animal is covered so the air cannot reach it. Gradually, parts of the plant or animal are changed chemically into such products as carbon dioxide, water, and marsh gas. As these products escape, a concentration of carbon is left which forms the outline and sometimes shows details like veins in a leaf or scales on a fish.

When we walk in soft mud, sand, or snow, we leave footprints. Anyone trained to interpret them could tell quite a number of things about the kind of creature that had passed by. Indians were able to know a great many things about the men and animals that passed through the woods by studying this kind of evidence. So today there are, in various parts of our Earth, footprints and body and tail marks which were left by animals in the soft mud or sand millions of years ago and which later were covered over and became hard. Such things as ripple marks, mud cracks, and raindrop imprints have also been preserved in the same way. Thus preserved, these fossils are invaluable guides to the past.

Petrified fossils are frequently brought into the classroom as treasures that some member of the family has collected on his travels. The

Dinosaur tracks in Neskla Nizzadi Canyon, Arizona. (Three Lions, N.Y.C.)

original structure of the plant or animal has been replaced, particle by particle, with mineral matter in such a way that it is faithfully duplicated. A log, for instance, may have been buried in a landslide of sand or by volcanic ash that later is covered with water. As the log's woody structure is slowly removed, the tissues are replaced, particle by particle, with silica, calcite, pyrite, or some other mineral. They are frequently colored by iron and various other minerals dissolved in the ground-water. Petrified trees in the Petrified Forest National Monument, near Winslow, Arizona, and in many other places even show

Petrified logs, the remains of ancient trees, buried and later uncovered by erosion. Petrified Forest National Monument, Arizona. (Josef Muench.)

details of cell structure, annual rings, or bark.

Children have little difficulty in learning how fossils were formed and in understanding that they may be used in deciphering the history of our Earth. Their own play with snow, sand, and clay prints may be utilized in developing the concepts involved.

EXPERIENCE. *To show how imprints are made.* Mix a plaster-of-Paris paste and spread it out on a flat surface. Press shells, leaves, or other objects into it. When the plaster hardens, the print is left. In this way some fossil prints were made in mud.

EXPERIENCE. *Where would fossils be found?* If you live in a region where there are sedimentary rocks, you may be able to find fossils in abundance. Fossils may also be found in some metamorphic rocks. You will never find them in igneous rocks, since all such rocks were once molten.

The Meaning of a Geologic Timetable

A geologic timetable is included here in order to give a bird's-eye view of the past history of Earth and its living organisms as it is exhibited in the rocks, and to show the progression of events. It is intended to be a source of reference for the teacher, not to be memorized. Such vast amounts of time are involved in the development of living things upon Earth that man's imagination is challenged to the utmost.

In order to help us in this particular, the history of Earth has been divided into eons, these divided into eras, the eras into periods, and the periods into epochs. Appropriate names have been given to each of these divisions. The names of the eons and eras end with *zoic,* which comes from the Greek word *zoe,* meaning "life." Thus we have them named for the kind of life that was typical of the various times; namely, in the two eons, *Cryptozoic* means "concealed life;" *Phanerozoic* means "visible life," and the words *recent, medieval,* and *ancient* describe life in the eras.

The names of the periods, with some exceptions, come from the names of the places where rocks of that time in Earth history were either first found and recognized or are especially well exposed. For instance, the Jurassic period was named for the Jura Mountains between France and Switzerland, and the Cambrian period was named for Cambria, the Latin name for Wales.

These eons, eras, periods, and epochs are neither haphazard nor equal divisions of time, but mark the beginning and close of outstanding events in Earth history. They are based on the development of living things and on physical events in Earth history, as found in the rocks all over the world. They are also based on the principle that if the rocks are undisturbed the oldest will be on the bottom and the youngest on top. A great deal of study must take place before a place can be given to rocks and their fossils in the timetable of Earth history.

Geologic *revolutions* are times of tremendous readjustment in Earth's crust—a readjustment which goes on very, very slowly, however, and which may take millions of years. In a general way, these revolutions mark the end of the eras. For instance, the Appalachian revolution took place toward the end of the Paleozoic era. The rocks identified as having been formed during an era are often spoken of as a group, as the Paleozoic group.

Geologic *disturbances* are of less magnitude han revolutions. They, too, are gradual and low readjustments of Earth's crust. They letermine the length of the periods in the imetable. The rocks of each period are poken of as systems, as the Permian system.

Periods are composed of epochs, a shorter ime during which rocks called a series are ormed, as the Upper Jurassic series. Smaller livisions of time have been made and the rocks formed then have been given such names s formations and members of formations, all of which have characteristics which distin- guish them from rocks formed at other times.

The geologic timetable has been changed ince it was first conceived, as new knowledge vas acquired, and may be changed again for he same reason. Knowledge gained from new exploration has been added that gained rom the use of radioactivity in dating rocks.

Throughout the long history of Earth, liastrophic movements, or elevations and sub- idences of Earth's crust, have been going on (p. 284). Water, wind, heat, and cold have been present on Earth for many mil- lions of years. The timetable shows that there have been cycles of land emergence, or uplifts, when continents changed their shapes; other cycles of erosion and sinking, when seas slowly invaded vast sections of the continents, only to leave their sediments as the land rose again. Icecaps crept over some parts of the land on at least four different occasions. All these events had their effects on the climate and hence on the life of those eras. The timetable shows at a glance that there have been periods when certain types of living organisms were in the ascendancy. The zigzag lines found in the column marked "Mountain-making Times" indicate in a general way the duration and intensity of the outstanding rock movements in North America.

The time during which Earth and its oc- cupants have been intelligently studied is ex- tremely short; yet the amount of knowledge that has already accumulated and the under- standing and elimination of fear and supersti- tion that have resulted is considerable.

Life Begins on Earth— The Cryptozoic Eon

We have no record of how life began. The evidence shows, however, that the first life was very simple and very small and that it began on Earth a long time ago. It may have been smaller than anything that we can see through the microscope.

The universe is composed of living and non- living things. Living things are dependent on nonliving things. Living matter is made up chiefly of carbon, hydrogen, oxygen, nitrogen, sulfur, sodium, calcium, iron, and phosphorus, together with small amounts of many other elements (p. 376), and is dependent on such things as light, water, and heat. In general, living organisms are very sensitive to slight changes in environment. They require a narrow range of temperature, a moderate supply of light, and supplies of the elements listed above in the form of food. Living or- ganisms also require a machinery to permit the suitable circulation of food and waste material.

Unless the chemistry of living organisms in the Cryptozoic eon was different from what it is now, deductions may be made concerning early forms of life. Many of these have been verified in laboratories. Organic substances such as urea and amino acids have been made

EVENTS IN THE EARTH HISTORY OF NORTH AMERICA[1]

Eras	Periods and Epochs with Dates	Changes in Climate, Plants, Animals	Mountain-making Times	Ages Plants	Ages Animals
PHANEROZOIC EON — **CENOZOIC, OR RECENT-LIFE, ERA** (Has lasted 63 Million Years)	**Quaternary Period (1 Million Years)** RECENT EPOCH 11,000	Man becomes dominant	Cascadian revolution	Age of Modern Seed Plants (angiosperms)	Age of Man
	PLEISTOCENE, OR GLACIAL, EPOCH ½ to 2 m[2]	Social life begins among men — Large mammals become extinct — Four advances of great ice sheet, with long interglacial periods			
	Tertiary Period (Lasted 62 Million Years) PLIOCENE EPOCH 13 ± 1 m	Transition of man's remote ancestors into man — Transition stage of other modern mammals — Elevation of land; cooling of climate			Age of Mammals
	MIOCENE EPOCH 25 ± 1 m	Mammals continue development — Grasses widespread — Climate more arid and mild			
	OLIGOCENE EPOCH 36 ± 2 m	Modernized mammals prevail — Spread of modernized types of life — Last of archaic mammals			
	EOCENE EPOCH 58 ± 2 m	Spread of modernized mammals — Rise of modern types of birds — Spread of grasses and cereals — Climate becoming warmer			
	PALEOCENE EPOCH 63 ± 2 m	Archaic mammals spread — Valley glaciers and lower temperatures	Laramide revolution		
MESOZOIC, OR MEDIEVAL-LIFE, ERA (Lasted 167 Million Years)	CRETACEOUS PERIOD 135 ± 5 m	Extinction of toothed birds, pterodactyls, and dinosaurs — Spread of flowering plants and modern insects — Last of ammonites — Rise of archaic mammals — Last great spread of seas	Nevadan revolution	Age of Medieval Seed Plants (Continued) (gymnosperms)	Age of Reptiles and Ammonites
	JURASSIC PERIOD 181 ± 5 m	Toothed birds appear; pterodactyls spread — Dinosaurs become common — Ammonites reach greatest development — Climate mild — First mammals appear	Palisade disturbance		
	TRIASSIC PERIOD 230 ± 10 m	Reptiles are dominant; dinosaurs and pterodactyls appear — Cycads and conifers spread — Climate arid and cool			

[1] Adapted by permission from Charles Schuchert and C. O. Dunbar, *Historical Geology*. John Wiley & Sons, Inc., New York, 1933, pp. 64 and 65. Figures are taken from J. L. Kulp, "Geologic Time Scale," *Science*, Vol. 133, No. 3459, 1961, pp. 1105–1114.

[2] The abbreviation "m" stands for "million years." The dates are years *before* the present.

EVENTS IN THE EARTH HISTORY OF NORTH AMERICA *(Continued)*

Eras	Periods and Epochs with Dates	Changes in Climate, Plants, Animals	Mountain-making Times	Ages Plants	Ages Animals
PHANEROZOIC EON — PALEOZOIC, OR ANCIENT-LIFE, ERA (Lasted 370 Million Years)	PERMIAN PERIOD 280 ± 10 m	Many ancient plants and marine animals die out / Reptiles become more numerous; amphibians decline / General rise of land; colder, more arid climate	Appalachian revolution	Age of Medieval Seed Plants	Age of Amphibians
	PENNSYLVANIAN PERIOD 310 ± 10 m	Earliest known reptiles appear / Largest insects of all time / Spore-producing plants dominant / Greatest coal beds formed / Warm humid climate—arid locally	Repeated	Age of Spore-Bearing Plants	Age of Amphibians
	MISSISSIPPIAN PERIOD 345 ± 10 m	Abundance of shell-crushing sharks / Crinoids flourish and then become less numerous / Trilobites almost extinct / Shifting seas and local dry areas; coal swamps	Disturbances	Age of Spore-Bearing Plants	Age of Fishes
	DEVONIAN PERIOD 405 ± 10 m	Amphibians appear / Fish and brachiopods numerous / Ammonites appear / First forests appear	Acadian disturbance	Age of Spore-Bearing Plants	Age of Fishes
	SILURIAN PERIOD 425 ± 10 m	Land plants appear / First air-breathing invertebrates (scorpions) / Climate mild; north half of continent arid / Marine animals are dominant; corals widespread / Deposits of salt, gypsum, and iron	Taconic disturbance	Age of Marine Plants	Age of Marine Invertebrates
	ORDOVICIAN PERIOD 500 ± 10 m	Rise of fresh-water fish and earliest vertebrates / Spread of shell-bearing sea animals / Trilobites reach greatest development / Sixty per cent of North America under water	Taconic disturbance	Age of Marine Plants	Age of Marine Invertebrates
	CAMBRIAN PERIOD 600 ± 50 m	Trilobites and brachiopods are abundant / Shell-bearing sea animals (snails, etc.) appear / Large variety of invertebrate animals in seas / Mild climate / Long period of erosion	Vermont disturbance	Age of Marine Plants	Age of Marine Invertebrates
CRYPTOZOIC EON	PRECAMBRIAN PERIOD 4500–5000 m	Living things, probably small and soft-tissued / An early and late glacial period / Oldest known life, probably lime-secreting algae / Gold, silver, copper, nickel, uranium, cobalt, platinum, and iron deposits / Volcanic activity / Sediments formed; Earth history indistinct / Oldest meteorites, about 4500 million years / Development of Earth and other planets	Killarney revolution / Algoman revolution / Laurentian revolution		

from inorganic substances such as were present on Earth even before there was an atmosphere as we know it. Much is being learned about the electrical forces between the particles that make up matter (p. 375). These are steps toward a larger body of information in this area.

The Cryptozoic Eon. The division of geologic time by the American Commission on Nomenclature at the beginning of the Cambrian period in the Paleozoic era is based on the fossil record. There is an abundance of fossils in the Cambrian rocks, but most of them are conspicuously absent before that time.

The first large division, the Cryptozoic eon, or Precambrian time, as it is often called, covers most of geologic time. It is that vast length of time *before* the Cambrian period, reaching back about 4.5 or 5 billion years.

Ancient rocks are found in many places, but the relative absence of a fossil record makes the correlation of rock ages on the basis of radioactive dating the most reliable.

With the advent of radioactive dating of rocks, it has seemed wise to abandon the effort to separate the Cryptozoic eon into well-defined eras until enough dates can be obtained to make a more comprehensive correlation than can now be made. However, it is correct to speak of rocks as belonging to early, middle, or late Cryptozoic or Precambrian time.

Rocks with an age of 3500 million years have been found in South Africa. Certain meteorites have an age of 4500 million years. Such figures are checked in every possible way. Nowhere has any rock been found that can be identified as rock of the original Earth-nucleus.

Early Fossils. Fossils are not readily found in any Precambrian rock. Life in the Cambrian period seems relatively simple compared to the life of later periods, yet living things must have been developing for a very long period of time to have reached even that simplicity of form. Precambrian forms probably had few hard parts, and therefore could not retain their identity for long. Many Precambrian rocks are igneous rocks represented by ancient granite batholiths intruded into sediments. These would contain no fossils. Both the igneous rocks and the sedimentary rocks of that time have been twisted and metamorphosed so that fossils, were they ever there, cannot be recognized. However, spots are found in a few rocks that may be the remains of bacteria and lime-secreting algae. Graphite is present in other rocks, which may mean that plant life and an atmosphere existed; yet some think the graphite has an inorganic origin due to chemical reactions in the ancient rocks. In some of these rocks are indications of an atmosphere, such as ripple marks, mud cracks, and other markings.

Fossils have recently been found in the Ediacara Hills of South Australia resting well below the oldest Cambrian rocks, which seem to belong to the late Precambrian and are related to some fossils found in England and South Africa. The strata in which they were found is composed of ancient sediments that have been undisturbed. They contain no radioactive elements, and therefore cannot be dated in that way. Weathering and erosion had exposed these fossils, consisting of molds and casts of numerous jellyfish, soft corals, segmented worms with strong head shields, which may possibly have been related to the trilobites that came later, and several other water-dwelling animals, some with spicules— needle-like growths of calcium carbonate. It seems certain that efforts in the coming years will reveal a great body of information concerning life in past ages.

Ancient Rocks. In North America, ancient igneous rocks of the Precambrian can be observed, because they occur under some deeply eroded mountains. Examples of these are to be found in the Adirondack Mountains of

...aces where the oldest rocks known—those of the Precambrian— ...bear on the surface. They are shown in black.

feet of sediments were laid down on more ancient rock as the area sank. In many places the sediments reached a depth of 35,000 feet. In general, these ancient sedimentary rocks have not been deformed to any extent, but in places they have been greatly tilted. They are to be seen in Glacier National Park, Montana, and in Jasper National Park, Alberta. After having been uplifted, they have been carved by weathering and erosion into the most impressive scenery.

In a number of regions studied it is clear that great events occurred. Great and prolonged periods of erosion when the surface became worn down to a peneplain were followed by long periods of sedimentation, as evidenced by two such breaks in the rocks toward the bottom of the Grand Canyon of the Colorado. Ancient mountain systems were worn down until only roots were left. In Canada, the Laurentian disturbance occurred early and was followed by the Algoman revolution and, toward the end of the Precambrian, by the Killarney revolution. There were two periods of glaciation, one midway and the other near the close of the Precambrian.

Economic Deposits. Precambrian rocks have yielded prodigious amounts of minerals. Some of these minerals and the areas where they are found are iron ore from the Lake Superior region, Michigan, and northern Quebec; copper from northern Michigan, eastern Ontario, western Quebec, Manitoba, and Saskatchewan; nickel from eastern Ontario and Manitoba; gold from eastern Ontario and the Black Hills of South Dakota; uranium from northwestern Canada around the Bear Lake district and Lake Athabasca; platinum, cobalt, and silver from Canada; and lead and zinc from British Columbia, New Jersey, and Idaho.

It is difficult for anyone to imagine the vast reaches of time; the slow, relentless forces in-

New York, in the northern parts of Minnesota, Wisconsin, and Michigan, and in parts of the Appalachian and Rocky Mountains. They are exposed in the bottom of the Grand Canyon of the Colorado and in numerous smaller areas and are partly uncovered in the great Canadian Shield. In fact, they are exposed as a *shield area* on every continent where they tend to remain relatively flat, above sea level, and rigid, and nearby areas became geosynclines or basins of some kind. Yet on the whole, their exposure is limited to perhaps one fifth of the land surface of Earth, the rest being covered by younger formations. The shields are the result of long and intermittent intrusions of molten rock. It is certain that these areas were never one big lake of this material.

During the earlier part of the Precambrian there was a great trough, or geosyncline, and probably several smaller ones, in what is now the Rocky Mountain area, extending from Montana, Wyoming, and Idaho through British Columbia and Alberta. Thousands of

volved in the uplifts; the countless intrusions of molten rock; the mountain-building times, now here, now there; the unremitting wearing down and deposition of Earth materials; the long sinking of land in the geosynclines and the consequent invasions of the seas and the filling in with sediments from some higher region; the intricate chemical changes within rocks; and the vast concentration of minerals that went on during that eon of time.

Significant Events of the Cryptozoic Eon. The entire geologic history of Earth up to the

beginning of the Paleozoic era is spoken of as the Cryptozoic eon, or Precambrian time.

Rocks of this eon are exposed in various places, but none have been found of the original surface of Earth.

This was a tremendously long period of time, with long periods of mountain-building and long periods of wearing down and sedimentation. Great deposits of ore were formed during this eon. Two periods of glaciation have been recognized. A few fossils of living things have been found in rocks of the late Cryptozoic eon.

The Beginning of an Abundant Fossil Record— The Phanerozoic Eon—The Paleozoic Era

It was long thought that the rocks of the Paleozoic era contained the first evidences of living things; now, however, fossils have been found in more ancient rocks, and indirect evidences of life have been found in still older rocks. It is in the rocks of the Paleozoic era, however, that the first abundant supply of fossils, representing all the major invertebrate groups (pp. 518–520), is found. Fortunately, over large areas of North America, many of these rocks were comparatively undisturbed by the folding and mountain-making movements which affected the rocks of earlier eras. This makes of these areas grounds of happy hunting for those who wish to study the rocks and life of this era.

Through the long ages large parts of the North American continent have tended to remain elevated, while other sections have tended to sink, letting in the marine waters, and then to rise again, sometimes to considerable heights. Throughout Earth history, the sea has repeatedly invaded the principal geosynclines, or troughs, remaining for millions of years at a time, so that vast quantities of sediment were deposited.

During the estimated 300 to 400 million years of the Paleozoic era, these depressed areas varied greatly in size, at times being almost absent, at other times stretching over at least one half of the continent.

This map shows how the North American continent was floo in early Cambrian times, many millions of years ago. The tro in the west is called the Cordilleran geosyncline and the one the east is the Appalachian geosyncline.

Water Life in the Cambrian Period. In the early part of the Paleozoic era there were two large inundations, one in the east and one in the west; the one in the west later spread over a portion of the Great Plains. These shallow seas swarmed with living things, among them being gastropods, or snails, worms, coral-like animals called archaeocyathids, brachiopods, and trilobites. There were many soft-bodied forms, as shown in the early Cambrian Burgess shale near Field, British Columbia. Trilobites and brachiopods are considered the dominant creatures of this time; and throughout the ages when they existed, they presented many variations. The trilobites ranged in length from a fraction of an inch to about twenty-seven and one-half inches. The shell on top, which covered head and body, was hard. Some were slow-crawling creatures, while others were able to move faster. Most were well equipped with eyes, but some were blind.

Lime-secreting algae existed throughout the period, and spores and plant tissues from the middle Cambrian have been reported from Siberia. Lichens may have existed, and there seems little doubt that there was an abundance of water plants having soft stems. The moderate mountain-making in Eastern North America is known as the Vermont disturbance.

Vertebrates Appear—The Ordovician Period. During the next interval of time the North American continent probably underwent its greatest inundation. Some geologists say that half of it was covered by seas; others say that considerably more than half was under water. At any rate, it was a period of widespread limestone deposition of great thickness. The greatest oil and gas deposits are found in the strata of this period. The uniform climate of the period and the great expanses of the shallow inland seas made the period especially conducive to the development of plant and animal life. In fact, the number of species of fauna was twice that of the preceding Cambrian period in North America.

Invertebrates (animals without backbones) of the last era, with a few exceptions, still flourished in the salt waters, and to these swarms of life were added graptolites, true corals, clams, bryozoans, crinoids, or sea lilies, protozoa, and sponges. Trilobites reached their greatest development. Lime-secreting seaweeds constitute the most common plant fossils of this period.

There is no proved record of either land plants or land animals at this time. However, an outstanding event of the time was the appearance of a vertebrate (an animal with a backbone); its importance lies in the fact that it was the forerunner of the vast hordes of vertebrates which were to follow. It is believed to have been a fishlike inhabitant of fresh water.

The marine waters at length gradually withdrew, and a new local uplift took place, the Taconic uplift, extending from Newfoundland through the eastern provinces of Canada, nearly to Alabama.

Air-breathing Animals Appear—The Silurian Period. In this period air-breathing animals appeared. They were scorpions, much like those of today. Primitive fresh-water fish inhabited the streams. Trilobites and graptolites were declining; but corals, brachiopods, and eurypterids, or sea scorpions, were much more abundant than before. Fossils of the first land plants have been found in England and Australia. The plants were small but bore a relationship to those which followed later. Soft algae and fungi probably flourished in spots.

During the first part of the period sandstones and conglomerate deposits were characteristic; then the sea again placed about two fifths of the continent under water, and the third great period of limestone deposition took place. During this time reef-building corals flourished as far north as the arctic. This was followed by a long period with desert conditions. An inland sea in the Great Lakes region finally dried up, leaving enormous beds of salt and gypsum. In eastern North America there was considerable volcanic activity during the period, the lava and ash in some areas showing a thickness of 4000 feet; in others, 10,000 feet. The Caledonian Mountains, a ridge thought to have extended in an arc from northern Greenland to Europe, was formed. The whole period was quiet and relatively uneventful when compared with other periods.

In North America, iron, salt, and gypsum were the important economic deposits of the period, although petroleum and rocks now used in building were formed.

The Age of Fishes—The Devonian Period. During this period fish continued to develop in numbers and varieties; indeed, the period is often called the Age of Fishes. The fish of the Devonian period, however, did not have well-developed internal skeletons. Their skeletons were, in fact, not so much bone as cartilage (elastic tissue). Some of these fish were small sharks; there were a great many ganoids, remotely related to our sturgeons and gar pikes; and there were many other kinds. The teeth, spines, and bony armor of these fish are abundant in many rock formations of this period. Lung breathing developed on the part of certain fish during this time. Two varieties of these lungfish became common: the fringe-finned ganoids and the true lungfish. Both had a swim bladder attached to the throat in such a way that air could be taken into it and the oxygen absorbed when it was

Cambrian marine life. This shallow sea bottom depicts a typical Cambrian scene. From left to right: sponge, crinoids (with stalks), shrimplike forms, octopus-like cephalopods, lampshells or brachiopods, clamlike forms, jellyfish, trilobites, starfish. (Thomas W. Voter.)

impossible for the gills to function properly. Of these two the fringe-finned ganoids are believed to have been the ancestors of the higher vertebrates.

One footprint alone leads paleontologists to believe that other and larger vertebrates lived at that time. It suggests that its maker might have been a salamander-like animal about three feet in length called a stegocephalian, probably an amphibian.

During this period, at least seven hundred different kinds of brachiopods flourished in North America alone. Pelecypods (clams) became common, and ammonites, a kind of shellfish, had their beginning at this time. The ammonites became the dominant mollusk (shellfish) during the Mesozoic era. The trilobites were slowly dying out, though in local areas they were still numerous. Blastoids (sea buds), starfish, and echinoids (sea urchins), as well as other invertebrates, were among the host of living forms of that day. The warm climate permitted the widespread growth of coral reefs from Alaska to Kentucky.

Toward the end of the period there were forests widely distributed over eastern North America. The warm, though somewhat arid, climate permitted a growth of plants in valleys and around small swamps or water holes. These forests consisted of fernlike plants, rushes, and primitive evergreens. Some of these grew to a considerable height and were as much as two feet in diameter.

The fossil remains of spiders and mites have been found in early Devonian deposits in Scotland, showing that they had their beginnings previous to that early time.

About the middle of the period the Acadian ranges were pushed up, and there is reason to believe that they extended far into the present Atlantic Ocean. This disturbance was accompanied by considerable volcanic activity. The granites of Nova Scotia, of the White Mountains of New Hampshire, and of Mt. Katahdin in Maine were intruded at this time. In other places volcanoes burst forth and spread lava and ash about.

By the end of the period both the Cordilleran and Appalachian geosynclines had sunk wholly or in part, and a great thickness of sediment had been deposited. By the end of the period the continent had emerged.

And thus this period passed on—a time of shifting seas and shifting rivers, with periods of equable climate followed by periods of aridity, all having their effect on the life of the time.

More Shifting Seas and Local Aridity— the Mississippian Period. As the centuries passed, the seas again encroached upon the land, stretching from the south along the Cordilleran geosyncline to the arctic and from the southern coast into what is now the Mississippi Valley. These seas were warm but not warm enough for the growth of coral reefs. They did not persist, however. At times they joined; at other times they all but dried up, while seas formed in other places. During the Mississippian period the Wichita Mountains of Oklahoma were formed, and there is evidence that other mountains were being pushed up in the east. At the close of the period an uplift occurred which formed a rim from Texas along the coast to the Acadian Mountains.

By this time the trilobites were nearly gone. Shell-crushing sharks had become more plentiful and powerful, while the sea lilies, or crinoids, became profuse and mingled with the sea urchins and corals. An abundance of sea urchins and bryozoans added to the variety of marine life. Foraminifera were so numerous that thick limestone deposits were formed from them in Indiana and Illinois. Apparently there were few changes in the land life of the times. Amphibians continued, as evidenced by a variety of tracks which have not yet been identified. There is no evidence of insects; yet there is a strong belief that they emerged during the preceding period.

The Mississippian period, like the Devonian, was a time of shifting seas and periods of local aridity, as evidenced by the salt beds in Michigan and the gypsum deposits in Nova Scotia. In some widely scattered areas red soil, colored by iron compounds, suggests that these places may have been alternately wet and dry.

The Coal Age—the Pennsylvanian Period.
The cool, dry climate finally gave way to a much warmer and more humid one the world over. Vast fresh-water swamps appeared which supported a luxuriant growth of plant life; from this plant life has come coal, which is so intimately linked to the daily lives of most human beings. Over three thousand species of these coal-forming plants have been described. They were of rapid and luxuriant growth—a mixture of tall varieties and smaller ones, the latter forming an undergrowth. Shades of green predominated, for there were no true flowering plants. There were no bright colors or sweet odors, such as we associate with flowers. Most of these plants were spore-producing (pp. 524–525); layers of coal have been examined which are almost entirely composed of vast quantities of spores. The plants which produced seeds were fernlike and grew as high as 40 feet. Scale trees grew to be 100 feet high and 6 feet in diameter. Giant rushes were numerous, and there were great numbers of short, tall, and climbing fernlike plants. Cordaites, growing tall and slender, were among the many other varieties. These were evergreens having long and narrow leaves.

Certain conditions are necessary for coal-making. These are the conditions that existed during the Pennsylvanian period, the greatest of all coal-making times.

At that time the whole eastern interior of the United States was a vast lowland covered with swamps. In addition, it was a lowland that was subsiding. It was hemmed about by the higher plains, comprising the Canadian

Life of the Pennsylvania period. Typical scene of a coal-forming swamp. (1) Treelike relative of a present-day horsetail. (2) A scale tree. (3) Cordaites. (4) Another scale tree. (5) Ferns. (6) A giant dragonfly. (7) A large amphibian. (8) A small salamander-like amphibian. (Thomas W. Voter.)

shield on the north, by the high mountainous region, called Appalachia (illus., p. 342), on the east, and by a similar high region on the south. These gave to the lowlands a basin-like form and were partly responsible for the abundant supply of water that gathered in them. The warm, moisture-laden winds blowing up the steep sides of Appalachia dropped their moisture. All the ordinary processes that wear the land down were going on, except those due to ice; three great deltas of material, weathered and washed down from the bordering highlands, were being deposited in this low basin. A lush and abundant vegetation bears evidence of a mild, humid (very moist) climate. Large and succulent foliage gives evidence of rapid and luxuriant growth.

These plants, then, furnished abundant material for coal-making. They accumulated as peat, being covered with water and with the inflowing sediments. In the meantime, a shallow sea irregularly advanced and retreated from the southwest and now and then overran the region. In the main, however, the filling of the basin kept up with its subsidence, so that most of the time it was essentially swampy. By the time the period of accumulation ended, the basin had subsided between 2000 and several thousand feet below sea level. The picture that remains is one of vast thicknesses of plant remains alternating with layers of sediments. And now after time, heat, and pressure have done their work, we find hard or soft coal, and the sediments have become sandstones, shales, and limestones. The coal fields formed during this period alone in North America are estimated to cover 250,000 square miles. Coal at this time was being formed elsewhere too—in the Acadian basin in Canada and in the Old World—but not in such quantities as in the eastern United States. Coal has been formed in spots during every period since plant life became abundant.

During these ages another landmark was established when certain invertebrates became adapted to living part of the time in the air. They were the first insects. Some, however, think that the life history of insects had its beginning in a preceding period. These insects were not like ours of today, for not only were they carnivorous but they were far larger than any of the modern insects. There were many kinds, including 4-inch cockroaches and dragonflies with a wingspread up to 29 inches. Many of these varieties died out later, although dragonflies have come down to us in a much smaller form and with certain adaptations. Cockroaches also have come down with little change except in size.

Amphibians persisted; and it is believed that reptiles, real lung-breathing land forms whose young resembled their parents at birth, developed during this period. A great many of these were plump, sluggish creatures with broad, flat teeth, indicating a diet of shelled creatures, such as the crustaceans of the period. Others of these primitive reptiles had curved teeth for holding their prey. This and the structure of their bodies indicate a swifter-moving variety, with a diet of more agile creatures.

The Pennsylvanian period was a time of great crustal unrest in local areas. A small mountain range, the Oklahoma Mountains, was pushed up and eroded, giving way to the Arbuckle Mountains, Wichita Mountains, and Amarillo Mountains, which were pushed up from Arkansas west to New Mexico, as were the Marathon Mountains in southwestern Texas. Another group of mountains whose uplifts continued through this and the following period were the Colorado Mountains in the west, extending from southern Wyoming, through Colorado and along the Arizona-New Mexico border. Fresh-water swamps were numerous, and the climate in general was warm and humid.

Coal, petroleum, and natural gas, along with limestones widely used in buildings and clay used in bricks and fine porcelains, are the most important economic products formed during this period.

A Time of Widespread Change—The Permian Period. During this, the closing period of the Paleozoic era, the Appalachian revolution occurred. The region along the Atlantic coast, from the southern borders of the continent to Newfoundland, was pushed up and folded from the south and east, forming our present Appalachian Mountains. It has been said that the whole area that lies between the present sites of Philadelphia and Altoona, Pennsylvania, was made shorter by 100 miles by this intense faulting and folding. This revolution destroyed the geosyncline in the east where, time after time, through the ages, the land had subsided and become a shallow sea. The new mountains now covered this area. Many faults developed in this section, the two greatest being 500 and 700 miles long. The Martic fault extended from Georgia to Pennsylvania and the Blue Ridge fault from Alabama to Pennsylvania. These compare favorably in length with the San Andreas fault in the west, along which so many earthquakes have been felt in recent times. The Appalachians of that time probably would have compared very favorably with the Alps of today in size and beauty.

Granites in this area were largely due to volcanic activity during this revolution. The volcanic activity which was a marked feature of the next era had its beginning along the Pacific coast at this time.

Mountain-making forces were also pushing up mountains in what is now the region of the southern Rockies. The Ouachita Mountains and other small ranges in the southwest were formed by faulting and folding in the same way as the Appalachians. The height to which they were raised, however, was in no way comparable with that of the Appalachians. Thick deposits filled the great Midland,

Delaware, and Marfa basins in western Texas and part of New Mexico.

The warm, humid atmosphere of the preceding period gave way to a dry, cold climate. The continental seas of those days were surrounded by deserts, as evidenced by vast deposits of gypsum, and by the enormous salt beds stretching from Kansas to New Mexico. The glaciation of the Permian period was greatest in the Southern Hemisphere. With this change in climate came a change in living forms. It was a period of struggle for existence during which many forms of life died out, but which resulted in the evolution of plants and animals hardier and better adapted to living under such rigorous conditions. This period saw the end of the trilobites, and many brachiopods and echinoids (sea urchins) died out. Warm-blooded animals may have had their beginning during this time, and metamorphosis (p. 590) among the insects probably became established.

Petroleum, salt, potash, gypsum, and phosphate are important economic products of the Permian period.

Significant Events of the Paleozoic Era. The Paleozoic era was indeed one of tremendous change and development. Side by side with the great changes in Earth's surface and the consequent changes in climate, there was the development of living forms, both plant and animal, from very simple forms to a multitude of infinitely more complex forms.

The first half of the era, through the Devonian period, was a time when large areas of North America subsided and were invaded by shallow seas; it was in the Ordovician period that the continent underwent its greatest inundation. These were periods of limestone deposits.

The Caledonian Mountains were formed toward the end of the Silurian Period, probably forming a land bridge from Greenland to Europe.

The close of the era, the Permian period, was a time of mountain-making, during which the Appalachian revolution occurred. It was a critical time in the lives of those plants and animals that could not migrate or become adapted to new conditions which were due to the elevation of the land and the consequent change in climate.

Hordes of invertebrates lived in the seas of the Cambrian period. The plants left few remains.

The first vertebrate appeared during the early part of the era in the Ordovician period.

A scorpion, the first air-breathing animal, appeared in the Silurian period.

Trilobites and brachiopods swarmed through the shallow seas during most of the era.

Fish became numerous during the Devonian period and amphibians appeared.

The time of greatest coal-making in our Earth's history was the Pennsylvanian period. It was a time of many fresh-water swamps with an abundant vegetation in them. It was a time of giant insects. Arid conditions abounded in some regions, however.

The Age of Reptiles—The Mesozoic Era

The uplift which occurred at the end of the Paleozoic era was world-wide. The continents were probably larger then than at any other time since the close of the Devonian period. With this long, slow emergence of the land and the consequent change in ocean currents, air currents, and supply of moisture on the land, a change came in climate as well. It is quite possible that the climate became colder and more arid.

The gradual drying up of the inland seas caused the widespread destruction of a great many kinds of living creatures; those animals were affected least that were able to move about or migrate freely. Because of these profound changes the closing centuries of the Paleozoic era were a most critical period in the lives of enormous numbers of plants and animals. Such climatic conditions continued well into the Triassic period of the Mesozoic era in North America.

Land and Water Changes of the Mesozoic Era. During the Triassic period records show that the Pacific coast gradually subsided until it was under shallow marine waters. Here are found marine deposits, mainly limestones, shales, and some sandstones, with fossils of such salt-water animals as corals and ammonites mixed and interbedded with volcanic ash and lava.

Of early Jurassic age and to the east are found the deposits formed by fresh water; gypsum, characteristic of arid conditions; and vast beds of sand shading from white to yellow to red. Today some of these great deposits may be seen in the steep sandstone walls of Zion Canyon, as well as in many other places in that section of the West. Still farther to the east the gradual wearing down of the Appalachians continued. Vast quantities of this material gathered in the valleys and in the long, narrow fault troughs which developed through Nova Scotia and Connecticut, and from the Hudson River as far south as North Carolina. Today shales and sandstones to a thickness of 15,000 feet may be found in some of these regions. Throughout these areas, as well as along the Pacific, are found evidences of igneous activity during the early part of the Mesozoic era. There were no large volcanoes; only the remains of small ones have been found. A vast amount of the igneous rock occurs as intrusive flows in the form of dikes and sills and as extrusive flows which in some places have a thickness of 900 feet. The most famous of these intrusive flows is exhibited in the Palisades, extending a number of miles along the west shore of the Hudson River north from New York City. Here may be seen the exposed edge of an ancient sill of diabase, a fine-grained igneous rock.

Somewhat later there was a period of faulting and elevation east of the Appalachians—commonly called the Palisade disturbance. A series of mountain ranges appeared, due to the steep tilting of the fault blocks. The ranges varied in length, but were scattered from Nova Scotia to the northern border of South Carolina. The Triassic period ends with this disturbance, which extended over into the following period.

The records show that as time went on into the Jurassic period three fourths of eastern North America was reduced by erosion, and a general leveling off of the continent took place. In what is now the Rocky Mountain region and extending to the arctic another sea developed, which, although somewhat extensive, was of short duration compared with many that had previously existed.

Toward the end of the Jurassic occurred the greatest deformation along the Pacific coast since Precambrian times. Long ranges of mountains were folded from California up through British Columbia, while vast intrusions of granite took place. This was the first uplift of the Sierra Nevada. At the same time flows of lava took place farther to the east. This is known as the Nevadan disturbance.

During the early part of the Cretaceous period another and the last great cycle of inland seas appeared. They finally extended from the arctic to the Gulf of Mexico, from the newly elevated Sierra Nevada to Wisconsin and Iowa, and from Texas to the Atlantic Ocean, covering nearly half the North

American continent. Again the seas receded and, among other sedimentary rocks, left the formation known as Dakota sandstone, the steeply-tilted edges of which form some of the low hills, called hogbacks, that lie east of the Rocky Mountains and in the region of the Black Hills. Shale and limestone may be found covering the Dakota sandstone in places from Texas to the arctic.

In this basin may be found sediments from much of the Paleozoic era and, on top of these, sediments laid down during most of the Mesozoic era. These are probably the thickest beds of sediments that have been laid down in any one place in our Earth's history.

The chalk cliffs of England and France and large deposits in Colorado, Kansas, Nebraska, Texas, and Oklahoma were formed from innumerable one-celled sea animals during the same period, the Cretaceous.

Since the great Coal Age and up to the beginning of the Cretaceous period, the Gulf states had been somewhat elevated, forcing the drainage to flow westward. Thus the Mississippi River, after becoming established, may have flowed into the Gulf of California. During the early Cretaceous period, however, a gradual subsidence of the Gulf states took place, turning the Mississippi toward its present bed and letting in the marine waters. Since the late Cretaceous period, elevation has taken place and may still be going on. The deltas of the Mississippi extend from Cairo, Illinois, into the present Gulf of Mexico.

Great crustal disturbances marked the close of the Mesozoic era. In the eastern United States a slight general uplift took place in the region of the then completely worn-down Appalachians. The present appearance of those mountains is due entirely to further uplift and erosion since that time. Along the entire Pacific coast mountain-making activities were going on. In South America the Andes were folded, and in North America the Laramide revolution took place, during which the Rocky

Mountain system was formed, the crustal disturbances extending from Mexico to Alaska and from Colorado to Nevada and Idaho. It was, indeed, the most widespread disturbance in all North America since Precambrian times.

Flowering Plants Develop. Deposits of coal, formed during the first period of this era, the Triassic, are found in Mexico, Argentina, parts of Europe and Asia, Australia, and the states of Virginia and North Carolina, which indicates that there were places where there was moisture enough to support an abundance of plant life for considerable periods of time. Cycads, tall conifers, tree ferns, and rushes were prominent among the common plants of the period. The sequoias emerged during this time, although they were not in their ascendancy until the latter part of the era. Fossil forests have weathered out of the deposits of this period in many Western states. The trees are now silicified, without bark, and have the appearance of having been brought by water or some other means from other places. In the Petrified Forest near Winslow, Arizona, a few of the logs are as long as 120 feet and 8 feet in diameter; other remains are only fragments of logs.

Perhaps a still greater period of coal formation occurred during the latter part of the era in the Cretaceous period, when there was again a lowering of the continent, with long periods of fresh-water swamps in the West. Luxuriant vegetation, warm humid climate, and the pressure of the rocks during long ages produced coal. This period of coal formation ranks next in importance to that of the great Coal Age.

During this same time the rushes and numerous varieties of cycads died out, and such modern flowering plants as the oak, walnut, beech, maple, birch, hazelnut, magnolia, sassafras, fruit trees, and our common vegetables and other annuals developed. Evergreens were still numerous but were forced to make way for many new varieties. Grasses and sedges appeared at the very end of the era but were not abundant for a long time. This development of plants was an important event, and it has been said that "human civilization could not have evolved, but for the presence of this group of plants."

Animals—Variation and Specialization. This era stands out as a time when many forms of life became specialized, and a considerable number of new forms emerged. There was wide variation among animals. The reptiles, for example, showed wide differentiation in form and manner of living. Some of the ichthyosaurs developed fishlike forms and habits and passed their existence in the water, although they definitely came from land forms. Their bodies were slender, necks short, and tails obviously adapted to pushing them through the water. Their front feet and legs became paddles which were larger than the paddle formed by the tail. Crocodiles and turtles were abundant in the middle and latter part of the era, as well as about a hundred kinds of odd-looking aquatic reptiles called plesiosaurs. Yet all these forms, except certain crocodiles and turtles, together with the toothed birds, described later, disappeared by the end of the era. Specialized varieties of invertebrates too were either dying out at this time or had become extinct.

Dinosaurs—Predominant Reptiles of the Mesozoic Era. Among the many vertebrates of the era, by far the most prominent were the dinosaurs, believed to have developed from a lizard-like reptile of the late Paleozoic era. This primitive reptile, called a thecodont, was carnivorous and rather small, with a range in size about like that of our modern lizard. Apparently, however, it possessed some unusual potentiality, for from it came the crocodiles, the flying reptiles, and the dinosaurs.

The dinosaurs divided into two great family lines, the saurischians and the ornithischians. The former were reptile-like in their structure, and the latter were birdlike. While different in structure, the two stocks were similar in that at first the forms were small and swift, but as time went on they tended to increase in size, although there may have been small forms to the very last. In each of the family lines there was at least as much variation as is found in a group of modern animals, such as dogs or cats.

The saurischians, or reptile-like dinosaurs, were for the most part carnivorous; some were herbivorous. The early saurischians were small, about the size of a rooster; they were swift flesh-eating creatures, running about on their hind legs, with insignificant front limbs.

They preyed upon other small reptiles and possibly upon the primitive mammals, which were emerging at that time.

Prominent members of this carnivorous bipedal group were the saurischians that left so many tracks in the Connecticut-valley Triassic sandstones. They were active and swift-running. Some were about six feet long, but not bulky or very intelligent. Their feet were birdlike in appearance, and when they ran they used the three center toes only.

Later, in the Jurassic period, a huge type of carnivorous dinosaur developed, called *Allosaurus*. They looked much like the small saurischians. They had long balancing tails and insignificant front limbs, and became of goodly size, as long as thirty-four feet.

Life of the Jurassic period. Left foreground: *a small flesh-eating dinosaur called* Allosaurus. Upper right: *a plant-eating duck-billed dinosaur.* Middle left: *a turtle.* Left background: *a herd of plant-eating four-footed dinosaurs. A long-tailed flying reptile (greatly enlarged). (Thomas W. Voter.)*

Tyrannosaurus, in the Cretaceous period, was even larger—some fifty feet or more at his largest. He was a formidable creature to meet, with his six-inch teeth; but he was sluggish and very stupid, and for that reason his prey often escaped.

Some of these saurischians were herbivorous. Beginning in the late Triassic period, they lived through the remainder of the era but reached their peak about the end of the Jurassic period. They were amphibious, living both in water and on land. Among them were *Diplodocus, Brontosaurus, Apatosaurus,* and *Brachiosaurus.* They were all huge, the largest land animals of all time, reaching such lengths as fifty, seventy, and eighty feet. These amphibious dinosaurs walked on all four feet, and some were capable of living in water of considerable depth.

The birdlike dinosaurs, or ornithischians, developed somewhat later than the reptile-like dinosaurs. By the middle of the Jurassic period they were well established and continued until the end of the era. They, like the saurischians, were swift and ran on their hind legs. Unlike the saurischians, however, their front limbs were not reduced in size, and they were probably used as the need arose.

The dinosaurs of this group were all herbivorous. Among these developed many curious types: the duckbills, with and without crests; dinosaurs with armor; dinosaurs with horns. Of the duckbills, *Lambeosaurus* shows the curious development of a bony crest and a prong of bone pointing backward from the crest, in addition to the bill shaped like a duck's bill. The duckbills had webbed feet and no doubt fed in swampy places.

Stegosaurus is a fine representative of a later Jurassic armored dinosaur. Stegosaurs were heavy-bodied, small-headed creatures with fairly short front legs, which, however, were well able to support them. The tail was a double line of huge heavy plates shaped much like poplar leaves.

Among the horned dinosaurs, *Triceratops,* of the late Cretaceous period, is a fine type. The protective adaptations were centered around the head and neck. Over the neck, a region of attack no doubt, was a strong frill, or plate, of bone connected to the skull. On top of the head were two sharp horns and on the nose a third one.

A dinosaur whose head armor was not so well developed as that of *Triceratops* and whose size was not so great was *Protoceratops;* it lived in the late Cretaceous period. The plates covering its head and neck were well developed, but no horns were present. This one is believed to have produced the famous dinosaur eggs found in Mongolia.

And so, after such a variety of forms and specializations, the tribe of dinosaurs became extinct. There are several theories which attempt to account for this; yet there is no proof that any one thing caused their extinction. Some say that the cause was change of climate and the drying up of their swampy homes as the inland seas receded and, consequently, that the cause was at least partially a matter of lack of food. Others say that the tiny mammals may have eaten their eggs and destroyed their young, so that few were left to hatch and grow up. The real cause may be discovered some day.

Dinosaurs, then, were numerous in many of their varied forms over the whole Earth. Some were small, and others became the largest land animals to live during the entire history of our Earth to the present time. Some were carnivorous, some ate plants, and others ate both plants and animals. Some were quadrupeds; others were bipeds, using their short front legs and feet for reaching and holding food. Some were heavily armored; some had tremendously long tails and necks with tiny heads. None were intelligent. Some must have weighed as much as forty tons or more. Their tracks range in size from one inch to two feet, and show that they had three, four, or five toes. Many tracks have been found in the Connecticut valley, New Jersey, and Pennsylvania, as well as in the West. Many skeletons are well preserved. Specimens may be found in museums.

Other curious animals that appeared about the beginning of this era were the pterodactyls, or flying reptiles, which have the distinction of being the first animals to practice true flight. They too were grotesque creatures, but were much smaller than the majority of the dinosaurs. In size they ranged from the size of a sparrow to that of an albatross; yet none probably weighed more than thirty pounds. Their tails varied in length, and their bodies were without any covering but the skin. They were mainly carnivorous, probably securing their food from inland waters. They are believed to have had their origin in a primitive reptile of

This reptile-like bird, an Archaeopteryx, *was carnivorous. Wings have changed through long periods of time.*

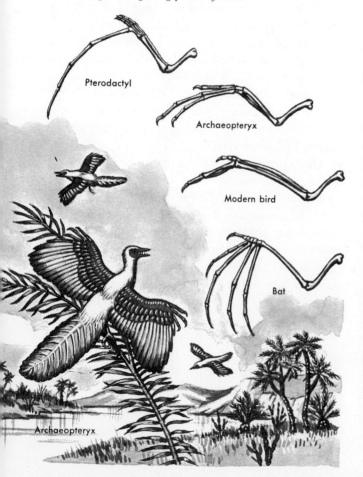

the previous era; and the fossil records show that they became extinct along with the dinosaurs, toward the end of the Mesozoic era.

Reptile-like Birds Emerge. In deposits of the middle part of the Mesozoic era (the Jurassic period) have been found the skeletons and in a very few instances the fossil feathers of an early bird. The development of these creatures constituted a landmark in bird history, for they were the first to bear feathers of which there is any record. Since the fossil record of bird life is unaccountably scanty, even when one takes into account the fragile skeletons of birds and the fact that they furnished food for many other animals, it is entirely possible that other variations existed at that time and certainly somewhat later, for other skeletons are found in deposits of a later date. Feathers were, indeed, an innovation in the way of adaptations; yet these creatures were very much like reptiles in spite of their plumage. They had reptilian heads with long jaws containing teeth; and they had long tails with 20 or 21 vertebrae, on which the feathers grew in pairs, whereas the tails of modern birds consist of feathers growing fan-shaped from a very short extension of the backbone. Modern birds have horny beaks instead of bony jaws. *Archaeopteryx* was about the size of a pigeon and was carnivorous.

The next bird fossils were found in deposits laid down several million years later, toward the end of this era, in the Cretaceous period. The two kinds whose fossils are most complete are called *Ichthyornis* and *Hesperornis;* they are similar only in their possession of jaws with small pointed teeth, instead of beaks. *Ichthyornis* was small and was more like modern birds, especially in its wings and breastbone; yet it retained many reptilian characteristics, such as the structure of bones, a long head, and jaws with teeth. *Hesperornis* was a large aquatic bird with a long head and jaws with teeth. Its small, underdeveloped wings were covered with fine hairlike feathers. No doubt a long line of ancestors preceded these primitive birds for even that much development to have taken place; some day the fossils of these ancestors may be found. Fossil records show that there were many other types of birds in the Cretaceous period, but the skeletons are incomplete.

Marine Invertebrates of the Mesozoic Era. The invertebrates seem not to have suffered the fate of many other animals at the close of the Paleozoic era. The ammonites became the predominant shelled animal of the seas and reached a perfection in their strength and ability to move quickly that few, if any, other shelled animals have attained. A great many, however, died out at the end of the Triassic period. Whether this was due to the newly developing marine reptiles or to a cooling of the water, no one knows. Nevertheless a group survived, and from them came a numerous and varied kind during the Jurassic period. Finally they declined, and became extinct by the end of the era.

Cephalopods (squids and devilfish), and gastropods (snails) became very common during the era. Brachiopods did not prosper; and, though there are brachiopods living today, they have never been common since the Triassic period. Reef-building corals appeared during the Jurassic period. Oysters and clams were common, and also crabs.

Modern Insects and Primitive Mammals Emerge. The history of insects during the era shows that considerable change took place, especially during the middle of the era. In Mid-Mesozoic deposits are found a great many insects— true dragonflies, locusts, crickets, moths, butterflies, beetles, and a number of others. Insect fossils are usually very much crushed and mixed together, except for those preserved in fossil gums, such as amber. While it is doubtful that bees and wasps originated during this era, many of the insects show a definite relationship to present-day species.

Primitive mammals emerged in the early middle part of the Mesozoic era. They had many characteristics of their mammal-like reptilian ancestors; yet the structure of their heads and the teeth, which included incisors, canines, and molars, definitely place them in the mammal class. From the teeth it is inferred that they were carnivorous. Worms, insects, eggs, and other foods of various kinds composed their diet. They were most insignificant little creatures, about the size of mice and rats; they probably inhabited trees and showed little of the development, during the millions of years of their existence in the Mesozoic era, that they exhibited in the next era. Some authorities, however, maintain that marsupials and the placental (p. 362) mammals, which dominated the following ages, had emerged by the end of the Mesozoic era, although they were then small and inconspicuous. Since the soft parts of a body do not fossilize readily, we have no evidence of the time when certain characteristics, such as hair or the suckling of young, originated in mammals.

Significant Events of the Mesozoic Era. During the early part of the Mesozoic era the Palisade disturbance occurred. The mountains formed then have since been worn down.

The first uplift of the Sierra Nevada took place on the Pacific coast in the middle of the era.

The Rocky Mountain system was formed after a long series of mountain-making movements which extended into the Cenozoic era.

The Appalachians were being worn down during all this time, and by the close of the era the region had become a peneplain. A slight uplift then occurred.

The whole era was a period of sedimentation. Sediments from the Appalachians spread over the east. In the great area occupied by the Rocky Mountain system, more sediments were laid down on top of those that had already accumulated there during the Paleozoic era.

The last great invasion of shallow seas took place during the closing period of the era.

Flowering plants, among them fruit and nut trees, developed. Most important of all for future generations of animals were the sedges and grasses which appeared at the very end of the era.

Dinosaurs, large and small, became the pre-dominant animals of the Mesozoic era, at the end of which they became extinct. Toothed birds appeared during the Jurassic period and became extinct toward the close of the era. A great many forms of life died out.

Modern insects emerged near the middle of the era. Primitive mammals emerged some-what earlier. They were about the size of mice and rats, and probably were tree-dwell-ing.

Important deposits of coal, gold, and ura-nium were made during this era.

The Age of Mammals—The Cenozoic Era

Cenozoic era is the name given to the period of time that extends from the Mesozoic era through the Pleistocene epoch, or Ice Age. The time since then is called the Recent era and has been dominated by man. The Ceno-zoic era is about half as long as the preceding era; and in comparison with the other pre-ceding eras, it seems very short indeed. Even so, it lasted for some 60-odd million years. It will be noticed that the whole Cenozoic era is not much longer than some of the periods of other eras, and hence the deposits are not deep when compared with those of other eras.

This era has great appeal to the imagina-tion because it produced every feature of the present landscape. The mountains took on their present appearance, the streams assumed their present courses, the lakes were produced and the marked temperature belts became established during the era.

Inundations of the Cenozoic Era. The con-tinents were high during the era; probably not more than 6 per cent of North America was ever under water at any one time, and most of the time much less. The areas of in-undation were the borders of the Atlantic Ocean, some sections of the Pacific coast, and the Gulf states. Central America was sub-merged during the middle part of the era; at other times it formed a land bridge over which animals from both North America and South America migrated back and forth, though not to the extent that might be expected on account of the volcanic and jungle-like na-ture of the country. At various times a land bridge existed between Alaska and Asia and between northeastern North America and Europe over which animals passed, adding to the variety of types on each continent.

The Gulf Region. The Mississippi Valley was the only other important area of inundation in North America. Here, in the early part of the era, waters from the Gulf of Mexico invaded the land as far north as Cairo, Illinois. From that point southward were deposited sedi-ments of fresh and brackish (salty) water, as well as the remains of plant life growing in the swamps which followed the receding shallow sea—now found as beds of lignite. Sediments from ancient deltas of the Mississippi are in-cluded in these deposits. A small portion of Florida appeared, but as an island; the re-mainder of it was covered by shallow water. Only recently has it become a peninsula.

The Pacific-coast Region. On the Pacific coast, notably in the region of Puget Sound, appear other ancient deltas with their deposits of sand and clay. With these are mingled volcanic ash and lava from the volcanoes which were active during the latter part of the era. This area filled in so rapidly that, though it gradually sank a total distance of 2 miles, it remained a relatively shallow estuary bordered by marshes. In these rather extensive marshes gathered sediments and the remains of plants now found as beds of coal.

The sediments of this era have remained soft and unconsolidated except in those regions along the Pacific coast where they have been altered. Along the Pacific coast most of the deposits older than the Pleistocene epoch are consolidated into rock.

Intermontane Basins. The importance of the continental and fresh-water deposits of this era cannot be overestimated. In the areas of these deposits is found the most complete fossil record of the mammals of this era that is to be found anywhere. Large areas between the ranges of the Rocky Mountains formed natural basins for the sediments brought down from the surrounding highlands. Streams flowed into and through these areas, dropping sediments on their flood plains. Vast quantities of volcanic ash and other igneous material from the many surrounding volcanoes greatly added to the accumulation. In time, grasses and forests covered these areas, providing homes and protection for vast numbers of animals. Here these animals died, and thus their development into modern forms can be traced.

A few of these areas were covered with fresh water. For example, the Green River basin of Wyoming and Colorado contained a lake which covered an area of 350 miles by 150 miles. Shallow and near sea level, it persisted for about 6,500,000 years, as shown by the deposits of annual layers of sediment called *varves.* In the bed of this ancient lake are found the remains of a great many species of plants, insects, and fish. A few species of these fish were of marine origin, which probably migrated up some ancient stream for spawning.

The Plains Region. East of the present Rockies lie their foothills and the Great Plains. Here also the record of mammalian development is unsurpassed. As the great basins just described became filled with deposits, the sediments of streams flowing eastward were dropped on the plains east of the Rocky Mountains. Deep but unevenly distributed deposits brought by wind and the many large and small meandering streams that flowed intermittently provided the means of preservation for the remains of many animals. These deposits spread as far east as Nebraska, southward into Mexico, and for some distance into Canada. They vary in depth up to several thousand feet and help to make of this region a high and comparatively level plain sloping gently toward the lower lands of the Mississippi Valley. Many of these strata are exposed to view in the Bad Lands of the now semiarid West.

Much of this sediment came from the Rocky Mountains, which were pushed up at the close of the Mesozoic era and the beginning of the Cenozoic era. The weathering and erosion of these mountains proceeded as they were elevated, and continued during the early Cenozoic era until they were reduced to a peneplain, with only a few scattered monadnocks (isolated hills) left.

Great Crustal Unrest Characterizes the Cenozoic Era. The Cenozoic era was a time of great crustal unrest which is probably still going on. As evidence of this we may recall the not infrequent earthquakes in California and Montana and various parts of the eastern United States and in Japan, as well as the volcanic activity in many areas.

Life of the Oligocene and Miocene epochs. This is a typical scene in western North America. Left background: *three-toed horses; shovel-tusked mastodons.* Right background: *primitive camels.* Left center: *a rhinoceros-like animal.* Right center: *the largest of the titanothers or "giant beasts" which were far larger than a present-day rhinoceros.* Left foreground: *tortoises, and a small, flesh-eating animal.* (Thomas W. Voter.)

The Cascade Range and the Columbia Plateau. The greatest volcanic activity since Precambrian times took place up and down the Pacific-coast region and farther inland during the early part of the Cenozoic era. Remnants of these great and small volcanoes can be found scattered over the West. During the latter part of the era the Cascade Range rose from California northward across Oregon and Washington. These mountains are volcanic in nature, and among them are Mt. Shasta, old Mt. Mazama, in whose crater beautiful Crater Lake now stands, Mt. Hood, majestic Mt. Rainier, and Mt. Baker, with Mt. Lassen farther south.

In addition to the volcanoes, there were enormous quantities of igneous material which were poured forth from fissures from the middle of the era on. The liquid rock filled in hollows and covered hills and mountains until a great plateau of basalt was built up. This plateau, covering about 200,000 square miles in the Columbia River region, is called the Columbia plateau. There were other smaller fissure flows, somewhat more recent, in the Snake River valley; these flows were rather extensive in what is now Yellowstone National Park. Evidences of still more recent volcanic activity, probably fissure flows with small cinder cones, are found in the Craters of the Moon National Monument.

The Sierra Nevada. The Sierra Nevada, a long fault block uplifted in the middle of the Mesozoic era, underwent the usual constant wearing down and was peneplained by the middle of the Cenozoic era (Miocene epoch). Faulting again took place, and the area was again tilted upward toward the west and uplifted to a height of 3000 feet. At the beginning of the Pleistocene epoch came the final tilting, and an uplift of 6000 feet took place. Erosion continued and was intensified by the glaciation of the Ice Age at the end of the era. This wearing down has given to the mountains their present form.

The Coast Ranges and the Great Basin. West of the Sierra Nevada the Coast Ranges were also formed from great fault blocks, some blocks being elevated to form mountains and others being depressed, with the formation of such features as the Gulf of California, the Valley of California, and Puget Sound. Sediments from the highlands were brought down to the valleys, forming thick, fertile soils. To the east of the Sierra Nevada lies the Great Basin, which probably had its beginning when the first mountain ranges rose on its western border, shutting off the supply of moisture which the region had previously received.

East and north of this basin many relatively short mountain ranges were formed from uplifted fault blocks. This faulting took place in Miocene time and is said to be still going on.

The Colorado Plateau. The Colorado plateau is an area which was once well covered by Eocene deposits laid over a well-eroded surface. A period of erosion was followed by a general uplift; it is hard to say just how many cycles of erosion followed. At any rate the

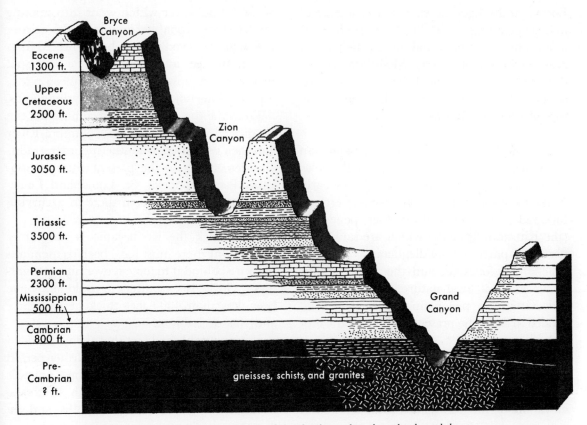

| Eocene 1300 ft. |
| Upper Cretaceous 2500 ft. |
| Jurassic 3050 ft. |
| Triassic 3500 ft. |
| Permian 2300 ft. |
| Mississippian 500 ft. |
| Cambrian 800 ft. |
| Pre-Cambrian ? ft. |

gneisses, schists, and granites

The sedimentary rocks of the Colorado plateau have been deeply eroded.

present high cliffs, deep canyons, plateaus, and mesas are all the result of weathering and erosion during the Cenozoic era.

The Grand Canyon of the Colorado is a spectacular feature of this plateau. The district around it is domelike and about 100 miles wide; it is the part of the plateau that shows the greatest uplift. About 6000 feet of sedimentary rocks laid down in the Mesozoic era have been removed, leaving it some 2000 to 3000 feet lower than the plateau regions to the north. At that time the whole region was lower than it is now; the final uplift, during Pleistocene times, changed the drainage and started the Colorado in its present course. The present canyon and other features have all been made since then.

The Rocky Mountains. The Rocky Mountains were reduced to a peneplain during the Eocene and Oligocene epochs, but a general uplift, beginning in the Pliocene epoch, gave a new impetus to erosional forces; the present appearance of the Rocky Mountains is due entirely to these erosional forces. Remnants of the old peneplain can still be seen on the tops of a few mountains.

The Appalachian Mountains. The Appalachian Mountains, worn to a peneplain by the close of the Mesozoic era, were gently uplifted early in the Cenozoic era. A long cycle of erosion followed and produced another peneplain (the Kittatinny), bits of which are said to be visible in parts of the Alleghenies. Still another uplift followed, and then other uplifts of a somewhat local nature, pushing up the old Kittatinny peneplain, which has been eroded to show the present features of the Appalachians.

The Last Ice Age. The widespread elevation of mountains on the continents and the elevation of the continents themselves gave rise to a changing climate. Whether the new elevation was responsible for the Ice Age, however, is not known. After the middle of the era ice began to gather in the north of Europe, Asia, and North America. All over the world the snow line on the mountains descended, and before the end of the Pleistocene epoch great valley glaciers (p. 324) flowed down the sides of the mountains. There were three great centers in Canada from which the ice radiated, covering all of northern North America except the northern end of Greenland, islands to the west of Greenland, a small spot in Wisconsin, and a portion of Alaska. A portion of Siberia also was not covered, and here developed the great tundras. That areas free from ice existed so near the ice sheet seems rather odd, but geologists tell us that the reason was the lack of precipitation. Precipitation, of course, is necessary for the formation of ice. The water which went into making the ice sheet probably came from the oceans, which are believed to have been lowered from 200 to 400 feet at that time. The little spot in Wisconsin, however, may have been partly due to protection from the ice by highlands.

From the three centers of accumulation the ice dipped southward to the Columbia River and then retreated, its southern border gradually descending to the present cities of Spokane, Pierre, Topeka, St. Louis, and Louisville, and extending from there in a curving line up to Long Island.

How thick the ice became is not surely known, but there must have been tremendous pressure behind it to force it over hills and valleys. Geologists say that it could not have been less than 4000 feet thick at its center and was probably more.

It is an established fact that the ice receded three or four times; and in the warmer period which followed each recession animals adapted to a warm climate, such as horses, peccaries, tapirs, camels, giant sloths, and sea

Ice covered many parts of the Northern Hemisphere during the last Ice Age (Pleistocene epoch).

cows, migrated northward. After a warm, interglacial period, lasting many thousands of years, five or six times as long as the period of expansion of the ice fields, the ice crept forward again. The southern species of animals were again gradually crowded southward, and animals that were adapted to the cold, such as woolly mammoths, caribou, moose, and musk oxen, followed the ice southward and took their places. That is why the remains of such animals are found in the southern United States today.

Drainage was changed, and the basins of the Great Lakes, as well as the basins of thousands of small lakes, were dug out by the ice. It was after the last retreat of the ice that Niagara Falls was formed. Since then, a matter of about 10,000 years, the falls of the Niagara River have worked back to their present location, forming the great gorge.

Since the formation of the Great Lakes that region has been tilting southwestward. This is going on very slowly, but it is estimated that in 1600 years the Great Lakes will drain into the Mississippi instead of the St. Lawrence.

Before the Pleistocene epoch, streams northeast of a line roughly drawn between Montana and Virginia flowed north into Hudson Bay and the St. Lawrence River. Then the continental ice sheets blocked these river channels, forcing them to find new outlets. The present drainage pattern of the Mississippi River was formed in the last 2,000 years.

Plants and Animals of the Cenozoic Era. The great and continuous crustal activity of the Cenozoic era throughout the western part of the North American continent necessarily brought a change in climate over the whole area, resulting in changing forms of life and ways and places of living.

In the early part of the era swamps that supported coal-forming plants covered many parts of Wyoming, Montana, Dakota, and Alberta.

By the middle of the era the grasses had become thoroughly established and widespread. Such forms as cycads, magnolias, and figs flourished in the Yukon region of Alaska; in Greenland, and elsewhere—there were forests of walnut trees, oaks, elms, and redwoods; and somewhat later, crocodiles and palm trees prospered in the Dakotas, Saskatchewan, and Alberta.

With the rise of the Western ranges, however, moisture-laden winds were cut off. The forests died out, and grasses took their places over the Great Plains area. This marked change in the vegetation had a profound influence on many forms of life. Certain animals became adapted structurally to the change in food. This adaptation may be observed especially in the structure of the jaws and teeth.

The ammonites (shellfish), characteristic of shallow marine waters, passed away with the Mesozoic era. During the Cenozoic era brachiopods and crinoids (sea lilies) became very scarce. Gastropods (snails) were numerous, and cephalopods (squids and devilfish) were represented by the nautilus and the squid. Large Foraminifera (usually microscopic shelled animals) called nummulites were abundant in spots. These were great builders of limestone. Oysters attained a length of 13 inches. Corals were about as numerous as they are now.

About 6000 species of Cenozoic insects have been found, among them 100 kinds of ants preserved in fossil gums (amber) of the early part of the era. Of these hundred kinds of ants 24 kinds are still living.

Fishes of this era are quite similar to the modern ones. Early in the era a mammal, a whalelike animal, became adapted to living in the water. Later came sea cows, and still later in the era came the true whales, seals, and sea lions.

The reptiles of the Mesozoic era had almost completely vanished. All that were left to "carry on" in the new era were the alligators, crocodiles, a few nonvenomous snakes (the venomous ones developed later), and enormous land turtles.

Large ostrich-like birds, as high as 7 or 8 feet, marked the beginning of the era. These feathered creatures had huge heads and underdeveloped wings which were unable to carry them in flight. Later, modern toothless birds emerged, among them eagles, vultures, shore birds, and songbirds.

The predominant animals of the Cenozoic era, however, were the mammals, just as the reptiles were the predominant animals of the Mesozoic era. Hence a brief survey of mammals, including some of their outstanding adaptations, follows.

Mammals Appear. By the time the great reptiles had died out, at the close of the Mesozoic era, mammals are believed to have developed from the very primitive forms that laid eggs into the two groups which produce their young alive—namely, the marsupials and the placentals (p. 523)—with a wide variation in their ways of living. With only a few exceptions, such as the duckbills and spiny anteaters of Australia, all present-day mammals retain their young within their bodies for varying lengths of time, giving the young greater protection and an opportunity for greater body development.

The eggs of mammals are very small and, unlike reptile and bird eggs, they contain practically no food for the nourishment of the embryo. This alone means that further protection and nourishment are necessary until the young can care for themselves. This has probably led to the production of fewer young, as well as to greater protection before and after birth.

Marsupials. In the mammals called marsupials the young have always been especially immature when born. Long ago a pouch evolved on the abdomen of the mother into which the tiny animal crept after birth. There it found safety and warmth, as well as nourishment from the mammary glands located within the pouch.

Small opossum-like mammals eating all kinds of food became widespread early in the Cenozoic era, and from them came our present-day marsupials. The early marsupials migrated far and wide but seem to have had the best chance for development in South America and Australia because of the isolation of these continents for long periods of time. South America was isolated from the early part of the Cenozoic era to the latter part, during the Pleistocene epoch, when there was a general uprising of continental masses and the present land bridge was restored. Many curious forms arose in South America, many of them closely paralleling the placental mammals in outward form, although not necessarily in inner structure. Marsupials resembling cats, dogs and wolves became flesh-eating, and many plant-eating placentals developed. But during the Pleistocene epoch most of these died out, leaving only small marsupials.

Australia, isolated since late Mesozoic times, became a place of opportunity for the early marsupials; for apparently no placental mammals inhabited the region until man introduced them. Here the marsupials developed into such strictly herbivorous forms as the koalas (which have now lost their pouches) wombats, and kangaroos. Giant forms of many of these animals, including wombats and kangaroos, are now extinct. Carnivorous forms developed, such as Tasmanian devils (the "wolves" which inhabit the wildest parts of Tasmania) and the common dasyures, squirrel-like animals about twelve inches long. There are many that eat both plants and animals. Opossums are the only marsupials found in North America and South America today.

Placental Mammals. The placental mammals developed several steps farther in their manner of caring for their young before birth. In the case of these animals, too, the young remain within the body for a period; but the membranes surrounding the tiny embryo come in close contact with the uterus of the mother. The union of the embryonic and maternal membranes forms the placenta, by which food and oxygen are carried to the embryo and waste materials, including carbon dioxide, are carried off in the blood stream of the mother. This manner of bearing the young makes possible the development of a far more complicated body than would otherwise be the case (p. 531).

Many Archaic Mammals Flourish and Die. Little is known about all the many different kinds of mammals that must have existed in very early days. It is reasonable to believe that there was a widespread development of many different forms. However, the fossils of four differing groups have been recognized in sediments laid down during the Jurassic period in different parts of our Earth. These are thought to have risen from a mammal-like reptile during the early part of the Mesozoic era. Of these four groups three became extinct by the end of the Mesozoic era; from the fourth group, during the Cretaceous period, came the marsupials and insectivores (placental mammals, mainly insect-eating). By the close of the Cretaceous period a wide variety of mammals had evolved.

It was not, however, until the dinosaurs died out and the cereals, fruits, and grasses became more widespread that the mammals could really prosper. So we find that with the beginning of the Cenozoic era many new types appeared.

In the deposits of the early Cenozoic era (Paleocene epoch) at least five groups of archaic mammals can be recognized; Marsupialia, Insectivora, Creodonta, Condylarthra, and Amblypoda. Of these, marsupials still exist and are represented by opossums and kangaroos. Insectivores are living today as shrews, hedgehogs, and moles. The creodonts were flesh-eating; and, though most of them became extinct, one small group is believed to have given rise to modern dogs, wolves, and cats. The condylarths and amblypods were herbivorous. They too became extinct early in the Cenozoic era. These animals showed a wide diversity of size and form; teeth and limbs were adapted to different kinds of food and places of living. They did not, however, have the power to live on among the mammals which migrated into their habitats.

The Rise of Modern Mammals. The fossil record tells us that soon after the beginning of the Cenozoic era new types of animals appeared in North America among the archaic mammals. Some of these were undoubtedly developments from native forms of life; others migrated from Asia and Europe, for there were land bridges connecting North America with these continents at that time. By long and careful study many have been found to be the direct ancestors of many present-day forms. Some of them, however, lived only for a while and then became extinct.

Tendencies in Mammalian Development. Mammals are distinguished from other animals by being warm-blooded, by having hair at some stage in their life history, by suckling their young, and by a diaphragm separating the thorax from the abdomen.

There are certain general trends in the development of mammals through the centuries that set them apart from other animals. There has been a tendency toward increase in the size of the body, including the skull and brain. The increase in brain power seems to be the quality that has allowed mammals to become dominant. The skull differs from the reptilian skull by a separation of the food and nasal passages, allowing mammals to eat while breathing. Mammals have but one bone in the lower jaw fastened directly to the skull, whereas the reptiles have seven bones in the

lower jaw, which is fastened to the skull in an entirely different way.

Among the structural parts of mammals that show the widest variation in their adaptation to certain specialized ways of living are the teeth and the feet. The teeth of mammals are adapted for the tearing and eating of flesh and for the cutting and chewing of plants. The grass-eaters especially developed high-crowned teeth with deeply folded enamel to withstand the enormous amount of grinding necessary with such food. In some species the teeth continue growing throughout the life of the animal, replacing the wear which goes on at their surface.

Mammals, again, are distinguished from the reptiles by having two sets of teeth composed of incisors, canines, and molars, as compared with the reptiles' indefinite number of sets, all the teeth having the same shape.

There is great variation in feet and mouths. Each is used helping an animal to survive.

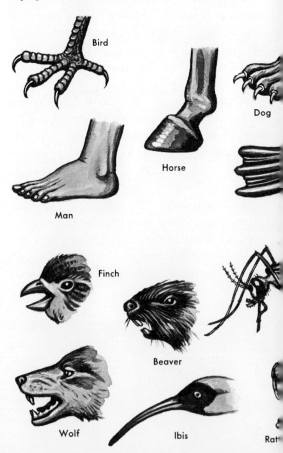

In locomotion, adaptations seem to have been made for speed. The four limbs have changed position so that backward and forward motion is easiest. As the bony structure of the limbs changed, the muscles changed also; these are placed nearer the body, where they can be used to better advantage.

The feet became adapted to various habitats, such as trees; for example, claws developed for climbing. Claws developed, too, for catching and holding prey. Horses, over a period of nearly 40 million years, gradually lost four of the digits on their feet, finally coming to stand on the much enlarged third toe.

All in all, if any one word could characterize adequately the structure of a mammal, it would be the word *action*.

Adaptation among Animals. The special fitness which many animals possess for the particular environment in which they live has attracted attention for a long time. In frogs the fishlike gills of the tadpole stage, which is lived entirely in water, largely disappear during metamorphosis, and lungs take over the business of respiration when the animal begins life on land. During the tadpole stage the frog resembles a fish, with its tail and absence of legs. It becomes adapted to living on land by the absorption of its tail and by the growth of feet.

The webbed feet and broad bills of ducks are adaptations which permit them to secure food from water and swampy places. Hence they are able to live more successfully in such an environment than a chicken could.

All animals must either control their environment, become adjusted to changes in their environment, or be destroyed. Beavers build houses, and ants built nests; and there are other animals that change their environment to a small extent. Man alone changes his environment constantly to suit his convenience, although even man is frequently confronted with environments or with aspects of an environment which he has not yet learned how to control.

Adaptations may occur either in the structure of an animal, in the uses made of certain structures, or in the way in which the animal meets a new situation. These adaptations to environment are not voluntary on the part of the animal; they are brought about through a long, slow process. When animals are placed in a new environment, often they are either all destroyed or all destroyed with the exception of a few which are better able to cope with the situation than the rest. The ability to cope with a situation may be a matter of color. This is true in the case of many insects and in the case of young deer, whose dappled coats closely resemble the pattern made by sunlight falling through leaves. Some animals' necks may be slightly longer than those of their fellows, and thus the animals are better able to secure food in the new environment; some animals may be slightly more fleet of foot than others, and thus they escape their enemies a little better. These individuals, then, are the ones that survive and reproduce. With each new generation the weeding-out process goes on until, after thousands of years, an environment may support animals that fit into it very well indeed. They may look quite different from their early ancestors, and yet show definite connection with them in many details.

Of the ten orders of modern mammals it is the Ungulata, or hoofed mammals, whose fossil record shows most clearly and completely the continued change in certain structures of the body.

The hoofed mammals are distinctly a development of the Cenozoic era; the new environment of extensive grassland areas, which had never before existed, probably was a guiding factor in their evolution. The hoofed mammals live in herds and are herbivorous, although there are some exceptions. Swine, for instance, eat anything and everything. The molar teeth of most hoofed mammals have become flattened and enlarged for the chewing of grasses. The canines of swine have developed into tusks of varying sizes, and the snouts of swine have become adapted to digging for near-surface roots.

Among many of these mammals there has been great development for speed. Rapid flight is their best means of escape from predators, although most of them strike, bite, and kick when cornered. Some have horns, which are an aid in their protection.

In the development leading to rapid flight the foot was raised from the flat position characteristic of bears and man to that of running on the end of the third digit in the odd-toed ungulates and on the third and fourth digits in most of the even-toed ungulates.

Significant Events of the Cenozoic Era. Land masses were high during the Cenozoic era. Only areas along the Atlantic Ocean, the Gulf, and parts of the Pacific coast were submerged.

Mountain-building and general and local uplift accompanied by erosion mark the era. The Sierra Nevada and the Coast Ranges, as well as many other ranges farther inland, were pushed up. The Colorado plateau was uplifted, and the Grand Canyon was cut through it. The Rocky Mountains and the Appalachian Mountains were uplifted and eroded to their present appearance. The greatest volcanic activity since Precambrian times took place. The Cascade Range, containing many

volcanic mountains, arose, and the Columbia plateau was built from fissure flows.

Great deposits of sediment were made as the highlands were eroded. These deposits contain a valuable record of the animal life during these times.

An ice sheet spread over much of the North American continent during the Pleistocene epoch.

Grasses became widespread, thereby influencing the animal life of the times.

Mammals became the predominant animals of the era, showing wide variety and adaptations.

Man made his appearance during the Cenozoic era.

Economic deposits of the era include petroleum, lignite, placer gold, veins of gold, silver, copper, and diatomite—earth made of diatoms used in filters and as fillers.

Changes in Earth's surface have vitally influenced living things. Favorable environments have allowed living things to flourish. The development and spread of plants permitted the development and spread of many different kinds of animals. Lack of suitable temperature or food acted as a check on plant and animal alike. Plants and animals often seem to undergo adaptations to slight changes in environment, through long periods of time. Such interrelationships and adaptations have been going on through the long history of plants and animals.

The Age of Man—The Recent Epoch

The fossil remains of man and manlike creatures are indeed scanty; yet such is the interest today in man's origin and past that increasing effort and care are being used in the search for the truth. Such finds as have been made have, for the most part, been made in Europe and

Africa, although a few fossils have been found in Java and China. Nevertheless, Asia or Africa is believed to have been the "incubator" of early man. Not only are these continents large, but huge sections of them have long had a climate that was favorable to man. There too were centers of development for many other mammals contemporary with early man. These regions have only been dipped into so far as exploration is concerned, and there, probably, will be found the secret of man's past. Many important discoveries of fossils and artifacts (products of human workmanship) have been made in the last twenty-five to fifty years.

At present little can be said of early man in America. The Indians and Eskimos have been here for a very long time and may have come from Asia by way of the Alaskan land bridge. Evidences of Folsom man have been found in many places and have been successfully dated as having lived 10,000 years ago. This means that these rather skillful people were here before that time. Their artifacts have been found with the remains of bison, now extinct. An elephant bone has been found near Mexico City carved with pictures of extinct animals. Preliminary tests give this bone an age of 30,000 years. Along with the bone were found other bones shaped for use as tools and about 500 stone tools.

Human history goes back to the Ice Age. Yet at most this was only between 700,000 and 1 million years ago, a very short time in our Earth's history. Well-developed apes were present during the two epochs preceding the Ice Age, and it is presumed that man's remote ancestors were undergoing transition at that time as well.

From artifacts a great deal can be learned about the way in which the men lived who made and used them. The age of the rock in which the artifacts are found tells approximately the time when their makers lived. The kind of material of which artifacts are made and the design or lack of it indicate the mode of living and especially the degree of intelligence attained by the makers. Hence a vast storehouse of information is being accumulated which sometime will reveal the true history of man.

Man's teeth show considerable modification, the canines becoming less prominent and pointed and tending to become more like the incisors. This correlates closely with man's feeding habits. With the shortening of the jaw, the nose has become more prominent and the chin has developed. The feet have remained primitive in that there are five toes. Compared with the toes of other primates, those of man are short; but the foot has become elongated, and the great toe is not opposite the other toes, as the thumb is opposite the fingers, but lies alongside them. The weight of the body is centered over the legs; and a heel has developed, which is used as a brace, or support. Structurally man's chief development has been his brain, and only because of it has he survived and become in large measure the master of his environment.

Fossil Man and Manlike Primates. The following fossil remains are from Europe and Asia:

A fossil of *Pithecanthropus erectus,* or erect ape-man, found in 1890 in Java, is one of the earliest fossils of mankind yet found, if it really is man. This fossil consists of part of a skull, some teeth, and a thighbone. The brain was larger than any ape's but much smaller than modern man's. However, it may have been sufficiently developed to permit a small amount of primitive speech. The creature walked erect, probably resembling man more than ape in this respect, but was only about half the size of modern man. It is believed to have lived in the early part of the Pleistocene epoch. This would make the age of *Pithecanthropus erectus* less than 1 million years. In the 1930's similar and related kinds of fossils dating back to about the same time in Earth history were found in Java.

The remains of Heidelberg man consist of a lower jaw found in sand of the early Pleistocene epoch near Heidelberg, Germany, in

1907. The jaw was heavy and of a chinless type and the teeth were primitive. This species of human being lived at some time in the first interglacial period, making it the oldest fossil so far discovered. This makes Heidelberg man somewhat less than 1 million years old.

About 1927 some fossils were found in a cave near Peking, China. In 1929 a skullcap and later a number of different bones were found. These creatures were given the name *Sinanthropus pekinensis*, or China man of Peking. The intelligence of these men may have been somewhat ahead of that of Java man, if one may judge by the size of the brain. The chin was retreating, and the teeth were primitive. The evidence shows that they not only ate the animals living at that time but also ate others like themselves. From carbonized remains found near the fossils it is believed that these men were familiar with fire for warmth and were users of stone tools. Their remains were found near those of animals that lived during the early Pleistocene epoch. This would make them, too, about 1 million years old.

The remains of Neanderthal man were first found in the Neanderthal, a valley in Germany. Since then the remains of many others of this race have been found. They had prominent ridges above the eyes, low, sloping foreheads, and undeveloped chins. Their heads were large in the back and on the side, so that their brain capacity was equal to that of modern man. The jaw and teeth were large, but the teeth were quite different in structure from present human teeth. These men walked bent over, with their heavy heads sagging forward. They were short and stocky. They lived in all parts of Europe for about 100,000 years, during the last interglacial period and last glaciation. They used bows and arrows, made fairly good stone tools, and knew the use of fire. They lived in caves and sometimes buried their dead.

Olduvai Gorge, in a remote section of Tan-ganyika, in eastern Africa, has proved to be a rich source of remains of very early types of man. One type is called *Zinjanthropus boisei*, or East Africa man. He had a small brain, large jaws, and very heavy teeth adapted to chewing coarse vegetation. Stone tools and small animal bones found with the remains indicate that he was learning to kill animals for food. From potassium-argon dating tests it is believed that he lived nearly 2 million years ago.

Other recent discoveries in the same regions are the remains of *Homo habilis*. This race used both plants and animals for food and seems to have been more skilled in the use of crude tools than *Zinjanthropus*. *Homo habilis* probably lived before, at the same time, and after *Zinjanthropus*.

Evidence is accumulating that may make it possible to trace man's development as far back as 14 million years.

Some authorities think that the forefathers of modern man and many other kinds of erect manlike primates were all living when the Pleistocene epoch began, but that *Homo sapiens* (man) was the only one to survive. This was undoubtedly due to his superior brain.

The men of the Cro-Magnon race were highly developed, having a large brain, a well-developed chin, and a high forehead with scarcely any brow ridges; in height they resembled modern man. Their culture placed them well forward on the road to modern man. They closely resembled many of the Neolithic people, who followed them. They were physically and mentally superior, having well-formed tools of stone and bone. They used ornaments and bows and arrows, and they dressed in furs. Picture writing done by them is found on the walls of caves; they carved pictures on their bone and stone tools; and later they decorated the walls of caves with colored pictures. They persisted through the last glacial period and are believed to have been the direct ancestors of modern man.

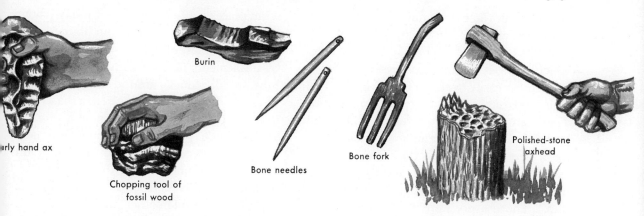

Through thousands of years, people learned to make tools that were more efficient than those used by primitive man.

There is some evidence of other races. Fossils found in the Grimaldi Caves, in Italy, bear striking negroid characteristics. The development of the different races is still shrouded in the distant past. Some authorities think that racial characteristics are the organism's adaptation to varying degrees of heat, visible light, and ultraviolet radiation.

Ancient Cultures. Time was when man knew no metals. His only tools were made from stone, wood, and possibly hide, bone, and sinews. Tools of these materials, except for those made of stone, have long since crumbled to dust; only the stone artifacts remain to indicate the degree of man's intelligence and his mode of living.

In the very beginning primitive man picked up and used for tools sticks for the digging of roots, and stones that fitted his needs. These were of different shapes and formed by the forces of nature. Many water-rounded stones have been found that were split open. This would give a badly-needed sharp edge for cutting points on digging-sticks and for numerous other uses. Such instruments are called *eoliths*.

The different Stone Age cultures which followed the use of eoliths are classified as the Old Stone Age, or Paleolithic Age, and the New Stone Age, or Neolithic Age. The Paleolithic Age is subdivided into the Lower, the Middle, and the Upper Paleolithic Age. The Lower Paleolithic Age was the earliest and extended over a long period of time, well back into the early part of the Pleistocene epoch. The hand ax made from the core of a nodule of flint is typical of this time. One end was pointed and the other left large and rounded. The chipping of the first axes was by no means perfectly done, but this work improved as time went on. In size they range from two inches to two feet, and during the 250,000 years in which they were widely used, they changed very little. They are found from England to Palestine, South Africa, and India. No human remains have been found with these axes.

The Middle Paleolithic Age was of shorter duration. The hand ax was abandoned, and fairly well-made tools were formed from chips instead of the core of flint nodules. A few bone artifacts of this same time show that some progress was being made by their makers. During this time men became skilled hunters with the newly devised sharp-pointed stones, and rituals developed for healing the sick.

The Upper Paleolithic Age presents an entirely new group of tools in addition to many of the old ones. Associated with these artifacts are the Cro-Magnon remains. A new technique was employed in the making of the old tools. A tool called a *burin* had been invented which made it possible to carve bone, ivory, and antler easily without breaking the tool. This apparently was a great step forward. Then came the technique of polishing, and probably from all this came the polished stone ax, a stronger tool than they had ever possessed. Scratchers, knives, and gravers were made from long flakes struck from flint nodules. The gravers were used for engraving pictures and for fashioning artifacts from bone, reindeer horn, and ivory. These took the form of harpoons, darts, and needles with eyes, which indicate the use of clothing. Cro-Magnon men developed new arts as well: working and modeling with clay and the use of ocher and the oxides of iron and manganese. Through this period progress can be noted in art. Greater detail and better proportions appear in the engravings, in the drawings, and in relief. The Cro-Magnons made wide use of caves as places to make their drawings, and thus some of these drawings have been preserved to this day. During the Upper Paleolithic, a time covering roughly from 35,000 to 8000 B.C., human beings spread into the colder regions of Europe and Asia and crossed into Alaska and from there to South America. Inasmuch as the oldest remains of man in the western hemisphere found so far are in the southernmost part of South America, some wonder if there could have possibly been a migration from some other direction than the north. With the recession of the ice following the last glaciation this culture came to an end.

The Upper Paleolithic culture merged into a nondescript culture called the Mesolithic, which lasted to the beginnings of agriculture. In those places where agriculture was invented the population passed more quickly into the Neolithic culture. In regions remote from such centers the transition was slower and in

some places it is even going on today. Some phases are characterized by an abundance of painted pebbles; others, by their absence and by implements of bone with a ring of microliths (small stones) around them. Another phase produced a tool chipped to a sharp point from an oval stone. Later came a phase in which crude pottery was made and used, along with objects made from bone and antlers. Yet another phase with its pottery and milling stones gives evidence that men had begun to secure food in other ways than by hunting. In these same deposits are found the remains of horses, stags, and oxen, along with ash and oak trees.

This culture merged into the Neolithic culture, which began roughly about 8000 years ago. During the Neolithic, or New Stone, Age, man learned to domesticate plants and animals and thus produce part of his food. Dogs are believed to have been the first wild animals to be domesticated. Milk is believed to have been used. Man learned to live in villages.

Many of the flint instruments of the Neolithic Age are works of art; articles made from stone were polished as a final touch. Pottery was improved, and sewing, weaving, braiding, spinning, knitting, and basket-making were among the many accomplishments. The wheel and the loom were outstanding inventions of the time. Homes were built over swamps and streams and over the water on lake shores. Dugout boats were used widely in transportation.

This culture spread all over Europe, and with it civilization really began. There are many countries today where aspects of this culture are a part of everyday living. These people were herdsmen and tillers of the soil.

The Bronze Age began about 3000 B.C. in some parts of the world. As men became acquainted with their environment and techniques for using it, the use of iron, gunpowder, coal, oil, and hydroelectric and atomic power followed in quick succession.

Man, then, has been on Earth only a very short time compared, for example, with the length of time that the race of dinosaurs covered Earth. When compared with the geological age of Earth, man's approximately one million years on Earth are but a moment. Thanks to his enlarged and more powerful brain, he has risen above the dinosaurs and all the other animals and has made a place for himself in the world that is unique. He alone can change his environment to any considerable extent. He alone is learning how to study the universe. He can use his intelligence to make life easier and longer for himself.

EXPERIENCE. *The geological study of a locality.* Many teachers trace with their group the geological history of their particular region. This can be done with the aid of federal, state, or provincial geological bulletins.

Groups working out such a history should visit places in the region which are of interest geologically.

If a museum is near, much information may be gathered there.

Some children have been able to help other groups by keeping records of their findings with slides, murals, and "picture shows."

EXPERIENCE. *To integrate art with the study of our Earth.* Much excellent work has been carried on in public schools in recent years in using art as a means of developing a conception of time and change. In some schools children make clay models of prehistoric animals, later baking the clay. In some school museums, exhibits have been made of the prehistoric past. The children may be encouraged to make drawings and paintings of these earlier times.

EXPERIENCE. *To develop murals concerning prehistoric times.* Encourage children to develop ideas of how the region in which the school is now located looked at times in the past. Was the region ever covered with ice? What kind of animals lived at that time? Were there mountains in the region? The children may draw an imaginary picture, and often these pictures can be mounted in such a way as to make a classroom mural. This co-operative kind of activity can be stimulating and constructive for children.

EXPERIENCE. *To develop a play based on the story of life in your vicinity.* Children sometimes like to dramatize the past. By developing a number of imaginary episodes of the past, they can develop a concept of time.

EXPERIENCE. *To develop a movie of the story of our Earth.* By making pictures on large pieces of wrapping paper, a movie can be made of the history of Earth. Broomsticks can be used for rollers for the wrapping paper. The class may develop the narration to go with the movie.

CHAPTER 11

What the Universe Is Made Of

Our Ever Widening Frontiers

The more knowledge man acquires about what the universe is made of, the more he recognizes how much there is still to be learned. Thus the study of what the universe is composed of is a continuing one. In spite of the rapid progress which has been made in recent years, we are still only at the beginning. Children frequently do not recognize this. They sometimes express the belief that soon we shall know everything, and there will be no need for further investigation. They seem to have formulated in their own minds a preconceived limit to the amount of knowledge that man can acquire. We can help children recognize that there is always more and more to be learned, and that with each advance comes an ever widening frontier of new knowledge which is yet to be obtained and understood. Through constant research new hypotheses and content are developed. One discovery usually leads to another.

With increased knowledge man is able to create new materials that serve him better; he can make unused resources useful and valuable; he can continue to improve existing materials in order that they may serve him more effectively; and he can develop new substitutes and synthetic materials to take the place of scarce or depleted substances. There are still huge quantities and sources of materials about which we know very little. The ocean, for example, is a huge reserve whose potentialities have not been fully explored. No one can foresee what will be possible in the future.

Man's Dependence on Substances and Energy

Man has always used substances and energy. His own body could not function without them. However, in the past he had a very limited understanding of his immediate environment and possessed even less information about what went on outside of it. Modern man has a much better understanding of substances and energy. He explores the oceans, the crust of Earth, the atmosphere, and the objects out in space. Before man could use

Scientists Distinguish One Chemical from Another

It seems at first almost unbelievable that one can hand a substance to an expert chemist and after an examination have him tell just what is in it. If he is familiar with the procedures and has the equipment and time he can make such a determination.

Substances Have Characteristic Properties. As stated earlier, all matter is composed of chemicals. All matter is made up of about one hundred elements. Children recognize some of the elements which go to make up the materials around them, and observe many differences in things both at home and at school. In doing so they make use of the same sorts of information that the chemist does. Some substances are harder than others; some are heavier, darker, more soluble, more brittle, or have more odor than others. Substances have specific colors and react to heat in different ways. A child, as well as the professional chemist, makes use of such differences in determining of what materials an object is composed.

EXPERIENCE. *Substances differ in a number of ways.* If possible, gather some scraps of different kinds of substances such as quartz, plastics, glass, iron, steel, aluminum, lead, stones, oak wood, pine wood, and other materials. If one tries to cut some of these substances with a knife he will find that lead is quite easily cut, and that pine wood can be cut more readily than oak. He will find that the glass and quartz are brittle, while the metals, wood, and plastic substances are not. Lead can be flattened by pounding it with a hammer, showing that it is softer than the steel of the hammer. Some of the materials will flatten when pounded while others will break.

The children will find that even though they may have two things of the same size, one may be much heavier than the other. The lead pipe is heavier than an iron one of the same size, while the iron pipe is heavier than a similar pipe made of aluminum.

Note the colors and odors of each of the substances listed above. Are differences to be observed?

Children may observe in their own homes some of the effects of heat on substances. They can see that vegetables are softened by heat when boiled in water and sometimes change color. Fats commonly used melt easily but some faster than others. When foods are baked, heat is applied and changes take place. Perhaps the children could name a few differences that they have observed.

Many common substances in use in a kitchen show differences in solubility. Among them are salt, sugar, soap, soap flakes, soap powders, vinegar, gelatin, oil, and instant coffee. Some dissolve faster when heat is applied in the form of hot water.

These kinds of experiences can be done at many different levels. In the first grade the common substances with which the children are most familiar could be used and the observations and discussions could be much more fragmentary than with older children. Older children might devise a chart or mural indicating the characteristics of certain substances and compare them in this manner.

Odors. Many substances have characteristic odors that everyone, including the chemist, takes into consideration in helping to recognize them. The children will readily identify by their odors such substances as apples, peaches, onions, oranges, lemon, pineapple, vinegar, cheese, bacon, laundry soap, fish, and many other things that they can mention. They know what their mothers are cooking before they get into the kitchen. They also recognize the drugstore, the paint store, the grocery store, the meat market, the feed store, the fish market, the hardware store, the garage, and the filling station, as well as many other places, by the odors given off by the products there. They will, of course, notice that some substances have no odor.

Colors. (P. 866.) While man is able to give a particular color that he wishes to many of the things that he has, each substance has a natural color that is useful in helping to identify it. A geologist may secure an idea of what is in a sample stone or rock by the colors of the different parts of it. The children are familiar with the fact that some stones are of one color while others are of another, or that different parts of a single stone may differ in color. Naturalists use colors to help them name the birds, the fish, the flowers, the trees, and many other things. The farmer takes the color of the soil into account when deciding whether a field has good or poor soil. The children may be able to distinguish copper, iron, aluminum, and zinc they find at home and at school by the color, as well as by other characteristics. The color of the water in the stream tells us much about whether it is carrying away soil. A chemist always considers the color of the substance that he is trying to analyze.

It has been found that each particular substance produces its own color when heated to a high temperature. One can identify some chemicals by holding them in a flame; for example, strontium gives a red flame. If one heats table salt (sodium chloride) he will notice the yellow flame which is due to the presence of sodium. The color of a substance is also affected by a change in temperature. As an iron wire is heated, it will first give off a yellow color, then red, and finally as it is heated still hotter the color will be white. A copper wire will first turn red when it is heated in the flame, and as it gets very hot will then give a green color to the flame.

The children may wonder how scientists learn so much about the chemical constitution of the stars when they cannot visit them.

Almost everyone has noticed that light from the sun is broken up into different colors as it passes through glass prisms, or through the corner of an aquarium. The scientist refers to this color combination, which he also can see in the rainbow, as the *spectrum.*

When the light from the stars is passed through an instrument known as a *spectroscope,* different combinations of colors, or spectra, are seen, and may be recorded on photographic plates. By examining these different color combinations scientists can detect the presence of certain chemicals. Using the spectroscope is simply an elaborate and accurate way of identifying chemicals by the colored light they give off.

Reaching far out into space by means of astronomical instruments, astronomers discover that the other bodies in the universe seem to be made up of the same chemical elements as those we find on Earth. Perhaps at some time in the future more delicate instruments will enable scientists to understand more about what is happening in the stars.

Melting Point. If one were watching a chemist check to see of what element or elements a particular substance was composed, he would probably see the chemist determining the melting point of the substance as another means of verifying his conclusion. The children are familiar with the fact that water freezes and ice melts at 32°F. They know that solder melts at a lower temperature than iron. They may have watched a plumber melt some lead, or they may have been in a printing shop and noticed that type metal can be melted by heating it in an iron container. Other children may have seen butter melt on a hot day or their mother melt sugar in a skillet to be used for flavoring or sweetening in a cake.

When heat is applied to solids their molecules vibrate and their orderly and regular arrangement is disturbed. The vibration of the molecules becomes so great that even though they remain together, they slip past each other and begin to move more freely as the solid approaches the liquid state. The temperature at which a solid becomes a liquid is called the *melting point*. The melting point often determines what a substance is and also the use to which it is put. An example of this is that of sugar melting in a skillet. The melting point of sugar is lower than the melting point of the material of which the skillet is made. In other words, it takes less heat to melt the sugar than it takes to melt the skillet. The skillet retains its shape and the sugar does not.

Solutions. Another test that comes within the experience of the children is that of solubility. They, as well as the chemist, make use of it in becoming acquainted with the characteristics of different substances. A sample of very fine white sand may look much like a sample of sugar, but the sand will not dissolve in water, while the sugar does so readily. Some things that are not soluble in water are soluble in other liquids. The mechanic uses gasoline to dissolve the oil and grease off his hands, as these substances are not soluble in water. Water can be used for cleaning a candy or sirup spot off clothing, while it will not remove a grease spot. Gasoline, which removes the grease spot, will not dissolve the candy spot.

Substances tend to dissolve in other substances that are similar in chemical make-up.

About Chemical Reactions. Chemists always take chemical reactions into consideration when finding out what a substance contains. Chemical reactions are those that involve the processes that change one substance into another. A chemical change takes place when acid is put on limestone. The reaction produces carbon dioxide. Carbon dioxide can be detected by bubbling it through limewater. It gives a milky white substance (p. 385). Baking powder when moistened and heated gives off carbon dioxide and sometimes ammonia gases, which escape during baking. Carbon dioxide has the property of being noncombustible. Therefore, it is excellent for putting out fires. Most substances that contain carbon will char, producing charcoal when heated (p. 396). That some substances contain hydrogen can be shown by holding a cold object in the flame produced by burning a substance such as a candle or gas (p. 382). Hydrogen from the burning candle or gas combines with oxygen from the air and forms water, which contains hydrogen.

Every substance has something about it that is different from other substances. These properties can be observed, and they help to determine what a substance is and how it can be used. In determining what a particular substance is, children as well as the professional chemist can make use of many of the procedures mentioned. Many simple tests can be made that do not require complicated equipment.

Man Makes Use of Chemistry

Man has benefited from the use of chemical forces in his work for a very long time; however, only in modern times has chemistry been studied in a scientific manner. Some would say that chemistry had its beginning with the ancients; others would state that it had its origin long ago in the crude laboratories of the alchemists. Alchemy lacked a basis in scientific theory, and contributed little to the advancement of chemistry.

Alchemists were looking for the "elixir of life" which they thought would enable them to conquer death. They also tried to change other metals into gold. They mixed substances in a more or less hit-or-miss fashion, hoping for the best. However, in this way they did make some valuable discoveries. Today, chemists have the experiences of the past from which to profit. They have a better understanding of matter and energy. Present-day chemists also have developed better equipment, and they have been much more successful. The alchemists were not familiar with what is known as the scientific approach to the solution of problems.

According to some, chemistry had its beginnings as a science when oxygen was discovered in the late eighteenth century. Until that time, it is believed that no one understood the

process of burning. The combining of oxygen with fuel in the process of burning was worked out on a scientific basis. Since then the science of chemistry has made tremendous strides. The areas for investigation are very extensive. Most scientists have limited their study to a specialized field.

With few exceptions, the world of the past had the same elements as the world of today. Earlier civilizations, however, did not understand and hence could not take advantage of the available resources.

Fire and Explosions Are Used in a Variety of Ways. One of the most spectacular phases of chemistry, and hence one which attracts the child's attention and interest, is that concerned with explosives. "What is an explosion?" and "How can we make an explosion?" are questions often asked by children. In any discussion of explosions and explosives

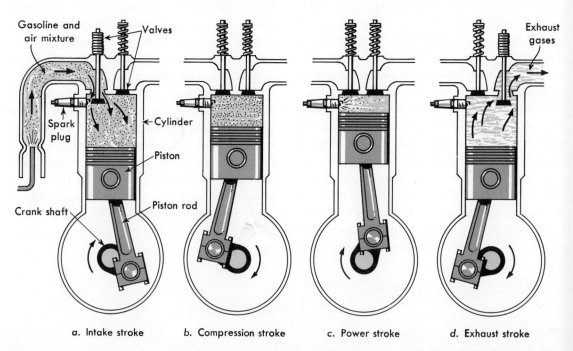

A four-cycle gasoline engine. (a) Intake valve is open, fuel mixture is drawn into cylinder. (b) Valves closed, gas is compressed by rising piston. (c) A spark is fired, exploding the fuel, producing power. (d) Exhaust valve is open, burned gases are driven out.

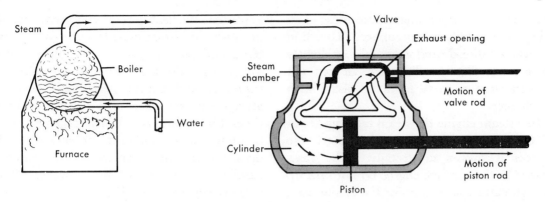

A steam engine and boiler.

one must also consider related controls and necessary safety factors. For it is wise to recognize that dangers are involved, and should therefore be avoided. Some things which are useful can also be harmful. Fire, for example, does a tremendous amount of damage and is often difficult to manage, and yet it is one of the most valuable things with which man carries on his work.

Explosions are made use of in many different ways. Blasting is often utilized to break up large masses of mined materials, to construct roads, to make excavations for buildings, and to accomplish other related kinds of useful work. Sulfur is broken up by this means before being loaded on cars for transportation. Coal is blasted from the walls of the mine in order that it may be loaded on cars and removed from the mine. In digging canals explosives are often used.

Gasoline-Engine Explosions. An entirely different use of explosions is the use made in the operation of a gasoline engine. Gasoline mixed with air is taken into the cylinder of the engine and is exploded when a spark is made by the spark plug. It is the explosion which causes the piston to move down to the other end of the cylinder. The walls of the cylinder have to be made strong enough to withstand the explosion without breaking.

The obvious thing about an explosion is the fact that it can do a great deal of pushing. It can push pieces of rock apart or push a piston from one end of a cylinder to the other. Why is it that exploding substances can push with such force? This brings us to the question of what an explosion is. How can we find the answer to this problem?

The gasoline engine is somewhat like the steam engine. Each has a piston which moves in a cylinder. It is an explosion that does the work in a gasoline engine. No explosion takes place in a steam engine, but perhaps we can get some hint of what an explosion is by considering what it is that does take place in a steam engine. The pressure in a steam engine is due to the fact that steam takes up much more room than the liquid water from which it was made. In other words, steam must expand until it has enough room. This would lead us to surmise that perhaps something is expanding in the cylinders of the gasoline engine.

A mixture of air and gasoline enters the cylinder. We know that the air and gasoline are changed to different chemicals in the cylinder because it has been found that the gases coming out of the exhaust are mostly carbon dioxide and steam. Could the pressure be caused by the fact that the steam and carbon dioxide take up more room than the original gasoline and air? How much more room these gases take up can readily be determined. They find that carbon dioxide and steam take up slightly more room than gasoline and air but not enough more room to push the piston with much force.

In a steam engine the steam takes up about 1750 times as much space as the water! No wonder it pushes so strongly. The gases formed in the gasoline engine do not take up enough extra space to make the engine run. They help the engine to run, but we must look for a further explanation. We need another force which will cause the gases to take up more room.

Perhaps you have noticed that the rails of a railroad track are laid so that there are small spaces between them in winter. When the weather is hot, these spaces nearly disappear. The iron rails have actually become longer and almost filled up the spaces. They have expanded because of the heat. Not only do metals expand when hot, but liquids, such as the alcohol in alcohol thermometers, and gases, such as air, also take up more room when they are hot than when they are cold. Will this fact help us to explain an explosion? We know that a great deal of heat is produced in a gasoline engine, because the engine will get very hot if we do not keep plenty of water in the radiator to cool it. The heat produced by the explosion makes the gases expand, or take up a great deal more room than they occupied when they were cooler. It is believed that this is the main cause of the force of exploding gasoline.

But we still do not know all about an explosion of gasoline and the oxygen of the air. We know that it makes a great deal of heat. We know that carbon dioxide and steam are formed by the explosion. A little carbon monoxide is also formed. This is the substance which can cause the death of a person who stays in an insufficiently ventilated garage in which the engine of a car is running. We

know that the heat generated is great enough to cause the carbon dioxide and steam to expand and push a piston. But there is still something about gasoline which we have not explained, and that is the fact that it does not always explode when it is lighted. Sometimes it burns instead. When gasoline is used in a torch, we do not want it to explode. If it does, it injures the workman. We do want the gasoline in a torch to burn, however. The torch would be useless if the gasoline did not burn. How can we make gasoline explode sometimes and burn at other times?

Speed of Burning. The speed of burning is affected by the amount of contact between the fuel and oxygen. When there is more contact burning is more rapid. One fans a fire, thus giving it more oxygen, to make it burn faster. It is easier to burn a magazine if the sheets are torn out and crumpled a bit. When the sheets are torn out there is more space between them for oxygen from the air. Sometimes one reads of coal-dust explosions. They result when a mixture of fine coal and air is ignited. In this case each little particle of coal is in contact with oxygen, so that the entire quantity burns almost simultaneously. When this occurs there is much expansion due to the formation of new gases and the high temperature that accompanies burning.

Gasoline, oil, or kerosene will burn when there is contact between them and oxygen with a sufficiently high temperature at the points of contact. When one ignites a fine mixture of one of these combustible substances and oxygen, the entire quantity *burns simultaneously. If this burning takes place in an enclosed area, great pressure is developed.*

In a gasoline torch the gas burns as it makes contact with oxygen, which means that it burns close to the nozzle. If some gasoline or alcohol is burned in a dish, the combustion takes place as the gasoline is vaporized at the borderline between the hot vapor and the air.

In the cylinder of the automobile engine a spark ignites a mixture of gasoline vapor and air. Since each particle of vapor is in contact with air, the burning takes place *very rapidly*. This accounts for the *explosion*, the pressure of which pushes the piston of the gasoline engine. If combustion takes place too quickly in an automobile engine it may cause a knock. Chemicals such as tetraethyl lead are added to gasolines in order to slow down combustion and reduce knocking. They are called antiknock compounds.

As fuel combines with oxygen, it forms large quantities of very hot gas under great pressure. This pressure may be used to drive the pistons of a gasoline engine, to push a jet plane through the air, or to lift a rocket far into space (p. 702).

EXPERIENCE. *To learn about gasoline engines.* Perhaps an excursion can be made to a local garage. There the children can see the parts of an engine. A mechanic will probably be glad to answer questions and to show different parts of an engine. The children can see the cylinder in which explosions take place. They will note the pistons that move up and down in the cylinders. The pistons are fastened to a crankshaft. The crankshaft goes round and round as the pistons go up and down. The children will be interested in seeing a spark plug and in noticing where the spark is produced.

In this excursion both boys and girls, in addition to learning about the gasoline engine, should gain an increased appreciation of the important role of mechanics and technicians in our modern life.

Heat from Fire. Fire is used to produce heat. Coal, oil, gas, and other substances are burned to produce heat for our homes. The heat from burning coal or oil is used to form steam for use in steam turbines, which turn electric generators or drive the propellers of ships.

For centuries men have used fires to furnish heat to cook their food. We could not live comfortably in some parts of the world without heat for our houses. Fire is used to furnish this heat (p. 373).

In industry, fires serve many purposes. They are used to provide heat to melt metals, to separate substances in the process of distillation, to soften plastics so that they may be molded into desired shapes, for the making and shaping of glass, to evaporate water in the purifying of salt and sugar, and for many other purposes. Fires provide high temperatures, as in the heating of limestone to a temperature at which it decomposes to give quicklime and carbon dioxide. Fire enters into the chemical process of refining some metals, as for example, in the production of iron from iron ore. Iron ore is generally an oxide of iron, somewhat similar to rust. Coke and iron ore, along with some other materials, are put into the blast furnace. In effect, the hot coke (carbon)

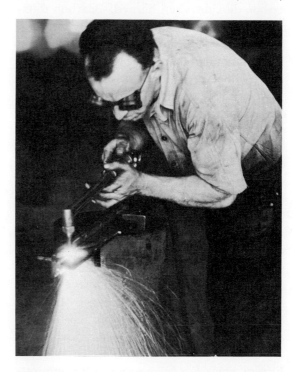

Acetylene welder using a torch to cut a steel plate. (G. A. Douglas from Gendreau, New York.)

unites with the oxygen, forming carbon dioxide and setting the element iron free. The molten iron is drawn off at the bottom of the furnace.

The cutting of iron with an oxygen-acetylene torch is a chemical process in which the iron is burned. In this case, the hot iron oxidizes in a stream of oxygen. High-temperature torches are used in a similar manner in cutting holes in stones in preparation for blasting. This speeds up the process of mining, as holes can be cut much faster than by drilling in the conventional manner. One of the first steps in the manufacture of sulfuric acid is the making of sulfur dioxide by burning sulfur. It has been estimated that for every person in our country about 163 pounds of sulfuric acid is used each year.

EXPERIENCE. *What are ashes?* It may seem strange that ashes are left after coal has been burned, since coal is mostly carbon and forms carbon dioxide when burned. Carbon dioxide is an invisible gas, and certainly does not form ashes. The ashes are that part of the coal which is not carbon. They represent the part which either does not burn or forms a solid substance when it does burn. A little of the carbon may remain unburned as part of the ashes.

EXPERIENCE. *What is smoke?* Some fires make smoke, and others do not. Smoke is made up of millions of tiny particles of ashes which are light enough to float in the air. If the ashes are made up of large pieces, there may be no smoke; but if they are made up of very small particles, there may be a thick smoke. Some of the smoke may be unburned bits of carbon. It is often possible to make smoke by blowing on ashes or by dumping ashes which have come from a coal furnace or a coal stove.

EXPERIENCE. *Fire has many uses.* It is interesting to note the different types of uses fire may

have. Fire is often used not only to furnish heat but also to destroy unwanted waste material, as in the burning of rubbish. It may be used to burn a chemical so as to turn it into a different chemical, as in the production of sulfur dioxide by burning sulfur in the manufacture of sulfuric acid, described earlier.

EXPERIENCE. *Making soot.* When we burn a candle and hold a glass over the flame, the glass becomes covered with soot. Soot is car-

Carbon from the burning candle is deposited on the glass plate.

bon which has not burned. It is often collected on a large scale, and used for making printer's ink. It is called lampblack when made commercially. A kind of lampblack, called carbon black, is used in making automobile tires.

Some Substances Preserve Other Substances.
Coverings. If a piece of iron is left exposed outdoors, everyone knows what will happen to it. It soon rusts. It combines with oxygen. If one leaves a piece of unpainted wood outside, it will soon rot unless it has been specially treated or unless it happens to be an unusually resistant variety of wood, such as California redwood. In order to preserve certain materials outdoors, one must protect them from the weather, and in some cases from insects, by painting or varnishing. Children are often curious about why steel and iron structures, such as fences and bridges, are first painted with a red-orange paint and then covered with black paint. The orange paint contains lead oxide, which gives it its color. This paint sticks to the iron surface and protects it from the water vapor and oxygen of the air. Some paints would come off too easily. The second coat of paint, which may be black or any other color, will stick to the orange paint better than it will stick to the iron itself.

If it is not desirable to paint iron, it may be protected by a covering of another, more resistant metal. This is necessary in a can which is to hold a liquid which could dissolve a protective coating of paint or varnish. Tin is plated over the iron which is used in tin cans. *Galvanized iron* is iron which has been coated with zinc. A tin can will not rust so long as the tin covering is intact; but as soon as it is cracked so that air can reach the iron, the can rusts rapidly. Since tin is so much more easily preserved than iron, one may wonder why pure tin is not used. This is partly because tin is much more expensive than iron. We could not afford to have cans made wholly of tin.

Moreover, tin is weaker than iron, and would not be sufficiently strong for many purposes for which iron is used.

Lacquer and varnish also furnish a tough protective coat; they can be put on colored articles without obscuring the color. Iron household utensils, such as stoves, refrigerators, and cooking ware, are covered with enamel or porcelain; trimming and bumpers on cars and such fixtures as faucets may be coated with chromium or nickel. It is often a matter of separating an object in some way from a corroding agent.

Iron ships corrode rapidly in the water in the same way that the plates of a storage battery are eaten away by electrical action (p. 818). The hull of the ship divides into countless minute areas, each electrically charged. These areas pair off to form tiny electrical cells or batteries, using the water for an electrolyte or current carrier (p. 813).

Atoms of iron, by way of a chemical reaction, may collect on the surface of the ship as cakes of rust. The iron outer part of the ship is thus subjected to an intense electrical and chemical attack that rapidly destroys it unless it is kept constantly painted or otherwise protected.

Cathodic Protection. This is a method that is proving quite successful. Plates of magnesium metal are attached to the hull. Magnesium is more active than iron and with the iron forms a battery: the magnesium is one pole and the iron is the other. The magnesium is eaten away, but the iron remains untouched as long as any magnesium is present. The magnesium plates can be replaced as often as necessary, and the ship is thus protected.

Hot-water tanks may be protected in the same way. A rod of magnesium protects the iron tank from corrosion and keeps the hot water free from rust. Steel pipelines laid deep in the ground may also be protected in this way.

Resistant Materials. Substances may be mixed, producing other substances that can resist corrosion. For instance, chromium may be mixed with iron, producing stainless steel, an alloy, which is more resistant to corrosion than iron by itself (p. 416).

EXPERIENCE. *Painted wood does not rot as rapidly as unpainted wood.* If the children are old enough to sustain interest in an experiment which takes a large part of the year to complete, they may enjoy testing wood. A piece of unpainted white pine and a painted piece may be left outdoors. After a number of months it may be possible to see which one is going to deteriorate sooner. In connection with this experience, wood fences, sheds, or other buildings could be observed. Perhaps there is an old frame building in your community in good condition because it has been painted regularly. Perhaps someone who is interested in the preservation of buildings will talk to the children.

EXPERIENCE. *What is the effect of paint on iron?* Many nails will rust if they are exposed to the weather or are left in a damp place. Paint one large nail carefully, so that no part of it can come in contact with the air. Place it, together with a similar unpainted nail, outside on the window sill. The unpainted nail will rust.

EXPERIENCE. *Tin protects iron.* Obtain two tin cans. These cans are composed of iron that has a very thin coating of tin. Make some scratches on one of the cans and leave the other with its coating of tin undamaged. Put both cans in a damp place for a few days. Notice that the one on which the tin coating has been damaged rusts more quickly.

EXPERIENCE. *Some substances help to prevent rusting.* Get two other undamaged cans and scratch some places on each of them. Cover the scratches on one of the cans with varnish or nail polish then put them both in a damp place for a few days. You will notice that the scratches that were protected by the varnish or nail polish did not rust so quickly. Some types of varnish may be used, instead of tin, to prevent cans from rusting.

EXPERIENCE. *To what extent does zinc preserve iron?* Take two pieces of galvanized iron which can be obtained from an old pail or sheet of roofing. Scratch the zinc coating in some places on one of them and leave the other undamaged. Put them in a damp place for a few days to see how much more rapidly the iron rusts where the zinc has been scratched off.

EXPERIENCE. *Oil and grease will also prevent iron from rusting.* The children can carry on some experiments to see how much less readily oiled nails or wire rust. Workmen oil their tools before putting them away for long periods of time. Hunters also keep their guns oiled. Have the children had experience with rusting of their own toys?

Food Preservatives. Through science man has improved his health by providing for a variety of foods at all seasons of the year. He has perfected ways of sterilizing food, using heat and then sealing the food in airtight containers; by radiation with gamma and beta rays; and by the use of chemicals such as salt, nitrates and nitrites, organic acids, and smoking. Certain antibiotics have been found of value in preserving fresh fish and poultry. Artificial refrigeration and dehydration inhibit the growth of bacteria. Man can preserve food when enough is available for this purpose with the assurance that he can eat it at another time and place. He can, for example, have fruits and vegetables when they are out of season. He can also have them in parts of the country where they do not grow. Wrappings made of plastics protect foods, and when they are used, as much as half of the previous waste of fresh vegetables is avoided. Molding in bread is inhibited by chemicals such as calcium and sodium propionates. During the evaporation of milk, curdling is prevented by the use of sodium phosphates. Baked goods and confections are prevented from drying out by the chemical, sorbitol. Molds are prevented from forming on cheese by sorbic acid. Sanitary chemicals are necessary for the proper maintenance of the plants and equipment that are used in the processing of food.

The government spends large sums of money and employs many people to keep a constant check on food supplies. The people have this protection which assures that only food that is safe should be sold to them. Unfortunately, some food preservatives are slightly harmful. Food producers must be educated not to use, and if necessary prevented from using, harmful chemicals as preservatives.

EXPERIENCE. *Learn about the duties of health officers in providing for safe food.* In case the teacher does not know who the health officers in the community are, a physician or nurse will be able to tell her. From them she can get information as to the facilities provided by local, state, and national departments of health. One will find that there are numerous people at work to safeguard our food, water and medical supplies.

EXPERIENCE. *What foods are preserved?* Have the children make lists of foods that would not be available during the winter if it were not possible to have them preserved. They will also be interested in making a list of the foods that come from another place than the one in which they live.

EXPERIENCE. *How are chemicals used in preserving foods?* Arrange for someone who is familiar with the process of curing meat to tell the children about it. Cook some fresh and some cured bacon and notice the difference in the odor and taste.

EXPERIENCE. *How does cold storage affect the chemical action responsible for spoiling food?* This can be done by putting one glass of milk in the refrigerator or outside during cold weather, and leaving another in a warm room. Also try this with fruits and with vegetables. Perhaps the teacher can arrange for the children to visit a frozen-food locker.

EXPERIENCE. *Canning preserves foods.* In the process of canning, food is heated to a high temperature to destroy bacteria that might be in it. It is then sealed in the can so that bacteria cannot get in. This also prevents the air from coming into contact with the food, and thus prevents chemical reactions with oxygen. Perhaps the teacher with the children can arrange to can some food. If the teacher wishes she may ask one of the mothers to help with it. In some localities arrangements can be made for a trip to a canning factory.

Foods packaged in cans or bottles are labeled with the name of any preservative used. Cider often contains sodium benzoate, which is added to check the "hardening" process. Maraschino cherries are treated with sulfur dioxide as well as sodium benzoate. Vinegar is extensively used in preserving, or pickling, certain foods—especially cucumbers and olives.

Preserving Dead Plants and Animals. It is at times desirable to preserve dead organisms. This is usually done in order that biological and medical students and research scientists may study them. Such specimens are generally preserved in a formaldehyde or an alcohol solution. These solutions prevent bacteria and other decay-producing organisms from growing.

Some Substances Change the Properties of Other Substances. *Color and the Appearance of Substances* (p. 418). Most human beings are sensitive to color. Children are especially fond of bright colors. People get tired of looking at the same color constantly and like a variety of colors. Children do not like to wear clothes of the same color all the time. Adults do not like to drive cars or to live in houses that are all the same color. Much money has been spent, and chemists have spent much time, in developing methods of making a variety of colors which will not fade.

A very important source of dyes is coal tar. Coal tar is made from soft coal (bituminous coal). The tar can be broken down into several substances. Some of these substances may be treated with additional chemicals and made into dyes. Dyes of many different colors can be made from coal tar.

EXPERIENCE. *The effect of chemical change on some colors.* Put some material such as red cabbage or red flowers into washing ammonia. Let it soak for some time to see whether there is a change in color. Put some blue flowers or some red cabbage that has bleached out into vinegar and note the effect of the acid in the vinegar on the color.

EXPERIENCE. *Focus attention on the variety of colors.* Have the children make a list of the colors of different things at home. Keep a list of colors that are visible outside and in the classroom at different seasons of the year. Have them inquire at the grocery and at the hardware store to learn what colors can be purchased to color foods and wood surfaces. The art-supply store or toy store will have paints, colored pencils, and crayons. Certain dyes can be purchased at the drugstore.

EXPERIENCE. *Advances have been made in creating colors.* If the children read in the library or inquire at a museum they can learn how their great-grandparents obtained different colors. Perhaps the children will be interested in trying out some of the old-time procedures. Cut an old bedsheet into small pieces, or have the children bring some clean, white cloths from home and arrange to color them as their grandparents did. Try to obtain some dyes from the store and color some other cloths with them. The children will observe that through modern procedures we can be more sure of getting the desired colors.

There are some things such as sheets and pillowcases which we may prefer to have white or colorless. Since some of the materials of which these things are made, such as cotton, are of a brownish color naturally, the problem becomes one of removing the color. This is often done by adding a chemical which will combine with oxygen so readily that it will take the oxygen away from the colored chemical. This may change it to a colorless chemical. The chemical which is added to do this is known as a *bleaching agent*. Sulfur dioxide sometimes bleaches because of this action.

On the other hand, some colored chemicals are made colorless by the addition, not the removal, of oxygen. Chlorine and water, when put together, form hydrochloric acid and give off oxygen. If a colored chemical is immersed in the solution, it may combine with the oxygen and lose its color. Hydrogen peroxide also furnishes oxygen for bleaching in this way. There are some bleaching processes in which a chemical is made colorless without the addition or the removal of oxygen.

EXPERIENCE. *Observe the effects of some bleaching agents.* Call attention to the effect of the sun in bleaching some colors. Perhaps one of the children can bring an old window curtain, partly bleached by sunlight. Wash two pieces of unbleached muslin. Dry one in the sun and one inside. Repeat several times. The sun-dried piece should become the whiter.

Soak materials of different colors in Clorox to find the ones that Clorox bleaches out more readily.

Some dyes or stains are easily removed from clothing, while others are difficult or impossible to bleach out. Have the children learn how their mothers remove stains of different kinds. Blood stains, for example, can be easily removed if the garment is washed first in cold water. If the cloth that is stained with blood is put into hot water, the stain becomes much more difficult to remove.

Chemicals May Change Odors. Articles are sometimes made attractive by a change in odor or by a change in taste, which is often the result of a change in odor. Thus maraschino cherries are artificially flavored.

Odors, like colors, are changed by changing the chemical which is producing the odor. Face powders and talcum powders are often made attractive by the addition of perfumes. When one realizes that many perfumes have some disagreeable substance such as civet or musk as a base, he realizes what a decided change in odor must occur in the manufacturing process.

By Means of Chemicals Man Is Able to Take Photographs. One of the most useful tools which scientists have produced is the camera. Besides affording entertainment, motion pictures and television may be a means of education. They make it possible for one to travel extensively and cheaply without ever going far from home. Snapshots or films of a trip preserve the high spots, so that one can enjoy it again years later, simply by looking at the pictures.

Photographs are very useful in scientific work. A picture preserves the evidence for everyone concerned to see for himself. Sometimes an action takes place too rapidly for us to see it in detail. If one has a motion picture of it, he can run the picture slowly or stop it at

Developing

1. Load developing tank with film

2. Pour in developer

3. Spin agitator

4. Pour developer back into bottle and rinse

5. Pour in fixer

6. Return fixer to bottle and rinse

7. Hang film up to dry

Printing

1. Place negative and printing paper in a print frame. Dull side of negative against shiny side of paper

2. Expose to white light

3. Develop and fix prints

4. Wash prints in running water

any place he wishes, and so study the action in detail and at leisure. At certain observatories the sky is photographed every night, so that new objects can be discovered in the sky and so the past behavior of known objects can be studied from the old photographs. Sometimes discoveries are made by astronomers merely by examining these photographs.

What part do chemists play in making these pictures? In the first place, there is a film, or glass plate, which is coated with a chemical containing silver. This chemical (silver bromide) is very sensitive to light. When light touches the film, metallic silver is formed. The greatest amount of silver is formed where the greatest amount of light touches the film. If one should examine the film immediately after it has been used, there would be no apparent change in the silver bromide distributed over the surface of the film. The change caused by the light becomes apparent only after further treatment of the film with chemicals. After the pictures have been taken, the film is put into a mixture of chemicals known as the *developer*.

The silver bromide on the film was affected in proportion to the intensity of the light that shone on it. That which received the most light reacts fastest and most completely with the developer. The film is left in the developer only until the silver bromide which was exposed to light has had time to produce metallic silver. The *negative* is a reverse copy of what was in front of the camera, with the part that was the lightest in the object being darkest on the negative.

When the film is taken out of the developer it is washed briefly to remove the developer. Then it is put into the *fixer,* which dissolves all of the silver bromide that did not react with the developer. If the film is not left in the fixer long enough, the negative will get darker later on, as the silver bromide continues to be affected by light. In other words, the fixer treats the film in such a way that light no longer affects it. When one has a portrait taken at a professional photographer's, he receives rough proofs to choose from. Sometimes these rough proofs have not been put into the fixer. They often get dark after one has had them for a few days.

When the films are taken from the fixer (after about twenty minutes), they must be washed in running water for an hour or so to remove the fixer completely. They are then dried.

When one looks at a film, he notices that the dark part of the picture looks light, and the light part looks dark. This is why it is called a negative. To get the picture the way it should look, one must print it on paper which has silver bromide on it. The negative is placed with its dull side against the paper and its shiny side upward. The film and paper are usually held in a frame with a glass over the front. The paper has to be taken out of the envelope in which it comes and put into the frame in the dark or in a room with a red safety light. A bright light would ruin the paper, since light also causes a change in the chemicals on the printing paper. The frame, with the film and paper in it, is held in front of a light for a few seconds, and then the paper is put into the developer and the fixer, just as the film was. Since the greatest amount of light shone on the light-sensitive paper through the lightest portions of the film, and the least amount of light through the darkest portions, the printed picture appears with the light objects light and the dark objects dark. Black-and-white pictures may be made brown and white by putting them into a different solution of chemicals.

Blueprints are made in much the same way as the silver photographs except that different chemicals are used to develop them. Some of them are developed in water, without other chemicals. Blueprint paper is coated with chemicals which contain iron instead of silver.

Left: *This is a positive, the way a picture looks after printing. the camera. (Lawlor, Boston.)*   Right: *A negative is the reverse of whatever was in front of*

EXPERIENCE. *To develop snapshots.* Ordinary camera snapshots can be developed by means of developers which may be purchased from the drugstore. These materials are available in very small quantities. They are sold in little envelopes on which the directions are printed in sufficient detail so that anyone can follow them. Materials for developing pictures are usually available at camera shops and drugstores.

EXPERIENCE. *To examine a film.* Place a film on its printed picture so that the picture of the film fits the printed picture exactly. Now turn the film over so that its shiny side is next to the printed picture. What would have happened if the film had been placed on the paper in this way when the frame was held in front of the light?

If a film is examined, it will be found that the light objects are dark, and the dark objects are light. It is for this reason that a film is often called a negative. The finished picture is called a positive because the light parts are light and the dark parts are dark, as they should be.

Electricity Can Be Produced by Chemicals. The electricity we use in our homes and schools generally comes from a central power-house, which furnishes electricity to the city or town and the surrounding region. In some localities electricity comes from hydroelectric stations which may be many miles away. This electricity is produced by generators which can make it in large quantities.

Sometimes, however, we wish to use such a small amount of electricity that a battery or batteries or even one dry cell are sufficient for its production. Batteries produce electricity by means of the action between certain chemicals. For further information about batteries see the discussion of the dry cell and the storage battery on pages 817 and 819.

Chemical Change through the Use of Electricity. Many substances are changed chemically when a current of electricity is passed through them.   The chemist decomposes water into hydrogen and oxygen by using electricity. The storage battery in the automobile is charged by passing a current of electricity through it.   Electric currents are used in refining many metals.   Formerly aluminum was a very expensive metal, even though it was a part of many common compounds.   Man now understands how to use electricity in getting the metal from ore.   Electroplating is also dependent on the changes brought about by a current of electricity.

EXPERIENCE. *Electricity is important in the production of aluminum.* Perhaps the children can read about how aluminum is made. Suggest that they examine a map showing natural resources to learn if aluminum is manufactured close to where electricity is produced.

EXPERIENCE. *The use of current in electroplating.* For this activity a piece of copper, something to be plated, a dry cell (commonly called a battery), some copper sulfate, a glass tumbler, and two short lengths of wire conductor will be needed. A small coil of copper wire about the size of a penny can be used as the piece of copper. The children will be interested in plating belt buckles and various other things. A dry cell such as is used for doorbells can be purchased at the hardware or electrical-supply store. Copper sulfate is commonly called blue vitriol and can be purchased at the drugstore. A tablespoonful will be a sufficient quantity. Door-bell wire will be needed for use as a conductor. It can be purchased where one gets the dry cell.

After you have all the materials, dissolve the copper sulfate in a tumbler of water. Grinding and stirring will make it dissolve more quickly. Cut two pieces of the bell wire, each about a foot in length. Strip the cloth or paper covering off about an inch of each end of the wires. The top of the dry cell has two

Using electrical current in electroplating.

connections. One of them is in the middle of the top of the dry cell and the other is at the edge. Fasten the bare end of one of the wires to the middle connection and the other end of the wire to the piece of copper. Fasten one end of the other wire to the second connection on the dry cell and the other end to the object to be plated. Try to avoid having the two objects touch, as it will weaken the dry cell. Put the copper and the object to be plated into the solution. After a few minutes pull them out of the solution and the children will notice that copper has been removed from the coil of copper wire and deposited on the other object. If current passes through for a long enough time all the copper will be moved to the other object. Reversing the connection will send the copper back.

The Sources of Necessary Materials

The Ocean an Old, yet a New, Storehouse. Although for many years substances, both living and nonliving, have been obtained from the oceans of the world, man is just learning what they really have in store for him. If we consider that about three fourths of the surface of Earth is covered by water, we can appreciate some of its potential values. It is interesting to note that some estimates indicate that there are about 320 million cubic miles of sea water.

The kinds of substances as well as the amounts of such substances found in sea water vary from place to place and from time to time. In spite of these variations there is an over-all constancy of substances found in all the larger bodies of water. Thus all nations which are located near oceans have this vast resource from which to obtain these materials.

The ocean is a huge solution. Many chemical reactions may take place in it. The amount of a dissolved chemical found in water is sometimes indicated in terms of the quantity of that material which can be derived from a cubic mile of ocean water. Very large quantities of sodium chloride (common salt) can be derived from the oceans of the world. In addition to sodium chloride, magnesium and potassium are also available in sea water. Bromine gas is a by-product from the extraction of salt and magnesium. Both plants and animals accumulate elements from sea water in their life processes. Seaweeds take iodine from sea water as they grow; some algae accumulate bromine, others concentrate potassium, copper, vanadium, or beryllium. In addition to these substances, the ocean contains silver, gold, and radium. Although possible, it has been found unfeasible to extract gold and many other substances from sea water, for the cost of the process is more than the value of the substance obtained.

Oozes, diatomaceous earth, and red clay found on the ocean floor are sources of material for portland cement, filtering agents, and aluminum and copper, respectively, if ways can be found to mine them economically. Phosphorite nodules occur near shore usually in less than 300 feet of water. They are a sources of phosphorus, useful in making phosphate fertilizers. Manganese nodules are coated not only with manganese, which is important in steel making, but with several other important metals—nickel, copper, and cobalt.

Although we are concerned here about chemicals, let us not minimize the values of the living things present in the sea water (pp. 172, 267, 533). Under suitable conditions thousands of tons of carbohydrates to the square mile are produced by marine plant life. Tremendous quantities of carbon dioxide are involved, for the changes discussed under the carbon cycle (p. 432) take place in the water as well as on land. As on land, plants form the base of all life in the ocean. Most of these are one-celled algae and bacteria that can be seen only with a microscope. There are hundreds of different kinds, and they may be so numerous as to color the water brown, green, or red. It has been estimated that there may be as much as 100 pounds of these tiny plants drifting around in an acre of surface water. Associated with these minute plants are extremely small animals that feed on the plants or on any animals smaller than themselves. These animals consist of protozoa, minute crustacea, and the larvae and eggs of many species of larger animals, including fish and other forms. Together, these plants and animals form the plankton on which larger animals feed (p. 267). These slightly larger animals, in turn, are eaten by still larger animals. After this has been repeated again and again, large fish, rich in protein, are available for man's use. Certain sharks, smaller fish, and whales feed directly upon plankton.

Experiments have shown that when the same amounts of fertilizer are added to ponds as to an equivalent amount of land, more protein can be derived from life in the ponds than can be obtained by raising food on that same amount of land and feeding it to beef cattle.

Man has only begun to utilize the substances available from this vast storehouse. Where he has succeeded in the selective extraction of substances, he has utilized processes that are essentially chemical in nature. There are many new processes yet to be developed.

Fresh water is essential for land plant and animal life, and its cheap production from salt water in quantities is of major importance to mankind. Several processes for doing this are being used. Among them are *distillation, evaporation, freezing,* passing an *electric current* through it, and *chemical reaction.* When a process becomes sufficiently economical, irri-

gation projects can be set up in deserts, and cities that need it can be assured of a supply of fresh water (p. 172).

Man-Made Molecules and the Process of Synthesis. Sometimes man desires a substance which can be used for some particular purpose. If this material is not already available in a natural form he tries to make it. When a substance is made according to some preconceived design, we refer to this process as *synthesis.* It is the building up or combining of one or more substances to make a different substance. How is it possible to build up custom-made molecules? Just as a printer starts with a limited number of kinds of type, the chemist starts with certain kinds of atoms. It is his task to try to put the atoms together so that the molecules which are formed possess the desired properties. Before this can be done, he frequently has to learn how he can control or encourage the desired changes and how he can check unwanted changes. When the process or design for making a synthetic product is worked out, the product will always have exactly the same properties, because chemical reactions under a given set of conditions are exactly the same. Similar *combinations, formations, dispersals,* and *recompositions* of molecules in new forms have occurred without man's control for millions of years.

Some even consider the process of synthesis equal in importance to the release of nuclear energy. There is scarcely an aspect of everyday life that is not affected by the products of synthesis. Each helps man to have the things he wants and to do more efficiently the things he wants to do.

Raw Materials from Which Man Makes Better Substances. Over a century ago, chemists began taking substances apart to learn what elements they were made of. They have continued to broaden and perfect their procedures, and it is the atoms and molecules

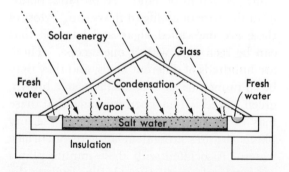

A simple solar still. Much-needed fresh water may be obtained from salt water by condensation. The sun provides the energy. (Adapted from McGraw-Hill Encyclopedia of Science and Technology, *Vol. 12, p. 12.)*

from some of these substances that the chemical and metal industries use as a basis for synthetic products.

Man's use of cellulose began thousands of years ago and proceeded slowly, step by step, until he began to use it as a chemical about a century ago. It is now one of the important raw materials used as a basis for a great variety of complex products.

Cellulose is a product of the cell walls of living plants in greater or lesser amounts. For instance, cotton is 88 to 96 per cent cellulose. Cellulose is made up of 44.4 per cent carbon, 6.2 per cent hydrogen, and 49.4 per cent oxygen by gross weight. Considering the origin of cellulose, there is every reason to think there will always be a plentiful supply. It is a renewable resource.

Air, water, salt, silica, limestone, natural gas, coal, and *petroleum* are fully as important as cellulose as sources of raw materials. Chemists take these substances apart and use their constituents in building new products. From air comes nitrogen, oxygen, carbon dioxide, and the less abundant gases, argon, krypton, neon, and xenon; from salt comes sodium and chlorine; from water comes oxygen and hydrogen. Limestone is composed of varying amounts of calcium, magnesium, carbon, oxygen, and sometimes other substances in lesser amounts. From natural gas and petroleum come thousands of hydrocarbons,

substances whose molecules consist of combinations of different numbers of hydrogen and carbon atoms. These are replacing coal to some extent as a source of raw materials. From coal come the aromatic hydrocarbons from which are obtained important substances for synthesis.

Complex *ores* are broken down to secure the metals that give to other metals such properties as strength, toughness, or great resistance to corrosion, heat, or cold.

From Abstractions to Realities. It sometimes takes a period of time between the proposal of an idea and its practical application. The idea that synthetic fibers could be made is an example. As long ago as 1665 Robert Hooke proposed the possibility of producing artificial fibers. More than two hundred years passed before man possessed sufficient knowledge to accomplish this goal. To produce the first truly synthetic fiber, nylon, it took eleven years, over a quarter of a billion dollars, and the work of over two hundred chemists and chemical engineers to contrive ways and machinery to make the material and then produce it economically. The production of nylon was not the only reward for this great labor and expense; other technological processes were discovered then that are now used in building additional synthetic fibers and plastics.

Man-Made Substances with Special Properties

Custom-Made Fibers. Many man-made fibers have been developed. Originally some of these fibers were created as substitutes for natural fibers; however, some of the fibers possessed characteristics which made them superior in some respects and they became valuable for their own intrinsic properties.

Just as properties of wrinkle resistance, lightness of weight, and attractiveness of appearance are obtainable with selective use of these synthetic fibers, so too can durable, strong, and resilient materials be made with the same fibers.

Some fibers which are normally considered

synthetic are not really synthesized. Rayon, for example, is merely another form of cellulose. Rayon is only partly synthetic. Several different kinds of fibers are included under the term rayon. Although they are prepared differently they are made from cellulose. Frequently natural fibers are combined with the rayon yarns. The rayon called viscose is the material used in some automobile tires. Acetate rayon has a remarkable ability to combine with all the other fibers. Partly synthetic fibers need not all be made from cellulose derivatives. Some are made from modified protein fibers.

Nylon, the first completely synthetic fiber, has many uses due to its properties. It is light in weight; it can be boiled or dry-cleaned; it can be made to retain its shape, hold pleats, and decrease wrinkling by setting with heat; it dries quickly, and it is very tough and strong. As a fiber, it is used in products ranging from parachutes, carpets, and toothbrushes to the sheerest hosiery. Nylon rope is noted for its strength and light weight.

There are many other synthetic fibers with properties that make them desirable for specific purposes. Orlon has great strength, resistance to molds, acids, outdoor exposure, and sunlight. It is widely used in clothing, sewing thread for special purposes, and industrial uses. Teflon is noninflammable, and resists acids, alkalies, oxidizing agents, and heat up to about several hundred degrees Fahrenheit. These properties make it valuable for such things as filter fabrics, gaskets, belting, and packing for valves. No fiber is perfect for every use; hence chemists seek to make fibers that will fill special needs.

Alloys. An alloy, with a few exceptions, is a metal made up of two or more metals intimately mixed or in combination. Probably the first alloy to be made was bronze, an alloy of copper and tin known in prehistoric times. Brass is a similar alloy of copper and zinc.

Today, most commercially used metals are alloys. The pure metals may be too soft or may be lacking in other properties that are needed. The number of alloys runs into the thousands. There are even series of alloys, each containing the same basic ingredients but in different proportions, with small amounts of other metals added to give them properties that fill a special need.

The iron alloys may contain nickel and chromium and different amounts of cobalt, copper, molybdenum, tungsten, or silicon. By mixing nickel with steel, an alloy of iron and carbon, in the right proportion we get Invar, an alloy which does not expand very much when heated, or contract very much when cooled. Such a metal is extremely useful—for example, for railroad rails. By mixing certain quantities of aluminum, nickel, and cobalt into steel we get an alloy which makes a more powerful magnet than any plain steel magnet could ever be.

There are many alloys that can be made into magnets. They grade from soft temporary magnets of cast iron to hard permanent magnets of nickel-iron, steel, steel with cobalt, chromium, and tungsten, and others containing aluminum, nickel, cobalt, iron, copper, and sometimes titanium and columbium (niobium).

Ceramic (ferrite) magnets are made from iron and oxygen and some other metal, such as copper, nickel, cobalt, zinc, magnesium, manganese, or barium. These materials can be magnetized easily and have many uses.

Chromium added to steel gives the stainless variety used, for example, in tableware and kitchen utensils. In fact, we can make steel harder, tougher, lighter, stronger, more magnetic, or almost anything we wish simply by the introduction of various other metals.

Some of the properties of alloys are surprising. Lead, for example, will melt if it is heated to 621°F. Tin will melt at 450°F. But when a solder is made which is half lead and half tin, the melting point of the solder is not the average melting point of the lead and the tin, but is lower than the melting point of either, namely, about 437°F.

The problems of materials for space work are directly related to stresses and temperatures resulting from either high speeds or high altitudes. Jet aircraft bodies and engines require light-weight materials that maintain their strength even at elevated temperatures. Alloys based on titanium provide these properties. Platinum metal alloys are used in aircraft spark plugs to withstand high temperatures and resist corrosion and wear. The materials to fill tomorrow's needs in space work may not yet have been invented.

Mixtures of metals and compounds, such as oxides and carbides, form materials called cermets. These have great strength at high temperatures, although they do not possess all the desirable properties of some other alloys.

New alloys to replace older alloys are constantly being developed. In the future it may be possible to make alloys with almost any characteristics we wish.

Plastics. Plastics offer many characteristics which are not found in more traditional materials. They can be made light in weight and yet durable, attractive, colorful, and strong, and with special insulating properties. By improved molding processes they can be made in a variety of intricate shapes and designs. Plastics can frequently be used where wood or metal would have previously served. There are many uses of specific plastics which are determined by their properties. For example, polyethylene has been used widely in the preparation of "squeeze" bottles and in a variety of household and consumer materials. Like some other plastics, it is useful for packaging purposes. Plastic boats, shoes, and even tactical field mine detectors of this substance have already been produced.

Many plastics have proved useful to industry. Plastics can be made from a variety of sources. Some are made from vegetable materials. Others are made from chemicals derived from petroleum and natural gas. Probably the best-known plastic material is Bakelite. This is made from carbolic acid and formaldehyde. Many objects can be made from this material.

Lucite is a light, clear, tough plastic with a great many uses, an important one being its use in dental and surgical instruments, because it permits light to pass around a curve.

Nylon and Teflon are both used as plastics as well as fibers. As a plastic, nylon is used in combs, toothbrush handles, unbreakable tableware, gears and bearings, and many other things. Cookies do not stick when baked on a Teflon-coated sheet. It is used commercially where an extremely smooth, heat- and corrosion-resistant surface is needed, such as in bearings when lubrication is undesirable and where chemicals would destroy working parts.

Many plastics are used in building materials. Since plastics can be made that are durable and colorful, and because they are quite easy to maintain, they are used for floor and counter coverings, wall surfacing, and a variety of fixtures. Plastics can be used combined with other substances, such as wood and glass fibers and magnetic materials, and when properly utilized they improve the properties of substances such as pitch and tar.

For plastics to be useful in the manufacture of automobiles and aircraft, it is necessary that they last for a long time and that they be durable under a wide variety of weather conditions. A vinyl-plastic layer is used to produce safety glass. The linings of brakes are frequently made of plastics. Plastic-covered fabrics and foam plastic cushions help make interiors more attractive and comfortable. Molded plastics are used in the instrument panels, steering wheels, lenses, reflectors, and other parts of an automobile.

Synthetic Rubber. World War II gave the impetus to efforts to produce synthetic rubber. Now, in varying degrees it surpasses natural rubber in its resistance to oils, chemicals, oxygen, ozone, and sunlight. Synthetic rubber is built from various raw materials that can be derived, for example, from coke, limestone, water, and coal tar, salt, or refinery gases.

Synthetic Dyes and Pigments. Synthetic dyes and pigments are more varied in shades and more brilliant than dyes derived from plants and animals. They are based mostly on aromatic hydrocarbons with acids added. Dyes are made that will successfully color the natural fibers—wool, linen, cotton, and silk; the partly synthetic fibers—viscose and acetate rayon; and such synthetic fibers as nylon, Dacron, Orlon, and Teflon. There are dyes tailored for paper, wood, leather, food, oil, cosmetics, and soap and for use in photography.

Pigments are made from certain dyes for use in paint, lacquers, plastics, and other products. They are mechanically mixed with materials, as opposed to dyes, which are absorbed by the material to be dyed.

Chemicals. Fertilizers, insecticides, weed killers, disinfectants, explosives, ammonia, camphor, drugs, poultry and livestock feeds, and a long list of other chemicals are prepared from simpler raw materials. They promote greater health and comfort, better crops, and better livestock.

EXPERIENCE. *To call attention to the wide use of man-made substances.* Older boys and girls may note whether the substances they use in one day at home or in the classroom are natural or synthetic. They may wish to make a list, such as: desk—wood and a metal, probably an alloy; telephone—plastic; bicycle—handles, plastic or synthetic rubber; seat—plastic or leather; bell—an alloy, probably; dishes—plastic or china; knives, forks and spoons—alloy of silver or steel or silver plated on an alloy of nickel, copper, and zinc; lunch money—alloy of silver or copper; books—covers may have a plastic coating; and so on.

EXPERIENCE. *To draw attention to the properties of alloys in common use.* Boys and girls may examine an electric toaster, a washing machine, a skillet or other article. They may describe parts of it and their uses and the properties needed in the materials of which it is made. For instance, no part of a toaster should corrode; part of it must be able to withstand heat; it should look well and be easily cleaned. A certain amount of strength and toughness is needed to retain its shape and to withstand several years of use. The heating element may be an alloy of nickel, iron, manganese, and carbon; the body may be chromium-plated steel, an alloy, and the base may be an alloy or plastic.

Substances and Health

As was mentioned earlier, green plants are able to make food from carbon dioxide of the air and from water and the minerals of the soil, while animals must depend on plants for food. To be sure, there are animals which never eat plants, but the animals upon which they feed do eat plants. Human beings get their food from both plant and animal sources. In the process of digestion foods are changed into simple soluble substances which can be used by the body. These changes take place in the presence of substances in the digestive juices that are known as enzymes.

Along with the foods that man obtains from plants and animals, he must have many other substances, including water and minerals. Some of the minerals are contained in our other foods, and one does not usually have to concern himself with them. Most people are familiar with the need for salt (sodium chloride). Man's body cannot function without this chemical. During hot weather a person may lose salt by perspiration in such large quantities that the supply in his body becomes insufficient. When this occurs he suffers from what is called heat exhaustion. Many factories provide salt pills beside the drinking fountains during hot weather, and encourage workmen to take these salt tablets when they drink water. In case the food supply is deficient in compounds of iodine, the thyroid gland, which uses iodine in the manufacture of thyroxine, may become enlarged. This brings about a condition that we know as goiter. Iodized salt contains small quantities of iodine compounds and may be used as a means of securing an ample supply of this element.

When the body is not functioning properly, the physician may prescribe medicine of some kind. A physician will be able to tell whether the trouble is an infection, a dislocation, or a deficiency of some particular substance, and will prescribe appropriate treatment. Medicines should generally be taken only on the advice of a physician. A deficiency of insulin, a substance secreted by the pancreas, may result in a condition known as diabetes. Before scientists had discovered the relationship between this disease and the glandular secretion, many people's lives were shortened and made unpleasant by this condition. An overactive thyroid gland may lead to too high a metabolism rate, while an underactive one may cause the opposite effect. Medical science provides means for discovering these and many other

defects, as well as the procedures for coping with them.

In addition to carbohydrates, fats, proteins, water, and certain minerals, our bodies must have vitamins, which we usually get from our food. Most of us are familiar with the relationship between a deficiency of vitamin D, the sunshine vitamin, and rickets in children. The teacher in any community can probably find health officers who are willing to provide her with information as to whether the food of the school children is deficient in certain vitamins. They will help in making recommendations to parents in order to provide for improved health in the area.

Through science man has improved his chances of survival from surgical operations. We no longer think of ourselves as having to endure infected tonsils or appendixes, for when necessary these structures can be removed with little discomfort and danger to the individual involved. Surgical skill, anesthetics for easing the pain, and antiseptics for preventing danger from infection contribute much to our well-being. The person who is deformed at birth or by disease is not necessarily crippled for life. Many defects, whether they be of the vital organs or of other structures, can now be corrected by surgery.

When one works with children, he can appreciate how vaccines and serums have helped to alleviate childhood diseases.

Progress has been made in other fields as well. Nutritional standards have been raised. New hormone compounds, antibiotics, and chemotherapeutic agents further help to improve man's health. Man is also attempting to develop substances which can better control the degenerative and infectious diseases.

Many infectious diseases which were once quite lethal are no longer responsible for such large numbers of deaths. Antibiotics have helped to cause this decline. The duration of time for recovery in many cases has also been shortened. Antibiotics are capable of destroying or inhibiting the growth of micro-organisms. Penicillin is an antibiotic. Because the substances are so potent, very small amounts of penicillin and other antibiotics are necessary for therapeutic purposes. Some penicillin formulations are prepared so that they are now retained in the body and not excreted as quickly as they formerly were.

Chemicals such as those which cause a person to relax or become more tranquil can also contribute to the therapeutic practices in the field of mental diseases.

Radioactive substances are used in determining whether or not parts of the body are functioning properly. Radioactive iodine will show up in the thyroid after being taken orally. From the amount taken up, it can be learned whether the gland is functioning properly. Leukemia is sometimes treated with a radioisotope, and cobalt 60 is used for radiation therapy.

In the food and drug industry radioisotopes are used to sterilize food and certain drugs.

Recent advances in medicine are indicated by the fact that some sources have reported that about 80 to 90 per cent of present-day prescriptions for medicines are for substances that did not exist as medicines fifteen or twenty years ago.

As more and more is learned, perhaps we will be able to obtain medicinal chemicals which not only cure diseases but also foster and promote good health, in order that many may live a longer and more useful life.

Man through Science Continues to Provide for Better Living

Each development brings new problems. In earlier days the number of people inhabiting any locality was small. *Sewage* or home waste was disposed of by flowing it into streams or lakes. Decay usually rendered such waste harmless after a period of time. Improved living conditions, however, make it possible for people to live longer. Populations of today's cities are large and these congested areas are close together. Thus the sewage from one city or town may not have time to be rendered harmless by decay before the stream enters the next one. Thus pollution becomes continually worse, creating health hazards, and making the regions along streams unpleasant for human habitation.

Sewage consists chiefly of partly decomposed plant and animal matter. Such material is changed, by the process of decay, into soil (p. 393). Such decomposition also liberates gases which may be used as fuel. Decomposition of plant and animal matter is a chemical change. These changes take place more rapidly when the material is warm than when it is cold.

Through the application of scientific principles many cities solve their sewage-disposal problems cheaply. Sewage-treatment plants may be operated so as to cost the city very little. The fuel gas, mentioned above, is burned to heat the buildings during cold weather. Heat from this source is used to increase the rate of decomposition of sewage. This fuel gas also runs engines which operate pumps and other mechanical devices used in plant operations. Fertilizer is made from the sewage. The sale of this fertilizer provides funds to pay operators and help with other expenses of the plant.

EXPERIENCE. *How do cities dispose of their sewage?* Children might be interested in finding out

actory dumps its industrial waste into the Ohio River. (Three ns, N.Y.C.)

An understanding of chemistry entered into providing the enamel on the kitchen table, the paper on which this book is printed, the clothing one wears, the power of an automobile engine, or almost anything that man has made for himself. Not only did chemistry enter into the making of the things that man has, but the large industries, whether they manufacture paper, automobiles, foods, clothing, medicines, paints, tools, building materials, or something else, employ chemists who are constantly learning about the products. These chemists are always looking for more economical ways to make the materials and for procedures by which they can make new and better ones.

In the manufacturing of many things, *materials are left over.* Formerly these waste substances were thrown away. Now the manufacturers employ chemists who try to find ways in which useful products can be made from waste materials (Chapters 6 and 21). For example, in the manufacture of lumber tremendous quantities of sawdust and scrap wood are left. These leftovers constitute a rather large part of the total wood in the tree. Formerly the scrap wood was burned and the sawdust was left in piles to rot or was thrown into lakes or rivers. There it had a detrimental effect on the fish and other forms of life. It also made the water less desirable for drinking and recreational purposes. In modern factory operations up to 70 per cent of a tree is used. New glues and new uses permit greater use of odd-shaped and odd-sized leftovers. Glues, fuels, fertilizers, plastics, and other products are made from bark. Sawdust is used as a base for plastics, as a soil conditioner, as a fuel, and as many other things. Better and thinner saws make less sawdust, and better methods used in the seasoning of wood cut down on the amount of poor and useless material. Newer methods of cutting wood may eliminate sawdust as a by-product.

what type of sewage-disposal system is used on their farm, in their city, or nearby. It may be possible to take the children to visit a city sewage-disposal system. Visit the bank of a stream below a city that has an effective sewage-disposal system. Compare this stream with one below a city that does not have a sewage treatment plant.

Many times the entire classroom group cannot make a trip such as the one above. Some teachers arrange for a committee of children to make investigations of problems that come up. Such a committee can represent the interest of the group in securing the desired information. This type of procedure gives an opportunity for all children to work in small groups. Teachers sometimes help such committees after school or on Saturdays. On other occasions such committees are accompanied by a parent.

Through the study of chemistry man is providing the things that he needs and enjoys.

Industries have found that wastes in the form of fumes and smoke that were allowed to escape into the air may be utilized in making useful material. It is likely that as industries learn to make useful materials out of the fumes and smoke that escape from their flues and chimneys, industrial communities can be completely freed from smoke, industrial fumes, and smog. The installation of devices that return automobile fumes to the combustion chamber for burning go far toward eliminating one of the chief sources of smog.

In some sections of the world streams are polluted by waste from paper mills. The annual per-capita consumption of paper and paperboard in the United States is over 400 pounds. For each pound of paper produced, approximately a pound of material is left over. When one multiplies the quantity per person by all the millions making up the population he sees how extensive the problem of waste material is.

Smoke and gas from this old blast furnace were eliminated when new gas-cleaning equipment was installed. (U. S. Steel Company.)

Paper manufacturers look forward to the time when all this waste material will be utilized. Much progress has already been made in this direction.

EXPERIENCE. *The use of resources.* If the children live in an industrial community they can learn the different products that are produced there. They will be interested in learning what raw materials are used; and they will be surprised to learn the variety of different places from which the materials are obtained.

EXPERIENCE. *Research in a factory.* Arrange for the children to visit a factory. They can then see the changes that are made in material as it is changed into the finished product. The proprietor may be willing to indicate new developments that are in progress. If the factory is a large concern, it probably employs a number of scientists who spend their time in trying to improve the processes used. Some of these research workers will undoubtedly be looking for ways to make useful articles from waste materials. Others will be investigating possible new products.

EXPERIENCE. *New developments in food preparation.* Take the children to the grocery store. Make advance arrangements and go when the store is not crowded. Learn the ways in which the grocer keeps food from spoiling. Study the labels on food so as to see what preservatives are used and where the food was produced. The grocer can tell the children about new developments in the preparation of foods for sale. Compare a grocery of today with pictures and articles about those of the past. Consider differences in methods of storage and packaging.

EXPERIENCE. *New appliances for home use.* Take the children to a home-appliance store. Arrange to have someone tell them ways in which the new things are better. A home survey will give an idea of the modern appliances commonly used. By checking as to how long particular appliances have been in use, the children will learn how long they last. They may also want to figure the cost per week of having the use of particular devices.

EXPERIENCE. *New uses for farm products.* The children may be surprised to learn of the different products that are made from farm crops. They will find, for example, that starch, sirup, sugar, alcohol, and cloth, as well as many other things, are made from corn. They will find that even the stalks may be used in the making of other things. Farm magazines and newspapers are sources of information on such developments.

EXPERIENCE. *Appraisal of the air in your region.* Alert the children to the condition of the air in their region. Do you have smog? Do you find the air smoky and dusty? Have them help with dusting the tables and chairs. Do you have to clean the room frequently? Have them smell the air. Do they detect industrial waste products? Give them a feeling of hope that the air can be kept clean in the future.

EXPERIENCE. *Appraisal of streams in your region.* Are the streams free from rubbish and industrial waste products? Are there fish in the streams? How can the streams be improved? Keep in mind that most industries want to co-operate with communities.

The chemists learning how to make new materials search for a plentiful source from which they may make them. They may find that a clay bed, a pile of sawdust, or coal tar may be utilized. Newly discovered chemical processes often make it possible to use materials that were once considered wastes. Cheap, plentiful sources of raw materials make it possible to produce new materials cheaply. So we find that today one need not be wealthy to have the modern conveniences. A family with a small income today can have better living conditions than the wealthiest family living two or three decades ago.

Many chemists believe they have made only a small percentage of the possible compounds that can be made with carbon. They believe that many more new and useful substances can be made using carbon. Some chemists believe that silicon can be used for the making of many fine, new substances. When one realizes how much silicon is in sand, one can imagine that many useful discoveries are yet to be made. The children in our classrooms are living through a chemical revolution. They can look forward to the future with confidence.

CHAPTER 12

The Atmosphere

The Ocean of Air That Surrounds Our Planet

We are completely bathed by air from birth to death. We live in it, move in it, and grow old in it. Fortunately we do not have to buy this vital substance, for it exists in great quantities right at our very nostrils, ready to rush into our lungs at all times. We live at the bottom of a vast "ocean" of air which completely envelops Earth. We are not surprised, therefore, to find a host of phenomena which can be explained only through a knowledge of principles related to the atmosphere. This accounts for the fact that the atmosphere is an essential part of science in childhood education.

The Atmosphere and the Basic Patterns. Perhaps no part of a child's environment makes him more aware of continuous *change* than does the atmosphere that surrounds him. In the content and Experiences listed in this chapter a teacher or parent can use the experiences that children have with changes of weather and ventilation, to provide profitable teaching and learning situations.

The atmosphere furnishes for everyone dramatic and dynamic performances with its cloud formations, varied sunsets, haze, wind, rain, hail, snow, lightning, and thunder. All of our senses are involved in our observations of such phenomena. Yet perhaps we need to be even more conscious of the tremendous display of *energy* involved in the daily sequence of atmospheric phenomena. The energy in-

424

volved in the movement of great masses of air from the tropical and polar regions into the temperate regions—or the energy of a hurricane, a tornado, or a summer thunderstorm—is tremendous.

It is well for a child to become aware of the role of energy; aware that almost all, if not all, of this energy comes from the sun; understand something of the interplay of the sun's energy; understand something of the gravity of Earth; and to become aware of Earth's rotation and revolution. This appreciation is not to be developed fully in a day, a week, a year, or even in eight years, but the basis for a lifetime appreciation of the role of energy can be built in childhood.

Teachers are referred to the section on the Pattern of Equilibrium and Balance (pp. 99–100), for nowhere, it seems, is this pattern better illustrated than in the atmosphere. The hurricane, tornado, anticyclone, and the summer thunderstorm are thought to be caused by the lack of balance of forces growing out of the sun's energy and Earth's gravity and movement. If we did not have these forces creating this lack of balance we might have a static planet unsuitable for life. Meteorologists frequently speak of turbulence, atmospheric disturbances, or instability. The resulting cyclone, anticyclone, or thunderstorm is the result of the interaction of forces tending toward a balance.

How Far Outward Does the Atmosphere Extend?

The atmosphere is an envelope of gases. It is densest at Earth's surface. There are many indications that it extends a considerable distance from Earth's surface. The duration of twilight shows that there is enough dust and vapor at a height of forty-five miles to scatter light. The aurora borealis (northern lights) in the region of the arctic and the aurora australis (southern lights) in the antarctic are believed to be due to bombardment of thin gases of the upper regions of the atmosphere by charged particles that have been emitted by the sun. The borealis displays have been reported at altitudes from fifty to seven hundred miles above Earth.

From these evidences and others, scientists have concluded that the atmosphere extends to a height of hundreds of miles. It should, however, be borne in mind that air is exceedingly thin at such heights. We can gain some idea of how great the height of the upper atmosphere is by comparing it with the highest mountain, which is about five and a half miles high. The air is very thin at the tops of high mountains. Above 3.6 miles there is as much air as there is below that point. In other words, half of the air is above and half is below the 3.6-mile level. Above this point the air grows thinner, until above the fifteen-mile level there is only about one twenty-fifth of the entire atmosphere.

EXPERIENCE. *To describe twilight.* Have children observe twilight and talk about it at school the next day. Suggest that they look at the horizon in different directions. Repeat such observations at various times. Perhaps the children may wish to make murals to illustrate what they have seen. Keep in mind that as one goes towards the equator the twilight period becomes briefer.

EXPERIENCE. *Do other planets have an atmosphere* (pp. 212–221)? Frequently there is information in current periodicals on this subject.

In this work have the children learn the importance of going to reliable sources, rather than to science fiction and astrology.

EXPERIENCE. *To make a mural of the atmosphere.* Depict in a mural the height of the atmosphere, the height of Mt. Everest, and the record heights attained by such means as airplanes, manned balloons, sounding balloons, rockets, or other vehicles.

EXPERIENCE. *The atmosphere is different at higher altitudes.* Perhaps some of the children or their parents have been in the high mountains and can talk with the children about the difficulties of breathing at high altitudes. They may have had some difficulties with nose bleeds, due to the pressure being higher inside their bodies. If they drove a car in the mountainous country they can perhaps tell of some of the adjustments that had to be made so that the motor would operate at higher altitudes. Even experiences in the elevators of tall buildings may be used.

EXPERIENCE. *Learning about high altitudes.* Perhaps someone on a flight on a commercial airline can secure a copy of a flight log. This will show differences in pressure and temperature at the high altitudes at which some of the planes fly. Some child or one of the parents who has flown at high altitudes can tell the children about the adjustments that are made so that the passengers are comfortable while riding; also of the discomfort that follows a rapid change in pressure.

EXPERIENCE. *Current events and the atmosphere.* Frequently there are current events which relate to the atmosphere in some way or another. Some of these events may be local in character, while others may be described on television, over the radio, and in the newspapers. Dry conditions and heavy winds may contribute to the formation of a dust storm; a wind may carry smoke from a forest fire for hundreds of miles and influence the colors of the sunrise and sunset; at times northern lights may be observed in some regions; volcanic eruptions may scatter much volcanic dust into the air, where it may hang suspended for a very long time. Children should develop in this kind of work a feeling for the importance of securing information from reliable sources.

Air Sourrounds Us at All Times. The atmosphere is held close to Earth by gravity. If Earth were smaller, it would have less gravity and be able to hold less air. Possibly, a very long time ago, when Earth was very young, it was smaller than it is now, and as a result exerted less force of gravity and therefore held very little air. As it grew older and larger, its gravity increased, and it held more atmosphere.

The effect of gravity is to hold the atmosphere close to Earth, causing the air to be denser near the surface. The air, being constantly pulled to Earth, covers Earth's entire surface. It enters our houses, even though windows and doors are tightly closed, penetrates the soil, and goes down into valleys and deep mines. We can find no place on the surface of Earth where air is absent; in fact, the air pressure on the surface of Earth is so great that man has never been able to make a perfect vacuum. We never need fear walking into places with no air; for air is all around us, pressing into and filling every space.

Everyday experiences of children reveal to them the fact that air surrounds them. They feel the air in motion in winds; sometimes they are forced to brace themselves to walk against it. They may have seen how it turns umbrellas inside out, or, after a windstorm, how it has strewed the ground with branches. It can be brought to their attention that air carries the sounds which reach their ears. All living things depend upon the air that surrounds them (pp. 548–549). Our constant dependence on air is revealed by our need of breathing.

EXPERIENCE. *To become aware of the atmosphere.* At all levels of education children, including preschool children, can make new interpretations about the atmosphere. Observation from windows will reveal moving clouds, swaying branches, the clothing of people being blown about, the direction of blown smoke, damage of wind storms. Experiences on the playground will help children to feel the air against their bodies—the cooling effect of cool air and the warming effect of warm air. A teacher aware of possibilities can help children to have much in the way of personalized experiences with air. Children can be encouraged to extend such observation beyond the school day, to the home and to their journeys from school to home, whether they make the trip by bus, by car, or on foot. Airplanes can be observed in relation to clouds: sometimes, as we stand on the ground looking up at an airplane flying overhead, we will see the airplane disappear into a cloud or above the cloud. In this work a teacher should assist children to secure a feeling for the "depth," or "height," of the atmosphere. High clouds may help to build this feeling on the part of children.

EXPERIENCE. *To become aware of the changing aroma of the atmosphere.* In many regions the atmosphere has different odors at different times. The odor of the desert after a shower, the odor of an industry, the odor of spring, or the odor of autumn.

Take children where they can smell the air. Have them close their eyes. What do they think they smelled? Ask them if they think they can remember the odor? Repeat on other days and at different times of the year; after a dust storm; before and after a rain, or after an electrical storm. Older children can note the direction of the wind and whether the wind brings industrial odors with it.

Some smells can be associated with different seasons of the year; some smells are typically "country" smells, while others are typically "city" smells. Some smells are typical of the ocean shore; others of the pine woods; others of grasslands or desert lands. Many smells are "man-made"; others are to be found in nature. Can the children give examples of man-made smells which try to copy those found in nature?

From the developmental point of view, children begin to learn about the atmosphere at birth. As they are exposed to the conditions of the atmosphere, such as temperature, breezes, odors, and so on, they form experiential meanings (p. 4).

Sailboats are propelled by air in motion. (Lawlor, Boston.)

Experience. *We do not see air.* We can feel air, smell it when it has an odor, and breathe it. We can use it for such purposes as to fill automobile tires, but we never see it. However, dust and moisture in the air can interfere with our seeing.

Take children to a place where there is a distant view. Perhaps the classroom window will provide such a view. Have them point out some landmarks. Note that on some days the atmosphere contains so much moisture and dust that distant visibility is impossible. On some days fog may permit only the nearest objects to be seen. Older children may be interested in using the aviation term "ceiling," and other useful, meaningful terms.

The Atmosphere Is Made Up of Gases

The air is not one substance, but is a mixture of several gases. These gases behave in different ways. Some of them are very important to man and other living things. The names of some of these gases—for example, oxygen and neon—are common words in children's vocabulary.

The air around us is composed of about 78 per cent (by volume) nitrogen, 21 per cent oxygen, 0.93 per cent argon, 0.03 per cent carbon dioxide, very small amounts of certain rare gases (helium, neon, krypton, and xenon), varying amounts of water in gaseous form, and dust. Using exact values, we find that nitrogen, oxygen, argon, and carbon dioxide together account for 99.99 per cent of our air. The water vapor contained in the atmosphere was not considered in making up the percentages above, because its amount varies between 0 and as much as 4 per cent in the tropics.

Water vapor and dust practically disappear in the stratosphere (p. 447), as there are no storms there to keep the air mixed. The proportions of the other ingredients do not seem to differ greatly in the stratosphere from those at the surface of Earth. Rocket soundings and other upper-air studies show that the composition of the air, while it grows "thinner" or less dense, maintains a uniform composition at heights of not less than seventy-five to one hundred miles above the surface of Earth.

Oxygen. Oxygen, as stated above, makes up about one fifth of the atmosphere. It is very important to all living things.

Oxygen is a very active substance; that is to say, it readily unites chemically with a great variety of other substances, and in doing so energy is released. When it unites with other substances rapidly, light energy and heat energy are produced, and we call the process burning. The oxygen that we breathe unites inside our bodies with the food that we eat to supply us with the energy for work or play (p. 373). Even things living in water are dependent upon oxygen. They secure it by breathing the air which is dissolved in the water or by coming to the surface from time to time.

At first thought, one might be afraid that the supply of oxygen would be exhausted by all the furnaces, motorcars, and living things which constantly use it. Instead we find a practically stable supply, as far as the present geological period is concerned. The composition of the air, however, may have been different in other geological ages. One of the sources of supply is to be found in the growth of green plants. A green plant, in common with all other living things, must have oxygen to live; but in its life processes it gives off considerably more oxygen than it uses. The net result is that a green plant actually puts oxygen into the air (p. 395). Green water plants put oxygen into the water. This is one reason for having them in an aquarium, since they help to supply oxygen for the fish to breathe (p. 541).

EXPERIENCE. *There is air in water.* Fill a jar or tumbler with cold water. Allow it to stand undisturbed for a few hours. Small bubbles will collect on the side of the jar or tumbler. These bubbles are air which was in the water. Cold water can hold more air than warm water; as water warms, air leaves it. It is this dissolved air that is used by fish in breathing.

EXPERIENCE. *To remove the air from water.* Put some water in a pan which can be heated. A clear cooking dish may be better if one is available. Heat the water over a hot plate. Watch for the bubbles of air that come out as the water is heated. The bubbles that come out before the water starts boiling are mostly air. The bubbles that rise to the surface after it is boiling are mostly steam. Steam is water vapor at the temperature of boiling water.

EXPERIENCE. *Air affects the taste of water.* Put some water in a clean pan or kettle so that it can be heated. Heat it until it has boiled for a few minutes. Most of the air which is dissolved in the water will be driven out. Set the water aside while it cools. Then, being careful not to stir it, thus mixing it with air, pour samples into cups for the children to taste. They will notice that it tastes different from what it did before it was boiled. Now mix the remaining water with air by stirring it vigorously or by pouring it back and forth from one container to another several times. After it has been mixed thoroughly with air, have them taste it again. The children will notice that putting the air back into water improves the taste.

EXPERIENCE. *How much oxygen is there in air?* Obtain a straight-sided jar, such as an olive

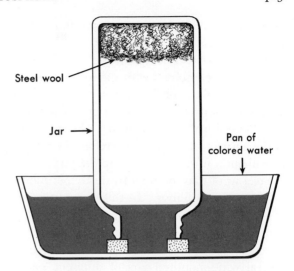

The water may be colored by a few drops of ink.

or a pickle jar. Fill it with water and empty it, leaving some droplets clinging to the bottom and sides. Put into it one or two spoonfuls of iron filings or pulverized steel wool, and roll and shake the jar until a good many filings are clinging to the sides, held in place by the water droplets. Pour out the excess filings. The inside of the jar should be fairly well coated with iron filings.

Invert the jar and plunge the mouth well below the surface of a pan of colored water. Carefully mark the point to which the water rises inside the jar. A rubber band placed around the jar is a good way to mark this point. Secure the jar firmly in this position by placing two or three small objects such as wooden blocks or rubber erasers under the mouth of the bottle (see diagram). The objects should not obstruct the mouth of the bottle. In about two days note the position of the water inside the jar. It should be found to have risen about a fifth of the distance between the rubber band and the bottom of the jar.

Slip a glass plate under the mouth of the jar and remove the jar from the water. Insert a burning splinter of wood in the jar. The flame should go out. This does not prove that *all* the oxygen has been removed from the air in the jar (p. 383), but it proves that at least some of it has.

About a fifth of the air in the jar was oxygen. This oxygen combined with the iron filings to form iron oxide, or ordinary iron rust. Almost all the oxygen was thus taken out of the air and "locked up" with the iron. About a fifth of the air was taken away; therefore the water rose about a fifth of the way up the jar.

Steel wool may be used in this experiment in place of iron filings. In this case put a bit of the steel wool in the bottom of the jar.

EXPERIENCE. *Fire needs air to burn.* Secure several wide-mouthed jars of different sizes. Stick upright to the top of the table (or to small squares of cardboard) as many birthday candles as you have jars. Light the candles. Then have several children (one to each jar) invert the jars over the candles, as nearly as possible at the same time by a spoken command or word, or by some form of signaling device such as they may use in games. Watch the candle flames. Soon one will go out, then another. Which one goes out first? The one in the smallest jar—that is, the jar with the least air in it. (Repetition of this experiment, using a number of jars of different sizes, will make this experience quite dramatic.) Now quickly lift one of the jars, trying to "spill" as little of the "old" air as possible; relight the candle and replace the jar over the candle. This time the candle goes out much sooner. Force out the old air by filling the jar with water and emptying it. Again light the candle and again replace the jar. This time the candle may burn as long as it did the first time. The candles used something in the air.

The candles did not use all the oxygen. They merely used it to the point where they could no longer burn.

EXPERIENCE. *Putting out a fire.* On an asbestos or metal pad make a very small fire out of bits of paper. When the fire is burning well,

Fire needs air to burn.

pour sand on it. The sand keeps air from the fire, putting it out. Perhaps the concept of smothering can be used with this Experience (p. 383).

EXPERIENCE. *Working with jack-o'-lanterns.* In making a Halloween jack-o'-lantern children sometimes cut the holes for the eyes, nose, and mouth too small, so that the candle inside does not burn satisfactorily. This provides an opportunity to lead them to see that fire must have air.

Safety Instruction and Fire Prevention. (P. 101.) The foregoing activities offer an excellent start for safety instruction and fire prevention (p. 385). No experiments with fire should be performed without a bucket of water (or sand) at hand in case of accident. A discussion may easily be started about what to do in case one's clothes catch fire. One should never run, as running supplies more air to the flames. Instead one should roll on the floor or, better still, wrap oneself in a rug or coat or blanket. The first essential is to be calm.

Nitrogen. Nitrogen, which makes up about 78 per cent of the air, is, in some ways, the exact opposite of oxygen. It is extremely inactive, in contrast with the activity of oxygen. It is with great difficulty made to combine with other substances.

The nitrogen which we breathe takes no part in our body reactions but passes out into the atmosphere unchanged when we exhale. It serves only to dilute the oxygen.

Plants and animals contain nitrogen compounds. Animals must obtain them from other aimals or from plants; plants must obtain them from the soil. In spite of the fact that there are millions of tons of nitrogen in the air, it is useless to most living things. If the nitrogen compounds in the soil are exhausted, plants cannot grow in it. The soil is replenished with nitrogen compounds by natural forces. Some of the blue-green algae and tiny living plants called bacteria are able to take nitrogen from the air and convert it into compounds in their body processes. They are the only living things which can do so. Im-mense numbers of these bacteria live freely in the soil or in little swellings (nodules) on the roots of peas, beans, clover, alfalfa, and other leguminous plants. Where these plants are growing, the bacteria help to replace the nitrogen compounds in the soil. That is why farmers occasionally plant clover or alfalfa in fields where other crops have been growing.

EXPERIENCE. *To observe the nodules on a leguminous plant.* (P. 552.) Perhaps a clover, bean, pea or other plant can be removed carefully in such a way that children can observe nodules on the roots. A kitchen knife or a garden trowel may help to remove the plant without disturbing the roots and tearing off the nodules. Permission should be secured from the owner of the plant and the children should do as little harm to the spot from which the plant is taken as possible. The plant may be carefully returned to the soil.

During electrical storms, air masses may be heated to exceedingly high temperatures, and also subjected to high-voltage electrical charges. Man has for a long time associated a pungent odor with discharges of lightning. It is thought by many authorities that the pungent odor is in part due to the formation of nitrogen compounds during a lightning discharge.

Nitrogen compounds—ammonia (composed of nitrogen and hydrogen) and oxides of nitrogen (composed of nitrogen and oxygen) —are washed out of the air and fall to the ground when it rains. Each of these types of compounds unites with other substances to form materials from which plants can get the nitrogen needed for growth.

Since very ancient times, man has used decaying plant or animal material to supply nitrogen compounds to the soil. Such material is usually decaying leaves and stalks of plants and the waste material of animals (manure). Guano, the waste material of sea birds, is

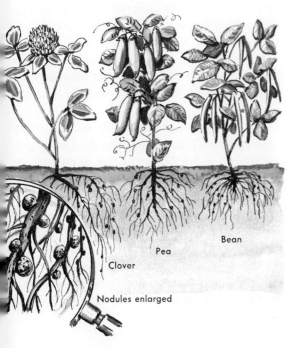

Bean

Pea

Clover

Nodules enlarged

Nitrogen-fixing bacteria form nodules on the roots of leguminous plants.

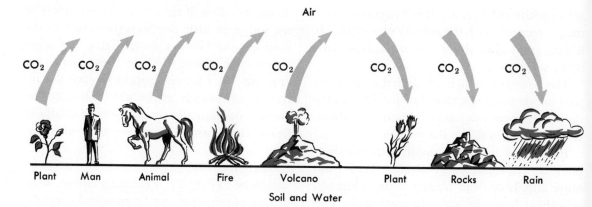

Air

CO₂   CO₂   CO₂   CO₂   CO₂   CO₂   CO₂   CO₂

Plant   Man   Animal   Fire   Volcano   Plant   Rocks   Rain

Soil and Water

A simplified diagram of the carbon or carbon-dioxide cycle.

highly prized as fertilizer. In some sections decaying fish are used as fertilizer.

In some desert parts of the world, notably central Chile, nitrogen compounds (nitrates) are found on top of the ground, where they have been left by evaporation since ancient times. In that extremely dry climate there is no rain to carry these nitrates away. Until World War I, Chile was the world's principal source of nitrates for fertilizer. Since that time, many nations have made rapid strides toward the development of processes by which nitrogen compounds can be produced synthetically. These processes are in many respects analogous to the process by which nitrogen compounds are formed in lightning discharges. Man thus becomes independent of the natural sources such as the deserts of Chile. Nitrogen compounds are used for many purposes, including explosives, fertilizers, and plastics.

Carbon Dioxide. Although carbon dioxide forms only about 0.03 per cent of the atmosphere, it plays a very important part in life processes. Living things are composed largely of carbon, which plants derive from the carbon dioxide of the air. Green plants are able to combine carbon dioxide, which they take from the air, with water, which they take from the soil through their roots, to make complex carbon compounds. They get the energy to do this from sunlight. In a very real sense, energy from the sun is stored up in plants. Animals then eat the plants, thereby getting the benefit of the energy which the plant has stored up. The animals may then be eaten by other animals. When plant or animal materials burn or decay, the carbon dioxide is returned to the air. The stored energy reappears in the form of heat energy or light energy. This whole process is sometimes referred to as the *carbon cycle* or *carbon-dioxide cycle*.

It is easy for children, reasoning along these lines, to see that the energy that they have for working and playing came originally from the sun.

We give off carbon dioxide whenever we breathe out. This comes from the food which we "burn" in our bodies to give us energy. It is also a waste product of respiration in plants.

Under ordinary circumstances we are able to breathe without giving the process any thought. But we are unable to hold our breath beyond a certain point. Breathing is very largely automatic. Scientists have discovered that this automatic breathing depends on the action of carbon dioxide dissolved in the blood.

EXPERIENCE. *Making and using carbon dioxide.* (P. 374.) Place a handful of washing soda

The carbon dioxide flows like water over the lighted candles and extinguishes them.

(baking soda will do also) in a fairly tall tumbler. Set the tumbler inside a large glass or tin jar. (A large cannister or other large container with wide mouth will do.) Pour into the soda about half a cup of strong vinegar. The soda will bubble vigorously as it gives off carbon dioxide. The glass jar now contains a large supply of carbon dioxide.

Arrange three or four lighted candles on a slanting board with pieces of cardboard tacked to the sides so as to form a trough (see diagram). Quickly remove the tumbler from the jar, and *pour* from the jar the carbon dioxide down the trough, just as you would a jar of water. The candles should be put out. Carbon dioxide is much heavier than air and will run downhill, just as water does. Carbon dioxide puts out a fire by shutting off the oxygen from it.

Prepare another jar of carbon dioxide. Fasten a candle to a piece of wire and lower the lighted candle into the jar. As it becomes immersed in the carbon dioxide, it goes out instantly. Many commercial fire-extinguishers are based on the principle that carbon dioxide puts out fire. The effect of such ex-

tinguishers is to surround the fire with a blanket of the gas.

EXPERIENCE. *To show there is carbon dioxide in soda water.* Soda water, such as is sold as bottled "pop" and at soda fountains, is made of water which contains carbon dioxide. When the pressure of the gas is released, as in removing the cap from a "pop" bottle, the gas escapes and produces bubbles.

EXPERIENCE. *To test for carbon dioxide.* Pour some fresh limewater (p. 385) (obtainable at a drugstore) into a jar of carbon dioxide and shake vigorously. The limewater turns milky; and if it is left undisturbed for a while, a white substance may be seen to settle at the bottom. This is the way that chemists test for carbon dioxide.

EXPERIENCE. *To test breath for carbon dioxide.* With a rubber, straw, or plastic tube, blow breath through fresh limewater. Does this test show carbon dioxide in the breath?

EXPERIENCE. *To test the air for carbon dioxide.* Allow a small jar of fresh limewater to be exposed to the air for a few days. What happens? Is there carbon dioxide in the air? Why should limewater be freshly prepared?

Water Vapor. Water vapor and dust are the only substances in the air which vary widely from time to time and from place to place. There are regions on Earth where the air is very dry and other regions on Earth where it is very moist. Some days the air in the place where we live seems dry, and evaporation (as, for example, from clothes on a line) takes place rapidly. At other times the air is holding nearly all the moisture it can, and wet things dry very slowly (p. 477).

Dust in the Air. Like that of water vapor, the quantity of dust in the atmosphere varies

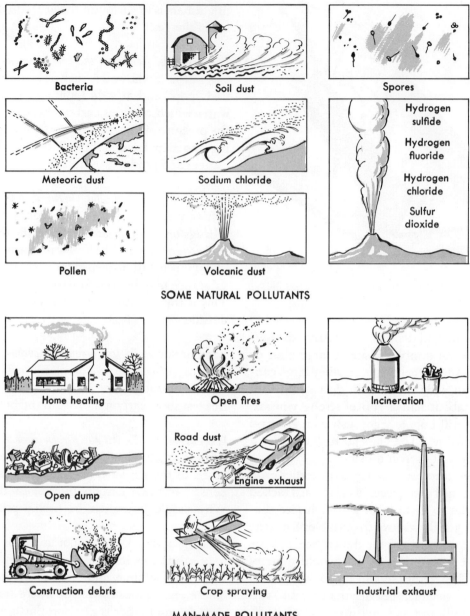

SOME NATURAL POLLUTANTS

Bacteria   Soil dust   Spores

Meteoric dust   Sodium chloride   Hydrogen sulfide / Hydrogen fluoride / Hydrogen chloride / Sulfur dioxide

Pollen   Volcanic dust

MAN-MADE POLLUTANTS

Home heating   Open fires   Incineration

Open dump   Road dust / Engine exhaust   Industrial exhaust

Construction debris   Crop spraying

from time to time. After a rain there may be very little dust in the air, whereas when a strong wind blows over deserts or plowed, dusty fields, there will be a great deal of dust in the air. The dust of the dust storms which sometimes trouble certain parts of the world is composed of good soil which is being carried away by the wind.

EXPERIENCE. *The dust in the school may be soil.* If some of the children go to a part of the school building that is seldom used, they will probably be able to gather a cupful of dust. After gathering it, add water, and then plant some seeds in it. Seeds should also be planted in some good soil so that the results can be compared.

All solid particles in the air may be called *dust*. Some of these are particles of soil, tiny bits of volcanic material, dust from meteors, bacteria, smoke, yeast cells, pollen, spores of plants, or salt from sea spray. Violent volcanic eruptions cause great quantities of fine dust to be distributed in the atmosphere. Dust in the air so scatters the sun's light as to produce brilliantly colored sunsets. Dust from the eruption of the volcano Krakatoa in 1883 floated in the air all the way around Earth, and caused brilliant sunsets for over three years.

Smoke consists of fine particles of carbon. Frequently the smoke from extensive forest fires floats in the air and causes a haze for weeks at a time. Such a smoke cloud may drift with moving masses of air, producing a haze extending hundreds of miles from the source. The smoke and other dust of large cities often serves to cut off a considerable portion of the sunlight.

Strange as it may seem, although dust may form into great clouds which obscure the sun, it also helps us to see, because each little particle acts as a mirror, *reflecting* light and helping us to see indoors and in other places where the sun does not shine directly. If it were not for dust particles, we should not have daylight inside our houses except when our windows received the direct rays of the sun; and there would be complete darkness in shadows. One is only aware of light when it falls directly on him or on some other object which reflects it on him. Anyone who has directed the beam of a flashlight into the night sky is aware of the fact that light becomes evident only when it falls on something and is reflected back. The observers are aware of sunlight only when they are on the same side of Earth as the sun, or when the light is reflected back by an object such as the moon.

When light passes through Earth's atmosphere it is absorbed by air molecules and by dust particles of many kinds and set into vibration. It is then given off by them in different directions. It is scattered. The short waves of light, violet and light blue, are scattered most readily, followed by green, yellow, orange, and red. This accounts for the light blue of the sky on a clear day when there is relatively little dust, and the varying colors of a sunrise or sunset. The amount of dust in the air, and the miles of it through which we look, more or less determine the colors we see.

EXPERIENCE. *There is dust in the air.* Dust, unfortunately, is common enough in our houses and schools. Children are usually interested in speculating about where it comes from. They will probably conclude that dust is wholly a nuisance. The teacher might point out that even dust has its importance in the composition of the air. Without dust there might be no snow.

If the window shades are arranged so that a small ray of bright sunshine enters the room, dust particles can be seen and the path of the ray can be easily followed.

EXPERIENCE. *The effect of dust particles on light.* One will need a black or dark-colored cloth, a flashlight, a source of dust such as blackboard erasers, and a room that can be darkened. Put the black cloth on the wall at one end of the darkened room and notice that when the beam of light is directed onto it, the room is lighted up to only a slight extent. The black cloth *absorbs,* rather than reflects, light. If there is already some dust in the room, it will make the beam of light visible to some extent. Clap the erasers together, procuring a quantity of dust between the flashlight and the dark cloth. The room will be lighted to a larger extent as each particle of dust becomes a reflector of light.

Rare Gases. The rare gases—helium, neon, xenon, krypton, and argon—are extremely inactive. So far as is known they do not occur as a part of any of the compounds that enter into the make-up of living things. Despite this inactivity, or in some cases due to it, man makes use of some of them. Argon is used to fill some types of electric light bulbs. If ordinary air is left in the bulbs, the filament soon oxidizes. To prevent the oxidation of the filament, the makers of bulbs learned to evacuate them. However, when there was no air in the bulbs, the heated filaments soon evaporated, blackening the inside of the glass. The manufacturers of bulbs discovered that if they were filled with the inactive gas, argon, the filament did not oxidize, and it evaporated much more slowly. Neon is used in the neon lights for advertising signs, as well as for lighting airports or other places where brilliant lights are desirable. Neon and argon are also used in fluorescent tubes. Helium is light in weight and does not burn. It is thus useful for filling dirigibles and air ships. It is also used instead of nitrogen in the air provided for people who work in places where the air pressure is very great. When men work under great pressure, as in diving to considerable depths, large quantities of air are dissolved in the blood. When the men come back to where the pressure is less, some of the air may come out of solution forming bubbles in the blood stream. Such a condition is known as the *bends,* or caisson disease. Helium is much less soluble in the blood, and it is therefore used instead of nitrogen in order to reduce the danger of the men contracting the bends.

Air Exerts Pressure

The weight of the upper portions of the air presses down against the lower ones, causing the latter to become denser. As a result of this there is great pressure at low altitudes and less pressure at high altitudes. Miners who work at great depths experience greater pressure than that found at Earth's surface, and must adjust themselves to it.

At sea level the average pressure is about 14.7 pounds to the square inch. Draw a square one inch on a side (one square inch) on the blackboard or on paper. With the scales used in weighing, the children can determine how many books are necessary to make nearly 15 pounds. This is about the amount of pressure which the air exerts on *every square inch* of objects at sea level on the surface of Earth. In the later grades children will learn how to determine the number of square inches there are on a given surface, such as a book, a table, or a hand, and from that they can calculate the total pressure on the surface. Ordinarily we do not feel the air press on us, because it presses on all sides. It enters our bodies and presses from the inside, as well as from the outside.

Air pressure changes slightly from day to day. It seldom remains the same for any great length of time. The "highs" and "lows" on weather maps refer to high-pressure and low-pressure areas. Air is denser in high-pressure areas than it is in low-pressure areas. One can watch how the air pressure changes in a given locality by observing a barometer from day to day, or by following the daily weather maps published in the newspapers.

Winds, which will be explained more fully later, are caused by the flowing of air from regions of high pressure to regions of low pressure. Storms are accompanied by changes in air pressure (pp. 455–463).

When we suck lemonade through a straw, we remove some of the air which is over the liquid inside the straw. Since there is now less air pressure on the surface of the liquid inside the straw than there is on the surface of the

Atmospheric pressure on the surface of the lemonade forces it up the straw.

liquid outside—in other words, since a difference of pressure is created—the liquid is pushed up in the straw. When the mouth is removed from the straw, this difference of pressure is destroyed. The pressure on the liquid inside the straw becomes equal to the pressure outside, and the liquid falls back until it is level with the liquid outside the straw.

The fact that air can be displaced reveals that it is a real substance. It occupies space and exerts pressure. Children may be reminded that we usually speak of a container, such as a tumbler, as being empty when it is really filled to the brim with air. One of the Experiences listed below reveals that "empty" containers are filled with air.

EXPERIENCE. *Air occupies space.* We can push an inverted "empty" glass into a basin of water, and the water will rise only a very little way into the glass.

The Experience can be repeated. This time place an object that will float on the water. Now push the inverted "empty" glass over the floating object. Note that the floating object is lower than the water around the container.

This Experience can be varied again by showing that a paper towel placed in the bottom of the glass will not be moistened when the tumbler is inverted over the water.

If we tip the glass so as to allow the air to escape (this is indicated by the bubbles), then the glass will become filled with water as the air escapes. This shows that the empty glass was not really empty, but contained air; in other words, the air occupied space.

Another way to show that air occupies space is to use an empty bottle closed with a two-hole stopper. Insert a plastic funnel tightly in one of the holes. While one child holds his finger tightly over the uncovered hole, let another try to pour water down the funnel to fill the bottle. Little, if any, water should enter. Have the child remove his finger. The water now enters the bottle readily, for the air has a chance to escape through the open hole, and in so doing it makes room for the water.

Another way to show that air occupies space is to use a narrow-necked bottle and a funnel which fits snugly into the neck. Children will have difficulty in filling the bottle with water because the air cannot escape readily. If the funnel fits tightly enough, the water may enter the bottle very slowly and intermittently as air

The glass is full of air, and water will not enter it until some of the air has escaped.

bubbles escape up through the funnel and a small amount of water enters to take their place. If the funnel is lifted slightly, so that air can escape, the water enters freely. Many funnels in household use have the stems fluted or corrugated so as to provide an air passage around them.

The following is another way of showing that air occupies space: Place the thumb firmly over the end of an inverted funnel and force the large end of the funnel under water. The water will come only a little way up inside the funnel, and air can be felt pressing against the thumb. Now release the thumb. The air can be felt rushing out of the funnel as the water enters. An ordinary metal household funnel may be used, but children cannot so readily see what is happening.

Greater air pressure outside the bottle forces the egg into the bottle. The numbers indicate the sequence of events.

EXPERIENCE. *Air pressure is needed in order to suck milk through a straw.* Sometime when the children are drinking milk, perform this experiment. Make a hole in the stopper of a milk bottle just large enough for a straw. The place where the straw passes through the stopper can be made airtight by applying melted candle wax or sealing wax. After you are sure that the opening has been made airtight, ask a child to suck the milk through the straw. If the bottle is really airtight, this will be difficult or impossible. Now make another hole in the stopper. The milk can now be sucked up easily; for the air that comes into the bottle through the second hole pushes the milk up when air is drawn from the straw.

EXPERIENCE. *Air exerts pressure.* Fill a glass tumbler with water. Place a piece of paper over the glass and hold it in place with the hand. Invert the glass and carefully remove the hand from the paper. Water remains in the tumbler because of the pressure of the air against the paper. To prove that air pressure causes this, gently pull a corner of the paper away from the glass. A large bubble of air

will be seen to enter, and the water will fall out. The glass tumbler need not be completely filled with water to perform this experiment, if it is carefully done.

Boil an egg hard and remove the shell. Set fire to a small strip of paper, place it in a quart milk bottle, and place the egg *quickly* in the mouth of the bottle. The egg will dance up and down for a moment, and then will go down into the bottle, usually with a loud "pop." The heat of the burning paper expands the air in the bottle, and forces some of it out past the egg, causing the egg to dance. As the air in the bottle cools, it contracts. But no air can get into the bottle past the egg to make the pressure of the air inside the bottle the same as that outside. As a result, the pressure of the air inside the bottle is less than the pressure outside, and the outside pressure forces the egg in. To remove the egg, hold the bottle upside down and blow forcibly into it. Blowing air into the bottle causes the pressure to be greater inside than outside. This will force the egg out.

EXPERIENCE. *Air supports weight.* Deflate a basketball and place a shallow box over it. Be sure that the valve is exposed. Have a child sit on the box. Pump air into the basketball, and the child will be lifted off the floor.

EXPERIENCE. *The siphon—using air pressure to do work.* It is often necessary in the classroom to empty an aquarium or other container of water. This may be done by means of a siphon. A siphon may be made of a piece of rubber tubing. Fill the tube full of water and close both ends with your fingers. Put one end into the container to be emptied and the other end into the sink or a pail, which should be at a lower level than the aquarium. Now remove your fingers. The water should flow freely from the container through the tube into the pail or sink. This method may be used to remove dirt and fine sand from an aquarium or to empty part of the water without disturbing the plants or fish. The siphon operates by air pressure. Water falling because of gravity in the *long* arm creates a partial vacuum inside the tube. The air pressure on the surface of the water in the container is sufficient to force water *up* the *short* arm and over the bend, where the process is repeated. Do you see now why the sink or pail must be lower than the container?

EXPERIENCE. *The aquarium dip tube—another use for air pressure.* An aquarium dip tube may be used to remove small bits of dirt from the bottom of the aquarium. Take a straight piece of glass or plastic tubing, or a soda straw, from eight to twelve inches long. Close one end with a finger. Dip the open end in the aquarium, placing it directly over the dirt to be removed. Now remove your finger. Water ascends into the tube, forcing out some of the air and carrying the dirt with it. Replace your finger over the upper end; remove the tube from the aquarium and carry it to the sink. Again remove your finger, and the water and dirt will run out. The water stayed in the tube when it was lifted from the aquarium because the air was pressing on the lower end. The air was prevented by the finger from pressing equally on the upper end.

EXPERIENCE. *The pressure of the air in the schoolroom can crush a tin can.* Take an empty gallon varnish or maple-sirup can (be sure *for safety* that there is no inflammable material in it) and pour into it enough water to cover the bottom to a depth of about an inch. Place the can on a burner and boil the water for about five minutes. Remove the can from the flame. Stopper it tightly. The cooling may be hastened by holding the can under a cold-water tap. The pressure of the air on the can will crush it in a few minutes.

To demonstrate that a great deal of force is needed to crush the can, place a board across it and have some children stand on the board, before doing the experiment. The weight of several children will not crush the can, but the pressure of the air can do so easily.

Water expands about seventeen hundred times in turning into steam. This expansion causes steam to rush out of the opening, carrying with it the air that is in the can. Allowing the water to boil for several minutes gives time for most of the air to be driven off. The inside of the can above the water is now filled with steam. The steam condenses as the can cools, and turns back into water. Since the can is stoppered, no air can enter, and a partial vacuum is created in the can. A low pressure now exists inside the can, while there is the usual atmospheric pressure outside. The higher pressure outside the can causes the can to be crushed.

In this experiment it is important to make clear that the pressure of the atmosphere was resting on the can all the time and not just at the moment when the can was crushed. Air presses on everything about us at all times. We cannot change the pressure of the air around us, and probably would not want to if we could. We can change only the pressure in small vessels, such as the tin can. Later we shall see that the pressure of the air around us does change slightly from day to day because of the operation of natural forces and that this is one of the principal causes of changes in the weather.

EXPERIENCE. *Air resists the movement of objects through it.* Take a flat stick from three to five feet long and not over two inches wide (a lath or a yardstick will do very well). Place this on a table so that one end projects about a foot beyond the edge of the table. With the fist or a hammer strike downward on the projecting end, to show how easily the stick can be moved. Replace the stick on the table in its former position. Now stretch a large piece of paper, such as newspaper or wrapping paper, over the part of the stick that is on the table. Again strike the projecting end. This time the stick can scarcely be moved. In order to move it, it is necessary to displace the air that is resting on top of the large surface of the paper. Considerable force is required to do this suddenly. To make it clear that the effect is caused by air resistance and not by the weight of the paper, use only one sheet of paper and fold it into as small a bundle as possible. Now repeat the experiment; the stick is easily moved. The folded paper has the same *weight* as the unfolded paper, but it presents less *surface* to the air.

One of the objects in *streamlining* motorcars and trains is to reduce the amount of surface which must be moved through the air and thereby lessen air resistance. Some of the children may be interested in collecting pictures of locomotives, automobiles, and airplanes that illustrate streamlining.

Air has *mass,* just as any other substance has, and it takes work to push it aside. The less air we have to push aside, the less work we must do to force any object through the air.

Streamlined vehicles are (theoretically) designed to push aside and stir up as little air as possible.

EXPERIENCE. *We do less work when we have less air to push aside.* Get a large rectangular piece of strong cardboard. Hold it at arm's length while you swing it, first narrow edge forward and then broadside. Notice the difference when you are not pushing so much air to one side.

EXPERIENCE. *Air and falling objects.* Have a child hold a coin in his right hand and one in his left hand. Have the child allow both objects to fall to the floor at the same time. Note that gravity causes the two coins to reach the floor at the same time. This may be repeated several times.

Now place the coin in one hand and a sheet of paper in the other. When they are allowed to fall at the same time the coin reaches the floor more quickly than the paper. Note that the paper flutters down because there is more air in its way than there is for the coin. There is more air to resist the paper. This can be repeated several times if necessary.

Now take two sheets of paper and repeat the experiment with these, dropping them from a high place. Both papers flutter down at approximately the same time.

Now crumple one sheet into a ball. Drop this and the sheet that has not been crumpled. Note that the ball falls much faster than the uncrumpled sheet. These experiences can be used to build up a feeling for the air.

These experiences can be improved if the child performing the demonstration will stand on a chair or table to provide a greater distance for the objects to fall.

What Causes Air Pressure? In order to guide children properly in their interpretations of atmospheric phenomena, teachers need some fundamental understanding of what causes air to behave as it does. They will probably have little occasion to use the explanation given here as something to be taught to the children in its entirety; it is to be regarded rather as a statement of helpful guiding principles which will prove useful without regard to the direction the instruction may take or of the level at which it is given.

Matter is composed of tiny particles called molecules (p. 375). The solids, liquids, and gases with which we have experience in everyday life are all composed of molecules. The atoms composing the molecules need not concern us in the explanations at this point.

Molecules are so small that we have difficulty in imagining their minuteness. It has been estimated that the average molecule has a diameter of about a hundred-millionth of an inch. There are more than a hundred billion billion molecules in a pint of water. In order to write a number representing the molecules in a pint of water, it would be necessary to write 1 followed by twenty zeros. We take into our lungs many billions of gaseous molecules with every breath.

These molecules are in motion. The molecules of liquids move more rapidly than those of solids, and the molecules of gases move more rapidly than those of liquids. In solids molecules are held closely in place. In liquids molecules are more free to move about. In gases molecules move very freely, so that they are able to travel in all directions.

EXPERIENCE. *Gas molecules move rapidly.* Pour a little of some pleasant-smelling substance in one corner of the room. Have the children in different parts of the room indicate when they detect the odor. A sample of flavoring extract or perfume would be suitable.

If we wish molecules to move more rapidly, we have only to heat the substance. For instance, if we apply heat to ice (a solid), the motion of the molecules is speeded up, and the solid ice becomes the liquid water. Continued heating of the water still further increases the speed of motion of the molecules. They begin to escape from the liquid, and steam (a gas) is formed.

EXPERIENCE. *Molecules in cold and hot liquids.* Fill one glass tumbler with hot water and another with cold water. Put a drop of ink or some other coloring substance into each of them. Notice in which tumbler molecules of the coloring matter seem to move through faster.

Air is composed of molecules of gases in rapid motion. If we light a fire or turn on the heat in a radiator, we speed up the movements of the air molecules in the room. Then we say the air is warmer.

Every time one of these rapidly moving molecules strikes an object, the object receives a slight blow. The sum of many millions of these blows each second acts on the object as a push. This is precisely what air pressure is —the *push produced* by *millions* of *tiny blows.*

If we wish to increase the pressure of a gas, there are two ways of doing so. We can increase the number of blows per second; that is, we can increase the number of molecules in a given volume of the gas by squeezing them closer together. Or we can increase the speed with which each molecule strikes the object; that is, we can heat the gas. Furthermore, if we heat a given volume of an *unconfined* gas (such as the atmosphere), each molecule, moving more rapidly, takes up more space, and the gas expands.

Since the atmosphere near the surface of Earth is squeezed by the weight of all the air above it, the molecules are packed closer together (or, as we say, the air is *denser*); therefore the pressure of the air is greatest at the surface of Earth and decreases as we ascend to higher altitudes.

We have grown so accustomed to air pres-

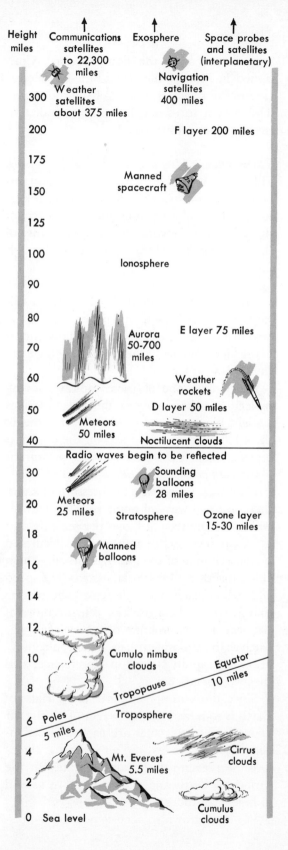

Communications
satellites
to 22,300
miles

Exosphere

Space probes
and satellites
(interplanetary)

Navigation
satellites
400 miles

300

Weather
satellites
about 375 miles

200

F layer 200 miles

175

150

Manned
spacecraft

125

100

Ionosphere

90

80

70

Aurora
50-700
miles

E layer 75 miles

60

Weather
rockets

50

D layer 50 miles

Meteors
50 miles

40

Noctilucent clouds

Radio waves begin to be reflected

30

Sounding
balloons
28 miles

Meteors
25 miles

20

Stratosphere

Ozone layer
15-30 miles

18

Manned
balloons

16

14

12

10

Cumulo nimbus
clouds

Equator
10 miles

8

Tropopause

6 Poles

Troposphere

5 miles

4

Mt. Everest
5.5 miles

Cirrus
clouds

2

0 Sea level

Cumulus
clouds

sure that we seldom notice it either inside or outside the body, except when some rather sudden and extensive change occurs. Such a change occurs when we ride up or down in an elevator in some tall building or when we ride in a rapidly moving automobile, up or down a mountainside.

EXPERIENCE. *To show that air expands when heated.* Cool an empty soft-drink bottle in a pan of ice or in a refrigerator. Remove, wet the top, and place a penny on it. Place warm hands or cloth on the bottle. Raised by the warmed and expanding air, the penny will give a series of tiny "plops!"

EXPERIENCE. *Air expands when heated and contracts when cooled.* Place a small amount of air in a small plastic or rubber balloon so that the balloon is not rounded out. Tie the opening of the balloon so that the air can not escape by making a tight knot with the neck of the balloon. Now place the balloon in a cold place such as in ice water. Immerse it well and then examine the balloon. Note the size of the balloon. Now heat the balloon by holding in a very warm place as over a radiator or by holding it in one's hands. Note that the air in the balloon expands in the warm place and contracts in the cold place.

This Experience can be varied by the children if they wish. This time blow the balloon so that it is just a little too large for the top of a tumbler. When the balloon has been cooled in ice water, it may fit into the tumbler. When the balloon is heated it is much too large for the tumbler.

The concept of the words *expand* and *contract* should be developed carefully.

The Bernoulli Effect. Differences in air pressure are important in lifting an airplane off the

A vertical section through the nearest parts of Earth's atmosphere.

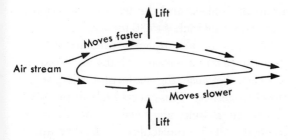

The difference in the speed with which air moves over the upper and lower sides of an airplane wing results in greater pressure upward than downward. This upward pressure is called lift.

ground. Early airplanes had flat wings, which furnished poor lifting power. Later research in wind tunnels showed that a hollow wing that bulged on top provided greatly increased lift. This is explained in this way.

Molecules of air passing across the rounded top surface of the wing travel farther and faster than those passing along the straight lower surface. According to the Bernoulli principle, when the velocity of a fluid increases, its pressure decreases. In other words, air that is moving uses up some of its energy in moving. It therefore has less energy left with which to press. This discovery made it possible to build airplanes that fly well. Air, passing farther and faster over the rounded top of a wing, presses less than does the air passing over the flat lower surface of the wing. The difference in air pressure is responsible for the major portion of the lifting power of the wing.

EXPERIENCE. *To observe how motion reduces pressure.* Hang two ping-pong balls or two filled balloons so they are about an inch apart. Blow between them. What happens? Where is the pressure of the air greatest? Why? You may need to make the balls or balloons stop moving and try this again.

Another way to show that motion in air reduces pressure is to take a strip of paper about one inch wide and five to eight inches long and place one end against the lower lip so it can be blown across. It should rise. Air moves faster across the top than across the lower side of the paper. Hence, it presses less on the top side. This is the same principle that is used in designing efficient airplane wings.

How Air Pressure Is Measured. The pressure of the atmosphere is usually measured by an instrument called a barometer. The *mercury barometer* was invented by Torricelli over three hundred years ago. It consists of glass tube closed at one end. This tube is filled with mercury so that most of the air is driven out; then it is inverted and the open end immersed in mercury. The mercury in the tube now sinks to a certain point and no farther. Since practically all the air was driven out of the tube before it was inverted, and since no air can enter after it is inverted, there is practically a vacuum in the upper end of the tube. There is, therefore, nothing pressing down on the upper end of the mercury column, but air is pressing on the mercury at the lower end of the tube. Under these conditions, the pressure of the air holding the mercury column up is exactly balanced by the weight of the column pressing down. The instrument thus becomes a means for measuring the pressure of the air.

EXPERIENCE. *To show how atmospheric pressure holds up a column of water.* Fill an olive jar or any similarly shaped jar with water. Place a piece of cardboard over the open end, and while keeping the cardboard in place, invert the jar into a beaker of water. When the open end of the jar is below the level of water in the beaker, remove the cardboard, and let the jar rest upright in the beaker. The atmospheric pressure keeps the column of water in the jar higher than the level in the beaker.

At sea level, under normal conditions, the column of mercury will reach a height of 30 inches. Thus, a reading of 30 inches signifies

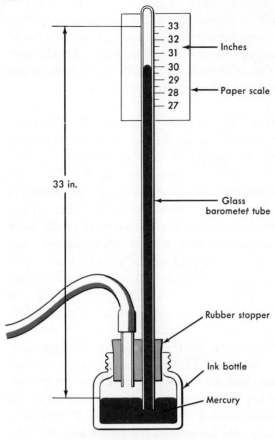

A homemade mercury barometer.

that the atmospheric pressure is just right to support a column of mercury 30 inches high. Such a column of mercury one inch square will weigh 14.7 pounds. This 14.7 pounds per square inch is considered the normal, or *standard, atmospheric pressure.*

The standard pressure is also sometimes designated as a pressure of *one atmosphere.* Thus, a pressure of ten atmospheres will support a column of mercury 300 inches high. This unit is used for measuring very large pressures. So we see that pressure may be measured in terms of pounds per square inch, in terms of inches of mercury, or in terms of atmospheres.

Atmospheric pressure varies somewhat. At sea level the extreme variation in the height of a mercury column is from about 26 inches to about 32 inches, and the normal variation is from about 29 inches to 30 inches.

Changes in atmospheric pressure accompany or precede weather changes. Cold air is heavy because the molecules are packed closely together. This causes high air pressure. Warm air is light air, because the air is expanded and the molecules are farther apart. Therefore, warm air has low pressure. Thus, one reason that air pressure varies is due to temperature differences. Another reason stems from the fact that dry air has more pressure than moist air. A third reason is that air pressure is greatest at sea level (p. 451), and it decreases the higher we ascend. A rapidly falling barometer frequently indicates an approaching storm; a rising one may indicate fair weather. If the barometer continues to rise, the weather is likely to be settled and fair (p. 490).

The mercury barometer is simpler and more accurate than any other type, but it is too cumbersome and fragile to carry about, so a more rugged and portable instrument, known as an *aneroid barometer* (*aneroid* means "containing no liquid"), is used. The aneroid barometer is a small, round metallic box from which most of the air has been removed. This box is kept from collapsing by a spring inside it. Slight changes in pressure

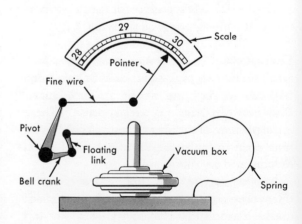

The parts of an aneroid barometer.

alter the curvature of the box. These movements, magnified by a system of levers, move a pointer over a scale. The scale is calibrated to read in inches or millimeters of mercury.

Because it can be easily carried, mountain climbers and aviators find the aneroid barometer useful. Since the pressure of the air decreases with altitude, the barometer may be used to determine the height above sea level. Ordinarily air pressure decreases 0.1 of an inch for every 90 feet of increase in altitude. The altimeter used by aviators is a kind of aneroid barometer.

In order to obtain a written record of the variations in atmospheric pressure, an instrument called the *aneroid barograph* is used. An aneroid barometer connected to a tracer draws a continuous record of pressure changes on a revolving drum. This information is very useful to the forecaster.

It is desirable to have an aneroid barometer in every elementary school. This barometer can be placed in a location in the building where it may be read for atmospheric changes by older groups of children. In fact, since everyone talks about the weather, and since it is a matter of interest most of the time, a barometer can be used whether there is a special study of weather being carried on or not.

In most cases, a mercurial barometer is unnecessary for use in an elementary school. The discussion of the mercurial barometer has been given here since the numbers 29 and 30 with appropriate decimals which are found frequently on weather reports can only be explained in terms of the mercurial barometer.

It should be kept in mind that the mercurial barometer was invented before the aneroid. When the aneroid barometer was invented, it was thought necessary to take the mercurial barometer scale for reading the aneroid.

How Temperature Is Measured. One of the first instruments with which children come in contact is the *thermometer*. Fortunately, the principle involved in a thermometer is easily explained. Thermometers are usually filled with mercury or alcohol. This expands when heated and contracts when cooled.

The most commonly used scale is the Fahrenheit scale. On this scale water freezes at 32° and boils at 212° at sea level. This scale was named for Gabriel Daniel Fahrenheit, a German physicist, who invented the thermometer. The symbol F. is used to indicate Fahrenheit. We say, "Water freezes at 32 degrees Fahrenheit," or write it thus, 32°F.

Another scale, used in laboratories and general scientific work, is called the centigrade. On this scale water freezes at 0° and boils at 100°. The symbol C. is used to indicate centigrade; we write, "Water freezes at 0°C."

About 1949, at an International Conference on Weights and Measures, scientists representing twenty-eight nations voted unanimously to change the name *centigrade* to *Celsius* in honor of the eighteenth-century Swedish astronomer, Anders Celsius. The change was made to standardize the name. It may take some years before the new name is generally used.

Scientists often use the Kelvin scale, abbreviated K. Zero on this scale is at −273°C., sometimes referred to as absolute zero. This

is regarded as the absolute limit of possible coldness, where the motions of atoms and molecules are stilled. Temperatures somewhere in space may approach this limit, and it can also be closely approached in the laboratory for experimental purposes. Except for the location of the zero point, the scale is the same as the centigrade scale, so that high temperatures, as found in the stars, are roughly the same in either scale (p. 724).

Children for the most part will be using Fahrenheit thermometers.[1]

EXPERIENCE. *To use a thermometer.* Take a thermometer with the class on a walk. Read the temperature in the shade, in the sun, indoors, and so on. Do this on a warm day and on a cold day. Note the differences.

Every school should have an outdoor and an indoor thermometer hung in a convenient place for observation by children. The outdoor thermometer may be of the type that can be read from indoors.

EXPERIENCE. *To develop a weather station.* An aneroid barometer, a thermometer, weather maps, weather records, and perhaps drawings by children of weather conditions may be kept in a central place available for all children.

EXPERIENCE. *To keep weather records.* Weather records can be kept in various ways at various educational levels. Younger children may wish to make drawings of how weather affects them or in terms of their observations such as umbrellas, flags fluttering, dark clouds, rain coats, etc. Older children may keep more exact recordings.

[1] The difference between the melting of ice and the boiling of water is 100° on the centigrade scale and 180° on the Fahrenheit scale. Therefore, this relationship can be expressed as 180/100, or 9/5. Conversely, a Fahrenheit degree is 100/180, or 5/9 of a degree on the centigrade scale. For instance, to change 50°C. to F., 50° × 9/5 = 90°F. above the 32° mark. By adding 32° to 90° the correct reading of 122°F. is obtained. The following formulas may be used to change one to the other: $F = 9/5C + 32; C = 5/9(F - 32).$

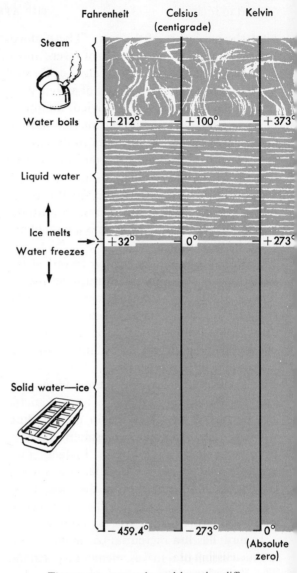

Three temperature scales and how they differ.

EXPERIENCE. *To use school windows in noting changes in weather.* School windows should be utilized many times a day. Note with children the conditions in the morning and the changes during the day. Note the direction of the wind. Are the clouds moving? Sometimes one has to hold his head still and sight on some object such as an antenna or steeple to detect the motion of clouds. Personalize instruction by raising questions such as, "Can you imagine yourself moving the cloud around?"

The Layers of the Atmosphere

Most people are familiar with the fact that much is known about the upper atmosphere. They read and hear reports of space explorations, of heights in the stratosphere, of ordinary radio waves being turned back by the upper atmosphere, and of radar waves going to the moon, a planet, or a satellite and being reflected back. As a result of this interest, the terms *stratosphere* and *ionosphere* may be a part of the vocabulary of children.

The atmosphere may be thought of as consisting of four more or less distinct regions, layers, zones, or spheres, as they are called: the troposphere, the stratosphere (with a transitional region, the tropopause, between them), the ionosphere, and the exosphere. These layers, or regions, do not have sharp boundaries; each one merges into the next. Furthermore, they are not always exactly the same, and many different figures for locating them will be found. Research into their nature will continue for some time.

The Troposphere—The Part of the Atmosphere in Which We Live. The troposphere extends outward from the surface of Earth from five to ten miles. It extends to the higher altitude in the equatorial regions and to the lower one in the polar regions. It is the region of the atmosphere in which we live, and consequently the region about which we have considerable information. It is the region of great weather changes, as we all know; for there are wind, rain, blizzards, clouds, hail, and the like in the troposphere, particularly in the lower half. These changes in the troposphere are due to its being so close to Earth's surface. The surface of Earth, being heated unequally, causes the air close to it to move,

as explained more fully on page 452. As one ascends from Earth's surface into the troposphere, the air becomes colder and colder, the temperature decreasing with altitude at the rate of about 1°F. per 300 feet although it varies. Aviators going to extremely high altitudes find it necessary to have heated planes or specially designed warm clothing. The lowest temperatures in the troposphere have been found directly over the equator, and not over the poles as one might think. A temperature of − 134°F. was reported over Java.

The Tropopause—The Region between the Troposphere and Stratosphere. The tropopause, as has been said, is a transitional region, possibly of a thickness of from two to four miles, which separates the stratosphere from the troposphere. As one ascends through this region, the temperature is constant or increases only slightly. The height of the tropopause varies greatly, as has been indicated in the diagram on page 448.

The Stratosphere—Another Part of the Atmosphere. Beyond the troposphere and tropopause lies the region known as the stratosphere, or, as it was formerly called, the isothermal layer. It begins at a height varying from about 5 miles at the poles to about 10 miles at the equator. At any one place its height varies somewhat with weather conditions in the troposphere and also with the seasons.

As one ascends in the stratosphere, the temperature does not gradually decrease with increasing altitude, as it does in the troposphere. In the stratosphere the temperature has been found to alternately increase and decrease up-

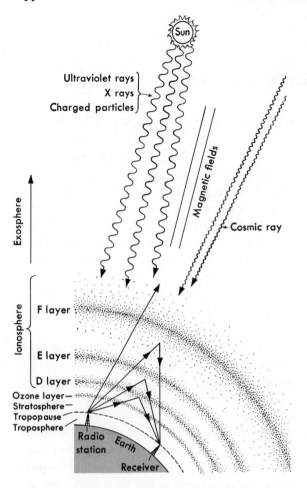

Energy from the sun and from space alters the outer regions of Earth's atmosphere, forming the ionosphere and ozone layer. Some radio broadcast waves pass through the ionosphere, others are reflected back to Earth. (After T. C. Ridout.)

to learn as much as possible about the nature of the world. Another reason is that knowledge of the stratosphere is giving us more information about the factors producing our weather. The stratosphere, free from storms and other changing weather conditions, is an excellent region for air transportation by means of specially designed airplanes. Another reason for the interest of scientists is their desire to know the origin of the charged particles called cosmic rays. These rays are stronger in the stratosphere than on Earth (pp. 200, 208).

The Ionosphere, Which Reflects Our Radio Waves. Beyond the stratosphere is a region known as the ionosphere, because of the presence of large numbers of ions. Radiation from the sun (p. 870), particularly ultraviolet, breaks up atoms of oxygen and nitrogen in the upper atmosphere, forming ions of these atoms and releasing free electrons (p. 379). This region is thus an *electrical conductor*. It can reflect certain *radio waves* back to Earth, and is for that reason important in long-distance radio communication (p. 200).

The ionosphere, sometimes called the thermosphere, begins at an altitude of about 30 or 35 miles and is important in radio communication to more than 250 miles. Beyond this, considerable ionization is believed to extend for at least 600 miles into space. The amount of ionization is measured and studied with the aid of satellites and space probes.

The particular layers or regions of the ionosphere used in radio are known as the D layer (50 miles), the E layer (75 miles), and the F layer (200 miles). These layers, so called, are not stationary, nor are they clearly defined. Because they depend on energy from the sun, they tend to disappear at night, particularly the lower layers. During daylight hours, especially in winter, radio signals up to a maximum frequency of around 50 megacycles per second may be reflected around the curve of

ward. Few clouds exist in the stratosphere, because of an insufficient amount of water vapor (pp. 433–434). It is a relatively stable region, although there are winds, both east and west winds, that follow a seasonal pattern. All air movement is horizontal. There is very little dust to scatter light; so the sky looks nearly black, and the stars can be seen even in the daytime.

Why are scientists so interested in the stratosphere? There are many reasons for this. For one thing, it is intellectually satisfying

Earth, and thus are received at distant points on the globe. At night it is likely that only lower frequencies may be received. Strong seasonal variations occur, depending on the position of Earth in relation to the sun. Conditions vary widely with the 11-year sunspot cycle and with the sun's rotation period of 27 days.

Due to its importance, a world-wide network of observation stations corresponding to those of the Weather Bureau keeps in constant touch with ionospheric conditions and forecasts the "radio weather." This enables radio technicians to select the best times and frequencies for long-distance transmissions.

It is expected that the somewhat uncertain conditions of the ionosphere "radio mirror" will be supplemented by the use of communication satellites. In this way television programs, for example, which are broadcast at frequencies too high to be reflected back by the ionosphere, may be relayed to distant parts of Earth.

While ordinary radio waves are reflected by this region, the very short waves referred to as *radar waves* pass right through the ionosphere. The fact that radar waves are not reflected back by the ionized layers makes it possible for man to transmit such waves to the moon or to other bodies outside Earth's atmosphere. Since these waves are reflected back by more solid objects, it is possible to send them to the moon or to other planets, and then to note the time of their return. Thus another means of obtaining information about distant objects in our universe has come into existence.

The Exosphere—The Outermost Region of the Atmosphere. Regions beyond the ionosphere are sometimes referred to as the exosphere, meaning "outer sphere." Here, satellites and space probes are making many important discoveries. Here, the atmosphere of Earth merges with the "atmosphere" of the solar system. This region includes the magnetosphere (p. 788).

The Ozone Layer, Which Protects Us from Ultraviolet Light. Everyone is familiar with the need for oxygen on the part of all living things. It may be surprising, however, to learn that life such as is known could not exist if it were not for a different form of oxygen in the stratosphere. Ordinary oxygen has two atoms per molecule. Ozone has three atoms per molecule. It is present as one part to 5 million parts of the upper atmosphere in a layer 15 to 30 miles up. Its chief significance to mankind rests in its ability to absorb ultraviolet radiation. Without this absorption, the radiation would cause excessive and, perhaps, deadly sunburn.

On the other hand, if more ozone were present, the decreased amount of radiation reaching the surface of Earth would result in a stoppage of vitamin D production, and without this necessary vitamin our bones would not develop properly.

The Atmosphere Is a Part of Earth

It is well to find out what kind of ideas children have about air and the atmosphere. These can be discovered by inviting them to talk freely and to raise questions with them. During the year it is well to discover what kind of ideas they are developing. They should never be humiliated for misconceptions.

Sometimes children think of the atmosphere as extending throughout the universe, with

Earth, moon, sun, and other bodies moving through the air. This may be based upon their own experiential backgrounds, since they have never been anywhere that there hasn't been air.

From the content given in the preceding sections it is indicated that the atmosphere is a part of Earth. It is held to Earth by gravity. It goes along with Earth as Earth moves in space.

The air which is around us may be somewhere else tomorrow (p. 452), but it does not leave Earth. It may be moved along Earth's surface to a new place or it may be moved upward above Earth's surface.

EXPERIENCE. *The atmosphere is a part of Earth.* Whether we think of the atmosphere as very large and extensive or very small and of no great depth is a relative matter. If we think of the total depth of the atmosphere as compared with a distance between two cities or two farms, we may state quite truly that the atmosphere extends far above the surface of Earth. But if we drew a circle to represent the solid and liquid parts of Earth and attempted to shade in the atmosphere around the circle, we would find only a small band of shading. (See p. 276 for the diameter of Earth.)

In connection with this instruction it is well to have the children look up into the atmosphere for clouds, birds, or airplanes to secure a conception of depth, realizing, of course, that the atmosphere extends far above all of these objects.

It is well to have them look toward the horizon. In this horizontal view they are looking through more air. Encourage them to look for the rising or setting sun when they have an opportunity and also to look at the night sky. They should learn that the stars, planets, moon, and sun are far out beyond our atmosphere.

EXPERIENCE. *The atmosphere is constantly changing and causes changes in the solid part of Earth.* This Experience is based on some of the content found in Chapter 9 which treats with forces that produce changes on Earth. As a result of the atmosphere the solid and liquid parts of Earth are changed. Because of all the dynamic forces growing out of the effect of Earth's rotation and the sun's energy, we have rain, snow, and other forms of precipitation, as well as winds. With these come weathering and erosion and changes on Earth. So whether we think of the atmosphere as shallow or deep, we know it produces changes.

A current event may help to make this vivid. Reports of floods, hurricanes, or other wind storms may be of interest. A flood is related to the atmosphere, since the water in the flood has at some other time been moisture in the atmosphere. This learning can be related to smaller events such as the erosion or washing on the streets or on the school grounds by a rainstorm.

Why Are Mountaintops Cold?

The rays which reach the atmosphere directly from the sun contribute very little to the heat of the atmosphere. Only about 19 per cent of the direct radiation received from the sun is absorbed by the atmosphere, and that mostly in the upper regions. Roughly 47 per cent is absorbed by Earth, which is thereby warmed and itself gives off heat by radiation. This Earth radiation is nearly all absorbed by the atmosphere, which in its turn becomes warm. Furthermore, most of this warming is done in the lower and denser parts of the atmosphere, where dust and water vapor help to absorb the heat radiation. Some compare the atmosphere to the walls of a greenhouse because it lets in radiation from the sun but hinders its outward loss.

The farther we get away from the level surface of Earth, then, the farther we are away from the place where the atmosphere is being warmed. Also, as we leave the lower portions of the air, we leave behind us most of the dust and water vapor, which help to absorb the heat radiation.

The result of these two factors is that the atmosphere becomes cooler as we ascend to higher altitudes, whether in a balloon or on a mountainside.

The atmosphere may be likened to bed clothing, which serves to retain the heat of our bodies. There is less and less "bed clothing" over us as we ascend into the air.

Far out from Earth the gases of the atmosphere become so thin that the word *temperature* no longer has its usual meaning. The high temperatures of these regions refer to the kinetic (moving) energy of each particle.

Water Boils at a Low Temperaure on Mountaintops. Those who attempt to cook food by boiling at high altitudes have difficulty because the water boils at a low temperature. This may be explained somewhat as follows:

When we change liquid water to a gas, we speed up its molecules by heating them until they move so fast that they begin to escape from the liquid into the air (p. 441). This is called *boiling* when it proceeds rapidly, and takes place when the water is heated to a temperature of 212°F. at sea level. After water (or any other substance) has reached the *boiling point,* further application of heat only makes it boil faster. It does not make it any hotter.

Anything which interferes with the escape of molecules raises the boiling point; anything which aids the escape of molecules lowers the boiling point. The air, pressing down on the surface of the water, interferes with the escape of molecules and so raises the boiling point. If

The sun's rays have little warming effect on the high peaks. (Armstrong Roberts.)

we remove some of the air, we lower the boiling point correspondingly. That is to say, the boiling point changes as the pressure changes. We can boil water at any temperature, provided we adjust the pressure accordingly. To raise the boiling point we increase the pressure.

The air pressure on the tops of high mountains is low, and so the boiling point of water is also low. Now the cooking of food in boiling water does not depend upon the boiling but upon the temperature. Hence, if the boiling point is low, cooking is slow, difficult, or impossible. To overcome this difficulty, peo-

ple living in cities at high altitudes may use pressure cookers, in which water is boiled under steam pressure. This pressure is much higher than the pressure of the mountain atmosphere. In fact, pressure cookers, because of the high temperature at which they operate, are widely used even at ordinary altitudes.

EXPERIENCE. *How does air pressure affect the ways in which people live?* Find out everything you can about the manner of living of people who reside in places at high altitudes in the Andes, the Rocky Mountains, and the Alps. How does the low air pressure affect them?

Winds and Their Causes

Earth is heated unequally. The equator receives more heat than the poles. The oceans retain their heat better than continents. There are local differences due to surface features. This unequal heating of Earth causes differences in Earth's atmosphere (p. 202). We have had occasion to learn and to apply the principle that the molecules of a substance move more rapidly as the substance is heated. This is true of air. As air becomes warmer, its molecules move more rapidly and require more space for their motions. Therefore the heated air expands. The situation is somewhat analogous to that of children sitting quietly and the same children playing a game which involves running: in the latter case much more space is required than in the former.

Air expands when heated, and in doing so spreads in all directions. As this happens, the air becomes less dense; that is, it becomes lighter for a given volume. Then the colder, denser, outside portions push in and force the lighter air up. The air pressure is greater in the denser regions of the atmosphere than it

is in the less dense regions. This difference in pressure, brought about by temperature, causes air to flow from the regions of high pressure to those of low pressure. A convenient summary would be this: air is warmed, expands, and is pushed up by cold air, which moves in to take its place. This motion of air is *wind*. In general, the greater the difference in pressure, the stronger the wind.

The cause of the circulation of air is the same, regardless of whether the process occurs on a small scale in a schoolroom over a radiator or on a grand scale over a whole continent or even the entire Earth.

Air is always moving. Outdoor air is likely to move more rapidly than indoor air. Stoves, radiators, warm places on Earth's surface, all help to keep the air of Earth in motion.

Winds blow at various speeds. A breeze is a wind blowing at the rate of from four to thirty-one miles an hour. A gale has a speed of from thirty-two to sixty-three miles an hour. A hurricane blows at more than seventy-five miles an hour, and is believed to reach a maximum of nearly two hundred miles an hour.

The speed of the wind in tornadoes is so great that it has never been measured (p. 467). A scale of wind velocity, called the Beaufort scale, is used by the United States Weather Bureau. It employs numbers from 0 to 17, representing calm, light air, breeze (slight, gentle, moderate, fresh, and strong), gale (moderate, fresh, strong, and whole), storm, and hurricane.

The speed of wind is measured by an instrument known as an *anemometer*. This usually consists of three or four metal cups placed at the ends of arms arranged to revolve about an axis. The faster the wind blows, the harder it pushes against the cups, and the faster the arms revolve. The speed is measured by a meter somewhat like an automobile speedometer.

The measurements of upper winds are determined by releasing a balloon. Mathematical calculations give the observer the direction and the speed of these winds. Radar may also be used in this method.

The direction of winds is ascertained by a *wind vane,* often miscalled a weather vane. This device points in the direction from which the wind is blowing. Wind vanes, frequently made in fanciful shapes, can often be seen on buildings or poles.

Winds do much good. They carry raingiving clouds about; they cause large amounts of air to move about Earth's surface and so help to equalize temperatures; they blow smoke away from cities; they draw away polluted air; they drive windmills and sailboats. Carbon dioxide, essential to plant life, is distributed about Earth's surface by winds. Cool winds help to relieve suffering in hot weather.

Winds can also do much harm. In the form of tornadoes and hurricanes they cause destruction. Winds spread forest fires. They blow away loose soil in the form of dust. Hot winds destroy vegetation. Violent winds at sea cause shipwreck and raise high waves, which may do damage along the shore. Sudden warm winds may melt the snow too quickly and cause floods. In short, winds, like other forces of nature, both aid and hinder man in his activities on Earth.

The Air Distributes Heat. One is generally unaware of the fact that the air gives or takes up heat. If the temperature of one's surroundings is entirely comfortable, then the air feels neither hot nor cold. It is when the temperature of the air is higher or lower than is desirable that the person becomes aware of its capacity to give up or take on heat. During hot weather, the temperature of the air may be so high that it is very uncomfortable. When the air is too hot for comfort, one can feel the heat "beating down" on him and one realizes that the mass of air has a large quantity of heat. On the other hand, during cold weather, if one steps outside without adequate clothing, he can literally feel the heat leaving his body as it is taken up by the cold air.

Since the air can take up or give off heat, it can be used as a medium for transferring heat from one place to another. Heat is transferred from one part of a room to another by the air. Even in homes equipped with steam or hot-water heat distribution systems, heat is transferred from the radiator to other parts of the room by air. In those homes that have hot-air heat distribution systems, the heat is transferred from the furnace in the basement to the rooms above by air. Air next to the furnace or stove becomes warmer. As this warmer air comes into contact with cooler objects, some of its heat is given up to the cooler objects. The air, after giving up some of its heat, contracts and is as a result more dense than the warmer air. As a result, it may sink down to the floor. It may go back toward the furnace where it is again warmed. This process in which the air gets heat from a warmer object and then gives it up to a cooler one goes on all of the time. The only condition under which heat is not being transferred from warm

to cooler objects is one in which every object in the room has the same temperature.

Air Rises When Heated. Warm air is lighter than cold air. (See p. 443 for a more detailed statement.) As warm air is lighter it tends to be lifted or pushed to one side by cold air. Therefore, warm air rises as it is pushed up by the heavier air. Children will have noticed that cigarette smoke rises up around a lighted lamp as the smoke-filled air is warmed by the lamp. As warm air around a flame is pushed up, it points the flame up.

Arrange a box with two holes in the top, as shown in the accompanying illustration, and a glass front which can be raised or lowered. Insert two ordinary lamp chimneys in the two holes, and place a candle on the bottom of the box under one of the holes. Light the candle and close the glass front.

Hold a piece of lighted punk or Chinese joss

stick, some smoldering moistened paper, burning incense, or some other smoking material,[2] first over one chimney, then over the other. In which chimney is the air rising? In which is it descending? Trace the course of the smoke down one chimney, across the box, and up the other chimney.

Hold the smoking material over a stove, steam radiator, or hot-air register. Hold it near a window open at the top and at the bottom. Where is air rising? Where is it descending?

Why does the flame of a match or candle always rise? Air, when heated, doesn't rise as a result solely of its own energy. Rather, when air is heated, it expands. Naturally anything that expands becomes less dense because the individual molecules are farther apart. Since it is less dense, or lighter for its size, than the surrounding air, it is pushed up by the cooler, heavier air around it. So, while we can say that the air rises, we can realize it rises because it is pushed up by other surrounding air. This cooler and heavier air coming into the warm place becomes warm too, and is in turn pushed up by other air, and so it continues as long as the place is warmer than other places. The expression "circulation of air" is a good description for many things that go on in the air, because air is forever circulating. When heat is transferred in gases, such as air, or in liquids, such as water, due to unequal heating, the currents are called *convection currents*. The word should not be used with children until it has meaning for them.

EXPERIENCE. *Wind is air in motion.* Let one child fan another. What is it that is felt? Is it wind? Is it air?

Blow feathers or other light objects about.

[2] A lamp wick covered with vaseline provides an excellent source of smoke. Some teachers have children cover the inside of the box with asbestos. (See p. 430 concerning teaching safety and fire prevention.) Children should feel responsible for having a bucket of sand nearby in case the box should catch fire.

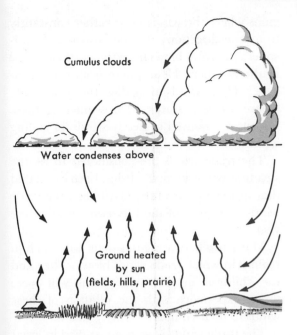

Cumulus clouds

Water condenses above

Ground heated
by sun
(fields, hills, prairie)

Cumulus clouds become larger as heated air rises and cooler air descends.

What is it that comes out of our mouths when we blow? Is it something like wind?

On a windy day a discussion may easily be started as to what it is that blows leaves about and presses against us as we walk. What useful devices have we that use wind for power?

EXPERIENCE. *Cold air descends.* Obtain a piece of iron pipe 18 inches long and at least 1 inch across. Place the pipe in a refrigerator or outside on a cold day. When the pipe is cold, light a match, then blow out the flame. While the match is smoking, hold it above the open end of the cold pipe and notice that the smoke goes down, coming out the bottom. If the smoking match is held at the bottom of the cold pipe, the smoke will go off to one side instead of rising up the tube. When the pipe is full of cold air, the air will not rise in it.

EXPERIENCE. *Air rises over a burning match.* We use this principle of air currents when we hold a burning match. If one wants to increase the size of the flame, the burning match is held with the flame below the rest of the match. In this way the unburned part of the match, which is the fuel, is above the flame. The flame moves upward because the air, including the burning gas from the match, is being pushed upwards by the surrounding cooler air. The flame is in the direction of the fuel and the match burns more rapidly.

If we wish to retard the burning of the match we turn the match upward so that the fuel, or unburned part of the match, is below the flame. In this way the flame does not reach the unburned part of the match. In fact, the match may go out before it is completely burned.

EXPERIENCE. *Warm air expands when heated.* Stretch the mouth of a balloon over the neck of a small bottle or jar. Cup your hands around the bottle and notice the balloon beginning to fill up. Your hands warmed the bottle, which in turn warmed the air within. The warm air expanded, thus filling the balloon.

Wind Belts of Earth. There are several wind systems, or belts, on Earth. All of them are caused by Earth's being hot at the equator, cold at the poles, and rotating on its axis. We shall first describe the wind belts, and in the next section briefly explain their causes.

In any discussion of the great wind systems of Earth, it must be emphasized that, for the purposes of the discussion, it is not the real Earth that is considered but a highly idealized one. The surface of the real Earth is broken into land and water areas. There are mountains and valleys, lakes, and streams. The color of Earth's surface ranges from the brown of deserts through the green of forests to the white of polar snow fields; and color affects the degree to which heat is absorbed or radiated. All these highly important factors are neglected in the discussion which follows. We shall describe the winds as they would be on

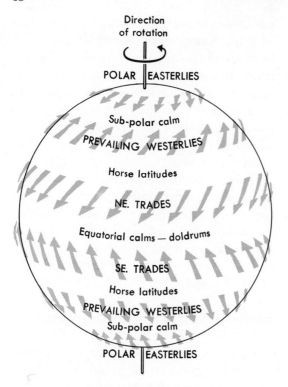

Earth has great wind systems.

Earth if the surface were perfectly uniform, either all land or all water.

The children will need to use a globe frequently while studying this subject.

The Equatorial Belt of Calms, the Doldrums. Over a belt lying very roughly between 5° north latitude and 5° south latitude, calms and light variable winds prevail. What little breeze there is may blow from any direction and shift abruptly. The weather is hot and humid. In many regions in this belt much rain falls.

This region was greatly feared in the days of sailing ships, for a vessel which entered it might be becalmed for days or weeks, perhaps until her food or drinking water or both were exhausted.

The Trade Winds. North and south of the belt of the doldrums, extending to about 30° or 35° north latitude and south latitude, are two re-

gions where the winds blow rather constantly from one direction. In the Northern Hemisphere the wind blows from the northeast, and in the Southern Hemisphere from the southeast. These winds are called the *trade winds*. There are few storms. Ships entering these regions are assured of steady winds for sailing westward.

The trade winds are considered to be the steadiest winds known. It has been estimated that in some parts of the Caribbean the trade winds blow fifty of the fifty-two weeks in the year.

Many teachers using this book will teach in regions in which trade winds blow. They and the children in their classrooms will have much experience with the relation of these winds to their comfort.

The trade winds have been studied in great detail since World War II. The conditions in the upper atmosphere above the trade winds have proved to be much more complicated than was thought. This is another illustration of the fact that man has much yet to learn.

The Subtropical Belts of Calms, the Horse Latitudes. North and south of the region of the trade winds, roughly from 30° to 40° north latitude and south latitude, are two more belts of calms and light variable winds. In contrast with the weather in the doldrums, the weather in these regions is dry and fairly cool. There are few clouds, and the sun shines most of the time. The gentle winds blow from any direction.

The name *horse latitudes* is possibly derived from the fact that vessels carrying horses were frequently becalmed in these regions. When supplies were exhausted, it was necessary to throw the horses overboard.

The Prevailing Westerlies, the Region of Cyclones. North and south of the horse latitudes come the regions of the prevailing westerly winds, sometimes called the stormy westerlies. They extend roughly from 40° to 65° north latitude and south latitude. These belts are characterized by alternate stormy and fine weather.

Within the regions of the westerlies, large movements of air called *cyclones* and *anticyclones* move from west to east. These movements are particularly well developed in the regions occupied by much of North America and Europe.

Cyclones and anticyclones, in the sense in which the words are used by scientists, should not be confused with tornadoes or with hurricanes. Both the latter are violently destructive storms. A cyclone is *any* mass of air that moves spirally around a center of low pressure (p. 467). Tornadoes and hurricanes are special kinds of cyclones. People who live in the regions of the prevailing westerlies are constantly being visited by cyclones without being any the worse for it. In fact, cyclones are beneficial, not only because of the general weather changes which they bring with them, but also because of the invigorating effects of the changes in temperature and humidity. In this book we shall use the word *cyclone* to mean the winds that cause the ordinary storm which occurs every few days in the regions of the prevailing westerlies, and we shall call the special kinds of cyclones by their distinctive names, such as *hurricane* and *tornado*.

If cyclones and anticyclones did not move, we should probably have rather monotonous weather, with little change from day to day.

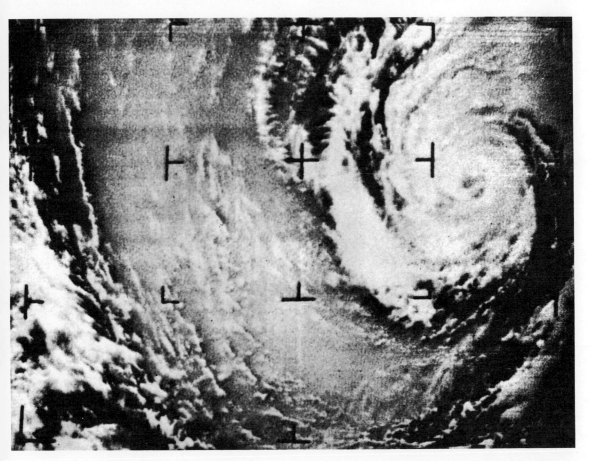

A hurricane is one type of cyclonic storm. Hurricane Ethel, photographed by the Nimbus I weather satellite, September 11, 1964. (Three Lions, N.Y.C.)

Cyclones, or low-pressure areas, usually bring stormy or cloudy weather. Anticyclones, or high-pressure areas, bring fair, clear, cool, or cold weather. As cyclones and anticyclones move around Earth from west to east, it is possible to predict weather by observing the direction and speed of their movement.

Although the large movements of air are from west to east in this belt, the wind may blow from all directions of the compass. Observations made by children and teachers from windows of the school or out of doors will demonstrate that this is true.

Westerly winds are said to prevail for two reasons: first, on an average, the wind blows more often and more strongly from the west, northwest, and southwest than from other directions; second, the general circulation of the air is from west to east. This is shown by the west-to-east movement of cyclones and anticyclones. In this belt there will be cloudy days as well as fair days. Storm winds may be common. Weather in this belt is highly changeable. Mark Twain, commenting about part of this region, advised that if anyone didn't like the weather, he should wait a few minutes and it would change.

Almost all of the United States, Canada, Alaska, northern Mexico, and most of Europe are within this belt.

The westerlies are much stronger and more noticeable in the Southern Hemisphere than in the Northern Hemisphere, for there is less land there to interfere with them. Sailors call the region of from 40° to 50° south latitude the "roaring forties" because of the strong winds encountered there.

Winds in Polar Regions. Not a great deal has been known about the winds in the regions of the north and south poles. Now, however, extensive studies are being made of the weather in the polar regions of Earth. Wind appears to flow out from the poles in a more or less easterly direction toward zones in the regions

of from about 60° to about 65° north latitude and south latitude. Here these cold easterly winds come into violent conflict with relatively warm westerly winds. It is now believed (p. 461) that this interaction between conflicting air currents may produce cyclones and anticyclones.

Much remains to be found out about the winds in the regions of the poles. It is one of the principal objects of modern polar explorers to do this, as it is believed that more knowledge of polar conditions may make possible long-range weather-forecasting.

EXPERIENCE. *To consider the wind belt in which we live.* In studying weather children might consider the weather of regions other than their own. Children who live in the area of the trade winds may compare their weather with that of the temperate and arctic regions, and vice versa. They may, in addition to reading the barometer and thermometer, observe the direction and intensity of the wind. Small children can observe how flags fly. Is the wind blowing the flag? If so, in what direction? Or does the flag hang limp on the pole?

Teachers may help children to learn in what belt of winds they live.

Can the children think of any ways in which the winds in their wind belt affect their daily lives or do they remember special times when winds have affected them?

The Causes of the Wind Belts. The causes of the wind belts are not simple. Any simple explanation must leave out much useful information. Furthermore, scientists themselves are not yet sure of all the causes. Nevertheless a brief and necessarily incomplete explanation will be attempted here.

On page 454 we saw that air moves from a cooler to a warmer place. The pressure of the air at the warm place is slightly less, owing to expansion and the rising of the air, than it is at the cool place. Another way of stating the same thing would be to say that air moves from a place of greater pressure to one of less pressure. This principle also holds true of other substances than air. Water, for instance, tends to move from a place of greater pressure to one of less pressure.

If Earth did not rotate on its axis, the explanation of wind systems would be simple, somewhat as follows: The rays of the sun strike Earth vertically at the equator, and this causes Earth in equatorial regions to become very hot. In the polar regions, the sun shines on Earth obliquely or not at all, consequently these regions are usually cold (p. 203). The air near Earth in equatorial regions gets heated, expands, and becomes less dense, while polar air is cold and sinks as it spreads out away from the poles. So we see air circulating as hot-air masses rise from equatorial regions and move toward the poles, while cold polar-air masses move toward the equator near Earth's surface.

Earth's atmosphere may be thought of as a great dynamic circulation system with the air in continuous motion and with the sun furnishing the energy. Children are challenged by such ideas even though they may not care for or be prepared to understand the details. There would be a north[3] wind everywhere on Earth's surface in the Northern Hemisphere, and a south wind everywhere in the Southern Hemisphere. At the equator the wind would blow neither from north nor from south, but instead there would be rising air currents. These currents would not be felt by an observer at the surface, and the air would appear to be calm.

The foregoing explanation, however, does not take into account the fact that Earth does rotate. This rotation profoundly modifies and complicates the explanation.

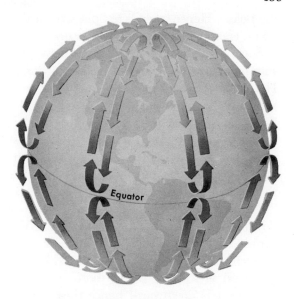

The heating of Earth causes air to move.

It has been shown by Ferrel that anything moving freely over the surface of the rotating Earth will tend to be turned to the right in the Northern Hemisphere and to the left in the Southern Hemisphere—assuming in each case that you are facing the equator. If you will work this statement out on the school globe, you will see that the winds which begin blowing from the north and south blow more and more from the east. If you start walking from north to south, but turn a little to the right at each step, you will presently find yourself walking from east to west. In the same way, if you walk from south to north, but turn to the left, you will also find yourself walking from east to west.

According to Ferrel's law, as the air which was heated and forced up over the equator proceeds toward the poles, it is turned more and more toward the east, until at from about 30° to about 35° north latitude or south latitude it has become a wind blowing from west to east. Bear in mind that all this takes place high in the air. More and more air is constantly being forced into this region from the equator, but it cannot proceed farther toward

---

[3] Winds are named according to the directions *from* which they blow; thus a north wind is a wind blowing from the north.

the poles. Hence it tends to "pile up" at this point, creating a zone of high pressure.

Some of the air from this zone of high pressure flows downward to the surface of Earth. Here it flows away from the area of high pressure. Some of it flows southward (in the Northern Hemisphere). This portion is turned to the right and becomes the northeast (that is, from the northeast) trade wind. Another portion flows northward and becomes the prevailing westerly wind.

A place where air is flowing upward or downward appears calm to an observer on the surface of Earth. The areas of high pressure which we have been discussing (the horse latitudes) are places where most of the air movement is downward; hence they are regions of light variable winds and calms.

In the doldrums air is rising; in the horse latitudes air is descending. We shall see later that areas of rising air currents are usually rainy or cloudy, whereas areas of descending air currents are usually fair. This accounts for the difference in the weather of the doldrums and the horse latitudes.

Just as air is heated and forced up at the equator, so it is cooled and sinks at the poles. This cold air flows out from the poles, turning in accordance with Ferrel's law, in two currents, one from each pole. These are the polar easterlies. They flow south or north until they meet the prevailing westerlies. It is the interaction of these two wind belts (the polar easterlies and the prevailing westerlies) which, it is believed, forms cyclones and anticyclones (pp. 461–463).

To summarize: The atmosphere circulates between the poles and the equator. This circulation is due to unequal heating of Earth's surface. The movement of the atmosphere is greatly modified and complicated by the rotation of Earth. It is also greatly modified by irregular distribution of land and water, differences in land elevation, Earth's revolution around the sun, inclination of Earth on its axis, and by other natural features and forces. Scientists do not yet fully understand the circulation of the atmosphere.

Monsoons. Land surfaces heat faster and cool faster than water surfaces. In some parts of the world, notably India, parts of China, Australia, and parts of Africa, large masses of land become much hotter than the surrounding ocean in summer, and much colder in winter. Under such conditions, hot air is pushed up in summer, and cool moist air from the sea flows in. In winter the wind reverses its direction, and dry cool air flows out from the land. This wind, which changes its direction with the season, is called a monsoon. It is of vast importance to the people who dwell in monsoon regions because the moist sea air brings rain for their crops.

In the United States there is a small monsoon in the southern part of the country, especially in Texas. This is also true for parts of Mexico, Central and South America. Many teachers using this book will be living in the various regions of the monsoons.

A similar phenomenon occurs at the seashore during a summer day. The water is colder than the land. The hot air above the land rises as the cool air over the water moves in under the warm air. Thus, we feel a cool breeze coming from the sea during the day. At night, the reverse happens. The land is cooler than the water so a land breeze blows toward the sea.

Storms and Other Weather Phenomena. Having discussed the great wind systems of Earth, we now turn our attention to a consideration of some of the more common weather phenomena which occur within them.

Cyclones and Anticyclones, Which Make the Weather of the Middle Latitudes. Of these phenomena perhaps the most important from the point of view of people living in the middle latitudes are the cyclones and anticyclones, which occur in the regions of the prevailing westerlies; for they bring about most of the weather changes in both the north and south middle latitudes. We have already discussed cyclones and anticyclones, in the section on the prevailing westerlies.

A cyclone is a mass of air moving spirally inward toward a center of low pressure. An anticyclone is a mass of air moving spirally outward from a center of high pressure. So the cyclones and anticyclones which are continuously moving across the United States, Canada, and most of Europe are spiralling in opposite directions. Cyclones are usually oval in shape. They vary in size, sometimes extending over several thousand miles.

The Weather Bureau of the United States and the Meteorological Branch, Department of Transport of Canada use the word *low* in referring to a cyclone and the word *high* in referring to an anticyclone. We shall follow this convenient practice in the remainder of this discussion.

If at any place on Earth's surface a space occurs where the air pressure is low, air will immediately move in from the surrounding atmosphere to fill the space. Owing to the rotation of Earth, however, the inflowing air is deflected to the right (in the Northern Hemisphere), in accordance with Ferrel's law. Thus it is easy to see that the winds about a low in the Northern Hemisphere are spiralling *inward* in a *counterclockwise* direction, and the winds about a high are spiralling *outward* in a *clockwise* direction. In the Southern Hemisphere winds spiral clockwise about a low and counterclockwise about a high.

To make this clearer, draw a circle. Imagine that the center of this circle is the center of a low. At several points on the circle draw short arrows pointing toward the center. These arrows show the directions in which the wind would blow on a nonrotating Earth.

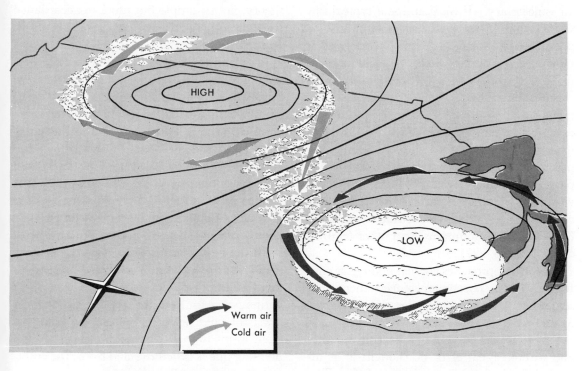

Cold air from northern regions is flowing south. (Top of the illustration is North.)

Now turn all the arrows to the right. You will see that they indicate a counterclockwise rotation.

The air that rushes in toward the center of a low piles up, is forced upward, and is cooled. Some of the cooling is caused simply because the air is moved to a cooler region at a high altitude; but much of it comes about because the incoming air, rising from the surface to a region of decreased pressure, expands. In expanding it does work. In doing work it loses energy and becomes cooler because of the loss of energy. Thus it comes about that, through the combination of these two causes of cooling, any given mass of air, as it rises above the surface of Earth, cools about 1° F. for every 300 feet of rise. Warm air is capable of holding much more moisture than cold air (p. 479). Therefore, when warm air holding considerable moisture is forced to rise, it cools and drops its moisture. In this way clouds, rain, and snow are formed.

For condensation a supply of warm, moist air is necessary. If we examine a typical low we see that in its southeastern and eastern parts (in the Northern Hemisphere) wind is blowing from warm, moist tropical or subtropical regions. In its western and northwestern parts wind is blowing from cold dry regions. It is probable, therefore, that the eastern and southeastern parts of a low will have rain or snow and relatively warm temperatures, while the western and northwestern parts will experience cool or cold clear weather. In different parts of the world these conditions are modified somewhat by the location of oceans, mountains, and other features of the land (p. 327).

As a low approaches a given point, it is easy to see why a barometer placed there falls somewhat. As the low recedes, the barometer again rises.

Highs, or anticyclones, may conveniently and without great error be thought of as directly opposite in characteristics to lows. The air flows spirally in a clockwise direction outward from the center. The northeastern portion of a high, which receives the north wind, is cool, while the southwestern and western parts are likely to be warm. A high generally is an area of fair weather.

No single explanation seems able to account for the origin of all cyclones and anticyclones within the middle latitudes. It was formerly believed that lows were caused directly by unequal heating of Earth's surface, as are the great wind systems and certain types of storms. It was supposed that when a region became warmer than its surroundings, the air there expanded and was forced up by cooler air moving in. This theory may account for the origin of some lows, but it is now considered inadequate for several reasons, notably for the reasons that most lows originate in winter and in very cold polar regions and that the temperature of the upper air in the center of a low is often lower than that of surrounding regions. For these and other reasons, another theory, not so simple but more in accordance with the observed facts, has been advanced.

Simplified, the modern theory of the origin of lows is this: Along the line where the prevailing westerlies meet the polar easterlies two kinds of air currents having very different characteristics come in contact. The westerlies are warm and moist, while the polar winds are cold and dry. Furthermore, the two winds are moving in opposite directions. These two kinds of air do not mix readily, but tend to preserve their own characteristics. As a result of their interaction, great tongues, or hooks, of cold air are forced equatorward, while tongues of warm air are forced poleward creating a somewhat circular wave-like movement of air which develops into a low. The lighter warm air from the tropics helps to form lows; the cold heavier air from the polar regions forms highs. The poleward side of the dividing line is called the cold front; the equatorward side is called the warm front.

One of the principal objects of modern polar expeditions is to learn more about the winds, which, we believe, give rise to many storms in the middle latitudes. Much remains to be learned about the factors influencing our weather.

Air Masses. From the description of highs and lows given above, the reader will realize that almost all of the United States, a large part of Canada, and a portion of Mexico may be compared to a battle ground in which there is a continual struggle between the masses of cold, polar air from the north and invading masses of warm, tropical air from the south.

To follow the weather forecasts intelligently it is well to have some acquaintance with air masses. This acquaintance can be secured by older children in the elementary school. The air currents indicated above are produced in large part by what have been called air masses. More and more weather reports, whether they are to be found in newspapers or received by radio or television, mention air masses. A teacher can use weather information secured through such reports in developing an acquaintance with air masses and their influence on the weather of a region.

One of the important developments in weather forecasting and meteorology in recent years has been the increased knowledge of air masses. Much of this knowledge has come about from the study of the air at high levels (p. 491). However, much more needs to be learned in this field and future discoveries may cause scientists to revise their present ideas.

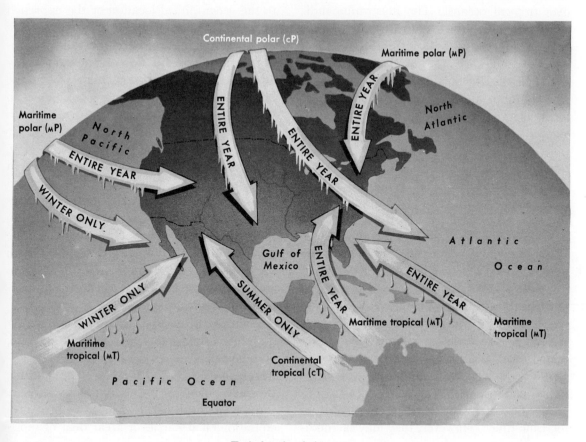

Typical paths of air masses.

It has been discovered that if bodies of air remain for any length of time over relatively large areas, they take on some of the characteristics of those areas. The air currents over these regions will be hot or cold, wet or dry, high or low pressure, depending on the conditions of the surface over which they have passed. These air masses tend to keep their characteristics and carry them along as they move on. Air masses may be several hundred miles long, several hundred miles wide, and several thousand feet deep. By wind movements of which these air masses may become a part, they are carried to distant parts of the world, hundreds or thousands of miles away.

There are areas of the world which are sources for air masses. These areas are large regions having rather uniform conditions of temperature such as prevails in the Arctic or over tropical oceans. The illustration indicates the great source regions for the air masses that invade the middle latitudes in North America.

Frequently, the air masses are indicated on weather maps. If the air mass originated over a continent it is marked on weather maps by a small c. If it originated over the continent in polar regions, it is marked cP. If it originated over the ocean it is called a maritime air mass and is marked with a small m. So if it formed over polar oceans it would be marked mP. If the air mass formed over the tropics it would be marked T, with cT for air masses formed in the tropics over continents and mT for air masses formed over tropical oceans.

A third letter, w or k, is used to indicate whether the air mass is warmer or colder than the surface over which it is traveling. Therefore, an air mass called cPk tells us that it originated over land near the polar regions and that it is cooler than the surface of Earth over which it passes.

Air masses tend to keep their characteristics for some time. However, they may be modi-fied by the regions over which they flow later on. Sometimes an air mass that has been cold becomes warm because it has moved over a hot land surface. So, while an air mass may have inherited certain characteristics from the region in which it began, it may change as it moves on, getting warmer or cooler, drier or wetter, denser (high pressure) or lighter (low pressure), depending upon the prevailing conditions in the regions over which it passes. If it moves over water, it may become moister; if it moves over land, drier. If it moves slowly over a region, it has a longer time in which changes may occur.

Fronts. Children will find that weather fronts are marked on the weather maps in the newspapers. Also in reports of weather by television or radio, reference is frequently made to the geographical location or the approach of cold and warm fronts, and sometimes one may hear references to occluded and stationary fronts. There is no need of forcing any extensive study of fronts on children. On the other hand, children can observe changes in the weather, and these can be associated with the fact that a different body or mass of air with a front is passing through their region, perhaps every few days. It is well to keep in mind that the meteorologists themselves did not know much about fronts for many years and that there is still much to learn and understand at present. However, children in the middle latitudes experience fronts, and there are desirable attitudes and meanings for the children if they are to be intelligent and resourceful in the years to come.

Polar and tropical air masses differ greatly in temperature, moisture content, pressure, and density. There may be a very great contrast between them. The greater the contrast, the more violent are the accompanying storms. If the warm air is dry, there may be little precipitation; if it carries a great deal of mois-

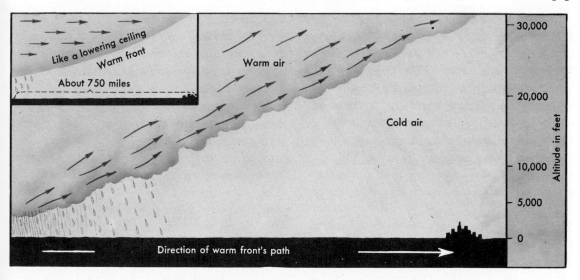

Like a lowering ceiling
Warm front
About 750 miles

Warm air

Cold air

30,000

20,000

10,000

5,000

0

Altitude in feet

Direction of warm front's path

A warm front riding over a cold air mass. Note precipitation.

ture, the precipitation may be greater. Since cold polar air is more dense than warm tropical air, it tends to push the warm air up; in other words it displaces the warm air (see the wind box Experience on p. 454). All storms are modified by the topography of Earth. Therefore, as cold polar air masses and warm tropical air masses meet, there is developed a boundary or border between them known as a *front*. Some meteorologists have compared it to a battle front where two armies are fighting. These masses may collide in almost any part of the middle latitudes; in fact, cold polar air has invaded Mexico at times. As would be expected, the warm tropical fronts move farther north in the summer than they do in winter. We would also expect cold polar fronts to move farther south in winter, which they do.

There are two general types of *cold fronts*. One kind moves slowly; it may take a wedge-like shape with a long, sloping forward edge over which the invaded warm air mass slowly ascends. As the warm air is gradually pushed upward, it is cooled and therefore it cannot hold as much moisture as it did. There may be showers, squalls, and thunderstorms along a front hundreds of miles long, and rain may

fall hundreds of miles to the rear of the cold front.

A second kind of cold front moves rapidly. These cold fronts have steep front slopes. The warm air mass is pushed rapidly upward. High winds are present, and thunderstorms may occur along the border of the front or somewhat ahead of it for some miles, due to the rapidly advancing and overturning of the cold air and rapidly ascending warm air near the border.

If the warm air is dry, there may be few or no clouds and little or no precipitation. If the cold air behind the front becomes warmed, there may be no great change in temperature. But there will be drier air, better visibility, and a change in the direction of the wind.

When a warm air mass is moving into a region of cold air, we have a *warm front*. Here, again, the cold air remains on the ground and the warm air is forced to rise over the cold air. The warm air ascending over the cold air may form a long ramp far back over the cold mass. Rains and cloudy weather may follow.

EXPERIENCE. *To discuss cold waves.* There is a cold spell almost every winter in many parts of our Earth. There are periods of cool weather in the summer as well. Have children discuss a cold spell. When did they first notice it? Were there any clouds? Did they notice the wind? In what direction did it blow? Did the direction change later? Was there any squally weather? Was there rain, snow, or other precipitation? Was there fog? Where was this air mass formed? Was the cold wave expensive to the community, that is, was there any damage? Were people inconvenienced?

EXPERIENCE. *To discuss hot spells of weather.* Often there is a period, even if brief, in which the weather is unseasonably hot. Were there clouds in the sky? What were the clouds like? Was there any wind? Were there any squalls? Was there any damage to crops? Was it a dry hot spell or was it a humid hot spell? How did it affect people?

One condition that produces an *occluded front* is when a cold air mass advances so fast that it overtakes other less-cold air masses as well as warm air masses. The cold air of the fast-moving cold front remains next to the ground, forcing both the warmer and the less-cold air up over it. The warm air is said to be *occluded* since it has been completely forced off the ground. The warm air is cooled and may, if sufficiently moist, produce clouds and rain. This is called a cold front occlusion.

There are warm front occlusions, too, when a cool air mass overtakes a warm air mass flowing up the slope of another cold air mass. The cool air pushes up the warm air and itself flows up the slope of the colder air mass.

There are combinations of these types called composite occlusions.

So we see that if cold air is displacing warm air at Earth's surface, the front is called a cold front. When the warm air is displacing the cold, the front is a warm one. If a front is not moving, it is a *stationary* front. And the name occlusion has been given to other ways in which the fronts behave.

Hurricanes. Hurricanes, sometimes called tropical cyclones or typhoons, are storms of great violence and may cause widespread destruction. They seem to originate in the warmer parts of the oceans, along the poleward margins of the doldrums. They occur in both the northern and southern hemispheres. They occasionally pass over the West Indies and to the interior of North America, sometimes causing great damage and loss of life. They also occur in the China Sea, the Arabian Sea, the Bay of Bengal, the Indian Ocean, and the waters northeast and northwest of Australia. Tropical cyclones are often called by different names. They are called cyclones in India, hurricanes in the West Indies, and typhoons in East Asia.

Hurricanes are from fifty to nine hundred miles in total diameter. The wind velocities in them may, in the most violent part, be as high as two hundred miles an hour. At the center of the storm, there is a calm, clear area, from five to thirty miles in diameter called the *eye* of the storm. Hurricanes are usually accompanied by torrential rains. Barometric pressure in the center of the storm is very low; in one Florida hurricane, for example, it was 27.61 inches.

Since the winds are spiralling inward toward the center, as the eye of the storm passes over a person at the surface of Earth he will find that the wind shifts its direction.

After hurricanes enter the region of the prevailing westerlies, they gradually lose their violent characteristics and become ordinary cyclones. Likewise, after passing over extensive areas, they tend to lose their intensity after several days, and having travelled many miles.

Hurricanes are believed to originate in an upward-moving column of hot moist air in a calm region. This column is probably started by unequal heating of a portion of Earth's surface. As air moves in to fill the space left by the upward-moving air, it is turned to the right by Earth's rotation, in accordance with

A Wind Scale

	MILES PER HOUR	TYPE OF WIND
1. Smoke rises straight up; leaves still	Less than 1	Calm
2. Leaves on trees barely rustle	2–7	Slight breeze
3. Leaves and twigs in motion; flags snapping	8–12	Gentle breeze
4. Dust and loose papers flying; small branches swaying	13–18	Moderate breeze
5. Small trees in leaf swaying; crests appearing on waves	19–24	Fresh breeze
6. Larger branches in motion; whistling heard in telegraph wires; hard to walk with open umbrella	25–31	Strong wind
7. Whole trees swaying; hard to walk against wind	32–38	High wind
8. Twigs broken off branches	39–46	Gale
9. Branches of trees broken; signs torn down; chimneys blown down	47–54	Strong gale
10. Trees uprooted; barn roofs torn off; buildings damaged	55–75	Whole gale
11. Buildings destroyed; trains overturned; telephone poles snapped off; automobiles lifted off the highways	Above 75	Hurricane

Ferrel's law. The result is that a vigorous whirl is soon set up. The air which is carried aloft cools and drops its moisture in the form of rain thereby releasing vast amounts of energy. Since there is an immense amount of warm, moist, calm air available in the doldrums, a storm of great violence is presently built up. This storm is carried, first westward by the trade winds and then eastward by the westerlies, in the characteristic curved path of a hurricane.

Note that hurricanes differ from ordinary cyclones. Cyclones are caused by interacting currents of warm and cold air; hurricanes, by upward movements of warm, moist, calm air. Cyclones originate in the regions of the westerlies; hurricanes originate in the regions of the doldrums but may move into the regions of the westerlies. Cyclones originate over either water or land; hurricanes only over water, where there is little friction with the surface. Although hurricanes originate over water, they frequently pass over a part of the North American continent before expiring. In fact, hurricanes have been known to go far inland. The inward moving air in a hurricane is whirling so violently that it never reaches the center. This forms the *calm eye*. Ordinary cyclones have no eye.

The Weather Bureau keeps careful watch for these hurricanes and issues "advisories," which give the location, intensity, and direction of the storm. Bulletins are also issued to keep the public informed as to the progress of the storm so that people can take the necessary safety precautions.

Tornadoes. Tornadoes, often miscalled cyclones, are the smallest storms, but they are nevertheless the most violent. Most of them occur between the Rocky Mountains and the Appalachians. However, tornadoes have been reported in every state in the United States. They have been reported in Canada, in many countries in Europe, in Australia, India, China, Japan, in the Bermuda Islands and the Fiji Islands. They are usually associated with thunderstorms. A tornado consists of a mass of air whirling with great speed about a center of low pressure.

There has been considerable difficulty in measuring the barometric pressures and wind velocities in a tornado accurately since frequently the necessary instruments are destroyed by the storm. Some scientists have estimated the wind velocity to be in the neighborhood of five hundred miles an hour, and the pressure to be three fourths of its normal value.

The most striking characteristic of a tornado, aside from its violence, is its funnel-shaped cloud. Writhing and twisting, a long funnel of vapor seems to hang from greenish-black clouds overhead. Wherever this funnel touches Earth, havoc and destruction take place. The roar of the tornado has been said to resemble that of a hundred jet planes.

Tornadoes seem to originate, as whirls in mid-air, in the southeastern section of an ordinary cyclone. These whirls are probably started where a current of cold, dry air meets one of warm, moist air. Since the whirl starts above the surface of Earth, there is little friction to retard it, and it develops great velocity. It now extends nearer and nearer the ground, finally touching the surface.

Since the air mass is whirling with extreme rapidity, the motion tends to throw the air away from the center, creating in the center a region of very low pressure. This is perhaps one of the lowest air pressures to be obtained by natural processes at the surface of the land. Expansion of the air inside this partial vacuum produces cooling and condensation; hence the funnel-shaped cloud.

The conditions described above as necessary for the production of tornadoes (conflicting currents of cool dry air and warm moist air above Earth's surface) are found to a marked degree in the Mississippi Valley and other tornado areas. In many of these regions it is a quite common practice to carry insurance on property for damage done by tornadoes.

The path of a tornado may vary in width from a few feet to a mile, but generally is between five hundred and two thousand feet. In length, it is commonly from twenty to forty miles, though it may be as long as three hundred miles. A tornado travels at a speed of between twenty and forty miles per hour. The direction of a tornado tends to follow that of the cyclone with which it is associated.

The destruction caused by a tornado is due to two factors: the great velocity of the wind and the low pressure at the center. Trees are uprooted or broken, buildings blown down or carried away, trains blown from their tracks, straws driven through boards. When the center of low pressure reaches a house, the air pressure inside the house is so much greater than that outside that the house often seems to explode. Strange stories are told of freak occurrences in tornadoes. There have been records of water being "sucked up" from river beds into this center of low pressure.

Tornado approaching the town of Vulcan, Alberta, Canada. (Th Lions, N.Y.C.)

Many people dwelling in tornado areas have constructed cellars (called storm caves, or tornado or cyclone cellars), beneath the ground level, where they can take refuge in case of a tornado. Of course the chance of being hit by a tornado is rather small, owing to the limited area which the storm covers.

Tornadoes usually travel from southwest to northeast with the prevailing westerly winds. If a person is caught in the open by an approaching tornado, he should run as fast as he can at right angles to the path of the storm. This may take him out of the path of danger. The next best thing to do is to lie flat in a surface depression such as a ditch or a gully.

In homes, the corner of the basement nearest the tornado is the safest place. The house is likely to be carried away from that corner rather than toward it, and the basement walls offer some protection against the wind and the flying debris.

It would be well for the teacher and children to know what they should do if a tornado is reported as approaching. Advice should be sought from a competent authority who has knowledge concerning how tornado-proof the school building is. In tornado regions it would be well to provide children with information as to desirable behavior if a tornado strikes when they are in the open. This kind of information may be a result of joint consideration by school authorities, teaching staff, parents, and other representatives of the community.

In recent years a tornado warning system has been developed with its center at Kansas City. Data is collected from weather stations all over the country. When conditions favorable to the development of tornadoes are found, the local organizations are contacted and warnings are issued so that people may watch for tornadoes and take the proper safety measures. The boys and girls we are teaching today will live in a period when more will be known about tornadoes, how to predict them

more accurately, and how they are formed. They may know more about how to build their houses and public buildings to resist the destructive effects of these, the most violent storms known to us.

Thunderstorms. Few phenomena have been "explained" with the use of more superstitious ideas than have thunderstorms. The Norsemen believed that thunder was caused by the god Thor's chariot and that the thunderbolt was his hammer. The Greek and Roman god Zeus or Jupiter was represented as hurling thunderbolts when angry. Even today we can find many erroneous ideas concerning thunderstorms. One of these is that the storm itself is caused by the thunder and lightning. It is well known, however, that, though thunder and lightning are very spectacular, they are entirely secondary to the real cause of a thunderstorm.

Thunderstorms occur everywhere. They are more frequent, however, near the equator than at the poles and in humid regions than in desert regions. Over land there are more thunderstorms in summer than in winter.

Clouds producing thunderstorms, when seen from the side, are frequently shaped like an anvil and may occupy a space from one to ten miles high and from three to several hundred miles long.

Studies which have been made by aircraft, radiosonde stations, and long-range radar have increased our knowledge of thunderstorms. It has been discovered that most thunderstorms consist of several *cells*. Each of the cells is characterized by an updraft, or chimney of air, in which air is being carried upward. Usually with each cell there are associated downdrafts.

Some thunderstorms occur in warm air masses that are very humid. This kind seems to be started by the heating of the air near the ground. The air expands and the cooler surrounding air forces the warm air up. The hot

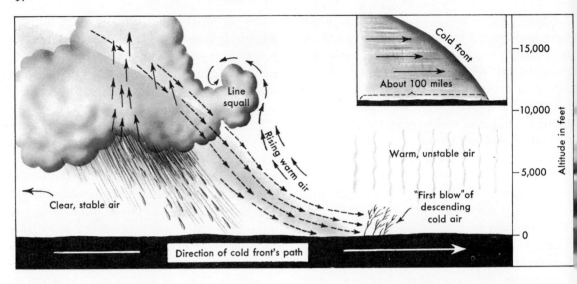

A cold front pushing under a warm air mass may produce thunderstorms.

air is pushed up so fast that, with the cooler air rushing in, becoming warm, and in turn being pushed up, a strong updraft or chimney of rising air is produced. The hot air reaching higher altitudes expands still more because there is less pressure resting on it to compress it. Air is cooled in this process. This causes its great load of water vapor to be condensed quickly into rain (p. 479). The cold rain, falling through the air, cools it and causes a downdraft inside the storm. The difference in temperature between the bottom and the top of a thunder cloud may be as much as 100°F. We may, therefore, anticipate a thunderstorm when the air is warm and quiet and contains a large amount of water vapor.

The principal air currents in a thunderstorm, then, are a rising current of warm air in the front of a storm and a descending current of cool air toward its rear. This descending current seems to be essential to provide the violent circulation necessary to form a thunderstorm.

A thunderstorm moves at a rate of from twenty to fifty miles an hour along a path ranging from a hundred feet to forty or more miles in width. In the region of the prevailing

westerlies its direction of movement is eastward. As it moves, it continues to take up air from the heated land over which it passes, forming an intense updraft, which maintains the storm.

One can easily distinguish between the two air currents in an actual thunderstorm. Shortly before the storm arrives, the wind dies down or blows gently toward the storm. This is the upward-moving air current, which appears to the observer to be a calm or a gentle breeze. Just before the first rain falls, there is a gust of cool wind, often violent, blowing outward directly away from the storm. This is the descending current, which strikes the ground and blows outward.

Some thunderstorms are caused by the passing of a low and the coming of a high. We may think of them as occurring along rapidly moving cold fronts of cold continental air. Usually this change is gradual, but sometimes it comes suddenly. When this occurs, cold dry air is brought violently into contact with warm moist air. The cold current may either trap the warm air beneath it or force the warm air to rise over it. In the first case, the warm air then tends to overturn the cold layer above

In either case, the warm air expands and produces a storm. Thunderstorms of this type are frequently more severe than those of the first type, and may occur at any time of night or day. Sometimes a line of thunderstorms, or squall line, moves ahead of the cold front.

Some thunderstorms develop over hilly and mountainous belts where air masses that are warm and humid are forced upward over the hills or mountains. The Ozark Mountains of Arkansas and Missouri and the Black Hills of South Dakota have been called breeding grounds for thunderstorms.

On the whole, thunderstorms are beneficial. They usually bring a maximum of rain with a maximum of sunshine, since the entire storm may pass by in an hour or so, leaving the sun shining brightly. This is helpful during growing seasons, when crops need moisture without loss of sunshine. In some sections thunderstorms provide much-needed rain at seasons when ordinary cyclonic rainstorms are at a minimum.

Thunderstorms can also do damage, not only because of lightning, but also because of hail, which frequently accompanies them, and occasional violent winds. A tremendous amount of energy is released in a thunderstorm, independent of lightning discharges. It is often comparable to the energy released by ten bombs of the World War II type.

People often may be heard to say, "The shower is coming back." A moment's thought will show why this is impossible in the zone of the prevailing westerlies, for thunderstorms follow the normal direction of all storms in middle latitudes—from west to east. If one thunderstorm comes soon after another, you may be sure that the second is a new storm.

Lightning and Thunder. Lightning and thunder, as has been stated, are by-products of a thunderstorm, and by no means causes of it. Benjamin Franklin was the first to prove that lightning is a huge spark of electricity.

After great differences of charge have accumulated between cloud and Earth, a bolt of lightning restores the balance. (Westinghouse Electric Corporation.)

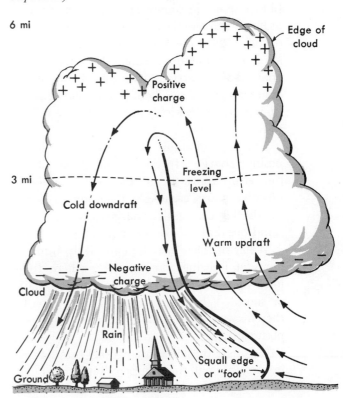

Some events taking place in a thunderstorm: warm updrafts, cold downdrafts; storm advancing with a squall line leading; generation of opposite electrical charges; lightning restoring balance; moisture cooling and condensing. (Adapted from McGraw-Hill Encyclopedia of Technology, Vol. 13, p. 617, after G. A. Suckstorff, H. R. Byers, and R. R. Braham, Jr.)

Since lightning is electricity, the teacher is advised to read the section on electricity (pp. 804–898): the portion on static or frictional electricity (pp. 806–811) will be especially useful to the teaching and learning situations concerning lightning. Scientists have much to learn about the electrical charges that occur in a thunderstorm. The ideas that have been developed as explanations of these phenomena by various authorities are not always in complete agreement.

Experiments have proved that when drops of water are broken into a spray they become electrically charged. (See Experience, p. 806). In a thunderstorm the rush of air currents is so great that raindrops in the great updrafts are blown apart, in somewhat the same manner as fluid in an atomizer. It is thought that most of the larger drops become positive, while the air surrounding them becomes negative. The charged air is carried to higher portions of the cloud; and the drops, being larger and heavier, remain at the bottom and eventually fall as rain.

The tops of many thunderclouds have a positive charge. In the middle of the cloud, but far up above the ground, will be found a negative charge created by the updrafts carrying the lighter negative charges upward. The raindrops that fall are positively charged.

Water droplets are also carried up into regions of freezing temperatures, where they form various types of ice crystals, pellets, hail, or snow. When freezing occurs too rapidly they may explode, forming particles with opposite charges.

No single mechanism is wholly satisfactory in explaining all that happens, but it has been found that thunderclouds, for the most part, are positively charged in the upper parts and negatively charged in the lower parts. When the difference between the charges becomes great enough, a bolt of lightning, like a huge spark, is discharged and tends to restore the electrical balance. The bolt may flash between parts of the same cloud, between clouds, or between a cloud and the ground. Lightning flashes follow the easiest course, which accounts for their zigzag appearance. The first bolt is likely to form a one- to six-inch channel of ionized air through which as many as thirty or forty later bolts may pass.

Studies indicate that in normal fair weather the solid part of Earth usually has a negative charge. However, several thousand thunderstorms are occurring on Earth at any given moment, and as each moves along, electrical interactions take place not only within the clouds but also between the clouds and the ground. A negative charge builds up in the lower part of the moving cloud, and at the same time, a positive charge appears in the ground below it, *induced* by the charge in the cloud. That is, the negative charges in the ground are driven away from under the negatively charged clouds, and it is left with a positive charge. Then, attracted by the negative charges in the base of the passing clouds, the positive charges move up trees, high steeples, or buildings, leaving Earth with a negative charge. Lightning, too, while restoring balance, tends to leave Earth with a negative charge.

In fair-weather regions, these negatively charged electrons then steadily "leak" upward through the air, which acts as a weak conductor, and may finally reach the ionosphere. This fair-weather current also tends to restore balance.

To summarize: violent air currents in a thunderstorm separate electrical charges. There are positive and negative charges within the clouds and on the ground, and these are discharged by lightning between oppositely charged clouds or between clouds and Earth. It is only the latter that may do damage to objects on the ground.

In a discharge of lightning the electricity passing through the air heats it suddenly, causing very rapid expansion. The sudden expansion sets up a wave in the atmosphere which reaches our ears as the sound which we call *thunder*. Since the sound from the farther end of the path has a longer distance to travel than the sound from the nearer end, we do not hear it all at once, but rather as the characteristic roll of thunder. Some of the sound may be reflected from the clouds, which adds to the rolling effect.

Sound takes about five seconds to travel a mile; light, an exceedingly small fraction of a second; therefore, if we count the number of seconds between the time we see the flash of lightning and the time we hear the thunder, and divide by five, we can get a rough idea of how far away the storm is. Usually the sound of thunder cannot be heard more than ten to fifteen miles.

If we provide a path by which electricity can pass between Earth and the cloud without a violent spark, we secure protection from lightning. Lightning rods help to provide such a path. If they are well connected to Earth, they allow some of the electric charge to leak harmlessly off. When a building protected by well-installed lightning rods is struck, even then the lightning rods tend to lead the electricity away and prevent damage.

When lightning rods are poorly installed, they actually increase the danger from lightning. Instead of leading the charge away, they may simply lead it to a point where it may more easily do damage. They should be installed by a person thoroughly competent to do such work. Special care should be taken to see that the rods are properly connected to the ground below the level where the ground is always saturated with water. Since the object of lightning rods is to lead electricity to or from Earth, they should be connected to the ground as effectively as possible. Ground water is a good conductor; so the connection is better if it is made in permanently wet ground. If this is impossible, seek competent advice on an alternative method of grounding.

Steel-frame buildings, such as the skyscrapers in cities, form a cage of steel about their occupants; and even when they are struck, which they very frequently are, they lead the electricity away harmlessly. One should remain indoors in a city during a thunderstorm. Isolated buildings in the country are more hazardous and should be protected by lightning rods.

When a person is caught out in the open in a storm, he should avoid standing near an isolated tree. Tall, isolated trees are more likely to be hit than short ones in a forest. Do not remain in the water of a lake or standing upright in a large flat area, thus becoming a target. Seek a depression, or lie flat on the ground. Wire fences may conduct electricity a long distance; avoid them. Do not take refuge in isolated structures or under bridges. It is better to remain out in the open and get wet than to move into lines of natural conduction between a cloud and Earth. Persons in a car are shielded by the steel cage surrounding them.

In any case, relatively few people are ever killed by lightning. Many of the discharges we see and hear are between cloud and cloud. Many of the discharges between cloud and Earth strike where there are no people.

When a thunderstorm is so far away that we cannot hear the thunder, we can sometimes see the lightning reflected from clouds. Such indistinct flashes, sometimes lighting up the sky all around the horizon, are called "heat lightning" or sometimes "sheet lightning." They have no more to do with heat than other lightning; most thunderstorms are hot-weather phenomena.

EXPERIENCE. *To observe a thunderstorm.* Thunderstorms are gigantic displays of energy in nature. If they were as rare as total eclipses of the sun and could be predicted far ahead, it is likely that thousands of people would travel to see this lavish display.

Should a thunderstorm develop during a time when children are in school, it might be well to use it as a part of the instruction about weather and electricity. Describe the period of calm before the storm. Keep the children calm by talking to them in a calm voice. Encourage them to talk calmly also. Do you see an anvil-shaped cloud? Do you see any evidence of updraft or downdraft? Point out that the thunderstorm is the result of the air getting out of balance (unstable). The sun is the great source of energy that has heated Earth, and some places have become much warmer than others. Cool air may be rushing forward, replacing masses of rising warmer air. Observe the lightning. It is a beautiful display. It is an old-fashioned Fourth of July celebration multiplied a thousand times. The amount of energy can be personalized by considering whether we could puff up a great cloud like that. Compare with the little clouds one's breath makes on a cold day. Note what happens after the thunderstorm passes and the forces of the atmosphere have become more stable.

If the period of the development of the thunderstorm is quite long, it might be well to plan to have children work at something else which need not interfere with observation or discussion. Have children discuss safety during a thunderstorm.

Land and Sea Breezes—Local Winds. The pleasant climate of many seaside and lake resorts is largely due to the cool breezes which blow upon them from the water. During the day the land heats much faster than the water; the air over it rises and creates an area of low pressure. Air moves in from the cooler (and therefore higher-pressure) area over the water. At night this condition reverses itself; the land cools off more rapidly, and a breeze blows in the opposite direction.

Often one side of a valley is exposed more directly to the rays of the sun than surrounding regions. This side becomes warm, the air over it rises, and a breeze blows up the slope. After dark, cooling takes place, and conditions reverse themselves.

Cold air, in sinking, flows downhill precisely as water does. If, then, there is a supply of cold air from a high, cold plateau draining down a valley, a wind will be set up. The *bora* of the northeast Adriatic, the *mistral* of the Rhone valley, and the winds of many smaller valleys are of this kind. Extensive winds of this general nature blow steadily from the interior of Greenland and the antarctic continent, and may greatly modify the world's weather. Scientists are attempting to learn more about them.

Jet Streams. During World War II, some air pilots flying at altitudes between 20,000 and 30,000 feet above sea level came back with stories about air currents. Flying one direction, they seemed to make hardly any progress as viewed from the ground, but when they turned around they found that they passed over the ground surface at a speed almost twice as fast as their motors could move them. In one direction they were flying against a great speeding stream of air; in the opposite direction, the air stream carried them along.

Winds at high altitudes blow in different directions from those near the surface of Earth. In the Northern Hemisphere, southward from the pole to northern Mexico, Africa, and India, and to the southern part of the United States, winds blow from the west with increasing speed until the region of the easterly trade winds is reached; south of this region toward the equator these westerly winds decrease in speed, and finally gentle winds from the east are encountered. At their strongest, these winds are called *jet streams*. Jet streams are always present in the upper troposphere but they vary in velocity and position—north or south. In the Northern Hemisphere they are farther north and weaker in summer, and

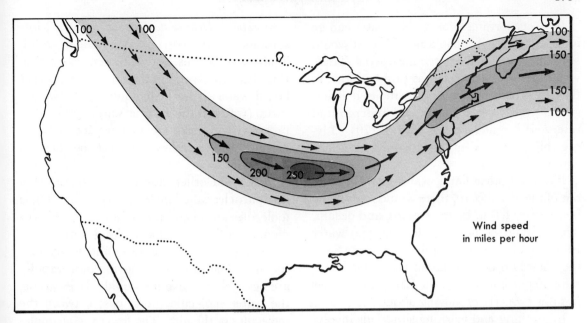

The position of a jet stream may shift from time to time.   The wind speed within a jet stream varies.   (Adapted from Aviation
Series, *Leaflet No. 3, U.S. Department of Commerce, Weather Bureau.)*

farther south and stronger in winter.   Great
turbulence along their edges has been reported
by those who have flown into them.

Sometimes two or more single streams of
air connect and form a great river of rushing
air which meanders about, encircling our
Earth somewhere between the Arctic Circle
and the Tropic of Cancer in the Northern
Hemisphere.   There are also jet streams in the
Southern Hemisphere, but not as much is
known about them.

In the jet streams, speeds of more than 200
miles an hour have been encountered at high
levels, although there is great variation in
speed within a single jet stream.   When they

get as low as 10,000 feet their speed becomes
much less.

The heat of Earth is distributed by its winds.
The jet streams are probably a part of this heat
distributing mechanism.

From time to time there may be news items
about the jet streams.   Teachers can use such
items as information to be thought over, not
necessarily accepted.   There is a great possibility that the study of jet streams will help
meteorologists to give long-range forecasts of
the weather.   It is known that they have a
steering effect on air masses moving in an easterly direction and the weather conditions that
accompany them.

The Water in the Air

**Water Cycle—How Water Gets into the Air
and out Again.**   Water is never still for long.
It is constantly going into the air and constantly coming out again; this constant inter-

change is called the *water cycle*.   If we are to
understand rainfall, clouds, and other phenomena connected with weather, we must
know something about the behavior of water.

It is very fortunate for us that water can go into the air; for if it could not, all of it would soon sink into Earth or swell the oceans. There would be no water to fall as rain or snow, to flow in brooks and rivers, to moisten fields, gardens, and forests, and to refill underground reservoirs (aquifers, p. 171 and p. 270). Living things, including man, would soon lack water.

If, on the other hand, water could not get out of the air, once in, there would soon be no more water left in lakes, streams, and oceans. There would be no rain, no snow, no water left to supply the needs of living things. Soon the air would be holding all the water. It is most important for life on Earth that water has this property of moving about.

In teaching and learning situations involving weather, a teacher and children have opportunities to internalize learnings better than in almost any area of learning, because children have so many sensory experiences with weather, and their activities are accordingly affected. Even interpretations of things that are invisible, such as water in the air, energy, and steam can be internalized. An individual should *personalize* his learning, making it his own.

Evaporation—How Water Gets into the Air. Most substances can exist in three states—solid, liquid, and gaseous; and water is no exception. If we heat ice (water in the solid state), we get liquid water; if we heat liquid water, we. get steam (water in the gaseous state). When the process is reversed, steam must lose heat to become water, and water must lose heat to become ice.

Water, like other substances, is composed of tiny particles called molecules (p. 375). These molecules are in constant motion. Under ordinary conditions, some molecules move fast enough to fly out of the water and escape into the air. The molecules moving most rapidly are best able to leave the liquid. In escaping, the water molecules must pass between the molecules of the air. The fewer the air molecules, the less difficulty the water molecules will have in escaping. This is why water boils at a low temperature when the air pressure is low, as was explained on page 451. This flying off of the molecules is called *evaporation*. It is the means by which water gets into the air. Water is constantly evaporating from puddles, lakes, rivers, and oceans—in fact, from all bodies of water, whether large or small.

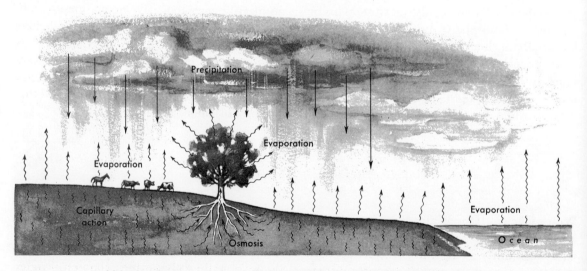

Molecules of water move about. Condensation of water takes place within the clouds.

The warmer a liquid is, the greater is the speed of motion of the molecules, and therefore, since more of them go fast enough to fly off, the higher is the rate of evaporation. When evaporation proceeds violently, we say that the liquid is boiling.

The more surface a liquid has exposed, the greater are the opportunities for the escape of molecules into the space above. Water, therefore, will evaporate faster from a wide-mouthed jar than from a narrow-necked bottle.

EXPERIENCE. *To observe evaporation under different conditions.* If the blackboards in the school are of the kind that can be moistened, have the children moisten a section. Watch it dry as the water evaporates into the air. Now have two children moisten two spots, being careful that they are equal in size and approximate amount of moisture used. This will provide children with an opportunity to use their critical thinking in an activity. Have a child fan one spot, but make certain the other is not fanned. Observe that the water from the spot that is fanned evaporates the more rapidly, because new air is being brought to the moist spot. If the blackboards are of the type that cannot be moistened, perhaps a cement walk or breezeway can be used.

Cloths such as dish towels can be used in studying evaporation. Place one wet cloth in a cool place and another near a source of heat. How does heat affect the rate of evaporation? Place a wet cloth in a place where the air is quiet and one in the wind. Observe the difference in the rate of evaporation. Children may have a hand in making certain the cloths are the same size, made of the same material, and equally moistened.

Air at a given temperature can hold no more than a certain amount of water. When, at the given temperature, it contains this amount, it is said to be *saturated*. If air is in motion over the surface of water, the saturated air is removed and replaced with fresh, unsaturated air, which in turn becomes saturated, and so on. Thus air moving over the surface of water increases the rate of evaporation. We shall encounter this idea of saturation in another and more important place presently.

Obviously the more water there already is in the air at a certain temperature (that is, the nearer the air is to saturation), the more difficult it is for additional water molecules to get in. Therefore water (or any other liquid) evaporates faster into dry air than into moist air (p. 433).

To summarize, the factors that affect the rate of evaporation are the temperature of the liquid, the air pressure, the exposed surface of the liquid, moisture in the air, and the movement of air above the liquid.

Living things give off much water to the air. Water transpires from the leaf surfaces of plants. Enough water may transpire from corn plants during one growing season to cover the field in which they grow with seven inches of water. On a warm summer day a sunflower gives off a pint of water, and an oak tree as much as two hundred gallons.

Animals too put much moisture into the air. The air we exhale contains considerable water vapor, which has evaporated from our lungs. When we perspire, water evaporates from the surface of our skin. This can in large part account for our discomfort in a crowded room which has poor ventilation.

Strange as it may at first appear, water is formed in the air by fires. Water is composed of hydrogen and oxygen. There is much hydrogen in ordinary fuels. When these burn, the hydrogen combines with the oxygen of the air and forms water. A cold glass held over a candle flame will be covered with moisture from the flame. In cooking, one notices that if a vessel of cold water is placed over a gas flame, moisture forms on the outside of the vessel. This moisture comes from the hydrogen of the gas, which, when the gas burns, unites with the oxygen of the air, forming water (p. 382). The water condenses on the outside of the cold container. When the container has been over the flame long enough to become warm, water no longer condenses on it.

EXPERIENCE. *To observe that water is formed in a flame.* Hold a tin or aluminum cup or pan over a candle flame or over a Sterno stove. Have the pan about half full of cold water. Note that moisture is formed on the lower part of the pan when the pan is *first* put over the flame. There may also be a black soot which is carbon from the candle or stove. See above for explanation of the formation of water.

When water (or any other liquid) evaporates, it is the fastest-moving molecules that leave the liquid; the slower-moving molecules remain behind. This evaporation of a liquid has a cooling effect upon the liquid, since slower-moving molecules indicate that the liquid has a lower temperature than it had before evaporation began. This is the reason why our hands feel cool when we dip them in water and allow them to dry in the air. When we perspire, the cooling effect as the perspiration evaporates helps to keep our bodies at a proper temperature. This cooling effect is used in hot desert countries to keep supplies of drinking water cool. The water is kept in somewhat porous containers, such as jars and canvas bags, and the evaporation of some of the water serves to keep the rest cool. Children who are living in dry regions or who have traveled in such regions may have observed canvas bags that are carried on automobiles to furnish the occupants with cool water.

Some substances evaporate more rapidly than water. This is true of gasoline, alcohol, and ether. Owing to the rapid evaporation of these substances, they have an unusually cool-

ing effect. Alcohol baths have been used in the treatment of fevers. Anyone who has washed things in gasoline knows the cooling effect of gasoline on the hands.

EXPERIENCE. *To observe that water disappears when it evaporates.* With young children arrange for evaporation as an experience in the simplest fashion, possibly with water in a pan. After a while the water disappears. Where did it go? Young children may say, "Who did it?" (That is, "Who emptied it?") By repetition and thinking, they can come to accept that it has gone into the air.

EXPERIENCE. *To study the evaporation of water in vessels of different shapes.* Secure a pan, a tumbler, a pitcher, a flower vase, and a narrow necked bottle with a stopper. Have the children place exactly the same amount of water in each vessel. Stopper the bottle after the water has been placed in it. Set all of the vessels on a table where the conditions such as temperature and air movement will be the same for all vessels. Have the children and the custodian make certain the vessels are not disturbed. Observe these over a period of several days. The water in the open pan should evaporate first because the water is exposed to more air and to more changes of air, allowing for more evaporation. There should be very little if any indication of evaporation in the bottle.

EXPERIENCE. *To study the effect of temperature upon evaporation.* Place equal amounts of water in two similar containers. Set one on the radiator and the other in a cool place. From which one does more water evaporate?

This series of experiments illustrates one of the techniques for solving problems; we carefully varied one factor at a time. In the first part, we varied the exposure of the water to the air; in the second part, we closed one portion of water from the air and not the other;

Bubbles forming from air dissolved in water

Steam

Large bubbles form and break. Water is now boiling.

The boiling of water is a complex process that is not yet fully understood.

in the last, we varied the temperature of the water.

EXPERIENCE. *Boiling water.* Place a container of cold water over a heater such as a small electric heating plate. After a while bubbles will be seen to form on the inside of the container. These are formed of air which was dissolved in the water. Next large bubbles of water vapor will form, rise to the surface, and break. The water is now said to be boiling. A white cloud forms near the surface. This white cloud is composed of tiny drops of water. Most people call it "steam," but it is not really steam. Steam is invisible.

If water is boiled in a teakettle, it is easy to see that there is a space between the spout and the white cloud. This space contains steam. Children may put their hands in the white parts and feel that it is moist. They must *not* put their fingers in the invisible part, for they will surely be scalded. The steam is very hot.

EXPERIENCE. *Plants give off water into the air.* Cut a small hole in the center of a circular piece of cardboard; then cut a slit from the hole out to the edge. Fit the cardboard around the stem of a small potted geranium plant. Around the stem of the plant and over the slit in the cardboard, paste gummed paper tape or adhesive tape. Over the cardboard invert a large glass jar. If the preparations are carefully carried out, no air or water vapor can enter the jar unless it is carried in by the plant. In a day or two the inside of the jar will be covered with droplets of water which have been given off into the air by the growing plant.

EXPERIENCE. *Cooling by evaporation.* With a cork, close the hole in the bottom of an empty unglazed flowerpot. Fill the pot with water, standing it in a pan to prevent water damage to the table. Fill a glass jar with water also. Water will soon penetrate the porous pot and evaporate. In an hour or two take the temperature of the water in the pot and in the jar. Which is cooler? It is best to do this experiment in a very dry place—a heated schoolroom on a winter's day, for instance, unless the room is artificially humidified. (This information can be secured from the custodian or principal.) Under such conditions evaporation is rapid. Why may such devices be used to cool drinking water in dry desert countries? Why not in hot moist countries?

Condensation—How Water Gets out of the Air. We have seen in the previous section that by heating liquid water we can get water vapor or steam. The reverse is also true; by cooling water vapor we can get liquid water. The process of changing water vapor to liquid water is called *condensation.*

Warm air can hold more moisture than cold air. The warmer the air is, the more moisture it can hold. If we cool moist air sufficiently, it loses part of its moisture. At any given temperature air can hold only a certain amount of water. Air which is holding all the moisture which it can at any given temperature is said to be saturated. If saturated air is cooled, it must lose some of its water. We may become aware of this water in the form of rain, dew, snow, and other forms of precipitation (see below). If the air is heated, it becomes able to hold more water, or, in other words, it becomes unsaturated.

When we speak of the humidity of the air, as we frequently do in talking about the weather, we usually mean the relative humidity. This is true of almost all weather reports. *Relative humidity* means the ratio between the amount of water the air is actually holding at a given temperature and the amount it could hold at this temperature. It is always expressed in a per cent. Thus a relative humidity of 70 per cent means that the air is holding 70 per cent as much moisture as it can, or that it is 70 per cent saturated. Air that is perfectly dry has a relative humidity of 0 per cent, and air that can hold no more moisture (saturated air) has a relative humidity of 100 per cent. If we lower the temperature of air, without adding or subtracting any moisture, we increase its relative humidity; if we raise its temperature, we decrease its relative humidity; so we can see how much relative humidity is dependent upon temperature. Occasionally the per cent sign is omitted in writing about relative humidity, but it should always be understood.

If for any reason moist air is cooled to a point where it can no longer hold all its moisture,—that is, if it is cooled below its saturation point,—condensation occurs. When condensed water vapor in any form falls to Earth from the atmosphere, the process is called *precipitation*.

Condensation may take place in a small way—for example, when one's eyeglasses become clouded with moisture when one comes indoors on a cold day or when moisture forms on the outside of a glass of cold water. It may also occur in a large way when warm moist winds are cooled in storms.

Another term is sometimes heard in connection with moisture in the air. *Absolute humidity* refers to the actual moisture present in a specific volume, generally a cubic foot. The term "absolute humidity" has little significance in most of the instruction in the elementary school.

EXPERIENCE. *There is water in air.* Fill a shiny metal cup or drinking glass with cold water. (Any cup or glass will do, although moisture will be more readily visible on a shiny surface.) Does moisture form on the sides of the cup? If not, add ice to the water. In case the air is very dry, you might add salt to the ice in order to cool the water even more. However, in many climates the moisture will be formed by using cold water from the faucet.

Young children may say that the water forms on the outside of the cup because the cup leaks. If so, it may be a matter of trying to show whether this is so. The cup filled with warm water will not be covered with moisture.

How can we show that water forming on the outside is different water from that inside? Perhaps some child will indicate that we can mark the water inside. That can be done by coloring it with a few drops of ink. This shows the water formed on the outside does not come from the inside. This moisture can quite properly be called *dew*.

This entire series of experiences can provide children and teacher with an opportunity for planning together and for critical thinking.

In summary, it should be kept in mind by the teacher that the water found on the outside of the cup comes from the air. Cool air can hold less moisture than warm air. The air next to the cup was cooled and the moisture was deposited on the cup.

When children make cold drinks, such as lemonade, they frequently notice this phenomenon. When dishes are taken from the refrigerator, they quickly become covered with moisture. Cold-water pipes "sweat" in damp weather. Spectacles "cloud up" when one comes indoors on a cold day. Windows become covered with moisture or with frost (frozen moisture) on cold days, especially if cooking is going on in the room. Why? The windows of closed automobiles "cloud up" on cold days. The latter case is interesting, for most of the water in the air is given off by the passengers in breathing. If we breathe on a cold mirror, it "clouds" with moisture.

Children should see that the process just described (called condensation) is just the opposite of evaporation. In evaporation the water is going into the air; in condensation the water is coming out of the air. The *words* themselves are not necessary for small children, but they should be able to observe the processes and see their relationship.

EXPERIENCE. *Determining the relative humidity (for older children in the upper grades).* There are two simple instruments for determining relative humidity: the wet-and-dry-bulb thermometer (called a psychrometer) and the hygrometer. A crude wet-and-dry-bulb thermometer is easy to construct and interesting to use.

Secure two thermometers as nearly alike as possible. Chemical thermometers are best because their bulbs are exposed, but ordinary wall thermometers will work. Wrap the bulb of one with a single layer of thin cloth; linen or silk is best. If a wall thermometer with a little brass cage around the bulb is used, the cage must first be removed. Be sure the cloth is as snug around the bulb as possible. Leave an end of the cloth two or three inches long dangling. This will serve as a wick. Hang the thermometer from a stand, with the end of the cloth dipping into a small dish of water. Hang the other thermometer, to which nothing need be done, near by.

Since, as we have seen, evaporation has a cooling effect, evaporation of the water from the cloth will cool the bulb of one thermometer. The more rapid evaporation is, the more the wet bulb will be cooled.

We have also seen (p. 477) that the drier the air, the more rapid is the evaporation. In other words, evaporation is rapid when the relative humidity is low. Therefore the wet bulb will be cooler than the dry bulb, and the difference will increase as the relative humidity becomes lower. If the air should become saturated, as it does in a fog or during a heavy rainstorm, there will be no evaporation, and the two thermometers will read the same.

In use the two thermometers are hung up, and the cloth around the wet bulb is thoroughly saturated. The thermometers are then fanned for a few minutes. This is done to blow away the air next to the cloth, and keep it from being surrounded with a layer of saturated air. The thermometers are sometimes in a position so that they may be whirled in a circle. The two thermometers are then carefully read.

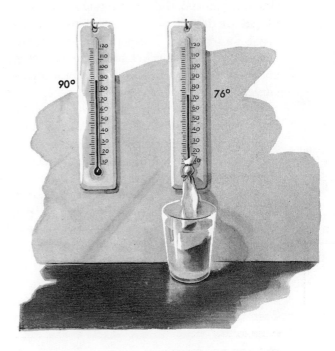

If the dry-bulb thermometer reads 90 degrees and the wet-bulb reads 14 degrees lower, the table shows that the relative humidity is 52 per cent.

DRY-BULB READING	DIFFERENCE BETWEEN DRY-BULB AND WET-BULB READINGS (FAHRENHEIT DEGREES)																	
	1°	2°	3°	4°	5°	6°	7°	8°	9°	10°	11°	12°	13°	14°	15°	16°	17°	18°
64°	95	90	84	79	74	70	65	60	56	51	47	43	38	34	30	26	22	18
66°	95	90	85	80	75	71	66	61	57	53	48	44	40	36	32	29	25	21
68°	95	90	85	80	76	71	67	62	58	54	50	46	42	38	34	31	27	23
70°	95	90	86	81	77	72	68	64	59	55	51	48	44	40	36	33	29	25
72°	95	91	86	82	77	73	69	65	61	57	53	49	45	42	38	34	31	28
74°	95	91	86	82	78	74	69	65	61	58	54	50	47	43	39	36	33	29
76°	96	91	87	82	78	74	70	66	62	59	55	51	48	44	41	38	34	31
78°	96	91	87	83	79	75	71	67	63	60	56	53	49	46	43	39	36	33
80°	96	91	87	83	79	75	72	68	64	61	57	54	50	47	44	41	38	35
82°	96	92	88	84	80	76	72	69	65	61	58	55	51	48	45	42	39	36
84°	96	92	88	84	80	76	73	69	66	62	59	56	52	49	46	43	40	37
86°	96	92	88	84	81	77	73	70	66	63	60	57	53	50	47	44	42	39
88°	96	92	88	85	81	77	74	70	67	64	61	57	54	51	48	46	43	40
90°	96	92	89	85	81	78	74	71	68	65	61	58	55	52	49	47	44	41
92°	96	92	89	85	82	78	75	72	68	65	62	59	56	53	50	48	45	42
94°	96	93	89	85	82	79	75	72	69	66	63	60	57	54	51	49	46	43
96°	96	93	89	86	82	79	76	73	69	66	63	61	58	55	52	50	47	44

The difference in their readings may be found by subtracting the wet-bulb reading from the dry-bulb reading. Using the dry-bulb reading and the difference in readings, one can find the relative humidity from the accompanying table.

The *hygrometer* is an instrument which shows the relative humidity directly. A convenient form is a combination thermometer and hygrometer. The relative humidity may be read directly from a pointer on a scale.

Another form, a hair hygrometer, depends upon the change in length of a human hair due to moisture present in the air. The small change is magnified by levers, and moves a pointer over a scale indicating the relative humidity.

Fogs and Clouds. Water is continuously evaporating from oceans, lakes, rivers, mud puddles, and other wet places on Earth's surface. When this moisture evaporates, it is invisible and is known as *water vapor,* which is an invisible gas. (However, a great deal of

moisture in the air, although itself invisible, does interfere with distant observation. Usually one can see for longer distances in dry climates.) When the temperature of the air is lowered sufficiently, the water vapor condenses into fine droplets. These droplets are often so small and light that they are kept aloft by the rising currents of air, and they often collect in such numbers as to form clouds or fog in the air. Clouds and fog are therefore made up of droplets of condensed water vapor.

Fogs. When these droplets collect near the surface of Earth, we call them a fog. When they collect above Earth, they form clouds. The only difference between a fog and a cloud is the location. If we look at a mountainside from a distance, we may see masses of vapor. We say we see clouds. If, however, we were to climb the mountain until we were in the clouds, we would say that we were in a fog. "Fog is a cloud seen from the inside; clouds are fogs seen from the outside."

Fogs are of two kinds. The first kind is

caused by the cooling off of the surface air at night. Such fogs, often called land fogs, are likely to be of small extent.

If the air next to Earth has a high relative humidity and is very still, then some of the water condenses out as dew as the layer of air is cooled. If there is a slight bit of turbulence such as might be present when there is a wind blowing only a few miles per hour, then a layer of air several feet in thickness is cooled. Under these conditions, fog is formed as the air gives up some of its water to form tiny droplets. This is the type of fog that may be seen in the hollows and valleys on comparatively still nights. It is sometimes referred to as *radiation fog,* since it is associated with the cooling by radiation of the surface of Earth when the sun's rays are not warming it. Earth is then colder than the air. This reminds one of the Experience on page 480 when dew was formed on the outside of the glass or cup.

The second kind of fog is caused by a current of warm, moist air when it *blows over* a cold surface. Such fogs are apt to occur in the winter, and may be dense and extensive. The dreaded sea fogs of the north Atlantic are often caused by warm winds from the Gulf Stream when they blow over the cold Labrador Current. Sometimes, on a cold, fall day, a fog is noticed rising from the surface of a lake, giving an appearance such as might occur over a body of steaming water. This occurs when the air is comparatively still and is colder than the water. The air next to the water is warmed by it. Water evaporates into this air. Then this warmer, moist air rises slightly, mixing with the colder air above. It cools and gives up some water to form droplets of fog. This type of fog, like others, occurs only when the air is relatively still. Of course, if there is a strong wind, it mixes up the air and blows away the fog.

Anyone who has blown his breath into the outside air on a frosty morning has noticed the fog that is made as his breath makes contact with the cold air. The air, as it comes from the lungs, is warm and humid. It cools on contact with the colder air. As it cools, it cannot hold so much water vapor. Some of the water vapor condenses out into droplets of fog. As the little mass of fog mixes with more air, the droplets are revaporized, much as a fog is vaporized when the wind mixes it with the air. One also notices a fog when the refrigerator is opened in a warm, humid kitchen. In this case cold, heavy air from the refrigerator flows out through the door and down to the floor. As it flows out, the warm, humid air mixes with it and is cooled. As the moist air is cooled, it gives up some of its water to form droplets of fog. The exhaust from the automobile contains water vapor, which is one of the substances formed when gasoline burns (p. 401). As the exhaust makes contact with the air on cold days, some of the water vapor is condensed out as droplets of fog. The children will probably think of other situations in which fog is produced.

Clouds. Clouds are usually formed by the expansion and consequent cooling of rising masses of air. Heated air, in rising, expands and cools. It comes to a final temperature which is lower than its original one. When the air has been cooled to a point at which it cannot hold all its moisture, water vapor begins to condense into droplets. Now it is a fact of common experience that we must supply heat to change water into water vapor, as for instance, in boiling. When this change is reversed and we turn water vapor into water, it seems logical that the heat should be returned. This is exactly what happens in a cloud. The heat is returned and slows down the cooling of the air, thereby forcing it still higher. In the end it is made still cooler. Let us restate this sequence of events for the sake of clarity.

Heat warms air. As this warm air is pushed up, it expands still more because there is less pressure resting on it. Since there is less air pushing down on this rising air, it is free to get larger. Air, like all gases, cools when it expands. Cooling air releases moisture, giving up heat. This heat in turn causes the air to rise more and become still cooler. This process keeps up until equilibrium is reached and there is a balance of all the forces concerned.

If the temperature at which condensation begins happens to be below the freezing point of water, ice crystals instead of water droplets are formed (p. 487).

Scientists have shown that water vapor must have something about which to condense, that is, a nucleus must be present. A blade of grass on the ground is a sufficient object around which dew can form. In the air, the *condensation nuclei* can be salt crystals or smoke or dust particles. To be a condensation nucleus, it must have an attraction for water vapor. As it absorbs water, it grows until it reaches a size where one of two processes causes it to fall as precipitation.

Clouds may be classified by their formation or by the altitude at which they are found. Of course, clouds of certain formations are found at specific altitudes.

The international classification of clouds comprises four main divisions: High clouds, 20,000 feet or above; middle clouds, 6,000 to 20,000 feet; low clouds, near ground level to 6,000 feet; clouds with vertical (extending upward) developments, which cut across horizontal layers and are found between 1,500 and 20,000 feet. There are four principal types:

1. *Cirrus clouds.* These are the high, white, wispy clouds often seen in fair weather. They are composed of ice crystals. Traveling at great heights (five to seven and a half miles) and at great speed (as fast as two hundred miles per hour), they are the highest and fastest moving of all clouds. They originate at the front of cyclones, but on account of their speed they are ahead of the main cyclones. Hence they are often forerunners of storms.

2. *Cumulus clouds.* These are the white, fluffy clouds with flat bases, like great bunches of cotton, frequently seen in fair summer weather. They are caused by rising currents of air. The rapid and violent upward moving currents which accompany thunderstorms produce the towering cumulus clouds called thunderheads. All thunderheads are cumulus clouds, but not all cumulus clouds are thunderheads.

3. *Stratus clouds.* Stratus clouds are low sheets of clouds covering the whole sky.

4. *Nimbostratus clouds.* Nimbostratus clouds are formless, dark-gray clouds. Frequently rain or snow falls from them. Nimbostratus clouds are "rainy day" clouds. They include the type formerly called "nimbus."

It is hardly necessary for us to point out that clouds play an important part in our everyday affairs. They provide us with rain. They may give us relief from the hot sun. They are studied by the Weather Bureau as a help in predicting the weather. Clouds sometimes screen growing plants and thus prevent excessive sunshine from reaching them. Some regions—for example, the coast of Maine—depend to some extent upon heavy fogs for moisture for crops.

Cirrus clouds. (U.S. Weather Bureau, F. Ellerman.)

Stratus clouds.   (U.S. Weather Bureau.)

Cumulus clouds.   (U.S. Weather Bureau, C. E. Depperman.)

Fogs and clouds are not always beneficial to man.   They frequently interfere with transportation.   The dangers of navigating vessels in a fog are well known, while fog is one of the aviator's greatest perils.   Fogs so dense as to interfere with the operation of railroads by obscuring the engineers' vision and as to render automobile travel hazardous are by no means rare.   Clouds also interfere with aviation.   Aviators speak of a "low ceiling" when the clouds are low and of a "high ceiling" when they are high above Earth's surface.   Actually, of course, clouds are not at any great height from Earth when compared with the total depth of the atmosphere.   Clouds are known to have reached more than 10 miles in the air.   Many of them are less than a mile high.

Clouds passing between Earth and the moon often give us the impression that they are nearer to the moon than to Earth.   This is an illusion.   The cloud is only a few miles away, but the distance to the moon is about 250,000 miles.   Sometimes the clouds are so thin that we can see the moon right through them, and it then looks as if the moon were nearer than the clouds.

Noctilucent Clouds.   Occasionally in summer in the far north and south, clouds can be seen very high in the sky at twilight.   They are found to be about 50 miles high, and the sun still shines on them after Earth's surface is in shadow.   Being so far above the region of Earth's weather, people have wondered what they are made of.   Recent studies show they

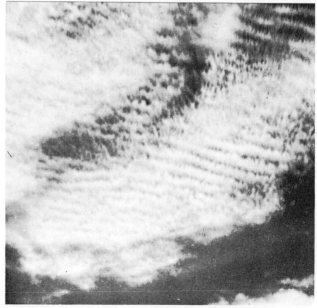

Cirrocumulus clouds.   (U.S. Weather Bureau, E. E. Barnard.)

may be composed of solid particles, some of which are coated with a substance that evaporates. News items about these will be of interest to all.

Haze. When it is difficult to see distant objects, there is said to be haze in the air. Haze is frequently produced by dust in the atmosphere. This occurs especially in September and October when dry leaves are falling and being blown about. Forest fires may also increase the amount of haze in the atmosphere by creating smoke.

Sometimes haze occurs high in the air, giving the sky a whitish appearance and at night making some of the stars invisible. This kind of haze is made of ice crystals. It is something like a very thin cloud.

Sometimes distant objects appear to be indistinct on warm days when the atmosphere is comparatively free from dust. This is caused by the bending of the rays of light by layers of air of different densities. This phenomenon is something like the shimmering "heat waves" one may see over a sidewalk on very hot days or over a hot steam radiator.

EXPERIENCE. *To observe fog and cloud formation.* Have children report experiences with fog, smog, and haze. Observe with them the opening of a refrigerator door on various days on a trip to the school cafeteria or to the home of one of the children. Observe breathing out of doors on a cold, dry winter day. Have them observe the exhaust of an automobile. The school bus might be used for this. Or these experiences may be done by children individually, rather than as a part of a group excursion. This work can be combined with art instruction and the development of murals.

Different Kinds of Precipitation That Provide the Ground with Moisture

Meteorologists, or scientists who study the atmosphere and its phenomena, use the word precipitation. We recall that condensation referred to the change from water vapor to liquid or ice. *Precipitation* refers to the depositing of this liquid or ice on the ground from the air. It includes rain, snow, sleet, hail, and dew. Although the word need not be taught to children, it is convenient for grouping many atmospheric phenomena.

EXPERIENCE. *To become aware of the weather changes.* Have children keep records of the weather changes and compare them with weather reports given by newspapers, television, and radio. Have them note the weather predictions. Do the predictions prove to be right? Note the sequence of weather changes in your region from day to day.

Older children can clip weather maps from newspapers and place them on a bulletin board. If possible, get weather maps from other countries. Canadian weather maps will interest children in the United States and vice versa. Sometimes weather maps for Mexico can be secured by children in the Southwest.

Rain. If for any reason the droplets in a cloud unite or grow in any manner to form drops large enough to fall in spite of the rising air currents in the cloud, rain falls. These cloud droplets must grow greatly in size, since the average raindrop contains one million times the amount of water of a cloud droplet.

In the center of most raindrops will be found a small particle. As we explained previously, salt crystals, smoke, or dust particles are necessary for the formation of clouds and raindrops.

Drizzle droplets are larger than fog droplets but smaller than raindrops. Rain, of course, is one of the most important of all weather phenomena, since it provides most of the moisture necessary for growing crops. Rain makes the difference between garden and desert.

Snow. If condensation takes place below the freezing point of water (32°F.), ice crystals are formed (p. 484). If these crystals unite, snow may fall. Snow is *not* frozen rain, but is formed by condensation directly from water vapor to ice crystals. If you check the temperature during a heavy snowstorm, you will see that it is generally near 32°F.

This process of changing directly from a gas to a solid or from a solid to a gas, without going through a liquid state is likely to be quite challenging if one stops to think of it. The process is called *sublimation*. This term, however, is

Government snow markers in Oregon. Brightly painted iron pipes are used to measure the depth of the snow. (Soil Conservation Service.)

not needed in the development of science in the elementary school.

When any substance crystallizes, the crystals take on a form peculiar to the substance. Water crystallizes into six-sided crystals, which determines the shape of snowflakes. Snowflakes are among the most beautiful forms of nature. They seem to have an infinite variety of detail, all based on a six-sided figure. No two of them have been found alike.

Like rain, snow may be beneficial. It forms a blanket which protects many plants from sudden changes of temperature. It is especially helpful in regions that grow winter wheat. Heavy snows may provide moisture for growing crops during the early spring. In many regions farmers fear the result of a winter that has had little snowfall, for the immature plants are left exposed to the winter's extreme cold.

From the standpoint of pleasure, snow brings with it the opportunity for a number of excellent winter sports. Winter sports are fast developing into a profitable industry in many parts of the world.

On the other hand, snow imposes a heavy burden on cities and states, which must spend vast sums of money to remove the snow from highways so as to keep them open for automobile travel. Railroads must also spend money to keep their tracks clear of snow. Snow can interfere seriously with transportation, especially since so much of our transportation of products and materials depends on motor trucks.

Weather stations measure rain and snowfall with special instruments called gauges. Rain falls into a funnel-shaped collector and collects in a cylinder. A ruler measures the depth. Snowfall is measured in a similar manner: it is the water equivalent of snow that is measured.

EXPERIENCE. *Catching snowflakes.* A piece of black or dark-blue cloth, preferably stretched

No two snowflakes are exactly alike, yet each has six sides.

over a wooden frame, makes an excellent device for catching and studying snowflakes. Catch the fairly small flakes that fall after it has been snowing a while. Do not bother with the large, fleecy flakes which sometimes fall. These are several snowflakes which are sticking together. Out of doors they may be examined closely by means of a hand lens. Notice that each one is built on a six-sided pattern, but that each is different.

Allow some snow to melt, and observe that it is really water. Sometimes children in playing squeeze snow together and partly melt it, so that it turns to ice. Ice and snow are really forms of water.

EXPERIENCE. *Water can exist in three forms. Heat is required to change water from one form to another.* Bring some ice into the room. As it warms up, what happens? Heat the resulting water to boiling. The water turns to steam. What happens when we add heat to ice? to water? What happens when we take heat away from steam? from water? (It will be recalled, p. 487, that snow in being formed does not go through the liquid state.)

Sleet. Sleet, too, is formed when water vapor condenses on nuclei in the atmosphere and freezes. It is thought by some that the water droplets encounter ice crystals, resulting in at least some of the droplets freezing on the ice and eventually falling as small pellets of ice. Or it is possible that water droplets encounter such temperatures that they freeze, gather more moisture and then fall as ice pellets called *sleet*. It is an exceedingly uncomfortable experience to be out of doors in a storm when sleet is being driven by a high wind. One should not confuse sleet with hail, which falls during a summer thunderstorm, or with glaze, which produces destructive ice storms.

Hail. Hail occurs only during thunderstorms, when there are very strong ascending and descending currents of air. It is estimated that to sustain a hailstone 1 inch in diameter, the upward moving air must have a velocity of at least 59 miles per hour. If the stone were 3 inches in diameter, a velocity of 116 miles per hour would be required. Temperatures are low in the upper parts of the thunderstorm-producing clouds and much higher in the lower parts of the clouds. In the middle latitudes hail occurs normally only during spring and summer.

The initial formation of hail is similar to that of sleet. Water droplets may encounter ice particles, resulting in the water, or part of it, freezing on the ice particle. As the pellets grow in size they are called *hail*. The hail as it falls may be caught up by an ascending air current and come in contact with still unfrozen, or liquid, water droplets which freeze on the growing hailstone. This process may go on again and again until the hailstone becomes too heavy for the ascending air currents to carry upward.

Sleet falls in small pellets, but hail varies in size. Sometimes hailstones are small, but at other times they may be as large as or larger than hens' eggs.

If we were to cut open a large hailstone, we might find that it was made up of layers, looking something like the layers of an onion. These layers vary in appearance, some being cloudy, others clear. This is due to the hail falling through areas with a low liquid-water content and through others with a high liquid-water content. The cloudy layers are due to rime ice, ice with air spaces between the frozen particles. The clear layers are due to the freezing of some of the water that is encountered by the hailstone. In addition to the part that freezes on the hailstone, some water remains as a film; some may evaporate and some may flow away. The water that flows away takes the form of tiny drops. These and other similar drops may combine to form larger ones or they may freeze at any time conditions are right. Some hail has a clear center which points to its origin as being these frozen raindrops.

Hail causes a great deal of damage. Aviators usually avoid thunderstorms by flying around or above them. Hail beats down growing crops and smashes windows in greenhouses. Sometimes it even breaks windows in homes. Many people living where large hailstones commonly fall carry insurance against hail damage.

Glaze, or Ice Storms. Glaze is often incorrectly called sleet. It forms when rain or drizzle falls on objects the temperature of which is below the freezing point of water. The rain freezes as it strikes, covering the objects with a beautiful but highly destructive coating of ice. The weight of the ice causes trees and electric wires to break, while the slippery coating on roads and sidewalks renders travel hazardous.

Ice sometimes forms on airplane wings for the same reason. Such happenings are extremely dangerous; for unless the aviator can find a warm layer of air, he will be forced down. Planes are now equipped with deicing-devices which break the ice off and various devices which prevent the formation of ice, such as those which distribute alcohol over areas on which a concentration of ice would be hazardous.

Dew. At night, objects on or near the surface of Earth may become cooler than the surrounding atmosphere. Warm, moist air coming in contact with such objects may be cooled sufficiently to deposit moisture upon them. This moisture is called *dew*. It does not fall, as is commonly thought, but forms directly on the object (p. 480).

Dew forms on still, cloudless nights. If the wind is blowing, it stirs up the air and does not give it a chance to cool off enough to deposit moisture. Clouds serve as a sort of blanket to prevent some of the loss of heat from Earth's surface, and so objects are kept from becoming cold enough to cause dew to form.

Dew has been the subject of many superstitious ideas. Magical medicinal powers have been frequently ascribed to it. In reality, of course, it is merely water.

Gardeners and farmers often think that dew is very beneficial to their crops. Instead it is very often a nuisance, for it makes the grass and plants wet enough to hinder the farmers in working in the fields, without providing enough moisture to do the plants any good.

ice storm in upstate New York. (N.Y. Power and Light Co., any.)

Even in fairly moist regions the total amount of dew which "falls" in a year amounts to only about one inch.

The *dew point* is the temperature to which the air must be cooled in order to cause condensation of its vapor or dew formation. When the air above Earth's surface is cooled to the dew point, clouds or fog form.

Frost. If the dew point is below 32°F., the water condenses directly into ice crystals on the surfaces, producing the white coating we call frost. Frost is formed somewhat like dew, except for the matter of low temperature. However, it is *not* frozen dew, any more than snow is frozen rain.

The word *frost* is used by the Weather Bureau in two senses: (1) the white deposit on leaves, etc., mentioned above, and (2) the low temperature necessary to produce frost. This temperature, because it kills vegetation, is of great economic importance, and its prediction is of vital interest to farmers. A "light frost," in the language of the weather reports, is one in which the temperature of the air drops only low enough to injure the more delicate types of vegetation. A "killing frost" is one in which the temperature falls so low as to kill staple crops of the vicinity. In many places the length of the growing season, and hence the type of crop raised, is determined by the date of the last killing frost in the spring and of the first in the autumn.

Frost, like dew, occurs on still, clear nights. It frequently occurs in low places into which cold air drains (p. 474), while on the same nights higher locations receive no frost. Frost-sensitive crops, therefore, are often grown on valley slopes rather than in valley bottoms. Smudge fires which produce dense smoke are sometimes used to protect delicate crops, such as oranges. This smoke acts somewhat like a cloud to prevent the ground from cooling off quite so much as it otherwise would.

EXPERIENCE. *Natural forces both aid and hinder man's activities.* Think of each of the forms in which water may get to Earth (rain, snow, sleet, etc.), and list ways in which they may help or hinder man in his activities. The children might list such activities as agriculture or travel, and such industries as the taxicab industry, the coal industry, and the clothing industry, and the industries of light, of power, and of transportation. Also think of things about which children may have considerable knowledge, such as delivery service and recreation, including sports, picnics, and celebrations. Children may wish to tell about their own experiences.

Weather Prediction—The Work of the Weather Bureau

When we plan a picnic for tomorrow, we wish to know if the weather will be fair; if we plan winter sports, we need to know whether or not a warm spell will spoil the snow. On a cloudy day, shall we take umbrellas or leave them home? Sea captains need to be warned of approaching storms; aviators, of fogs and unfavorable winds. Farmers are benefited if they know of storms or dry spells beforehand so that they can care for their crops. Merchants need to be warned if their shipments of vegetables are likely to be spoiled by heat or cold. A rainy spell even affects the great mail-order houses, for on rainy days people are more likely to remain indoors and write orders for things that they need.

Weather around the entire Earth must be known before a manned space flight is undertaken. Photographs of clouds made by weather satellites are used in addition to reports from the weather stations. There is scarcely anyone who is not better off if he knows what the weather is likely to be.

It was Benjamin Franklin who first found that a cyclonic storm as a whole moves from west to east, no matter in which direction the winds within the storm may be blowing. After the telegraph was invented, the idea came to some people that with the aid of this means of rapid communication it would be possible to secure information about storms which were coming from the west. This idea was embodied in the United States Weather Bureau, first founded in 1870 as a part of the United States Signal Service and later placed under the Department of Commerce. Similar service is maintained in Canada.

Man Learns about Air Masses. Direct information about air masses was not accessible until means were found for observing and measuring weather conditions in the upper air. This is done by means of pilot balloons and radiosonde.

Pilot balloons are small, helium-filled neoprene balloons sent aloft. Ground observation of these gives the observer wind direction and velocity. The *radiosonde* is a very small, light-weight weather station with a light radio transmitter carried upward by a balloon. It sends out radio signals, giving information about pressure, temperature, and humidity. A ground receiver records these signals. This instrument goes to an average of 75,000 feet. When the balloon bursts, the radiosonde floats by means of a parachute to Earth, where it may be recovered.

Tracking the balloon with such electronic equipment as radar or radio-theodolites gives information on altitudes, wind directions, and speeds. Such an observation is called a *rawinsonde*. Radiowind apparatus carried aloft measures at the same time the upper winds.

Pilot-balloon observations are usually made four times daily, while radiosonde observations are made twice or four times daily.

Weather satellites carry equipment for making photographs of clouds and for relaying these to receiving stations on Earth. When a receiving station is remote, the pictures are stored on magnetic tape, then relayed when the station is near. These are of great value in predicting weather, and children might wish to watch for developments in this type of weather exploration.

It has already been stated that in the Northern Hemisphere certain sections of lows (no-

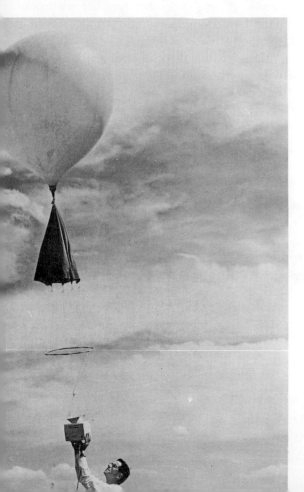

Radiosonde apparatus. The balloon carries aloft a radio transmitter which broadcasts minute-by-minute reports of temperature, pressure, and humidity in the upper air. Finally the balloon bursts and the instruments are returned to Earth by the parachute. Observations which include direction and speed of winds are called rawinsondes. (General Electric Company.)

tably the southeastern one) tend to be areas of storminess. As a rule, lows are accompanied by storms and highs by fair weather. Furthermore, lows and highs tend to follow certain tracks or paths, and to move at a rather definite speed. Weather prediction, then, seems to be a simple matter of determining the location, path, and speed of the lows and highs over the country, putting them twenty-four hours ahead on the paths they are following, and thus predicting tomorrow's weather. Unfortunately there are very many factors which affect the movement of lows and highs, and it is not easy to take all these into proper account. Lows and highs occasionally "jump the track." They are influenced by the presence of other lows and highs. Their courses are influenced by land features, such as mountains and lakes. During the period for which the prediction was made, new lows or highs may have developed to change the picture. As a result, long experience, as well as thorough knowledge, is necessary to be a successful weather forecaster.

Of course the first step in forecasting is to locate the lows and highs over the country. This is done by means of the weather maps. After the observations from all over the country are received, they are charted on an outline map of the United States. Lines (called isobars) are then drawn through places having equal barometric pressure. These give a series of closed curves. The centers of these curves are the centers either of lows or of highs. Other data, such as wind direction, kind of precipitation, and temperature, are also shown on the map. By studying the weather map, comparing it with the maps of previous days, using his judgment based on past experience and his understanding of the principles governing atmospheric behavior, the forecaster makes his prediction.

Weather stations in North America, the West Indies, and adjacent areas, ships in the Atlantic and Pacific oceans, hundreds of commercial aircraft and scheduled military weather reconnaisance planes, as well as stations in foreign countries, send thousands of weather observations to the National Meteorological Center in Suitland, Maryland, and several large cities. In addition, there are thousands of volunteer weather observers. Among these observations are the following: (1) air pressure, (2) temperature, (3) precipitation, (4) wind direction and velocity, (5) clouds, (6) fog and other weather conditions. This data is supplemented by upper-air information by many of these stations.

The weather report is a synopsis of the weather conditions in a locality at a certain time, and the name, synoptic weather report, is given to it. Thus the first step in making a weather forecast is to obtain a composite view of the weather from the many observation points mentioned. The next step is to plot the composite picture a day or two ahead. Fi-

The International Ice Patrol broadcasts information on weather and the movement of icebergs. The Coast Guard Cutter Mendota *is shown on patrol. (U.S. Coast Guard.)*

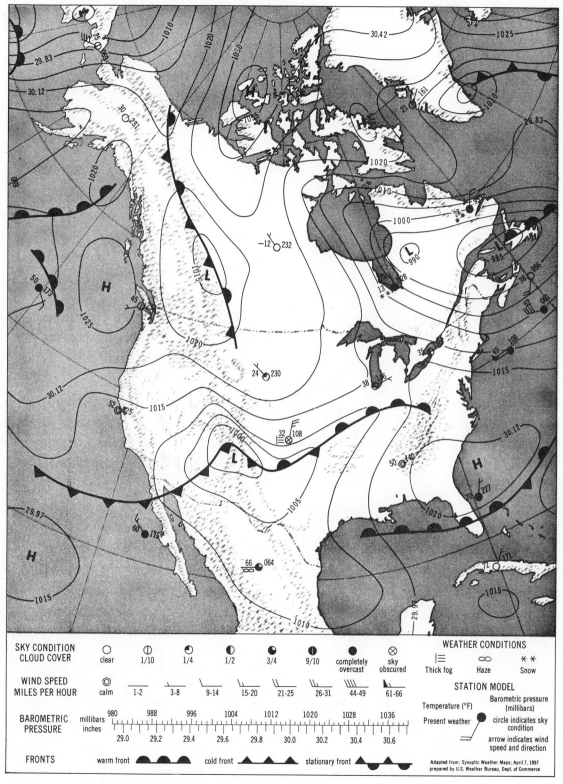

SKY CONDITION CLOUD COVER: clear, 1/10, 1/4, 1/2, 3/4, 9/10, completely overcast, sky obscured

WEATHER CONDITIONS: Thick fog, Haze, Snow

WIND SPEED MILES PER HOUR: calm, 1-2, 3-8, 9-14, 15-20, 21-25, 26-31, 44-49, 61-66

STATION MODEL: Temperature (°F), Barometric pressure (millibars), Present weather, circle indicates sky condition, arrow indicates wind speed and direction

BAROMETRIC PRESSURE: millibars 980, 988, 996, 1004, 1012, 1020, 1028, 1036; inches 29.0, 29.2, 29.4, 29.6, 29.8, 30.0, 30.2, 30.4, 30.6

FRONTS: warm front, cold front, stationary front

Adapted from: Synoptic Weather Maps; April 7, 1957 prepared by U.S. Weather Bureau, Dept. of Commerce

This map shows a summary of weather conditions on one day over most of North America.

nally, the analysis is transferred into a weather forecast for the next thirty-six or forty-eight hours.

The study of weather is not a national but an international problem. The cyclones which determine the weather may (and often do) originate thousands of miles away, in another country or even in another continent. The causes which produce, let us say, the great wind belts of the world are at work all over Earth. The nations of the world are learning to co-operate more in the exchange of weather information. Better knowledge of world conditions is enabling each country to increase its understanding of the causes of its weather and to improve its predictions.

One of the many activities of the World Meteorological Organization is that of coordinating the taking of weather observations among nations.

EXPERIENCE. *Predicting the weather.* Young children can become interested in observing the weather. A large calendar may be made by the teacher or the children. On it the children can mark each day what the weather is. They may use words or invent symbols. Some may be interested in using the Weather Bureau's symbols. They may write "cool," "cold," "warm," or "hot," or mark down the actual temperature.

An aneroid barometer in the room provides a continuous center of interest for children of almost any age. The barometer should be read and the movable hand set at a definite time each day. Then, when it is next observed, it is easy to see whether the other hand has risen or fallen. Children may be led to observe that the barometer frequently falls before a storm and rises before clear weather. They may decide that it is a fairly good means of predicting the weather six to eight hours ahead.

Some children may be interested in attempting to predict tomorrow's weather from the barometer. They will find that they will often fail, and decide that more data are necessary. Weather maps may be obtained from the newspapers. Children can readily see that the weather map is made up of data from all over the country. They should now be able to predict more accurately, but will still go wrong a great many times. In the end the children may conclude that a great deal of skill and experience, as well as knowledge, is necessary to predict the weather.

Climate and Weather

Much confusion frequently exists in the minds of children (and adults as well) about the difference between climate and weather. Climate is generalized weather. It is, let us say, the ordinary course of the weather of a given area. The word *weather* denotes the state of the atmosphere at any given moment; *climate,* the normal run of weather conditions over a long period of time. Moreover, *climate* implies a larger geographic area. Thus one may speak of the weather of Winnipeg, Manitoba, on a spring day, and of the summer climate of the prairie provinces of Canada.

Since all the types of weather that a place has go to make up its climate, it follows that the same physical forces that control the weather, acting over a longer period of time, produce the climate of that place. The prevailing winds, the location of mountains, and all the other factors which we have seen make the weather, also make the climate. For example, a place located in the belt of the doldrums, where the warm, moist air gives rise to heavy rainfall and the rays of the sun are hottest, would probably have a hot, damp climate. A place located in the interior or on the west coast of a continent in the path of the trade winds would probably be partially or wholly a desert. The trade winds do not have much moisture in any case; and if they are forced to rise over mountains on the east coast (as is frequently the case), they drop most of the moisture they have. As a result, by the time they reach the west coast, they are hot and dry. Many of the great deserts of the world are located in these regions. In the same way, all other climates may be traced back to the forces which produce the weather.

There is a great variety of climate on Earth. Climatologists, or scientists who study the climates of Earth, have recognized as many as twenty-five different types. Some are dry; some are wet. Some are hot; some are cold. Some have dry seasons and rainy seasons; others are continuously wet or dry; still others have moderate rainfall. Some have hot summers and cold winters; others have no extremes of temperature.

Climates profoundly modify the activities of the people living in them. The occupations, recreations, houses, and clothing of people living in southwestern California, for example, are vastly different from those of people living in Newfoundland; and these in turn are different from those of people in Madagascar. No doubt their customs and philosophies differ also. Some of these differences are due to climate.

Is the Climate Changing?

It is certain that the climates of Earth have changed profoundly over the periods of geologic time. There is abundant evidence that regions now well-watered were once deserts. Great ice sheets at various times covered large portions of Earth. On the other hand, the fossil remains of tropical plants are found in Antarctica.

There are some indications that minor climatic changes may occur in cycles, but even these cycles are not agreed upon by scientists. Thus it is probable that a number of rather wet years may occur, followed by a number of years of somewhat deficient rainfall. Possibly these changes occur with some degree of regularity. We do not know. One thing seems certain: when people speak of an "old-fashioned winter" they have probably not studied weather and climates very closely.

One often hears such comments as, "I tell you the climate is changing; the world is getting warmer (or colder)." Such comments are not to be accepted quickly. To determine whether the climate is changing requires the careful keeping of records over many years. Almost no nation has kept weather records long enough to draw a conclusion about present climatic change. It is a problem on which many scientists from many different fields are working. Information is published from time to time on the subject.

It should be recalled that many comments made by adults involving comparison of present experiences with those of their childhood are likely to be questionable. Adults may recall a winter of snow and cold and forget the warmer winters, or they may forget that there was little equipment for removing snow when they were young, or they may have forgotten periods of drought or excessive rainfall, and so on.

This is not to say that the climates of Earth

are remaining the same. The very fact that there are evidences of changes of climate in regions on Earth in the past indicates there could be changes going on today. Geological processes that influence climate, though often extremely slow, are constantly at work.

Many anthropologists are of the opinion that certain civilizations ceased to exist because there were climatic changes. They also point out evidences of the migration of prehistoric peoples that may have occurred in the past when regions became dry. The cliff-dwellers of southwestern United States are thought to have moved southward when their

water supply dried up in a great drought about A.D. 1300.

Teachers can be willing to listen to new information about present-day changes in climate, but that does not necessarily involve accepting any or all of this information.

Regardless of whether or not the climates of Earth are changing, we know that Earth has had an atmosphere suitable for life for millions of years, and we may anticipate that Earth's atmosphere will be favorable for life for a long time to come. Teachers can give children a feeling of confidence and resourcefulness.

Can Man Change the Weather?

Many things have been said for and against man-made snow and rain. In 1940, Dr. Irving Langmuir and Vincent Schaefer studied stratus clouds that were below freezing temperatures (32°F.) containing snow crystals, but from which no snow was falling. Their belief was that there were not enough snow nuclei (p. 487). They found that a tiny grain of Dry Ice could cause millions of ice crystals to fall from certain clouds. The cold temperature of the Dry Ice (−40°F.) was an important factor in this. Tests by Dr. Bernard Vonnegut showed that ice crystals would form around silver iodide smoke particles.

The first man-made snowstorm took place in 1946 as a result of scattering six pounds of dry-ice pellets from an airplane.

Attention now was turned to seeding cumulus clouds at temperatures near the freezing point in order to yield rain. This project lasted for five years beginning in 1947. Silver-iodide seeding on two separate days over New Mexico resulted in an estimated 480 billion gallons of rain.

Of course, conditions must be ideal for seeding, and it is not possible to cause rain to fall exactly when we want it. Moisture-laden clouds must be present.

"Fresh Air"—Ventilation

Almost everyone recognizes that we need what we call "fresh air," but not every scientist is agreed as to just what "fresh air" really does to us. Certainly we are all aware that something in an overheated, stuffy room

makes us feel unambitious and sleepy, and that opening the windows or otherwise changing the air in the room stimulates and arouses us. Cases are on record in which people have died from lack of proper air conditions.

We have learned that in breathing we use up some oxygen from the air and give off some carbon dioxide. It was formerly thought that the ill effects from staying in badly ventilated rooms were due to a lack of oxygen in the air. It was later found that so much air is able to leak into a room, even with windows and doors closed, that it is impossible to reduce the supply of oxygen to a dangerous point by breathing. In fact, it was found that people may breathe quite comfortably, if they are not moving about, in air which contains so little oxygen that matches will not burn.

Another theory has been advanced. It is that the carbon dioxide content of the air in a poorly ventilated room is so increased as to be harmful to persons breathing it. It was shown, however, that persons are able to breathe without ill effects air containing much more carbon dioxide than may be found in any ordinary room.

Still a third theory was held by some. The body odors of a group of people served to render the air of a room sufficiently unpleasant or even poisonous to account for the effects noted. Experiments, however, seem to indicate that odors must be quite strong to affect people seriously, and even then the nature of the effects is not entirely clear.

A group of people in a closed room affect the air in two ways. They give off heat and moisture, thus slowing-down the cooling of the body and producing discomfort.

The most important points to consider for good ventilation are temperature and humidity for comfort; air free from such things as dust, odors, smoke, and industrial wastes; and a change of air.

For comfort the temperature should be adjusted as nearly as possible to the amount of clothing worn and the degree of activity of the persons using the room. Comfortable indoor temperatures for winter have been cited at 68° to 72°F., and 80° to 82°F. for summer.

It has been found that one of the best ways to ventilate a schoolroom that does not have air conditioning is to have outside air admitted at the windows and stale air removed through an opening at the opposite side of the room, near the ceiling. Ordinary living-rooms may be ventilated by having windows open at the top and bottom. The essential thing is to provide an opening for the entrance of cool outside air and another opening to allow warm, stale air to escape, without subjecting the children to drafts. The principal factor to be watched is the temperature. It should be kept between 68° and 72°F.

Air Conditioning

The health and progress of man are linked to climatic conditions, in which humidity is even more important than temperature.

Air conditioning is the artificial control of temperature, humidity, cleanliness, and purification of air, and of air movement to assure a level most conducive to comfort, health, and productivity.

Attempts to change the moisture content of the air in cotton mills began about the middle of the nineteenth century. Developments of the idea followed here and there, and in 1906 important contributions were made which made possible the development of air conditioning for industries and private uses. It was not until after 1930 that smaller units were developed and began to be used in private homes.

In cold weather, air conditioning involves warming the air. The warming process lowers the relative humidity, since warm air can hold more moisture than cold air. Therefore, moisture is generally added to the air. In hot weather, air conditioning implies cooling the air and removing water from it.

Whenever it is feasible, a teacher may help the children to take some responsibility for the ventilation of their schoolroom.

EXPERIENCE. *Reading the thermometer.* Every schoolroom should have a thermometer, and it should be used. It is well to have in the school a large thermometer at a height low enough so that young children can have beginning experiences with interpreting temperature. Learning to read the thermometer is in itself an activity which interests smaller children. They like to see the line go up and down as the room gets warmer or cooler. Many thermometers have a division on the scale for every two degrees. This gives the children an opportunity to count by twos. The thermometer may be moved about the room to see which places are warm and which are cool. Children may take turns in being responsible for seeing that the thermometer reads between 68° and 72°F. The essential thing is that the temperature should as far as possible be kept within these limits. The thermometer should be placed so that children can read it without stretching.

Practice in reading the thermometer.

EXPERIENCE. *The humidity in the classroom.* On page 481 will be found a description of a wet-and-dry-bulb thermometer which the teacher can make, and of a simple hygrometer. With either of these instruments the children can tell the relative humidity in the room. It will frequently be found very low in the winter. (This can be associated with the increase in electric shocks—static electricity—experienced by teachers, parents, and children; p. 808.) This condition comes about because warm air can hold more moisture than cold air. The cold outdoor air of winter may be holding nearly as much moisture as it can at that temperature. In other words, its relative humidity may be high. If, however, we warm this same air without adding any water to it, it becomes able to hold much more water. But since we have added no water, its relative humidity becomes very low.

We can do something to relieve the dryness by putting pans of water on the radiator. Some mechanical ventilators found in schoolrooms have pans to be filled with water. This water evaporates and goes into the air of the room.

In general, however, we cannot raise the relative humidity in the classroom much. If we raised the relative humidity to any great extent, water would condense on the cold windows in the form of frost or "steam" (dew) (p. 479). Condensation might even take place on the walls.

Evaporation from a large uncovered aquarium in the room adds some water to the air. Children are interested to see that they must put more water into the aquarium regularly to replace that lost by evaporation. Leaving an aquarium uncovered, however, affects the living things in it, for the water becomes covered with a film of dust from the air.

EXPERIENCE. *Tracing the movement of air in the classroom.* Carry some smoking material (p. 454), or some light streamers made of crepe paper to various parts of the room. By noting the direction the smoke or streamers blow, the children can tell which way the air currents are moving. Be sure to test the direction of movement of the air through the ventilators in the walls, if the school is equipped with them. Open some windows at the top and bottom and test the air movements. Be sure that the air is moving *out* at some place, either through an open window or a ventilator.

EXPERIENCE. *To compare the rates of evaporation in different places.* Get a number of identical containers such as flat pans or dishes. Fill each of them to the same level with water. Measuring the depths with a foot rule will be one way of determining if the levels are the same. Put a pan in each of several different places, such as the classroom, the attic, the cloakroom, the coal bin, and outside. A more exact experiment will result if the temperatures are determined for each of the places. Keep records of time, temperatures, and rates of evaporation. Results will probably show that the rate of evaporation was faster in places in which the air was warmer.

The children may be interested in determining the rate of evaporation at different times of the year. They will find that when the air is very humid, on so-called "muggy" days, the rate of evaporation is very slow.

The children can determine how long it takes the water level to go down an inch. They would probably be surprised if they knew how many barrelfuls of water leave a lake the size of the school yard in the same period of time. A barrelful of water will evaporate from a little pool about eight feet deep for every inch that it drops in level.

EXPERIENCE. *Following weather maps.* Obtain weather maps from the newspapers for a period of several weeks. Trace the course of lows, highs, cold fronts, and warm fronts. Make your own weather predictions after studying these maps.

EXPERIENCE. *Check up on the weather man.* Obtain weather forecasts from the newspapers, radio, or television for several weeks. Each day, notice if the forecast was accurate.

Part III

THE LIFE
OF
EARTH

CHAPTER 13

Plants and Animals Differ

Our Environment Contains Living and Nonliving Things

At birth the child begins his experiences with living and nonliving things. He learns at an early age that some things are capable of movement, and that other things remain where they are placed until some outside force moves them. The experiences of very young children include contact with people and with other living things. The kinds of plants and animals with which children are familiar will depend upon the part of the world in which they live. Experiences with nonliving things are also numerous and important. Toys, "mud pies," rocks, dishes, buildings, and roads all provide early contacts with nonliving objects.

Many children by the time they come to school will be aware of the chief differences between these living and nonliving objects. For other children, critical examination of objects will be a new experience. Most groups of children can be led to the conclusion that living things (1) grow, (2) reproduce their own kind, (3) need food, water, some things from the air, and warmth, and in some cases (4) show movement.

Some children will have difficulty accepting the idea that every living thing is either a plant or an animal. It may be necessary to let this concept grow from many observations made during several years.

In the case of other children, however, there may be a keen awareness of the fact that some living things can move about, and some can even talk and think.

EXPERIENCE. *To determine some of the differences between living and nonliving things.* Young children might look at pictures in books, objects in the classroom, objects that can be seen from the windows, or be asked to bring into the classroom both living and nonliving objects for observation.[1] It is from the looking at objects around them or pictures of such objects that the children should be able to draw simple conclusions as to the differences between these two large groups of objects found on this Earth. Such observations should lead the child to a better understanding of his community.

---

[1] One should consider the value of living things in their natural surroundings before requesting that such things be brought into the classroom. See pages 62–74 and 146–149 for suggestions on conservation.

Plants and Animals Differ in Many Ways

Children who have observed carefully will be unable to find two living things that are exactly alike. Living objects can be found that resemble each other very closely. If one looks carefully enough, he should always be able to find such differences. Children will be able to see differences in the size, shape, color, and in some cases the structure of living objects. There are also many differences in development which can be observed by older children. Human twins are often so much alike in gross appearance that confusion of identity results, but the details are different. Even in the case of identical twins it has been found that the fingerprints vary sufficiently to make identification by that means fairly simple to the fingerprint expert. To say that two things are as much alike as two peas in a pod gives considerable latitude for differences; for two peas from the same pod may vary in color, shape, and size, although the differences may be very small.

EXPERIENCE. *To observe the differences between two similar living things.* Suggest that the children look anywhere they go after leaving school for two living objects that are very much alike. For example two leaves, two flowers, two birds, two fish, two grasshoppers, two people, etc. Suggest that they look at the objects very closely. A hand lens or reading glass will be found useful here. Ask each child to bring to school, if this can be done according to sound principles of conservation (p. 73), those objects in which they have difficulty in finding differences, so that others may have the opportunity of examining them.

Another example would be to examine the peas or beans in a pod, or the grains on an ear of corn, noting the differences in size, shape, and color.

Plants Differ Considerably in Size. Perhaps the most obvious variation among living things is the variation in size. Some plants are so large that their height compares favorably with that of a twenty-five-story building. Some of the sequoia trees of California are over 300 feet tall. They are the tallest plants in existence. Their circumference at the base of the trunk is so great that in at least one instance a road has been cut through a tree, so that vehicles may pass through it. In order to attain their enormous size, these trees must have grown for many centuries. The age of some of them has been estimated to be four thousand years. If this estimate is approximately correct, the sequoias were already huge trees at the time of the birth of Christ. They probably existed for centuries before the founding of the ancient Roman Empire, and were very old at the time of the discovery of America by Columbus. Only two species of sequoia, commonly called Giant Sequoia and Coast Redwood, have survived in North America.

Most of our familiar trees do not approach the sequoias either in size or in age. On the whole, however, trees are the largest and longest-lived plants of today. They vary greatly in size, as children can readily observe. Two trees of the same age and same species or kind (p. 97 will be found to be unlike each other in this respect. Different species of trees grow to different heights. A white oak may be 100 feet tall; the basswood or linden seldom exceeds 80 feet; pin oaks have been found to grow to a height of 140 feet.

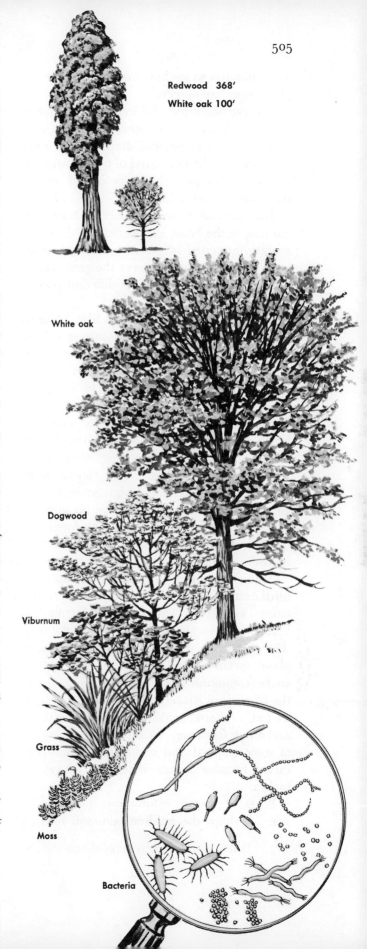

Other common plants further illustrate difference in size. Some cedars may grow to a height of fifty feet, but the flowering dogwood is not nearly so tall. Shrubs and bush plants, such as the elderberry, seldom grow more than about eight feet tall. Grasses may grow to a height of three or four feet, while other plants like the strawberry grow close to the ground. Ferns show a considerable variation in size, some being taller than some of the grasses and others much shorter. Mosses generally grow very close to the ground and are shorter than ferns.

Even the simplest plants—those without roots, stems, flowers, or leaves—exhibit considerable variation. Some of the seaweeds may be several feet long, while others are much smaller. The simple plants (algae) which grow in fresh water may be so small that they escape notice. Many of them are microscopic in size and cannot be seen with the unaided eye. They are not, however, the smallest plants.

The smallest plants known are the bacteria. None of them can be seen without the use of a microscope. Some of them are so small that five thousand of them laid side by side would make a line scarcely an inch long. Some of them are even smaller. They are present in the milk and water we drink and on the food we eat and in the air we breathe. They are on our skins and in our mouths, but we are unaware of their presence because of their extremely small size.

Plants, then, show a considerable range in size. Largest of all are the giant trees, and smallest are the bacteria. All the other plants range between these two extremes.

EXPERIENCES. *Opportunities to study variations in plants.* Take the class on a field excursion to notice variations in sizes of plants.

Ask the children to look out the window for

Plant life flourishes on Earth in many sizes, from microscopic plant life to towering trees.

Redwood 368'
White oak 100'

White oak

Dogwood

Viburnum

Grass

Moss

Bacteria

a few minutes so see how many differences in plants they can observe.

Observe with the children a tree that is growing out away from other trees. Be sure to note the symmetrical shape of the tree. Next observe the same kind of tree growing in a group. Compare the shape of this second tree with that of the first.

Take the class to visit a nursery, a botanical garden, or the home of a person in the community interested in growing different kinds or species of plants. Observe the great variations in the size and shape of different plants.

Animals Vary Considerably in Size. Variations in size occur among animals as well as among plants. Whales are perhaps the largest of all animals. One species, the sulfur-bottom whale, has been reported to weigh as much as 150 tons. This means that one of these huge marine creatures may weigh as much as one hundred and fifty large draft horses. There are, of course, other large warm-blooded animals. The elephants of India and Africa often weigh several tons. In temperate climates there are no animals to compare with them in size. The American bison, for example, does not weigh so much as an ordinary horse.

Animals like the fishes, frogs, snakes, and birds exemplify the great variety of size in the animal kingdom. The python of Burma has been known to attain a length of thirty feet. The anaconda of South America averages about seventeen feet in length. The black snake (commonly called the blue racer west of the Mississippi River) attains a length of about six feet. A garter snake may grow to be three and a half feet long. Worm snakes, residents of some tropical and semitropical countries, rarely become longer than ten to twelve inches.

Birds, of course, exhibit much variety in size. Perhaps the smallest common bird in

There is a great variety in the animal life of Earth.

North America is the ruby-throated hummingbird, whose nest is less than one and a half inches in diameter. At the other extreme are such birds as the wild geese, buzzards, and eagles, which are among the largest birds.

Insects range in size from moths which have a wingspread of several inches to aphids, or plant lice, which are less than an eighth of an inch in length. Sponges which grow in fresh water are often less than an inch in length, while the kind which grow in warm ocean waters and which are used to make bath sponges may be large enough to fill a small tub.

The smallest of all animals are the many thousands of kinds of one-celled Protozoa, which may be found wherever there is water. Even these vary considerably, some of them being approximately one twenty-fifth of an inch long and visible to the unaided eye, and others being so small that many hundreds of them may live in a small drop of water. Some of the Protozoa are no larger in size than some bacteria.

EXPERIENCES. *Opportunities to study variations in animals.* Take the children on an excursion to a nearby creek, river, lake, or pond and study the animal life found in and near the water. Use a dip net to collect small animals living near the edge of the pond. A white enameled dishpan will be found useful for emptying the "catch." After the animals have been observed and discussed, they may be returned to the water. The teacher might call attention to the fact that it is desirable to look and study but not needlessly to destroy living things. (NOTE. A dip net can be made from cheesecloth, wire, and an old broom handle. A small strainer also makes a good dip net.)

Take the children into a vacant lot to observe variations in the size of the animals found there. Remember that under rocks, bricks, bottles, and boards many interesting animals may sometimes be found. Use a long stick to overturn these objects, and take the proper

safety precautions in those regions where a poisonous animal might possibly share such habitats.

Make a visit to a nearby farm or a zoological park to observe the great variations in size of the animals.

Variations Exist within Each Kind, or Species, of Living Thing. Variations occur not only over the whole range of the plant and animal kingdoms, but also within any particular kind. Each kind of living thing, such as horses, dogs, corn, and apple trees, is a *species*. As was previously noted, no two living things are ever exactly alike. Within each species many differences may be found. Only one species of man exists today, but the species has several *varieties*. These varieties correspond to what are sometimes called the races of man. The white race differs from the black; the yellow race differs from each of the other two. Color is not the only variant. The average weight and height, the facial features, the structure of the hair, and other characteristics show variation. The same thing is true of other species. All domesticated dogs belong to the same species; but there are over a hundred varieties, or breeds, ranging from the large Newfoundland and great Dane to the small rat terriers and poodles. Among wild animals similar variety may be noticed.

Plants too show many varieties within the same species. Any gardener's catalogue lists the many varieties of plants of any single species. Popcorn, field corn, and sweet corn are all members of the same species. There are many varieties of apples, for example, and many varieties of tomatoes.

EXPERIENCES. *Observations of variations within each kind, or species, of living thing.* The children might be directed in the observation and discussion of the variations in size, color of skin, color of hair, color of eyes, of the members of the class. These are good examples of variations, but the teacher conducting this type of discussion must be very careful that no child be made to feel that his size, physical proportions, or coloring, is a handicap. Of equal importance, one should not be made to feel that having his particular size and coloring makes him superior or inferior.

Secure several garden catalogues and let the children look through them. Call their attention to the great number of varieties of plants within the same species.

Suggest that the next time the children go to the grocery store they might be interested in noticing the different varieties of pecans, apples, grapes, corn, squash, beans, peas, potatoes, and other fruits and vegetables.

Let the children examine books on dogs, cats, horses, cattle, rabbits, pigeons, fish, and other animals. See how many varieties of each kind of animal are pictured or discussed.

Variations Exist within Each Variety. Within each variety there are many noticeable variations. In the same litter of purebred dogs no two puppies will be exactly alike. Two peach trees of the same variety and growing side by side under the same environmental conditions will be different, producing different quantities of fruit. Wheat plants growing close together may be very different.

Variations may even be found on a single plant. No two leaves on a tree will be identical in size, shape, and color. Apples growing on the same limb are different from one another. The range of these differences may be narrow, but they exist nevertheless. There is no end to variety.

EXPERIENCES. *Observations to show variations within each given variety of plant or animal.* It might be interesting, if several children in the group have dogs or other pets of the same variety, to arrange for these pets to visit the school at a time when the children might have class on the school ground. For example, three children might have cocker spaniel dogs that would show variation in size, possibly color, and also considerable variation in behavior.

The teacher or children might bring in several branches from different plants. Let the children study these for variations in color, size, shape, edges, and veining of leaves from the same branch.

Variations Exist within Nonliving Things. While this chapter deals with living things, it should be noted that there is a great variation in soils, rocks, and other nonliving things. (NOTE. See Chapter 6 for a more extensive discussion of rocks and soils.)

EXPERIENCES. *To observe variations in rocks and soils.* Ask children to bring in small quantities of different kinds of soils found near their homes. Note variations in color and size of particles.

Ask children to study the rocks found at or near their homes. Do they see variations in size, shape, hardness, and color. They may wish to make a display of rocks. If so, caution against bringing in more rocks than are necessary. Children should have a feeling for the place of rocks and soils in their neighborhood.

Plants and Animals Are Alike in Many Ways

Despite the fact that there are many obvious differences in the structure of plants and animals, there are also numerous similarities. All living things, both plant and animal, are made up of *protoplasm*. It is the basic, fundamental stuff of life. It is usually described as a granular, gelatin-like substance, somewhat resembling in consistency and appearance the white of an egg. It is colorless, semi-transparent, and present in the cells of all living things.

If we accept the doctrine that all living things are made up of protoplasm, then the question may be asked, "What is protoplasm composed of?" There is no simple answer to this question. Analysis shows that protoplasm is made up of a number of chemical elements and that these are the common ones of our experience. Carbon, hydrogen, and oxygen are always found in protoplasm, as are potassium, phosphorus, iodine, sulfur, nitrogen, calcium, iron, magnesium, sodium, and chlorine. Often traces of copper, boron, and silicon may be found in it.

The elements in protoplasm are combined together in a number of exceedingly complicated compounds, the exact nature of which has not yet been determined. It is significant,

however, that the protoplasm in each species of living things is specific for that species; that is, it is different from the protoplasm of other species.

Protoplasm is not found in a haphazard, unorganized arrangement. Within any organism it is found as tiny *cells*, microscopic in size, each of which has a cell wall, or membrane. Toward the center of each living cell may be found a denser, more or less spherical mass of protoplasm, called the *nucleus*. The nucleus is a vital part of the cell and is concerned with cell division.

Not all cells are alike. The cells vary according to their function, or work. In an animal, cells in the nervous system are unlike those which make up the muscles, and cells in the liver are different from either of the other kinds. Within a single leaf several kinds of cells are found.

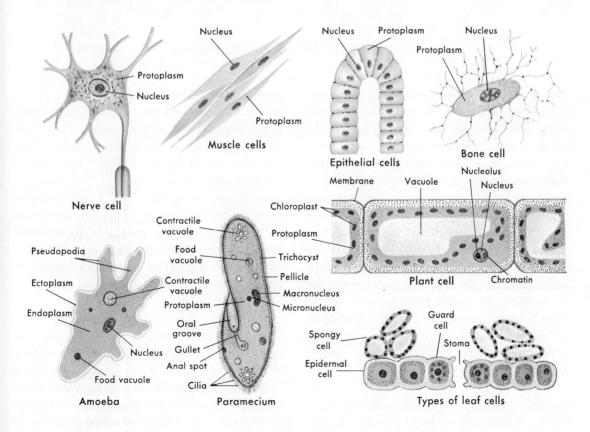

Varieties of cells.

A number of cells performing a similar function make up a *tissue*. The heart of an animal, for example, is made up largely of muscle tissue. A group of tissues make up an *organ*. The brain is made up of nerve-cell tissue; muscles are groups of muscle tissues made up of muscle cells working together. A group of organs doing the same kind of work and performing the same function make up a *system*. Thus the human body is made up of the skeletal, muscular, respiratory, circulatory, and other systems. The aggregate of systems makes up the individual. In a plant the tubes which conduct minerals and water to the leaves, and food made in the leaves to the stem and roots, make up the vascular system.

Both plants and animals, then, are made up of protoplasm. Both are made of cells, and in both the cells make up tissues, tissues make up organs, and organs make up the individual.

Nor is this the end of the similarities between them. Both are adapted to their environment. Both need oxygen in order to utilize the energy in the food they use. Both manufacture special chemical substances called enzymes to aid in the digestion of foods. Some types of plants can even move about from place to place. Among these are some of the bacteria, and other larger plants, yet very small, called diatoms. On the other hand, some animals, such as sponges, corals, oysters, and clams, lead a sedentary existence during a large part of their life cycle. As a matter of fact, some living things exhibit so many of the characteristics of both plants and animals that biologists have not yet agreed on their proper classification although some favor a new phylum, Protista. An example of this is the microscopic organism *Euglena,* which moves like an animal, but manufactures food like a plant.

Plants Differ Widely in Structure

Some Plants Have No Roots, Stems, Flowers, or Leaves. There are thousands of species of plants that have no roots, stems, flowers, or leaves. Some authorities broadly classify them as bacteria, algae, and fungi. Many cannot be seen without the aid of a microscope; others are fairly large. Some are composed of a single cell, and others are multicellular. Some of them contain chlorophyll and make their own food, and others do not. Some can live on ice and snow, and others live in hot springs. Some can live in the soil, and others live in the air, in water, or under great pressure at the ocean bottom. Some may live within or upon the bodies of other living things, or upon dead or inorganic materials. Many are destructive, but many are extremely useful.

Bacteria. Plants vary not only in the gross details of their appearance, but also in the complexity of their structure. Bacteria are simple nongreen plants. They are extremely small, single-celled, and primitive. They have no definite nucleus, and, being single-celled, can have no tissues or organs. They are of three general shapes: they may be spherical, rod-shaped, or spiral. Many variations of these shapes may occur. They are sometimes without any definite means of locomotion. Some of them, however, have very fine hair-like projections called flagella by means of which they can propel themselves through a liquid medium.

Algae. Another group of simple plants includes the algae, which live wherever moisture is abundant. One of the commonest kinds known to children grows in almost any pond or stream, and is sometimes called pond scum, or frog spit. It consists of a long filament of cells, the entire filament being surrounded by a sheath of a slippery, gelatin-like material. Each individual filament is usually much finer than a human hair. Microscopic examination reveals the cell wall, nucleus, and protoplasm. In addition, each living cell contains a green material, known as chlorophyll, which is important in the process of food-making. Chlorophyll is found in all green plants and gives them their color.

Some species of algae live on the bark of trees on the shady side, or on fence posts which have been exposed to the weather a long time, or even on stones where moisture is apt to gather. Many of the plants commonly known as seaweeds are algae. These are often red or brown rather than green in color. None of the algae have roots, stems, leaves, or flowers. In the simpler kinds each cell is an individual plant, and can exist independently of the others in its colony. It can manufacture its own food, secure oxygen from the water, and reproduce its own kind.

Mushrooms and Toadstools. Mushrooms and toadstools represent another type of simple plant, a fungus, with which children may have had experience. These are composed of many cells, but they do not have true roots, stems, leaves, or flowers. Neither do they make their own food. In the case of mushrooms, the main

Edible mushrooms can be a tasty delicacy, but only an expert should pick them.

part of the plant grows underground for two or three years. When it has reached maturity and conditions are favorable, that part of the plant (the umbrella-shaped structure) with which children are familiar grows rapidly after a heavy rain.

EXPERIENCE. *To observe toadstools.* Show the children pictures of toadstools and ask them to look for plants like these near their homes or near school. Suggest that they not pick them, but show others where they are. If toadstools are close to school, it might be interesting for the class to observe them.

Yeasts. Yeasts are still another example of simple plants with which children will be familiar. They are very small, more or less spherical or ovoid, and contain no chlorophyll. Yeast cells have a definite nucleus. They live largely upon sugar present in various substances, and change it into alcohol. Special chemical substances called enzymes, which the yeasts produce, enable them to do this. Because of their ability to change sugar into alcohol, yeasts are used for many commercial purposes. A cake of yeast consists of millions of these plants mixed with damp starch to keep them moist and alive.

When a cake of yeast is mixed with bread dough and kept in a warm place, the yeast immediately begins changing the sugar in the dough to alcohol. As a result of this chemical reaction, much carbon dioxide gas is released, which gathers into bubbles within the dough, so that it occupies more space, and the dough is said to rise. Then, when the dough is placed in the oven to be baked, the heat of the oven causes the carbon dioxide gas to expand; the alcohol evaporates; the bread is light and palatable.

EXPERIENCE. *To show the effects of yeast on dough.* Children may find a recipe for a loaf of bread and make it, being sure to *include the yeast*.

They may mix exactly the same ingredients again, being sure to *omit the yeast*. Set both mixtures together in a warm place. Note that the dough containing the yeast rises, and the other does not.

EXPERIENCE. *To test the effects of temperature upon the activity of yeasts and the consequent rising of bread.* Make the same recipe for bread again, being sure to *include the yeast*. Divide into 3 parts. Place one part in a refrigerator or other cold place; another should be kept at room temperature, and the third in a very hot place, such as an oven. Note which of the three rises best.

EXPERIENCE. *To show that yeast acts upon sugar.* Place about one fourth of a fresh well-crumbled cake of yeast in a small glass containing some well-sweetened water. In another small glass place a similar quantity of yeast and a similar quantity of ordinary tap water. Keep both at the same temperature. Note that the yeast in the sweetened water is causing bubbles of gas to be given off, while no such change is taking place in the other glass. In a third glass place some water in which there is dissolved some table salt, and add yeast. No change will take place. The bubbles of gas given off in the glass with the sweetened water are carbon dioxide.

EXPERIENCE. *To demonstrate that the gas which is given off when yeast acts upon sugar is carbon dioxide.* Place some limewater—which may be purchased inexpensively at any drugstore or made (see p. 385)—in a small glass. Then have one of the pupils exhale through a straw into the limewater in the small glass. The limewater will turn milky, or cloudy, in color because of the chemical effect of the carbon dioxide in the exhaled air. Now take a small glass of sweetened water in which fresh yeast has been placed, and fit the glass with a one-hole cork, a rubber stopper, or modeling clay which can be molded around the glass tubing and also molded to fit the opening in the small glass. Get a curved piece of glass tubing at a drugstore; put one end of it into the modeling clay in the glass which contains the yeast water, and put the other end into a glass of limewater. Keep the yeast glass fairly warm. The carbon dioxide gas given off by the yeast will then bubble out into the limewater, causing it to turn milky, as did the carbon dioxide in the exhaled air.

EXPERIENCE. *To observe yeast plants.* If a microprojector is available make a slide of fresh yeast. To do this, place a drop of water on a clean glass slide and put into it a very small piece of a yeast cake. Smear the yeast in the drop of water so that it seems to be dissolved. Then place a cover glass on the smear and focus the microprojector. The yeast plants will appear to be very small, ovoid or round in shape, and more or less colorless.

Molds. Molds are another type of simple plant with which most children are acquainted. They too cannot manufacture their own food, since they lack chlorophyll, and consequently live upon bread and other organic things. They need moisture in order to thrive, and do not grow well under dry conditions. The best-known mold is probably the bread mold, found commonly on stale bread, decaying fruits and vegetables, and other organic matter. Some molds are found on living insects as parasites, while other kinds are common in streams and ponds on the bodies of dead insects and other decaying matter. A few species attack living fish or fish eggs, and may be very destructive when they infest the eggs and young fish in hatcheries.

In structure molds resemble rather closely certain of the algae, since the plant body is made up of filaments called hyphae and since they reproduce in somewhat the same way.

EXPERIENCE. *To obtain the type of molds which live in the water on the bodies of dead insects.* Place a few dead flies in some stagnant water. Within a few days the flies generally become surrounded by a whitish growth of mold.

EXPERIENCE. *To obtain the common bread mold.* Moisten a slice of bread, expose it to the air in the classroom, and keep it at ordinary room temperature for three or four days. By that time molds should develop. These will probably be whitish in color at first. The molds develop from mold spores which settle from the air upon the bread.

EXPERIENCE. *To determine conditions under which molds grow best.* Take six slices of bread. Toast one slice, making sure that it becomes very dry. Place another on a plate and keep it fairly moist, but not soaked. Take a third slice and immerse it completely in water, keeping it that way. Keep all three of these at the same temperature, and note which slice of bread shows the greatest development of mold. Also, take another slice of bread, keep it fairly moist, and place it in a refrigerator or other cold place; the fifth slice should be moistened similarly and kept at room temperature; the last slice should be as damp as the other two and, if possible, should be kept in a relatively hot place. Note which mold grows best. The second and fifth slices should show most mold growth, indicating that molds grow best at fairly warm temperatures and under conditions of dampness without excess of moisture. Remember that the molds growing on the bread will be of a different kind from those in the earlier experience with the water mold.

Mildews. Mildews are simple plants without chlorophyll and that are parasitic on other living things. They have been responsible for much damage to fruits, vegetables, and other plants. Mildews need suitable food, dampness, and plenty of warmth to grow.

Smuts. Children in rural communities are often familiar with smut growing on corn. The black powder, or dust, found within the mature smut growth is simply a large number of spores. Carried by the wind, they may germinate into new smut plants, and thus the infection spreads.

Rusts. Rusts are also common simple plants that are parasites on various plants, chiefly on their stems and leaves. They often cause great economic loss. In cool climates some rusts live their life cycle on wheat, then on the common barberry, and then go back to wheat. The white-pine blister rust completes its life cycle by alternating between white pines and wild gooseberries or currants.

Some Plants Have Roots, Stems, and Leaves. *Mosses.* Mosses represent plants of a higher degree of complexity. They are usually found in places where water is fairly abundant, and have leaves, short stems, and the suggestion of roots in underground structures called rhizoids, through which they can take in water. These rhizoids are not well-developed for their function, and consequently mosses generally cannot thrive under arid conditions. Mosses all contain chlorophyll and manufacture their own food. They have no flowers and do not reproduce by means of seeds.

Ferns. Ferns are more highly complicated plants than the mosses and are generally better adapted to living on land. They have well-developed leaves, which are called fronds, on whose lower surface spores develop in tiny cases. They also have well-developed roots and stems. Ferns are widely distributed over the surface of Earth and flourish best in moist, shady places. Some kinds, however, grow in very dry places. In the tropics some ferns attain a height of forty-five or more feet. All ferns have a well-developed vascular system for conducting water and minerals from the roots to the stems and leaves and the food made in the leaves to the stems and roots. They are much more complicated than the mosses, since there is more differentiation of cells according to function.

Seed-Bearing Plants. The seed-bearing plants are of exceptional importance to man, furnishing him with many materials for food, clothing, and shelter. They are the ones most people think of as plants. In addition to having a well-developed system for conducting nutrients and food to all parts of the plant, these are plants whose chief distinguishing characteristic is the formation of seeds and a pollen tube. The latter structure will be taken up in the discussion of plant reproduction (p. 526).

One group of seed-bearing plants has no flowers. These are the *gymnosperms*. These are chiefly woody evergreen trees, shrubs, or vines with needles or scalelike leaves. The most familiar ones are pines, firs, cedars, spruces, redwoods, junipers, and others commonly called conifers, and the ginkgoes used for ornamental purposes. Many grow best in the cooler parts of the middle latitudes, although some kinds grow in deserts and others in the tropics. Many lose their leaves gradually, rarely keeping them longer than four years (p. 660). Most species bear woody seed

cones as well as the much smaller and less woody pollen cones on the same tree. However, in some species there is only one cone that produces both pollen and seed. Although they produce pollen and bear seed, they do not have highly specialized flowers as do the flowering plants. Their seeds develop on the *surface* of the scalelike parts of a cone.

The other large group of seed-bearing plants are the flowering plants, or *angiosperms*. These represent the highest type of plant development. There are approximately 250,000 species in this largest and most complex group of plants. For the most part they have broad leaves, woody or herbaceous stems, and well-developed flowers. Unlike the gymnosperms, the seeds of flowering plants are *enclosed* in a fruit or protective covering. There is great variation in length of life, in size, and in structure. Their organs for absorbing, conducting, and conserving water make it possible for them to exist under a great variety of conditions. They can live almost anywhere there is light— in water, in polar regions, in hot dry regions, and in hot wet regions.

Seed-bearing plants have vascular tubes called *xylem* for conducting to the stems and leaves the water and nutrients taken in through the roots. Other tubes called *phloem* carry food manufactured in the leaves down to all parts of the stems and the roots.

The roots themselves are often very long and serve to anchor a plant. In addition to carrying water and dissolved nutrients to the stems, roots may also store food to a greater or lesser degree (p. 653).

The tip of every root is protected from injury by a *root cap* as it pushes through the soil. Cells of the root cap are constantly being formed as the root grows. At the same time younger cells in the root become increasingly more mature and more specialized (p. 589).

Water, with nutrients and gases in solution, is absorbed through the growing section of a root and through very fine root hairs. A *root*

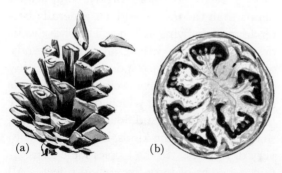

(a) *Pine seeds develop on the surface of the scales.* (b) *The seeds of flowering plants are enclosed in a fruit or protective covering.*

hair is a delicate, tubelike expansion of the outer wall of a surface or epidermal cell. As roots grow longer, old root hairs die and new root hairs are formed just back of the growing root tip and at once begin surrounding minute particles of soil (p. 550). Thus they come into close contact with the film or coating of water enveloping the soil particles, and due to a rather gummy coating, they adhere closely. Root hairs never become roots, but they greatly increase the absorbing area of a root system. Nearly all ordinary land plants have root hairs.

EXPERIENCE. *To observe roots and root hairs.* Place radish seeds on a wet blotter and cover with a glass. If the blotter is dark they can be seen more easily. Keep *well moistened,* and when roots appear, observe with a hand lens and note the parts of the root and the size of the area for taking in water. In what ways are the root hairs helpful? Where do they grow?

EXPERIENCE. *To see differences in root systems.* Children may examine the root systems of various plants. A root system is composed of *all* the underground roots of a plant. For instance, they may dig up a whole dandelion plant and a whole grass plant from a place where it will not injure or disfigure the surroundings. Carefully soak off the soil in one or more pails of water so as not to injure the roots. Did they secure a whole root system with root hairs intact? Does soil still cling to the root hairs? Examine with a hand lens. A dandelion has a *tap root,* a long main root with smaller branching roots. A grass plant has a network of small roots. Grass has a *fibrous root system.*

Road cuts and excavations may provide opportunities to observe the root systems of trees, shrubs, and many other plants. Some root systems are shallow, and some extend deep into the soil. Children may discuss the advantages of each type of root system. These systems vary in different species of plants and under different growing conditions.

The leaves are very complicated in structure. A typical leaf consists of three parts: the blade; its slender stalk, or petiole; and the broadened attachment to the stem, or leaf base. The water- and food-conducting tubes extend into the leaves, where they are called *veins,* which are parallel to one another in some species and branching (net-veined) in others. The leaf blade itself may be simple, with lobes, as in the case of most oaks and maples, or it may be a compound leaf, as in clover, in which three leaflets make up a single leaf. Other examples of compound leaves are potato, horse chestnut, and walnut leaves.

The outer layer of cells in a leaf make up the *epidermis,* which covers the whole leaf surface and protects the tissues within. Beneath the upper epidermis are relatively long, large cells closely packed together and forming one or more layers. Under these, other cells, irregularly shaped and loosely packed, extend to the lower epidermis. Spaces extend between all the leaf cells, forming a network and connecting with similar spaces in stems and roots. By means of this network gases may reach the plant cells. The spaces are called *air spaces.* All the leaf cells are rich in chlorophyll, which is contained in minute packets called *chloroplasts.* These are the food-making structures in plants, and are present not only in the leaves but also in the green stems of many plants. As one observes a plant leaf it is easy to understand that all cells are microscopic.

Some of the cells in the epidermis may be modified to form hairs of various kinds. Other epidermal cells are modified into structures—pairs of *guard cells*—between which is an opening called a *stoma* (plural, *stomata*). It is through these openings for the most part that carbon dioxide enters and water vapor and

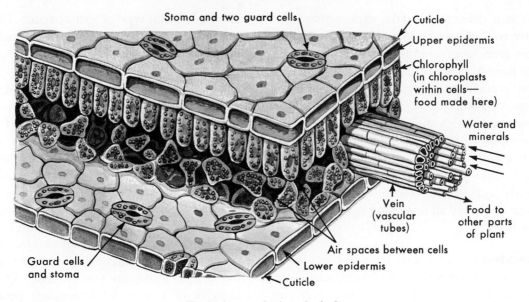

Stoma and two guard cells

Cuticle

Upper epidermis

Chlorophyll
(in chloroplasts
within cells—
food made here)

Water and
minerals

Vein
(vascular
tubes)

Food to
other parts
of plant

Air spaces between cells

Lower epidermis

Cuticle

Guard cells
and stoma

The intricate mechanism of a leaf.

oxygen leave or enter a leaf. Small amounts of water vapor and other gases enter or may leave a plant from the stem and other surfaces. The loss of water from plants as water vapor is called *transpiration.*

In the presence of sunlight the guard cells change shape, due to an increased concentration of sugar within and therefore an increased intake of water from nearby cells. As their shape changes, the stomata open and transpiration occurs. Then, as light decreases and photosynthesis decreases also, the guard cells become less rigid, the stomata close, and the gradual passing in and out of gases comes to a stop, or nearly so. Hence, shade or a dark day tends to reduce transpiration. Also, when water is not available to a plant, the stomata tend to close, thus bringing the outgoing and incoming supply of water into balance. This may serve to keep plants alive under adverse circumstances.

When the humidity is high and transpiration cannot take place readily, water may leave a plant in liquid form. This is called *guttation.* Special cells at the ends of leaf veins secrete the water, which continues to rise,

even though the rate of transpiration is slowed down. The water is seen as drops hanging from the tips or margins of leaves.

EXPERIENCE. *Children can distinguish between dew and guttation.* On humid mornings children may observe the leaves of such plants as grass, corn, tomatoes, potatoes, and others for drops of water hanging from leaf edges or tips. They may observe that dew appears as dampness over the whole surface of a leaf, whereas guttation appears as drops only on tips or margins of leaves. Guttation may be observed in a classroom by placing and leaving a glass jar over small, *well-watered* corn, tomato, or grass plants. Can the children explain why the glass jar promotes guttation? The amount of moisture that accumulates in the small amount of air in the jar does not permit transpiration to continue to take place readily.

Plants Take In and Use Water and Nutrients. Water enters a plant root in different ways: by osmosis, or active absorption, and by passive absorption. Osmosis is a process of far-reaching importance, because it is involved in the life processes of plants and animals, including man, in medicine and in many related fields. There is still much that is not understood about the process. In order for water to enter or leave a root or root hair by *osmosis,* it must pass through the membranes or tissues of the cell walls. In this process the cell membranes permit the passage of water but not everything that is in solution in the water, especially sugar. For instance, when the amount of sugar, a common constituent of cell sap, is greater within a cell than in the water outside, then water can pass through the cell membrane into the cell. Osmosis may take place in either direction, depending upon which side of the membrane has the highest concentration of substances in solution.

Passive absorption involves pressure. This process depends on the difference in pressure on the water in the soil and the water in the plant. The pull from transpiration reduces the water pressure inside the plant, thus promoting the inward flow of water.

The absorption of the many substances in solution may occur as ions (p. 379), and at different rates, depending on the characteristics of the substances and the environment of the plant. They are not necessarily absorbed as part of the water.

As in animals, food must be digested before it can be of use to a plant. However, plants have no special organs for digestion, as animals have. Digestion goes on in any living cell when food is present. During digestion, enzymes change such things as starch, fat, sugar, and protein into a soluble form. In solution they can be transported to cells all over the plant by the vascular tubes called phloem. Other enzymes control oxidation or slow combustion of food, in which energy is released and is used in the building of tissues. This takes place in the plant cells. Another name for this process is *respiration.* The use or conversion of foods into living tissue is *assimilation.* This, too, takes place in the plant cells.

How Water Rises in Plants. The rise of water in plants, and especially its rise to the top of tall trees, is not fully understood by scientists. In tubes such as xylem tubes, water molecules cohere, or hold together, partly due to the attraction between the molecules. Water molecules also adhere to the walls of the tubes. They move from cell to cell, upward. When a plant transpires, the cells surrounding the xylem tubes in leaf veins draw water from them. This produces a pull on the column of water in the stem or trunk. Other factors may influence the process, but some think that transpiration pull and the cohesion of water molecules are sufficient to raise water to the tops of the tallest trees.

EXPERIENCE. *To observe the great variation in stems.* Boys and girls know that lumber comes from trees. They may be interested in knowing that it comes from the stem or trunk. They may examine the stems of many plants, note the many variations and their function as part of a plant. Discussion of the uses of stems might follow with older girls and boys.

Viewing a cross section of different stems with a hand lens will give greater insight into the structure and function of stems.

EXPERIENCE. *To help children broaden their conception of a plant.* This experience might be started with children by suggesting that they draw a picture of a whole plant or of someone setting a plant in the ground. Or children may transplant a young cabbage, zinnia, or tomato plant into a pot, or in a garden. Show them how the roots should be carefully spread out and soil scattered over them. Water is used to wash the soil closer about the roots and also to provide water for the roots to take up. Soil should be added until the roots are well covered and the plant seems firmly placed. The children might notice whether or not the plant wilts. When a wilted plant stands upright again, it shows that the roots are taking

Water passes from the ground into a plant where some is used and some is given off into the air.

up water and dissolved nutrients from the soil. What parts of the plant did the children observe? Call attention to the fact that each part of the plant—the roots, the stem, the flowers and the leaves—has a use in the life cycle of a plant.

EXPERIENCE. *To help children to see the veins in the leaves and leaf stalks.* A good hand lens is very helpful in this experience. Leaves of different plants look quite different; some are fuzzy and some are shiny; some are thick and some are thin. A thin leaf will be easier to see through. Hold the leaf and its leaf stalk in a strong light and use the hand lens to look through them. Note the many veins of different sizes in the leaf and consider their uses. The children will notice that the leaf is at the end of a leaf stalk which in turn grows from a stem that is attached to the roots of the plant.

The Structure of Some Animals Is More Complicated than That of Others

That animals vary considerably in structure is obvious. Since some of the animals are so small that they cannot be seen without a microscope, and since some are not a familiar part of our daily experience, the complete picture of this variety of structure is not available unless special attention is given to it.

Some Animals Have No Backbone. *Invertebrate Animals.* The microscopic *one-celled* Protozoa are generally spoken of as the simplest of animals. This is true, but it must be remembered that they are by no means so simple as their unicellular structure may lead one to believe. They have no systems or tissues, as do the higher animals. The cell generally consists of a cell membrane, a nucleus, and cytoplasm (protoplasm outside the nucleus); and sometimes food materials are found in it which have been taken in by the animal. Very fine threadlike projections of protoplasm, called cilia, are found on the outer surface of the cell in some species, by means of which the animal propels itself through the water. Other protozoans appear to be not much more than a blob of protoplasm within which the nucleus is embedded.

Despite this simplicity of structure, it must be borne in mind that each one-celled animal carries on all the functions of life which characterize the most complex members of the animal kingdom. Each cell must take in food and oxygen, carry on digestion, circulate the digested food around the cell, dispose of car-

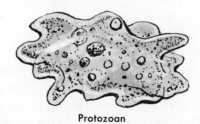

Protozoan

bon dioxide, undigested materials, and other wastes, and carry on growth and reproduction. Protozoa are sensitive to environmental conditions, such as light, heat, and gravity. Most of them move about actively, and some kinds even have means of stinging and thus paralyzing others and using them for food.

EXPERIENCE. *To set up a zoo of microscopic animals.* If a microscope is available, take an ordinary quart or pint Mason jar and put into it some tap water (about three-fourths full) and a few bits of hay or dried grass. Allow this infusion to stand at room temperature for a few days; then examine a drop of water from the surface under a microscope. Protozoa of various kinds should be easily found. Since a variety of microscopic animals may be found in such an infusion, the jar represents a zoo of microscopic animals. Older children might find this a very profitable experience.

Sponges represent the next degree of complexity in animals. They are made up of *many cells,* not one cell. Most sponges known to children are the skeletons of marine sponges which grow in shallow tropical waters, but there are several species which live in fresh water. These, however, are so small that they generally escape notice, for they seldom exceed a length of one inch and do not look like the common sponge. Some marine sponges are made up of an aggregate of cells, with skeletons of limy or glassy particles. They live attached to stones, and, since they do not

move about, they were until rather recently believed to be plants. The cells of sponges show a slight differentiation according to function.

Members of a third group of animals are the corals and fresh-water polyps. Corals are found in warm, rather shallow seas, and have the ability to secrete small lime cups, within which they live. Members of this group of animals are found in ponds and lakes in this country. The commonest form is a small animal known as *Hydra,* of which there are several species. Hydras have no skeletons, but are small, tubelike in structure, and have tentacles and a mouth at one end of the body. The body wall of *Hydra* consists of two layers

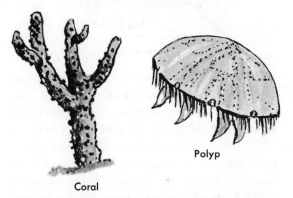

Polyp

Coral

of cells, between which is a thin noncellular layer of a gelatinous material. The outer layer of cells is called the ectoderm, the inner layer is known as the endoderm, and the layer between the two is known as the mesogloea. The cells of the inner layer carry on digestion, while the ectoderm serves as a protection for the body.

Next to be considered are the flatworms and roundworms. The roundworms are usually

Sponge

Roundworm

quite small, often are found in fresh water or as parasites in animals, and are rarely seen.

Flatworm

The best known of the flatworms is probably the tapeworm, which infests man and other animals as a parasite.

Earthworm

Earthworms, which are classed in a separate phylum of the animal kingdom, are highly complicated animals. The plant and animal kingdoms are divided into phyla (p. 523). They possess rather well-developed systems for the circulation of blood and have muscles, nerves, an efficient digestive tract, and a highly specialized reproductive system.

Starfish represent a group of animals which are always found in oceans and seas and never in fresh water. Included with them are such animals as the sea urchin and the sand dollar, as well as the brittle stars, common on the coasts of the United States.

Starfish

One of the largest and most important groups of animals is the phylum which includes the insects. Classed together here are

such diverse forms as lobsters, crabs, crayfish, spiders, barnacles, and insect species. All members of this phylum have many characteristics in common, chief among which are a segmented body, jointed legs, and an external skeleton made up of a horny substance called

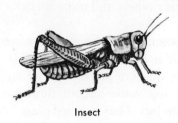

Insect

chitin. None of them have lungs, but breathe by means of gills or by openings in the skeleton called spiracles, or breathing pores. Many of them have well-developed senses of sight, smell, and hearing. The insects have highly specialized mouth parts for chewing or for sucking plant juices. Many of them can fly. They are among the greatest pests of man.

The phylum including oysters, snails, and clams is characterized by shells of lime, although some members of this phylum, like the common garden slug, may be without shells. The shells of some species consist of two halves, each called a valve. Animals of this kind are

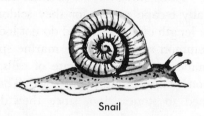

Snail

called bivalves. Others have shells which are spiral in shape and so consist of only one piece, as in the snails.

Some Animals Have a Backbone. *Vertebrate Animals.* All the animals thus far discussed are called invertebrates, since they have no vertebrae or backbone. The highest phylum of animals is characterized by a spinal cord, which is always located along the top surface, or back, of the animal. Earthworms are invertebrates which have a nerve extending the length of the body, but in this case it is found along the lower, or ventral, surface. All animals with spinal cords, or with backbones within which the spinal cord is located, are called vertebrates.

Each phylum of animals is divided into classes. Thus far no attention has been given to the various classes of animals in each phylum, but the classes of vertebrates are so commonly a part of the experience of the school child that some attention must be devoted to each of them. The main classes of vertebrates are the *fishes,* the *amphibians,* the *reptiles,* the *birds,* and the *mammals.*

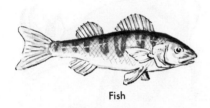

Fish

Not everything which swims is a fish, any more than everything which flies is a bird. Sharks, dogfish, and rays, or skates, resemble the true fishes in form, but differ from them so widely that they are placed in a class by themselves. They have no air bladder, for example, and no scales. The skeleton of a dogfish is made up entirely of cartilage rather than true bone. The true fishes have scales or bony plates which furnish a protective covering for the body. Their skeleton consists in part or wholly of bone. They breathe by means of gills and are well adapted for life in the water. The gills are covered by a plate called the operculum for protection from injury. The fins are an extension of the skin by means of rays of cartilage. They may be used as oars when the fish is swimming slowly. The tail fin

and the fins on the back aid in keeping the fish in a vertical position in the water.

The skeleton of a fish generally consists of a skull, backbone, ribs, and a number of bones called the pectoral girdle. The latter lie just behind the head on either side and furnish a strong support for the muscles that move the fins located there. Muscles in fishes are well developed and are used in locomotion, in breathing, and in obtaining food. Other systems are also well developed.

Amphibian

Frogs, toads, and salamanders belong in the class Amphibia. While fish always breathe by means of gills, the amphibians breathe in this manner only in the early stages of their development, while they are in the water. Later they develop lungs and live on land. Amphibians in the adult stages have legs and consequently can move about on land. The heart of a fish is usually made up of two chambers, an auricle and a ventricle, whereas the heart of an amphibian is made up of three chambers, two auricles and one ventricle.

The third class of animals with backbones includes snakes, turtles, lizards, alligators, and crocodiles; these are called reptiles. Some of these animals are found in or near water, but they always breathe by means of lungs and do not breathe by means of gills at any stage of their life cycle. They generally hatch from eggs laid on dry land and, like the Amphibia, possess a three-chambered heart. While the skins of amphibians are generally smooth, those of reptiles are covered with scales and frequently with bony plates. The popular notion that snakes and other reptiles are slimy is false.   Contrary also to popular belief, the majority of them are harmless to man, and even beneficial.

Reptile

Some Vertebrates Are Cold-blooded; Others Are Warm-blooded.   All the animals, including the invertebrates, which we have considered so far are known as cold-blooded. This means that their body temperature is not constant, but may vary considerably as the temperature of the air or water around them varies.   The next class of animals, the birds, have a constant body temperature which varies but little.   Since this temperature is generally higher than that of the atmosphere, these animals are known as warm-blooded.   It must be emphasized that birds and mammals alone are warm-blooded animals.

EXPERIENCE.   *To observe some of the differences between warm-blooded and cold-blooded animals.* Children might bring to class a cold-blooded animal, such as a frog, and a warm-blooded animal, such as a rabbit or kitten or guinea pig.   Show them how to touch each one to determine why some animals are said to be cold-blooded and others warm-blooded.   Help children to develop behavior in reference to living things consistent with sound conservation.

Birds are distinguished easily from all other animals by the fact that they alone possess feathers.   It is sometimes surprising to children to learn that a hen or a turkey is a bird, since

Bird

often they associate that term only with the wild songbirds.   Birds have a four-chambered heart, consisting of two auricles and two ventricles; and their average body temperature is usually much higher than that of man, in some cases reaching 110°F.   They have light bony skeletons, wings, strong muscles, and scales on the feet; and they show many adaptations to their environment and to their mode of living.

Mammal

The last class of backboned animals is the class Mammalia.   It is in this group that most of the animals with which we are most closely associated are found, including the human species.   They are warm-blooded, breathe by means of lungs, are covered wholly or partly with hair or fur, suckle their young on milk secreted by mammary glands, and have a large sheet of muscle called the diaphragm in the body cavity, separating the lungs and heart from the stomach, intestines, and other internal organs.

From this brief survey of the animal kingdom it is evident that animals, like plants, have complexity of structure and exhibit many large differences. It must be remembered, however, that the divisions discussed here are only the major ones, and no attempt is made to include them all. The animal kingdom is divided into phyla (singular, phylum), and each of these is divided into classes. Each class is further arranged into subclasses. In the class Mammalia we find such a division. The first subclass is that of the egg-laying mammals; the second includes all the other mammals. The former lay eggs, but the young of the latter develop within the body of the female.

The egg-laying mammals are found in Australia, New Guinea, and Tasmania. Their most conspicuous peculiarities are their egg-laying habit and the fact that in certain respects their skeleton is somewhat like that of a reptile.

An example is the duckbill, an animal which is about the size of a muskrat. It possesses webbed feet, a thick fur which is waterproof like that of a beaver, and a ducklike bill with which it probes in the mud for worms and insects.

Each subclass is further divided into orders and suborders, which, in turn, are divided into families. Each family consists of a number of genera, and each genus is made up of a number of species. The species, in turn, may have subspecies and varieties.

The opossums of America and the kangaroos and wallabies of Australia are representatives of the order Marsupialia. Their young are born in an extremely immature condition, and so must be carried about in the pouch of the mother. Some very small mammals, the insectivores, live chiefly on insects. Typical of these are the moles, which often burrow underground in our gardens and lawns. Bats, which are sometimes mistaken for birds because of their habit of flight, belong to the order Chiroptera. The flesh-eating mammals are carnivores, characterized by their small incisor teeth and well-developed canine teeth.

There are eleven families of carnivorous mammals, not all of which are exclusively flesheaters; for some of them are omnivorous, and others are vegetarians. The five families of carnivores found in North America north of Mexico are the dog family, which includes the foxes, wolves, coyotes; the raccoons; the bears; the martens (including the otter, mink, weasel, skunk, wolverine, and badger); and the cat family, which in North America includes the wildcat, puma, Canada lynx, and jaguar. Lions, tigers, and leopards are other members of the cat family.

Rabbits, squirrels, beavers, muskrats, mice, rats, and other gnawing animals are rodents. They are characterized by their long chisel-shaped incisor teeth and the absence of canine teeth. Whales, porpoises, and some other sea mammals belong to the order Cetacea, while the hoofed animals, such as the horse, pig, deer, and cow, are ungulates. Man, the apes, and the monkeys belong to the order Primates.

Both plants and animals are classified according to their development and characteristics. All the members of the same phylum or plant division have some characteristics in common and some differences. In each of the smaller categories the animals have more similarities in common than in the larger groups. Thus all vertebrate animals have backbones, but only mammals have fur. Of the mammals, only those with hoofs are classed together as ungulates. Some hoofed animals have an even number of toes, and hence are classed separately from those which, like the horse, tapir, and rhinoceros, have an odd number of hoofed toes. To a scientist the classification of an animal is the process of giving an exact description of its structure and appearance.

Living Things Reproduce in Different Ways

It has been said that living things are characterized by two dominant urges: to preserve the life of the individual and to perpetuate the species. Perpetuation of the species necessarily involves the reproductive processes. That all life comes from life is an established and accepted fact today, but less than a century ago this belief was hotly disputed. Formerly even scientists believed that it was sometimes possible for living things to arise by spontaneous generation, and the eminent French scientist Louis Pasteur found it necessary to perform experiments to disprove claims which others were making concerning the origin of simple life.

At one time it was an accepted idea that mice could be engendered by putting some dirty linen rags in a box with some grain and cheese. Fish were thought to arise from water, and tadpoles and frogs were thought to grow out of mud. With the discovery of bacteria came the belief that these originated from decaying foods; flies were supposed to arise from decaying meat, and mosquitoes from stagnant water.

To this day some people believe that a horsehair placed in a container of water will develop into a snake. Even as late as the year 1905, Bastian, in a treatise entitled *The Nature and Origin of Living Matter,* maintained that he had actually observed the origin of bacteria in infusions which he claimed had been heated to the point where no life could have remained.

We believe now that all things that are living today are the offspring of other living things. But what was the origin of the first bit of life? It is apparent that there must have been a beginning somewhere. When, where, and how life began can only be surmised. It is thought by some scientists that hundreds of millions of years ago, when conditions on Earth were markedly different from those which exist today, pools of rather warm water existed on Earth. Water is a solvent; that is, many substances dissolve in it. Among the elements or compounds present in a dissolved form may have been carbonic acid. Chemical reactions may have taken place, many carbon-containing compounds being formed. Some of these may have exhibited the fundamental properties of protoplasm.

The masses of protoplasm must have become better and better adapted to their environment; they must have developed somehow. As time went on, further changes probably took place, and plants and animals of a very simple kind and of very primitive structure may have arisen. The question of the origin of life invites speculation and imagination, for there are few facts upon which reliance may be placed.

One of the hypotheses which has been advanced is that life did not originate on this planet at all, but that living matter in the form of spores may have fallen on Earth out of space, having had its origin on another astronomical body. There is no evidence to substantiate this idea, though it is well known that spores may stay alive under adverse conditions of extreme heat and cold for surprisingly long periods of time. Yet this is not an explanation, even if the hypothesis were true, for it simply transfers the problem from Earth to some other astronomical body.

Some Plants Reproduce by Cell Division, Some by Spores, and Some by Conjugation. Although the origin of life may be a complete puzzle, the method of its perpetuation is not. Reproduction occurs in a number of ways. Bacteria reproduce by a process of *cell division,* or fission, in which, when the cell attains maturity, it divides into two halves, each called a daughter cell and each a complete organism in itself. In a favorable environment and under optimum conditions this process of reproduction may occur every half-hour. At first glance the latter statement seems to have little significance. Simple calculation, however, quickly indicates that if one bacterium divides, and each of the resultant bacteria divide again hourly, the original organism will have become the progenitor of more than thirty million of its own kind in twenty-four hours.

Many other plants reproduce similarly. Some of the algae undergo division of cells. Yeasts reproduce by budding, which is a similar process, except that instead of dividing into two equal halves, a portion of the protoplasm forms a lateral outgrowth, or bud, which is surrounded by a cell wall. Yeasts and bacteria sometimes form spores when conditions are adverse, and remain as spores until the environment is favorable again, when the spores develop into the usual plants.

Mushrooms and puffballs reproduce by means of *spores,* and do not divide. That part of the mushroom which grows above the surface of the soil, and which is gathered for culinary purposes, is the spore-producing part of the plant. If one looks at the lower surface of the umbrella-shapped structure, one may notice the gills, which are thin plates radiating from the stalk to the outer margin of the cap, or pileus. The whole surface of the gills is covered with structures which produce the spores. Mushrooms produce immense numbers of spores. It has been calculated that an average-sized mushroom may liberate as many as one billion five hundred million spores. Puffballs reproduce similarly, except that the spores are produced within the saclike ball.

When the puffball is dry and the spores are mature, it may be kicked by an animal and the spores liberated. They produce a cloud of brown or black dust, and are scattered far and wide by the winds.

EXPERIENCE. *To observe plant spores.* Have children bring to class an unbroken dry puffball. Open it in class and shake some of the spores on a sheet of smooth white paper and examine them. Observe the spores under a hand lens, a bioscope, or a microscope if one is available.

Conjugation is a form of reproduction which occurs in some of the green algae. If two filaments are growing side by side, a protoplasmic bridge may be formed connecting two adjacent cells. Over this bridge the protoplasm, nucleus, and other cell materials from one of the cells pass into the other. This double portion of cell contents then forms a thick wall and sinks to the bottom of the water, where it remains for some time before germinating and forming a new filament of cells.

Some Animals Also Reproduce by Cell Division, Some by Spores, and Some by Conjugation. Animal reproduction is basically like that of plants. The same principles are involved. Among the Protozoa, cell division occurs. The nucleus divides into two halves, which migrate to opposite ends of the cell. Other changes take place. While these are in progress, a constriction arises around the body of the cell wall at about the same distance from each end. This constriction cuts deeper and deeper until finally the two halves separate, each a complete single-celled animal which will grow and repeat the process. In *Paramecium* this process of division takes about two hours, and may occur every twenty-four hours for weeks and even months.

Protozoans also conjugate. Two paramecia may come in contact with their mouths, or gullets, together, and remain in this position apparently because the protoplasm is of a sticky nature. At about the middle of the surface of contact a protoplasmic bridge forms, thus uniting the protoplasm of the two individuals. Then there is an exchange of materials from the nucleus of each paramecium to that of the other, after which separation occurs. Each remains alive and separate.

One entire class of Protozoa, known as the Sporozoa, reproduce by means of spores. Thus we see that plant and animal reproduction is similar in principle.

No mention of sex has been made in the reproductive processes so far discussed, because no sex is involved. Reproduction by budding and by cell division is known as *asexual* reproduction, as is reproduction by spore formation. Sponges often reproduce by buds which form internally in the parent organism. Aggregations of cells known as gemmules are formed which become separated from the parent, float out of the body of the sponge, become rounded in shape, and drift long distances in the sea. The following spring they develop into new sponges. Other animals, such as *Hydra,* develop external lateral buds. A miniature of the parent organism grows at its side, usually near its base. After reaching a certain stage of growth the bud breaks off and leads a separate existence.

Some Plants Reproduce Both Asexually and Sexually. Mosses and ferns have a complicated life cycle known as alternation of generations. The familiar fern plant produces spore cases on the lower surface of the leaves. They are small round structures, brown or reddish-brown in color. Within these spore cases spores develop, mature, and fall to the ground.

If conditions are favorable, the spores germinate and grow into small heart-shaped structures about half an inch in diameter, each known as a prothallium. The prothallium has

rudimentary roots, or rhizoids, and develops specialized organs called archegonia and antheridia. Within these organs reproductive cells form. Those which are formed in the archegonia are known as egg cells and correspond to female reproductive cells. The reproductive cells produced by the antheridia are male in character and are called sperm cells. These sperm cells are generally smaller than the egg cells. Thirty-two sperm cells are usually produced by each antheridium, but only one egg cell by each archegonium.

When conditions are such that the prothallium is partly or wholly covered by water, the sperm cells are liberated. Each of them possesses one or more whiplike structures known as flagella, by means of which the sperms can swim about in the water. A sperm by chance comes in contact with an egg cell. The sperm and egg cell unite. This union of a sperm and egg cell is known as *fertilization,* and the egg is said to be fertilized.

Following fertilization the egg, which is now called a *zygote,* begins to divide. Division results in growth; for the new cells do not become separated from the zygote, but are parts of a new individual. Successive divisions of the zygote cells result in the development of a small fern plant which has a root, leaf, and stem. Further growth results in a mature fern plant which can produce spores. Thus the fern plant reproduces asexually (by means of spores), while the prothallium resulting from the spores reproduces *sexually* (by means of sperm and egg cells). A similar alternation of generations is found in mosses.

Briefly, in pines, representative of the gymnosperms, spores develop into male cells in the pollen grains in the staminate cone, and into egg cells in the carpellate, or ovulate, cone. The two cones correspond to the stamens and carpels in flowers, and derive their names from them. Pollen carried by the wind from the staminate cones falls on the partly open scales of the carpellate cones bearing the egg cells or ovules. The pollen grains sift downward and come into contact with a sticky substance secreted by the ovules. As this dries, pollen passes through the micropyle, a small opening in the region of the ovule or seed. A pollen tube and two new sperm cells develop. The fertilization of an egg occurs about a year later, and growth of an embryo proceeds on the upper surface of a scale. The scales of a cone close after receiving the pollen, and the seeds will usually have matured by the end of another twelve-month period. A mature pine cone gradually turns downward in some species, the scales open as it dries, and the seeds fall out. There is great variation among gymnosperms, and in some species the seeds remain in the closed cone for five or six years.

Flowering plants, the angiosperms, produce seeds by the sexual method of reproduction, thus perpetuating their species. They have a wide variety of flowers, both in size and make-up. In many instances these may be so inconspicuous and so different from the common idea of a flower that they are not recognized as such. The flowers of maple trees, for example, which appear before the leaves in the spring, are not often noticed. For purposes of study in the elementary school it is best to select a large flower which has all the structures present. It will be noted that most kinds of flowers have a whorl of green leaflike structures. These are called sepals individually; collectively they make up the calyx of the flower. The colored petals make up the corolla. The corolla and calyx together make up the perianth.

Within the perianth are found the essential parts of the flower. In the center is the pistil, the expanded tip of which is called the stigma. Its stalk is called the style. The base of the pistil is the ovary, within which the egg cells develop. Around the pistil are a number of stamens, each consisting of a slender filament, or stalk, at the tip of which is the anther, which produces the pollen.

EXPERIENCE. *To call the attention of children to the many sizes, shapes, and colors among flowers.* Some flowers are very small and some are very large. Children might find it interesting to find one of the smallest and one of the largest in their garden or community. They will find flowers with many, many different colors and shapes. Children should be advised to note the kinds of insects found around certain flowers. This study might be carried on in the fall or in the spring, and those who are especially interested might continue their observations through the summer.

When the pollen grains within the anthers have matured, the anthers open and the pollen escapes. It must reach the stigma of a pistil in order to carry out its function. The pollen of grass plants is generally blown about

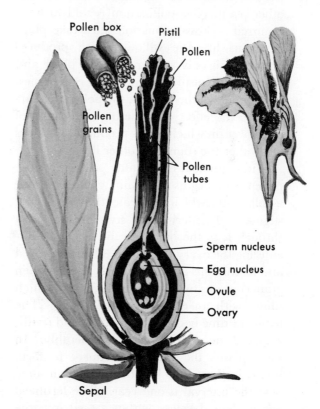

The reproductive parts of a flowering plant. Insects may carry pollen from plant to plant.

by the wind and may be carried considerable distances in this way. This is also true of plants with inconspicuous flowers, such as the poplars, alders, birches, oaks, hickories, and others. In many flowering plants, however, pollen is transferred from one plant to another by insects, especially bees. In visiting a flower in search of nectar, which is made into honey, the bee brushes against the anther and some of the pollen grains adhere to the insect. When the bee visits another flower, some of the pollen may be brushed against the stigma of the pistil, which, in many cases, secretes a sticky fluid that holds the pollen grains. The transfer of pollen from the anther to the stigma is known as *pollination*. If the pollen is transferred to the stigma of the same flower or to another flower of the same plant, self-pollination is said to have taken place. If, however, the pollen reaches a stigma on a flower of another plant, cross-pollination is said to have occurred. Cross-pollination must take place in plants like the willow, which produces flowers with only stamens on one plant and flowers with pistils on another. Sometimes, too, in some of the orchids, the pollen appears to have the effect of withering the stigma of the flower on which it was produced, but does not wither the stigmas of other flowers.

Within an hour or two after pollination, the pollen grain begins to germinate and sends out a pollen tube which penetrates the tissue of the stigma and, entering the style, grows down through it to the base into the ovary. After entering the ovary the pollen tube is ruptured and its contents are discharged. Each pollen grain contains two sperm nuclei, one of which unites with an egg cell in the ovary. The length of time between pollination and fertilization of the egg cell varies considerably. In some plants the interval is thirty to forty hours; in the crocus it is thirty days; in some oaks the interval is one year. The fertilized egg nucleus develops within a seed into the *embryo* of the plant. Meanwhile some of the

tissue within the ovary develops into the *endosperm* of the seed, in which food is stored. When the embryo plant begins to grow as a result of germination, it draws upon the endosperm for its food (p. 587).

Corn, or maize, is a good example of a plant which produces both pollen grains and eggs, but in separate parts of the plant. The tassel is made up of flowers which produce the pollen. The ear bears the ovaries with their eggs. The silky hairs of the ear are very long pistils. When the pollen in the tassel is mature, any slight breeze will shake it loose from the anther, and it floats about in the air. As it slowly drifts toward the ground, a grain of pollen may come in contact with the silky pistil. There it germinates, as in the other flowers, and grows a pollen tube, which may be twenty inches long, through the style to the ovary at its base. Each grain of corn has its individual pistil; and if a pollen grain does not fall on it, no kernel will develop. This may be experimentally proved by tying a paper bag over the ear just before the pollen is mature, so that no pollen can fall on the silk. An ear of corn treated in this way will be entirely barren of kernels. If, one the other hand, all the tassels were cut off in a field of corn, before the pollen matured, no kernels would develop. In both cases, fertilization would not occur, and the eggs within the ovaries would die.

Reproduction by flowers is sexual reproduction. Many flowering plants, however, can be propagated successfully in other ways. Black raspberries may be propagated from old plants by burying their tips in the soil and covering them. Potatoes are not usually grown from seeds, but from the underground stems, the eyes of which are really buds from which roots and new stems arise. Many grasses produce underground stems bearing buds from which new plants arise. Dahlias are not ordinarily grown from seeds, but from tubers. Sugar cane is grown from cuttings of stalks, and grape plants are often grown from cuttings of the vine. Many kinds of fruit trees are propagated only by grafting and budding, since trees grown from their seed may produce less desirable plants or fruit.

Some Invertebrates Reproduce Both Sexually and Asexually.

Sexual reproduction in animals varies from a relatively simple process in the lower animals to complexity in the higher types. In *Hydra,* for example, certain of the cells near the base of the animal assume the function of producing sperm cells. The structure within which these are produced is called the testis, while eggs are produced in a structure again known as the ovary. The sperms possess flagella, as do those of ferns. They swim about in the water until they come in contact with an egg, with which one of them unites in fertilization. The fertilized egg is called the zygote, as in the ferns. It begins to divide, and soon it forms a hollow ball of cells. Such a hollow ball of cells, resulting from the division of a zygote, is known as a blastula. The cells of the blastula divide; the outer ones form the ectoderm, and those on the inner side the endoderm. The ectoderm cells then secrete a thick shell of a horny material covered with sharp projections. The blastula then separates from the parent and falls to the bottom. There it remains unchanged for several weeks, after which development is resumed and the horny covering breaks away. The larva within escapes and elongates into its normal form. Mesogloea is now secreted by the endoderm and ectoderm cells and the hydra grows into an adult.

It may be noted here that *Hydra* reproduces both asexually by budding and sexually by means of sperms and eggs. It is also interesting to note that the sperms and eggs are produced by the same individual, so that both sexes are present within the one hydra. Whenever the same individual produces both sperms and eggs, it is said to be a *hermaphrodite.* Earthworms are another example of herma-

phroditism, for each specimen produces both kinds of reproductive cells. In their case, however, sperm cells are exchanged by two individuals, so that the eggs of one are fertilized by the sperm of another.

It has been emphasized that sexual reproduction involves both sperm and egg cells, but there is one exception. Among certain invertebrate animals, notably some of the insects, males are not produced for comparatively long periods of time. Eggs, however, are produced by the females; and, although these are not fertilized, since no males are present, they develop into new individuals like the parent. These reproductive cells are identified as eggs by their origin and method of development; hence sex is obviously involved, even though only one parent is concerned.

This development of unfertilized eggs is known as *parthenogenesis,* and occurs among plant lice and the scale insects, such as the San Jose scale, which infests apple trees, and among the bees, ants, and wasps. Bees may be used to illustrate the point. Both males and females are usually present in the colony, but the female lays both fertilized and unfertilized eggs. She is able to do this because the sperms are stored within her body in special structures, in which she seems to be able to retain them or release them to fertilize the eggs. Unfertilized bee eggs develop into drones, or male bees; fertilized eggs develop into workers and queens, both of which are females. Some species of insects, such as the brown chrysanthemum aphid, never produce males. Their reproduction is therefore entirely parthenogenetic. This is also true of some of the insects which produce galls on plants.

The principles of reproduction in most insects are the same as for other animals which reproduce sexually. The sexes are usually separate; the eggs are fertilized within the body of the female, after which they are laid on a supply of food for the larva which will hatch out of them.

Vertebrates Reproduce by Sexual Methods Only. The sexes are always distinct in the vertebrates; that is, each individual produces only eggs or sperms, and is a female or male accordingly. Frogs, for example, illustrate the type of reproduction which occurs in vertebrates. Within the body of the female the ovaries produce eggs in large numbers. Within the body of the male testes produce sperm cells. The female migrates to a pond in the spring of the year and lays her eggs in large masses. As the eggs are being laid a gelatinous material is secreted and deposited with the eggs, so that they become embedded in it. Simultaneously the male frog sheds sperm cells in the water as he clasps the female with his forelegs. The sperms swim about in the water until they come in contact with an egg, bringing about fertilization. Unfertilized eggs die. Within the fertilized egg the nucleus of the sperm unites with the nucleus of the egg, and the zygote begins to divide.

Division continues, and a hollow ball of cells, the blastula stage, results. This is followed by further development until there are two layers of cells, the ectoderm and the endoderm. Between these two layers, and from the division of cells in them, a third layer of cells, called the mesoderm, arises. From these layers of cells the various organs develop. The nervous system and the skin have their origin in the ectoderm, for example, while the muscular system arises from the mesoderm. The cells become differentiated according to their function, and development proceeds. Soon the embryo frog, or tadpole, wriggles free of the gelatinous mass and attaches itself to the stem of a water plant. It lives in the water until it has developed legs and lungs, when it emerges as an animal that can live on land.

Reptiles reproduce in the same way, except that the eggs which they lay have shells of a leathery nature and are not deposited in water. These eggs develop within the ovaries of the female. By a special male structure the sperms are deposited within the body cavity of the female, where fertilization occurs. After fertilization has taken place, the food is deposited around the zygote, and lastly the shell is formed; the eggs then leave the body of the female. The embryo lives on the food within the egg, and gets oxygen through the shell, which is porous and permits air to pass into the egg. Reproduction of birds is very similar to that of the reptiles. The yolk and albumen within the egg serve as food for the developing embryo. The albumen is used up first; the yolk is not entirely used up until the bird is hatched. The zygote has begun division even before the egg is laid. Heat is necessary for the continued development of the egg, and consequently the eggs are incubated by either the female or the male bird, according to the species. If an egg is kept at a cool, fairly constant

Stages in the development of a frog.

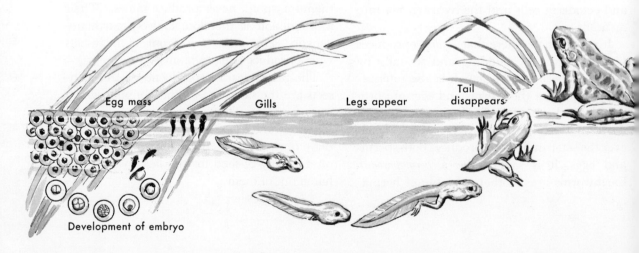

Egg mass   Gills   Legs appear   Tail disappears

Development of embryo

temperature after it is laid, development of the embryo is checked. If it is kept cool for too long a period of time, the embryo may die.

With a few exceptions, such as the duckbill of Australia, mammals do not lay eggs. As in the case of egg-laying animals, the eggs are produced by ovaries and the sperms by testes. The eggs of mammals, like those of birds and reptiles, are fertilized within the body of the female after the sperms have been placed there by the male in the process of copulation. No shell is deposited around the egg, however. Instead the dividing zygote passes into a structure known as the uterus, where it soon attaches itself to the walls of this organ.

As development continues, a connection is established through which food and oxygen from the blood of the female pass by osmosis into the blood vessels of the embryo. Carbon dioxide and other wastes from the embryo also pass through this connection by osmosis into the blood of the mother. In normal development there is no direct connection between the blood of the embryo and that of the mother. When the young have reached a certain stage of development, the muscles in the walls of the uterus contract, the young are expelled from it, and birth has occurred.

The period of development within the body of the female varies in length with each species of animal. It is called the *gestation* period. The gestation period of a rabbit is about thirty days; of a dog, about three months; of cattle, about nine months.

Since man is a mammal, human reproduction is essentially the same as that of other mammals. There are some differences of detail, but none of principle. The period of development from fertilization, or conception, until birth varies, but averages about two hundred and eighty days.

EXPERIENCE. *To observe the development of an animal from the egg stage.* There may be an opportunity to observe the development of frogs from the egg stage. If possible place the eggs in water from a pond that has not been polluted. In some cases, tap water can be used if the water has not been treated with harmful chemicals. Place the eggs in a fairly large container and place some water plants in with them. It may be necessary to change the water rather frequently to make sure that the developing embryos will not die because of excess carbon dioxide. Have the class watch the development of the eggs into tadpoles. Keep the tadpoles on hand until there is no further need for them in the classroom. Then they may be placed in a pond. Frogs' eggs can be obtained only in the spring. Sometimes unfertilized eggs are brought into the classroom, which naturally fail to develop. If this occurs, the necessity of fertilization in reproduction may be stressed.

Often it is possible to secure eggs which are being incubated at a chick hatchery. Or one may borrow a small incubator for use in the classroom. In either case, secure and open eggs that have been incubating for various lengths of time. Good incubation intervals at which to open the eggs are those of three, six, nine, twelve, fifteen, and twenty days. This will help the children to study the progressive development of the chick.

In this work the teacher should be on the alert to help the children develop wholesome attitudes toward the experience. She should indicate to the children that what they learn from their observation of how the chick develops is considered of sufficient importance to make it worth-while to open these eggs, even though it means the death of several chick embryos. Help children learn to consider, before doing an experiment which involves taking the life of a plant or an animal, whether the learning experience is important enough to justify taking such a life. If this consciousness of the importance of all living things can be developed, it will be a valuable step in advancing the whole concept of conservation and wise utilization of natural resources.

CHAPTER 14

Plants and Animals Live in Communities

Living things are not scattered over the surface of Earth in an accidental or haphazard manner. Every species has its own particular place in the scheme of distribution. Many young children know that to catch fish one must go to a pond or stream or some other body of water, and that to pick daisies one goes to a meadow and not deep into a forest. Whales and sharks live only in oceans and seas, and polar bears are to be found only in the arctic regions. Muskrat and beaver colonies are found in swamps and near running water, and cacti reach their greatest development in arid or semiarid areas.

Plants and Animals Live in Many Kinds of Communities

Plants and animals live in characteristic communities. These communities are of many different kinds. Generally speaking, it may be said that some living things are found in water and others on land. The water environment of animals and plants may be divided into many different types. Living things found in a pond will be different from those found in a lake; those found in a lake will again differ in many respects from those found in rivers and streams. Nor is it true that all streams contain identical kinds of living things; for one would not expect to find the same plants and animals in a tropical stream that are found in a river in Alaska. Streams which have their origin in the water of melting mountain snows, and which are consequently extremely cold and swift-running, support kinds of life not found in the sluggish currents flowing through low swamp lands. Underground streams and streams flowing through large caves often contain types of life never seen elsewhere.

Oceans and seas complicate the question still further. Because of the ability of water to dissolve a great many substances and because rivers are constantly transporting these dissolved substances and depositing them in the ocean, the chemical composition of ocean water is quite different from that of fresh water. It contains sodium chloride and calcium and magnesium compounds in comparatively great abundance. Consequently it is of greater density than fresh water, weighs more per cubic foot, and has a lower freezing point. Because of some of these conditions, most of the plants and animals which can live in fresh water could not exist in the oceans of the world. On the other hand, most of the ocean life could not survive in fresh water.

Conditions are as variable in the oceans as they are in bodies of fresh water. Some of the living things in it are found only near the surface, where sunlight is abundant. In shallow water and down to a depth of about 300 feet many marine plants are found, and in conjunction with them are found animals, such as fish, which feed upon them. This surface stratum of the ocean is generally fairly warm. At a depth of 3000 feet, however, no light penetrates, and no plants are found. Animals living at that depth necessarily feed upon other animals, which, in turn, feed upon plants nearer the surface. In the very deep seas, below 6000 feet, the temperature of the water rarely varies, there is great pressure, and there is much that we do not know about environmental conditions. Each of these depths is characterized by typical kinds of life (pp. 267, 413).

Depth is but one of the factors determining the character of the marine community. Tides exercise an important influence on living things. Those plants and animals which cannot endure exposure to air for any length of time cannot live so close to the shore line that they are uncovered by the movement of the tides. In the tidal zones living things are also exposed to considerable variations of temperature. On the New England coast, for example, the winters are severe, and the air may be extremely cold. The ocean is warm enough so that it does not freeze, and is considerably warmer than the atmosphere when the temperature of the latter drops to a low point. In the tidal zone, then, the animals and plants are for some hours of the day covered by com-

paratively warm ocean water. As the tides recede, however, they are exposed to the much lower temperature of the atmosphere; and since not many living things can survive such extreme and continual variations in temperature, only certain special kinds of life are found there.

In the summertime the air may be considerably warmer than the water, and again the sudden variation of temperature is sufficient to kill many types of living things, as a result of which only those adapted specially to these variations can survive. The movement of water during the tides causes strong currents in many places, so that living things not securely attached to some object are swept out into the ocean. The heavy tides of the Bay of Fundy prevent the mackerel from spawning there, and the absence of heavy tides in the Gulf of St. Lawrence makes it an important spawning place for many species of fish. The large ocean currents have an effect on the type of life found in various parts of each ocean. The cold waters of arctic currents moving southward along the coast of Labrador lower the temperature of the water there sufficiently to cause the development of a community different from that found in the Gulf Stream.

EXPERIENCE. *To observe the kind of life found in different water communities.* It may be worth while to take the class on a field trip to a pond or lake and stream if there is one near the school. Observe safety precautions on all such trips. Have the children observe the kind of life found in each. If possible, a trip to the ocean shore should be made if a place where natural conditions prevail is available. Emphasize both plant and animal life. Some questions that might be considered are these: Where are the plants growing? Is this the habitat best suited to their needs? Is the pond covered with plants? What would this lead one to think about the depth or movement of the water? If a stream runs swiftly or is stagnant, where do the plants grow? Are there many kinds or sizes? Is any animal life to be seen? Where?

When such first-hand experiences are impossible, children who have had similar experiences with their parents or others may tell the class what they have observed. Pictures of different habitats, with the plant and animal communities they support, may be used to show the differences between the communities and the relationship between the habitat and the plants and animals living there.

Communities exist because of a diversity of environmental conditions. Certain plants and animals are found together in communities because they happen to be more or less adapted to conditions in a particular place. This is true of both land and water communities. Land communities are also of many different kinds, varying as conditions vary. In the arctic regions animals are fairly common, since some plant life exists on which animals may feed. These animals are different, however, from those found in temperate or tropical regions, for climatic conditions are different. *Climate,* then, is an important factor determining the type of community. Altitude is another prime factor. A valley at the foot of a high range of mountains may have a temperate climate, adequate rainfall, and rich soil for the support of plant life. The valley may support great forests of deciduous trees (p. 659). In these forests may be found deer, antelope, and other grazing animals. Squirrels may be plentiful if oaks and beeches are numerous. If a stream runs through the forests, minks, which prey on fish, frogs, crayfish, and other smaller animals, occur. Forest birds abound, and insects adapted to forest life serve as food. The insects in turn may feed upon the plants.

As the mountain range is ascended, however, all this changes. The deciduous trees

Life is different in each type of community.

gradually disappear; evergreens like the spruces and the pines are found instead. With the change in the kind of trees it will be found that the smaller plants are also different from the kinds found in the valley. Since the plants are different, other types of insects not found at the lower levels are in evidence. Near the top of the mountain range the large evergreens give way to smaller ones, stunted and gnarled from constant exposure to strong winds and extremely low temperatures. Finally, if the mountain range is sufficiently high, there may be a region where conditions are so rigorous that no plant life exists. With the disappearance of the plant life animals become scarce or are absent. High peaks may be covered with snow the year round, and will then be just as barren of life as the northernmost arctic lands. Or perhaps the snow melts in the early summer, and the temperature is sufficiently high to permit the growth of plants for two or three months. In that case the vegetation will be alpine in character and very different from that found under more favorable conditions. Environmental conditions change with *altitude,* and consequently the kinds of living things found at the various levels change also.

At lower altitudes and under what might be considered more favorable circumstances there is again a great variety of conditions, and therefore a great variety of communities. The chemical make-up of the soil often determines the kind of plants found in a given place. In the bluegrass region of Kentucky there is sufficient lime in the soil to support the luxuriant growth of bluegrass, which will not thrive in soils lacking in lime. This fact has had a considerable effect upon the type of agriculture carried on there. Similarly, wild plants are often found only in certain kinds of soils and will not grow well in others. Children often have the experience of digging up plants in the woods (p. 73), taking them home, and planting them in their own gar-

dens. Despite the best of care, the plants often fail to survive because it is difficult to duplicate the amount of sunlight and moisture, the temperature, and the kind of soil in which the plants were growing in the woods. Rainfall is an important consideration, for the plants in a desert region are much different from those found in humid lands. Plants in a swamp are very different from those on a hillside.

Land communities, then, differ with conditions. Plants may thrive or fail to thrive because of the amount of rainfall, temperature changes, the chemical make-up of the soil, and for other reasons. The type of animals found in a community depends upon the type of plants growing there. Plants and animals are thus linked by environment into characteristic communities.

EXPERIENCE. *To observe the kind of life found in different land communities.* The class may wish to go on a field trip through a meadow, woods, swamp, and pasture. Observe the kinds of plants and animals found in each and compare with the others. In city schools where a trip to the country may be impossible, a trip to a vacant city lot to determine the kinds of living things there may be profitable. Often a surprising number of insects, earthworms, and plants may be found.

EXPERIENCE. *To observe a wide range of habitats.* Children may look out of the classroom window, go out on the playground, possibly up on the roof of a nearby building or up on a high balcony, to see how many different habitats or environments they can see. What is seen will depend upon the location, the point of observation, and the keenness of the observer. Some of the habitats one might find are: fresh water, salt water, bog, woodland, sun, shade, plant foliage, in and under rotting logs, under rocks, boards, or bricks, in sand, among rocks, and in dry, almost desert areas. After such observations, it should be brought out in discussion that one does not have to go great distances to observe different kinds of habitats.

The soil itself is full of living things. Usually these are quite close to the surface. Termites may burrow to a depth of five feet; earthworm burrows have been found six feet below the surface, while those of the prairie dog are sometimes as deep as fourteen feet. Under favorable conditions the number of animals in an acre of soil may be enormous. Protozoa may occur at the rate of fifty million per quart of topsoil; and there may be five times that many bacteria, or even many times more than that, in the same amount of soil. Earthworms have been estimated at hundreds of thousands per acre in deep rich soil. There may be a million or more insects to the acre, especially if the soil is rich in organic matter. The total number of animals in the soil reaches a staggering figure when calculated by the acre.

The type of animals living in the soil and the number per unit of area depend upon many factors. Clay, humus, and rock soils each have their characteristic plants and animals. The presence or absence of air in the soil, the amount of moisture in it, and its temperature, all influence the type of life found. Because wet soil is often poorly supplied with oxygen, without which living things cannot exist, it contains fewer forms of life than a soil that is drier. On the other hand, an extremely dry soil is so lacking in moisture that few animals and plants can live in it. Porous soils are generally best for insects in the larval form because they contain plenty of oxygen.

EXPERIENCE. *To determine what animals live in the soil.* If possible, bring to class from rich soil a piece of sod about a foot square and six inches deep. It might be wise to replace this sod as soon as the study is completed in order to make sure no damage is done. Children may look for animals in this sod and the soil.

They may be able to find earthworms, adult and larval insects, roundworms, millepedes, centipedes, and many other animals. Have them count the number of animals they find. The number and kinds of animals living in a sandy environment or habitat of the same size would be different, because the amount of food and water contained in the soil and the physical make-up of the soil would be different.

EXPERIENCE. *To provide opportunities for the study of various types of plant and animal communities.* One may be teaching in a place where there are many different types of plant and animal communities. They may be communities living in habitats of many types, for each habitat supports certain kinds of communities. It is frequently possible to find several of these types within a very small area. If the community that the teacher and the students select for study is one that is accessible to the children, it might be desirable to study the plants and animals in their natural surroundings. If one wishes to set up in his classroom aquariums or terrariums which are stocked with plants and animals from the out of doors, there are several questions that should be considered by the teacher and pupils before active collecting work begins. *1. Is it possible to set up an environment or habitat sufficiently like that in which the plant or animal lives in order that it may continue to live and grow? 2. Are there enough plants and animals of the kinds that one wishes to collect in the locality? 3. What effect will their removal have on the entire community?* If one finds that he can answer these questions in a satisfactory way, then he may wish to proceed with the setting up of an aquarium or terrarium. One must next decide what kind of an aquarium or terrarium he wishes to set up. (See Experiences that follow.)

EXPERIENCE. *To set up aquariums in the classroom.* What one does will depend largely upon the kind of a water habitat that the teacher and children wish to study. Perhaps several types of water communities might be wanted, in order to contrast the kinds of plant and animal life found under different conditions. One might study the kinds of life found in a mud-bottomed shallow pool; or the life found in a gravel-bottomed shallow pool; or the life found in shallow salt water. (While it would be interesting to discuss the kinds of life found in deep bodies of water, it would be very difficult to study them by observation in the classroom: to supply the proper amount of light, temperature, pressure, and other conditions necessary to life would require equipment more elaborate than most would find available.) Another type of water habitat that one may wish to study in the classroom is that needed by tropical fish or by goldfish. For these, most of the necessary plants and animals may be purchased from a pet store or biological supply house.

There are many types and sizes of containers that may be used to house a water community. The rectangular aquarium tank made of a good quality of glass with a metal frame, and if possible a slate or glass bottom (preferably the former), may be purchased from pet shops or scientific supply houses. The size needed will depend upon the space available for the tank in the room, upon the purpose for which it is to be used, and upon the cost. Many find that a tank which holds from five to eight gallons of water is a convenient size. If you cannot buy an aquarium tank, do not give up the study of a water community. Collect large, wide-mouth glass jars such as the ones in which the school cafeteria or the neighboring restaurant buy mustard, mayonnaise, pickles, or cucumbers. After the container has been secured it should be washed both inside and outside with a solution of salt water in order to remove whatever dust or grease may be on the surface. An aquarium tank should never be washed with soap, scour-

ing powder, or similar substances. A thorough rinsing after washing is advised.

If children are studying a water habitat that is in their own community, they may wish to take their large jars to the pond or stream. *In the interest of conservation* the class might work as two or three groups, rather than have each child set up an individual aquarium. After studying the stream or pond, they would select a spot whose conditions they could most nearly duplicate in their jar and classroom. Each group would transfer the needed materials, placing them carefully in the bottom of the jar. The jar might be filled about half full of water. The plant or animal life needed would then be selected and planted in the jar and the jar carried back to the classroom. Additional water may be brought back in other jars. If one has the usual commercial aquariums, it would be better to bring all materials into the classroom in other containers. The children should participate in the selection of a suitable place for the aquarium. They should consider the amount of sunlight needed (if any), the temperature, and whether the aquarium can be easily observed without its being jarred or moved. A bowl-shaped aquarium—one with curving sides—should be filled to the point where the jar begins to curve in toward the mouth. This will allow for maximum contact of the water surface with the air. If a larger aquarium—one with flat glass sides and a metal frame—is being set up in the classroom, one should be careful not to move it after the water has been poured in, for leaking is likely to occur. It is usually desirable to let the water settle several days before adding the fish or other large animal life.

If one is buying his plant and animal life, he may wish to follow the more usual routine in setting up an aquarium. In the clean tank, well-washed sand should be placed to a depth of about half an inch. If tap water is used, allow it to stand in open pans for a day or so. (Chlorinated water is not safe to use other-

Types of container

Sand $\frac{1}{2}$ inch

Sagittaria

Cabomba

Ceramic pitcher

Ludwigia

Elodea

Vallisneria

Red spotted newt (aquatic phase)

Wax paper

Method of filling tank

Sheet of glass

Japanese snail

Feeding ring

wise.) You will frequently find in ponds both floating and rooted plants suitable for aquarium use. Sometimes these plants are sold commercially at pet shops or other stores. The plants listed in the discussion which follows may be found in many local ponds. Rooted plants such as *Vallisneria* and *Sagittaria* may be planted by spreading their roots on the aquarium bottom and then adding sand until they are held firmly in place. After the plants are in place, sand to a depth of about two inches should be added.

The tank should now be placed in a spot already carefully chosen for it. Since plants depend upon sunlight for the manufacture of food, it is important to place the aquarium in a spot where there will be plenty of light. Direct sunlight should usually be avoided, however, for it heats the water too much. It is also best not to place the aquarium too close to a window. If the aquarium is receiving sufficient sunlight, bubbles will be seen to rise from the plants.

When the tank has been placed in its permanent location, place two sheets of newspaper or wax paper over the plants, and then add water until the tank is about three-fourths full. The sheets of paper wil protect the plants from the water that is being poured in, so that they will not be washed out of place, and will also keep the finer particles of sand from floating in the water and causing it to lose its clearness. When the tank is about three-fourths full, other plants such as *Elodea, Cabomba,* and *Ludwigia* may be planted. They should be tied in small bunches of four or five plants, and should be anchored with small pieces of lead or stone so that they will remain upright and will not float horizontally.

If a floating plant is desired, *Salvinia,* which is floating fern, or *Lemna,* frequently called duckweed, may be added. The tank may then be filled to within half an inch of the top. The tank should then be permitted to settle for a day or two before the animals are introduced.

If after that time the water appears cloudy, it may be necessary to siphon it off (p. 439) and refill the tank once or twice. All decayed leaves should be removed from the plants before they are placed in the aquarium.

A variety of goldfish may be bought. They are very hardy and do not require much attention. Many pet shops also sell a great variety of tropical fish. Some of these are live-bearing and will reproduce even in a small aquarium. Most children will find it interesting to watch the development of the young fish. It is hard to keep tropical fish in regions other than the tropics unless one can heat the water and keep it at an almost constant temperature. Five or six medium-sized snails in the tank will help to keep it clean by eating the algae which may grow on the sides and by acting as scavengers.

If the aquatic phase of the red-spotted newt is used, feed it by placing it in a bowl of tepid water in which particles of lean beef or liver have been placed. When eating is finished, rinse off and replace the newt in the aquarium. Feed only once a week, unless it is obviously hungry.

Overstocking the aquarium must be avoided. If too many animals are present, there is likely to be an excess of carbon dioxide in the water. Fish, as well as other animals, die in an excess of carbon dioxide. A general rule is to have about "one inch of fish" for each gallon of water. It is best to introduce only a few animals at a time, gradually increasing the number until a safe maximum is reached.

An aquarium which has the proper amount of plant life in proportion to animal life will need no attention beyond the regular feeding of the animals and the occasional addition of water made necessary by evaporation. Even the evaporation of water can be reduced to a minimum if a glass cover which fits neatly on the top of the tank is provided. Water evaporating from the surface will condense on the lower surface of the glass top, form large drops, and fall back into the aquarium, minimizing the loss by evaporation. A glass cover also helps to keep out dust and dirt.

In feeding the fish, it must be remembered that it is easier to overfeed than to underfeed. Fish and other cold-blooded animals are more active at higher temperatures than when the temperature is low, so that if the water is above 70°F., the feeding should occur daily. A glass feeding ring should be used, and the food placed inside it as it floats on the water, so that the food will not spread over the entire surface of the water. After the fish have been feeding for about fifteen minutes, the remainder of the food should be removed; and any food which has dropped to the bottom of the tank should also be removed. This will prevent the water from becoming foul and will also prevent over-feeding. If the temperature of the water is below 70°F., feeding every other day is sufficient.

No special provisions are necessary during periods of short vacations, for the fish and other animals will live, even though occasionally they are not fed for a week or ten days, provided other conditions in the tank are good. Fish may be fed the balanced fish foods which are on the market; and their diet may occasionally be varied with such things as dried shrimp, mosquito larvae, and very small pieces of earthworms, as well as the larvae of such an animal as *Daphnia,* which may be purchased at many pet shops. The aquarium should be watched closely. If the fish come to the surface for air, it may be due to an excess of carbon dioxide.

Animals are subject to diseases. Sometimes aquarium animals are attacked by a fungus growth, in which case black spots appear on the skin of the fish. Such individuals need to be treated. Any sick fish should be removed from the aquarium at once and placed in a separate tank or jar. The water in this tank should contain salt, about one ounce to a gallon of water being a good proportion. The fish should be left in this solution for a day or two and should not be fed. If the fish shows no signs of improvement the strength of the solution may be doubled. A solution of potassium permanganate in water, using five or six crystals to a quart of water, may also be used as a disinfectant in which the fish may be placed for a period of about fifteen minutes. Fish should not be picked up in the hand unless absolutely necessary. Most fish have a thin protective covering over their scales or skin. If the fish is picked up with dry hands much of this protective covering is removed. The removal of this covering allows parasites easier entrance under the scales or into the skin of the fish. Should it become necessary to pick up or to touch a fish, it is desirable to first wet the hands. Then there will be less destruction of the protective covering, and the fish is more likely to remain healthy. (If you are teaching in a region where the children go fishing, it would be helpful to show them the relation between the care of the fish in the aquarium and the care of small fish that are caught and returned to the water.)

It has been found that the oxygen content of a body of water remains fairly constant. If an excess of oxygen is present, it easily escapes from the surface of the water until equilibrium exists. If there is a deficiency in oxygen content, then oxygen freely and quickly enters the water from the air above. Carbon dioxide is much slower in its movement from air to water or water to air.

It has also been found that in some fish a small amount of carbon dioxide is useful in stimulating the blood to carry oxygen to the tissues. At the same time, carbon dioxide causes the blood to take in less oxygen at the gills. Thus, in the presence of an excess of carbon dioxide, the fish may not be able to take the oxygen that it needs from the water.

The plants in an aquarium actually help the fish in two ways. One is the giving off of oxygen during the process of food-making.

The other is the using up of carbon dioxide in the process of food-making. Since oxygen can rapidly enter the water from the air, it is no longer thought that the fish are in this way dependent on plants. The important thing is that the plants during daylight use a much greater amount of carbon dioxide than they give off in respiration. During cloudy, dark days, however, and at night the plants actually add to the carbon-dioxide supply through the process of respiration. Thus, in a successful aquarium, the plants during the day must by photosynthesis lower the carbon-dioxide content enough so that the respiration of both plants *and* animals during the night will not bring the carbon-dioxide content high enough to kill the fish.

The animals in an aquarium *help* the plants by supplying them with carbon dioxide.

Aeration is the forcing of air into the water. The aeration of the water in an aquarium is a desirable practice, since it acts to speed up the movement of the carbon dioxide from the water into the air.

When the water is cold, the decreased activity of the animals may be noted. The function of the snails and crayfish as scavengers in an aquatic community is noticeable. If tadpoles are present, their activity may be observed. Snails may be obtained, either of the egg-laying type or of the kind which bear their young alive. The effect of sunlight on plants is also evident; and when strong light is falling on the tank, bubbles of gas are given off as a result of photosynthesis.[1]

EXPERIENCE. *To set up terrariums of typical plant and animal communities.* Children often show sufficient interest in their study of various types of land communities to justify setting up terrariums in which they can reproduce conditions found out of doors. These may then be used to carry on further study conveniently

[1] James W. Atz, "The Myth of the Balanced Aquarium," *Natural History,* Vol. 58, No. 2 (February 1949), p. 72.

in the classroom, and may be as great a source of interest as the aquarium. In this work, as with the aquarium, *it is most important that children consider whether they should remove the needed plants or animals from the environment. They also may consider whether the plants and animals can survive in the classroom.*

Aquarium tanks, if they are available, may be used for terrariums. However, if aquarium tanks are not available, substitutes for them may be made by the children and the teacher. A shallow, rectangular tin pan may be used as a base. Two pieces of glass to fit the ends, and two other pieces of glass to fit the sides, should then be cut. Ordinary window glass cut to the proper size may be secured inexpensively at any hardware store. The glass is then bound together with adhesive tape so as to form a box, and this is then set into the tin pan. Waterproof adhesive tape may be used, or a thin coat of shellac may be painted over the adhesive tape to make it waterproof, so that it will not loosen when it becomes moist.

When the glass box has been placed in the pan, it may be found desirable to pour a plaster of Paris bottom on the pan. This may be done by mixing plaster of Paris with water and quickly placing the mixture in the pan while it is still soft. It must be immediately leveled, for it hardens quickly. When it has hardened, the soil may be placed in the terrarium. Clean sand may be used for the bottom instead of the more permanent plaster of Paris, and the soil may be placed on top of it. The use of sand makes it easier to take the terrarium apart for storage purposes when necessary. For the *woodland* terrarium, the base should consist of leaf mold or rich garden soil, charcoal, and gravel. The gravel ensures aeration of the soil and drainage. These should be mixed together well and then placed in the bottom of the terrarium.

The soil may be sterilized by heating in an oven or by pouring boiling water over it. However, this not only removes any pests that

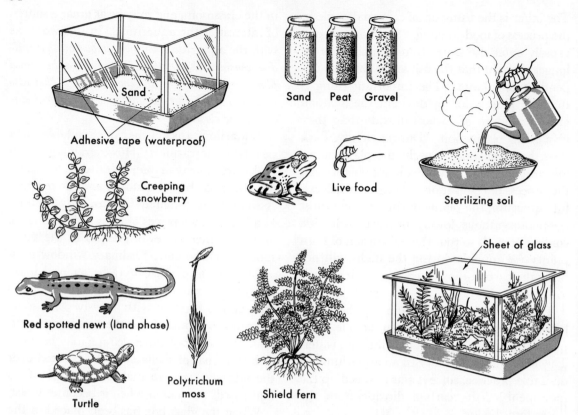

Sand

Adhesive tape (waterproof)

Sand   Peat   Gravel

Creeping snowberry

Live food

Sterilizing soil

Sheet of glass

Red spotted newt (land phase)

Polytrichum moss

Shield fern

Turtle

might be in it but also bacteria and fungi that are beneficial to plant life. It is often more interesting to observe what comes from unsterilized soil.

For the *bog* terrarium the base should consist of one part sand, one part peat, and one part gravel; or it may be taken from a bog directly and used in the terrarium. A *desert* terrarium should have as its base ordinary garden soil, for cacti and other desert plants grow best in garden soil in which there is an adequate amount of moisture. The arrangement of these materials in the terrarium should suggest the topography most suited to the plants and animals being used.

The plants may now be added. The spot where the plant is to be placed should be moistened; the roots of the plant may also be moistened, and the plant then set in place. Moss plants should be set very shallowly, while other plants such as Venus's-flytraps and pitcher plants should be set deep into the soil.

Plants for each type of terrarium should be obtained from the environment with conservation in mind. If this cannot be done, they may be purchased from scientific supply houses which furnish them in habitat groups, such as woodland plants, bog plants, desert plants, and so on.

After the plants have been introduced into the terrarium, it should be kept in a place where the temperature is not over 70°F. for about two weeks, if possible. This will give the plants an opportunity to establish a good root system. For the desert terrarium a screen top should be provided; the other types should have glass tops. The desert terrarium should be placed where it will receive considerable light, while the others should be placed in subdued light. If the terrarium is kept covered, it will need additional water only occasionally.

To complete the terrarium, small animals may be added. Tree frogs, salamanders, or toads may be placed in the woodland terrarium; in the desert terrarium such animals as horned toads will add to the effectiveness of the scene. If the terrarium is small, the secretion from a toad's skin may harm a salamander or a newt.

Care must be taken not to use too much water in any terrarium. If there seems to be too much moisture, the glass top may be removed for a time, permitting some of the excess to evaporate. Molds sometimes appear if there is too much moisture. They may be eliminated by the use of a little powdered sulfur or slaked lime. If aphids appear, the animals from the terrarium should be removed and the plants sprayed with a solution of nicotine sulfate, which may be purchased from any drugstore and used according to the directions furnished with it.

Salamanders and turtles should be removed from the terrarium when they are to be fed. If the animals cannot be easily removed, the terrarium should be cleaned after each feeding. Otherwise the decaying food will produce undesirable odors. They will live on small earthworms, swatted flies, raw fish, or small pieces of raw meat which has been finely ground. Toads will eat live flies placed in the terrarium; horned toads and other lizards must have living food. They will eat meal worms, cockroaches, grasshoppers, and ants. Small snakes will eat cockroaches, earthworms, and small fish.

Terrariums may be utilized to introduce children to the variety of land habitats in the vicinity. Several terrariums may be developed at one time or at different times to illustrate life in such places as a hillside, a field, a meadow, the desert, and woods. Terrariums may be considered as a means of securing certain observations and interpretations that may not be made conveniently by the children in the out-of-doors. The various habitats established in the schoolroom should be integrated with the study of those outside.

EXPERIENCE. *What differences have been noted between water plants and animals and those living on land?* From the children's knowledge of land and water plants and animals, they may be able to discuss and point out some differences. These differences may pertain to form, size, color, and ways of moving or covering. Their own experiences in swimming may help them to think of other differences.

EXPERIENCE. *To provide for the return of living things to the environment.* Frequently living things are kept in the classroom beyond their period of usefulness in the instruction. Before plants and animals are brought into the classroom, *the teacher and children should study the requirements of the living things and plan where they should be kept and how they should be cared for.* Along with this planning, or at a later date, *plans should be made when and how the plants or animals are to be returned to the environment. In making and carrying out these plans, the children might consider not only the survival of specific plants or animals, but also the effect that their presence or absence in the environment would have on the survival of the species.* An experience of this kind would give children a chance for active participation in the large program of conservation.

Communities Tend toward a Balance between Plants and Animals

Plants and animals are so interdependent that any variation in the number of one affects the other. In Chapter 13 it was pointed out that carnivorous animals feed upon those which use plants as their food supply. Since plants are the basic elements in the community, and since their food-making activity makes it possible for all animals, including man, to exist, it may be well at this time to consider the process of photosynthesis, or food-making, by plants.

Plants Are Able to Manufacture Food. To make food, a plant must first of all contain the green material called chlorophyll. Chlorophyll is found within the cells of the leaves and stems in microscopic packets called chloroplasts. The structure of the leaf is such that certain cells, analogous perhaps to pores, may open and thus permit air to enter the leaf. Present in the atmosphere everywhere is a small percentage of carbon dioxide gas. The roots of the plant absorb water from the soil. The water is conducted by tubes from the root, through the stems, into the leaves, where it enters the cells containing chlorophyll. The carbon dioxide also enters the cells.

Present in the leaf cell, then, are carbon dioxide gas, water, and chlorophyll. A chemical change takes place in which it seems that six molecules of water unite chemically with six molecules of carbon dioxide gas to produce one molecule of sugar. The following simple chemical equation summarizes the chemical change which takes place:

$$6CO_2 + 6H_2O \rightarrow C_6H_{12}O_6 + 6O_2$$
carbon dioxide + water $\rightarrow$ sugar + oxygen

It will be observed that a by-product of this chemical action is oxygen, six molecules of which are given off for every molecule of sugar formed. It is significant to note that this process can take place only in the presence of light. The sugar is converted by the plant into starch, in which form it is then stored in seeds and other parts (p. 648).

EXPERIENCE. *To show that a plant without light loses its chlorophyll.* Take a fairly small but healthy potted plant and place it in a box from which all light can be excluded. Keep it in the box until the chlorophyll has disappeared

and the plant has a bleached appearance. Then place it in sunlight again, and notice that in two or three days it regains much of its green color.

EXPERIENCE. *To demonstrate that starch is present in plants.* Establish the idea that iodine on starch causes a blue color by taking some starch, putting a small quantity of it in a small bottle or glass of water, and adding a drop or two of iodine. The water with the starch in it should turn to a blue or purple color. Then try testing various plants for starch, using potato, onion, and others. Determine which contain starch and which do not.

If the children show continued interest in learning how we know that starch is manufactured in the leaves of plants, the teacher may wish to do the following Experiences as *demonstrations.*

EXPERIENCE. *To demonstrate that starch is present in leaves.* Take the leaf of a plant, such as geranium, and boil it in alcohol until all the green chlorophyll has been boiled out of it. Remember that evaporating alcohol is inflammable, as is the liquid alcohol. To do this experiment without danger, place the leaf in alcohol in a pyrex glass; then place this glass in a large container of water and heat the water. The water vapor given off by the boiling water will eliminate danger. After the chlorophyll has been boiled out of the leaf, test the leaf for starch by putting a small drop of the iodine solution on the leaf. If starch is present, it will turn blue.

EXPERIENCE. *To demonstrate that leaves without chlorophyll do not manufacture sugar and therefore have no starch in them.* Take a plant which is growing well, and put an envelope made of black paper over one of its leaves. Seal this paper envelope in such a way that no light can come upon the leaf. Let the plant stand four or five days; then remove the leaf from the envelope and test for starch, as in the previous activity. If the leaf has been allowed to stand without sunlight for a sufficiently long period of time, no starch will be present.

Animals Depend on Plants for Food. Since plants manufacture the food in any community, and since animals are either directly or indirectly dependent on this food supply, there is a definite limit to the number of animals which can exist in a community. If there are too many animals, they will devour most of the plants, and a scarcity of food will then cause the animals to migrate to an area where it is more abundant, thus altering radically the make-up of that community. Insects feed to a great extent on plants. If there are more insects in the community than the plant life can support, many of the plants may be killed off. The insects may then die off also.

Often one kind of animal may feed on a special plant. If these special plants become scarce, then the animals which feed on them become limited in number. As the number of the animals is decreased, the plants have a better opportunity to develop, and consequently begin to flourish. But with this increase in plants, animals find it easier to get food and to survive, and thus their numbers increase correspondingly. Simultaneously the specific animal itself may be the *prey*— become the food—of a carnivore, or meat-eating animal. As the numbers of plant-eating animals fluctuate, so the carnivores will in turn vary in numbers.

Each animal and each plant in a community usually has its *predators,* other living things that use them for food. These predators tend to keep animals and plants in check. If predators are removed, the species may become so numerous as to become a pest. A well-known example of this is the situation created by the importation of rabbits into Australia from England. In England there were predators that kept the rabbits in check. In Australia,

however, there were none. Being fecund mammals, the rabbits multiplied until they became a definite scourge, because they fed upon grasses that were a source of food for sheep kept by ranchers.

The climate of Australia is rather dry, and in large parts of the country the amount of rainfall is insufficient to promote the rapid growth of grass. In the competition for food between the sheep and the rabbits, the latter threatened to become victorious, until extermination campaigns were waged against them. Today rabbits are still one of the main problems with which man must contend in that continent.

In our own country the English sparrow was imported to help to keep an insect pest in check. Instead it became adapted to life in the cities and has since become one of our pest problems. Thus the importation of a new plant or animal may result in the disturbing of a natural community.

When there are just enough plants in a community to support the animals therein, we say that the community is *balanced*. No natural community is ever in a static state of balance, for conditions are continually changing sufficiently to cause alterations in the character of that community.

To illustrate this, it may be pointed out that changing weather conditions may be sufficiently different each year to cause an unbalance in a community.

An extremely dry summer may cause a pond to dry up slowly. The pond may be teeming with life in early summer. It may contain tadpoles, turtles, aquatic insects, protozoans, roundworms, algae, bacteria, and even flowering plants. The community is well balanced. Then drought sets in, and the water begins evaporating and seeping away. As the pond grows smaller, the animals in it are more crowded. They use up the oxygen rapidly, and the carbon dioxide they give off combines with the water to form carbonic acid, which increases the acidity of the water. A slight change in the acidity of the water may be sufficient to kill some of the algae, bacteria, and protozoans. They are supplanted by other species, which thrive better under the new conditions. New kinds are found in the water.

As the pond continues to dry up, the frogs and turtles may leave it to migrate to another body of water. Their absence may make some of the other animals, particularly the insects, more numerous. Eventually the pond becomes entirely dry. Many of the animals die for lack of water. Others become temporarily adjusted to the new conditions. Some of the protozoans change in form, looking very much like microscopic grains of sand, remaining in this state until they are immersed in water again. If the drought continues for a number of years, the seeds of land plants may fall on the bed of the pond. The soil there is fertile, and they flourish. Land animals feed upon them.

Then comes a series of years with heavy rainfall. The pond again becomes filled with water. The terrestrial, or land, plants die off. Protozoans, bacteria, and algae reappear. Frogs lay their eggs in the pond, and turtles return to it. The pond has once more become a typical aquatic community.

There is a constant tendency toward a balance, but a shift in environmental conditions disturbs it. Since environmental conditions are continually changing, lack of balance rather than absolute balance is characteristic of a community. Deep snowfall during an entire winter is disastrous to birds. Those which normally remain in the region are deprived of their food supply when the ground is covered. Extremes of weather kill them off. Their numbers diminish, and during the following summer insects thrive, since the birds, their natural predators, are fewer in number. Some of the winter birds feed on weed seeds. Deep snows cover the weeds, so that their seeds are protected from birds. The following year weeds are more numerous than ever. In other words, deep snow has caused an unbalanced community.

EXPERIENCES. *To show relation of animal population to plant food available.* Encourage children to observe in their own community the changes in animal population brought about by a change in plant food. In some parts of the world this is most easily observed by noting the appearance of certain kinds of birds at the time a given plant fruit or seed begins to ripen. Such observations would provide materials for interesting class discussions.

Encourage children to determine through observation the kinds of animals and plants that are frequently found living in the same environment.

Older children may discuss and compare the continent as they think it was 150 years ago and the way it is today, as to numbers and kinds of plants and animals.

Communities Have a Number of Physical Aspects

The character of each plant and animal community is determined to a large extent by the physical aspects of that community. One of the most important of these is the abundance or scarcity of water. This liquid is per-haps as important to life as any other single thing. A plant may be 90 per cent water by weight, while many animals are as much as 75 per cent water by weight. A jellyfish is more than nine-tenths water.

Water is the medium in which mineral substances are dissolved in the soil and then taken into the roots of plants for use in food-making. The blood of animals is largely water with a number of chemical compounds in solution in it. Water is also the medium by means of which poisonous or undesirable waste materials in living things are eliminated. Most animals can survive much longer without food than they can without water.

Water Is Essential to Life. The availability of water, then, is an important factor in determining the types of plants and animals that will be found together in a community. In addition to its properties as a solvent of many substances, water is a storage place of heat energy. Any large body of water, such as a lake or ocean, is exposed to long periods of sunshine during the spring, summer, and autumn months. Because of its great capacity for absorbing heat energy, water warms very slowly. Conversely it also loses its heat energy more slowly than many other substances. This property of water has a decided effect on living things which exist in the neighborhood of water and in the water itself. Children living near a large lake or one of the oceans may have had experience with this property of water when swimming during the early spring or late fall.

The temperature of land and soil varies much more rapidly, and therefore much more frequently, than does that of water. As a result of this many interesting differences may be found in the development of plants and animals living near the water and those existing inland.

Along the Great Lakes the weather remains cool for a long time in the spring because the cold water has a cooling effect on the atmosphere. The development of buds of fruit trees is thus delayed noticeably. Trees which bloom very early in the spring, especially peach trees, do not blossom so quickly here as they do inland. This is an advantage to the fruitgrower, for it means that the tree will not blossom until the danger of frost is past. Thus there is a better chance for the development of fruit than there is inland, where a few warm days may cause the trees to bloom and where a sudden sharp frost may ruin the crop. The same thing is true of grapes and other crops. In the fall of the year the warmth which the water has accumulated during the summer months is slowly given up, keeping the atmosphere warm and postponing frosts, thus giving crops a longer growing period in which to mature.

Many nurseries are located on the southern shores of Lake Erie because of the effect of water on the weather, and peaches and grapes are important crops in that area. Along the Pacific seacoast the same effect of water on weather and climate is apparent, but to an even greater extent.

Because water temperature rises slowly and falls slowly, changes of temperature do not occur rapidly and conditions are more stable in the water than on land. Plants and animals living in water are therefore not subjected to extremes of temperature. The fact that water expands upon freezing is also a factor which cannot be overestimated in its importance to water life. When water freezes and expands, it becomes lighter for each unit of volume. A cubic foot of ice weighs less than a cubic foot of water. Being lighter, ice rises to the surface. The formation of ice on the surface of a pond or lake protects the waters beneath it from exposure to cold air, so that living things do not freeze.

If ice were heavier than water in its liquid form, it would remain at the bottom, where the water would freeze first. During a continued cold period a pond would be frozen solid with ice, and fish and other kinds of animals in the water, as well as the plants, would be killed. Furthermore, the ice at the bottom would thaw very slowly in the spring. Under such conditions life in fresh water would either be impossible or else very difficult. Deep lakes would probably never thaw to the bottom. Under such circumstances living things would have to be very different in order to survive.

Other properties of water must be carefully considered. As the temperature falls, water becomes denser until it reaches a temperature of about 39°F., or 4°C. It is only below this temperature that water begins to expand and become lighter per unit of volume. As a pond, lake, or ocean becomes cooler with the coming of winter, its surface water becomes cool and is denser. Since it is denser, it is heavier than the warmer water beneath it, and so it sinks to the bottom. By sinking to the bottom it displaces the warmer water below it, making it move in an upward direction. The warmer water from the lower levels is then exposed to the cold of the atmosphere, and it in turn is cooled, becomes denser, and sinks to the bottom. In this manner the freezing of a pond or lake is considerably delayed, and temperature changes are gradual rather than rapid.

Other Aspects Are Essential to Life. Air is another important physical necessity for life. The relations of the gases that are in the air to life have been discussed (p. 426).

The atmosphere acts as a blanket for retaining heat. Light energy from the sun is absorbed by Earth, and the air is thus warmed. Like water the air acts as a storehouse of heat energy. If Earth had no atmosphere, great variations in its temperature would occur daily and with the seasons. During the day Earth is receiving energy from the sun; this energy is to some extent absorbed by the air. As Earth rotates on its axis and night comes, the temperature drops more slowly than it otherwise would because of the heat energy which the air holds.

Without an atmosphere surrounding Earth, darkness would result in bitterly cold nights, and the days would be extremely hot. The daily variation of temperature would be so great that life as we know it could not exist. During the day the extremely high temperature would cause such rapid evaporation of water from both plants and animals that they would die. If they survived the extreme heat, the sudden change to bitter cold and the subsequent freezing would destroy the kinds of living things which exist on Earth. All life is more or less adapted to conditions as they are, and a change of these conditions, if it is abrupt, results in death.

Water and air are important, therefore, to all living things because they enable chemical reactions to take place in the cells of plants and animals, and because they act as regulators of temperature, thus determining weather and climate.

Heat and light are other factors in the environment that are important to living things. Without light, plants could not carry on photosynthesis, and no food supply would be available. Hence animals could not exist. It is true that such plants as bacteria, yeasts, molds, and mushrooms can grow in dark places and do not carry on photosynthesis. But in each case these plants live either as *parasites,* drawing their nourishment from other living things, or as *saprophytes,* getting their food from organic matter which has resulted from the decomposition of living things after they have died. Their existence would be impossible without light, which influences them in this indirect way. Without light, life as we know it would be impossible.

EXPERIENCE. *To observe and compare different communities.* A meadow or piece of grassland, the edge of a forest or a wood lot, and the forest itself with either large trees or with trees growing close together are three habitats which will show marked contrasts in the plant and animal communities. Why is this true? Consider the amount of sunlight, shade, water, temperature, and kinds of soil to the degree

There are three habitats in this photograph. Santa Fe National Forest, New Mexico. (U. S. Forest Service.)

that it has meaning for your particular group of children.

Chemical Changes Take Place in Living Things. Life has been defined as the sum total of all action, reaction, and interaction in protoplasm. In other words, life is characterized by a series of chemical changes which involve the liberation of energy. These energy changes result in heat; it is significant that where the quantity of heat is slight, resulting in low temperatures, life cannot and does not exist. If the temperature around a plant is very high, water evaporates from it too rapidly, it wilts, and finally dies. If the temperature is too low, the water in the cells may freeze, killing the protoplasm and resulting again in death.

Seeds and spores of plants sometimes survive extremely low temperatures, but in such cases the plant is in a resting stage; its chemical changes go on very slowly, and the water content is very low when compared with that of the growing plant. These things minimize the effect of the low temperature.

Children sometimes ask, "What is most needed in order to live?" There is no single answer to this query. Life as we know it could not exist in the absence of any one of several elements. Each of the elements has its own significance, no matter how small its quantity may be. Iodine is found in the human body in extremely small quantities; yet its absence causes an underactivity of the thyroid gland which, if the condition persists from birth, may result in the kind of feeble-mindedness known as cretinism. The body contains traces of copper which are so slight that only the best chemical methods can show its presence; yet without copper, anemia may afflict the individual. Boron may not be found in large quantities in plants; yet in its entire absence seeds do not mature as they should. Such elements are called *trace elements*. No single element can be said to be the most important, for they are all necessary to the proper development of the organism and to the proper functioning of its cells (p. 418).

EXPERIENCE. *To show that living things contain much water.* Have a child bring to school a potato, which is a plant that is alive but dormant. Grate the potato to show its water content. Have other things brought in, such as a piece of meat, a celery plant, and a carrot. Heat the piece of meat after having weighed it. Be sure not to burn it; merely dry it. Weigh it again after it is thoroughly dried over the flame of an alcohol burner. The difference in weight is due to loss of water. Keep the stalk of celery and the carrot on the desk, and note daily the changes which take place because of the loss of water by evaporation.

Many children are familiar with dried apples, apricots, or prunes. These are fruits that have had the water removed by evaporation. They are usually soaked and then cooked in water before being used.

EXPERIENCE. *To show that water expands when it is heated.* Place some cold tap water in a pan or other container. Fill the container very full. Heat gently and notice that the water overflows because of its expansion.

EXPERIENCE. *To show that water contracts on being cooled.* Fill a Pyrex bottle or a flask very full of hot water carefully so that it will not crack. Place it in some ice water. Notice that the container of water is not so full when the water has cooled as it was when the water was warm. This illustrates the principle that water contracts upon cooling.

EXPERIENCE. *To show that water expands on freezing.* On a cold day fill a milk bottle full of water and put a milk cap on the bottle. Place it on the outside of the window sill; let it remain overnight so that it will freeze. Notice that the water has expanded sufficiently to force the cap off the bottle. A small bottle of water may be frozen by placing it in the freezing drawer of a refrigerator.

EXPERIENCE. *To demonstrate that ice is lighter than water in its liquid form and therefore floats.* Usually children are aware of this from previous experience, but it may be advantageous to place some ice cubes in a container of water in class.

Soil Is Necessary to Life. Still another factor in the environment of living things is soil (p. 301). Soils vary greatly, not only in their chemical composition, but in their physical properties as well. *Sandy* soils are usually formed by the erosion of sandstones. Since sandstones contain large quantities of silicon compounds, and since these are not easily dissolved by water, sandy soils are not so good for plant life as other kinds unless they are rich in organic matter. Plants must have nitrogen, potassium, phosphorus, and other elements with which to make protoplasm; and without decaying animal and vegetable substances sandy soils usually lack these elements. Unless sandy soils contain humus, they do not support a great deal of plant life. Water is not retained well by a sandy soil, since its porous structure permits rapid drainage and evapora-

tion, and this reduces the number of plants which can be supported.

Clay soils, on the other hand, are generally much richer in the elements which plants need. They result from the erosion of igneous rocks, which are rich in a variety of chemical elements. In addition, clay is composed of much smaller particles than sandy soil, so that it holds water better and does not permit its rapid evaporation. Clay is generally richer in humus than sand, contains more plant food, and supports more plant life. Some plants do not grow well in clay, however, because, when dry, the clay often becomes hard and baked.

Perhaps the best type of soil for plant growth is *loam,* which is a mixture of clay and sand, holds water fairly well, and does not become hard when dry. A loam that is composed of more sand than clay is known as a sandy loam, while one that has more of the properties of clay than of sand is a clay loam. Loam is considered best for most agricultural purposes, since it is easy to plow and fit for seeding, and for cultivation after the crop has begun its growth. Seedlings grow better in clay loam than in clay, since clay loam is not so hard and compact. Seedlings grow better in sandy loam than in sand, since loam does not dry out as quickly.

The various kinds of soils differ in the amount of air they contain, as well as in the amount of moisture. Since sprouting seeds of all plants need oxygen in order to germinate and grow, the amount of air held in the soil is important. Clay soils in particular may lack oxygen because their compactness excludes air, particularly if the soil is so wet that the spaces between soil particles are filled entirely with water. It is to aerate the soil that the farmer plows and cultivates.

EXPERIENCE. *To experiment with different kinds of soils.* Obtain three flowerpots; fill one with sand, one with loam, and one with clay. Plant two or three different kinds of seeds in each,

Soil is composed of varying amounts of extremely small rock particles that are irregular in shape and differ in size. Clay and silt particles are smaller than sand grains. (After H. O. Buckman and N. C. Brady, The Nature and Property of Soils, 6th edition, 1960, Macmillan, N.Y.)

such as corn, beans, radishes. Keep each pot under exactly the same conditions, giving each the same quantity of water. Have children note the pot in which the seeds sprout first. Compare like seeds. In which pot does the soil dry quickest; plants grow best?

EXPERIENCE. *To show the difference in the size of the particles in clay, loam, and sandy soils.* If a microscope is available, place a little of each kind of soil on a glass slide without a cover glass, using the low-power objective. Which kinds of soils have large sand particles? If a microscope is not available, use a hand lens.

EXPERIENCE. *To show that soils contain air.* Place some soil in a bottle and pour water over it until the water entirely covers the soil. Note the bubbles of air which arise from the soil.

Some Plants Help to Enrich the Soil. When plant foliage dies it drops to the ground. Rainfall moistens the dead leaves and stems, enabling bacteria to grow on them. Using the dead material for food, bacteria cause it to decay or break down into simpler substances. As a result of this chemical process, many of the substances in the dead leaves and stems are then in a form that can be used by green plants in the future. The soil is thus gradually enriched.

Where this process has been going on for a long period of time, soil may be very fertile. This was the case in North America when it was first settled. The great forests had been undisturbed, and the accumulation of dead and decaying vegetable matter was so great that in many places it was not necessary to fertilize the soil artificially for many years.

Green plants thus furnish the substances on which bacteria may live; by breaking down the organic matter bacteria make food available in turn to green plants; the green plants are then better able to grow. As soil fertility increases because of bacterial action, the abundance of plant life becomes greater. As plants become more abundant, more animals find a ready food supply and thrive better.

Because we cannot see bacteria except under special conditions, we are often unaware of their great importance to all living things. They are instrumental in the decomposition of all organisms which have died. If it were not for their activity, the surface of our Earth would be littered with the remains of dead things, both plant and animal. It is also important to remember that plants take many substances from the soil to make food and to build up the plant structure. If there were no bacteria, this material would not be returned to the soil with any rapidity. It is possible that under such circumstances the supply of raw materials necessary for plant life might become depleted in the topsoil, in which most plant roots are found. A meadow, prairie, or forest soil would thus become less fertile as time went on, and might become incapable of supporting life. All living things are kept alive, directly or indirectly, by the materials found in soil; if the supply of these were to vanish, no kind of life could exist.

Bacteria not only return to the soil many substances taken from it; they also increase its fertility in another way. Next to hydrogen and oxygen, the element needed in the soil in largest quantities is nitrogen. Nitrogen is very important in the chemical make-up of protoplasm, and because it is needed in such quantities it is likely to become the element most lacking in the soil. This is true in cultivated fields, from which plants take large quantities of nitrogen and incorporate it in their seeds, stems, and other parts. When a crop is harvested, this nitrogen is taken away; and the supply of this element in the soil is thus diminished.

Bacteria are important factors in replenishing the supply of nitrogen in the soil. It has been shown experimentally that even in bare soils there are bacteria which increase the nitrogen content of the soil. When such a soil is placed in a container and kept under natural soil conditions of temperature, moisture, and air, its nitrogen content slowly increases. That this is due to the activity of bacteria is proved by the fact that if such a soil is sterilized by heating, so that all the bacteria are killed, its nitrogen content does not increase.

Bacteria do not actually make nitrogen. About 78 per cent of the atmosphere is nitrogen, however, and certain bacteria have the property of being able to make the gaseous nitrogen of the air available to plants (p. 431).

Some of the bacteria which carry on the process of nitrogen fixation are never found except in association with certain plants, such as the various clovers, alfalfa, and soybeans. Most of the plants with which these bacteria are found are legumes, or members of the plant family to which beans and peas belong. Bacteria in the soil gain entrance to the roots of the legumes when the latter are very young, and their presence causes the growth of small swellings called nodules, or *tubercles*. The cells of these tubercles on the roots are filled with *nitrogen-fixing bacteria*. When the farmer cuts the clover or alfalfa crop to make hay of it, many of the roots die and the tubercles on them decay as the roots decay. In this way the nitrates formed by the bacteria find their way into the soil, making it more fertile than before.

If a perennial crop like alfalfa is permitted to grow in a field for a number of years, the soil is generally richer in nitrogen than it was previously. However, if none of the nitrogen-fixing bacteria are present in the soil, nitrogen fixation will not go on.

Where a four-year or five-year rotation of crops is used, and the legume is grown only once in the period of rotation, the nitrogen-fixing bacteria of this type may all die off. To remedy this condition, the farmer is able to buy cultures of these bacteria under various trade names. He mixes the culture with the seeds before he sows his crops, and thus assures the presence of nitrogen-fixing bacteria in the soil. Alfalfa, soybeans, and the various kinds of clover are able to support only their special kinds of bacteria; thus each must be provided with its kind.

If there is present in the soil so much water that the soil is decidedly wet over a period of years, nitrogen-fixing bacteria cannot survive. Acid soils are also generally lacking in nitrogen-fixing bacteria. Some types of bacteria carry on a process which is the reverse of nitrogen fixation. They change nitrates into nitrogen in its gaseous form, thus making it unavailable to plants. These are known as *denitrifying bacteria*.

Since the presence of nitrogen-fixing bacteria in the soil increases its fertility, this evidently has a more or less direct effect upon the community. By enriching the soil they cause more luxuriant plant growth, and then a greater animal population may be supported.

EXPERIENCE. *To show the presence of nodules of nitrogen-fixing bacteria on a legume.* Bring to class an alfalfa or clover plant. Wash the soil off the roots so that the nodules may be seen. Select for this purpose a plant which is large and has been growing for some time.

Interrelationships in the Environment. The physical aspects of the environment are inextricably interrelated and cannot be separated in a consideration of their effects on living things. Soil contains substances necessary to plants, including water and air, and it possesses warmth. The water found in the air is important from the standpoint of weather, for it results in the formation of clouds and in rainfall, which replenishes the water supply of the topsoil, from which plants derive some of their raw materials for photosynthesis. Moreover, water contains dissolved oxygen, which makes it possible for animals and plants to exist in it; and as was previously indicated, both water and air contain heat energy, which affects life greatly.

EXPERIENCE. *To show that air contains water.* Note on a cold day the formation of water on windowpanes. This has formed from water vapor in the air. When the warm air of the room comes in contact with the cold windowpane, its temperature is lowered, the water vapor condenses and changes to liquid water, and is found on the windowpane. Place some water containing ice cubes in a glass or pitcher. Water vapor will condense on the outside of the container. If the atmosphere is so dry that moisture is not formed, add some salt to the water.

EXPERIENCE. *To illustrate how water vapor gets into the air.* Place some water in a saucer and allow it to evaporate.

EXPERIENCE. *To show that soil contains water, even though the water may not be visible.* Place some soil in a pan and heat it gently. Over the top of the pan hold a piece of cold glass. Water vapor will condense on the glass.

EXPERIENCE. *What kind of conditions exist in the universe?* The possibility that life may exist elsewhere in space, particularly on some of the other planets in the solar system, is one which has fascinated people for many years. Individuals with keen imaginations have debated this question from many points of view.

Some objects in the universe obviously cannot support any form of life. Stars like our sun have such high temperatures that it is doubtful whether matter of any kind can exist in organized form. Protoplasm is basic to life, and protoplasm, made up of chemical compounds, is of a very complicated nature. Chemists know that the atoms and molecules of any compound will lose their organization, or structure, under conditions of extreme heat, and so protoplasm could not exist in stars. Planets, however, possess much less heat and are very cold when compared with stars. For that reason planets have been picked as the most likely place for life to occur. Because of their different sizes, and because of their various distances from the sun, conditions on them are very different. It is likely that many planets throughout the universe are quite similar to Earth.

It must always be remembered that life on our Earth has become adapted to conditions as they are. This adjustment of life to environment is a delicate one. Living things are adapted to certain temperatures. If the climate of our country, for example, averaged 10° warmer or colder, the effect on plant life would be astounding. A slight variation in any environmental factor has a definite vital effect on life.

It must be borne in mind that Earth originated a long time ago, that many great changes took place before life appeared, and that life became adapted to conditions as they were and as they are. Given different conditions, life might still have developed; but if we judge by the behavior of living things in existence now and in the past, it seems plain that life originating under other conditions would have been very different from that which we know. It is possible, therefore, that life may exist on other planets, but such life might resemble our own in very few respects.

Organisms Compete for the Necessities of Life

Thus far most of the discussion of plant and animal community life has been confined to the effects of the physical aspects of the environment. Living things themselves are an important part of the environment and have definite effects on one another. It has been stated that green plants furnish the basic food supply for the community, and that without them animals cannot exist. Plants, however, not only affect animals; they also affect other plants. Moreover, animals also have an important effect on plants, while the relationship of one species of animals in a community to other species must not be overlooked.

Living Things Affect One Another. The competition of plant with plant is generally for space, sunlight, and moisture. In this respect the competition is not merely between various species of plants but also between members of the same species. The competition between species is generally quite obvious. In a forest area where the trees are dense and little sunshine reaches the forest floor, comparatively few of the smaller plants are found. This is because the dense foliage of the trees does not permit sufficient sunshine to reach the small plants, and they cannot carry on the food-making processes rapidly enough to maintain themselves successfully. Some kinds of plants which seem to prefer a shady place in which to grow may survive, but few others will.

EXPERIENCE. *To show the effect of a dense population of plants on each other.* Children could visit a weed patch and point out those plants they thought were thriving. They might wish to discuss their reasons for thinking so. Then they should look under these large healthy plants to see what they can find. Are these smaller plants of the same kind—do their leaves have much the same shape? If they are the same kind of plant, why do the children think they are smaller? Are there too many plants for them all to receive sunshine and room to grow?

If any of the children have had a garden of their own or if they have observed the care their parents have given to their garden, they may recall that some of the carrots, beets, or other young plants were pulled out before any of them had become very large. Why was this done?

Available light affects tree growth. (Caterpillar Tractor Compa

In a very dense pine forest the lower branches of the trees sometimes die because of the lack of sunlight. In such places young trees may be very scarce, since the seedling after germination finds it difficult to get sufficient light energy to carry on photosynthesis. It may also be noticed that trees in a dense forest tend to grow straighter and taller than in an area which is not so dense, since there is more sunlight available in an upward direction than in any other. Such trees are more slender than in locations where they have more room in which to develop. Children will often have opportunity to make such observations near their homes or as they travel with their parents.

Plants also compete for water. Water is necessary to plant life for photosynthesis and for the transportation of the manufactured food from one part of the plant to another. Under conditions of drought, when water in the soil is comparatively scarce, plants have difficulty in surviving. If there are too many plants in a given area, there may be too little water to enable them to carry on the functions of life, and some of them may die.

Children living in rural areas or where there are gardens know that weeds compete with cultivated crops for moisture, minerals, and sunlight. Weeds generally are better able to survive adverse conditions than cultivated plants; and if they are permitted to grow undisturbed, they may cause crop failure. They also produce seeds in great numbers; and if they are not checked, they may crowd out crop plants.

As a result of their food-making activities, which go on at a rapid rate during the long summer days, when both sunshine and moisture are abundant, plants often manufacture more food than they can utilize at the time. Such food may be stored in various parts of the plant, as will be noted later. Food in the form of starch, oils, and sugars may be stored in the leaves, in stems, in the branches and trunks, in underground stems, in seeds, and in

roots. This fact enables animals to survive during the winter seasons, for by feeding on the various parts of plants animals manage to get enough food to keep themselves alive. Many winter birds, for example, live on weed seeds. This is true of birds like the quail or bobwhite. When snow is deep in the winter and grass is unavailable to rabbits, these animals often strip the bark from young trees to get at the green cambium layer underneath, on which they feed.

The kinds of animals found in a community will depend on the kind of plant life found there. Grasshoppers, which feed largely on grass plants, may be very abundant in a meadow and very scarce in a dense pine forest. The same thing is true of other insects, such as the crickets. The bison roamed the Western prairies in multitudinous herds because grass was plentiful there. They migrated as their food supply ran short. Squirrels are numerous in regions where oaks, beeches, and nut trees thrive. In the forests deer and elk herds may be found.

EXPERIENCE. *To study where different animals may be found.* Encourage children to think of where they would look for different animals and why. For example, earthworms are found in the ground, fish are found in water, redwinged blackbirds are usually near water, bats may be found during the day in dark sheltered places such as caves or between bricks or stones in buildings where the mortar has fallen out.

Wherever animals which feed on plant life are found, with them will be found carnivorous animals to prey on them. The vegetarian rabbit is eaten by foxes, wolves, and coyotes. Grasshoppers and other insects form the main food supply of birds. Deer and elk are hunted by wolves, which also attack and destroy cattle, sheep, and horses. Every living thing nourishes itself at the expense of other living things. The killer whale in the ocean attacks

Minks and muskrats live in and near water.

and destroys many seals, often driving herds of them ashore and keeping them there for some time. Charles Darwin noted these things in various parts of the world and concluded that only the fittest survive. Birds which are slow on the wing, land animals which cannot protect themselves or run away from larger animals, are killed and devoured. Man himself depends partly on plants for his food supply and partly on animals.

Because of the constant feeding of one animal at the expense of another, the animal community changes both in the kinds of animals represented and in numbers. An increase in the number of rabbits in a community, caused by conditions favoring the growth of plants which serve as their food, will in turn cause an increase in foxes and other animals which hunt rabbits. As the number of foxes increases, they devour more of the rabbits, so that fewer of them are left to perpetuate the species. As the number of rabbits decreases, the foxes find it harder to get food; the weaker ones die off if the winter is rigorous. The decrease in the number of foxes permits the survival of a greater number of rabbits; these multiply rapidly, and the cycle is repeated.

Darwin and Huxley, two English scientists, are reputed to have said that the price of beef in England depends on the number of old maids. Old maids keep cats, and cats eat field mice. Field mice feed on the bumblebees which live in the ground and which are the only insects able to pollinate red clover. As the field mice are eliminated by the cats, the number of bumblebees increases; so clover-plant blossoms are more likely to be pollinated, and more seeds are produced, with a consequent drop in the price of clover seed. When the seed is cheaper, more farmers are likely to purchase it in large quantities and sow it in their fields. Larger crops of clover hay are thus produced; more beef cattle are kept to be fattened on the hay, which causes the supply of beef to exceed the demand, and thus the price is affected.

Mountain goats are adapted to living at high altitudes.

Bobolinks thrive in the meadows, where there is an abundance of seeds and insects.

Whether or not the story is truly credited to the two English biologists does not matter. It illustrates the *interdependence* of plants and animals and the multitude of effects which may result from a single cause. One might even carry the story a step farther by saying that cheap beef in England may mean a better-nourished and healthier nation, all because of the number of old maids found on that island.

Some animals have a beneficial effect on the soil. By digging their burrows in the ground, earthworms make it possible for air to enter. The presence of air in the soil assures an abundance of oxygen for root development, which in turn causes the plant to grow better. Ants have a somewhat similar effect. It is said sometimes that the presence of Protozoa in the soil also has a beneficial influence upon its fertility, although this is debatable.

EXPERIENCE. *To observe the effect of earthworms on the growth of potted plants.* Select two plants of the same kind and as near the same size as possible. Plant them in the same size containers, and in as near an identical soil mixture as you can. Put several earthworms into the soil in one pot and none in the other pot.

Keep the plants in the same amount of sunlight and keep them moist with equal amounts of water. There should be a noticeable difference in the rate of growth of the two plants. Earthworms help to distribute organic matter throughout the soil and their tunnels help in aeration of the soil.

Some Plants and Animals Are Pests. Most of the numerous species of living things inhabiting Earth today have either a direct or an indirect effect upon the prosperity of man and upon his welfare. It is the degree to which man's comfort and welfare are disturbed that determines when an organism is classed as a *pest*. The role of bacteria in human diseases has been so widely proclaimed that often bacteria are thought of as man's worst enemy. It has been shown, however, that without some species of bacteria there could be no animal or plant life as we know it today. But the vast majority of bacteria have no observable direct effect on man. Insects have often been named as man's chief competitor for biological dominance of Earth. It should be pointed out that, of the hundreds of thousands of species of insects in the world, only a small percentage actually directly affect man. If a majority of the bacteria or of the insects were distinctly harmful to man, his survival on this Earth would not have been possible. Of the thousands of species of plants, relatively few are harmful enough to be classed as pests. Both plants and animals may be pests in some situations and useful in others. As an illustration, rabbits may be pests around a garden, but very useful when raised for food.

Farmers and gardners usually consider weeds to be pests, since they would soon crowd out cultivated crops if they were left undisturbed. There are times when plants that are weeds in one area may be very useful in another (see p. 564). Plants may be considered as pests for other reasons. Poison ivy, poison oak, and poison sumac, for example, are well known for their harmful irritation of the skin of certain individuals. The pollen from some plants such as ragweed, Bermuda grass, and cedar trees is very irritating to the nasal membranes of some people.

Certain algae which grow in fresh water are sometimes found to be so numerous in city-water reservoirs that when they die off with the coming of winter they impart to drinking water a distinctly fishlike taste. Molds may spoil bread and foods kept in storage, while yeasts may cause the fermentation of preserved fruits. Certain kinds of bacteria may cause milk to become ropy or bitter. Dandelions are a nuisance on a well-kept lawn, and may spread so rapidly that it becomes difficult to control them. Daisies may completely dominate a meadow, crowding out the desired grasses and persisting year after year unless special measures are taken to kill them. Morning-glory or bindweed may make a field unfit for crops. Locoweed, Jimson weed, and some of the plants of the nightshade family are poisonous to livestock. The list of plant pests is a long one, but it includes a relatively slight proportion of all the species.

EXPERIENCE. *To observe some of the plants man usually consider pests.* If there is a vacant lot, an abandoned garden, or an uncultivated field near the school, it will provide a place where children can have direct experience with weeds and grasses. Encourage the children to observe the great number of seeds produced by the plants. They might like to discuss why they think such plants have so many seeds. If the place visited is one that can be revisited, it might be interesting to remove the weeds, grasses, and any other plants from a small area and observe after the next big rain. By contrasting what has happened to the area no longer protected by plants with the area which is protected, children will be able to see that plants considered as pests in cultivated crops may be very useful in other places.

Animal pests are also numerous. Mosquitoes and other insects annoy by their bite and do harm by the transmission of disease. Rabbits may girdle young peach or apple trees during a severe winter, causing serious damage in an orchard. Moles sometimes burrow just under the surface of well-kept golf greens, spoiling their smoothness. Crows are said to pull up the farmers' corn while it is germinating or just after it has begun to grow from the seed. Minks may raid hen-houses, causing considerable damage; weasels sometimes do likewise. In thinly settled regions wolves and coyotes may cause considerable damage to young livestock. Beavers sometimes build dams in streams, backing up the water and preventing proper drainage.

Rats have been successful in adapting themselves to conditions of civilization. They may be found in sewers of large cities, along water fronts of ports, in garbage and refuse dumps, in the cellars of buildings, and in granaries and grain mills; and sometimes they even make their homes in the drainage systems which drain wet fields on farms. They destroy millions of dollars' worth of property annually, often eating great quantities of foodstuffs. They reproduce rapidly and seem to thrive despite many efforts to exterminate them. They have been known to raid brooder houses in which chicks are kept, destroying them in large numbers. They are sometimes infested with a type of flea which spreads the dreaded bubonic plague. Thus they may be the cause of epidemics of human disease.

Some Organisms Are Parasites. Not all plants live on dead organic material or manufacture their own food. In the same way not all animals live on plant life or by killing and devouring other animals. Many living things exist at the expense of others without immediately killing and devouring them. Such living things are known as *parasites*. The animal or plant on which the parasite feeds is the *host*.

Practically all living things are subject to parasitism. Many kinds of mammals are parasitized by tapeworms which live in the intestines of the host. A roundworm called *Trichina* is sometimes found in pork. If this pork is not sufficiently cooked before consumption, the muscle fibers of the meat may contain living *Trichina,* which are thus introduced into the human system. Once they have been established within the human body, they may multiply rapidly and produce the condition known as trichinosis.

In some parts of the United States, where the natives often go barefoot during much of the year, and where sanitation is primitive, the soil may be infested with hookworms, which find their way into the human body through the skin on the feet and cause the hookworm malady. Some kinds of bacteria and Protozoa find their way into the blood stream of human beings and cause typhoid fever, sleeping sickness, and many other diseases.

Sheep are sometimes infested with liver flukes, which may cause death to the host. All such parasites may be considered internal parasites, since they are found within the bodies of animals. Birds, reptiles, amphibians, fishes, insects, and practically all animals have parasites which live within them and sap their vitality.

In addition to *internal* parasites, there are also many kinds of *external* parasites. Birds and human beings alike are infested with lice. Cattle in the Southwestern states are sometimes afflicted with ticks, which spread disease among them. Leeches, or bloodsuckers, attach themselves to fish, boring through the skin to a blood vessel and gorging themselves on blood.

Some kinds of parasites can live only within or on the host and will die if removed from it. Others are able to survive when removed from the host. There are many degrees of parasitism. In addition to those already described,

animals are found which are parasites to the extent that they steal the food of other species. Some, like the cowbird, lay their eggs in the nests of other species, which are obliged to rear the young of the parasite. Among ants it has been found that one species often captures members of another species, enslaves them, and thus becomes parasitic upon the enslaved ants. Parasitism seems to occur among water animals, as well as among land animals.

Migrating animals may have different kinds of parasites as they progress along the route of migration. The European salmon is infested with one kind of parasite when it is in salt water and with other kinds when it enters fresh water. Similarly, migrating birds in the south are infested by one set of parasites; in their northern habitats they may be infested by others. When conditions change in a community, animals may become parasites, even though they previously had not been.

Every parasite is adapted to its host. External parasites are generally flattened; their legs may be degenerate, and the organs by means of which they attach themselves to the host are well developed. Internal parasites show a tendency toward a loss of many organs important in free-living animals, but they are often able to reproduce at a rapid rate. Often, too, the digestive system and the entire body are adapted for rapid feeding and great storage capacity, so that the animal may gorge itself in a short time.

Many evidences of parasitism are found among the insects. Some wasps are able to paralyze certain kinds of caterpillars and lay their eggs in them. The paralyzed caterpillar remains alive but motionless until the eggs hatch. Upon hatching, the young wasp larvae find their food supply ready for them. Parasites in turn are sometimes infested by organisms which parasitize them.

There are, of course, plant as well as animal parasites. The parasitism of man and other animals by bacteria has already been mentioned. Most of the flowering plants are free-living, but there are some parasites among them. The parasite generally pierces the tissues of the host plant by means of small modified roots which may be considered sucking organs. These may grow from either the root or the stem of the parasite.

The mistletoe is a common parasite in the Southern states, and dodder is another. Many fungi are parasites and cause plant diseases which are often destructive. It is probable that fewer of the green plants are parasites because they contain chlorophyll and can manufacture their own food, while more of the fungi are parasitic because of their lack of chlorophyll and consequent inability to carry on photosynthesis.

With an increase in the knowledge of parasitism, man is beginning to use parasites for his own purposes. If a species of insects is so numerous and harmful as to cause great damage, entomologists (insect specialists) seek to find out which parasites normally attack the insect. Often a smaller insect is found to be the key to the problem; this smaller insect parasitizes the pest and may be used to keep it in check. With a large number of host insects present, the parasite will thrive, multiplying rapidly and thus destroying the pests. With the decrease in the number of pest insects, the parasite will also decrease.

There is a balance between the parasite and its hosts so far as numbers are concerned. If an animal is infected with too many parasites, it may die. Its death and decomposition removes the food supply of the parasites which, if they cannot live under other conditions, also die for lack of food. In this way the number of parasites is kept in check. It is when parasitism interferes with human welfare that man especially concerns himself with it.

EXPERIENCE. *To study plant and animal parasites.* Children may be helped to discover for themselves both plant and animal parasites found in their community. They may also learn the best ways of dealing with such parasites by reading available authoritative materials, or by consulting the city health officer, the county agricultural agent, or other members of the community that have had experience with parasites.

Some Organisms Live Together and Benefit. Parasitism is one kind of relationship between living things. Often, however, animals, plants, or plants and animals live together, and both may be benefited, or one may benefit without harm to the other. Such a relationship is called *symbiosis*, and the organisms involved are known as *symbionts*. Certain birds, for example, sit on the backs of cattle, rhinoceroses, and buffaloes, and eat the blood-sucking parasites found on their skins. Thus they secure food and also benefit the mammal.

In the digestive cavities of termites (white ants) are found protozoans which help in the digestion of the wood which the termites have eaten. Without them the termites would die, since they cannot carry on digestion alone. Some kinds of very minute fungi live within the fat bodies found in a number of insects.

Aphids, or plant lice, furnish food for ants and are protected and fed by them. The eggs of certain species of aphids are actually carried by the ants into their underground galleries; and in the spring the young aphids are carried out, placed on favorable plants, and are there visited by the ants. Termites and ants also raise fungi for food, a symbiotic relationship.

Animals depending on large amounts of vegetation for food are aided in digesting the cellulose by bacteria and protozoans in their digestive tracts. In turn, the bacteria and protozoans benefit.

Lichens are examples of this relationship among plants. A lichen is a close association of a fungus and an alga. The alga is provided with moisture and shelter from mechanical injury by the presence of the fungus, and the alga makes food, used by both, whenever sunlight and water are available. This type of symbiotic association is called *mutualism*.

Another type of association among living things is called *commensalism*. In this type the association results in benefit to one or more of the living things involved, but, unlike parasitism, results in injury to none. Many species are found attached to their hosts, though they do not injure them. Certain species of barnacles are found attached to whales. In this way attached animals are afforded protection; and as the host moves from one place to another, the attached animal, which may be called a *commensal*, comes into situations favorable for the finding of food. Some commensals live within the host or within its home. Crabs, worms, and other animals may live within the shells of snails. Some beetles have been found that live in moles' nests.

Some biologists consider parasitism, mutualism, and commensalism different degrees of symbiosis.

A Community Is Constantly Changing

Nothing in life is static; change is a characteristic of the community of living things. These variations may be due to any one of a number of events, a combination or a succession of events. Generally these changes are so slow that only careful observation reveals them, but occasionally natural catastrophes occur which precipitate a sudden change in the community.

Communities Show Seasonal Changes. Perhaps the most easily observed change in a community is that which is due to seasonal changes. As Earth rotates on its axis and revolves in its orbit, the amount of light energy received on various parts of it vary. Children know that there are fewer hours of sunlight in the winter than in the summer, and that the temperatures may be considerably lower in January than in July. It may be well to consider the effects thus produced.

During the summer months in either the Northern or the Southern Hemisphere much sunlight comes to Earth. Atmospheric temperature is comparatively high. Plants are very active in all their life functions and growth is rapid, while photosynthesis results in the formation of more food than the plant can use. With this abundance of food, animals find it easy to obtain more than enough to keep them alive, and consequently they store some of it in the form of fat. Insects abound, and many species of birds may be found even as far north as the Arctic Circle and as far south as the antarctic regions. All animals are very active, except for the few that estivate (p. 683).

As Earth continues to move around the sun, its changed position becomes such that the vertical rays of the sun no longer fall north of the equator. Northern regions receive less light and heat; from this fact a lower atmospheric temperature results. We say that it is autumn. Plants of many kinds lose their leaves; food-making activity has stopped.

Some animals change color with the seasons.

Sugars, starches, proteins, and oils have been stored in stems; or they have been stored in seeds or other parts of the plant. Birds of many species migrate southward, where the food supply is more plentiful. Snakes, frogs, turtles, and many kinds of animals bury themselves in the soil below the frost line and spend the winter there. Raccoons, oppossums, and the several species of bears seek out a shelter in which they may spend a quiescent period during severe winter weather. Squirrels seek out hollow trees, to which they retreat during cold spells. Many species of insects burrow into decaying logs, into the ground, or into any other place which gives them shelter from the cold.

Thus a community which, during the summertime, may have teemed with living things may be comparatively barren of them in the wintertime. Insects are not in evidence, many of the mammals are hibernating, and reptiles and amphibians are not seen. Fish in streams are apt to seek deeper and warmer waters; those found in lakes also tend to move into deeper water or to rest near the bottom. Only such animals as rabbits, minks, and weasels range the country in search of food.

Wolves, which during the summer and autumn were found only in small solitary groups, may now band together in packs to facilitate the hunting of large game. Field mice often migrate to farm buildings to live on such food as they can find there. Crows, which are usually solitary during the summer, may form large flocks, during the winter; and a community which had but few crows may then have hundreds. Animals which graze on mountain slopes may descend into the valley, changing in this way the personnel of both the mountain and the valley community.

Some bears are inactive intermittently but do not go into true hibernation.

With the coming of spring, the character of the community changes again. Migrating birds return from tropical and semitropical regions. A few adult insects survive the winter, reappear, lay eggs, and insects that spend the winter as eggs or in other stages of development continue to grow. Fish may move out of lakes into streams to spawn and die, while some, like the salmon, leave the ocean and seek fresh-water rivers in which to lay their eggs. As atmospheric temperature gradually increases, and as the ground thaws out and becomes warm, plants resume growth, living at first on the food manufactured the previous year and stored over the winter. These changes go on year after year. Each change of season brings about a change of conditions, which in turn brings about a variation in the community.

Seasonal changes are significant in their effect on communities because they occur often and because their effects are easily seen by casual observation of the environment. The coming of the first severe frost in the fall, for example, may produce remarkable changes in the community. Annual plants which have flowered and produced seeds may be killed. Many kinds of insects are reduced in number. Chlorophyll disappears from the leaves of trees, so that other pigments predominate, and a green tree may in two or three days become brilliantly colored.

EXPERIENCE. *To study seasonal changes in a community.* The teacher and children may wish to select a place near their school that would be accessible at all seasons of the year. Here they would make planned group trips and also individual trips, to note the changes in the plants and animals throughout the year. In some regions there may be great changes that occur in connection with *rainy* and *dry seasons*. Records might be kept of all observations, so that an accurate picture of the life in that area at different seasons might be studied and com-

pared. Some children may be interested in making murals that depict an area in different seasons.

Other Changes Affect Communities. There are slower climatic changes which have a definite effect on communities. A study of Earth's history indicates that areas which are now frigid must at one time have had a much warmer climate. Fossils have been found in both arctic and antarctic regions. These show that a plant life once existed there which was semitropical in nature. From this fact it is deduced that the polar regions were not always perpetually cold. Coal deposits in various portions of North America give evidence that the climate of that continent must have been semitropical at one stage of Earth's history.

Similarly it is known that large portions of Earth's surface now having what is considered a temperate climate were at one time subjected to glaciers. Any vegetation in existence during glacial periods must have been different from the kind now found in these regions because of the lower temperatures which prevailed. Many regions now considered deserts because they support so few living things were at one time able to support an abundance of life. These changes are gradual and therefore not spectacular, and are not noticed unless a special study is made. Such climatic changes occur so slowly that a single lifetime is not a sufficiently long period to notice them.

Other changes taking place gradually over a period of many, many years may affect the type of living things found in a community. Great areas of Earth are found to be slowly rising. Their elevation often results in colder climate and more arid conditions, with life becoming scarcer as altitude increases. If the fringe of a continent is rising or sinking, it may result in the formation of salt-water swamps, which become inhabited by plants and animals adapted to those conditions. As moun-

In some regions, when man abandons a field, it is soon covered by weeds, later by bush plants, and finally by trees.

tain ranges are slowly worn down, they tend to become more habitable for living things. The Appalachians, for example, are found to be covered with plant life, while at the higher altitudes of the Rocky Mountains there is little or no plant life.

Many kinds of living things may be found in ponds and small lakes. Fresh-water fish, insects, fresh-water sponges, amphibians, protozoans, and other animals may be found in or near them. In the shallower regions of a body of water many kinds of aquatic plants may be seen. With the coming of winter, these aquatic plants usually die and settle to the bottom. In this way they add layer after layer of organic matter to the lake bed, which makes the lake shallower each year. Eventually the shallower parts of the lake, usually the shores, become completely filled in, and the area of the lake is smaller. Land plants begin to grow in the filled-in portion; the decay of their leaves and stems builds up the level to a higher point.

The shore line thus advances toward the center, and eventually the pond or lake may be completely filled, so that it becomes a swamp. Aquatic plants and animals of a dif-

ferent kind are now found in the community; fish, for example, may disappear entirely. Other animals move in; the muskrat builds its home there, or the beaver. Such a change may take hundreds of years, but it results in a change in the personnel of the community.

The same kind of thing may happen on land. In many parts of North America the first settlers cut down the forests and farmed the land until it was no longer profitable to do so, and then moved to new unexploited territories. Farms were deserted and fields left unplowed.

Soon changes in the community occurred. A few of the farm crops, such as alfalfa and timothy grass, may have survived for a number of years. They were crowded out by weeds, such as goldenrod and daisies. The weeds in turn were crowded out by bushes which make up what is sometimes known as "brush." Here and there a tree seed may have fallen, and a young tree may have begun to grow. As it became older, it bore seeds, which were scattered over the fields, and more trees grew where once the farmer cultivated his crops. Eventually the trees grew large enough so that they shaded the bush plants and competed with them for water, making it impossible for them to survive. As the trees grew older and larger, the fields assumed a forest appearance once more.

With all these changes in the types of plants occur similar changes in the types of animals. In the farmers' fields such birds as the bobolink and meadow lark may have been common. These were supplanted by others as the weeds were crowded out and bushes appeared. Grasshoppers and other insects characteristic of meadows disappeared also. As the field became a woodland, new types of birds and insects appeared.

When trees begin to grow in a field, it is not to be assumed that the resulting forest will always be of the same species as the first one. Small and short-lived trees generally appear first. In the New England area birch trees are the first to be found in abandoned fields. Later these are crowded out by various species of oaks and hickories; maples, pines, and hem-

locks eventually take the place of the oaks and hickories. Because the maples, pines, and hemlocks will persist until some great change in conditions occurs, they make up what is known as the climax vegetation.

Not all the changes which occur in the characteristics of communities are gradual. Occasionally natural changes take place which are sudden and striking in their effects. One of the commonest of these on land is fire. Forest fires are well known for their destruction of trees, but their effects are far wider than is popularly appreciated. Not only are trees destroyed, but at the same time all the smaller plants are destroyed. Bushes, grasses, herbs, and other plants do not escape. The surface of the soil may be sufficiently heated so that many kinds of bacteria are destroyed also.

The character of the chemical composition of the soil may be changed considerably by the burning of the decaying organic matter on

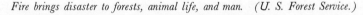

Fire brings disaster to forests, animal life, and man. (*U. S. Forest Service.*)

its surface and by the addition to the soil of large quantities of wood ashes. Mosses, ferns, lichens, and algae disappear for a time. Many of the less fleet animals perish, while others are forced to seek a new habitat. If a stream or river runs through the forest, enough ashes may be carried into it by subsequent rains to alter the chemical composition of the water, thus killing many forms of life found therein.

During the winter, snow may fall on the burned-over forests, resulting in floods which may wash away much of the topsoil. There is a tendency, however, for plants to invade the burned-over area. Seeds dropping here and there sprout, and annual plants grow. Lichens and mosses reappear. Gradually other forms of life are found, and after many years the region may again become heavily wooded.

Along streams and rivers sudden floods may cause great havoc to both plant and animal life. Floodwaters often strip the topsoil from one place, making that region incapable of supporting plant life. Much of this soil may be deposited in another place, thus burying what plant life exists there. Animals found in the soil are drowned in large numbers, and the community is thus altered. In other places they may be buried so deeply that they cannot survive. In the place where the soil carried by water is deposited, more luxuriant plant growth may result after the flood recedes, owing to the fact that the silt is often rich in the materials which plants need.

Less common, but perhaps even more spectacular, is the effect of such agencies as volcanic action on living things. A volcano may remain dormant for hundreds of years, giving no indication of its latent destructive force. Its sides may be covered with much plant growth in which may be living many kinds of animals. A sudden eruption of the volcano, with the attendant deposit of ash and lava on its sides, may bury all living things, so that temporarily at least it may present the aspect of a desert. If no further volcanic action takes place, the lava is weathered and eroded until it forms a thin layer of soil. Lichens may grow on the lava, helping to decompose it. Other plants begin to appear, and with them insects and other animals. In a few hundred years conditions become as they were before the eruption, and life goes on normally until another catastrophe occurs.

Man has been responsible for some great changes in his environment of living things. Some examples of his influence on the balance of nature have already been mentioned. Others, such as the rapid cutting down of forests, with the resultant loss of soil by erosion, are known to all. Within recent years much attention has been devoted to the erosion of soils by wind in various portions of the United States. It is probable that dust storms occurred before the advent of the white man on this continent, but those of the dust-bowl area of central United States seem to have been more severe recently than they were before the white man's time. Much of the soil in these regions is of a sandy nature. When the amount of rainfall is slight, the soil becomes very dry; and since it is loose, it is easily picked up by air currents and carried for many miles.

Before these soils were farmed, they were covered with a growth of buffalo grass and other plants. Agricultural methods are such that soils must be plowed before crops can be planted, and so the natural grasses disappeared. The soil was left without plants to hold it in place in those months when crops were not growing. A succession of abnormally dry years resulted in the transportation of the soil by winds.

Research on the proper control of wind erosion has resulted in a practical method that is being used for at least a partial solution to the problem. Trees have been planted to form windbreaks and shelter belts. Much of the land that was unsuited for farming has been planted with grass. Terracing and contour-plowing practices are being widely used. A study of plants most suited to this region has been made and their use, together with crop rotation and strip planting, is bringing about desirable results. It has taken time, but gradually these areas of shifting soil are being returned to usefulness.

Soils may be blown away in other places than in those states in which dust storms have been commonly observed. In some places, for example, sand dunes may be found sufficiently large to overwhelm small wooded areas, burying the trees and other plants so deeply that they die. In many places on Cape Cod grasses must be planted to hold the soil in place lest it be blown away. This is especially true along the shores of the ocean.

EXPERIENCE. *To observe changes in communities.* Frequently changes take place in habitats and communities that may be observed by children. When a habitat or environment changes, the community of plants and animals will change. The following are illustrations of ways in which habitats and communities are changed: the making of a garden; the work of a bulldozer; a garden or piece of ground no longer cultivated; the draining of a swamp; a forest fire or the burning of brush. The erection of a new school building produces new habitats and new communities, for a thicket, a weed patch, or grass may grow up. There may be a number of communities on the school grounds. When the observation or study of a plant or animal community is undertaken the children should have an opportunity to observe at first hand and to discuss the members of the community and their relationship to others in the community and to the habitat; but this should be done only to the extent that it will have meaning for them.

CHAPTER 15

Living Things Compete

Living Things Compete in a Struggle for Existence

Because reproduction in most plants and animals is lavish, there is a constant struggle for existence among living things. This results in perpetual competition for food among animals and for raw materials from which foods may be manufactured among plants. Since all animals feed on living organisms or on their dead bodies, they are continually busy with the destruction of other living things. The organism which is used for food must be able to hold its own in the struggle; else it will soon become extinct. It is for this reason biologically fortunate that plants produce more seeds than can possibly find room to grow, and more animals come into exist-

ence than can possibly survive. The struggle is a sharp one, for food is the basic source of energy for the activity of protoplasm. Because of changing environmental conditions which may result in a scarcity of food, each living thing must have sufficient food to be able to build up a reserve for a time when food may be scarce.

One of the means by which animals survive the struggle for existence is reproduction in enormous numbers. It has already been pointed out that a single bacterium may, in the course of twenty-four hours, become the ancestor of millions of its own kind, and that one average mushroom may produce a billion

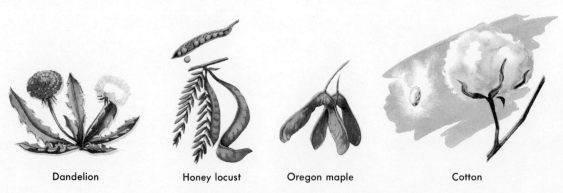

Dandelion   Honey locust   Oregon maple   Cotton

Thousands of seeds are produced for every one that germinates and grows.

568

and a half or more spores. Most of these are generally killed off before they have a chance to grow to maturity, but a few survive. These few are sufficient to carry on the reproductive process at a rate sufficiently great to perpetuate the species. Because of the tremendous numbers of the offspring some of them survive under the most adverse conditions through sheer chance. It has been suggested that if all Protozoa that were produced lived a normal life span, there would be enough of them in a short time to fill the oceans.

Each species tends to reproduce so rapidly that the struggle for survival is intense. Simple calculation shows that if all the descendants of a plant which produced only two seeds a year were to survive for twenty-one years, the plant would have at the end of that time more than a million offspring. There are hundreds of thousands of species of seed-producing plants, each producing great quantities of seeds; thus the reason for the competition for the necessities of life becomes apparent.

EXPERIENCE. *To show that some plants produce many seeds.* Have children bring to class a plant in seed, and ask them to count the number of seeds found on it. Dandelions, milkweed, corn, and sunflowers are desirable plants for this purpose. It may not be necessary to count all the seeds for the children to see that many plants produce a great number of seeds.

EXPERIENCE. *To give an appreciation of the rapidity of reproduction of bacteria.* Older children may assume that a bacterium will reproduce once each hour for twenty-four hours, and that all the resultant organisms survive. Have them calculate how many bacteria would be produced in twenty-four hours. Remember that the number doubles each hour.

EXPERIENCE. *To observe the rapidity of reproduction in some animals.* A pair of mice, rats, or hamsters might be kept in the room long enough to show the usual number of offspring in a litter, and also the time it takes for the young to become mature enough to reproduce. The eggs of frogs or toads may be brought into the classroom for observation. The children will see here the great number of eggs that may be produced by one female. They will also be able to observe that not all of these eggs develop into tadpoles. Egg cases of spiders may also be observed, to note the great number of young that emerge. The egg cases of cockroaches, praying mantes, or other insects might also be observed to show numbers of offspring.

It has been estimated that the conger eel lays about 15 million eggs, and the common fresh-water perch lays 100,000 eggs in a single spawning season. Some of the ocean fish produce millions of eggs yearly, and so do the oysters. Charles Darwin calculated that if the reproductive rate of man remained the same as it was during his lifetime, in a thousand years there would be no standing room for human beings. Insects sometimes lay thousands of eggs in a single summer. The female leopard frog may lay as many as 4500 eggs in one mass, while a toad may lay as many as 12,000 eggs.

Why, then, is not the world overrun by one

Many animals reproduce rapidly.

or another of these kinds of animals? There are many answers to this question. In the first place, many of the eggs which are laid in water must be fertilized there. Some of them are never reached by sperm cells, and die. Of those which are fertilized many are eaten by other animals; some of them are invaded by bacteria which cause diseases in them and kill them; still others may chance to come into environmental conditions unfavorable to their existence; some may die for lack of food or oxygen. Of the few surviving many are eaten before they reach maturity and before they can in turn carry on reproduction. Frogs often lay their eggs in ponds which are filled with water in the early spring, when the thawing of snow and spring rains have caused an accumulation of water in low places. Clear weather for a week or two causes these ponds to dry up, and the developing tadpoles are killed by this change in their environment.

The same sort of thing is true of plants. Many seeds are eaten by birds and other animals. Others are injured by insects and cannot germinate. Still others fall on stony ground or in the water, in which they cannot grow. Of those which germinate some are crowded out by plants which grow more rapidly than they, and are deprived of the things they need to exist. Some of them are succulent when they first appear above the ground and are hunted out as food by animals. A long dry summer may make water so scarce that many of them die for lack of water before they have had a chance to bloom and form seeds.

EXPERIENCE. *To show that not all seeds produced will grow.* Have children count out one hundred each of various kinds of seeds. Cut some blotting paper to fit saucers in which the seeds are to be germinated. Moisten this blotting paper, put it on the saucer, and place the seeds on it. Cover with another piece of blotting paper and keep continually moist. Note how many of each of the various kinds of seeds do not germinate.

EXPERIENCE. *To show that seeds falling in unfavorable places will not survive.* Place some seeds on a stone or brick which is kept moist, others on a dry stone, and others in a tumbler of water. Note that these seeds do not develop. Plant some in sawdust which is dry or in dry sand. To check on this experiment, plant some in soil that is kept moist and at room temperature to show that only those seeds falling in favorable places will develop.

Despite all these forces which act upon living things, organisms do manage to survive. But there is no end to the competition for the necessities of life. Food is constantly necessary, and often the animal must move over considerable areas to find it. Thus competition between animals of the same species occurs. All animals of the same species have similar food habits; and if the kind of food necessary to sustain them is scarce, the weaker individuals may die of starvation, while the stronger survive. Among predatory animals those least able to attack are the first to perish. Of the animals which are hunted those least able to escape are the first overtaken and killed. The weakest individuals of any species thus perish first, while the strongest and most able ones may continue to exist. This is a *selective agency.* Since only those animals most fit to cope with conditions survive, there is a gradual growth in the ability of the species to continue.

In the struggle of species against species some one of them may gain a slight advantage in numbers one year, and another the next. Unless something happens to upset the normal competition, a condition approaching stability of the numbers of each species is approached, and the numbers may vary only slightly from year to year. Sometimes animals become subject to epidemics of disease which decimate their ranks or wipe them out altogether. Plants too may become subject to new diseases to which they have no natural immunity. An example of this is the chestnut tree, which was once very common in many parts of North America. In recent years the chestnut blight has destroyed practically every tree of this species. This in turn has reduced the food supply of squirrels, so that they have become scarce in regions where they were formerly common. Often if one type of food becomes scarce, animals may develop new feeding habits and attack new prey.

A number of years ago young orange trees were attacked by an insect pest in California known as the cottony-cushion scale. There seemed to be no way of checking the ravages caused by it. Later it was determined that the pest had been introduced from Australia, and consequently entomologists were sent there to discover what natural predator might be found to help to keep the scale in check. It was found that a certain species of ladybird beetle attacked and fed on the cottony-cushion scale. Some of these ladybird beetles were then brought to California and released in infested orchards. Here the beetles thrived; and since the food supply was plentiful, they reproduced rapidly.

With the increase in the number of beetles, the cottony-cushion scales diminished in numbers, and were nearly eradicated. Then the number of ladybird beetles also decreased rapidly, for they had no other source of food. It became necessary to keep protected colonies of the cottony-cushion scales on which ladybird beetles were raised, in case of another serious outbreak of the pest.

Some Plants Survive Because of Protective Adaptations

Some species of plants are more likely to survive because they are protected against animals. Blackberries have thorns which tend to protect them against trampling by large animals, and which make them more or less unfit as food for animals. Many kinds of bush plants also have thorns which are so long and sharp that the plants are generally left undisturbed by the larger animals, though thorns are no protection against insects. Other plants are not used as food, because their leaves are such that they are neither palatable nor easily digested. Pine, hemlock, and other evergreen trees are seldom, if ever, eaten by the larger animals for this reason; their needle-like leaves are passed by for more palatable plants. The cacti of the desert regions not only have spines in some cases, but generally are so tough and leathery that they are not eaten by most animals.

Children who spend much time out of doors have learned to shun poison ivy because of its effects. Such plants as the skunk cabbage, often found in swamps, are not eaten, probably because of their characteristic odors. Milkweeds generally have a sticky, bitter, milky-looking liquid in their leaves and stems which is apparently distasteful to grazing animals, since many of them are shunned.

EXPERIENCE. *To show why some plants are not eaten by animals.* Have children bring skunk-cabbage leaves to class and note the odor. Milkweeds may be brought in and the "milk" noted. It might be desirable to take children to a pasture lot where there are many plants. In this environment children could examine the different plants and try to determine which plants are protected by having tough stems, sour or bitter liquids, or thorns.

Animals refuse to eat some plants.

Plants like the ferns are generally not found palatable by animals, and are not used for food. Mosses are not usually eaten unless other vegetation is very scarce. Some species of insects live on mushrooms and puffballs, but the larger plant-eating animals generally disregard them. Moldy food is avoided, too; if eaten, it may have a poisonous effect. Some species of plants are avoided because they are poisonous. Toadstools, which are poisonous mushrooms, may cause fatal poisoning to human beings. Some plants contain powerful poisons in sufficient quantities to be fatal. Others, like the horsetails, have no leaves and such unpalatable stems that they are not eaten. Each of these plant characteristics enables the plant to compete successfully in the struggle for existence, since it eliminates the possibility of the plant's being eaten.

EXPERIENCE. *To demonstrate that animals will not eat some plants.* One of the children might bring a domesticated rabbit to class, which may be kept in a screen-covered box. The children may try feeding it such various plants as pieces of cactus, pine and other evergreen leaves, fern leaves, mushrooms, lettuce, and celery. Note which the rabbit eats and which it rejects.

Plant adaptations: seeds are scattered and plants survive by means of various adaptations.

Cocklebur

Beggar's tick

Devils claw

Burdock

Plant adaptations

Blackberry

Cactus

Hemlock

Skunk cabbage

Milkweed

Poison ivy

Toadstool

The seeds of some plants are not eaten, because their fruits have barbs, or hooks, on them. Cocklebur and Spanish needles are examples. Others, like wild barley, are protected by long awns, or beards, which, if they get into the mouth of an animals, gradually work their way into the flesh and produce painful wounds. Some seeds have thick woody shells, or husks, which make them hard to open, so that the embryo plant within is protected to some extent from animals which might otherwise eat it. Some birds, however, and some animals like the squirrels, have learned to break open the nut or to gnaw through it, thus reaching the kernel.

EXPERIENCE. *To show why some plant seeds are not eaten.* Children may bring to class such fruits (commonly called seeds) as cocklebur, Spanish needles, and others like them, to be studied with the aid of magnifying glasses. This should make clear why some seeds are not eaten by animals. Fruits such as acorns and beech nuts may also be brought in.

Animals Are Protected in Different Ways

Animals escape predators in many different ways. Some of them run from their pursuers; others fly. Some crawl away, others may jump, and others swim. There are almost as many different ways of escape and protection as there are types of animals.

The tails of animals are made to serve many functions. Cows and horses use them to keep away, as much as possible, flies and other insects which may be annoying. The opossum uses its tail as a means of suspending itself from the branch of a tree. Some species of lizards have tails which are easily broken off without damage to the animal. The glass snake, which is not a snake at all, but a lizard, is an example. It cannot move rapidly when a predator approaches, and consequently is soon overtaken and seized by its pursuer. If the pursuer happens to grasp the animal by its tail, that appendage breaks off without damage to the glass snake. The muscles in the tail continue to contract and relax in such a way that the tail moves for some time after it has become detached. While the predator is occupied with the tail, the lizard crawls off to a safe place. Within a short time it has grown a new tail, although this one does not grow so long as the original, and its scales are somewhat different from those on the rest of the body. The red-backed salamander also loses its tail under similar circumstances.

Claws, Horns, Antlers, and Teeth Are Defense Structures. Many species of animals use their claws in self-defense and in getting food. Among birds the hawks and owls have talons with which they can if necessary protect themselves. Both wildcats and domesticated cats use their claws to good advantage upon animals which are pursuing them. Tigers and other larger members of the cat family do the same when in battle with other animals.

EXPERIENCE. *To illustrate the use of claws as a means of defense.* One of the children may bring to class a pet kitten, whose claws may be examined. Note how they are folded under when the kitten walks, and how they may be extended for protection.

Some animals use their antlers to charge upon their foes. Antelope, caribou, moose, and elk often beat off predators in this way. Occasionally in struggles between two members of the same species these antlers may become locked together in such a way that the combatants cannot extricate themselves. When this happens, they often grow so weak

Claw

Antler

Horn

Tusk

Tail

Teeth

Fangs

Tentacles

Claw

Stinger

Shell

Plates

that they die. In addition, they also use their hoofs to protect themselves. Cows, goats, buffaloes, and bison have horns with which they pierce the bodies of anything attacking them. When engaged in battle these animals sometimes show remarkable speed and nimbleness, which make them dangerous. Having transfixed their attacker, they throw him to the ground and then trample him with their hoofs. Some animals, such as the rhinoceros, have a single horn made of a horny tissue. Also their sense of smell is very keen, and they display great speed in charging.

EXPERIENCE. *To study the adaptations for defense of larger animals.* A trip to the zoo may be used to serve as a lesson to stress this point. Suggest that children note antlers of deer, horny plates of crocodiles and alligators, claws of bears, and other defense adaptations.

Many kinds of animals such as dogs, wolves, foxes, and coyotes have long sharp teeth well adapted for biting. Many kinds of rodents have long incisor teeth, which they use both in catching their prey and escaping from predators. A rat when cornered is able to bite viciously. The woodchuck, or groundhog, can inflict a severe wound when it bites. Squirrels protect themselves in the same way if they cannot escape by taking refuge in a tree. The mink and weasel have very sharp teeth, with which they defend themselves and attack other animals.

The canine teeth of some animals develop to such an extent that they are called tusks. The elephant uses these effectively when disturbed. One of the most dangerous animals to hunt is the wild boar, not only because of its fierce disposition, but because of the fact that it has tusks with which it can inflict a serious wound.

EXPERIENCE. *To study the teeth of a biting animal.* Have one of the children bring a pet dog of good disposition. The children should note the small incisor teeth and long sharp canine teeth.

Some Snakes Secrete Poison for Self-Defense. Some snakes have a means of protection in their fangs and poison glands. Fangs are modified teeth located in the upper jaw. Each fang is hollow and connects with a small gland located behind the eye in the interior of the head. In some species, when the mouth is closed, the fangs lie back against the roof of the mouth, but spring forward ready for use when the mouth is opened for biting. The venom is thus injected into an object when the snake bites. Uninformed persons often mistake a snake's tongue for its fangs. The sense of hearing is poorly developed in these reptiles, but the tongue is sensitive to vibrations. When a snake senses danger, this tongue, which is fork-shaped, flashes in and out of the mouth in an effort to locate sound vibrations which help to determine the position of the approaching animal. In some snakes there is a groove in the jaws through which the tongue is extended and drawn back again.

There are many untrue stories concerning the great danger from snakes. Children should understand that there are a few poisonous species, but that most of the snakes in North America are not venomous, and some are distinctly beneficial to man because of their insect-eating and rodent-eating habits. However, an unidentified kind of snake should *not* be molested or captured by a child.

EXPERIENCE. *To observe the tongue of a snake.* If one of the children brings to class a small garter snake, which may be kept in a box or terrarium for a short time, observe the tongue of the snake, noting that it is forked; also note that the mouth of the snake is not open when the tongue is extended.

In many instances pictures from books or magazines, or motion pictures, will suffice to show children a snake's tongue and the way it is used.

EXPERIENCE. *To study poisonous snakes found in one's own environment.* It is desirable that children be able to recognize the poisonous snakes living in their region. They may wish to check with the United States Department of Agriculture in Washington, D. C., or with their own State Department of Agriculture as to the kind and description of poisonous snakes found in their region. Children living in countries other than the United States may check with their government agencies dealing with education. The teacher may be able to borrow from a neighboring museum mounted speciments of the poisonous and nonpoisonous snakes found in his state or province. These can be studied and their characteristics learned. Lantern slides or mounted pictures may be useful in helping children to identify snakes. Museums or reptile displays in zoos will also offer excellent opportunity for observation of both harmful and helpful snakes. Children should gain confidence in their ability to recognize harmful snakes, and be encouraged to protect those snakes that are beneficial.

Some Animals Are Protected by Hard Coverings. Some species of animals are afforded protection by means of shells and horny skeletons. Oysters, mussels, and some species of snails have shells of lime which make them in-

A barnacle is securely anchored.

accessible to animals which would otherwise feed on them. It is well known, however, that starfish can open oysters by exerting a prolonged pull on the valves of the shell. Animals like the sea urchin, common along the eastern coast of North America, have long spines which make it difficult for animals to swallow them. Barnacles have what may be considered shells, the edges of which are sharp. Coral animals live within lime skeletons. Crayfish, lobsters, and crabs have horny skeletons. In addition, they have powerful pincers with which they ward off many predators.

EXPERIENCE. *To observe that some animals are protected by skeletons or shells.* Children may observe how completely protected the body of a snail is by the shell. Obtain some oysters in the shell if possible, and have children observe how strong and thick the shell is and how completely the oyster is protected by it.

Turtles have shells that are broad and flattened, into which the animal can withdraw itself more or less completely. Within this shell they have bones much the same as other vertebrates, double protection to the internal organs thus being provided and locomotion made possible. Some species of turtles are called snappers because they bite quickly when disturbed. Turtles do not have teeth. They have horny plates which form the margins of the jaws, by means of which they can seize their prey. The shell itself is made of bony material; in some species, however, it is leathery in character.

Some mammals are similarly protected by an outer skeleton made of bony material. One of these is the armadillo, one species of which is found from southern Texas as far south as Paraguay. When disturbed, these animals roll up into a ball; and since they present their hard armor to whatever disturbs them, they cannot easily be injured. They are generally about two feet long and live on open plains. They feed chiefly on worms and insects.

Another mammal which possesses armor protection is the pangolin, which inhabits Africa and eastern Asia. Its body is protected by overlapping scales which can be erected. When in danger, these animals, like the armadillos, roll themselves up into a ball. They are from one to five feet in length and feed on termites. Some of them live in trees, others burrow in the soil, while still others may live on the surface of the ground.

Crocodiles and alligators have horny scales on their skins which serve to protect them from injury. The backs of these animals, and sometimes the lower surface of the body as well, may be covered with bony plates similar to those of the turtle, but not forming a shell into which the animal can withdraw.

EXPERIENCE. *To study the protective shell of the turtle.* Someone in the class may bring a turtle to class if one is not at hand. Children should observe the reactions of the turtle when it is disturbed, and how completely the animal is protected when it withdraws into its shell.

Stings of Animals Are Used for Protection. Many species of animals possess structures by means of which they can sting and thus protect themselves. The protozoan *Paramecium* has in its cell membrane spindle-shaped cavities filled with a semifluid substance. Under certain conditions the substance is exploded out of the cavities into the water, in which it forms long threads, which are probably a defense mechanism. Jellyfish have tentacles which can inject slight quantities of poison into a disturbing animal. On the body of *Hydra* are found stinging cells within which there is an inverted, coiled, threadlike tube with barbs at the base. When the animal is irritated, these threads are rapidly shot out of the cell and are able to penetrate the tissues of other animals.

Insects are probably the best-known stinging animals. Many children have been stung by bees and are thus familiar with this means which animals have for their protection. The sting of a bee is a very complicated structure located at the end of the abdomen. Before the bee stings, a suitable place is located with the help of sting feelers. Two barbed darts are then thrust into the skin of the victim. These darts are guided by a sheath which aids in conducting the poison into the body of the animal being stung. The poison is secreted in a pair of glands and is stored in a reservoir from which it flows during the act of stinging. Usually when a bee stings another animal, the barbs on the darts make it impossible to extract the sting; and in the bee's struggle to escape, its poison glands and part of its intestine are pulled out. When this happens, death occurs within a few hours; however, if only the sting is lost and the intestine is not injured, the bee may recover.

EXPERIENCE. *To study the stinging apparatus of an insect.* If a dead bumblebee is available, children may be able to see the sting. A hand lens is helpful in this activity. Motion pictures are useful, or illustrations of a bee and its sting may be found in a book or magazine.

A turtle is protected by its shell.

Scorpions are able to paralyze some animals by means of a sting located on the end of the tail. The sting is not used as a method of defense unless the scorpion is hard pressed. Many species of spiders are often feared by children, although most of them are harmless. Spiders do not sting, but in some cases they do bite. Wasps and hornets are other examples of insects which can sting.

Some of the fishes with cartilaginous skeletons are capable of stinging in self-defense. The sting ray, which lives half buried in the sand along the coast of Florida, is one of these. Near the base of the whiplike tail is located a barbed spine capable of making a painful wound if driven into the hand or naked foot of a bather. No poison or venom is associated with this sting, however. One family of cartilaginous fishes is capable of storing up electrical energy in bundles of muscles lying on either side of the head. The electricity is discharged by means of electric organs and may be sufficient to paralyze large animals. These organs may thus be considered weapons of offense and defense. The electric eels of South America and the electric catfish of Egypt have similar ability to store up and use electrical energy in their defense. How this energy is generated and how it is stored is not well understood at the present time.

Some Animals Feign Death or Injury. Several different kinds of animals feign death when danger threatens them. Perhaps the best-known example of this means of protection is that of the opossum. It will remain entirely motionless, no matter how much it is pushed around, and continues its attempt to deceive its attacker until it departs. The insect known as the walking stick stiffens out and will not move, even though it is being cut to pieces. The cankerworm caterpillar assumes a twiglike attitude and remains motionless, even though a bird seizes it. Birds of many species feign injury in an attempt to lure a predator away from the vicinity of their nests. The killdeer, when its nest is approached by a predatory animal, hops slowly away and utters distressful cries, as though crippled. In this manner the animal may be induced to disregard the nest and pursue it. It manages to stay just out of reach of the attacker; and when it has enticed it some distance away, it suddenly flies off.

The hognose snake combines a number of ways of escaping possible harm. When first approached, it hisses in an attempt to frighten off the intruder. It also flattens its head and swishes its tail in a threatening manner. If the aggressor does not retreat after these manifestations of ferocity, the snake suddenly rolls over on its back and thrashes from side to side until it is covered with dust; soon it is limp from exhaustion. If the aggressor is still present, the snake will remain in this position for ten or fifteen minutes; when the danger seems to be gone, it lifts its head and uses its tongue to detect possible sound vibrations which will show where the animal is. If all is still, it will turn over very slowly and then glide away as swiftly as possible. If, however, when the snake is motionless on its back, an observer turns it over so that it is in its proper position, it swiftly turns over on its back again, thus revealing that it is not dead.

Some Animals Are Nocturnal in Habit. Some species of animals seek protection by remaining in hiding during the day and venturing out only under cover of darkness. Crows and owls seem to be natural enemies. Owls of the larger species often attack and kill crows during the night, seeking them out in their roosting places. During the night the crows are unable to see well, while the eyes of the owl are such that it has no such difficulty. The crow is thus handicapped and finds it difficult to escape. During the day, however, it is the crow which has the advantage, for its keen eyesight can be used to good advantage.

The owl, on the other hand, cannot see well during the day; and if it is caught in an exposed place by crows, it is attacked viciously by them and often killed. Crow-hunters sometimes use stuffed owls as a decoy. They place a stuffed owl in a tree in the vicinity of crows; these gather in flocks to attack the owl and are shot down by the hunters.

Rats and mice are also nocturnal in their habits. Bats seek insects for food only during the night, being first seen at twilight. During the day they roost in barns and other comparatively dark places. Muskrats seek food at night, and carry on much of their home-building activities only after sunset. They are less easily seen in the dark and therefore are more likely to escape predators. Earthworms crawl deep into their burrows during the day, coming to the surface at night to feed.

Some Animals Derive Protection from Their Coloration. The colors of animals seem to have some function in enabling them to escape the attention of possible predators. Animals may have either concealing coloration or coloration for warning and recognition. Concealing coloration makes animals so similar in appearance to the background in which they are generally found that it is difficult to distinguish them from it. The body color of some animals, for example, is streaked and the tail barred, which deceives the observer as to the general form of the body. The whippoorwill builds its nest on the ground, and the drab coloration of the female makes it almost impossible for the human eye to detect her on her nest even at a distance of a few feet. Female birds are generally less bright in color than males, although in some instances where both sexes incubate the eggs alternately, there is much less difference in coloration.

Fish like the suckers, which are found in muddy streams, are generally mud-colored when viewed from above. Many kinds of ocean fish, particularly those in warm waters, are gaudy in color. It might be thought that a bright color would make the fish more readily seen by their predators; but green fish are found where vegetation is plentiful, and the green of the fish blends in with the color of the plants. Nocturnal fishes, those which are active only during the night, are often red in color. In darkness red appears black, so that a fish which may appear to be very brightly colored is in reality adequately protected during the period of its greatest activity.

Toads, which are found away from water, are generally soil-colored and in addition have a very rough skin, so that a toad may appear to be a lump of dirt to the casual eye. Frogs, on the other hand, live close to water where grass and other plants are abundant; large parts of their bodies are green. In the tadpole stage, however, they are grayish-brown and match their environment, resembling mud. Desert animals like the horned toad are usually dull gray in color, or brown.

The praying mantis (an insect) has served as a subject for experimentation on protective coloration. When the green mantis is placed on dead grass, it is soon eaten by birds; and when the brown mantis is placed on green grass, it too is soon eaten. When the brown mantis is placed on dead grass, however, it generally escapes the attention of the birds, and the same thing is true of the green mantis on green grass. The female ostrich is brownish-gray in color, while the male is black. When eggs are being incubated, the hen sits on the eggs during the day and the cock at night. During the day the hen is the more inconspicuous of the two; at night the cock is less easily seen.

The colors and the pattern of colors of many animals change, matching their backgrounds, and thus they are protected under varying conditions. The tree frog, found in many parts of the United States, is one of these. Chameleons, found in the Southeastern states, are able to change colors with rapidity. *Fun-*

dulus, a marine fish found on the east coast of the United States, changes from a light gray to a very dark gray, according to the color of the ocean bottom beneath it. Flounders possess a quite remarkable ability to change their colors and the patterns of their colors in imitation of their background.

There are still many disagreements among biologists concerning the value of concealing coloration to the animal. It must be remembered that what may protect from one predator may be of no value at all as protection from another. Some animals are well protected by their coloration so long as they remain very quiet; these will often not stir, even though they are being killed. Those animals which are predators are also colored in such a way that they are not easily seen by their prey, so that coloration may be of value, not only to the hunted animal, but also to the hunter.

It has already been pointed out that some animals are protectively colored in one way during one stage of life and in another way in a later stage. Among mammals this is sometimes true of the deer. The fawn is usually brown and spotted, so that so long as it remains quiet in the forest, it is not easily detected. The feathers of young birds are drably colored, so that the birds are not easily discovered. It is only in their second year that many birds achieve their brilliant hues.

The coloration of some animals changes with the seasons. Thus the white-tailed ptarmigan, which is found only at high altitudes, is gray and brown during the summertime. These colors match the soil in the summer. During the winter, however, it becomes white, and is thus inconspicuous against a background of snow. The varying hare of arctic regions is found to be brown in the summer and white during the winter. Weasels, dark brown in the summer, also become white in the winter in some cases. Animals which live in regions of perpetual snow are white in color the year round. The polar bear does not vary, but remains white at all times. The same thing is true of the foxes of arctic regions, which are often pure white instead of brown, red, or gray like the foxes in temperate regions. The snowy owl is another illustration of white coloration which makes the animal blend with its surroundings.

Some animals have conspicuous colors or markings, which serve as warning or recognition marks to others. Not all conspicuously marked animals, however, are successful in thus avoiding the animals which hunt them, for in some instances the bright coloration seems to attract rather than repel predators. It seems, however, that there are many cases of actual protective coloration so conspicuous that it acts as a warning, as in skunks.

A polar bear on the ice is hard to see.

Many animals avoid close contact with skunks.

Birds often display their colors during courtship, and among many species some of the colors displayed during courtship are concealed at other times. The conspicuous white tail of the rabbit is thought by some to be a recognition mark by means of which other members of the species can identify one of their own kind. The same thing may be said of the white tails of antelope, although some biologists maintain that these markings are concealing, or protective, marks rather than recognition signals, serving to confuse the predator just as it attempts to grasp the prey during the hunt. It is also thought by some biologists that those sea birds which live in colonies are able to recognize their eggs because of their colors. In general, it may be said that the whole question of warning and recognition coloration is open to further investigation.

Resemblance to Objects in the Environment Seems to Afford Animals Some Protection. Some animals resemble their background not only in color but also in shape. Some insects,

for example, resemble sticks; it is this fact which gave the walking stick its name. Some brightly colored spiders are able to catch insects on account of the resemblance between the spider and flowers. There is a species of fish in South America which resembles a drifting leaf not only in appearance but also in movement. Those insects which feed on green plants are generally green in color.

Mimicry, or resemblance of an animal in shape as well as in color to its background or to objects upon which it may be resting, has already been mentioned. Numerous examples of this type of protection from predators may be cited. In the Sargasso Sea (that part of the Atlantic Ocean which is covered with great patches of the seaweed called sargasso, or gulfweed) many kinds of creatures exist which feed on the plants and live among them. These plants are olive-yellow in color, and most of the animals found there are also

A sargassum fish resembles a clump of seaweed. (The American Museum of Natural History.)

olive-yellow in color. Small fish, shrimps, crabs, one kind of flatworm, and other animals are all of this same hue. In addition, they have on their bodies small white markings which are also characteristic of the sea-weed.

Inchworms, or spanworms, which are the larvae of the geometrid moth, are twiglike in appearance. When they are disturbed, they erect themselves and stand out stiffly from the twig or branch upon which they rest, so that they resemble in position, as well as in color, a broken twig. The walking sticks have already been mentioned; another member of that family of insects is called the green-leaf insect and is found in South America. Its wings are green, broad, and leaflike, mimicking even the veins of leaves by their marking. On these wings are also found irregular yellowish or brown spots which resemble decaying spots on leaves. In our own country the common meadow browns (butterflies) have ragged edges on their wings. They appear in the autumn and flutter aimlessly about, looking much like falling leaves.

One of the most famous examples of mimicry is the large East Indian butterfly *Kallima*. The upper surfaces of its wings are dark with purple and orange markings which do not resemble a dead leaf. But the lower surface of each wing is exactly the color of a dead leaf. The markings are such that the midrib and oblique veins are mimicked, and there are two marks which resemble holes in leaves. These two spots are free of scales and consequently are transparent, thus imitating a leaf in which a hole has been eaten by an insect. When the butterfly is at rest, these markings of the lower surface are all exposed, since the butterfly holds its wings together in a vertical position over its back. In this position it looks much like a dry leaf that is still attached to the twig.

One of the most abundant butterflies in North America is known as the monarch butterfly. Insect specialists believe that the mon-

A Kallima butterfly resembles a leaf *(top).* The "walking stick" is almost indistinguishable from an ordinary stick *(bottom).*

arch butterfly is distasteful to birds, and that for this reason birds do not often eat it. It is conspicuously marked, being quite large and of a reddish-brown color. The viceroy butterfly resembles the monarch in many respects so far as marking and color are concerned, but it is found to be edible when fed to birds. It is thought that it derives a protection from its similarity to the monarch butterflies, since its close resemblance to them would cause it to be shunned by its predators. In tropical regions there are a number of similar examples of mimicry among butterflies.

Most instances of mimicry are found among insects, but there are also examples among other animals. The coral snake is venomous; it resembles in coloration the king snake, a nonvenomous species. Each of these species of snake has red, yellow, and black bands that surround the cylindrical body. An animal that has some characteristic that makes it undesirable as food, such as spines, a hard shell, or unpalatable taste, or an animal whose habits of movement make it difficult to capture, is called the *model*. The animal which resembles the model in color, shape, size, or activity and apparently derives protection in this manner is called the *mimic*. A very hungry animal, however, is often not deterred by any of these characteristics, so that either the mimic or its model may fall prey to it. Mimicry, like concealing and warning coloration, involves problems which have not been settled. There is doubt on the part of some biologists that mimicry can be explained in terms of protection to the animal.

EXPERIENCE. *To observe protective mechanisms of animals.* Suggest to the children that they observe animals in their community to see if they can determine which ones are protected from their predators by protective coloration or protective shape. Encourage the children to consider how well the protective mechanism of the animals they observe is helping to protect the animal. They should check their observations with authentic materials whenever possible.

Films and filmstrips are of value in a study of the protective mechanisms of animals, because they show many animals the children might not see otherwise.

Animals May Protect Themselves by Noxious Secretions. Some animals secure protection from predators by means of secretions which they produce. Perhaps the best-known example of such an animal is the skunk. This beast is famous for the two scent glands by means of which it produces a very strong-smelling, golden-colored liquid which it can eject for some distance behind itself. Its coloration is such that, once seen, it cannot be mistaken for any other creature, and one experience with it is sufficient to cause most animals to shun it ever after. Consequently the skunk thrives in almost any sort of environment in which its food is abundant. It feeds largely upon insects and small birds. It is an apparently stupid animal, being easily trapped by man; and it moves about at night seeking food in an unhurried manner, surviving despite its lack of speed because carnivorous predators give it a wide berth. Young dogs sometimes attack skunks, but they seldom do so a second time. Its protection is the strong-scented liquid it produces.

Toads are not often attacked or eaten by larger animals, because they can secrete a substance which seems to be distasteful. A dog may pick up a toad, but it will soon drop it again. Some snakes, however, eat toads despite this protective device. In Nicaragua there is a little red-and-blue frog which is abundant in the damp woods and which is so ill-tasting that it is not eaten.

Most of the various species of ladybird beetles, conspicuous for their red-and-black coloration, are not eaten by birds, because of their bad taste. Children who have had the experience of picking and eating strawberries know that occasionally they bite into a berry which is very ill-tasting. If they remove it from their mouths and investigate, they will find that on the berry was a flattened, green, shield-shaped insect commonly called the stinkbug. Its protection against birds seems to be its distastefulness.

The common carrot caterpillar, which is the larval form of the black swallowtail butterfly, has a "carroty" odor. This caterpillar has a V-shaped orange-colored pocket on top of its head. When this is touched lightly, structures resembling horns, orange in color, will appear and eject a liquid which is very distasteful. The distastefulness of the monarch butterfly has already been mentioned.

Human beings themselves generally avoid

Bison calves are protected by the herd.

eating the meat of carnivorous animals, thus indicating that the flesh of these is unpalatable. To this extent carnivorous animals are protected against man.

Numbers Are a Protection to Social Animals. The social habits of some animals are a protection against predators. Bison calves are protected from wolves by the herd, for no wolf dares to attack a number of bison when they face him with lowered horns. Bees and wasps generally attack their enemies en masse when the hive or colony is threatened. Quail, when they find a resting place for the night on the ground, form a ring in which the individuals face outward in all directions, thus making it possible to detect danger from any source. Deer and antelope, when grazing in small groups, generally post a sentinel to act as lookout; this animal warns the others of imminent danger.

EXPERIENCE. *To observe that some animals are very noisy and others are very quiet.* Encourage children to observe the noises that animals make. A trip to a farm, park, woods, or zoo might provide an excellent opportunity for children to listen to animals. A list of animals that

were heard to make very little or no noise, and those that were heard to make a great deal of noise may be helpful. Note also whether any of the animals that are noisy are social animals.

Protective Adaptations Make Survival Possible. The means by which animals are protected from predators are, then, numerous. Only a few of the many examples are given here. Those animals which are otherwise defenseless often have keenly developed sight or hearing, or they are capable of running away from their enemy very rapidly. Some animals can take to water if they are pursued too closely, and thus manage to escape. Others, like raccoons, opossums, and squirrels, may climb trees when the chase becomes desperate. A muskrat will dive into water very quickly when danger threatens, and so will a frog. A bird takes to the air and flies away as rapidly as possible, while frogs, toads, grasshoppers, and other animals may hop in long jumps in an effort to escape. A prairie dog jumps into its den in the ground at the approach of a predator; moles stay under the surface as much as possible.

EXPERIENCES. *To find how many animals escape from predators.* Through discussion and reading one may encourage children to become interested in the different ways animals escape from harm. Children might find it interesting to make a list of animals that are able to avoid close contact with predators. They might indicate on this list the structural adaptations that make escape possible. Examples are the long legs of the deer or antelope used in a speedy take-off. There might also be an interest on the part of some children in seeing how certain animals are superior to other animals, and sometimes man, in the development of their special senses. Examples which might be mentioned are the acute hearing and sight of the jack rabbit, the acute sense of smell of the armadillo, the well-developed eyes of birds like the crow, and the ability to see clearly in very dim light possessed by the owls.

Children could list all the protective devices they know of. Perhaps they might be interested in grouping the devices into divisions such as "escape" and "fighting."

Children might like to illustrate some of the protective devices in clay models, in sketches, or in murals. A horse or deer with its long, slender legs could show speed; animals with sharp teeth could show biting; animals with claws could show how they are used; animals with horns and antlers might illustrate how these are used for protection.

Every animal is adapted to its biological environment as well as to its physical environment. The protective adaptations are not the result of conscious or intelligent action, but rather they are the result of a process of natural selection and survival of the fittest which has been going on since the origin of life. Those animals least able to escape become the victims; those which survive are able to exist because of special defense adaptations. By heredity they transmit these defense characteristics to their offspring, so that these too can survive. Further elimination is constantly taking place, with a resultant improvement in the defense mechanism of the species.

Let us imagine, for the sake of clarifying this point, that a new species of porcupine without the protective quills should arise. The porcupine is a slow, witless animal, and it depends on its quills for protection; the quills are really adequate to keep most animals from attacking this beast. The new species of porcupine, without quills, would soon be killed by dogs, wolves, and other animals, so that the species would not be perpetuated. Similarly, if trout in a brook were not so very shy, they would be much easier to catch, and their numbers would be greatly depleted. If a new species of trout arose, lacking the shyness which characterizes others, man and other predators would soon put an end to the species.

Occasionally, through migration of animals or through importation by man, a new predator is introduced into an animal community. If the new animal is a bloodthirsty one, it may work havoc with the native species simply because sometimes these have no protection devices against the invader. Ferrets, which are very much like minks and weasels in appearance and habits, are sometimes acquired by farmers to exterminate rats and mice. Once having done this, the ferret will then often destroy the farmer's poultry flock, or it may destroy the wild rabbits in the neighborhood.

So man must ever be on his guard lest he upset the natural competition of living things to such an extent that he cannot control the forces he has set loose. The draining of a swamp, the construction of a dam, the burning of a forest, the plowing of a hillside, may have profound influence on all life in a community, including man himself. The extermination of a species that has lived in an environment or the introduction of a new one may affect the prosperity of man. All this means that man must conserve all his natural resources, including living things.

Porcupines are equipped with effective weapons of defense.

CHAPTER 16

Living Things Change

Plants and Animals Are Constantly Changing

Changes of various kinds are continually taking place in the environment, as we have seen, so that neither the physical nor the biological aspect of any community is ever static. Plants and animals as individuals are also continually changing, and a consideration of some of these changes in their development is necessary in any study of life.

With the exception of those plants and animals which reproduce by cell division, reproduction involves special reproductive cells, which are very different in appearance from the parent organism. The spore of a mushroom is not much like the mature plant which produced it. Similarly the egg and sperm cells of the ferns and mosses unite to form a zygote which at first resembles neither the sexually reproducing generation nor the spore-producing generation. Acorns grow into oaks, although the seed itself resembles the oak in no way which can be determined by a casual inspection; neither does a wheat seed resemble a wheat plant. The egg of a bird and the developing zygote within are not much like the brilliantly colored adults which produced it, except that both are made up of cells. A frog's egg does not suggest the adult or even the tadpole, and the fertilized egg of a starfish goes through several changes before it resembles the animal with which children who play on ocean beaches are familiar.

Most kinds of living things develop gradually and so change their appearance gradually from the time of the fertilization of the egg untile the maturity of the individual.

Animals grow and change.

586

Many Plants Develop from Seeds

Although most children have had the experience of watching the development of seeds of various kinds from the time they are planted until they develop into mature plants, the subject is one which generally interests them when studied in the classroom. Large seeds like Lima beans and sweet corn or field corn may be used profitably for study. For this reason these seeds need special attention.

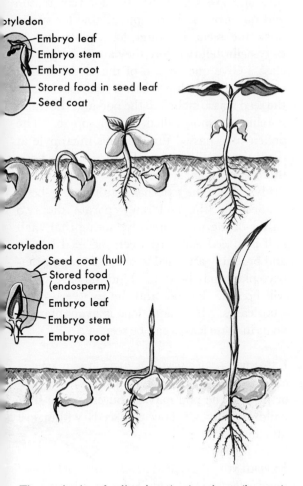

The germination of a lima bean (top) and corn (bottom).

Lima beans are known to most children, but their various structures may be pointed out to them. Where the bean was attached to the pod is a scar which is called the *hilum*. At one end of this scar there is a very small hole called the *micropyle,* through which the pollen tube passes. The seed has a membrane around it called the *seed coat.* Each of the two halves of the Lima-bean seed is called a *seed leaf,* and these contain starch, proteins, and other food substances on which the developing plant lives while the seed is germinating. The food supply stored here is sufficient to keep the plant alive until it has produced leaves and is capable of carrying on photosynthesis. By the time the plant has developed two or more large, green, true leaves, the food supply in the seed leaves is exhausted, and they drop off.

The bean is known as a *dicotyledon,* which means a plant whose seed has two seed leaves. Some plants, such as corn, the various grains, and the common grasses, produce seeds with only one seed leaf; they are therefore known as *monocotyledons.* In these, food is not stored in the seed leaf but in another part called the *endosperm.*

The Germination of Seeds. As seeds ripen, the growth of the embryo within stops completely. Seeds leave the plant that bore them and are dormant until conditions are right for them to germinate. They will need water, warmth, and air. During germination they soak up water and swell; the entrance of oxygen is made easier and respiration increases; finally enzymes are activated and food is digested; assimilation and cell division occurs. This results in the breaking of the seed coat and the growth of the embryo. First the young root emerges and gradually takes over its function of taking in water and nutrients. Then the young shoot pushes upward, and if conditions are favorable, the young plant continues its growth. It will continue to need water, warmth, and air and will also need light for the making of food.

Up to a certain point seeds can be dried and wetted many times without any effect on the growth of the embryo. Once the embryo begins to enlarge, the process cannot be reversed.

Not all seeds will germinate as soon as they mature. Some go through a period of dormancy lasting from a few months to several years. Other seeds have such hard seed coats that they will not soak up water nor take in oxygen. Ordinarily, freezing and thawing and the action of microorganisms in the soil will soften such seed coats.

Children can have experiences with living things.

EXPERIENCES. *To observe some conditions that influence the germination of seeds.* (1) Children may prepare three identical pots of soil. Plant 5 to 10 lima bean seeds in each pot. Number the pots 1, 2, and 3. Set them side by side so that all will have the same amount of warmth. Keep pot 1 soaked with water. It might be set in a dish with water in it. Keep pot 2 moderately moist at all times. Do not water pot 3 except right after planting the seeds. Examine the seeds in each pot after 10 days. Which germinated and grew best? (2) Prepare two identical pots of soil, and plant lima bean seeds in both. Place one in a warm spot and the other in the refrigerator (do not permit it to freeze). Give both pots the same amount of water, and keep moderately moist. After 10 days, examine the seeds. What conclusions can be drawn from these two experiences about water and heat?

EXPERIENCE. *To show children the different parts of a bean seed.* Secure some Lima-bean seeds from a seed store. Do not get Lima beans of the cooking kind from a grocery store; for

these are often picked when they are immature and are kiln-dried, and for that reason will not grow and are not suitable for study. Soak the seeds in water for twenty-four to forty-eight hours before they are to be used in class. Give one or two of the seeds to each child, and have him observe the scar where the seed was attached to the pod and the small porelike opening called the micropyle. The pollen tube passed through this micropyle at the time of pollination. If the seeds have been thoroughly soaked, the seed coat will slip off easily. After the external features have been studied, let the children separate the two halves of the seed carefully, noting that each half is a seed leaf. Between the seed leaves, and probably attached to one of them, the embryo plant may be seen. Find the part which will become the root and the two very small true leaves. If a hand lens is available, the veins in these leaves can be seen.

EXPERIENCE. *To show how beans or peas grow in a pod.* In a grocery store sufficient Lima beans or peas in the pod may be purchased so that children may see how the seeds within are attached to the pod.

EXPERIENCE. *To show that seeds contain food stored in the form of starch.* Take some bean, pea,

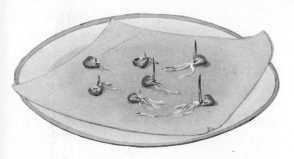

Seeds will sprout between layers of moist blotting paper.

or corn seeds and grind them up thoroughly. Mix a little of the flour thus formed with a little water and add a drop or two of iodine solution. Note the blue color, which indicates the presence of starch.

EXPERIENCE. *To watch the germination process of seeds.* Take some corn, bean, clover, and any other kinds of seeds which may be available. Cut some blotting paper to fit saucers in which the seeds are to be germinated. Moisten this blotting paper, put it on the saucer, and place the seeds on it. Cover with another piece of blotting paper and keep continually moist until they germinate. The children will notice that the plant then develops roots and leaves and is able to live for some time without soil. The plants will usually live until the food material in the seed leaves has been used up.

EXPERIENCE. *To watch the changes which take place in a plant as it develops.* Plant some corn, bean, and other seeds in small boxes or flowerpots. Keep the soil moist. The children may watch how long it takes each kind of seed to appear above the ground and the subsequent development. If glass jars are used and the seed placed next to the glass, children will be able to watch the early development of the root and stem. Plants in such containers should be transplanted after a short time to containers from which moisture can enter or leave through a hole or holes in the bottom.

Most Animals Develop from a Fertilized Egg. Most animals, like most plants, go through a series of changes from the time the egg is fertilized until the individual reaches maturity. As was noted previously, the fertilized egg divides and redivides until it forms a hollow ball of cells; then further changes take place, and the various layers of cells—the ectoderm, the endoderm, and the mesoderm between them—are formed. From these layers of cells the various organs and systems of the adult animal are produced. The entire process thus far is a fairly rapid one in most animals. There follows a slowing down in the process, marked by a sort of transition from the unspecialized cells in the hollow-ball stage to the highly specialized cells of the animal just before birth or hatching. By "specialized cells" is meant cells which have assumed certain functions; some cells become muscle cells, others form the lungs, still others form skin or nerve tissue, and so on.

The changes that take place in animals following birth or hatching are sometimes very great. Frequently the young resemble the parents, but usually even in these cases many changes take place as the young mature. For example young jack rabbits, guinea pigs, snakes, turtles, colts, calves, and many other young animals resemble their parents, but all of these animals change in size, activity, food requirements, and in other ways as they mature. Animals such as opossums show little resemblance to the parents at birth and undergo many changes during development.

There is also a great difference in the time it takes animals to mature and become capable of reproduction. For example, field mice mature in four weeks, whales mature in three years, humans usually mature between the ages of ten and one half and eighteen years, and elephants do not reach sexual maturity until they reach an age of thirty years or more. Usually the female of the species matures earlier than the male. There is also variation in age of maturity within each species. Differences also occur in the average length of life of different species of animals. Changes take place very rapidly in animals like field mice that live only 1½ years, whereas in elephants that have a live span of 130 years or more the changes are more gradual.

EXPERIENCE. *To observe changes in the growth and development of animals.* Children might like to compare their growth with the growth of a pet such as a dog, cat, or rabbit. Some very young children have had a puppy given to them during its first year of life and are success-

ful in keeping the dog until its death from old age. These children will have an excellent opportunity to compare their rate of maturity with that of the dog. Children may become aware of great differences in rate of growth and in the age when maturity is reached by keeping a pair of mice until several litters have matured. If records are kept, these may be compared with records of the children's own rate of growth or that a dog, cat, or chicken. The use of art in showing the differences in growth might be of interest to children and also give opportunity for originality in interpretation of records.

Metamorphosis—A Type of Change

In some animals the development from the fertilized egg to the mature individual is so marked by definite stages that it is called *metamorphosis*. Metamorphosis is characterized by sudden changes in the form of the animal, and some of the stages are very unlike the adult which finally develops. Children see animals in these various stages and find it difficult to understand just what happens; for they often do not associate the caterpillar with the butterfly, the grub with the beetle which it becomes, or the tadpole with the frog unless they have had considerable experience with these animals.

Metamorphosis Is Characteristic of Many Kinds of Animals. Metamorphosis is generally studied in connection with insects, but it is also typical of many other animals. The fertilized egg of the starfish develops in such a way that it passes through a number of stages, in some of which the young animal in no way resembles its parent. These changes take place in from two weeks to two months.

When the eggs of mussels are fertilized, they first develop into larvae which in some cases attach themselves to the gills of a fish for a number of weeks, and metamorphosis takes place there. The larvae live during this time as parasites. Mature oysters are sedentary animals; but at first, in the larva form, they are able to swim about freely for a short time, after which they settle to the bottom of the ocean in fairly shallow water, attach themselves to some object, and from that time on lead a sedentary life.

Because frogs and tadpoles are within the experience of many children, and because they may be watched as they develop in the classroom, they make interesting objects for a study of metamorphosis. The eggs of frogs and toads are laid early in the spring. Frogs' eggs are laid in rather large, more or less round masses, and are embedded in a mass of a gelatinous material which is deposited in the water by the female at the time that she lays the eggs. They are generally dull black in color on the top surface; since black absorbs sunlight, they are able to develop quickly, because the light energy of the sun is absorbed and transformed by absorption into heat energy. The lower surface of the egg is generally light in color.

As the egg develops, it seems to lengthen; and within a few days the tadpole may be seen wriggling within the gelatinous mass in an attempt to free itself. Within the egg there is a quantity of food which the embryo uses as a source of energy, and thus it can nourish itself until it is able to find its own food. After the tadpole breaks out of the egg, it begins to feed on microscopic plant life found in the water. At this stage careful inspection of the tadpole reveals, on each side of the head, structures which are gills, by means of which the animal gets its supply of oxygen from the water. Later these gills disappear; they have been replaced by four pairs of internal gills, which have taken over the function of breathing.

At this stage of its development the tadpole has many of the characteristics of a fish. It has no legs, and breathes by means of gills. It subsists entirely on plant food. It has a tail, and it moves through the water by the manipulation of this tail and its body in a fishlike manner. If its food supply is plentiful, the tadpole grows rapidly and eats voraciously. The tadpoles of most frogs begin the development of legs during the summer. The hind legs appear first, and later the front legs appear. While this is happening, the gills are disappearing, lungs are being developed, and the tail is being absorbed. The cells of which the tail is composed are being broken down, and the protoplasm found in them in transported by the blood stream to other cells, where it is used as a source of food. Soon the tadpole has all the external and internal characteristics of a frog, but it is much smaller in size.

At this time it emerges from the water and leads a land existence, although it does not stray far from the pond or stream in which it developed. Toads are more apt to wander some distance from the pond and return to it only the following spring to lay their eggs. The metamorphosis of a frog or toad occurs during one spring and summer. Bullfrog tadpoles, which are generally much larger and can be distinguished from frog tadpoles by the black spots on their back, need two and sometimes three summers in which to change from the egg to the adult stage. Thus the metamorphosis of frogs and toads is characterized by a change from an aquatic, fishlike, planteating animal to a terrestrial animal which breathes by means of lungs, possesses four legs, and feeds on insects and other animals of that general type (p. 530).

EXPERIENCE. *To demonstrate the metamorphosis of frogs.* Children may bring to class some frog or toad eggs. These may be found in ponds early in the spring when the first frogs are heard at night. Keep the eggs in a well-balanced aquarium or fairly large water tank. If they are kept in a tank, change the water frequently, so that there will not be an excess of carbon dioxide. Keep in a place where there is light but not too much direct sunlight. Have children study the development of the eggs and note the movement of the tadpoles as they attempt to wriggle free of the gelatinous mass; have them note the external gills at this time. Keep the eggs on hand as long as is practical. If an aquarium which has a growth of algae on its sides is available, they may be kept until the close of school. They need not be fed. Remember that sometimes the eggs brought in will not be fertile, because they have not been fertilized, and so they will not develop but will "spoil."

Insect Development Is of Three General Types. In the phylum Arthropoda, to which belong the numerous species of crabs, lobsters, shrimps, spiders, millepedes, insects, and other joint-legged animals, metamorphosis is best illustrated because it occurs very frequently.

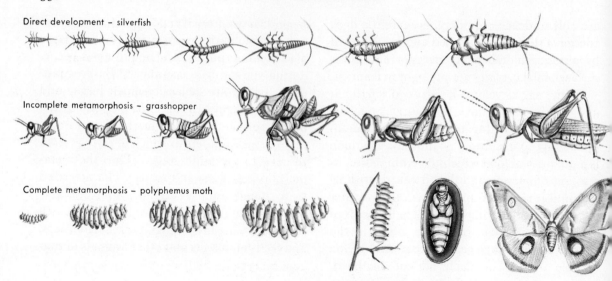

Direct development – silverfish

Incomplete metamorphosis – grasshopper

Complete metamorphosis – polyphemus moth

Three different types of development.

One species of shrimp hatches from the egg as a larva which has three pairs of appendages. All the arthropods *molt;* that is, they shed their outer skeletons as they grow larger. After the first molt, the shrimp larva, which originally had three pairs of appendages, now has six. Later it molts again, this time having eight pairs of appendages, and subsequent molts result in thirteen and as many as nineteen pairs of appendages, thus showing a considerable degree of change as its development progresses.

The development of insects is characterized by three kinds of changes. Some of the primitive, wingless insects do not go through metamorphosis at all. When they emerge from the egg, which has been laid by the female, they resemble the adult in every respect except that they are not capable of carrying on reproduction at once and are smaller. The fish moths, which are found in places where they can feed on dry starchy foods, are such insects. These have been known to include even starched clothes in their diet. Another example of *no metamorphosis* among insects is the snow fleas. Early in the spring they infest maple-sugar camps, being attracted by the sap which is

being collected and in which they are often found.

Many kinds of insects develop by what is known as *incomplete* metamorphosis. When the young insect emerges from the egg, it resembles the adult in many respects; but it is lacking in wings and other structures, the reproductive organs are immature, and it is much smaller than the adult. Incomplete metamorphosis is found in such insects as lice, aphids (or plant lice), dragonflies, stone flies, termites, cockroaches, walking sticks, praying mantids, grasshoppers, locusts, katydids, crickets, and May flies. In those insects in which the metamorphosis is incomplete, the young insect is often called a *nymph;* if the immature insect passes part of its life cycle in water, it is at that time called a *naiad.*

Most of the numerous species of insects go through four distinct stages of development in their metamorphosis, which is called *complete metamorphosis.* Included in this category are such well-known insects as honeybees, moths, butterflies, ant lions, caddis flies, ants, wasps, gallflies, beetles, fleas, houseflies, and mosquitoes. The first stage in the life of any insect is the egg stage. In those insects which undergo complete metamorphosis, this is followed by the *larva* stage; the larva is followed by the *pupa* stage; and the final transformation occurs when the *adult* insect emerges from the pupa.

Grasshoppers Illustrate Incomplete Metamorphosis. Grasshoppers are fairly common insects, which may be used as examples of incomplete metamorphosis. When the young has just emerged from the egg, it resembles in general the adult and can easily be recognized as a grasshopper. It is, of course, much smaller; it may be so small that it must be examined rather carefully in order to determine its features and structures. It is usually much greener in color than the adult and possesses no wings. Almost immediately after hatching it begins to feed on the vegetation around it, consuming comparatively great quantities of food.

If conditions are favorable, it soon grows so large that its outer skeleton becomes too small; the skeleton splits and is cast off. The insect then resumes the feeding process, and growth continues until another molt occurs. The young insect molts a number of times; each time it is larger and more like the adult. After a time rudimentary wings appear; these develop with the molts from time to time until finally the adult stage is reached. During all this development the insect is active and at no time passes into a quiescent state. With the approach of maturity the reproductive organs become functional, and soon reproduction is possible. When the female has matured, she lays fertilized eggs in the ground by means of a structure found at the tip of the abdomen. This structure is called the ovipositor.

Four Definite Stages Characterize Complete Metamorphosis. *Insect Eggs Represent the First Stage of Metamorphosis.* Insects which pass through complete metamorphosis, like those which develop by incomplete metamorphosis, begin life as a fertilized egg. In a few instances the insect egg remains within the body of the female until it hatches, but these are exceptions to the general rule. The eggs of insects are usually laid on or near a supply of food suitable for the larva which will hatch from them. The female walking stick, however, simply drops her eggs on the ground beneath the tree upon which she happens to be feeding at the time.

The apple-tree tent-caterpillar moth lays her eggs in a ringlike cluster around the twig of a wild cherry or apple tree, in the fall of the year, and they remain there about nine months before they hatch. The larvae emerge from the eggs just as the leaves of these trees are developing in the spring. The lime-tree winter moth lays her eggs under loose bark and in crevices on the trunks of trees. Some mosquitoes lay their eggs side by side in raftlike clusters, from which they hatch in a few days. Many kinds of insects lay their eggs on the ground or just beneath the surface of the ground; often larvae of these species feed and remain in the soil until they emerge as adults. Bees lay their eggs in cells in the honeycomb. Some flies deposit their eggs upon the carcasses of decaying animals or plants, and the young larvae feed on the decomposing organic matter.

Some insects lay their eggs in manure piles and similar waste matter. Carrion beetles, when they discover a dead mouse, bird, or other small animal, dig under it until it is beneath the surface of the ground. Then they cover the carcass with soil. The female beetle digs through the soil until she reaches the carrion, upon which she deposits her eggs, thus ensuring the larvae a supply of food.

The currant-borer lays its eggs on the twigs of currant bushes; and when the eggs hatch, the larvae penetrate through the stem of the twig and devour the pith in the center of it. The eggs of the peach-tree borer are laid on the bark of the tree just below the surface of

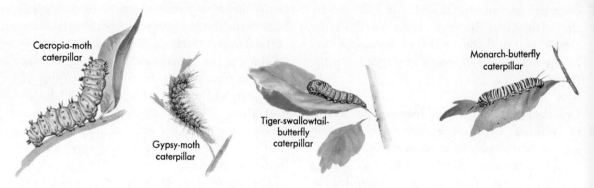

Plant destroyers.

the ground. Chinch-bug females lay their eggs in the spring in fields of grain on the roots or underground stems of the plants. In about two weeks these eggs hatch, and the larvae attack the plants and cause much destruction.

The water boatmen lay their eggs on the stems and leaves of water plants. The tussock moth, whose larva does so much damage to the foliage of shade and fruit trees, lays her eggs on the cocoon from which she has emerged. One method of controlling this insect is to gather these cocoons, from which the female has emerged, and destroy them, thus also destroying the eggs. Tachina flies lay their eggs on the backs of caterpillars. When the larvae hatch from the eggs, they bore into the body of the caterpillar and feed on it until they are fully grown and ready for the pupa stage of development.

Some species of guest bees lay their eggs in the nests of bumblebees, and the larvae eat the food which has been stored by the host bumblebee. Many kinds of insects lay their eggs on the lower surfaces of the leaves of plants on which the larvae feed.

When viewed with a good hand lens or with the low-power lens of a microscope, insect eggs are found to vary considerably in size, color, and shape. The eggs of some insects have smooth shells; sometimes, however, the eggs are ribbed or pitted, and sometimes they have spines. Often they are exquisitely and delicately colored.

Larvae Represents the Second Stage of Metamorphosis. The larva stage is one in which the insect feeds voraciously. Various common names are applied to insects in this stage. The larvae of beetles are sometimes called *grubs,* while the larvae of flies, especially when they are found on decaying organic material, are referred to as *maggots.* The larvae of moths and butterflies are usually called *caterpillars.* Children sometimes make no distinction between the kinds of larvae, but call them all by one name, "worms." Insect larvae are not worms, however; they are very different from the earthworms, tapeworms, and flatworms, which are true worms.

The sole function of the insect in the larval stage is to feed and grow. All the molting which results from increase in size occurs during the larval stage; later molts occur when a change of shape of the insect is imminent. Because of the enormous quantities of food necessary to continue the growth of the larvae, it is in this stage that most of the damage they cause is done.

Tent caterpillars, for example, hatch from eggs in the spring of the year. They may hatch even before the leaves have appeared, in which case they feed on the unopened buds until the leaves expand. The larvae are social in habit, for the entire brood that hatches from a cluster of eggs remains together and builds the familiar nest, or tent, in which they live when they are not feeding. After hatching, the larvae often migrate down the branch toward the trunk of the tree until they reach a fork of considerable size. Here they build their tent, which may be as long as two feet. As the larvae leave the tent, they spin a silken thread wherever they go. Because they generally appear in considerable numbers, they may strip whole branches of foliage, injuring the tree in this way. The insect may be controlled to some extent by destroying the tents as soon as they are seen in the spring of the year. This must be done in the early morning or late in the afternoon, for at other times the larvae are not in the nest. They remain in the tent on cold days also.

Another insect larva which is very destructive is the army worm. It was given its name because it appears in great numbers; and after destroying the vegetation in the field in which it hatches from eggs, it marches like an army to other fields. It is the larva of a rather small moth which is dull brown in color; the larva itself is about one and a half inches long when fully grown and is striped with black, yellow, and green. Cabbage and other garden vegetables are often attacked by a caterpillar which is light yellow in color and has three broad longitudinal stripes of black, one on each side and one on the back. Cutworms which cut off the roots of corn and other plants in the early spring, and which are active at night, are the larvae of owlet moths. Some kinds of cutworms ascend trees during the night and cut off and destroy the young buds.

The larvae of the cotton-bollworm moth are the well-known cotton bollworms, which have done much damage to cotton crops. This larva also frequently infests tomatoes, eating both the green and the ripe fruit. It bores into the bolls of the cotton, thus destroying them. Another larva which infests cotton is the cotton worm, which destroys the foliage of the plant and thus hampers its growth.

The raspberry geometrid-moth larvae feed on the fruit of the raspberry plant. They have a curious habit of covering themselves with bits of vegetable matter. The ends of the leaves of pine trees sometimes are found to be brown in color and dead in appearance. This is because the larva of the pine-leaf miner has eaten out the interior of the pine leaf, or needle. The larvae of the basswood leaf roller have the habit of cutting more than halfway across the leaf, the cut portion of which then curls. Within the curled portion of the leaf lives the larva of this insect. The larvae of the melon worm live on the foliage and fruit of melon plants, often causing serious damage to the crop. Meal-moth larvae feed on flour, meal, and clover hay. The larvae of the bee moths feed on the wax in the honeycomb of bees, and spin silk-lined galleries in the honeycomb, thus destroying it for any use.

The adult female ox warble fly lays her eggs on the backs of cattle. The young larvae are licked by the cattle from the back and swallowed. They first live in large numbers in the esophagus of the animal, from which place they apparently migrate through the body until they come to rest just beneath the skin. The eggs of the sheep botfly are laid in the nostrils of sheep, where the larvae hatch. They then pass up into the sinuses of the bones of the head. Other species of flies infest rabbits, squirrels, deer, and reindeer.

The horse botfly, which somewhat resembles a bee, lays its eggs on the legs and shoulders of horses. There the larvae emerge and bore their way into the body of the horse. When the larvae reach the stomach, they fasten themselves to it and remain there until they have attained their full larval growth, when they are eliminated from the intestinal tract by the normal elimination of undigested food material. The larvae of all the botflies are parasitic on mammals.

Another group of flies, known as the thick-headed flies, produces larvae which are parasitic on locusts, bumblebees, and wasps. The larvae of the humpbacked flies are thought to feed on decaying vegetable and animal matter, while the larvae of the flatfooted flies live in decaying mushrooms. Horsefly larvae are carnivorous and feed on various small animals, such as the larvae of other insects and snails.

Some insect larvae are cannibalistic. The water scavenger beetles lay their eggs in waterproof cases of a silklike secretion. As many as one hundred eggs may be deposited in a single case. Sometimes the egg cases are fastened beneath the leaves of aquatic plants. Frequently some of the larvae attack and devour others in the same egg case. They also feed on insects which have fallen into the water and on snails.

The larvae of the ladybug beetle feed on many species of harmful insects and are therefore considered beneficial. The larva of the carpet beetle lives in the cracks of floors along the edges of rooms and beneath furniture, and eats holes in carpets. It is a short thick grub, only about one fourth of an inch in length when fully grown.

Wireworms are the larvae of the click beetles. The adults of this insect are sometimes called snapping bugs, or skipjacks, because when placed on their backs they remain in that position for a short time; then with a sudden click they spring into the air several inches, generally land on their feet, and run off. The larvae of this insect are called wireworms because of the hardness of their wormlike bodies. Some of these larvae live under the bark of trees and in rotten wood. Many, however, live in the ground, where they feed on seeds and on the roots of grass and grain plants. They infest a great variety of plants, work beneath the surface of the soil, where it is difficult to observe them, and often cause serious damage by attacking young plants which are unable to withstand damage to roots.

The larvae of the large stag beetles develop from eggs which have been laid in crevices in the bark of trees. When the larvae hatch, they may bore into the trunk of the tree, reducing the wood to a coarse sawdust as they go. Similarly the larvae of the long-horned beetles are borers, living within the solid parts of woody plants or just beneath the bark. These larvae, or grubs, as they are more commonly known, are white or yellowish in color, and the body is soft, but the jaws are powerful enough to enable the insect to eat its way through the hardest wood. The adult cucumber beetle feeds on the leaves of cucumber and squash and melon plants, but the larvae bore through the stems and roots of the same plants.

The feeding habits of several kinds of insect larvae have been given to illustrate the wide diversity of ways in which they may cause damage. Emphasis must be placed on the fact that the larval stage is a stage of feeding and growth, and that the insect devours many times its own weight in food. It grows so rapidly that several molts are generally necessary in order that the external skeleton may accommodate the larva. This external skeleton is made up of a more or less horny substance known as *chitin*.

As the larva grows, the external skeleton becomes so firm that it limits further growth. The process of molting must then take place. Before it occurs, a new skin is formed beneath the old; the old skin, or external skeleton, then bursts open, and the insect crawls out of it. The new skin is at first soft and elastic; as the larva grows within it, it in turn becomes filled and is cast off. The total number of molts varies from only four or five in some species to as many as twenty in others.

Insect larvae also vary somewhat in external appearance. The maggot of most flies is a footless, wormlike larva. The caterpillars of some butterflies have spines; others, such as the caterpillar of the swallowtail butterfly, never have spines. They are hairless, green in color, ringed with black and spotted with yellow, and can project yellow horns which give off an unpleasant odor. Caterpillars of all kinds generally have from eight to sixteen legs. Six of these, the thoracic legs, have a hard external skeleton, and finally become the three pairs of legs which the insect possesses in its adult form. The others are called abdominal legs and are shed with the last molt in the larval stage. These are thick and fleshy and without joints. They are also called prolegs.

The reason for the gluttonous feeding of insects in the larval stage becomes apparent when one remembers that the next stage is wholly quiescent, in which the animal gets no food whatever. The larva must eat enough not only to grow but to be able to store a future source of energy in the form of fat for the quiescent stage. It has been estimated that the weight of the caterpillar of one kind of moth is more than four times as great in two months as its original weight, and that this caterpillar in that period eats many thousand times its original weight. It is because of the fact that insect larvae consume so much food that they are so destructive.

EXPERIENCE. *To secure insect eggs for use in class study.* Children often find insect eggs on the lower surfaces of leaves, on twigs and trunks of trees, and other places. Late in the spring and in September mosquito eggs may sometimes be found in small pools of stagnant water. Have children bring them to class and study them with the aid of a hand lens or magnifying glass. Late in the fall or during the winter clusters of praying-mantis eggs may be found on twigs. They are laid in masses and overlaid with a hard covering of silk. If kept in the classroom, these insects will hatch, and children may observe the process. Eggs may also be found on parsley, carrot, celery, bean, potato, tomato, and other plants. Ordinary house-flies may be kept in covered fruit jars in which a piece of decaying vegetable has been placed. If a number of flies are thus kept, some of them are likely to be females, which will lay eggs on the decaying vegetable.

The hatching of these eggs may then be observed. The eggs of grasshoppers and other insects may sometimes be found if a square of dirt from a meadow is brought to class and examined carefully for eggs.

EXPERIENCE. *To watch incomplete metamorphosis.* Young grasshoppers, locusts, or crickets may be brought into class by children and placed in a terrarium containing growing grass. The feeding habits and the growth of these insects may thus be studied.

EXPERIENCE. *To watch insects lay eggs.* Have children bring several adult grasshoppers to class. Place these in a wire-covered box in which grass is growing. The females may lay eggs in the soil, in which case the process may be watched by the pupils.

EXPERIENCE. *To observe the feeding habits of larvae.* Children may look for caterpillars and note what kinds of plants they are found upon. Some of these plants may be brought to class with the caterpillars on them for further observation of the feeding habits. If possible, locate some apple-tree tent-caterpillar larvae and bring them to class with the twig on which the tent is found. Have children bring to class "wormy" apples or pears, which may be cut open and the larvae within studied. Decaying mushrooms may also contain insect larvae. Insect larvae may also often be found within the galls on such plants as goldenrod, oak trees, willows, elms, dogwood, and roses.

The Pupal Stage Is One of External Inactivity. After having grown many times their original weight, and after having stored considerable quantities of fat in the body, the larvae of insects which undergo complete metamorphosis approach a period of inactivity known as the *pupal stage.* The insect becomes very quiescent so far as general activity is concerned; it does not move from one place to another. In

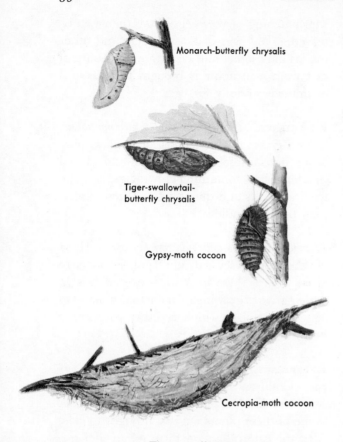

Monarch-butterfly chrysalis

Tiger-swallowtail-
butterfly chrysalis

Gypsy-moth cocoon

Cecropia-moth cocoon

These are all pupae.

many species the pupa, as the insect is called at this stage, can wriggle and squirm slightly, but that is all. When the last skin of the larva is cast off, the pupa is revealed.

If observed only casually, the pupa often seems to be headless and footless, although such is not actually the case. If the pupa is examined closely, the antennae, wings, and legs of the future adult insect may be distinguished. In moths and butterflies these organs are folded close to the body of the pupa; but in bees, ants, and beetles they are free for movement. The skin often appears to be shiny and is hard.

Butterflies form pupae which are called *chrysalises* (singular, *chrysalis*), a name given them because of their coloring and markings. The term is derived from a Greek word mean-

ing "gold" and is used probably because of the golden-colored dots and markings on the pupae. The caterpillars of the mourning-cloak, black-swallowtail, monarch, cabbage and other butterflies fasten themselves with strands of silk to some leaf, twig, or stick, or under some protective covering when they are ready to go into the pupal stage. The larvae of the tomato-worm butterfly, the emperor caterpillars, and other moth larvae which do not spin cocoons crawl into the ground, where they spend this period of inactivity.

Many larvae, especially those of the moths, when fully grown, spin about the body a silken case. When they are in the helpless quiescent stage, they derive from it a certain degree of protection from harm. These silken cases are called *cocoons*. They are sometimes made within leaves which have been rolled up. Sometimes the cocoons are made beneath grass or brush on the ground, while in other instances they are spun after the insect has descended below the surface of the ground. These cocoons are spun by means of silk glands which are similar to the glands in other insects.

The silk glands of moths are located on each side of the abdomen. They are often so tightly coiled together that they may be several times the length of the body of the larva. The silk glands are divided into two distinguishable parts: the thread press, which combines the two streams of silk into one common stream, and the directing tube, which is located in front of the thread press. Upon exposure to air the fluid silk hardens rapidly. The larva must therefore spin quickly. With its prolegs it clings to the object on which it will construct the cocoon, while the forelegs manipulate the silk into place. The silk glands in insects open on the lower lip of the jaw. Soon the entire larva is enclosed in the cocoon, where it remains until its pupal skin is molted.

The cocoons of moths are often very different. Those of the flannel moth, for example, are spun in such a way that a trap door is

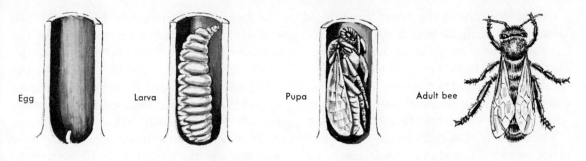

Egg   Larva   Pupa   Adult bee

Four stages in the development of the honeybee.

formed. Bagworm-moth caterpillars build for themselves a silken sac which is covered with little twigs. The larva of the grape-leaf folder moth folds grape leaves together by fastening them with silken threads, and the pupal stage is passed within the folded leaf. Clothes-moth larvae make cases out of bits of their food material, fastening them together with silk. As the larva grows, it enlarges its case by adding more bits of cloth to each end and by slitting it lengthwise and inserting a piece. The pupal state is passed within this case. The larvae of the currant-borer pass the pupal stage within the center of the stems and branches of currant plants.

The larvae known as measuring worms build very flimsy cocoons, in which they pass the pupal stage. A cocoon composed largely of the hairs of its body, spun together with silk, is spun by the harlequin milkweed caterpillar. The caterpillar of the Isabella tiger moth, which is reddish-brown in the middle and black at either end, spins a similar kind of cocoon. Royal-moth caterpillars simply crawl into the ground and spend the pupal stage there without any cocoon.

Some fly larvae also spin cocoons. The full-grown larvae of some of the black flies spin a boat-shaped cocoon within which the pupa transforms into an adult fly. The pupal stage of mosquitoes, like the larval stage, is passed in water, the head and thorax of the body being much enlarged. Other kinds of fly larvae do not shed the skin when they pupate.

They use it as an inflated watertight case which gives them protection from weather conditions. Such a pupa case is known as a *puparium*.

Honeybee larvae pass the pupal stage within the cells of the honeycomb. The larger species of ichneumon flies lay a single egg within the body of a Polyphemus-moth caterpillar. Within the caterpillar the parasite larva lives until it is ready to spin its cocoon, the caterpillar also remaining alive during this time. When the caterpillar spins its cocoon, the ichneumon-fly larva also spins its cocoon, within the cocoon of the caterpillar. The larvae of some bettles, ordinarily found in water during the larval stage, leave the water when pupation is about to occur, and bury themselves in the soil, from which they emerge as adults. The larvae of whirligig beetles leave the water and spin a gray paper-like cocoon which is attached to some object near the water.

Although the pupa gives no evidence of physical activity, it must be remembered that the internal structure of the insect is passing through some wonderful transformations which are not yet fully understood. The organs of the adult insect are being made from the organs of the larva. It seems that the larval organs disintegrate and are re-formed into new organs. At any rate, it is safe to say that during the pupal stage the insect is passing through crucial changes which result in the final form of the insect life cycle.

During this change the insect is nourished from the fat which has been stored during the larva stage, and from the oxidation of cells which are of no further use to the insect. The entire set of changes of metamorphosis is economical, for none of the previously constructed cells and none of the stored fat remain unused.

The length of time spent in the pupal stage varies widely. The eggs of some insects are laid in the spring or early summer; and during that year the larva feeds and grows, changing into a pupa in the fall. In insects of this kind the pupal stage may last all winter and until warm weather prevails the following spring. On the other hand, the pupal state of the mosquito lasts only a few days. Between these two extremes wide variations in the length of the pupal state occur.

EXPERIENCE. *To observe insects in their pupal forms.* If children find and bring to class mosquito larvae, which they often call "wigglers," keep these in a vessel of water and note their change to pupae. By means of a hand lens study the structure of the pupae. Children may also bring to class the cocoons of moths and other insects, and also the chrysalises of butterflies. Keep these in a box which is covered with screen wire. From some of them moths and butterflies may emerge. Because the air in any classroom is very dry during the winter months, the pupae must be sprinkled about once a week with a small quantity of water; otherwise the dryness may cause them to die. If a number of cocoons and chrysalises are brought in, have children open them at various times about two weeks apart to note evidences of internal change in the pupae. Sometimes it is best to keep the cocoons in a wooden box on the outside of the window sill, protected just enough to keep ice from forming on the box. They do not need to be kept warm, since in their natural environment they may be subject to severe weather conditions.

The Adult Insect Emerges from Pupation. When the internal reorganization of the insect has been completed within the cocoon, puparium, or chrysalis, the insect is ready to emerge in its adult and final form. In some cases it must liberate itself. The insect must pierce through the silk of the cocoon. Many moth pupae have beaks on their heads for tearing their way through the silk. Others have teethlike projections for cutting the silk. The most primitive moth pupae have mandibles, or jaws, by means of which they free themselves. The American silkworm, commonly called the Polyphemus moth, secretes a glandular fluid before it emerges. This fluid dissolves the gluelike substance which holds the fibers of silk together. Just before the adult emerges, the old pupa case of the insect splits longitudinally, so that the insect is freed from it. Then the Polyphemus moth secretes sufficient fluid to soak thoroughly the end of the cocoon from which it will emerge. When the cocoon end has dissolved, the moth forces its way out. Upon emerging, the adult will be completely formed. The excess body fluid in the abdomen is forced into the crumpled wings. When the wings are fully expanded and dried, the insect is ready for flight. Since flight is instinctive, the insect does not need to learn to fly. They frequently remain relatively quiet for thirty minutes or more after the wings expand, and then may travel quite a long distance during their first flight.

Having achieved maturity by passing through the egg, larval, and pupal stages, the chief function of the adult is reproduction. Perpetuation of the species is always a characteristic of the adult form of any animal, although a few isolated instances of reproduction by immature insects have been reported by observers.

Many interesting phenomena may be observed in connection with the reproductive processes of insects. Certain unmated female moths, for example, seem to emit an odor which attracts males of their species in large numbers. The French naturalist Fabre reports that when he kept the females of some moths in his room, many males were attracted to them. If an unmated female Promethea moth is kept in a screen-covered box in the classroom, and the windows are left open, it is possible that many males will gather in the room overnight, being attracted by the odor emitted by the female. After the female has mated with a male, this odor is apparently no longer emitted, for males then are not attracted to her.

Having mated and laid their eggs, some insects die soon after. The May fly, for example, may live under water for a period which varies from one to three years. It then emerges in the spring as an adult, flies a short distance, molts once, lays its eggs, and dies. Its adult life is a very short one, and it does not feed during this stage. The mouth parts are so rudimentary that it cannot eat. Often its adult life is only a few hours long. Some species of butterflies also have rudimentary mouth parts and thus cannot feed. They too die soon after they have fulfilled the function of reproduction.

Many adult insects, however, are capable of feeding and live for some time. Some butterflies and moths visit flowers and sip nectar from them; other kinds of insects feed on plants and animals during the final stage. Some of them hibernate during the winter and appear the following spring to carry on reproduction. Other insects are killed by the first frosts of autumn, and many others are killed by the more severe winter weather.

Most species of insects have one or two pairs of wings. Wings appear, however, only in the adult stage. Those insects which do not pass through any kinds of metamorphosis are always wingless. Nymphs of insects which pass through incomplete metamorphosis do not have wings until they reach maturity. Insects characterized by complete metamorphosis have wings only in the adult stage.

Sometimes children think that the very small flies which they see are young and not fully grown, but such is not the case. These are species of flies which have attained their full growth and which will never be any larger. Insects with wings do not molt, and consequently cannot grow further. The only known exception to this rule is the May fly, which molts once after it has become an adult and has wings.

Some Insects Spend Part of the Life Cycle in Water

Thus far the discussion of metamorphosis has been confined chiefly to insects which spend all their life cycle on land, and only brief mention has been made of those which live part of their lives in water. Many kinds of insects spend the larval and sometimes the pupal stage in the water; and since these are fairly common, some attention must be given them.

May flies, which have already been mentioned, damsel flies, stone flies, and dragon-flies all spend part of their life cycle in the water. Dragonflies attract the attention of children, and many superstitions concerning them are known to the child. They are sometimes called "snake doctors" and "ear-stingers" and are often believed to be vicious. They are almost always found near water, for they hover above it in search of insects which they catch on the wing and devour. They do not attack human beings, and because of their feeding habits they are distinctly beneficial.

They may be recognized by the relatively large size of their two pairs of wings and by the fact that the wings are extended horizontally when at rest. The eggs of dragonflies are laid in water. They may be found attached to water plants. Metamorphosis is incomplete, so that the larvae are called nymphs, although some authorities refer to them as naiads to distinguish between this stage in water insects and land insects.

Dragonfly nymphs have been described as ugly creatures. They are able to catch and devour small water animals. They have a peculiar mode of breathing. Adult insects breathe air; but since the aquatic nymph cannot obtain air, its breathing system is modified so that it breathes by means of gills. The gills of the dragonfly nymph are located in the cavity of the rectum, and the branches of the gills penetrate the wall of the rectum. The insect draws water into this structure and then expels it, obtaining from it the oxygen dissolved in the water. This process also helps the insect in swimming; for as the water is expelled from the rectal cavity, the insect is propelled forward. The nymph does not leave the water until it is ready for its last molt.

Very similar to the dragonfly, and often mistakenly taken for it, is the damsel fly. It differs from the dragonfly in being much slower in its flight, and the two pairs of wings are either folded parallel to the abdomen, or are tilted upward, when the insect is at rest. Damsel flies lay their eggs on the stems of water plants, sometimes just beneath the surface of the water. The nymphs possess leaf-like gills at the posterior portion of the body, which look like tails of the insect.

Nymphs of the May flies, which have such a short life in the adult stage, live on the bottoms of small streams, feeding on mud, water plants, and small insects. This nymph has strong legs and can both walk and swim. The gills by means of which it breathes are arranged along the side of the body in a sort of fringe. It may molt as many as twenty times; but after about the ninth molt there appear on the middle part of its body, the thorax, four little sacs, which are the beginnings of the wings. These little sacs grow larger with each molt, until finally the last molt of the nymph stage has taken place, when the gills are lost and the insect comes forth a winged May fly.

Stone-fly nymphs may be found under stones in the swiftest currents of small streams. The nymphs are about half an inch in length, but they vary from this size up to about one and a half inches in length. They cling very closely to the lower surface of the stones. The gills are located one behind each of the six legs, and are more or less white and hairlike. These nymphs are the favorite food of fishes, and consequently are often sought as bait by fishermen. The fully grown nymph crawls from the water and transforms into a greenish fly with four wings.

Caddis flies are four-winged insects which spend part of their life cycle in the water but have a complete metamorphosis. They have rudimentary mouth parts. Their larvae may be found in small streams, and they may be identified by their activities. Some species of caddis-fly larvae build small tubes made entirely of pieces of wood which are usually placed lengthwise on the body, and the larva lives within. Other species build these cases of bits of straw which float in the water, fastening some of the straws crosswise. Sometimes they fasten snail shells to the outside of their "houses." Others make their dwellings of bits of moss, or of small leaves so formed as to make a flat case. Still other species of caddis-fly larvae build houses of small pebbles and grains of sand, making them spiral in form and resembling snail shells. In each case the house is lined with silk, which is spun by the larvae in the same manner as the silk spun by caterpillars.

When the caddis larva approaches the pupal stage, it builds a door at the open end of

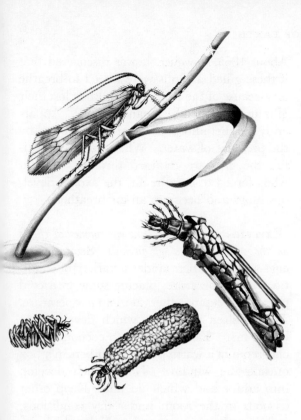

the top *is an adult caddis-fly. At the* bottom, *caddis-fly vae in cases in position for moving around under water.*

metamorphosis which spend part of the life cycle in the water are the dobson flies. In the adult stage these have four wings, mouth parts fitted for biting, and, in some cases, a wing expanse of five inches. The female lays the eggs in water, attaching them to stones or other objects which hang over the water. The egg mass may be almost an inch in diameter and may contain as many as three thousand eggs. When the larvae hatch, they immediately make their way into the water, in which they remain until they are fully grown. This means that they may remain in the water for almost three full years, feeding upon the nymphs of other water insects, such as May flies and stone flies. At the end of this period they emerge from the water and make a cell under a stone or some other object located on the bank of the stream. In this cell the larva changes into the pupa; approximately a month later the adult insect appears.

EXPERIENCE. *To study aquatic insect larvae.* Take the class on a field trip to a small stream. Have the children look for insect larvae in the water under stones and logs. Have them note the activity of the larvae in the water, and collect a few to bring to the aquarium (if you have a suitable one) for further study. Caddis-fly larvae particularly should be easy to find in a fairly rapid-flowing brook. At the same time have the children be alert for adult dragonflies and damsel flies, noting their characteristic flight. Their empty skins may be found on plants and rocks near the water.

the case which is sufficient to keep out intruders, but which allows free circulation of water. Often this door is only a silk wall spun by the larva. This enables the pupa to obtain fresh water, so that it can get oxygen from it for breathing purposes. When the insect in the larval stage moves about, it puts out the front end of its body, creeps along the bottom by means of its legs, and so drags its house along.

Another group of insects with complete

Environmental Conditions Affect Metamorphosis

Animals which undergo metamorphosis are subject to environmental conditions just as much as any others. If the weather is cold in the spring, amphibian and insect eggs may be

considerably delayed in their development, and hatching may be postponed. All invertebrate animals are sluggish when the temperature is low, and insect larvae are quite inactive when the temperature drops. That moth co-coons and butterfly chrysalises are sensitive to humidity may be demonstrated by keeping them in the classroom, in which the air is generally dry. Many of them will fail to develop properly. Frogs' eggs will fail to develop in water in which there is an excess supply of carbon dioxide.

One of the most interesting examples of the effect of environment upon metamorphosis is afforded by the small amphibian known as the axolotl. It is the larva of a salamander which is found from New York to California and south to central Mexico. The adult salamander may be from six to eight inches long; it is dark in color with yellow spots. Sometimes the larvae of this animal lose their gills when they become adults. Often, however, the larvae retain their gills during adulthood, and were for this reason long considered a separate species with external gills. This seemed like a logical conclusion, since the gilled adult carried on reproduction and laid fertile eggs.

About 1865, however, it was discovered that if these gilled axolotls were forced to breathe air because of the lack of water, they lost their gills and breathed by means of lungs. Apparently the metamorphosis is greatly affected by the presence of water. When water is plentiful, the gills are retained through life; but when forced to breathe air, the axolotl develops lungs and becomes an air-breather.

EXPERIENCE. *To determine environmental effects on the metamorphosis of animals.* Secure insect eggs and keep them under a variety of conditions of temperature, placing some in a cold place and keeping others at room temperature. The children may note which develop into larvae first. Keep some moth cocoons in the classroom in a warm place and others in a box outside the window. Note which develop into adults and which do not. Keep other cocoons in the room under dry conditions; sprinkle others occasionally. Note which develop into adults and which do not.

CHAPTER 17

Animals May Be Social

Many animals have habits of association with other members of their own species. Man is often called "the social animal"; but a survey of the remainder of the animal kingdom discloses that some of his biological contemporaries are far more social in their habits than he, though others associate to a lesser extent. Human society is undoubtedly extremely complicated; but when its efficiency is compared with that of some insect societies, it may be argued that men are not so well organized, from a biological standpoint, as some insects happen to be—for example, the termites.

Animal relationships are varied and of widely differing degrees of complexity. Often many of the individuals of the same species are found together because they are dependent on a habitat which is limited in its extent and because they feed and breed similarly. These are known as *gregarious* animals. Some animals are found to exist in *colonies* simply because they are connected together by a common skeleton or because they happen to be attached to a common object. Very often the individuals of a colony may be separated from one another. Under such conditions, the individuals may continue to lead a successful existence, often establishing new colonies.

Most complex of all is the organization of animals into *social life*. Among insects we find that ants have a definite caste system, and that the interdependence between the various members of the colony is so great that the absence of any one caste may lead to the eventual destruction of the society. This behavior is instinctive and is not the result of thinking through the various situations that confront a colony of ants.

Bees Are Social Insects

The best-known social insects are very common in the environment of the average school child. Bees, ants, wasps, and termites have a highly complicated social organization. Their communal life may be used to show some of the typical phenomena in insect social life.

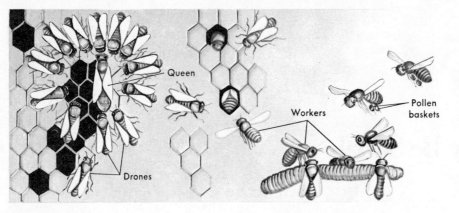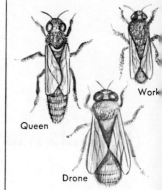

The honeybee society.

There Is Division of Labor in a Bee Society.
Honeybees live together in rather large societies, as many as fifty thousand individuals or more inhabiting the same hive. In the wild state, bees generally live in the hollow of dead or decaying tree trunks, in which they construct their honeycomb for the storage of honey. Three kinds of individuals may be found in each society: the *queen,* whose function is reproduction; the *workers,* which are infertile females; and the *drones,* which do not work but which are necessary for the fertilization of the queen's eggs before they are laid. The workers may be distinguished from the queen and drones by the fact that they are smaller. The queen may be distinguished from the drones by the fact that her abdomen is longer and more slender than that of the drones. The drones cannot sting.

Each of the three kinds of bees is necessary for the continuation of the bee community, for each has a function not carried out by the others. Without a queen no eggs would be produced to replenish the population of the hive; without the drones the eggs of the queen would not be fertilized. Without the workers no nectar, a sweet liquid, secreted in flowers and on some leaves, would be gathered and no honeycomb constructed, so that starvation would ensue and the queen and drones would die.

The worker bees make the wax from which the honeycomb is constructed and exude it in the form of small liquid drops from the skin on the lower side of the abdomen. When exposed to air the droplets run together and harden, and are then removed by means of the hind legs and used in constructing the hexagonal cells of the honeycomb. The worker bees visit flowers, gathering nectar from them, which they suck up by means of their mouth parts and swallow into a honey sac. When the worker has visited a number of flowers and is fully laden, it returns to the hive and regurgitates the nectar into the cells.

The nectar is at first very liquid and therefore unfit to be stored for any great length of time. Some of the water in it must be evaporated until the proper consistency and sweetness is reached. To accomplish this many of the workers assemble above those cells in the honeycomb which contain the nectar and vibrate their wings at a very rapid rate. This movement of the wings causes currents of air, which increases the rate of evaporation of water from the nectar and also raises the temperature of the body of the bees sufficiently to cause a rise in the temperature in the hive. Since evaporation is greater at higher temperatures, this increases the rate of evaporation. The nectar finally becomes honey.

In addition to gathering nectar from

flowers, the workers also gather a kind of resinous gum from certain trees, which is used in sealing up whatever cracks may appear in the hive, thus preventing water from seeping in. Pollen grains are brought into the hive by the workers in "pollen baskets," which are really not baskets at all. The hind leg of the worker is slightly concave on the outer surface, and this concave surface is lined with a row of incurved, rather bristly hairs. These stiff hairs hold the pollen, which is carried in this manner to the hive and stored in the cells. It is used as food, and is very rich in proteins.

In the spring of the year, when the first warm weather prevails, the hive stirs with activity. Ordinarily after a swarming has taken place, a young queen leaves the hive and is followed by the drones. She flies rapidly through the air, going higher and higher, leaving most of the drones far behind. Then, in mid-air, one of the drones still in pursuit overtakes the queen and mates with her, fertilizing the eggs, and dying as a result of the mating. The queen returns to the hive and begins the process of egg-laying. A thousand eggs or more may be laid daily, and are deposited in the cells of the honeycomb.

During the process of mating, the drone has transferred millions of sperm cells into the body of the queen. As the eggs pass from the organs in which they originate, they are fertilized by the sperms. The queen seems to have the ability to control the fertilization of the eggs she is laying. Fertilized eggs are laid either in small worker cells or in cells which are later made larger for the development of queens. Other eggs, unfertilized, are laid in special drone cells. It must be noted here that oddly enough the unfertilized eggs develop into the male drones, while the fertilized eggs develop into queens and the female workers. How the queen controls the fertilization of eggs is not known.

Bee larvae are footless grubs, white in color, soft-bodied, and helpless. Unlike the larvae of other insects described in the previous chapter, they cannot find food for themselves. Consequently they must be cared for, and this task is taken over by young workers known to beekeepers as nurses. These nurses stay in the hive and feed the larvae on a food called royal jelly, probably secreted from glands in their heads. When the larvae are about three days old, they are fed on pollen and honey, often called beebread. Finally a small mass of this food is placed in the cell, and the cell is covered with wax so that the larva is sealed within.

The larva then consumes all the food stored with it in the next two or three days and changes into the pupa stage. In this stage it lies quiescent for about thirteen days. During this interval it has changed into a fully grown bee. It then breaks through the wax cap of the cell with its jaws and is ready to assume its duties in the hive. The bees which have acted as nurses do so for about a week only; after this they begin the usual duties of gathering nectar and pollen, and their places are taken by other young workers.

Not all the larvae are treated as has just been described. Those eggs which are laid in some of the queen cells are not fed honey at all, nor are they fed pollen. From the time these larvae hatch until they pupate, they are fed on royal jelly; and when the pupa is transformed into the adult bee, it is a young queen and not a worker. The complete diet of royal jelly, together with the change in size and shape of the cell, are the only observable differences between the development of the worker and the queen. The eggs from which both the queen and the worker develop are thought to be identical. Thus it is believed that royal jelly causes the development of the reproductive organs in those that become queens. The richer food is also considered responsible for the larger size of the queen bees.

New Bee Societies Are Established by Swarming. When several young queens emerge, a battle occurs among them for supremacy in the hive. The young queens fight one another until there is only one survivor. This young queen becomes the new queen of the hive. The word *queen* is applied in a special sense, for there is no such thing as a ruler in the society. Earlier, when the weather has been suitable, the old queen and her followers have left the hive, gathering in a large cluster on a nearby branch, and then flying away to another place to establish a new society. This change of homes is known as *swarming*. A new society is thus founded away from the old, and the species distributes itself in new areas in this way. In the case of domesticated bees, the swarm is often captured by the beekeeper, who places it in a new hive.

Usually in late autumn the remaining drones are stung to death or driven out of the hive by the workers and thus perish. With the approach of winter and cold weather, the drones, which contribute nothing to the food supply, would menace the welfare of the hive by sharing in the food that has been stored. Since all of it is needed to feed the workers and queen during the winter, the elimination of the drones helps the other members of the society to survive. If an insufficient quantity of honey has been stored, many bees may die of starvation before spring, and the community is greatly weakened. None of the worker bees live very long, for the spring broods die in two or three months; those which develop later may live over the winter. The total number in a strong colony is not greatly reduced, however, because new bees are hatching while the old ones are dying off.

There are other activities which need to be performed in addition to those already mentioned. During warm weather many bees may be found near pools of water. This water is carried by workers to the larvae in the hive. Dead bees, pieces of old honeycomb, the excreta of the queens and drones, and other waste materials must be removed by the bees that tend the hive. Thus, by keeping a hive clean, the danger of disease caused by bacteria that grow and multiply in debris is lessened. Ventilation of the hive has already been described. Yellow jackets, bee moths, and other insects are attracted to the hive by the honey it contains, and they must be repelled. For this function bees are stationed at the entrance to the hive to repel any intruders. If the swarm is a weak one, the bees often fail in this task, so that the honeycomb may be infested by various organisms that prey on them.

In addition to insects there are a number of other organisms that disturb bees. Spiders, kingbirds, toads, and lizards feed on them. Rats invade the colony if it is weak. Skunks approach the hive at night, attract the attention of the bees by scratching at the entrance of the hive, and then eat the bees as they come out to investigate. Bears are well known for their habit of climbing trees containing bees and feeding on the honey in utter disregard of the swarm. Other bees often enter a weak hive and steal the honey. Foul brood is a bacterial disease which may kill off the bees.

In this discussion of the bee society, one thought must be emphasized. Each bee is born into a caste and has a special function to perform. The worker is destined to a life of toil, and the drone to a life of idleness, followed by sudden death either as the result of mating with the queen or of the stings of the workers. The queen does not gather food, for her sole function is reproduction. There is a sharp division of labor according to the caste.

EXPERIENCE. *To study the life of the bees.* Secure, if possible, a glass-sided section of a beehive which has been stocked with bees. Keep it in a place where it will not interfere with other activities, but where it may be readily observed by the children. Caution them about approaching too closely to the hive. Have them observe the activities of the bees.

Small groups of older children have built beehives with glass-sided sections for observation purposes. Local beekeepers are usually willing to co-operate with the children by advising them during the period that they are making plans and by stocking the hives with bees after they have been constructed. No project of this kind should be attempted without consultation with an experienced beekeeper.

Activities of Bees Are Important to Man. Bees are of importance to man, not only because they furnish honey for his food supply, but also because of the fact that in gathering nectar they are often responsible for the cross-pollination of many plants. Nectar is produced in a flower by glands located at the base of the petals. These glands are called *nectaries*. To reach the nectar, the bee must often crawl past the anthers, which produce pollen. Since the body and legs of the bee are hairy, some of the pollen grains become attached to the bee. When the bee makes a trip to another flower of the same species, some of these pollen grains are brushed off on the stigma of the pistil, where they germinate and fertilize the plant egg cells in the ovary. Some kinds of flowers will not produce fruit and seed unless fertilized in this manner. Hives of bees are often placed in orchards by farmers to ensure the pollination of the fruit-tree flowers so that a larger fruit crop will result.

Red clover will not produce seed except when cross-pollinated by bumblebees. The mouth parts of ordinary bees are not sufficiently long to get the nectar at the base of the red-clover flower, so that they do not visit them. But bumblebees can gather this nectar, and consequently they are necessary for the production of red-clover seed.

Certain moths and butterflies, as well as other kinds of insects, are also agents in cross-pollination.

EXPERIENCE. *To study nectar-gathering activities of bees.* Take the class on a field trip where blossoms are numerous. Note the way in which the bee enters a flower. Single one out and follow it as long as possible as it moves from one flower to another. (Each child may observe this again at some time.)

The Social Life of Ants Is Complex

Not all the numerous species of bees are social, some of them leading a more or less solitary existence; but all species of ants live in societies. More than two thousand species of ants are known, and all of these may be found in societies ranging in size from those having a few dozen ants to those having hundreds of thousands. According to some authorities, ants are the dominant insects of Earth, probably being more numerous than any other kind; and it is believed that this dominance is largely due to the high degree of social life and to the specialization of the ants within the society.

There Is Division of Labor in Ant Communities. Three types of individuals are always found in the ant community: the *males,* the *females,* and the *workers.* The workers are wingless, but the males and females both have wings. On a warm sunny afternoon swarms of these winged ants may be seen. This is the mating flight of the males and females. After the flight is over, they alight on the ground, and the males die soon thereafter. The females tear off their own wings and seek a place in which to lay their eggs, often establishing new societies, but sometimes being found by workers of their own species, which

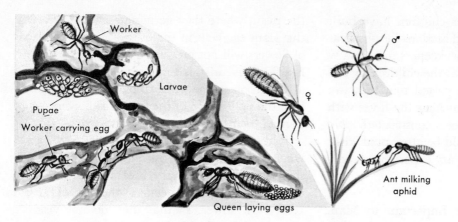
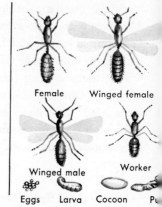

The ant society.

adopt them as their queen. Here again it must be noted that the queen, as in the case of the bees, does not rule over the colony in the usual sense of the word, but merely carries on the processes of reproduction for the purpose of maintaining the numbers of the colony.

When the larvae hatch from the eggs, they are white in color and have no legs. As in the case of the bees, the ant larvae are cared for by nurses, which carry them about from place to place in the ant nest.

When the larvae are ready to go into the pupal, or resting, stage, most species spin a cocoon, although some do not. When children disturb an anthill, they often discover in it oblong, egg-shaped, white bodies which they mistake for the eggs of the ant and which they see carried about by the workers. These are not the eggs, but cocoons of ants in the pupal stage. Children rarely see the actual eggs of the ants, for these are so small that they generally escape observation.

Ants Secure Some of Their Food from Aphids. Ants have interesting relations with other insects, particularly with aphids. It has already been noted that they care for these, placing them on suitable vegetation, and stroking them with their antennae, thus inducing the aphids to secrete a drop of a sweet fluid, which the ants immediately drink up.

Sometimes various species of beetles are found in the ant nest. Often the ants seem to take care of certain scale insects, deriving from them a sweet fluid similar to that secreted by aphids. Scale insects and aphids are rather soft-bodied and defenseless. They are often protected from predators by the ants, which drive away lady-bird beetles and other insects of predaceous habits.

In the Mississippi Valley there is a species of plant louse which lives on the roots of corn plants. It lays its eggs in the ground in the fall of the year, and the larvae hatch before the corn is planted the following spring. A little brown ant, common in that region, collects the young corn-root plant lice and places them on the roots of a weed until corn roots develop, and so protects them. Later they are transported to the roots of the corn plant, and are used as a source of the sweet fluid which the ants seem to crave. Other species of ants carry plant lice to their nests and care for them there. These various kinds of aphids, or plant lice, are sometimes called the cattle of the ants.

Some Species of Ants Have a Soldier Caste. Ant social organization sometimes goes farther than classification into males, females, and workers. Many species have a *soldier* caste. Individuals of this caste are wingless, like the workers, and cannot carry on reproductive functions. However, they have well-developed mouth parts which make them fit to do battle with other ants. It seems to be their duty to protect the ant colony from predaceous insects, especially other ants. Ants are warlike insects, for their soldier caste often invades neighboring colonies and attacks the ants in them. If successful in their invasion, they carry away to their own nest any food which may be stored. If any of the invaded and defeated colonies contain eggs or larvae, these are often carried off by the victors, and when mature, serve as slaves. The slaves collect food, assist in building the nest, and care for the young of the slave-making species.

One species of ants in South America has no real workers, only soldiers, so that the colony exists only because of its marauding activities. These ants are therefore known as robber ants. Here there are four castes: the winged males, winged females, small wingless soldiers, and large wingless soldiers. There are many more small wingless soldiers than large soldiers; and when they are on the march, the small soldiers move along in a long narrow column, while the large soldiers march along on either side, seemingly acting in the capacity of sentinels.

Among the slaveholding ants some species work side by side with their slaves, but in at least one instance it has been determined that the slaveholders are utterly helpless without their slaves. The Swiss naturalist Huber describes a European species which cannot build its own nest or even care for its young. If slaves are not present, these ants cannot even feed themselves, though there may be an abundance of food. These slaveholding ants seem able to do but one thing; they have remarkable ability to fight and thus capture slave ants, which do their work for them.

Ant Nests Differ. The ant nest is different in each species. Sometimes it is a simple tunnel in the ground; sometimes it is a fairly large mound with underground galleries extending many feet in all directions. Some species live in decayed trees; some tropical ants sometimes have more than one mound to the society. In addition to their dependence on aphids for food, ants seem to like the sweet juices of fruits and sometimes eat animal matter.

The social life of the ants rests on a caste system. The winged males and females carry on reproduction; the workers and slaves take care of the food problem; the soldiers act as guards and as pillagers to replenish the society with slaves.

EXPERIENCE. *To study some of the activities of ants.* Take children on a field trip to an ant colony. You may find one in or near the school yard. With a stick, open up the colony, noting the resultant activity of the ants, the way in which they carry into hiding their pupae, and the means by which they seek to protect themselves.

EXPERIENCE. *To keep ants in a classroom.* Fill a quart or gallon jar nearly full of loose soil. Place adult ants and pupae from an anthill in the jar. Place the jar in the center of a pan of water, so that the ants cannot escape. Wrap

A jar of ants for classroom study.

the jar with dark cloth. This cloth may be removed to observe the activities of the ants. The soil should be kept slightly moist. Sprinkle sugar or other food in the jar from time to time. Note that unless a queen has been brought in, the ant colony will not grow.

Termites Are Successful Social Insects

Much public attention has been focused on termites (sometimes called white ants) because of the damage which they cause to wooden buildings, telegraph posts, and wood piled in lumberyards. These insects, which superficially resemble ants but are members of a different and more primitive order of insects, are sometimes mistaken for ants because of their social organization and the fact that in addition to resembling ants they also build nests. Although they are found widely in the middle latitudes, they reach their greatest development in tropical countries. In Africa they build mounds which may be twelve or fifteen feet tall. Some species live in trees in nests which may be several feet thick. In North America they are found in old logs, under stones, and in old stumps, although they sometimes invade dwellings and cause much damage before their presence is discovered.

Their destructiveness is due to the fact that they bore through timbers and boards, hollowing out the interior. Externally the timber may appear to be perfectly sound until its collapse reveals the presence of termites. They are hard to control because they travel along underground burrows. A large tropical termite community may consist of many hundreds of thousands of individuals; in this country the community is generally not so large as that.

Castes in a Termite Society. As in the case of bees and ants, there are several castes of termites in each community. The workers are wingless, but they are both male and female; their function in the colony is the same as that of worker bees and ants. The soldier caste is also made up of both male and female termites; these too are wingless, but their heads are enormous in size, and they have powerful jaws projecting from the head. Neither the soldier nor the worker caste can carry on reproduction, for their reproductive organs are rudimentary.

In many species of termites both the workers and the soldiers are blind, having only very poor eyes or no eyes at all. The soldier caste may be equipped with a relatively long horn, which projects from its face. At the base of

King
Queen
Worker
Soldier
Close-up of jaws

Food compartment (small mushrooms)
Workers cultivating
Soldier on guard
Worker nurse carrying egg to nursery
Workers in attendance on queen
Nursery
Queen laying eggs
Soldiers on guard

The termite society.

the horn there is a gland which secretes a sticky substance. When a predator, such as an ant, approaches the termite colony, the soldier may discharge this sticky, semiliquid substance upon it, so that the ant is so thoroughly "gummed up" that it can neither flee nor advance.

In addition to the castes already described, there are in the community many individuals which have the rudiments of wings. These are members of the reproductive caste, for they are males and females which are able to carry on the processes of reproduction. As the summer advances, their wing pads become larger in size and their body color becomes darker, until they finally emerge from the nest in a great swarm and migrate some distance to found a new community.

Reproduction Is Limited to One Female in Each Society. These males and females, however, do not carry on the process of reproduction, even though they are capable of doing so. This function is assumed by two individuals, one of them a dark-colored male, the other a huge queen with a greatly developed abdomen. While most of the termites may not be over half or three quarters of an inch long, the egg-laying queen may be as long as six inches. Her great size is thought to be due to the enormous numbers of eggs found in her body. The male, of course, corresponds to the drone bee which fertilizes the queen bee, but in the case of the termites these males are not killed off. The "king" termite lives with the queen throughout her life.

In the termite society, then, there are eight different kinds of individuals: male and female workers, incapable of reproduction; male and female soldiers, also incapable of reproduction; males and females capable potentially of reproduction; and the reproductive king and queen. In addition, the society is sometimes complicated by the presence of males and females which are capable of reproduction but

are entirely wingless. Little is known of these except that perhaps they crawl away from their society and establish a new one.

The Development of a Termite Community. Let us trace the development of a termite state, or society. Much work on this subject has been done by members of the United States Bureau of Entomology. At the time of swarming, the termites make a short flight, settle to the ground, and by brushing against some object or by twisting the body they break off their wings, which would be an encumbrance in their subterranean existence. The young males and females pair off, and the female seeks out a dead tree or stump. She begins boring into the wood with her powerful jaws until a cavity sufficient to accommodate the pair has been made. On the floor of this narrow compartment the female lays her first eggs, about ten in number. Within ten days these eggs hatch.

The young termites are unable to feed themselves. The parents eat some of the wood which makes up the walls of the compartment, digest it, regurgitate it, and feed the young on the predigested and regurgitated wood. The compartment is thus enlarged and the insects are fed at the same time. Termites are able to use wood as food because of the presence in their digestive tracts of certain protozoans which can digest cellulose. When the regurgitated food is given the young termite, some of these protozoans are passed into its digestive cavity.

The young termites molt a number of times, like many other insects, but they do not develop into termites capable of reproduction. Instead they develop into workers and soldiers. About February the queen again lays eggs, more than at the first time. The young which develop from these are cared for by the previous brood of workers, which take over the task of caring for the young and enlarging the *termitary,* as the nest is sometimes called.

When the summer approaches, the society may consist of several dozen individuals; but all are soldiers and workers, with the exception of the original king and queen. During her second year the queen lays eggs at more frequent intervals and in greater numbers. This increased egg-laying activity causes an enlargement of the abdomen. During the third year still more workers and soldiers are produced, but other forms also begin to appear. It is at about this time that the winged males and females which are capable of reproduction appear. These may swarm and leave the original community. Finally the wingless males and females capable of reproducing appear in the society. If the queen does not die, she may lay eggs for a number of years; but if she dies, the king mates with one or more of the short-winged females, and the colony continues. The colony thus increases in numbers from year to year. No one caste could live apart from the others. They are interdependent.

There are many interesting facts concerning termites. Some of them bring into the termitary certain fungi, on which they feed, seemingly cultivating them in the nest. The workers of some tropical termites march abroad in large numbers, protected by their soldiers, in search of food, such as bits of leaves, dead stems, or lichens, which they bring back to their nests for consumption. It has been estimated that the queens of some species may lay as many as thirty thousand eggs daily, and that such a queen may lay 10 million eggs a year and 100 million in her lifetime. Because of her immense size she is practically helpless, and must be carefully tended by the workers. Her eggs are carried off by the workers and placed in nearby fungus gardens, where the young can feed without attention.

In Africa, Australia, and South America the species builds nests which are much more prominent than those maintained by the North American species. Some are simple mounds, while others are shaped like giant mushrooms. Termites which build nests in a tree also have colonies in the ground under the tree, and the tree trunk serves as a runway connecting the two colonies.

EXPERIENCE. *To observe termites.* Some children may be able to find old logs or pieces of lumber that are decaying. These should be examined for animal life. If termites are found, encourage the children to look at them with a hand lens.

If termites are found in lumber that is near a building, one should examine the foundation to see if the termites have entered the building. Frequently one is able to find along brick or concrete foundations a narrow tunnel made of mud leading from the ground to the wood above. It would be wise to call in termite exterminators if one finds evidence that termites have entered a house or other building.

In some warm regions such as the tropics, and even in more temperate regions, termites may be very destructive. Anyone planning to build a home should secure advice as to how homes can be built that are termite proof.

Societies May Be Comparatively Simple

Not all insect societies are so complicated or so large as those of the bees, ants, and termites. Bumblebees live in communities which are much smaller and much simpler in organization.

Their nests are found in the ground, and in the summer may contain a small quantity of honey. In the spring of the year the queen generally seeks out a deserted field-mouse burrow in which she places a ball of pollen upon which she lays her eggs. The larvae hatch from the eggs, eat the pollen, achieve their full growth, spin cocoons, and spend the pupal stage in the cocoons. All the first brood are worker bees, which take over all duties except that of laying the eggs. The honey is stored in the recently occupied cocoons, which are first strengthened with wax. Later broods of young bees develop into functionally reproductive males and females; but the young queens are not killed off, as in the case of the honeybee. The young bees remain together during the summer, but with the coming of winter all the young bees with the exception of the queens die. The queens seek a protected place and spend the winter there. Those that survive the winter emerge in the spring and begin new colonies, which will pass through the same cycle.

Some of the bees are not communal at all, but lead a solitary existence. The carpenter bee, green in color, is an example. The female bores out the pith from several inches of raspberry cane, divides the space into a few cells by means of partitions, places an egg and some pollen in each cell, and leaves the young to pass through complete metamorphosis. When they have done so, they begin life individually.

The social wasps show a similarity to the bumblebees in their habits. Only the fertilized females, or queens, survive the winter, and in the spring these females build nests of paper made by chewing weather-beaten, soft wood. In each cell the queen lays an egg, places in the cell some chewed insects or spiders, and the larvae emerge and feed on the prepared food. After pupation the young emerge as workers with wings, somewhat smaller than the queen in size. They enlarge the nest, add more combs, and make many cells in which the queen lays more eggs. This time the cells containing the eggs are provisioned with food by the workers. Several broods are produced each summer, only workers being produced at first; but later males and females appear. The females mate with the males in the fall; the workers and males die, and only the new queens are left to live through the winter and perpetuate the species.

Bumblebees and wasps, therefore, represent a stage between the highly developed societies of honeybees, ants, and termites on the one hand and the solitary insects on the other hand.

EXPERIENCE. *To observe social wasps.* If children live in areas where social wasps are found, they should be encouraged to observe their activities from a safe distance. The nest of the *Polistes* wasp consists of a single row of cells, and is frequently found hanging by a stalk from rose vines or bushes of many kinds, or under the eaves of houses and barns. In some regions large hornet's nests may be found and observed.

The Social Behavior of Insects Is Instinctive

Upon investigation of the social adaptations of ants, bees, and termites, a student of these insects is at once struck by the orderliness of their behavior and by an apparent submerging of the individual for the welfare of the group.

The behavior of the social insects seems to suggest that a strong intelligence is a guiding factor in regulating the community, but such is not actually the fact. The members of each caste in a society are born to their function; they have no choice whatever in the matter. They are structurally unadapted to carry on any function but that which they assume, and there is no question of choice or reasoning power on their part. Everything is done by *instinct,* and the instincts are so powerful and so exclusive of other possibilities that all activity seems to be automatic. There is no plasticity of behavior, no making of choices, no power to reason. A definite stimulus causes a definite reaction or set of reactions without involving thinking.

Insect societies are often compared to human society, but it is difficult to do so with scientific accuracy because much human activity is based, not on instinct, but on the power to remember, to reason, and to predict future developments. It has not been possible to prove satisfactorily that ants, for example, are able to solve successfully new problems which may arise in their environment. When confronted by a new situation they continue to react in the inherited manner. Neither do they seem to transmit to their offspring any new psychological qualities.

Advantages and Disadvantages Are Derived from Social Organization

That a highly complex society is advantageous to the species may be inferred from the biological success of the social insects. Numerical strength is one criterion of this success, and the fact that ants probably outnumber all other insects is testimony that social organization leads to the continuation of the species. It is obvious that when an organization is such that it facilitates the process of reproduction, enables the society to guard itself against enemies, and furnishes large supplies of food to the community, it will promote the survival and dispersion of the species.

The solitary insect must protect itself against enemies, secure its food, and carry on reproduction, thus being confronted with a number of problems. The task is much simpler when only one of the functions is assumed by one individual. Furthermore, the social insects give more attention to the care and feeding of their young than insects of solitary habit, so that a far greater percentage of the eggs laid by the females are likely to develop to maturity. Bees in a colony are able to keep themselves warm during the winter as a result of their bodily activity, so that they have a much better chance of survival during severe winter weather than solitary bees. Moreover, the food they have stored by common labor enables them to survive at a time when food is not obtainable. Social life also makes possible the keeping of aphids by ants and the culture of fungi by termites, for there are members of the community which do nothing but take care of these.

The society home itself is inherited by succeeding generations, so that they may devote all their attention to food-getting and defense. An ant society may easily exist for twenty-five years or longer, indicating a certain stability

Honeybees in their winter cluster.

not achieved by solitary animals. Man can profit from experience by means of language, and so preserve the knowledge gained.

Social life may be advantageous to the species as a whole, but it may be considered disadvantageous to the individual in some ways. It necessarily involves a subordination of the individual to the welfare of the community, although it may be pointed out that the protection and welfare of the community is only the sum total of the protection and welfare of the individual. Nevertheless an insect born into a social caste is limited in its activities by its heredity. Specialization of function has occurred to such a degree that the individual cannot live without others of other castes. The queen termite would soon starve without her workers, but without a reproductive queen the community would soon degenerate and be so weakened that it might cease to exist unless another queen were adopted. The interdependence of the castes is so great that the absence of any one of them may cause all the rest to perish. Sacrifice of individuality is the price paid for biological success among the social insects.

Some Animals Live in Colonies

In the discussion of the social life of insects the society was seen to be a highly integrated organization of interdependent organisms of the same species divided into a number of castes, each of which had a specific function or number of functions to perform. Colonial animals form a much looser organization, for there are no definite castes and often no specialization according to function. Many animals live in colonies only because they have not migrated far from the point of their origin or because they chance to be attached to a common object. Often, however, there is division of labor among the members of the colony and a specialization of structure according to the division of labor.

Colonial communities are common among the animals belonging to the group of which *Hydra* is a member. It will be recalled that *Hydra* often reproduces asexually by budding. When the bud has reached a certain stage of development, it separates and takes up independent existence. With many others of this group, however, the bud remains attached to the original animal; and when a number of these have formed, a colony is the result. One animal of this group, known as *Hydractinia,* may have nutritive and reproductive individuals in the same colony. The nutritive individuals seem to confine their efforts to securing food, while the reproductive forms specialize in perpetuation of the species.

The Portuguese man-of-war is even more complicated in its organization and division of labor. Some of the individuals which make up this colonial animal secure food, while others carry on reproduction. Some of them have large stinging cells, which they use for paralyzing prey and for the defense of the colony, while others form a float filled with air for buoyancy to keep the animal on the surface of the sea.

EXPERIENCE. *To observe the colony structure of the Portuguese man-of-war.* Children living near the Gulf Stream, tropical seas, or a large marine aquarium may have an opportunity to observe the parts of the Portuguese man-of-war. On some of the beaches along the Gulf and the Atlantic these animals are occasionally found where they have been washed in by the high tide or a storm. Care should be exercised in the handling of the specimens, because of the stinging cells.

The Portuguese man-of-war. (Courtesy of The American Museum of Natural History.)

Coral Animals Are Colonial. One type of colony with which many children may have had some vicarious experience through their work in geography classes is that formed by the coral animals. These live in tropical seas principally, but one species may be found along the north Atlantic coast. Each animal produces a cup made up of a lime compound (calcium carbonate), and it is this cup which is usually referred to as the *coral*. Within this cup the animal lives, with its tentacles reaching over the rim of the cup. The lime cup is only about half an inch or less in length; but as succeeding generations build their cups on top of the old ones, enormous masses of coral may be built up.

In the Indian Ocean among the Maldive Islands, near the Fiji Islands in the south Pacific, on the Great Barrier Reef near Australia, and in the region of the Bahama Islands, coral animals are well known for the great extent of their colonies. Some of these colonies are in the form of atolls. An atoll is a more or less circular ridge of coral within which there may be a lagoon of shallow sea water. Shore reefs are ridges of coral built up from the bottom of the sea so near the land that ships cannot reach the land, and navigation is impaired. Barrier reefs are separated from the shore by a wide and often very deep channel. The greatest of these is off the coast of Australia. It is more than 1100 miles long and in some places 30 miles wide. The channel between it and the shore is 50 to 150 feet deep.

Some of the species of sponges are also considered to be colonial. One of these may be found growing on rocks along the eastern seashores of our country, just below the water line

Coral reef. Small fish swimming past coral colonies. (Courtesy of The American Museum of Natural History.)

at low-tide level. It consists of a number of horizontal hollow tubes, and branches which extend upward into the water. These branches are also hollow, and each has an opening called the osculum at the top. The cavities within the branches and horizontal tubes are known to be digestive cavities. The entire mass of branches and horizontal tubes is considered a *colony,* and each branch, with its osculum, is considered a separate individual.

Colonies occur among some of the Protozoa. Such a colony may consist of a very few of these one-celled animals, or it may number many thousands of animals. Some of these colonies are linear, others branch out like a tree, and still others are spheroidal in shape.

Other Animals Live in Colonies. Among the animals which are more complicated than those so far mentioned, colonial forms are not so common. One species of segmented worms produces lateral buds which remain attached to the original individual, thus forming a branch colony. Tapeworms, which are parasitic in many mammals, are an example of colonial animals. They are made up of many segments, the first of which is called the head. It is not really a head in the true sense of the word, for any of the segments behind it may be considered a separate individual. This would be an example of a linear colony. Colonies are never formed among animals which perpetuate the species by means of sexual reproduction only.

EXPERIENCE. *To study the colonial structure of a coral.* Perhaps one of the children may bring a piece of coral to class. Note that the cup is divided into a number of chambers, and that the center of the cup is occupied by a structure formed by the fusion of the walls of the chambers. Note the height of each cup and the manner in which the cups are built one on top of the other.

Colonial Organization Is Relatively Simple. In conclusion, it may be said that a colonial organization of animals is much simpler than a social organization, and that some advantages may be derived for each individual when a division of labor occurs. There are no castes, as in the case of social insects, and colonial forms occur only among the lower animals.

Among plants the algae are often found to be colonial, the colony generally being round or spheroidal in shape. The individual plant cells in the colony may be embedded in a gelatinous mass. This type of colonial alga often grows on the inside walls of the class aquarium, causing it to appear green and dirty, although the water in it may be perfectly clear and clean.

One of the commonest kind of algae is often seen on rocks, fence posts, and trunks of trees, where superficially it resembles a thin layer of green. If some of this is brought into the laboratory or classroom and studied under a microscope, it is seen to consist of groups of two or four cells. Such a group of cells may be considered a simple colony which has arisen from the division of a single cell.

Some Animals Are Gregarious

The lowest degree of social life among animals is gregariousness. Because they are dependent on the same source of food, some animals are found together in fairly large numbers or perhaps in vast herds. Among gregarious animals there is very little division of labor. Unlike the caste system of insect societies all the individuals are much alike.

Wolves may hunt in packs.

The safety of the individual is seldom bound up with the safety of the herd, and each can live separately from the herd if necessary.

Gregariousness Has Advantages. One of the advantages derived from gregariousness is defense and protection for the individual Wolves might prey on individual bison detached from the herd, but they will not do so when large numbers of bison are present, for they would be attacked and quickly dispersed. On the other hand, a number of wolves may hunt together in packs, pulling down game which no one of them could kill alone. Rocky Mountain sheep, renowned among hunters for their extreme wariness, live together in

Prairie dogs live in "villages."

small bands and post sentinels while they are grazing or resting. These sentinels watch out for intruders and give warning of their approach. Prairie dogs in our Western states live in "villages" which may spread under many acres, and give notice to one another of the approach of an intruder by their shrill cries. Reindeer of northern countries migrate from one feeding area to another in large herds, thus enjoying a protection from predators which they would not have if they led a solitary existence.

Some kinds of sea birds are found in isolated places in great numbers, probably because they all find these spots free from animals which might attack their nests and destroy their eggs and young. In Oregon there is a wood rat which builds great nests in trees. Each of the rats has a separate compartment in the nest but runs about freely from one compartment to another.

Lions sometimes hunt singly, but more commonly one male and three or four females hunt together. Insect-eating birds commonly fly in flocks and are thereby enabled to catch insects which, because of their agile flight, might elude any one of them but cannot escape the flock. The tent caterpillar has been mentioned, and the habits of its larvae may be considered gregarious.

Pelicans practice a gregarious and mutually helpful habit. They feed on fish, and a number of them may choose an appropriate place near the shore, form a wide arc, and narrow it by moving toward the land. In this way they enclose the fish in an increasingly smaller area, which makes them easier to catch.

A buzzard may fly high in the air for a long time, until it spots carrion on which to feed. As it drops toward the carrion, it is quickly joined by others, and all share in the food found by one of them. Beavers live in groups, joining together in felling trees and damming streams to form ponds which will be used by all. Muskrat houses are often found to contain a number of these animals. Fish often travel in large numbers known as schools. Whales are frequently found in groups. Seals usually live together, and sometimes are found in very large numbers on the islands off the coast of Alaska.

Many animals may be more or less solitary during some seasons of the year and gregarious at others. Children are usually familiar with the fact that birds migrate in flocks; and many of them may have seen wild geese and wild ducks flying overhead, going north in the spring and south in the fall. During the spring, summer, and autumn crows generally lead a solitary existence, breaking up into family groups; but during the winter they often band together in large flocks, sometimes composed of thousands of individuals. Birds like quail are found in coveys during most parts of the year, but in the summertime they scatter to nest and to rear their young. Purple martins often nest together in large numbers, and so do barn swallows, several nests often being made in the same barn.

Practically all birds are gregarious to some extent. Some, however, like the butcher shrike, seem to lead a strictly solitary existence. They may be drawn together by the presence of a common food supply or by the presence of a nesting site peculiar to the species. Birds do not seem to derive much mutual protection from their gregarious tendencies, although occasionally they co-operate to drive away an intruder.

During the breeding season mating is facilitated by the presence of a large number of both sexes in an area. Sometimes the herd or pack is led by a male, sometimes by a female. Often the leadership is decided by battle among individuals which seem to compete for it. The strongest survives and leads the herd or pack until displaced from that position by a younger or stronger individual in combat.

When birds or other animals are migrating, the leadership is sometimes assumed by one individual after another, each leader being supplanted as he seems to grow weakened by fatigue. Sometimes gregarious animals are hostile to one another. Fiddler crabs fight with one another continually, and herring gulls when large and mature sometimes kill younger and weaker birds of their own species.

Gregariousness Has Certain Disadvantages. There are some disadvantages to gregarious life. If the herd is too large, the supply of food may become so scarce that the weaker members die. Too many tent caterpillars may strip all the leaves off a small tree; and if another tree is not to be found nearby, they may be forced to live upon plants which they ordinarily do not attack. Many predatory animals seek out their prey by means of the sense of smell; and the scent left by large groups of animals is so much easier to follow than that of the single animal that no difficulty is encountered in locating the quarry. Sometimes the instinct for following the leader is so strong that it is dangerous to the whole herd. It is well known that sheep will follow their leader anywhere, which sometimes leads to their destruction.

It may be noted that among living things, particularly among animals, there is a sharp competition for food and other necessities, which results in eliminating those least able to survive (the unfit) and permitting only the best-adapted animals to continue the species. This competition is of two kinds, the competition between *different* species and the competition between members of the *same* species. The latter is generally the more severe, although the former may be much more apparent.

This struggle for existence and survival of the fittest received much public attention from the work of two English biologists, Darwin and Wallace, who published simultaneously the results of the separate investigations which they had been conducting, each unaware of what

Ducks and geese migrate in flocks.

the other had been doing. The Russian scientist Kropotkin, however, has emphasized the fact that there is among animals a degree of mutual aid as well as competition, and that while the need of food tends to make animals competitive and antagonistic, the processes of reproduction have tended to bring them together. The burdens laid on the parents in bringing forth young and caring for them seem to have had a great effect on the gradual development of the varying degrees of cooperation among animals.

This is also true of the human species. There seems to be a tendency toward gregariousness, formation of colonies, or the establishment of societies in the entire animal kingdom, so that mutual aid exists in practically all species and even between species to some degree.

EXPERIENCE. *To observe animal relationships.* Some children may find it interesting to observe the habits of different animals in their community. A record kept of such observations showing which animals live a solitary life, which ones are social, and which ones are gregarious would be an interesting source of information for class discussions on this topic. Notice should be taken of how animals adjust to the ways of man.

Few Animals Are Truly Solitary

Only a comparatively few animal species are truly solitary. Most of these are predators and feed upon other animals. The presence of too many of such a species in a given area would cause the food supply to grow so small that all would be in danger of starvation. Eagles build their nests miles apart, and such birds as hawks are not found together in large groups. Polar bears are not found in groups larger than the family. The solitary habits of some of the insects have been mentioned. Animals like the weasel and mink, ferocious and bloodthirsty, do not form gregarious groups. It is noteworthy that those animals which are found in the greatest numbers are those which are at least somewhat gregarious or social, while the least numerous animals are the solitary ones. A solitary existence has its advantages in eliminating to a large extent competition within the species.

Parental Care of Offspring Varies in Amount

Thus far the social instincts of animals in their varying degrees of complexity have been considered from the standpoint of the entire society, colony, or gregarious grouping. Human relationship indicates that there is another kind of social organization, that of the family, and the same thing is true of many animals. The family is an important unit in social organization, and any animals otherwise displaying little tendency toward communal existence have a family life which is important for the protection of the young.

The largest such family is probably that of the termites, which, as we have seen, has its origin in a single pair of these insects, and which may grow eventually into hundreds of thousands of individuals, all of which develop from eggs laid by the reproductive queen over a period of years. In the case of the social insects, as has been noted, the young insects receive much care, being fed, aired, and cleaned by nurses, and protected from danger by the soldiers and workers. Other animals receive practically as much care, but because of the habits of the species cannot remain in such a large family.

Little Parental Care Is Given Some Animals. Some animals receive no parental care when they are young. The eggs and sperms of many fish are simply laid in the oceans or bodies of fresh water; fertilization is entirely accidental; and no further attention is given

them by the mature individuals which produced them. Starfish furnish an example of this lack of parental care. A female oyster may produce an enormous number of eggs; but their development is entirely a matter of chance, for no attention is given them by the mature individuals. The female codfish lays her millions of eggs in the water, and the fact that any of them ever reach maturity is not due to any care they receive, but only to chance. Animals like *Hydra* and the sponges give no care whatever to their offspring.

Some animals place their eggs where their development is somewhat facilitated by the environment. Thus, while the toad may be considered a terrestrial animal, it goes to the water to lay its eggs. Frogs and salamanders are closer to the water, usually; but they are adapted for a land existence, and they too lay their eggs in water. On the other hand, some mature turtles habitually spend most of their

New-hatched turtles heading for the water.

time in the water, but they come to land to lay their eggs, depositing them in warm sand.

The Australian brush turkey lays her eggs in a pile of decomposing litter which serves as a nest, and trusts to the heat of the decomposition of the litter to incubate the eggs. Some wasps, ichneumon flies, and other insects lay their eggs on either living or dead food of animal nature, while many other insects lay their eggs on plants suitable for the feeding of the larvae.

The nest-building habits of birds are well known, but some fishes also build nests by hollowing out a place in the bottom of a stream and depositing the eggs in the hollow. The eggs are then left to develop or to be eaten by other animals, as chance may dictate. Some cold-blooded animals remain near their eggs for a few days after they are laid; but since the body temperature of the parent is low, this probably does not hasten the development of the eggs.

Some animals carry their eggs with them wherever they go. The eggs of the crayfish are attached to the abdomen of the body of the female; and she waves them back and forth in the water, thus aerating them. Spiders sometimes carry their eggs around with them in a silken case, while some of the fresh-water mussels carry their eggs in the gill chambers of the female. As the water passes over the gills of the female, the eggs are furnished with oxygen so that they may develop properly. The eggs of some species of frogs are attached to the back of the male or the female. Sometimes the eggs are attached to the hind legs of the male frog, so that when danger threatens him, he carries away the eggs. The male of the curious little animal known as the sea horse has a brood pouch, and the eggs are carried about in this pouch until they hatch. The female marsupial frog, found in South America, has a pouch on her back which is formed from a fold of the skin. In this pouch the eggs are carried.

Some Young Must Receive Parental Care to Survive. Those animals which give their young no parental care, or which give their young only a very slight amount of it, usually hatch from the egg in a stage sufficiently developed to enable them to survive if they are not eaten by a larger animal or if they do not become subject to disease. In other words, they are able to take care of themselves sufficiently so that, barring accidents, they will grow to maturity, although most of them do not do so. Potentially each of them is capable of achieving maturity alone and without assistance.

Among animals which develop within the body of the female, birth often occurs when the young are so helpless that without parental care they would die within a short time. Thus young kangaroos and opossums are so very immature at birth that their development must be continued after they leave the body of the female. They are carried around in a pouch by her for some time. Mice and rats are born blind and hairless at birth, and are very helpless. Young rabbits, kittens, and puppies have a covering of hair, but they too are born blind. Such animals as calves and fawns, though they are able to walk around within a few hours after birth, are very dependent for a time on the female for their food. Bears are large animals, but their young are very small and helpless at birth, and must be given much care to survive.

Among birds there is considerable difference in the stage of development at the time of hatching. The young of most of the common songbirds are born practically without feathers, and in many cases are blind. Birds which are helpless at the time of hatching are said to be *altricial*. In direct contrast with the altricial forms, some species of birds are very active upon hatching, and in some instances are able to run or even swim almost immediately. Such birds are said to be *precocial*, and are covered with down. Some altricial birds, particularly the young of hawks and owls, are born with down, but are entirely helpless and blind. Both altricial and precocial birds receive considerable care; but the former type, being unable to seek its own food, receives more attention. Precocial young, like those of quail and pheasants, leave the nest soon after hatching and are led about by the female in search of food.

Children may get direct evidence of the care of young by parents in their own homes if there is a baby in the family. They realize that without a great deal of care the infant could not survive; for it is entirely helpless for a long time, and if it were not properly taken care of, would die. Most animals which care for their young provide them with food and shelter; in the case of the human species clothing must also be provided, and education itself is an example of care given to human young. It may be safely said that the young of the human race get more care than those of any other species of animals. The period of development of the human being, with the attendant parental care often given, is much longer than that of any other animal.

Reproduction May Result in the Formation of Families

In animals the reproductive process sometimes results in the development of families. In many cases when a male and female mate, they do so for life; for *monogamy* is the rule of some species. When this occurs and young are born to the mature individuals, a family is naturally formed. In many instances this results in much better care for the young, since two individuals are better able to care for a brood of young than one.

Most families in the animal world are not permanent. After the young have matured, they generally scatter and set up new families for themselves, seldom staying with the parents after they have achieved full growth. This dispersal is important, not only because it lessens excessive competition for food, but because it results in the invasion of new areas by the species, thus introducing it into places where it had not previously existed. Unless this dispersal is prevented by natural barriers, a species may be spread over great territories, often being halted only by large bodies of water and high mountains.

Both Parents May Co-operate in Caring for the Young. Birds are among those animals which give their young much parental care. In many species both the male and the female work on the building of the nest, and in many instances both birds participate in the incubation of the eggs. This is particularly true of those species in which the two sexes are similarly colored, as the robin and the mourning dove. After the young are hatched, both parent birds often seek food for the young and feed them. The Indian hornbill has a habit that is unique. The nest is in a hollow tree, much like a woodpecker's, with a large opening. Within this tree the female lays the eggs. She is sealed in by the male with mud, only a small opening permitting communication with the male. He seeks out food and brings it to her until the young hatch, when both birds work together to find food for the young. When the male is much more brightly colored than the female, only the latter incubates the eggs. In a few instances the female is more brightly colored, and the eggs are incubated by the male alone.

Among some mammals both male and female parents care for the young. When young beavers have cut their incisor teeth, they are weaned by the female and follow the parents about in their activities. From them they learn to gnaw down poplar saplings and other small trees, eat their fill, cut what is left into convenient lengths, and drag the small lengths of wood to the beaver lodge in which they live. During the coldest winter weather, when the ice is thick, they feed on the bark of the wood which was gathered in more favorable weather.

Among some mammals the females feed the young, while the males assume leadership and protect the family from predators. The apes are generally found together in family groups. The male chimpanzee guards his young as they swing from bough to bough among the trees. As the chimpanzee families move from one feeding ground to another, they go in single lines, with male sentinels running ahead of the party to make sure that the way is clear. If danger is sensed, their cries of alarm warn the others of the danger ahead. Gorilla families congregate together at night. Baboons also live in family groups. When they go from one place to another, several of the families often join together. When danger threatens, the males surround the females and the young and compel them to move more rapidly so that the danger may be avoided.

Some Females Rear Their Young Alone. Sometimes the association of male and female is a temporary one for the purpose of breeding only, and the male does not remain with the female while she cares for the offspring. The male may be hostile to the young, and will destroy them if he can, so that the female must protect them against him. Boys who have kept rabbits know that before the doe bears her young, the male must be segregated from her; else he will kill the young immediately after they are born. Female rats, mice, squirrels, domesticated cats, lions, tigers, and bears are among the animals which care for their young alone. While they are very young, the female nourishes the young in the den by

Animals vary in the care of the young.

means of her mammary glands, leaving them only long enough to secure food for herself. As they become older and stronger, she trains them in hunting and in eluding danger. Female bears have been observed in the forests with their young, cuffing them vigorously. To their young, foxes bring animals which are crippled sufficiently so that they cannot escape but which are still active enough to offer some resistance. In this way the young foxes learn a little about securing food, and later they accompany the female on foraging expeditions.

Deer, bison, cattle, and other grazing animals find new mates each year. The female alone takes care of the young, although the herd comes to her rescue if necessary. A cow can find her calf among hundreds of others, while a bison cow can do the same thing, picking out her calf by its call or scent, no matter how large the herd. As the calves become older and stronger, the instinct for protecting them seems to become weaker in the female, until finally she ceases to look after them altogether.

Males Sometimes Exercise Some Parental Care. Most species of fishes do not build homes for their young and take little, if any, care of them. There are some exceptions to this rule. Salmon leave the ocean, swim upstream to fresh water, and select a suitable place for laying the eggs. While the female is laying the eggs, the male emits sperm into the water, so that the eggs are fertilized.

At this time the male protects the female, and will fight marauders who attempt to attack her. If the male is killed, the female is protected by another male. During the breeding season the male stickleback builds a nest in an isolated place. When the nest is finished, the male seeks out a female and leads her to it. She deposits her eggs. He seeks out another female, or several others in succession, and more eggs are laid in it. The eggs are fertilized, and during their development they are guarded by the male. After the eggs have hatched, the male continues his guard, often forcing the young back to their nest if they attempt to leave.

Catfish lay their eggs in nests hollowed out under logs in the stream. The male cares for the eggs, catching them up in his mouth to prevent them from becoming embedded in the mud. In the Mississippi Valley and in sluggish waters of the Great Lakes region there is a fish which attains a length of about one foot and is dark olive in color. It is known variously as the bowfin, mudfish, and fresh-water dogfish, and feeds on other fish, crayfish, and other aquatic animals. During the breeding season, which is in the spring of the year, the male clears a space in vegetation in a quiet part of the stream. The female lays her eggs here, and the male guards them during the hatching period of eight to ten days and afterward for a period of about nine days while the young remain in the nest. At this time the young leave the nest, but they are accompanied by the male, who remains with them until they attain a length of about four inches.

The male smallmouthed black bass guards the eggs in the nest, which is made by clearing away a place near the shore where there are some good-sized stones. He continues to protect the young fish until they are about an inch and a quarter long. The pipefish, which lives in ocean water, is extremely thin, and has an abbreviated fin and bony armor; it resembles the sea horse in that it has a brood pouch in which the male carries the eggs about until they hatch.

The Length of Time of Parental Care Varies. Because animals are born at varying stages of development and because the length of time required for the attainment of maturity varies with the species, the amount of parental care also varies. An animal like a mouse, which matures within a few weeks after it is born, obviously does not need attention for so long a period as a human being. Generally the parental care is exercised until the young are able to seek food for themselves and to protect themselves from any predators. Young birds must take care of themselves when once they are fully grown and can fly, so that by autumn of the year in which they are hatched, they shift for themselves and even migrate south in flocks of young birds.

Those animals which give birth to young once a year usually take more care of their young than those which bring forth young at different times of the year. On the other hand, some animals may care for their young for a number of years. It is said that the young of the chimpanzee may remain with the parents until they are several years old. Instead of becoming entirely separated from the family, these apes may remain near it, thus giving rise to fairly large groups, each dominated by an old and powerful male who does not relinquish his leadership until defeated in battle by a younger and more powerful rival. Thus animals which mature slowly receive parental care over a much longer period of time than those which mature quickly.

EXPERIENCE. *To observe parental care of young.* Many children have opportunities to observe animal families. They will be able to see how much or how little care some parents give to their young. It should be noted at the same time whether both parents or just one provides this care. Children may also observe animals that give no care to their young, such as frogs, toads, turtles, and some insects.

Man Gives His Young a Constantly Improving Home Life

Since the activities of the lower animals are guided largely by inherited instincts, there is no improvement in the home life of these organisms except through a *natural selection* by which those whose adaptations for family life do not meet the test of a changing environment are eliminated. Such natural selection is an extremely slow process when measured in terms of years or generations of the animal. Consequently birds today are caring for their young much as they did thousands or hundreds of thousands of years ago. Termites are ancient insects, and it is probable that they were caring for their young in much the same manner as today long before the appearance of the human species on Earth.

Because of his reasoning power, his ability to learn and to transmit his knowledge, man has been able to gain some measure of control over natural resources and energy. He has used these abilities to improve his home life and to take much better care of his family than any other animal. He furnishes his offspring with warm clothes in winter and cool clothes in summer. He is able to diagnose and treat diseases which might cause the death of his young. He corrects their physical defects by various means and teaches them what he can about themselves and their environment, both biological and physical. It is true that there are wide individual differences, not only of a physical and mental nature, but also of social opportunity. But by and large, the human young receive more and better care during their immaturity than the young of any other animal.

CHAPTER 18

Animals Are Home-Builders

There Are Many Kinds of Animal Homes

The fact that many species of animals build homes has been noted in the study of the habits of the social insects, and here and there mention has been made of the homes of other animals. The honeycomb constructed in the

hollow tree by the wild bee, the underground galleries of the termites, which ramify in every direction, the anthills, which are so common in all parts of the world, are all examples of structures built by insects for their protection. In addition, the tubes made by the larvae of those insects which spend part of their life in water and the work of such insects as the carpenter bee have also been mentioned. Every child is familiar with the nests built by birds and realizes what these are for. Children living in rural and suburban districts may have seen houses built by muskrats, the nest in a hollow tree constructed there by the raccoon, the burrow of the woodchuck, or ground hog, the den occupied by the fox and skunk, and many others of similar nature. Man himself is perhaps the greatest of home-building animals.

Animal homes are made to serve many purposes. Sometimes they are built for purposes of hibernation, as a refuge for the animal during adverse seasons when temperature is low and food scarce. All the hibernating mammals of regions subjected to extreme cold during the winter seek out a shelter of some sort in which they stay until conditions are more favorable. Cold-blooded animals, like snakes, turtles, and frogs, dig down into the soil until

629

they reach a point below the freezing line and stay there. A discussion of the manner in which animals survive the changing seasons will be presented in a later chapter.

Sometimes homes are built by animals more for rearing the young than for any other reason. This is particularly true of birds, for they usually abandon their nests when they migrate. Most species build new nests the following breeding season. Mammals which rear their young in nests or burrows sometimes use them also for hibernation in the winter, and often food is stored in them for use during the unfavorable seasons.

Birds Build Nests for Their Young

Because bird nests are so well known to children, it may be proper to consider them first in a discussion of animals' homes. As has been stated, they are primarily an adaptation for rearing the young, seldom being used otherwise. Since birds are the prey of many animals, such as cats, other birds, skunks, squirrels, raccoons, snakes, and foxes, it is fortunate that most birds construct their nests in such a way that they are as inconspicuous as possible. This is accomplished partly by using materials very much like the background against which the nest is placed. Birds which nest on the ground in meadows use dead grass and leaves, which serve to blend the nest with its background, so that often it is not discovered unless one sees the female leaving it when she is disturbed. This is true of the nest of the field sparrow and the ground sparrow.

The Baltimore oriole makes its nest inaccessible by building it out on the ends of long branches, where it cannot be reached by squirrels, cats and other predators. The cliff swallow builds its nest on sheer cliffs, so that it cannot be invaded, while many birds build in hollow trees. Sometimes sea birds nest on uninhabited islands in large numbers, and find safety there. The killdeer builds its nest in open fields; but since it simply scoops out a shallow place in the soil and rings it with a few pebbles, its nest is not easily discovered.

The nest site is generally such that it affords protection from heavy rains, strong winds, and direct sunlight. The nest is located in a place where the food of the birds is abundant; thus long flight and prolonged absence from the nest in search of food are unnecessary. Nests of wild ducks and geese are found on the banks of lakes where the plant growth is sufficient to hide them from sight. For birds that build their nests in trees, adequate support is necessary; for a nest like that of the robin, built as it is partly of mud, would soon tumble to the ground if its support were insufficient.

Birds sometimes change their nesting habits, as is well illustrated by the chimney swifts and barn swallows. Before the coming of man to this continent chimney swifts built their nests in hollow trees; but now they often build inside chimneys, where they are relatively safe. Barn swallows have been given their name from their habit of building their nests in barns on the rafters and beams. Wrens, robins, and purple martins often nest in man-made boxes put up for them.

Some birds use their nests year after year, but this is not true of most species. Eagles are known to return to their nests repeatedly, rebuilding them each time to make them habitable. Robins also do this. They occasionally build a new nest on top of the old, especially if the location is a favorable one.

Different kinds of nests.

Ruby-throated hummingbird

Baltimore oriole

Chimney swift

Killdeer

Sparrow hawk

Barn swallow

Cliff swallow

Robin

Kingfisher

Pintail

Birds Build Nests at Different Levels. Some birds build their nests on the ground in more or less protected places. The whippoorwill nest is found on the ground of woods where the soil is damp and the smaller plants grow rather tall. Killdeers build their nests on the ground also, as do quail and ruffed grouse. Pheasants always build their nests on the ground and never in a tree or bush. Savanna sparrows, grasshopper sparrows, field sparrows, and vesper sparrows build their nests on the ground in tall grass. In places where there is an abundance of bushy growth the towhee builds its nest on the ground. Marsh hawks, ovenbirds, wild ducks, and wild geese build nests on the ground also.

Many species of birds build nests in fern thickets or weeds. This is true of the song sparrows. Red-winged blackbirds build nests at this level in marshy places where there is plenty of bush vegetation. Marsh wrens are found to nest similarly, and so is the Maryland yellowthroat. Some birds nest in thick underbrush on the edges of woods or in tangled undergrowth. The home of the rose-breasted grosbeak, cardinal, indigo bunting, catbird, cuckoo, and wood thrush may be located in such a situation.

Some birds nest in the lower branches of trees. This is true of the brown thrasher, which is found over many parts of this country. The mourning dove, well known for its plaintive call, builds a rather crude flat platform of twigs on the lower branches of a tree. Blue-jay nests are found in such a location, as well as those of the sharp-shinned hawks, hummingbirds, kingbirds, chipping sparrows, robins, redstarts, and goldfinches.

In tree tops may be found the nests of such birds as the bronzed grackle, purple grackle, crow, and hawk. Eagles generally select the tallest and largest trees in the neighborhood and build their nests high up among the branches.

In hollow trees may be found the nests of such species as the sparrow hawk, long-eared owl, screech owl, house wren, nuthatch, titmouse and red-headed woodpecker. Bluebirds nest in hollow apple trees in orchards, while chickadees nest in hollow trees in the woods. Screech owls often nest in barns; and house wrens, starlings, and English sparrows will nest in almost any available place. Bluebirds will often nest in birdhouses set out for them. English sparrows compete with bluebirds and robins for nesting sites, fighting with them in an effort to drive them off. One of the reasons why they are considered pests is that they occupy the nesting sites of song birds, making it impossible for them to occupy an area.

Birds Nest at Different Times of the Year. Not all birds build their nests at the same time. Those which do not migrate to the south in the fall, but which spend the entire year in the same vicinity, are apt to nest early, particularly if the type of food they feed their young is available early. Many species of hawks and owls feed their young on such food as mice and rabbits; and since such food is available early in the spring, owls nest very early. The eggs may be laid by the female in March or April.

Birds which feed their young on insects do not nest so early, since insects are not abundant until later in the spring. Some birds fly north later than others; usually the latecomers build their nests later. Often, however, two birds which arrive at about the same time show much variation in the nesting date. Robins and blackbirds arrive north about the same time, but the red-winged blackbird does not build its nest until after the sedges and grasses in the swamps have grown sufficiently to support the nest. By that time the first broods of robins have already hatched, since robins find nesting sites immediately available upon their arrival at the breeding place. Thus nesting habits may determine nesting dates. It is also true that birds with similar feeding habits may have different nesting dates. White-breasted nuthatches nest in the middle of April, but downy woodpeckers do not nest until the middle of May. Both feed on insects.

Screech owls generally nest in April, and so do crows, bluebirds, nuthatches, robins, phoebes, and song sparrows. Many common songbirds nest in May. Kingfishers, cardinals, flickers, quail, ruby-throated hummingbirds, redheaded woodpeckers, meadow larks, brown thrashers, catbirds, redstarts, wrens, red-winged blackbirds, and many others nest during this month. In June the nests of the scarlet tanagers, cedar waxwings, goldfinches, and wood pewees are built.

Types of Nests Are Characteristic of the Species. Nests are generally built according to their function and the type of young which will inhabit them. Those birds which have altricial young, which demand a comparatively great amount of care in the nest, build them carefully. The robin's nest consists of mud, dead grasses, horsehair, and other similar materials. It is sturdy and well constructed, for the young must spend some time in it before they are strong enough to leave it. The woven swaying structures made by the orioles represent one of the best developments of nests, for not only are they placed so that a maximum of protection is secured, but they are very skillfully constructed.

Birds whose young are precocial build nests which are much simpler in structure. For instance, herring fulls may even lay their eggs in hollows of bare rocks.

The type of nest varies with the species. Hawks build rather large platform-like nests, which are more or less bowl-shaped. The kingfisher digs a hole in a steep sandy bank, and the eggs are laid at the end of the tunnel thus formed. Swallows often assemble and build many nests close together, being somewhat gregarious.

Among some tropical birds it has been found that a common nest is built in which a number of females lay their eggs and then share the duties of incubation and feeding the young. Meadow larks have a covered runway to the nest. The marsh wren weaves a nest of grass attached to waterweeds; it has much the appearance of a small tuft of grass left on the weeds by high water, and the female enters the nest from the side, not from the top.

Birds do not learn to build their nests; rather it seems to be an *instinctive activity*. Each species builds a nest that is characteristic, so that when one learns to identify nests, each can be associated with a definite species. Mourning-dove nests are built co-operatively by both the male and the female, and this is also true of such birds as the robin and bluebird. The male house wren, however, does practically none of the work, but is to be found close at hand, usually singing.

The type of material used depends on the location of the nest and also on what is available. Woodland birds use twigs, rootlets, lichens, dried leaves, and mosses, while birds which nest in fields use dead grasses and animal hair. Birds nesting in marshes utilize dead rushes and grasses, while robins, wood thrushes, bronzed grackles, barn swallows, cliff swallows, and phoebes often use mud. Goldfinches, yellow warblers, and Baltimore orioles often use fibers taken from such plants as milkweeds.

Chimney swifts build their nests inside chimneys, of such materials as small sticks, which they fasten together and attach to the sides of the chimney by means of saliva which hardens and holds the nest together. Ruby-throated hummingbirds use cobwebs to fasten together bits of lichen, of which the nest is made. The nest of this bird is the smallest of all nests found in this country, generally not exceeding an inch in diameter at the top. Its eggs are very small, being about the size of peas. Petals of flowers are also used in the construction of the nest, as well as the scales of buds. Tree swallows build their nests of straw and line them with feathers. Occasionally birds will use such materials as paper or wood shavings in building their nest. The material is generally carried to the nesting site by the bird in its bill. Chimney swifts are thought to break off the small twigs they use while in full flight, and the robin carries the mud it uses in its bill.

The length of time required to build the nest also varies, although about six days is the length of time necessary for most birds. Once the nest is completed, the process of egg-laying begins.

EXPERIENCE. *To find the nesting sites of various birds.* Take a field excursion through meadows, underbrush, and into woods. Note which kinds of birds are found in each of these places, and note also where each species builds its nest.

EXPERIENCE. *To determine how a bird builds its nest.* Children may watch a robin or some other bird build its nest. Ask them to report the progress made by the bird each day. Warn them not to approach too closely to the nesting site, or the nest may be deserted by the birds and another one begun somewhere else.

EXPERIENCE. *To determine what substances birds use in building their nests.* Place in some rather secluded spot such things as horsehair, paper, bits of string, and other likely material. This should be done during the nest-building season. By observation children may determine which materials are chosen by the birds for nest-building.

EXPERIENCE. *To study deserted bird nests.* Since birds rarely use the same nests a second season, some children may find it interesting to study deserted bird nests. The children should be encouraged to keep notes telling when and where each nest was found, what kind of bird built the nest, and what materials were used in the construction. Some children may need guidance in determining whether or not a nest is deserted. A good pattern to follow would be to observe the nest at a distance at different times of the day on several succeeding days. If neither parent nor young is observed, the nest may be examined from a closer range. If there is still no visible activity, one is fairly safe in assuming the nest to be deserted.

Birds Will Often Use an Artificial Nest. Since birds are considered beneficial animals, they should be given every opportunity for survival. It is often profitable to build artificial nests or birdhouses which they can use when nesting sites are scarce. Many kinds of birds will use properly constructed birdhouses. Bluebirds, robins, wrens, martins, barn swallows, tree swallows, phoebes, chickadees, and nuthatches will occupy and use such nests.

Bluebirds like boxes placed in a shady spot on a fence post where they will not be disturbed by passers-by too frequently. If boxes are placed under the eaves of low buildings, wrens will often nest in them, returning to the same site year after year. Large birdhouses with many compartments may be built and placed on poles for martins. If boxes or hollow limbs are attached to branches of orchard trees, woodpeckers, flickers, nuthatches, and chickadees will often be attracted. Narrow ledges made of pieces of board nailed to rafters in a barn will be used by barn swallows if they can enter the barn through holes or spaces.

When birdhouses are built, they should not be painted in bright colors, since birds seem to shun them if they are conspicuous. Neutral shades of brown or gray may be used. If the house is well made and properly placed, it need never be moved, although it is sometimes wise to clean it in the fall so that wasps and similar insects will not occupy it. It may also be necessary to eject squirrels, mice, and simi-

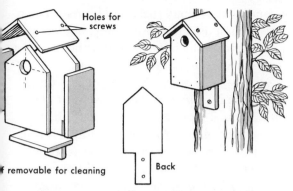

removable for cleaning   Back

For bluebirds and wrens — 4"square, 8"deep, opening 1"
For chickadees and nuthatches, same size, opening 1¼"
For bluebirds and swallows, 5"square, 8"deep, opening 1½"

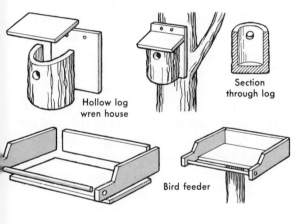

Birdhouses and feeding boxes.

lar animals in the spring; for these sometimes occupy birdhouses. At the end of the breeding season the old nest may be thrown out, al-though this is not absolutely necessary. The houses should be placed in position before they are to be occupied. In order to accommodate such birds as the chickadees, this must be done by about the first of February, since these birds have selected their nesting site by this time. When a house is built, the joints should be tight to keep out water. Pans of mud for building purposes may be provided near the birdhouse if it is intended for such birds as robins, swallows, and phoebes.

EXPERIENCE. *Constructing birdhouses.* During the month of February children may wish to construct birdhouses and place them in places where birds will be likely to use them during the nesting season. They may be used later for observation on how birds build their nests.

EXPERIENCE. *Constructing bird-feeding stations.* In the fall of the year bird-feeding stations may be constructed for those birds which remain in the vicinity during the winter months. When there is snow on the ground, and when the weather is cold, sunflower seeds, various grains, and other foods may be placed where birds can find them. Small pieces of suet may be tied to limbs of trees for birds to eat. Give the children opportunity to observe the feeding stations, noting what kinds of birds visit them.

Spiders Sometimes Construct Homes

Spiders often construct homes which are of interest to children. Many species spin webs of various kinds within which they live. These webs are often a means of trapping insects, which the spider then devours. This illustrates a type of home useful in aiding the animal in securing a supply of food. Flies, grasshoppers, and other insects alight on the web and are immediately entangled in its silken threads. They may struggle violently in an effort to escape. Often the spider waits until its prey is thoroughly fatigued, and then attacks it and devours it.

Spider webs show a wide diversity of structure. The commonest kinds perhaps are those of the orb-weaver spiders. These spin silk by means of spinnerets, which are located near the tip of the abdomen. Usually there are two or three pairs of these spinnerets. Upon the end of each spinneret there are many small tubes, called spinning tubes, from which the silk is spun. While it is within the body, the silk is in a fluid state; but it dries rapidly upon coming into contact with air. In addition to the many spinning tubes there are others which are larger and are called spigots. The ordinary thread of the web is spun from these.

Some spiders make two kinds of silk, one quite elastic and the other dry and inelastic. If the web of the orb spiders is examined, and the spiral line which forms the greater part of the web is touched, it will cling to the finger. When the finger is withdrawn, it will stretch. If one of the radiating lines or a portion of the outer framework is touched, however, it will neither adhere to the finger nor stretch. Some of the orb spiders live in the net and hang downward on its lower surface near the center of the net, while others stay near one side or edge of it. When an insect touches one of the sticky threads, the line sticks to it. Since it is elastic, it allows the insect to move a short distance, so that it comes in contact with other sticky threads and thus further entangles itself. When it has become so entangled that it is more or less helpless, the spider rushes to attack it.

The triangle spider is one of the commonest in North America, being found all over New England and as far to the southwest as Texas. The web consists of four lines of thread attached together at one end and radiating outward, with cross threads between them. When an insect becomes entangled in one of the sticky cross threads, the spider draws the web tight and then lets go of it suddenly, thus snapping the web and causing the insect prey to be further entangled.

Some of the running spiders build tubular nests in the ground, and these nests are lined with silk. Sometimes the entrance to the tube is concealed by small sticks and leaves. These nests are not used to capture prey, but serve as a retreat into which the animal withdraws except when seeking prey.

Some spiders spin what is called a funnel web, since it consists of a concave sheet of silk with a funnel-like tube at one side. The tube serves as the hiding place of the spider. It runs out of the tube whenever an insect is trapped in other parts of the web. The tube opens below so that the spider can escape from it quickly to the ground below if danger threatens.

In California and other Western states of the United States trapdoor spiders may sometimes be found. These dig a cylindrical hole in the ground, for which they provide a thick silken door, which is attached to the edge of the nest. This lid is slightly larger in diameter than the opening of the nest and is beveled at the edges, so that it fits neatly over the hole. The lid is often covered with bits of moss and other substances to make it inconspicuous. Soil, bits of wood, and leaves are also used for this purpose.

The nests of turret spiders are interesting examples of spider homes. These spiders make a small burrow in the ground and above it place sticks an inch or two in length in such a manner as to construct a five-sided turret. The sticks are laid one layer on top of another and are fastened together by means of silk; the entire structure may be two or even three inches high. The female turret spider carries her eggs about with her wherever she goes in the cocoon in which she has laid them. After being hatched the young spiders leave the cocoon and crawl up on the body of the female. She feeds them and carries them about for some time.

Not all spiders spin webs. Some of them wander about at night in search of prey and during the day hide under leaves and stones. The jumping spiders make no webs except nests in which they pass the winter or lay their

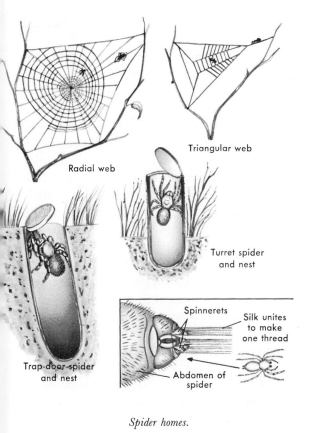

Radial web

Triangular web

Turret spider and nest

Trap-door-spider and nest

Spinnerets

Silk unites to make one thread

Abdomen of spider

Spider homes.

their bright colors and quick jumping movements. These spiders have three or four pairs of eyes and short legs, and they can move sideways or backward, being able also to make long jumps.

Spiders are unlike insects in that they cannot sting, but some species are able to bite. In species like the black-widow spiders and the tarantulas poison is secreted by glands. The bite of a black widow is dangerous to man, whereas the mild poison from a tarantula seldom gives trouble. The danger from most spider bites is usually exaggerated. They are seldom fatal, and are ordinarily not very painful.

EXPERIENCE. *To study the form and structure of spider webs.* Children may note the various kinds of spider webs they find. If the webs are simple, the children may wish to make sketches showing their construction. Note in which part of the web the spider is found. Have them determine which of the threads are sticky and elastic, and which are dry and inelastic. If an insect is caught in the web, note how it is entangled. If the spider is in sight, touch the web gently and observe how it acts.

eggs. They are common on plants and fences, and are often found also on the sides of buildings. They are often conspicuous because of

Some Solitary Insects Provide Homes for Their Young

Some solitary insects, as well as the social species, provide a shelter of one kind or another in which the young may complete at least part of their development. Several species of solitary bees build tunnels, or underground galleries. These shafts are about the diameter of a pencil and are made in moist sand. The walls are prevented from crumbling by the female lining the tunnel with a sticky substance which she secretes in her mouth. Several of these tunnels may be constructed each season by one female.

The *Halictus* bee builds a nest that is very similar to the one just described; but several females may co-operate in constructing it, and in addition to the main gallery there may be several tunnels branching off from it. The eggs of the females are deposited at the end of the branch tunnels. The large carpenter bees, which resemble bumblebees in size and appearance, build their nests by burrowing into the solid wood of fence posts and similar places. The entrance may be an inch or somewhat less in diameter, and the length may be as much as twelve inches in a downward direction within the wood.

Many species of mason bees build their nests under stones, logs, or in empty snail shells, constructing them of sand and clay mixed together with a sticky saliva produced by the bee. Another species selects empty oak-apple galls, reinforcing the walls of the gall with sand and clay mixed with saliva. In each oak gall there may be seven or eight cells, within each of which may be found a bit of beebread and an egg.

Mud-dauber wasps' nests are often seen under roofs, window ledges, and eaves of buildings. The nest is built by the female, who carries mud to the chosen site and plasters it into the shape of an oblong cell. The outside is smoothed over with a fresh coat of mud. The female seeks out a spider, paralyzes it with her sting, and places it in the cell. She then lays her eggs on the spider, seals the cell, and leaves it. The spider does not die; it remains alive, though paralyzed, until the wasp larvae hatch, when they proceed to feed on it. The potter wasp builds her nest upon thorn-bearing plants, such as wild blackberry or raspberry bushes. The nest is made of sand and mud mixed with saliva, and when complete it resembles a symmetrical jug. Each of the cells in it is provisioned with a paralyzed caterpillar, on which an egg is laid. The cell is then capped.

Wasps in tropical countries often use resins and gums from various trees in building their nests. Such nests protect the young from heavy rains, since they are waterproof. Other wasps stick together different materials, such as lichens and mosses. Some of them cover their nests with spines or suspend them from long threads. Some species do not provide a home for their larvae. They may lay their eggs in the cells of other species, destroying the egg which has previously been placed there by the wasp which constructed the nest. A species called the grasshopper wasp, which is found in our Western states, sometimes stings a grasshopper, thus paralyzing it. The wasp then carries the grasshopper to the abandoned nest of a carpenter ant, lays her egg on the grasshopper, and leaves it to its fate.

EXPERIENCE. *To observe the nests of some insects.* If the abandoned homes of various species of wasps are available, children might be interested in examining them. Discuss where the nests came from and note how they are constructed and of what materials they are made. If there is any doubt about whether or not a nest is occupied, naturally, it should not be disturbed.

Some Mammals Live in Underground Homes

Many different species of mammals dig subterranean burrows in which they spend a large part of their lives and rear their young. One of the commonest and best known of these mammals is the mole, which is found from Maine to Florida in this country. It lives in burrows which it digs, thereby causing damage to lawns, golf greens, and seed beds. This animal is often beneficial, however, for it feeds on insects and their larvae, and destroys in this way large numbers of them. These small animals are without external ears, and often their eyes are rudimentary, so that they see very poorly or not at all. The speed with which they dig is surprising, for one of them will tunnel a foot in about three minutes. Not all the moles live in the ground, for some of them are often found on the surface of the ground while other species are aquatic, and one or two species are known to live in trees.

EXPERIENCE. *To observe a mole burrow.* Locate a mole burrow and take the class to see it. Notice the direction in which it runs; and if it is not on a lawn or some similar place, the children may be permitted to open the burrow and follow its course. If they happen to come upon the mole, let them observe its progress through the soil. Do not pick up the mole, as it may bite.

Perhaps the children know of some other animals that make their homes in the ground and would like to tell about them.

Foxes generally make their dens by digging in the ground in some secluded and isolated spot where there is a minimum of danger. The young foxes are born in this burrow, and remain there or near it for some time after they are born. If pursued by hunters or other predators, the female fox will run, not to her home, but in any direction away from it until she has eluded her pursuers, thus preventing the discovery of the burrow. She returns to it to feed her young, bringing them small game after they have been weaned. The young foxes may be seen around the mouth of their burrow, playing in the sun; but at the first suspicion that something unusual is near they quickly disappear and do not come out for some time.

Many of the rodents make underground nests. In many parts of the United States woodchucks dig burrows in underbrush or along fence rows, from which they travel for short distances in search of food. They sometimes also make their burrows in hillsides or pasture lands. Ground squirrels (also known as gophers) inhabit open fields and dig burrows in the ground, in which the young are reared. Prairie dogs, common in the Western plains, live in large colonies of from forty or fifty to a thousand or more. They dig their burrows in the ground, the tunnels often being very long and usually communicating with one another. Grass and other vegetation is their food, and the colonies are always found where food is abundant.

Pocket gophers, found in Southeastern and Western states, have large claws for digging. They live in meadows, where they dig, throwing up mounds of dirt around the entrance to the burrow. These animals, like some other rodents, have internal cheek pouches, in which they carry food into their burrows. They cause considerable destruction if permitted to multiply.

Animals often take advantage of natural caves in which to make their homes. Bears

Homes underground.

often hibernate in caves (not true hibernation), and the young are born there. Wolves sometimes make use of caves also, and wander far from them in search of food. The otter, on the other hand, makes its burrows along the banks of streams, and is known to spend much of its time in the water. It has webbed feet and may grow to be three feet long. Fish are an important item in its diet. The mink has similar habits. It is much smaller than the otter. Its diet includes also birds and various small mammals, such as rabbits.

Badgers live underground and feed on small mammals. Skunks often find a den which has been deserted by some other animal and live in it during the period of hibernation, rearing their young there the following spring. Occasionally they dig their own burrows, but are as often as not found in an abandoned woodchuck hole, in a cave, a hollow log, a stone fence, or a haystack. The tunnel generally extends into the ground deeply enough to be below the frost line; and at the end of it is a rounded cavity which is lined with grass and leaves, thus making a nest. Here the young, blind and nearly hairless at birth, are brought forth in the spring, each litter numbering from four to ten young. The young are not able to see until they are three or four weeks old.

Many other examples of burrowing animals could be given from the mammal class. Chipmunks dig burrows the opening of which may be under the root of a tree or a stump. When a chipmunk digs, it carries the dirt away from the mouth of its new home, thus the loose soil does not betray the entrance. Red squir-

A muskrat's winter home.

rels often have two homes, one of these being a nest among the branches of a tree or in the trunk of a hollow tree, and the other an underground hole beneath the roots or stump of a tree. Nuts and mushrooms are favorite foods.

Some species of rabbits make more or less use of the abandoned burrows of other animals, or seek refuge in rock piles, among tree roots, and in similar places. Young jack rabbits are born with a covering of fur and with their eyes open, while young cottontails are born helpless and have their eyes closed. Field mice have underground nests in large chambers filled with dry grass, so that they are adequately sheltered in winter as well as in summer.

Some Mammals Build Nests on the Surface

Some species of mammals build their nests on the surface of the ground. Hares never dig burrows or occupy them, but instead make nests on the surface in tall grass. The nest is made up of dead grasses lined with fur from the body of the female. The muskrat has two homes: during the summer this rodent may be found in burrows along the banks of streams; during the winter it lives in a dome-shaped structure made from reeds and grasses found

Beavers build lodges.

in swamps. In this dome is a chamber above the water level, where the animals rest.

During the winter the animals remain within the house when weather is unusually severe; at other times, however, they go out in search of food. The entrance to the house is generally below the surface of the water, but even this does not deter bloodthirsty predators like the mink from entering the muskrat house and attacking and killing the residents. The young are not reared within the grass house, but are born in the spring of the year in burrows along streams.

Beavers make their lodges in swamps out of small branches which they plaster together with mud and grass sod. These are larger than the houses of muskrats, and have an underwater entrance much like that which leads to the muskrat house. The interior of the lodge consists of one "room," the floor of which is higher than the water, so that it is dry. Near the lodge the beavers store twigs and branches to be used as food in winter, when it is difficult to range far. The young are born and reared within these lodges.

Beavers sometimes build dams which impound the waters of a stream and cause the formation of a pond or lake. This is a beneficial activity when it results in the retardation of erosion; but sometimes the drainage systems built by farmers cannot function properly when a stream is dammed, and so the dam is destroyed. The beavers often promptly rebuild the dam.

Some Animals Live in Trees

Trees also serve as the sites of homes for animals other than birds and insects. Squirrels sometimes live in hollow tree trunks, and sometimes in the branches, where they build nests which resemble in some respects nests of large birds. During the winter gray squirrels live in the trunk of an old birch or maple tree. As many as five or six have been found in the same nest. In the spring of the year a second house may be built for rearing the young. This second house, or nest, located at the fork of two branches, is made of sticks, bark, and leaves, and is lined chiefly with grasses. The nest resembles that of a crow, but the entrance is from the side. If the nest is disturbed, the female will remove her young to a safer place, carrying them as a cat carries her kittens.

We have already noted that the red squirrel has two nests, one subterranean and the other in the branches of a tree. Flying squirrels may make their homes in knotholes, hollow limbs, and hollow tree trunks. They also build a nest in the branches similar to that of the gray squirrel, except that it is somewhat smaller.

Raccoons build their nests in the trunks of hollow trees, with an entrance high up off the ground level. In these hollows they rear their young, generally four in number. They also may hibernate in the nest during the winter-time. They are omnivorous and are easily recognized by their black-and-white ringed tails. When a raccoon is pursued by hunters or other predators, it will remain on the ground as long as possible, and will not take refuge in a tree unless escape otherwise is impossible.

Apes also build nests, or platforms, in trees, in which they may spend some time and in which they may sleep. Gibbons live mainly in the top branches of trees, where they construct nests for themselves made of twigs and branches and lined with leaves. Orangutans, which are found in Borneo and Sumatra, have a similar habit.

Many species of plants other than trees harbor insects and serve as homes for them for part of the life cycle. Oaks, chestnuts, willows, and elms often have *galls* upon them which are swellings or outgrowths caused by insects that puncture their tissues and lay eggs within the puncture. Galls are often seen also on blueberry, rose, and dogwood bushes, and goldenrods bear galls on their stems. Many of the insects which cause plant galls belong to the same order as the bees, ants, and wasps, and are known as gallflies. Galls may also be caused by mites, plant lice, and moths. A gall caused by a gallfly is closed, so that the insect must make a hole in it to emerge.

Each gall-producing insect infests only one particular part of a plant, and the gall is of a definite form, so that the insect causing it may be determined by the shape of the gall. When the egg begins to develop, some irritation seems to be set up within the plant tissues, so that an abnormal growth is produced; and it is this abnormal growth which constitutes the gall. Large spherical galls on oak trees are called oak-apple galls. In the center of the gall there is a small kernel-like structure within which the larva may be found. The larva develops within this gall before it emerges. On red oaks and black oaks the spongy oak-apple gall is found. It is densely filled with a mass of porous tissue which suggests its name. On blackberry plants the pithy blackberry gall is often found. It is often as much as three inches in length and one and a half inches in diameter, but its shape varies considerably. Galls on rose plants are sometimes hard and kernel-like. Sometimes two or more species of gallflies lay their eggs in a previously formed gall, and the various larvae live side by side, feeding on the plant tissues.

EXPERIENCE. *To study galls.* Some children may find it interesting to study plant galls and bring them to school. The external surface of the galls should be examined to see if there are any openings through which a mature insect may have emerged. If any such opening is found it may be interesting to cut the gall through the opening and examine the chamber in which the insect developed and the canal through which it escaped. If galls without openings are found, a few could be cut open to uncover the structure of the gall and to observe the egg or larva found within.

Some Animals Build No Homes

Homes are built by many animals, but there are others which build no shelter for themselves or for their young. Many of the larger animals, including those which are gregarious in nature, live in the open prairie or in the woods, with no special form of protection for their young or for themselves. Animals like deer, bison, antelope, and others seek a secluded spot, in which they give birth to the young. When the young are strong enough to accompany the adults, they are part of the herd and get no protection from a nest or burrow. Those animals which do not hibernate do not often build any sort of home. While some aquatic animals, such as the crayfish, may burrow in the banks of a stream, most of them simply exist in their habitat without shelter of any sort except the stones and other objects in the water.

Most fishes do not construct homes except in so far as a few species make some provision for the eggs and young for a short time. Frogs and toads dig down below the frost line at the approach of cold weather and remain there until the following spring, but they make no other provision for shelter. The same thing is true of reptiles. Alligators and crocodiles lay their eggs in nests constructed on the bank of a stream, but they do not live in them. Most species of insects build no homes other than the pupa cases, chrysalises, and cocoons, which serve to protect the animal during metamorphic changes.

The lower forms of animals, such as starfish, protozoans, *Hydra* forms, and others do not build homes in the sense that the word has been used here. Parasitic animals need no shelter or protection, for their presence on or within the body of the host gives them advantages which free-living organisms do not have. Thus the tapeworm within the body of the mammal host, the protozoan in the blood stream of a bird, and the larva mussel attached to the gills of a fish receive from their location the protection which some animals achieve only by the construction of a nest or the digging of a burrow.

In conclusion, it may be said that the building of a home is an adaptation which is made as the organism becomes adjusted to its environment. Those animals which pass the winters in middle latitudes, with their seasons of low temperature and food scarcity, often use the home as a place of hibernation until conditions are more favorable. The young of those animals which are born in a more or less helpless condition are protected from predaceous animals and also from adverse weather if they are in the nest or burrow. Such shelters as hollow trees and dens that are underground also serve effectively to protect the animal from excess heat. Many animal homes are furnished with a supply of food which has been gathered and stored and is used when food is scarce. The home is often a place of refuge from predators, although occasionally the animal may be followed into it and is thus trapped and cannot escape.

EXPERIENCE. *To learn about animal homes from expert sources and also through observation.* Children should be encouraged to learn about animal homes in their own community. If there are ferocious or poisonous animals in the environment, then it is best for children to learn about animal homes by talking with adults who have observed the animals and studied their homes. In areas where it is safe for children to make their own observations, they should be helped to observe and study homes that are in use, from a distance that will not disturb the animals. Many of the wild animals will move their young, or in some cases abandon them, if a person touches or comes too close to the nest.

Some children may find it interesting to keep records of their observations and to add descriptions of new animal homes as they are located and studied during the year. Both first-hand observations and conversations with adults may provide a stimulus for the children to read more about animals and their home life. This may be followed by interesting discussions which give children an opportunity to weigh the reliable character of tales that are frequently told about animals in the area.

Children may use various forms of art to describe their ideas of animal homes that interest them or of those they have seen. Modeling with clay, sketching, and the making of murals are forms of art that will provide a means for the expression of ideas.

CHAPTER 19

Plants Become Adjusted to Seasonal Changes

Seasonal Change from a World Outlook

Seasonal change is not the same the world over. Some regions have four definite seasons, with great contrast between winter and summer. In other regions there is little contrast throughout the year.

The difference in seasons has probably been a considerable factor in producing a great variety among plants. Plants are dependent in their growth on the amount of water that is available for use, and on the duration and intensity of sunlight. Most of the growth of the plant takes place during the hours of darkness, and most of the food is produced by the plant during the day. (The relationship of water, temperature, and light to living things is discussed on pages 546–551.)

In most of the middle latitudes there is a distinct seasonal change. The growing season in the different parts of these zones varies from a rather short period of three or four months to a much longer growing period which lasts almost the year round. The stunted trees, shrubs, and bushes of the Chaparral in California, for instance, are adapted so that all their growth takes place during the wet, cool winters—they remain relatively inactive during the remaining part of the year, which is likely to be hot and dry. This short period of growth, as compared with the period during which the usual forest trees grow, helps to account for their difference in size and shape from those in other forests.

The polar regions are usually considered to have two seasons, short summers and long, cold winters. The moisture present for most of the year is in a frozen state, and the light rays are less intense, because of the angle at which they strike these parts of Earth. The result is a very short growing season.

Tropical regions are areas in which there is little change in temperature during the year. In parts of the tropics there are wet and dry seasons. The wet season usually occurs when the sun's rays are nearly overhead. Most of the plant growth takes place during this wet season. The dry season usually occurs when the sun's rays are more slanting. In the Equatorial Rain Forest there is much rainfall, and the dry season is very short or does not exist. Because the rays of the sun are nearly vertical, the temperature is high the year round. The plants in this area have sufficient heat and moisture to enable them to grow almost continuously. This growth results in dense forests of broadleaf, evergreen trees with an impenetrable growth of small

Many living things can adjust to seasonal change.

trees and shrubs which are adapted to survive in the shade.

EXPERIENCE. *To see what seasonal changes take place in your community.* As shown by the material in this chapter, there are few if any places on Earth where there are not some seasonal changes. A study of such changes that can be observed in the community by children could be carried on throughout the year. This might include records of the differences in the length of day and night, in temperature, and in the amount of moisture throughout the year. Bird migration and the differences in the animal and plant populations might also be observed.

Sketches and other types of art work could reflect some of the children's learnings.

EXPERIENCE. *To relate movements of Earth to seasonal change.* Some teachers may want to associate the adjustment of plants to seasonal change with the demonstration of the cause of seasonal changes. It may be desirable to use the Experience given on page 202. In this case the children could work out the relationships of temperature and length of day and night to the effect of seasonal change upon plants.

Moisture, Light, and Heat Affect Plants

In those parts of Earth where the prevailing winds are from the west (Prevailing Westerlies, p. 456), there are generally four seasons each year. Each of these seasons is of about equal length, but conditions are different in so far as the amount of moisture, sunlight, and warmth of the air are concerned. During the winter season the atmosphere is cold, the hours of sunlight are short, and water is unavailable to plants for weeks at a time because it is frozen. All these factors make it impossible for most plants to grow, and consequently they must

Annual growth rings provide evidence concerning the age of a tree and the climate while it was growing.

the few species of birds which do not migrate, predaceous animals, such as the mink and weasel, and others, like the rabbits and musk-rats, which manage usually to find food, even though the ground may be covered deeply with snow. When temperatures are very low, however, many of these animals may seek a sheltered place and remain inactive until the weather moderates or until they are forced by hunger to venture out in search of food.

More attention will be devoted later to the various ways in which animals survive the winter season. At present it is important to note that plants also must make adjustment to winter conditions in order to survive.

make some adjustment to survive the adverse seasons. The teacher that is teaching in a region of wet and dry seasons should remember that the dry season is a time of adverse conditions for plants. In prairie and desert regions, where there is limited moisture, the adaptation of the annuals for quick flowering enables these species of plants to continue to live in an adverse region. It would be well for the children to know that the seed is an excellent adaptation for surviving the adverse conditions of such regions. Children living in a region of limited moisture should be encouraged to notice the effects of rain on plant growth. Sometimes a rain will cause a dry back lot or prairie to become a flower garden. Adjustments made by plants may result in a scarcity of food for animals, so that the latter are forced to migrate or to hibernate during the unfavorable seasons. Some animals remain active during the cold months, such as

EXPERIENCE. *To help children to realize that dry and cold seasons are frequently periods of adverse conditions.* If you are teaching in a region that has dry or cold seasons, have the children observe that there is no plant growth at such times; also have them observe the width of the annual growth rings on old stumps or newly cut timber. The width of tree rings has been used, along with other records, to determine the periods of severe drought and abundant rainfall in a given region; such rings may be found wherever there are annual cold and warm or wet and dry seasons.

EXPERIENCE. *To learn if plant and animal life passes through a cold period in frozen soil.* After cold weather sets in, collect a small chunk of frozen mud from the bank of a stream or ditch. Place in a jar, and if dry, apply some water free from chemicals. Watch for a week or more to see what plants and animals appear.

Three Groups of Plants: Annuals, Biennials, and Perennials

Flowering plants may be placed in three groups to make an understanding of their life cycle easier. Those plants which germinate from seed, grow, blossom, produce seeds, and die within a single year are known as *annuals*. Such plants include corn, oats, beans, peas, and many others familiar to us.

Some plants require two years in which to

grow from the seed and produce seeds themselves. These are known as biennial plants, or *biennials*. Beets, carrots, turnips, mullein, hollyhock, winter wheat, and many of the clovers are examples of the biennial type of plant.

Still other plants live for a number of years, and produce seeds each year after they mature. They are known as *perennials*. Trees, shrubs, and many herbs are examples of perennial plants.

EXPERIENCE. *Plants in the environment.* Discuss which plants are annual, which biennial, and which perennial.

Plants Store Food for Future Use

During the growing season, plants carry on the process of food-making at a rapid pace. Some of this food is used immediately by the plant as a source of the energy which it needs to carry on its functions, but much of it is not used and so is stored in various parts of the plant against future need. It is because of this fact that animals can feed on plants and derive energy from the plants for themselves, since they use the food which the plant has stored.

During that part of the year when conditions are unfavorable, the plant either continues the activity of photosynthesis only at a very slow rate or ceases to perform this function altogether. The activity of the plant is suspended during the months when water is unavailable, for without water no plant can carry on its life processes. There is some water present in the roots, stem, and branches; but since nothing can be added to this supply during a large part of the year, it must be conserved. Much transpiration of water takes place through the stomata of the leaves (pp. 477, 660), and the falling of the leaves of deciduous trees results in the conservation of the water supply of the plant. A decrease in the duration and intensity of sunlight will also cause a slowing down or a stopping of growth and food-making activities. The circulation of sap throughout the plant becomes less, and may cease completely. The color of the leaves changes from green to red, brown, or yellow; they die and drop to the ground. Leaf-fall is hastened by drought, frost, or wind. The loss of leaves prevents the further loss of water, so that what is left can be used by the plant.

Some Plants Store Food in Their Leaves. The *bulbs* of certain common plants consist of a short stem which is surrounded by a number of fleshy scalelike leaves which are filled with stored food. This is true of such bulbs as the onion, hyacinth, tulip, daffodil, and paper narcissus. If an onion bulb is examined, it will be found to consist of scaly leaves within which is a small disk-shaped stem. The dry, outer leaves are dead, and serve as a protection for the living leaves within. The internal fleshy leaves contain stored food in the form of sugar. In most plants, however, the food is stored in the form of starch which has been made from sugar.

When a farmer wishes to produce the green onions which are found on the market early in the spring, he does not usually plant onion seed, but instead he sets out small onion bulbs. Under favorable conditions these grow very rapidly, since they use the food stored in the leaves of the bulb until their roots develop. Bulbs are formed by many biennial plants and are an adaptation for surviving through the winter when the leaves are dead and no food is made.

If an onion bulb is planted in the spring and is permitted to grow throughout the summer, the plant will produce a seed stalk, at the top of which flowers and later seed will develop. If seed is planted, however, the plant will grow rapidly during the first year, and the bulb may become large if conditions are favorable; but no seed will be produced.

EXPERIENCE. *To learn the structure of a bulb.* Secure some fairly large onions from a grocery store. Children may see the layers of thin dead leaves on the outside and of the thick, fleshy, living leaves within. Have the pupils cut through the onion until they find the stem in the center.

EXPERIENCE. *To compare the growth of an onion bulb with that of onion seed.* Secure a small package of onion seed and a few onion bulbs. Plant the seeds just below the surface of the soil in a box; plant the bulbs in another box. Children may note which begin to grow first. Let them compare the rate of growth of the plants developing from the seeds with the rate of those developing from the bulbs.

EXPERIENCE. *To compare the weight of a bulb before and after growing.* Weigh some onion bulbs. Plant them in a flowerpot. When they have grown vigorously for some time, pull a bulb out of the soil and note what has happened to it. The bulb should be much lighter, since the food has been used up to a large extent.

EXPERIENCE. *To grow bulbs without soil.* Plant some narcissus bulbs in a shallow vessel in which stones have been placed and in which water is kept. Children should note that the bulb is growing without soil and that it may bloom. Emphasize the fact that much of the food needed by the plant comes from the bulb.

Food Is Sometimes Stored in Stems. Often plants store food in the stem. Children are familiar with the general type of plant stem, such as the stalk of corn or the trunk of a tree. But it should be pointed out that there are many kinds of *modified stems,* chief of which are the rhizome, tuber, corm, and runner, in which food is often stored.

Rhizomes are elongated stems which grow horizontally beneath the surface of the soil, and are characteristic of such plants as Canada thistle, quack grass, and iris. The rhizomes, like the stems above the surface of the soil, possess buds at their ends, and also produce lateral buds, which may give rise to vertical stems. These rhizomes are rich in food materials; and if one of them is cut off from the main plant, it will develop vertical stems and roots and proceed to grow. For this reason many of the worst weeds found on farms are difficult to eradicate. Morning-glory, Johnson grass, nut grass, and poverty weed are other examples of plants which become weeds.

If the stems of these plants aboveground are cut off, the plant may be prevented from blossoming and producing seed; but the spread of the weed is thereby only slightly checked, for the rhizomes will give rise to many new plants. If by the use of such farm tools as the hoe and harrow the underground stems are cut, the plant will develop roots; and each piece of the rhizome will grow, thereby increasing the number of plants. The rhizomes must be brought to the surface of the ground and dried thoroughly if the weed is to be eradicated. If the food-making leaves and stems above the surface of the soil are cut off, the plant draws on the food stored in the rhizomes to produce more shoots. If the weeds are cut down again and again, the food supply in the rhizomes may eventually be exhausted, and thus the plants may be eradicated through persistence on the part of the farmer.

Trees and shrubs also store food in their

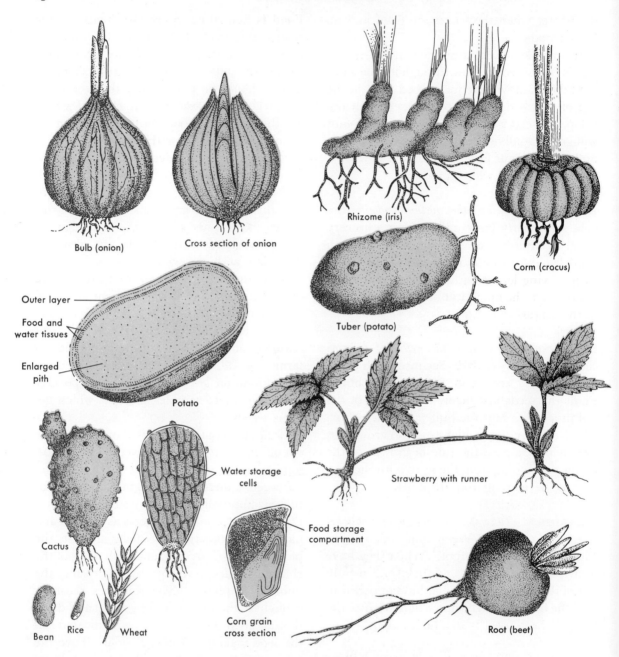

Bulb (onion)

Cross section of onion

Rhizome (iris)

Corm (crocus)

Outer layer

Food and
water tissues

Enlarged
pith

Potato

Tuber (potato)

Water storage
cells

Strawberry with runner

Cactus

Food storage
compartment

Bean

Rice

Wheat

Corn grain
cross section

Root (beet)

Plants store food in different ways.

stems. During summer months the food is being produced and stored in the branches of a tree and in its trunk. Much of the food is in the form of starch; but the following spring, when the buds are beginning to enlarge as the leaves within them grow, the starch is changed back to sugar. Circulation within the tree begins again, and the sugar is carried to all parts of it.

The sap of some trees contains much more sugar than others. It is for this reason that the maple tree is sometimes tapped in the spring,

Man can tap the food stores of the sugar maple.   (Vermont Development Commission.)

its sap collected in buckets and boiled until most of the water is evaporated.   The sugar is concentrated sufficiently to form the sirup.   Certain species of maple may be used successfully for making sirup from their sap; others do not contain enough sugar.   The sugar was formed during the previous year and stored.   In young apple twigs the starch may often be stored in the pith in the center; and sugar, fats, and proteins are also stored there.

Many plants store food in underground stems which are called *tubers*.   Tubers have so much food stored in them that they are much enlarged, fleshy, and generally rather short.   The common white potato is an example of a tuber.   The "eyes" of the potato are in reality buds, from which growth begins. The fleshy part of the potato consists mostly of starch and water.   If an elongated potato is studied, it may be observed that the buds, or "eyes," are arranged in a spiral manner.

Careful study of a potato which has been cut into halves reveals that the "skin" is really made up of cork and cambium cells and so is somewhat similar to the bark found on stems. Beneath it is found a ring of food-and-water-conducting tissues, while the central part of the potato corresponds to the pith found in stems.   When a potato is planted, roots and aerial stems develop from the buds, and the plant lives on the starch stored in the tuber until it is able to make its own food by photosynthesis.

The potato may be planted the season after the tuber was formed, and a new plant will develop.   The tuber is thus an adaptation for surviving through the winter.   Potatoes produce flowers and occasionally seed balls, which may be found on the aerial stems; but these are not used for the commercial growing of potatoes. The seeds are sometimes used in experimentation or in attempts to produce new varieties.

Some plants store food in short, vertical, solid, and much enlarged underground stems. These are known as *corms*. Common examples of corms are those of crocus and gladiolus. In shape corms are generally somewhat flattened from top to bottom. They bear a thick cluster of roots at the lower side, while on the upper side they have a tuft of leaves. They are much like bulbs in some respects, but differ from them mostly in being made up largely of the stem. They have only a few scaly leaves, while the bulb is made up of a small stem and many leaves. In the case of the corm the food is stored largely in the stem itself and not so much in the leaves. When a crocus seed is planted, it develops a corm the first year and does not blossom until the corm is of good size. When a corm is planted, the food in it is used up by the plant, and it decays. On its sides, however, new corms develop, and these may be used to propagate the plant.

Tubers, corms, and stems may be used in the propagation of plants, thus making seeding unnecessary. As we have seen, the potato tuber is the sole means of propagation of that plant which is used by the farmer or gardener, while onion plants are grown from bulbs which have been set out early in the spring. Corms too are used for the propagation of the plants which form them. Rhizomes are a means by which some plants spread.

There is another type of stem by means of which plants may be propagated. It is called the *runner*, and is commonly seen on the strawberry plant. Runners are much like rhizomes in that they grow horizontally, but they grow above the surface of the ground and do not have much food stored in them. Examination of a runner shows that new shoots and roots may develop from it. These roots grow

Stored food is used when potatoes sprout.

into the ground and begin to take in water and dissolved mineral matter for the new plant. When the roots are well established, the runner dies, and the new plant is independent of the old one.

EXPERIENCE. *To demonstrate that starch is stored in white potatoes.* Cut a slice from a white potato. Put a drop of iodine on the potato. The blue or purple color indicates presence of starch. Test a sugar cube in this same manner. The iodine spot remains brown because there is no starch in the sugar cube.

EXPERIENCE. *To show that potato eyes are buds.* Plant a rather small potato (or one cut so that there are two or three eyes to each piece) just beneath the surface of the soil in a box. After two weeks take the potato out and note from which part the growth began.

EXPERIENCE. *To show that the food in a potato is necessary to the development of the young plant.* Peel a potato and plant that part of the peeling which contains a bud. Keep it under favorable growing conditions. Note that the potato peeling will sprout at the bud, but will soon die for lack of food to support the young plant.

EXPERIENCE. *To show that the potato plant uses the food in its growth.* Plant one or more potatoes in sawdust; keep the sawdust moist and at a good growing temperature. After the potatoes have sprouted, let them continue growing until they die. Then take them out of the sawdust. Note that the seed potato is much smaller than originally and much lighter.

Some Plants Store Water and Waste Products in Their Stems. Some plants have fleshy stems which may store water, as well as food, in fairly large quantities. This is true of such plants as various species of cactus, the house plant known as begonia, glasswort, purslane, and others. In these the water accumulates in rather large cells which have thin walls. These cells may be located in the pith, or center, of the stem.

Waste products also accumulate in stems, and substances like resins, various oils, the milky material known as latex, and tannins. The resins are produced by coniferous trees, while the latex is produced by a number of plants, such as the poppy, milkweed, dandelion, and the rubber tree. The latex of the rubber tree is used in the production of rubber. Tannins are compounds which are found in the stems of many plants, but are particularly abundant in the bark of some oaks. Tannin is used in the process of tanning leather.

EXPERIENCE. *To observe liquids found in the stems of some plants.* Those children living in regions where either maple-sugar trees, pine trees, or rubber trees are tapped to secure sap for com-

mercial use will be familiar with the fact that some plants have liquids in their stems. Many children will be able to find milkweed, dandelions, or other plants common to their region in which much liquid is present in the stem.

Some Plants Store Food in Their Roots. Many of the vegetable plants which serve as part of our food supply are used because large quantities of food materials, mostly starches and sugars, are stored in their roots. While the common white potato is an underground stem, or tuber, the sweet potato is an underground *root*. Stored in it are considerable starch and some sugar. Beets are roots which are enlarged because of the food stored in them. The sugar beet, which is cultivated extensively in some parts of this country and in Europe, contains about 15 per cent sugar, so that it is used as a source of that product. The roots of the dahlia contain much food. Carrots are enlarged roots in which food is stored. They contain starch, as do such plants as radishes, parsnips, and turnips.

A plant known as the manroot, or man-of-the-earth, has storage roots in which so much food is deposited that they may weigh as much as an average man. Some roots, such as the mangel, are grown by farmers in large quantities and are used as feed for cattle and other livestock.

All the roots here mentioned may be used to propagate the plant. Thus a carrot does not produce seed the first year of its growth, but if permitted to remain in the soil during the winter it will resume growth the following year and produce seeds. Some plants, however, like the radish, will produce seed during the first year. Sweet-potato plants are propagated by the planting of those roots which are not used for food by man.

EXPERIENCE. *To demonstrate that plants will develop from roots.* Plant carrots in a box in such a way that the top of the root is just beneath the surface of the soil. Note from which part of the plant the leaves develop. Keep the plant growing for some time, noting meanwhile what is happening to the root. After the plant has been growing for some time, pull it out of the soil and note the changes which have taken place in the root.

Some of the children might be interested in having a sweet-potato vine in their room. If so, put a sweet potato in a glass bottle of water so that from a fourth to a half of the potato is exposed to the air. Then place the bottle where the potato will receive some sunlight. A vine will grow from the exposed end of the potato. Until the leaves begin the process of food-making, the plant will use food stored in the potato. Sometimes such a potato vine will grow for months and make a very attractive house plant.

EXPERIENCE. *To grow a new plant from the top of the root.* Cut about an inch from the top of a carrot. Place this piece, cut end down, in a shallow dish of water. A new plant will grow from the top of the root.

EXPERIENCE. *To determine whether starch is present in the roots of plants.* By the iodine test determine whether or not starch is present in the roots of radishes, parsnips, and carrots.

Plants Store Food in Their Seeds. Food is stored in the seeds of plants in order to provide the seedling with a source of energy until it is capable of manufacturing its own food supply. This means that sufficient food must be stored to last until a fairly good root system has developed and until leaves have grown and become active in the process of photosynthesis. Without a food supply the embryo plant could not survive.

Because of the food stored in them, seeds are valuable as a part of the diet of man. Wheat and rice are used by hundreds of millions of people as a staple article in their food supply, while corn, rye, and barley are used by many people. The soybean has been used for many centuries in China as a food for human beings, but in this country it is used largely because the plant is nutritious for livestock. The seed itself, however, is being used for many commercial purposes. Its oil is used in industry. By treating the seed chemically, it is possible to make from it a solvent for lacquer or substances for use in the manufacture of automobile parts. The oils of other seeds have been important commercial products for many years. Cottonseed oil and peanut oil have been used as substitutes for olive oil. Linseed oil, made from flaxseed, is used in the manufacture of varnish, paint, oilcloth, lino-

Different stages in the growth of a bean plant.

An avocado sprouting in water uses stored food.

leum, and artificial leather, as well as for a number of other things. From the seed of the coconut an oil is pressed which is used in the manufacture of soaps and butter and lard substitutes. Starches, proteins, fats in the form of oils, and sugars are all stored in seeds, as well as a substance known as hemicellulose, which is similar to cellulose. Rice is about 68 per cent starch, navy beans contain 45 per cent starch, and about 8 per cent of the almond seed is starch. Beans and peas contain a relatively large amount of protein when compared with other seeds, while castor-oil beans contain about 60 per cent oil.

For plants which have no other means of perpetuating the species, the seed is the only means of survival from year to year. The storage of food in such seeds is therefore part of the way in which the plant survives unfavorable winter conditions. Annual plants, which depend on seeds to carry on the species, produce large numbers of seeds. Because of this the species is not likely to become extinct. Annuals store food in no other part of the plant. In the seed, however, starch or other foods may be stored either in the tissue surrounding the embryo or within the embryo.

A perennial plant also produces large quantities of seeds; but since the plant persists from year to year, it is not so dependent upon each year's crop of seeds. If no seed is produced one year, seeds produced in following years will still perpetuate the species.

In summary, it is to be noted that food is stored by plants in leaves, stems, roots, and seeds in the form of sugars, starches, proteins, oils, and hemicellulose. In seeds the food is intended for the use of the embryo plant when it begins active growth. Since food stored in the forms named is generally not soluble except in the case of sugars, it must be digested by means of enzymes and made soluble so that it can be transported in the plant and made available where it is needed. Digestion results in the conversion of starches to sugars, fats into fatty acids and glycerin, and proteins into amino acids. As the food is used up by the plant, carbon dioxide is given off. Oxygen, also needed by the seed, thus combines with the food material oxidizing it. The reaction results in the liberation of energy (p. 516).

EXPERIENCE. *To observe that seeds have food stored in them.* Children might like to list the many different seeds that they eat and to examine the differences in size and internal structure. They might also want to experiment to determine if large seeds, those containing much food, will grow for a longer time than small seeds when both are placed in wet sawdust.

Buds Make Rapid Spring Growth Possible

In addition to storing food to be used the following year in various parts of the plant, trees and shrubs also develop *buds* during the growing season. These buds are formed from the time the plants are in full foliage until about the middle of July. They then remain dormant until the next spring. The bud consists of a very short stem and leaves which are rudimentary. The stem is enclosed by the rudimentary leaves, and in cold and arid climates the buds are covered by several layers of scales, which are arranged in an overlapping manner. The scales are themselves modified leaves and serve to protect the delicate inner tissues from conditions of extreme cold. Branches as well as leaves develop from buds.

The bud scales of many plants are covered with hairs, and in some cases they are covered with a waxy secretion. The hairs do not protect the bud from the cold, but both they and the waxy covering protect the leaves and stem within from mechanical injury and from the rapid evaporation of water. In moist, tropical countries trees have naked buds, unprotected by scales, and herbaceous plants in all parts of the world have naked buds.

Buds are classified according to their position on the stem, according to the number at each position, according to the structures which they contain, and also according to their development.

Buds Vary in Position and Number. Buds are *terminal* if they are found on the end of the branch. If a tree or shrub is examined, it will be found to have a bud at the end of each branch. This bud contains a short length of stem, which may be seen if the bud is removed and its interior is examined. This short length of stem grows rapidly under favorable conditions, causing the branch to become elongated. The new length of stem produced from a terminal bud is greater than that produced by any of the other buds on the same branch.

Other buds are found to occur just above the place on the stem or branch where a leaf is attached. Such buds are called *axillary* buds, and they give rise to leafy branches or to flowers. On apple trees there are buds located on very short stems called spurs, and on these spurs it is sometimes difficult to distinguish between the terminal, or end, buds and the axillary buds.

Adventitious buds are buds which may be found anywhere on the plant except at the tip

Longitudinal section
leaf bud

Butternut
(hairy bud)

Horse chestnut
stem

Bud found in warm climate
(cycad)

Longitudinal section
flower bud

Maple

Elm

Apple

Types of stems

Buds in spring.

of the stem or in the immediate vicinity of the leaves, where the axillary buds arise. They are often on roots as well as stems, and sometimes occur even on leaves. The rise of adventitious buds is often stimulated by some injury to a branch. If a branch of a fruit tree is cut off in the annual spring pruning, a number of adventitious buds arise at the edges of the cut surface, and from these may develop long stems known as water sprouts, or suckers.

Buds do not occur haphazardly on the stem. In the case of axillary buds, they are either *opposite* each other on the stem, as in maple trees, or they may be *alternate,* only one bud occurring at each node. This latter arrangement of buds is found in such trees as the apple, peach, and plum. The characteristic shapes of elms, maples, oaks, poplars, and other kinds of trees result largely from the arrangement of the buds along the twigs.

Buds Vary in Structure. Some buds contain only the leaf structures, and are consequently known as *leaf* buds. Others contain only *flower* structures, while still others are called *mixed* buds because they contain both leaf and flower parts. When a leaf bud is opened, within it may be found a very short stem bearing a number of tiny leaves. The flower bud contains no foliage, but it does contain one or more flowers. Each of the parts of the flower is present, so that the undeveloped pistils, stamens, and ovary may be observed if a flower bud is opened. Flower buds are usually not terminal buds; they are axillary buds in respect to their position on the stem.

Some buds when they develop in the spring unfold and produce a leafy shoot which generally terminates in a cluster of flowers. This is typical of such trees as the apple and pear.

Buds Vary in Activity. Buds may be called either dormant or active, according to their development. Dormant buds do not develop into branches unless the terminal bud is re-

moved, in which case they grow much like other buds. Active buds develop naturally and carry on the growth of the tree. Some of these grow only for a short time and then die because of an insufficient supply of food, attacks by insects, or diseases. There seems to be an active competition for food among the buds of a plant, and those less vigorous fail to survive from lack of it.

Buds Are of Great Importance to the Plant. Because they contain the flower parts, stems, and leaves of the plant for the next year's growth, buds are of great importance to the plant. They are an *adaptation* for rapid growth during that part of the year when conditions are most favorable. By forming the rudimentary structure a year in advance, the plant can resume its activities at once when conditions are right. A few warm days in the spring are sufficient to cause the buds of peaches to swell in size rapidly, owing to the growth of the structures within. This is sometimes the cause of much damage to fruit trees. If warm weather occurs for a week or so during February or early March, for example, the flower buds of such trees as the peaches and cherries may develop rapidly. Even though the trees are not yet blooming, subsequent cold weather may cause the buds to freeze, and the flowers are thus destroyed. When this happens, fruit is scarce. Farmers know as early as January of some years that there will be little fruit; for if warm weather is followed by very severe cold, the damage to the flower buds may be discovered by opening a few of them. If the flower within has frozen, as much damage has been done as if the freeze occurred while the trees were in full bloom.

Each species of plant has buds with characteristic structure and arrangement. From this fact it becomes evident that trees may be identified by their buds during winter months when they have no leaves, as well as by their general shape, bark, and location. The food-

and-water-conducting tissues of the roots and stem extend into the buds, so that the stem and leaves receive the food which is circulated through the plant. As the bud develops, the scales fall off, since they are no longer needed.

EXPERIENCE. *To learn the position of terminal and axillary buds.* If possible, bring to class one or two branches with winter buds. Help the children to find the terminal buds and the axillary buds. Determine whether the buds are alternate, opposite, or whorled (in groups of three or more at each node).

EXPERIENCE. *To determine the structure of a bud.* Children may wish to take the scales off the buds and examine them with hand lenses if such lenses are available. Notice whether or not the buds are hairy, or whether they are covered with a waxy substance. Help each child to see the small leaflets within a bud. Let them examine the small leaves with the hand lenses to note their similarity to large leaves. They may need help in finding the short stem which is covered by the leaves. The arrangement of the scales and leaves should also be noted by the children.

Lilac buds

EXPERIENCE. *To examine a flower bud.* If the children are interested, a few buds from fruit trees may be brought in. Carefully open a flower bud and locate the stamens and pistils. Note that the various parts of each structure are present. In some plants a bud may contain one flower; in others, such as the lilac and clover, a group of flowers may be present.

Some Plants Are Adapted to Survive Winter Conditions

Annual plants produce seed and die within one year, generally being killed by the first heavy frosts of autumn. Since they have fulfilled the biological function of reproduction, and since they are not adapted to meet the conditions existing during the winter months, they do not survive. The biennial and perennial plants, on the other hand, are adapted to the changing seasons, so that they can live through the winter in an inactive state and resume growth and food-making when conditions are favorable again. One of the most important factors in their survival has already been discussed, that of the storage of food in various parts of the plant. This food is used to furnish the plant with nutrition early in the spring, when it cannot make its food because of the lack of leaves.

The Stems of Some Plants Die in the Winter. Those plants which live for two years generally die down to the ground when winter comes. Thus clover leaves and stems do not live through the winter. Only the roots remain alive. In the spring of the following year, new stems and leaves are produced, which carry on growth and food-making as well as reproductive processes. The same thing is true of other biennial plants, such as carrots, beets, and parsnips.

Perennial grasses also lose their leaves when adverse conditions prevail, so that only the underground stem and roots remain alive, and new stems and leaves arise in the spring. Orchard grass, which is one of the first to produce seed heads in the spring, and which may be recognized by the characteristic clumps in which it grows, is one of these. Alfalfa is a leguminous plant which is similar in its adaptations for winter. Asparagus and rhubarb are other examples of perennials.

Some Plants Lose Their Leaves Annually. Many perennial plants do not die down to the ground in the fall, but lose only their leaves. This is true of the deciduous trees and shrubs. The stems do not normally die, although extremely low temperatures during the winter may kill the younger stems by freezing them. The shedding of leaves by trees in the autumn has been observed by many children. Maples, oaks, elms, poplars, birches, and a great many other species meet winter conditions by losing their leaves. Before the leaves fall, changes which are very striking take place. Food-making processes have stopped, and with the coming of autumn the chlorophyll in the leaves disappears. Light intensity is less as the rays of the sun become increasingly less vertical, and the average temperature drops.

The fading of the chlorophyll reveals the yellow and red pigments which are now present in the leaves. Yellow is the basic pigment, but because of the presence of other substances in the leaves they may assume red, brown, and other colors. Maple, dogwood, sumac, and sweet-gum trees may have red and orange colors, while in the oaks brown predominates. The colors on the same tree and even on the same leaf may vary considerably. The leaves of many shrubs, and herbaceous and climbing plants also change colors; poison-ivy leaves become conspicuously red, Boston ivy may turn brown. Other plants show similar changes.

Before the leaves drop from the branches, a number of things occur. At the base of the stem of the leaves a waterproof layer of cells is formed called a *separation layer*. This layer cuts off the circulation of water and food from the stem into the leaf. At the same time it forms a protective layer on the stem to which the leaf is attached, so that water is not lost from the stem and disease-producing bacteria cannot enter it. When this layer of cells is fully developed, the cell walls between it and the leaf disappear, so that there is nothing to hold the leaf in place, and a slight breeze is sufficient to detach it.

Some compound leaves, which are made up of a number of leaflets on a single leafstalk, form separation layers at the base of the leaflets first, and these drop off. Later the bare leafstalk, or petiole, becomes separated from the twig or stem and falls to the ground. In the case of certain oaks, ashes, and beeches, the separation layer of cells is imperfectly developed or even entirely missing, so that the leaves are sometimes retained on the trees during the greater part of the winter. They fall off when the buds begin to grow in the spring. The leaves are dead, however, and carry on none of the usual functions. Oaks that retain their living leaves far into the spring are called "live oaks" and are often considered evergreens. They grow in the southeastern United States.

Plants are unable to absorb water through their roots when the temperature of the soil is near freezing. In the leaf the structures known as stomata permit the loss of water by the process of transpiration. If the trees did not lose their leaves in the fall when temperatures are low and water cannot be obtained, the plant would be existing under conditions similar to those existing during drought. Since the leaves are lost, however, the loss of water through the stomata is stopped, so that the moisture needed by the plant to survive the winter is conserved. Plants containing a great deal of moisture cannot withstand cold temperatures so well as those which contain less water. During the winter months, then, most plants contain much less water than during the growing season.

Much damage sometimes occurs to fruit trees when a warm rainy autumn is followed by sudden low temperatures, for the plants contain so much water that they are susceptible to injury. The excess water in the cells may freeze and in so doing burst the cell wall.

Frosts seem to have nothing to do with the change of color of leaves in the autumn, for the process is seen to occur when plants are subjected to drought. Leaves will fall from plants in the summer months if moisture is not sufficient to enable the food-making and growth processes to take place normally. This illustrates the generalization that the fall of leaves is an adaptation to meet drought conditions. In the winter months there may be much moisture in the soil; but since the plant cannot use it when it is frozen, the plant is under drought conditions.

EXPERIENCE. *To illustrate the effect of low temperatures on plants.* This may be done by placing a succulent plant, such as a begonia, in a refrigerator for a few days. The leaves will fall off, and the plant will wilt, although the temperature in a refrigerator is generally a few degrees above the freezing point. This illustrates the fact that water is unavailable to plants, no matter how abundant, when the temperature is low.

Some Plants Do Not Lose Their Leaves Annually. The cone-bearing trees do not shed their leaves in preparation for winter. Their needles are in reality modified leaves, and photosynthesis takes place within them. However, so little moisture is lost through the stomata of these needles that there is little danger of the plant's losing too much water. The needles do not last forever, but they remain on the tree about two years in the case of the white pine and longer in the case of other evergreens. This accounts for the pine needles found beneath the trees. Photosynthesis may go on throughout the winter when there is sufficient sunshine, but at a very slow rate.

In tropical regions with an abundant water supply most plants grow luxuriantly and lose their leaves gradually throughout the year.

In some parts of the world, such as in the deserts of the southwestern United States, plants must be adapted for surviving under conditions of extreme heat and dryness. Such plants generally have leaves with a thick epidermis which is practically moistureproof, so that very little water is lost by transpiration. Often the leaves are densely covered with hairs, which are a means of preventing the escape of moisture. Some plants develop a large number of leaves when growing under conditions of sufficient water, and comparatively few leaves when growing under drought conditions.

Plants sometimes shed their leaves in the summer rather than in the winter. This is true in climates such as those on the coast of the Mediterranean Sea and in southern California, where the long hot summers are practically rainless. In those regions some trees and many shrubs lose almost all and, in some cases, all their leaves as an adaptation for meeting the period of drought. Plants in this leafless summer condition are known to lose only a very small amount of water in comparison with the amount lost when they are in full leaf.

Plants are sometimes classified according to their water environments. Such plants as cattails, water lilies, and sedges are known as *hydrophytes,* since they can live only in very wet soil or in water. Plants growing in meadows and forests where a moderate supply of water is available are known as *mesophytes,* while those living under desert conditions, such as the Russian thistle, sagebrush, and the many kinds of cactus are known as *xerophytes.* Some plants grow in salt marshes and in places where there is a great deal of alkali mineral matter in the soil. These are known as *halo-*

phytes. If there is too much mineral matter dissolved in water, plants are not able to use it unless they are adapted to such conditions. Examples of halophytes are greasewood and saltbush.

In conclusion, it may be said that plants are adapted for surviving conditions of unfavorable climate by the storage of foods in various parts of the plant, by the production of seeds, the loss of leaves, and the formation of buds.

EXPERIENCE. *To learn the effects of drought conditions on plants.* If two or more geranium, coleus, or begonia plants are available, keep some of them in the classroom without watering them for a few days. Keep the same kind of plant under similar conditions, but water it adequately. This will illustrate to children the effect of lack of water on plants. The plant kept under dry conditions will soon wilt; the leaves will turn yellow and drop off. If a third plant of the same kind is available, cut off some of the leaves and put some vaseline on the wound to prevent loss of water. Keep this plant without water also. Since it has fewer

leaves from which to lose water by transpiration, it should be able to withstand the dry conditions longer than the first plant.

EXPERIENCE. *To show the effect of short hours of sunshine on plant leaves.* Select two plants similar in size and kind. Cover one of these for a number of hours each day so that no light can reach it. Note the fading of the leaves from green to yellow as the chlorophyll becomes less abundant and the yellow pigment becomes visible.

Pine tree and cones.

CHAPTER 20

Animals Are Adapted to Survive Seasonal Changes

Animals Are Affected by Heat, Light, and Food Supply

Animals are affected by seasonal changes in many ways. In the middle latitudes, where periodic climatic variations occur, they are adapted to meet a number of very different conditions. During the summer months food may be very abundant, and animals may thrive without much difficulty. With the coming of winter, however, food may be so very scarce that survival is impossible, and animals may perish. Grasshoppers, for example, could scarcely survive the winter months even if they could withstand the low temperatures which prevail, for they feed upon plants. Since many plants die in the autumn, little food is available for them, and starvation ensues. Birds that live part of the time in the north and feed on insects usually migrate to warmer regions by the time the temperature is cold enough to kill insects.

Sunlight has an important effect on some animals. Bees, for example, seek nectar only in sunshine, so that with the shortening days of autumn their activities stop. British scientists have been able to predict roughly the catch of mackerel by determining the number of hours of sunlight in the month of May. That sunlight rather than temperature is the important factor has been shown to be true by the fact that a cold sunny May results in a greater catch than follows a warm month in which there are fewer hours of sunlight.

Frogs, toads, and other amphibians, as well as the reptiles, seek protection from the cold; for it makes them so sluggish that they cannot move. A few species of birds and mammals may remain active all winter, but they often die when conditions become extremely difficult for a prolonged time. Thus very cold temperatures and the absence of food kill quail and other birds which do not migrate.

It has been previously stated that the variation in the temperature of the cold-blooded animals is much greater than that of the warm-blooded animals. The great majority of animal species are said to be cold-blooded. That is, they are able to undergo great variation in body temperature. This variation in temperature usually follows that of the environment in which the animal is living. In other words, a snake on a warm rock will be warm, and the same snake in cold water will be cold.

Warm-blooded animals have a body temperature which remains almost constant.

Thus the temperature of birds and mammals will vary only slightly or not at all as the temperature of the environment changes. The temperature of healthy human beings stays at approximately 98.6°F. whether man lives in the tropics or in a frigid climate.

Birds and mammals are the only animals showing little variation in body temperature. The temperature of all other animals shows a greater variation, which follows more closely the differences in the temperature of their surroundings. Since activity decreases as temperature drops, animals with great variation in temperature must seek protection from cold; for a low degree of body heat may make them too sluggish to move.

Changing conditions of temperature, food supply, and sunlight are met by adaptations which enable the animal to survive. Where there are less pronounced changes in the seasons, the adaptations are not so marked. The greater the difference between the conditions of one part of the year and another, the greater the range of adaptations which may be noted.

EXPERIENCE. *To show the effect of low temperatures on an animal which can survive great variations in temperature.* This may be demonstrated by placing a frog in a container of water to which some ice is gradually added, so that the temperature of the water is slowly lowered. Children can then observe that the frog becomes quite inactive as its body temperature drops near to that of the water. After it has stopped all activity, the frog may be taken out of the water and placed where it will be warmed slowly. As its body temperature rises, it will resume normal activity. This demonstration may also be performed by placing insects in a bottle or other glass container and then placing the container in ice water for some time. As the temperature within the bottle drops, the activity of the insects decreases. Grasshoppers or other fairly large insects may be used.

Some Animals Remain Active during Unfavorable Conditions

Those animals which are protected by a heavy coat of fur, so that they are not much affected by low temperatures, may remain active during the entire winter, seeking shelter only when very cold weather sets in. Some species of carnivorous animals, like the mink, wolf, weasel, and fox, roam about in search of food at all times of the year. The gray wolf may find and kill calves, sheep, and colts, thus causing an economic loss to ranchmen. If these are not to be found, the wolf pack may find a small herd of deer, pull down one of them, and consume it.

Some of the rodents remain active during the unfavorable winter months, but many do not. A trip across farm fields reveals the tracks of rabbits, which seek plants as food. If the snow is deep, they may attack young trees, gnawing off the bark and consuming the green cambium layer beneath it. Deer, elk, and other hoofed animals, such as the bison, remain active all winter, feeding on dead grass beneath the snow. If this is not available, they may feed on the buds and young stems of plants. Mountain sheep and goats are also active during the winter season.

Some species of birds do not migrate, but remain at the same place throughout the year. In the colder regions the permanent residents are usually not insect-eaters exclusively, but are species which may feed on seeds or other available food. Crows move about in large

Some birds can survive the winter.

flocks from one place to another during the cold winter months, but they do not make the long migration which is characteristic of some birds. English sparrows remain in the same place, regardless of season, seeking food wherever they can find it. Quail and pheasants are permanent residents, feeding on weed seeds and the berries of various plants. Cardinals usually remain as residents throughout much of their range during the year. Blue jays do not migrate, nor do the several species of hawks and owls, the ruffed grouse, chickadee, tufted titmouse, and other birds. During some years robins, bluebirds, flickers, and mourning doves do not migrate, while cowbirds occasionally remain in the same place during the entire year.

EXPERIENCE. *To determine what birds may be found in a locality during the winter months.* This may be done by selecting a fairly secluded place which may be observed by children at a distance and establishing a bird-feeding station there. Sunflower seeds, cracked corn, and other grains may be placed there daily, so that the birds will visit it. Suet may be tied to the branch of a tree close by, for many birds will be attracted by it. A list of the various species of birds which visit the feeding station may be made. In this way the birds which remain in the vicinity during the winter months may be determined. It must be remembered that some birds, such as the brown creeper, slate-colored junco, red-breasted nuthatch, golden-crowned kinglet, and tree sparrow, are sometimes winter residents only. This means that they may spend the winter in the northern United States, having migrated from Canada. Such birds migrate farther north when spring comes.

Insects Live through the Winter in Various Stages of the Life Cycle

Most species of insects survive the winter in the egg, larval, or pupal stage. The severe frosts of autumn and the extreme colds of winter cause the deaths of most of the adult individuals, although some survive. When cold weather approaches, adult flies seek shelter in cracks between boards, under paper, and in similar situations. There they remain inactive all winter, emerging in the spring to lay eggs and carry on other functions. In the discussion of the social insects it was noted that bees, ants, and termites remain in an inactive state during the winter months. Some species of insects spend the winter in strawstacks, decaying logs, or piles of debris.

The adults of many species do not survive. They may lay eggs in the fall of the year. These eggs do not develop until the following spring, so that the species survive the unfavorable season in the egg stage. This is true of locusts, for example. The female locust lays her eggs in a small hole in the ground, which is later plugged with bits of vegetation. Some species of plant lice lay several broods of eggs, one of which is known as the winter eggs, since they are laid in the fall and do not develop until the following spring. Some moths and other insects have similar habits.

Many species of insects lay their eggs during the summer months. These soon hatch and feed voraciously, and by the time fall comes they have spun a cocoon in which they spend the winter months. This is true of many of the moths and butterflies. The cocoons and chrysalises may be gathered in the winter since they are easy to find then because of the lack of leaves on plants. One species of moth which infests pitch-pine trees spend the winter in the larval stage in small branches of the tree.

Some Animals Hibernate during the Winter Months

Many animals seek shelter in the ground, in trees, and in caves to escape the extreme cold of the winter months. Animals whose temperature varies a great deal seek out a place where they may dig themselves into the soil and remain there until the atmosphere is sufficiently warm to permit them to resume normal activity. During the summer months earthworms may be found close to the surface of the ground, but with the approach of cold weather they burrow several feet down in the soil to a point below the freezing level. There they remain until the ground has thawed again, working their way upward in the spring.

Amphibians Exhibit Various Body Changes during Hibernation. Toads and frogs also hibernate in the soil, burrowing deep to the point where there is no danger of freezing. Contrary to popular opinion, these and other animals cannot really be frozen without injury, so that if they do not burrow deeply enough into the ground to avoid freezing they may be destroyed. During *hibernation* the various physiological processes of the animal are slowed down, so that circulation of the blood, breathing, and other life functions go on at a very slow rate. If a hibernating frog is dug out of its burrow, it will exhibit few of the characteristics of a living animal.

The period of hibernation may be as long as five months, during which time the amphibian does not feed. It can survive because of the fact that several small bodies of fat are formed in the body cavity when food is plentiful during the summer months. These serve as a source of energy to the animal to keep it alive. During the summer months, then, sufficient fat must be stored to enable the animal to live through the period of hibernation. Since the animal is not active, it uses almost no energy, and so the supply lasts until spring, when food is again available. Because their hibernation generally occurs in damp soil, toads and frogs absorb sufficient moisture through their skins to keep them alive.

Reptiles Hibernate during the Cold Months. Reptiles react to winter conditions in a manner similar to that of the amphibians. Snakes often hibernate in sandy hillsides, where large numbers of the same species may occupy the same burrow, although sometimes two species hibernate together. Sometimes they hibernate in a hollow log or other suitable place. Snakes may return year after year to the same place for hibernation.

As the temperature drops in the fall of the year, they become sluggish. On a cold morning a snake may be so inactive that it may be picked up without making the least attempt to escape. For hibernating they generally choose a slope which faces south. The depth of the burrow may be three feet or more, which is well below the frost line in most parts of middle latitudes. Rocky places are sometimes selected if there are fissures sufficiently deep in the rocks. When spring comes, the snakes scatter to their natural habitats.

Turtles hibernate in the bottoms of ponds or along the margins of stream bottoms. There they dig down into the mud and remain buried in it until the coming of spring. They leave the water in the spring and soon thereafter lay their eggs in various places on the land. Box turtles may hibernate to some depth in soft earth rather than in the bottoms of ponds, emerging in the spring and laying their eggs under leaves or in soft earth. They lay from three to eight eggs.

Some Mammals Hibernate. While the variable-temperature animals like frogs, toads, snakes, and turtles hibernate throughout the winter and are therefore not seen until the coming of spring, many of the warm-blooded animals hibernate for a much shorter period. Squirrels may leave their winter dens when the weather becomes mild, even though it may be January; and their tracks may often be seen in the snow. They remain inactive only when the weather is very cold. They live through the winter on acorns and nuts which were stored in the fall. Hunters know that opossums and raccoons may be found in the woods during any of the winter months if the weather has been sufficiently warm to cause the snow to melt and the ground to thaw, especially if the warm weather persists for a number of days. During such periods these animals go forth in search of food, and return

Many animals survive adverse conditions in winter.

only when the weather becomes cold again. Skunks also leave their dens on warm, foggy winter nights, seeking birds and other prey.

Field mice are inactive while the weather is cold, but a few warm days and nights are sufficient to bring them out of their nests in search of food and water. Muskrats and beavers remain within their houses, or lodges, during severe weather; but when a mild spell occurs, they become more active and leave the residences to forage for food. Chipmunks generally go into hibernation during the month of November in northern latitudes, and remain in this state until March. At any time they may become active, they live on the supply of nuts and seeds which are stored in their burrows. One or two chipmunks are generally found in each burrow.

Gray squirrels do not hibernate but merely remain inactive during cold weather, and they do not store great quantities of food. Woodchucks feed heavily during the summer months and become very fat as autumn approaches. As the weather becomes colder, they appear less and less frequently, finally remaining in their burrows altogether. They go into hibernation at various times, according to the latitude, so that the beginning of hibernation may be at any time from the end of September until the first of November. They hibernate either singly or in pairs in burrows which may have been used by other animals or which they have dug for themselves. They do not emerge at any time during the winter, although during February they may be seen if there has been a prolonged spell of mild weather. Otherwise they hibernate until March, living on the fat stored in the body. In the spring they emerge very thin and with a voracious appetite. Skunks and other hibernating animals which do not store food are also dependent on stored fat for energy to keep them alive during the winter months.

Bats, the only mammals which can really fly, are among the animals which hibernate

Bats hibernate in winter.

during the winter months. During the warmer parts of the year they fly in pursuit of insects, which they catch while in full flight. With the coming of cold weather they seek out some dark secluded spot, in which they spend the winter. This may be a hollow tree or similar place. Sometimes they hibernate in caves in large numbers.

Most bats are nocturnal in habit, flying about only at night. In Africa, Asia, and Australia there are a number of fruit-eating bats, the largest species of which may have a body that is about a foot long and a wing expanse of about five feet. Vampire bats in South America have very sharp front teeth by means of which they make an incision in the skins of horses, cattle, and other warm-blooded animals, lapping up the oozing blood. One of the commonest species of bats in the eastern part of North America is the little brown bat, which measures not more than about three and a half inches in length. All the species of bats found in the United States live on insects, none of them attacking mammals or using fruit for food.

There are many superstitions concerning these mammals, none of which are true. For example, they are said to become entangled in the hair of human beings. Such superstitions are not substantiated in any way by observation.

Mention has been made of the fact that the body temperature of mammals remains almost constant. However, there is great variation in the body temperature of mammals during hibernation. Such mammals often possess a body temperature many degrees lower than normal.

For example, it has been found that hibernating ground squirrels in a temperature of about 35°F. may have a body temperature which is not much higher or which is the same as that of their surroundings. Respiration may be so slow that it may be imperceptible, and the heart beats very slowly. No food is taken by the animals which hibernate so profoundly, with the result that they are in an emaciated condition when spring comes. If conditions the previous summer were very unfavorable, so that the animal is not sufficiently

fat when the time for hibernation arrives, it may die before the coming of spring. Some warm-blooded animals, then, may at times show a variation in temperature similar to that found in the usual cold-blooded animal. It is interesting to note that if the body temperature of one of the warm-blooded animals should be reduced so greatly during that part of the year when it is normally active, death would result.

EXPERIENCE. *To learn which animals hibernate in your local community.* Inasmuch as climates differ so widely, this will need to be a local study. Learn what wild animals live in your community and then either ask someone in the community who knows about animals or obtain books to learn whether or not the animals hibernate and where. With this background of knowledge it will be easier to watch for them. What animals remain active all through the year?

Fur and Feathers Are a Protection against Cold Weather

All warm-blooded animals are protected against cold weather to some extent by a *covering* of feathers or fur. High temperature, hair and feathers are important; for without them so much heat would be lost that the animal could not survive during the winter. The fur of animals living in tropical countries is not so thick as that of those which live in the middle latitudes or in arctic regions. In those parts of Earth characterized by great environmental changes with the seasons, the animals have a thicker coat of fur in the winter than in the summer. It is for this reason that the trapping of animals whose furs are used by man is done in the cold winter months, not in spring or summer. With the approach of warm weather, much of the fur is shed by the

animal. The coat of fur need not be so thick in the warm months, and the animal is thus adapted to summer conditions.

On extremely cold mornings birds may be seen to appear larger than ordinarily because they have a way of fluffing out their feathers. One of the poorest conductors of heat is an air space in which the air is not circulating. By fluffing out their feathers, birds form a large number of small air spaces, which increase the insulating function of the feathers, so that little of the body heat is lost. Many mammals erect the hairs which make up their fur in a similar way. Animals which live in arctic regions generally have a thick layer of fat beneath the skin, which helps to preserve the body heat. Birds which swim on the water have feathers which are covered by an oil secreted by glands in the skin. This oil makes the feathers waterproof, and the skin is thus kept dry.

Man is the only animal which has learned to protect itself against changes of temperature by wearing clothing. Because of the slight development of hair on his body he is affected more severely by cold weather than other warm-blooded creatures. He obviates this by using the furs and skins of other animals and many plant products for clothes. Man has learned to vary the quantity of clothes he wears to suit changing conditions; this is one of the numerous ways in which he has adapted himself to his environment.

EXPERIENCE. *To observe how some animals are protected against cold weather.* Children might like to keep word or pictorial records of ways in which the animals in their neighborhood are protected from the cold weather. This might include such things as the difference in the way a bird's feathers lie on warm and on cold mornings, or the way the fur of some animals changes in color and in thickness with the coming of cold weather.

Some Animals Migrate Periodically

Many species of animals, especially the birds, migrate periodically and thus escape the rigors of a winter environment. The causes of *migration* are not yet well understood. Formerly it was believed that migration was due to the lower temperatures of the fall months; but this does not account for the migration of those species which leave the nesting grounds while the weather is warm, nor does it explain the migration of some mammals, such as the lemmings of the Scandinavian peninsula. Recent work indicates that the migration of some animals may be caused by the effect of shorter hours of sunlight, or that changes of a subtle nature occur in the ductless glands which arouse the migratory instinct. At any rate, a large number of animals migrate. In addition to birds, some species of fishes are known to migrate regularly; and such mammals as the seals which live in the ocean migrate also. Some land mammals make short and unspectacular migrations from one feeding ground to another, while some which live at high altitudes during summer months descend to lower altitudes for the winter. Migration is characteristic of animals in the middle latitudes.

The protection of migratory animals calls for close co-operation not only between states and provinces but between nations as well.

Migration Is a Distinctive Phase of Bird Life

Although a number of various animals migrate, more species of birds do so than any other class of animals. Migration is characteristic of a great many species, particularly those which nest in northern latitudes during the summer months. None of the migrating animals approach the birds in the extent of their travels.

No One Knows Why Birds Migrate. Before careful observations of the migrations of birds were made, many strange ideas concerning this phenomenon prevailed. It was known that birds which were seen during the summer months were not seen in winter, from which was drawn the conclusion that birds left Earth and spent the winter on the moon. Because of ignorance of conditions on the surface of the moon and its distance from Earth this idea was widely believed for centuries. Some people believed that birds hibernated like insects and some mammals; and those which lived along the shores were supposed to dig themselves into the mud and remain there until the coming of spring, when they reappeared. Swifts and swallows were believed to hibernate in decaying wood, and woodpeckers in the hollow trees in which they built their nests. Along the shores of some of the Mediterranean countries it was believed that birds rode across the sea on the backs of turtles. Now, however, birds are banded and thus their routes of migration are traced.

How the instinct of migration was developed in birds or other animals has not been satisfactorily explained. Migration is the result of a prolonged and gradual adjustment of the animal to its environment. It was once thought that migration may have started during the glacial periods, and that as the ice sheet encroached southward the birds were compelled by it to move southward. Later, as the ice receded, it was thought that birds moved northward again. Many difficulties make this explanation hard to accept.

Another of the older theories was that birds originated in tropical countries and spread northward from them because of their powers of flight. This theory is not acceptable, because it does not explain a number of things about migration. Perhaps the seasonal increase and decrease of food in northern latitudes was a factor in the development of the instinct of migration. At any rate, it seems that certain periodic physiological changes occur in birds which cause them to migrate northward in the spring and in the opposite direction in the fall.

Birds Follow Various Migration Routes. The migration of birds is along fairly definite routes; a given species follows the same routes year after year. There are almost as many routes as there are species of birds; but certain general routes are followed by most species, as has been determined by direct observation. Birds which nest regularly in the central part of the Mississippi Valley and eastward usually follow a route that brings them to western Louisiana and northwestern Florida. From this region they make a flight across the Gulf of Mexico, which necessitates a nonstop flight of five hundred or more miles. Other species fly from Florida to Cuba, Jamaica, and other islands in that part of the Caribbean, many of them remaining there during the entire winter. A less frequented route is one which takes the birds to Florida, Puerto Rico, the Lesser Antilles, and on to South America.

A few species of birds fly across the Gulf of Mexico from Texas to the vicinity of Veracruz in Mexico. Birds which feed on the wing, such as the swallow, often follow a route southward that is entirely over land, and feed on the insects which they find as they migrate. Those which nest in the western parts of the United States often winter in Mexico and Central America and follow a land route.

Some birds migrate great distances each year. One of the best known of these is the American golden plover, which nests along the arctic coasts of North America and winters in Argentina. The plovers arrive at their breeding grounds about the first week in June and build their nests in the moss on ground which is often still frozen. When the young are sufficiently strong to make extensive flights, the southern migration begins. The birds move slowly along the coast of Labrador, feeding as they go and becoming fat on their way. From Labrador they then cross to Nova Scotia, from where they proceed to South America. In their flight they pass over Bermuda and other islands in that vicinity, but if the weather is fair they do not stop until they

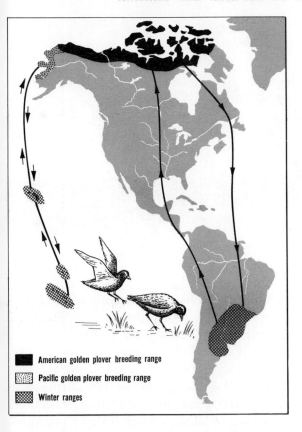

Migration routes, breeding grounds, and winter ranges of the American golden plover and the Pacific golden plover. Adapted from Migration of Birds, *Circular 16, Fish and Wildlife Service, U.S. Department of the Interior.*

- ■ American golden plover breeding range
- ▨ Pacific golden plover breeding range
- ▨ Winter ranges

have reached the coast of South America. By the time they have arrived there, the birds have become very thin, since they use the fat stored in their bodies as a source of energy to sustain them in their flight. They reach Argentina in September.

After remaining there about six months, or until March, the plovers start northward by a different route. They travel across the northwest portion of the South American continent, through Central America to Yucatán in Mexico, and across the Gulf of Mexico to the coast of Texas and Louisiana. Then they pass slowly northward along the Mississippi Valley. Early in June they are at their breeding site again.

The Pacific plover nests near the golden plover. It migrates, however, from Alaska to the Hawaiian Islands. Although these birds rear their young close to the breeding site of the golden plovers, yet the migrations of these two species take them to widely separated parts of Earth.

The greatest bird migrator is probably the arctic tern, whose nest containing young has been found within a few degrees of the north pole. As soon as the young are sufficiently developed, they migrate and several months later are found in the antarctic region.

Other birds make flights of comparable length. Black-polled warblers spend the summers in Alaska and the winters in South America. Their route takes them from South America to Jamaica, from Jamaica to Florida, and across the continent to Alaska. Some cliff swallows which nest in Nova Scotia spend the winter in northern South America, while the bobolink nest northward as far as Saskatchewan in Canada and spends the winters in Brazil. The scarlet tanager may migrate from Canada to Peru, while robins may winter anywhere from the northern states of the United States to the Gulf of Mexico. Kingbirds winter as far south as Bolivia, while the red-eyed vireo winters in southwestern Brazil. Yellow warblers often winter in Colombia, and the Baltimore oriole in Mexico and Central America.

Migrating Birds Travel at Different Speeds and Different Altitudes. When birds migrate, they do not ordinarily travel at top speed. The redstart, for example, takes seventy-seven days to make the journey from Florida to Nova Scotia, which is an average of approximately twenty miles a day. On the other hand, the gray-cheeked thrush makes a trip of about four thousand miles from Louisiana to Alaska in approximately thirty days, thus averaging about one hundred and thirty miles per day. Birds which migrate during the night may cover much longer distances in a single flight.

Wild geese

Geese migrate in v-shaped formations.

The speed of migration is increased as the nesting place is approached. This does not mean that the actual rate of miles per hour is increased, but that the birds fly for a longer period each day, the rest period being shortened. When a flight covering several hundred miles has been made, the birds may feed and rest for several days afterward. The average daily rate of the arctic tern is thought to be about seventy-five miles over a period of ten months.

On clear days and nights birds may fly at an altitude of more than 2000 feet, while on cloudy or misty days they often fly just high enough to clear trees and buildings. Sometimes the altitude of migration is so great that the birds cannot be seen with the unaided eye, and only their call notes give evidence of their presence overhead. Bird migration has been studied at night by training a telescope on the moon and counting and observing the birds as they pass within range of the telescope.

Night migrants generally spend at least part of the day feeding. Those birds which are timid in habits and which live in woods and thickets are generally night migrants. Such birds are the thrushes, tanagers, flycatchers, warblers, and vireos. The flight is usually begun soon after dark and ends just before dawn.

Birds like swifts and swallows, which feed on the wing, migrate during the day, making a comparatively slow daily progress. They generally avoid crossing over large bodies of water, going around them instead. Bluebirds, robins, and waxwings also migrate during the day. Ducks, geese, and birds which live along the shores of lakes and streams may migrate either during the day or at night. The calls of geese may sometimes be heard at night as they fly overhead in a V-formation, although they are often seen in the daytime too.

Birds Arrive at Their Breeding Sites at Different Times. There is some migration of birds going on at all times of the year, with the exception of the month of January. By that time the fall migrations are finished, and those birds which move into the United States from the north have arrived for the winter. During the month of March many species have arrived at their breeding grounds. Among these are such birds as the killdeer, bluebird, mourning dove, song sparrow, bronzed grackle, flicker, red-winged blackbird, cowbird, rusty blackbird, Canada goose, pintail duck, fox sparrow, vesper sparrow, chipping sparrow, and black duck.

During the month of April hermit thrushes often pass through the northern parts of the

United States on their way to Canada. Other birds which arrive then are the brown thrasher, ruby-crowned kinglet, yellow-bellied sapsucker, purple martin, barn swallow, chimney swift, house wren, tree swallow, white-throated sparrow, wood duck, Maryland yellowthroat, red-eyed vireo, black-and-white warbler, and lark sparrow.

In May the following birds arrive: crested flycatcher, scarlet tanager, water thrush, redstart, veery, white-crowned sparrow, rose-breasted grosbeak, nighthawk, ruby-throated hummingbird, bay-breasted warbler, wood pewee, whippoorwill, indigo bunting, cerulean warbler, least flycatcher, chestnut-sided warbler, magnolia warbler, yellow-breasted chat, yellow-billed cuckoo, black-billed cuckoo, black-polled warbler, and others.

The first birds to appear in northern parts of this country from tropical America are the barn swallows, which may be seen about the middle of April. It is interesting to note that some species of birds, such as the hummingbird, Baltimore oriole, and bobolink, appear each year on almost the same day. Often catbirds and brown thrashers appear almost simultaneously, and the chimney swift comes at almost the same time. In the spring migration the males generally appear first, preceding the females by several days. This is true of robins, red-winged blackbirds, yellow-bellied sapsuckers, orioles, and bobolinks. The later arrivals generally come in mixed groups, both males and females being present.

EXPERIENCE. *To observe that birds migrate.* Children living in the northern United States and in Canada may notice V-shaped flocks of geese and ducks going south in the fall and north in the early spring. There and in other places, flocks of small birds may be observed feeding in the fall of the year. These may be on their way south for the winter. In the early spring they may be observed feeding in trees or bushes, or on the ground, as they are returning to their summer nesting places.

Discussions may be held to see whether the children have noticed new birds in their community. Children may wish to keep a record of the birds they have seen and where they saw them. The children may work out their own method of recording, for this will give them an opportunity to study how to make records.

Birds Encounter Many Dangers in Migration. Not all birds survive the period of migration, for they encounter many dangers which they sometimes do not overcome. Those birds which can swim are fairly safe when flying over large bodies of water; for if they become fatigued or if a storm is encountered, they can rest on the water until the danger is gone. Birds whose feathers do not repel water cannot do this, however, so that a storm may cause hundreds of them to perish. Very strong winds sometimes drive birds off their migration route hundreds of miles out into the sea, so that they do not have sufficient strength to reach their destination. Moreover, birds sometimes fail to distinguish the surface of the water when they are flying in a heavy fog, and plunge into the water at full speed, thus killing themselves.

High, fixed lights in statues, monuments, and tall buildings cause the death of many birds. The lighthouses along the Atlantic coast attracted many birds which plunged against them and were thus killed, hundreds sometimes being found around a lighthouse in the morning. This situation is remedied by having lights which flash on and off rapidly, for birds seem to be repelled by such lights.

Other hazards exist during migration. Many birds are killed by flying against telephone and electric-power lines which are strung along highways and railroad lines. Small birds often fly against trees and buildings during heavy snowstorms. Others seem to be unable to distinguish ice on lakes during heavy snows which may overtake them while they are migrating, so that they dash against it and are killed. If the weather changes from warm to cold very suddenly, many birds may be killed; and many also perish from scarcity of food if the ground is suddenly covered by deep snow over a large portion of the migration route. Birds which arrive in the north too early in the spring may suffer from severe cold weather and deep snows which occur after they have arrived at their breeding site.

Birds' Bodies Reveal Many Adaptations for Flight. The migration of birds probably could not take place were these animals not developed along lines which make long flights possible. In no other animals is the power of flight so strong, with the possible exception of some of the bats. Many insects can fly long distances, but they do not range over so many hundreds of miles as the birds. A study of the body of a bird reveals that it is adapted in many ways to make prolonged flight possible.

A consideration of the anatomy of birds reveals that the bones which make up the hind limbs and the pelvis are modified in such a way that the bird can walk on what might be called its hind legs, the front limbs, called wings, being modified for flight. The entire body may be divided into three regions, the head, neck, and trunk. The bones which make up the framework of the trunk are joined together rigidly, and the bone which corresponds to the breastbone, or sternum, of man has a distinct crest which makes possible the attachment of large muscles that move the wings. The vertebrae which make up that part of the backbone located in the trunk are almost completely fused together, so that they form a rigid axis for the skeleton. This makes possible the support of the body while the bird is flying.

Many of the bones are hollow and have in them air cavities which decrease their weight without lessening their strength. The skull of a bird is composed of a number of bones which are so well fused that they appear to form a

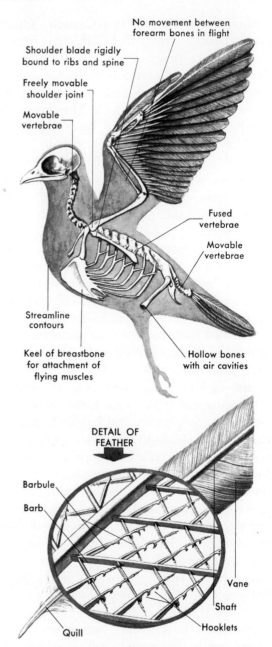

The anatomy of a bird.

single bone in an adult bird. The vertebrae in the neck are long and move freely on one another; thus the neck is very flexible, so that the head can be turned in almost any direction. The actual tail of a bird consists of five or six vertebrae which are not fused, followed by five or six vertebrae which are fused. This latter structure is known technically as the pygostyle, and it supports the large tail feathers. The free tail vertebrae make possible the movements of the tail which enable the bird to use it as a rudder while in flight.

In birds the muscles of the wings, tail, neck, and legs are very well developed. The downward stroke of the wings is produced by pectoral, or shoulder, muscles; these muscles are usually the largest in the bodies of birds which have strong powers of flight. Other muscles are similarly well developed, although in the case of birds which do not fly or whose powers of flight are very limited, their development may not be so pronounced.

The shape of the body of a bird in flight is such as to cause a minimum of air resistance, so that it may be said to be streamlined. Bird bodies are sometimes described as being spindle-shaped. Some birds when in flight draw the legs up close to the body, so that air resistance is further reduced. It is interesting to note that the legs of some birds are so weak that they cannot support the weight of the body. Chimney swifts are never seen except on the wing. It is said that they never rest except when they return to their nests, and that if by accident they are forced to alight on the ground, their legs will not hold them up. Such birds must of necessity feed while flying.

Feathers Are Peculiar to Birds. Birds are the only animals which have feathers, and so can be recognized without difficulty. It is believed that feathers are a modification of the scales of reptiles, and that they are evidence of the fact that birds are descended from reptilian ancestry. It is interesting to note in this connection that the legs of birds are covered with scales and that their skeletons show some similarity to those of reptiles. Fossils of birds have been discovered which show that at one time birds had much longer tails than at present, and that they had numerous teeth, which

are never found in modern birds. They also had hooked claws at the ends of the wings. Even today there exists a species of birds in Brazil, known as the hoatzin, which creeps among the branches of trees rather than flying. The fully grown bird is about the size of a mourning dove and feeds on the fruit and leaves of tropical trees which grow along river banks. The young of these birds have two claws at the tip of each wing, which they use in crawling about in the trees. At the base of the claws there is a pad, which aids the bird in grasping limbs as it climbs about. These claws and pads disappear as the bird matures and are not present in the adult.

Bird feathers are of three general types. The large feathers, which determine the general contour of the body, are known as *contour feathers*. Such a feather consists of a stiff rod which is called the stem. That portion of the stem which is closest to the skin of the bird is hollow and semitransparent and is called the quill. The quill pens, which were used before the invention of the steel pen, were made from this end of the shaft of goose feathers. The remainder of the stem is known as the vane. The vane consists of a shaft and a series of parallel barbs; each barb bears a fringe of barbules. These barbules bear hooklets on one side, which serve to hold together the adjacent parts, so that the whole structure is strong, pliable, and resistant to changes of atmospheric conditions.

A second type of feather is known as the *down*. Down feathers have a soft shaft and a vane without barbs. They are to be found beneath the contour feathers and form a covering for retaining the body heat of the bird. In some cases the down feathers arise directly from the end of the quill, so that no shaft is present.

The third type of feathers are known as *filoplumes*, and have a slender, hairlike shaft with very few or no barbs. The feathers are arranged in definite areas on the skin of the bird, not haphazardly, as may be observed when a chicken is plucked.

Feathers are important in the adaptation of birds to migration and to environmental conditions. It is evident that without strong well-developed feathers a bird could not fly and consequently could not migrate far. The feathers are waterproof, so that the body of a bird normally remains dry. Furthermore, the protection by feathers against cold temperatures is an important factor in enabling birds to survive sudden changes in the weather which might otherwise kill them.

EXPERIENCE. *To see the different kinds of feathers that a bird possesses.* Children may bring to school feathers which they have found. They may study them to locate the quill, vane, shaft, barbs, and barbules. They may be interested in noting how the barbules are held together. Use of hand lenses will make this interesting.

Children may also be interested in noting where the large, strong feathers are located on a bird. These will be found on the wings and tail, where they are useful in helping a bird to fly or to stop, and to guide it.

Birds Use Much Energy in Flight. That birds use much energy in flight can be easily understood when it is remembered how much energy a human being uses in climbing rapidly up two or three flights of stairs. Yet a bird can rise from the ground very rapidly and fly with great speed. Flight calls for the use of much more energy, relatively speaking, than does the activity of human beings, and so energy must be made available in large quantities. Two factors are involved in the liberation of large quantities of energy: the rapid digestion of foods and the securing of oxygen to liberate the energy from the digested food.

Birds are very active and consequently eat enormous quantities of insects, weed seeds, and other food. Since they have no teeth, this

A gull needs great wing power to snatch a fish from the water. (Wide World Photos.)

food is broken up by the beak and swallowed, entering the crop, where a large quantity of it is stored temporarily. Since food is not ground up by teeth, the head is light, since no powerful muscles to move the jaws are present, as in the case of mammals.

From the crop, where the food is moistened and softened, it passes into the gizzard, which is made up of very strong thick muscles. Birds are often seen to swallow pebbles, and many poultrymen feed their chickens small gravel. This is done because the grit is needed in the gizzard to enable the muscles to grind up the food by contraction, so that it enters the stomach in a pulverized state. Digestion in the stomach and small intestine is rapid, so that the food is soon available for distribution to the cells by the blood, where it combines with oxygen, and energy is given off. Since the gizzard, liver, and intestines are close to the center of gravity of the bird, it is easy for the bird to maintain its balance.

Birds have an efficient breathing system, as is shown by the fact that many of them sing while in full flight. When a lark is rising, its wings are beating at the rate of about two hundred strokes per minute; yet it may be singing as volubly as though it were not in motion. It is as though a human being were running rapidly up a steep hill and singing at the same time. The lungs of a bird are not very large, however, and have but little elasticity. The rate of breathing is generally high, small birds normally breathing from thirty to sixty or more times per minute when they are at rest. Because large quantities of food and oxygen are used, a bird's temperature is usually higher than that of a mammal. It may be as high as 110°F.

Birds are adapted for migration, then, by having light hollow bones, strong breast and wing muscles, strong pliable feathers, good digestive and breathing systems, and rapid oxidation of foods. They migrate periodically, generally nesting and breeding in northern latitudes and spending the winters in the southern part of the north middle latitudes, in tropical regions, or in the south middle latitudes.

EXPERIENCE. *To observe the eating habits of birds.* For children to make this observation may require a little time and patience on their part, but it is well worth the effort. A time when many birds are feeding their young might be a good time to watch the birds. If the children are quiet they will see the mother and father birds—robins, for instance—work from dawn until dark to feed their young. Great quantities of food are necessary for birds in order to generate the energy and maintain the high temperature they require.

Some Mammals Migrate

Migration of a periodic nature is not infrequent among mammals, but it does not approach that of the birds in range. This is probably due to the fact that the method of locomotion of mammals does not permit traveling over long distances in a comparatively short time. At any rate, only a few mammals migrate distances comparable to the hundreds of miles covered by birds. The hoary bat and the silver-haired bat, which spend the summer in regions that have cold winters, fly south in the autumn. They feed mainly on insects; and since their food supply is then limited, they migrate to warmer climates, where they can feed. Why some bats hibernate during the winter while others migrate is not clear. Their ability to fly, unique among the mammals, is due to the fact that they have four very long fingers on the forelimbs, between which is stretched the wing membrane. This membrane also extends along the side of the body between the forelimbs and the hind limbs. The hind toes are free, so that when the bat is at rest, it can suspend itself, hanging head downward. In other respects these animals are like all mammals; they have teeth, are covered by a coat of fur, bearing their young after some development within the body of the female, and nourishing the young by means of milk glands.

Fur seals, well known because of the value of their pelts, make annual migrations. They breed in northern latitudes, on the Pribilof Islands in the north Pacific. When the breeding season is over and cold weather is not far off, they migrate southward, returning again in the spring to the breeding grounds. Sea lions make a similar migration. In each case the migration is over a definite route. Many species of whales, which are marine mammals, also seem to follow definite migratory routes, moving north in the spring and south in the winter. It is probable that food is a factor in determining their migration.

Perhaps the most famous example of migrating mammals is the Norway lemming. These rodents, which resemble short-tailed rats but are somewhat larger than mice, not only make short seasonal migrations, but at intervals of a few years make large mass migrations.

Lemmings, relatively few in number, may exist in a community for several years. Suddenly, they will show great vitality and freedom from disease and multiply with great rapidity. Shortly, enormous numbers move away in any or all directions. They are joined by others as they move, and in spite of many being killed by predatory birds and other animals, vast numbers remain, because they continue to multiply. They move across hillsides, glaciers, or rivers. If they come to a body of water too large for them to cross, great numbers may attempt to swim, become exhausted, and drown. Others may eventually perish from lack of food or disease, and others may live out their natural lives. No one is sure what the factors are that trigger this type of migration, although studies are being made.

Other rodents make migrations. These, like those of the lemmings, are not necessarily seasonal in nature. Squirrels, for example, may be numerous in a wooded region for a number of years, when suddenly they may migrate to a new area some distance away. Since this sometimes occurs even when food is plentiful, it is difficult to find an explanation for the exodus. Prairie dogs have been observed to behave similarly, and rats sometimes leave places which they have infested for many years. They may move off for no apparent reason to a place which seemingly has no advantages over that which they have just left. Sometimes, however, the migration seems to be induced by a scarcity of food. Rats are remarkably fecund mammals, and their numerical increase may be so great in a place where predators are few that their food supply may be insufficient to support them. Under such circumstances, the entire population may migrate to a new area. Sometimes, however, only the younger animals leave, under the

Fur seals gather at their summer colony, Pribilof Islands.

leadership of an older animal. They may travel many miles in search of a new location.

Before the coming of European settlers to the western plains of the United States and Canada, the American bison migrated each fall and spring in great herds that must have contained hundreds of thousands of these animals. These migrations were apparently for the purpose of reaching satisfactory feeding grounds, since the animals ranged northward in the spring and early summer and then moved to the south with the approach of winter. Their numbers were once so great that they made broad trails. These trails were later used by engineers in laying out railroad lines and roads, since they led between hills and other elevations, following the easiest course.

African elephants make periodic journeys from one part of their range to another, sometimes in large herds. They may migrate when food in their locality is scarce, or when the ripening of some particular fruit on which they feed induces them to travel in search of it. In the Rocky Mountains the mountain sheep, or bighorn, remains above the timber line during the summertime; but when snow begins to fall, it migrates to the more protected valleys, where there is more food and where the temperature is not likely to be so cold. The American elk, sometimes called by its Shawnee Indian name of wapiti, travels to the higher ranges of the United States and Canada. There it remains during the summer. After the mating season, which is in the fall, these animals gather in large bands and descend to the lower levels, where food will be more plentiful. The caribou of northwestern North America gradually gather and join in a migration to better feeding grounds farther south as winter comes and to the north as spring arrives. Whether vast numbers of mosquitoes influence the caribou in their migrations is still a question.

Eels and Salmon Migrate to Reproduce

Some species of eels and salmon migrate periodically to spawn, but it is only recently that the migratory habits of the eel have been determined. While many fishes show a tendency to migrate from shallow to deep water at the approach of winter, eels and salmon spend part of their life cycle in one kind of water and reproduce in another kind.

The lamprey, or lamper eel, is a biologically primitive animal with a long cylindrical body. It has no jaws, but has instead a round sucker-like mouth, a piston-like tongue, and many sharp teeth. Its skeleton is made up of cartilage, not of bones. These animals may be found in the Atlantic Ocean along the shores of the Northeastern states of the United States, as well as in some fresh-water lakes. Those that live in sea water swim up fresh-water streams to lay their eggs. More than two hundred thousand eggs are sometimes laid by a single female and fertilized by the male. After spawning, both the male and female adults are carried downstream and soon die, thus reproducing only once in their life. The young live in the fresh water and feed on small plants and animals for four or five years, after which they migrate downstream into sea water, where they may reach a weight of five pounds.

Sturgeons are fish which live in both fresh and salt water. Those which live in salt water may ascend streams to deposit their eggs, of which there may be two or three million produced at each spawning. The eggs of sturgeons, when used as a relish, are called caviar.

Perhaps the greatest migration among the fishes is that made by the salmon. The Pacific salmon, largest and most valuable of this family of fish, spend most of their time in the Pacific Ocean. When they are mature, they ascend the Sacramento, Columbia, and other Northwestern rivers of this country after having traveled great distances through the ocean.

What causes a particular salmon to ascend one river rather than another is not known. However, there is some experimental evidence to support the theory that salmon return at spawning time to the stream in which they were hatched or were placed as fingerlings. Fish have a well-developed sense of smell, and it is possible that the young salmon "remembers" the individual odor of its native stream, and follows the scent back to it.

The migration routes of salmon have been studied for many years. In some experiments young salmon fingerlings were marked before being released at the hatcheries or various tributary rivers in the Northwest. Records of the returning salmon were kept for succeeding years. It was found that many of the returning adult fish were those that had been released in the stream several years earlier. All factors that may affect these experimental results have not as yet been thoroughly checked. But numerous experiments to date do show that at least when some salmon are ready to spawn and do not meet with insurmountable barriers, they return to the stream in which they were hatched or were placed as fingerlings.

Mature salmon travel about three miles a day up different rivers and streams to their spawning grounds. They may swim through rapids, leap through the air over natural waterfalls, or swim up man-made fish ladders to seek the headwaters of a particular stream.

The eggs are laid and fertilized in the month of November, and the adult fish float downstream but die before they reach the

Pacific salmon return to their birthplace, where they spawn and then die.

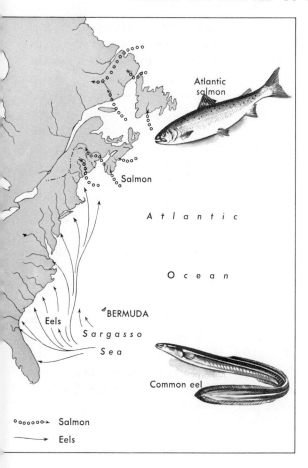

Migration routes of the Atlantic salmon and the common eel.

remain for several years until they are mature. They then swim toward land and ascend the rivers to spawn.

On the eastern coast of North America there is a species of salmon which migrates from the ocean into rivers to spawn. The rivers are those located north of Cape Cod, and cold streams are preferred. A female salmon lays about ten thousand eggs, which sink to the bottom of the stream. The adults do not necessarily die after spawning, as in the case of the Pacific salmon. The young remain in fresh water for about two years. Then they leave the streams and migrate into the ocean.

Common eels are the only fish known to live in fresh water that migrate to the sea to breed. Adult eels from both America and Europe move out into the ocean and swim to practically the same area, near the West Indies, to spawn. It has been estimated that a single female may lay about ten million eggs. The young are very thin and transparent. They are so unlike the adult that for many years they were thought to be a different species of fish. Those tiny eels returning to America usually spend one year in the ocean, while those going to Europe usually spend three years in crossing the Atlantic. When they reach the rivers they migrate upstream. Eels have been known to cross land and are sometimes found in inland lakes and streams. They live in fresh water until they are mature. When they are ready to breed, they migrate back to the area in which they were hatched.

ocean again. The eggs hatch in about two months, and the young fish remain in fresh water until they are from one-and-a-half to five inches long. Then they travel downstream until they reach the ocean, where they

Some Water Animals Migrate Vertically

Because water may change in oxygen and carbon dioxide content, temperature, and light, some animals make what are known as *vertical* migrations. This means that instead of moving long distances from one part of the sea or a lake to another, they rise from lower levels to the surface and then may descend to lower levels again. Herring fishermen trawl along the ocean bottom during the daytime, but at night they find the fish much nearer the sur-

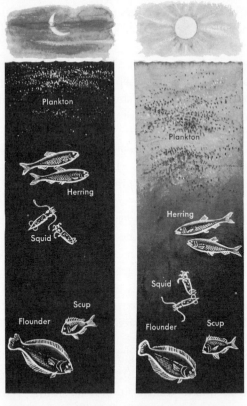

Some ocean life rises to higher levels at night.

face. Light probably causes them to seek lower levels; and at night, since there is less light, they migrate upward and then descend when day approaches. Squids are found at the surface of the ocean during the night, but during the day they too descend to lower levels, where light intensity is much less than at the surface.

The temperature of the water may play a part in vertical migration. Those animals which are usually found near the surface in the summertime, when the water is warm, may descend to a lower level in the winter; for in the wintertime the temperature at the surface is lower than at some distance below the surface. Sometimes vertical migrations cease entirely during the cold winter season.

In fresh water, particularly in lakes, certain movements of living things may be noted. Fish which may be found in shallow waters during the warm seasons, where they find an abundance of food, often migrate into deep water for the winter, remaining comparatively inactive and sluggish on the bottom.

Some Animals Are Inactive during Periods of Dryness

Many kinds of animals live in an aquatic environment under climatic conditions that cause ponds and marshes or swamps to become dry during some time in the year when temperatures are high and rainfall is at a minimum. Such animals, adapted as they are to conditions of an aquatic nature, must be able to survive the dry period if the species is to be perpetuated. These adaptations for alternate aquatic and dry existence may be noted in a variety of living things.

One of the most interesting creatures in existence is the lungfish. It is found in the rivers of Queensland, Australia, in the rivers and swamps of central Africa, and in the Amazon River and its tributaries in South America. It has gills, by means of which it breathes when water is abundant; and in this respect it does not differ from other fishes. But when the rivers and swamps in which it is found become dry, owing to the evaporation of water, the lungfish buries itself in the soft mud to a depth of about one and a half feet. The sides of this hole are lined with a mucus which is secreted by the fish and which keeps its skin moist. There is an opening in the upper end of the chamber, so that the fish can obtain air. All fishes have air bladders, which enable them

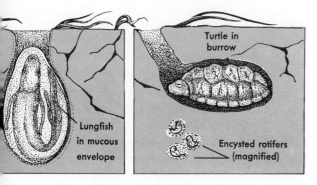

Some aquatic animals can survive extended periods of drought.

to rise or seek lower levels in the water; but in the case of the lungfish this air bladder has become so modified that it serves as a lung, so that the fish becomes an air-breather. This lung also makes it possible for the fish to live in water which is unfit for other fishes, since, if the oxygen content of the water is low, it can rise to the surface at frequent intervals for air.

While in its mud chamber this fish lives on fat stored in the body, as in the case of hibernating animals. It can remain in this condition for several months; with the coming of the rainy season it emerges from its chamber and resumes life as an aquatic animal. Lungfish have a body like that of an eel in shape. They have scales, but these are deeply embedded in the skin. The African lungfish may attain a length of six feet. It makes a nest in the mud of the marsh bottom, and in this nest the female deposits the eggs. The male stands guard over the eggs, and lashes his tail over them. A supply of fresh water is provided by the currents thus set up.

In the United States turtles and other reptiles, as well as some of the amphibians, seek shelter from drought conditions by digging into wet soil and remaining there until after rain has fallen. Turtles may often be found to have dug themselves into the wet soil on the bottom of ponds which have dried up.

Protozoans which live regularly in water escape death when ponds and other bodies dry up by forming cysts. As the protoplasm of the microscopic organism loses water by evaporation, it may form impervious membranes within which the protoplasm remains alive. The process of changing into this condition is known as encystment, and the cyst is so small and light that it may be blown about by winds with dust. The cyst resembles dust so much that a microscopic examination of it by an inexperienced observer may be disappointing. If a cyst happens to fall into water, the organism emerges in a few hours and becomes active in its more usual form. Encysted protozoans may be found also on blades of dry grass, leaves, and other vegetation.

Paramecium often forms cysts when there is a scarcity of water. Rotifers, frequently found in fresh water and often called "wheel animalcules," also have great powers of resisting dry conditions. Some species, if they are dried slowly, form a gelatinous envelope which prevents further loss of water; and in this condition they may live a number of years in an inactive state resembling that of the protozoan cysts. Upon being placed in water they resume normal activity.

The adaptation for meeting conditions of drought and high temperatures is known as *estivation*. Estivation differs from hibernation in that it occurs during hot dry seasons and is an adaptation to escape death by loss of water rather than as a protection against cold.

EXPERIENCE. *To learn where animals go in the winter (or summer) in your local community.* The children may wish to list as many of the animals living in your community as possible. They could find out how and where the animals live through the year and whether or not any of them migrate. If any of them do, they may watch for their return and for the time when they leave. There is great variety in the ways animals live during periods that are not favorable to them. How does migration benefit the animals?

Do the children know of any people who migrate, and why? They may be interested in considering how people sometimes follow migrating animals about from one season to the next.

EXPERIENCE. *To indicate migration routes.* Some children may be interested in locating some of the migration routes of animals on a globe. Cord or very narrow ribbon of different colors may be fastened to a globe with plasticine or modeling clay at the extreme limits of various migrations. This will help children to visualize the great distances sometimes traveled by migrating animals. The children may also be interested in learning about the feeding habits of animals during migration. This they may be able to observe in some instances; in other instances, they may secure information from books.

CHAPTER 21

Man Is an Animal

The human species is composed of individuals which have many of the characteristics of other animals. Although man has learned to control some of the factors of his environment, he is as truly dependent on it as any other living thing for his food, clothing, and shelter. Environmental changes affect him as greatly, in the long run, as they do other animals. He is dependent on plants for his food supply, for example, and consequently adverse weather conditions influence his existence. Periods of drought or of excessive rainfall wreak havoc on his crops; cold summers or severe winters may affect his welfare directly or indirectly. Periods of famine are not uncommon in some countries today; they are the result of food scarcity, which at some time or other affects many animals.

It is true that because man has learned to operate with some of the factors in his environment, he is able to exist over a wider range of territory than most other animals. He has existed successfully in the tropics and in the arctic and antarctic regions, thus illustrating that he is able to adapt himself to a variety of conditions. But his greatest success, as measured by his civilizations, has always been in regions of a favorable character. River val-

leys, for instance, are a favorite environment for man; for their soil is usually fertile, so that crops may be grown easily, and the river itself furnishes him with food. Thus man has been dependent on climate, soil, and other environmental factors; and where these have been most favorable, he has attained his highest peak of civilization. Like any other animal, man is affected by his environment and is adapted to it (p. 95–96).

Man Is a Mammal and a Primate

Man may be classified in the biological scheme of things just as any other living thing is classified. Because he has a backbone composed of a number of vertebrae, he is placed in the phylum Chordata, together with fishes, amphibians, reptiles, birds, and the other mammals. This phylum is divided into a number of classes, and man belongs to the last, the *mammals*. Animals in this class have a covering of hair or fur; they have a diaphragm which separates the heart and lungs from the digestive organs and the kidneys. Furthermore, man, like other mammals, nourishes his young after they are born by means of mammary, or milk, glands.

Primates Have Certain Characteristics. Each class of animals is further divided into a number of orders. The orders of the mammal class have been previously discussed. Man is a member of the order *Primates*. Most of the animals of this order are found chiefly in the tropical and subtropical parts of the world. Since they are similar to man in ways sufficient to be placed close to him in the system of classification, it may be well to consider them briefly.

Most primates are arboreal in habit, which means that they spend a large part of their life in trees and are able to climb about with ease and agility. Most of them are gregarious, going about in groups, although a few of them are solitary. They feed mainly on fruits, insects, and birds' eggs.

Perhaps the most important characteristic of the primates is the opposable thumb and great toe. This enables them to grasp objects with the thumb or great toe placed opposite the other fingers or toes, and makes is possible for them to handle things easily. To illustrate this, one need only pick up an object, keeping the thumb on the same side of it as the fingers, and the importance of the opposable thumb becomes evident. It has made it possible for man to use tools with a facility otherwise not approached. The opposable great toe of the primates is of great use in climbing, making them very proficient at it. Most primates produce but one young at a time, multiple births being the exception.

There are eight families of primates. A family is a subdivision of an order. The best-known families are the South American monkeys, the Old World monkeys, marmosets, lemurs, the anthropoid apes, and man. Of these the anthropoid apes are more like man in their structure than any other animal. They have no tail, often walk more or less erect on their hind limbs on the ground, and are divided into four groups. These four groups are the gibbons, the orangutans, the gorillas, and the chimpanzees. Gibbons are found in southeastern Asia and the East Indies; they generally grow to a height of about three feet. When they walk, they are not assisted by the hands. Orangutans are confined to Borneo and Sumatra. They live in treetops, where they construct nests for themselves; they grow to a height of about four feet; when they walk, they use their knuckles as well as their hind limbs. The brain of this animal is said to be more like that of man than is the brain of any other animal.

Gorillas are found in the forests of western Africa. They feed mainly on vegetation, reach a height of five feet and five inches, and sometimes grow to weigh five hundred pounds. They are very ferocious when disturbed, and cannot ordinarily be kept successfully in captivity, although one case is known of a gorilla born in an American zoo. Chimpanzees also live in Africa; they resemble the gorillas in some respects, but they are easily tamed and kept in confinement. The skull of the chimpanzee is smoother and rounder than that of the gorilla, and its arms are shorter.

Man is placed in the last family of the primates, the family *Hominidae*. Only one species exists today, which biologists call *Homo sapiens*. Man differs from other primates chiefly in the size of his brain and in his more erect locomotion. His body is not covered with hair to the same extent, although it is interesting to note that the human young before birth are covered by a rather heavy coat of hair over the entire body. This coat of hair is lost before birth occurs, and is called lanugo. While he has an opposable thumb in common with other primates, he does not have an opposable great toe, and consequently cannot climb with the facility of a monkey or an ape. For that reason it is easier for man to live on the surface of the ground than in trees.

Despite the fact that man is similar in some respects to the apes, the popular idea that man is "descended from a monkey" is not held to be true by biologists. It may be true that in the course of evolutionary development both man and the apes had a common ancestor, from which both are descended; but the various families of monkeys, apes, and man have been distinct for a long time.

The Structure of Man Resembles That of Other Mammals. Man's relationship to the other mammals becomes clear when his structure is compared with that of other members of this class of animals. Like them, he has a skeleton of bone and cartilage, and the chemical composition of his bone tissue is not very different from that of any other mammal, being made up largely of lime compounds. His backbone consists of a number of vertebrae through which runs the spinal cord, just as in a squirrel or horse. He has ribs and pelvic bones, which may be somewhat different in size and shape and arrangement because of his upright posture, but which in other respects are much the same. The bones in his arms and legs are found to correspond to the bones in the limbs of other mammals, and his teeth have a similar structure.

Other organs of the human body are parallel to those of other mammals. The muscles of man function in a way common to all mammals, and his digestive system is basically the same. He has such organs as the liver, pancreas, kidneys, and bladder, all of which may be found in any mammal picked at random. His heart is made up of muscle tissue and has two ventricles and two auricles, and his blood circulates through his body in arteries, capillaries, and veins, as it does in all mammals. The similarities are so numerous that there is no doubt of his relationship with other mammals. There are, of course, many differences; but differences exist among all animals. They serve only as a basis for setting man apart in a family and species by himself. His differences are not more pronounced than those existing among other species of the so-called lower animals.

Man's Body Functions Similarly to the Bodies of Other Mammals. Not only is man like other mammals in structure, but the manner in which his body functions is similar. He lives on foods which are also eaten by other mammals. He eats the seeds of such plants as corn, wheat, rice, oats, barley, and rye. He feeds also on the leafy parts of plants, their stems, roots, and even their flowers. He kills and eats other animals, as do the carnivores. Man is said to be omnivorous; that is, he eats both animal and vegetable substances. He digests these foods, as do all mammals, through a series of physical and chemical changes, so that the food is changed from the solid to the liquid state, and is then absorbed, principally in the small intestine. Special chemical substances known as enzymes are found to be necessary for the digestion of food in man, as well as in other mammals. The energy in these foods is liberated in the cells of man by chemical combination with oxygen. In this process carbon dioxide and liquid wastes are formed and must be eliminated. This is true of all living things.

The process of breathing is the same in man as in other mammals. He has two lungs, made up of very small air sacs called alveoli, in which are found numerous capillaries. Oxygen is acquired by the blood, and carbon dioxide is given off, in a way which is common to all mammals. Human reproduction involves the same principles that are involved in the reproduction of other mammals. Egg cells are produced by ovaries in the female, while sperm cells are produced in the testes of the male. Fertilization is always within the body of the female; and as with other mammals, the fertilized egg develops into an embryo and re-

ceives nourishment through the placenta by osmosis from the blood of the female.

All mammals have special glands which secrete powerful chemical substances known as hormones into the blood stream. These affect the temperament and growth of the individual. Man has these glands. One of them, the thyroid, is located at the base of the larynx, or "Adam's apple," and produces the hormone known as thyroxine. If the thyroid gland is not functioning properly, serious consequences may follow. Goiter is a manifestation of thyroid trouble.

Because of the numerous similarities between man and other mammals, and because his body functions much like that of the other animals in this class, it is possible to use mammals in experimentation the results of which are then sometimes applied to human diseases. Rats and guinea pigs have been used to determine the effects of certain diets and their vitamin content. The experimental work which formed the basis for developing the insulin treatment for diabetes was performed first on

Winter in different parts of the world.

(a)   (b)

Man can equip himself to survive unusual conditions.   (a) a test engineer in a Gemini-type pressure suit.   (Three Lions, N.Y.C.)
(b) a diver wearing a suit equipped with air and communication lines to the surface.   (Al Barry, from Three Lions, N.Y.C.)

dogs. Monkeys have been used in experimental studies of such diseases as infantile paralysis and colds.

Conditions Necessary for Life Are the Same for Man as for Other Mammals. Since he is so similar to other mammals in structure and function, the conditions under which man lives must be the same. He is dependent on the atmosphere for his supply of oxygen, and is affected by the lack of this vital element as other mammals are. He is just as much affected by such a force as gravity as any other living thing. He cannot live comfortably in a place where the humidity is too great or temperatures are too high without modifying his surroundings by such means as ventilation or air-conditioning.

Man invades the upper atmosphere, but to do so he must protect himself against changes in temperature, air pressure, and amount of oxygen. When he invades even relatively shallow water he encounters the problems of pressure and an oxygen supply. When descending into the deepest parts of the ocean, there are problems that arise out of living in a closed cabin as well as those of changing temperature, air pressure, water pressure, and oxygen (pp. 242, 263, 436).

The conditions necessary for life can be made more real to children by discussing any experiences they may have had in flying, swimming, or other activities. Wherever conditions are not favorable for his existence, he is found only in small numbers and has made special adaptations to his environment.

Man, then, is subject to the limitations of his environment. It is true that by using the materials he finds in Earth, and by utilizing plant and animal substances, he is able to overcome adverse conditions. But it is only where the environment is favorable or can be made more favorable that he is numerous. A sudden change of conditions affects man greatly, as is evident from the effect of droughts on farmers. Floods, earthquakes, volcanic eruptions, hurricanes, and other natural forces affect man as much as they do other animals in the community subject to the visitation of these phenomena.

EXPERIENCE. *To learn how people care for themselves during unfavorable times.* Even small children will be interested in the ways to take care of themselves in cold weather, when some animals hibernate or other animals migrate.

They may tell what they do to be comfortable when it is very cold and when it is very hot. Older children may proceed along the same lines, relating any ways they know of where man interacts with his environment in order to live. How do men live in places of extreme cold or extreme heat? Older children may be interested in the clothes devised for the use of the armed forces in different climates. They may also be interested in the methods of securing food. Art work may be used to describe children's ideas of different environments.

Man's Intelligence Gives Him an Advantage in the Struggle for Existence

Physically man is not superior to many animals, as comparison with some of them will show. He cannot run from danger with the speed of a deer, nor can he swim with the ease of an otter. His teeth are not so well adapted for biting as those of a wolf, nor can he use his fingernails in defending himself with as great effect as a lion uses its claws. He cannot climb away from an attacker with the effectiveness of a monkey, nor can he fly about in search of food with the facility of a bat. A large bear can kill a man with one blow of its powerful paw, and an unarmed human being is no match for an aroused gorilla. How, then, has man managed to survive in the ruthless and persistent struggle for existence?

The human brain is the answer to this question. Man possesses a brain with which he is able to reason, to remember, and to pass on to his offspring the results of his experiences. It is through this well-developed brain that man holds the advantage over all other living things. When he is confronted by a problematic situation, he is often able to recall past experiences which may have a bearing on the situation, and then attempt to solve the prob-

lem in the light of his past experiences. The thinking processes are complemented by his ability to make his ideas known to his associates through the medium of speech, so that it is easy for him to compare his own ideas with those of others and to profit thereby.

Moreover, man has learned to make marks which we call writing, and by writing or printing, he can circulate his ideas among a large number of his own kind. This exchange of ideas, aided by means of communication which have developed during the history of the human species and which are so complex today, has been of great assistance in giving man dominance over other animals. High mountain peaks and large bodies of water are barriers to the distribution of other mammals, but man has successfully overcome even these obstacles.

Another feature, a structural peculiarity common to the primates, has given man a great advantage. This is the *opposable thumb*. Because of it man is able to pick up things easily, turn them over in his hand, inspect them, and manipulate them to his advantage. Because of the opposable thumb

H. Armstrong Roberts

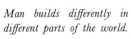

Man builds differently in different parts of the world.

Ewing Galloway

H. Armstrong Roberts

Scofield from Ewing Galloway

Ewing Galloway

man has become a tool-using animal. His first device was probably a tree branch with which he beat off the attack of another man or of some other mammal. He learned that he could pick up stones and throw them, thus bringing down small game which he could use for food. Later discoveries enabled him to tie the stone on the end of a stick, and the added leverage on the stone made it a more effective weapon.

Perhaps the greatest discovery man has ever made has been the *use of fire,* for by means of it he was able to keep warm when otherwise he might have perished of the cold. It enabled him to cook his foods and make them easier to digest. Eventually he learned to use fire in extracting copper and iron from their ores, and found that these made better weapons than stones or sharpened sticks. The story of man's development is a long but fascinating one. His language must have been very rudi-

mentary at first; but each new discovery made necessary a new word, so that his language expanded. Even today new words are being added to the many languages of the world as new inventions and scientific procedures make them necessary.

Man's chief advantage over other animals, then, is his superior mental ability, which resulted in his use of language and tools. These advantages enabled him to outwit predators and to cope with an unfavorable physical environment; they made his life more comfortable, and they made possible the leisure in which man has been able to reach his high artistic and cultural development. By domesticating animals, so that he no longer needs to hunt wild game for food, and by learning to cultivate plants, he has been able to meet the question of food so satisfactorily that in many parts of the world he no longer needs to expend all his energy in search of a bare subsistence.

When other mammals threaten his welfare, he shoots them or eliminates them by other means. Harmful insects he keeps in check by spraying; diseases he avoids in many different ways. Man's prominence in the biological scheme of things is due to his *intelligence,* which has made it possible for him to survive in situations that might otherwise have proved fatal to him. His greatest development has come in a period of time so short as to be insignificant when measured by the yardstick of the geologist (pp. 366–371).

Members of the Human Species Differ from One Another

That individual members of the human race differ from one another is, of course, a well-known fact. The species has been arbitrarily divided into a number of races, but the division is disputed by those who study man.

It is sometimes divided into three primary groups, the Caucasian, the Mongoloid, and Negroid. The Caucasian race includes most of the Europeans, and is characterized by soft straight hair, well-developed beard, prominent nose, small teeth, and retreating cheek-bones.

One variety of this race has fair skin, and ranges from northern Europe to northern Africa and western parts of Asia. Another variety includes the so-called Mediterranean races of southern Europe, southwestern Asia, and also northern Africa.

The Mongoloid race includes the Magyars, Turks, Eskimos, American Indians, and the inhabitants of northern and central Asia. They have black straight hair, a yellowish skin, a broad face with prominent cheekbones, teeth of a moderate size, a small nose, and sunken narrow eyes.

Negroid races possess tightly curled hair, dark skin, thick lips, and broad flat noses. Their teeth are generally large, and their eyes are prominent. Included in this race are the African Negroes, the aborigines of Australia and Tasmania, and the South African and Philippine Pygmies. It must be remembered that all these varieties of man are members of the same species, and that apart from the more or less superficial differences mentioned, they are alike in most other respects. Many students of the human races declare that because of numerous migrations it is difficult to find even small groups which may be considered truly representative of their type.

Individuals within the same race differ from one another in numerous respects. Within any one of the racial groups there are differences in stature, color of eyes, hair, and complexion. Thus the people of northern Europe are described as blonds, with fair complexions and light hair, but many dark-skinned, black-haired individuals are found among them. The Negroid people are found to vary considerably in color from a very dark complexion to one so light that it is not much darker than that of some of the Mediterranean people. There are also variations in the shape of the head and the face, the size and shape of the nose, and so forth. No two individuals are ever alike, the nearest approach to likeness being that perhaps of identical twins (pp. 97–98).

Man Is a Member of a Community[1]

Man lives in communities. He has a family life like that of some other mammals except that it is far more complicated. The family is an advantageous arrangement for rearing the young, for it gives the young a protection which is not possible without family life. Human offspring are helpless at birth and need much care. Man's community is so complicated that the young need much training before they are able to participate in its manifold activities, and the responsibilities are so numerous that without an adequate family life it is not possible to train the young to participate efficiently.

Families form the basis for further organization of the human community. Early in man's history a number of families clung together and formed tribes. The larger numbers gave man more protection against an attacker and made it possible for him to meet his changing environment more successfully. Man has probably always been a gregarious animal and has enjoyed the advantages and disadvantages of gregariousness. He has learned to co-operate to a great extent. His social life may not be so efficient as that of the bees, ants, and termites from a strictly biological point of view, but it is the result of intelli-

[1] The remainder of this chapter should be studied in connection with Chapter 6.

gent action rather than instinct alone. Furthermore, his society is such that the existence of the human species is not threatened by the collapse of one particular group, as is the case among the social insects, where the welfare of the society depends on the caste system. Heredity does not necessarily determine the fate of an individual. It is possible for a man born at the level of one social stratum to invade others successfully.

The whole Earth has been the scene of man's activity, so that he has not been limited to any particular zone. Other animals are found only in certain definite regions, but man has been able to overcome barriers which are impassable to other living beings. With the possible exception of some protozoa, no other animal has been able to exist from the north pole to the south pole and on all the continents as man has. The distribution of man over the continents occurred long before the invention of modern methods of transportation, for he was found everywhere, with only a few exceptions, before the development of steam and electricity.

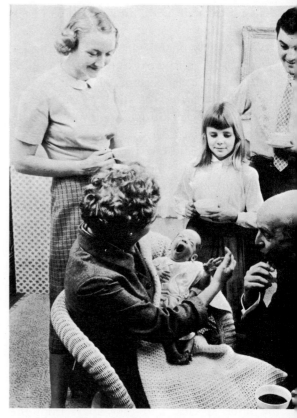

Three generations of one family.   (Courtesy of General Foods.)

Man Often Upsets the Natural Balance of a Community

Because of the control which he exercises over his environment, man often disturbs the balance which exists in communities of living things around him. He often thoughtlessly eliminates many species of plants and animals. Less than a hundred years ago the passenger pigeon was one of the commonest birds in North America. It was present in unbelievable numbers, the flocks often being so large as to obscure the sun when they were passing overhead. There seemed to be no limit to their numbers, but they were shot down so ruthlessly that today not a single pair of these birds is known to exist anywhere. Because they were fit for human consumption, the

passenger pigeons have become extinct. It is not possible to estimate the effect of this extinction on the biological community.

The same story can be told of many other species of living things. Beavers were once very common in North America, but they have become so scarce that most people have never seen one in its natural habitat. Today laws protecting both birds and mammals from hunters have been enacted; without these laws much wild life would soon disappear completely from the greater part of North America. Even small songbirds must be protected. Many species of beautiful wild flowers are now so scarce that laws protecting them have been passed. Man probably has a greater effect on the biological community than any other organism, so far as maintaining a balance is concerned.

Time and again man has disturbed the balance of a community by the importation of living things from other parts of the world. The English sparrow and the starling are notorious examples in North America of an animal which has succeeded in a new environment to the detriment of native species. The Hessian fly, which has caused many millions of dollars of damage to the wheat crop, was imported here in straw used for bedding during the American Revolutionary War. The common barberry, which is host to the fungus that causes black rust of wheat, was imported by early settlers from England. Wheat rust may be controlled by eliminating the common barberry, so that this plant is an example of a living thing imported to the detriment of other plants in the community.

When Australia was first settled there was no watercress in its streams; so it was imported from England and placed where it would grow. Since there was nothing that disturbed the plant, it grew so rapidly that soon the streams became choked with watercress. The mongoose was imported into some of the West Indies to eradicate rats, which had become very numerous there. After the mongoose had eradicated the rats, it turned its attention to birds and poultry and had to be controlled to prevent the elimination of the bird life. There were no Norway rats in North America before the coming of the white man. They arrived here on ships from European harbors and multiplied so rapidly that today they are one of the greatest pests we have. Such stories of man's effect on biological balance could be told almost endlessly.

Whenever a new species of plant or animal is introduced where it does not naturally exist, there must be a readjustment of the biological balance. This readjustment often works to

the detriment of man and is later regretted by him. Not all imported species maintain themselves successfully, however. An attempt was once made to introduce the camel into the southwestern part of the United States, but no great success attended the venture. This is in direct contrast with the way in which the horse thrived in our Western states. Before the coming of the white man there had been no horses on this continent probably for many thousands of years. Spanish exploring parties in the West had horses, some of which were lost during the expeditions of exploration. These found conditions suitable for their development and so multiplied rapidly. When the West was settled by the pioneers, it was necessary in some states to hunt the bands of wild horses and exterminate them to ensure sufficient grazing for cattle. Large bands of wild horses have existed in some places until quite recently.

EXPERIENCE. *To learn how man may have upset the natural balance in your community.* Do the children know of any animal in their community that is injuring in some way any of the plants? If such a situation is not readily noticed the children might find whether or not any animals or plants in the community are protected by law. Is there a limit to the number of fish caught or can only a certain animal be hunted and only for a short time? Are there any flowers that are protected? Why? Often man is responsible for such situations because he has destroyed those plants or animals which would hold others in check. Man is also responsible for nearly exterminating some kinds of plants and animals. Sometimes plants and animals have been brought into the country which crowd out others. Children may become aware of such conditions when they are found to exist and learn why they exist. They may become aware that certain things can be done to help such conditions. (See Chapter 6.)

Man Influences the Physical Conditions of the Environment

As a result of his numerous activities of an industrial and agricultural character, man has affected the physical aspects of his environment. Air is a part of that environment, and man's use of it is becoming increasingly important. The comparative cleanliness of the air enjoyed by our forefathers can become polluted by dusts and chemicals produced in providing for the needs of a large population. Construction, manufacturing, transportation, waste disposal, crop spraying, power production, defense activities, and other necessary work all contribute to making air unclean. The amount and kind of pollution will vary greatly from place to place. Many kinds of dust and gases, such as certain sulfur, nitrogen, and halogen compounds, hydrocarbons, formaldehyde, ozone, carbon dioxide, and carbon monoxide, may invade the air. This results in damage to building materials, textiles, and rubber; to materials in factories during production, to vegetation; to livestock; and to human beings by the intake of contaminated plants, and in decreased visibility and sunlight, and the irritation of membranes.

To control the output of these solid, liquid, or gaseous substances is expensive and may involve elaborate chemical or mechanical processes. It is often done by eliminating them during production by changes in processes or in equipment design, or by preventing their escape into the air by using collectors of various kinds. In selecting sites, new industries consider carefully the nature of possible pollution, damage to vegetation, damage to and from products of other factories and the local topography and weather conditions. The burning of trash by individuals is prohibited in some areas during certain weather condi-

tions, and the installation of devices for using the exhaust gases from automobiles is recommended.

The disposal of wastes to safeguard health is necessary, but sewage dumped into rivers and lakes makes the water unfit for fish to live in and unfit for human consumption as well. Cities on seacoasts often dump their garbage only a few miles from shore. Bathing beaches then become contaminated and diseases may be spread in this manner.

Factories located on riverbanks often dump waste chemicals into the water, so altering its chemical composition that it cannot support the living things naturally found in it. In order to protect their water supply and to make possible the conservation of fish and other aquatic life, many states and provinces have passed laws making it illegal to use streams for such dumping. Agricultural insecticides often contaminate the water supply as much as industrial wastes, and there may be a greater chain reaction affecting vital areas of community life. The dumping of waste from oil tankers and the cleaning of their tanks at sea has resulted in tremendous losses in birds and other water life and in contamination of beaches. This, and the disposal of radioactive wastes are international problems. Experiments are under way to find ways for making constructive uses of radioactive wastes and to determine the durability of the containers in which these wastes are now buried in the soil or sunk in the ocean.

Radioactive fallout, a product of nuclear explosions, can become a world-wide hazard. The radioactive products may attach themselves to dust particles and fall to Earth. The danger to living things is due to radiation from

Man's "improvements" may seriously upset the balance of the natural community. (Harold M. Lambert.)

these products. Atoms resulting from fission are unstable and give off such particles as electrons as they disintegrate to a more stable form. Close watch is kept on the amount of fallout.

Plant and animal communities are often disturbed by man's activities in rural areas. Farmers often drain swamps in order to increase the extent of their croplands, and thus make it impossible for animals like the muskrat and mink to exist. Red-winged black-birds, which nest in the swamps, must seek other breeding grounds. Brushland is often cleared of its vegetation and is used for crops, with the result that birds like pheasants and quails are driven out, and otherwise the community is disturbed.

In other places dams may be built to impound the water, and areas are flooded which are normally above the water line. Animals are then forced to migrate from the flooded land, while the plants existing there are drowned out. Dams built across some New England streams have made it impossible for Eastern species of salmon to reach their breeding places, so that they are not nearly so numerous as they once were. A dam may convert at least part of a swiftly flowing stream into a slow-moving stream, and this factor has a great influence on the kinds of living things which exist in the water.

The invasion of the Western Hemisphere by European cultures brought with it many changes in plant and animal communities (Chapter 6). It is difficult for the imagination to conceive the tremendous changes this has caused in the natural plant and animal communities which once existed here. Nor is the readjustment yet complete, for some animals and plants are becoming extinct even now. Not many years ago the last known heath hen died on the island of Nantucket.

A dam may flood a wide area and destroy much plant and animal [life].

EXPERIENCES. *To learn about ways in which man changes the country around him.* Children have only to look around them and think of the changes that are taking place to realize that man changes the place where he lives. The village and the city streets are different from the country it once was. The building of dams on the rivers, the cutting of trees, or the building of a new road may change an entire community. Children may wish to list the changes in the place where they live and possibly take one for study. If possible, they should choose one that they can observe easily.

To find out about substances in the air, children may spread a white paper or towel on a windowsill where it will not be disturbed for a few days. Examine any substances with a hand lens. Can they tell what the substances are? Do they have any evidence of other substances in the air that they cannot see? Why are they there? Children can become aware of air pollution, but for the most part the solution is an adult problem.

Man Exercises Control over Some of the Plants and Animals in His Environment

Some Animals Are Undesirable to Man. Despite his mental superiority, man is not able at present to carry on his activities without the interference of other living things. Many species of animals are harmful in their effects on his welfare, and so he must find means to combat them. Some kinds of insects have been injurious to man's interests, for they feed on the plants which he cultivates, infest his herds and flocks, and transmit diseases which are often fatal. There are far too many insect pests to mention them here with any degree of completeness. Grasshoppers sometimes occur in such large numbers that they are a plague and devour everything green. Corn is infested with the corn-borer; cotton has for many years been damaged by the cottonboll weevil. Potatoes must be sprayed with poisonous solutions regularly if the crop is to be saved from the Colorado potato beetle. The Mexican bean beetle infests the bean crop, while the codling moths make apples "wormy" as their larvae grow within the developing fruit. The plum curculio makes crescent-shaped incisions in plums and lays her eggs within the fruit, where the larvae develop. Cutworms are insect larvae which cut off young plants close above the ground. Every plant grown by man has its insect pests.

This is a serious problem for man. Millions of dollars are spent each year by governmental agencies and by private individuals in the battle against insects. Thousands of tons of chemical compounds are used annually in an effort to control damage done by insects. In some places certain crops have been abandoned entirely because of insect pests; in other places farming practice has been altered sufficiently to avoid infestation of the crops by insects. Winter wheat, for example, is often not planted until late in September or early in October. By that time the danger of infestation by the Hessian fly is past. The proper date is determined each year by agricultural experimental stations, and farmers wait until the best time for planting wheat is announced. Radio and television are used to dispense information to farmers on the proper time for spraying fruit trees to kill insect pests.

Other pests affect man's well-being in many ways. Seaports must protect themselves against invasion by rats from foreign lands, particularly those which may come from Asiatic countries. Rats are infested by fleas, and these fleas may carry the germs which cause the dreaded bubonic plague. The easiest way to forestall an epidemic of the plague is to prevent the rats from leaving ships. Airplanes carrying passengers and mail may become the means of spreading pests from one part of the country to another or from one country to another. Spraying such planes with disinfectants helps to lessen the danger of spreading disease-carrying pests. Local and international plant and animal quarantine helps to prevent the spread of pests.

Mammals are often pests in a number of ways. Rats, besides spreading disease, cause an enormous economic loss, for they damage many articles other than those which they use for food. Mice are much smaller, but they also cause a great deal of destruction in homes, farmers' fields, grain elevators, and warehouses. A single rabbit may ruin many young fruit trees during the course of a single severe winter by girdling them. Woodchucks often feed on bean and pea seedlings which have just appeared above the ground, causing much loss in the field. Prairie dogs may exist in such large colonies that their burrows make a field unfit for cultivation until the prairie dogs have been destroyed. Moles tunnel their way just below the surface of the ground in seed beds and lawns, leaving a ridge of soil behind them along which the plants may die. Weasels, minks, skunks, raccoons, and other animals invade poultry houses and kill chickens in large numbers. Muskrats may cause drainage systems to become plugged up, and beaver dams may flood land which man wants to keep dry. Wolves and other large predators kill calves, colts, and sheep. Lions and tigers may develop an appetite for human flesh and become man-killers, often striking terror into native villages until they are hunted down and killed. This, however, does not mean that all the harmful mammals must be entirely exterminated. To do so would upset the biological balance to such an extent that even worse results might follow. It is necessary to keep these animals in check by wise and cautious control.

Other animals besides insects and mammals may be harmful in their effects on man. Certain protozoans cause some of the most dreaded diseases, such as amoebic dysentery and malaria, and plant diseases, as the clubroot of cabbage. Starfish cause economic loss to man by invading the oyster beds which he has established and feeding on the oysters. Roundworms are often parasites on man,

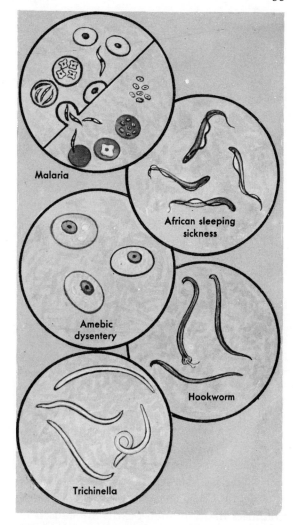

Some animal parasites (magnified). Top to bottom: malaria is caused by plasmodia; *African sleeping sickness is caused by* trypanosomes; *amoebic dysentery is caused by a certain type of* amoeba; hookworms *can stunt growth and cause severe anemia;* trichinella *in man cause trichinosis.*

causing such diseases as trichinosis and hookworm. Flatworms such as tapeworms may cause serious illness or even the death of an individual. One member of the mollusk phylum, the shipworm, is injurious to wooden ships and wooden structures which are sunk in water. These small animals are not worms at all, but are classified with oysters, snails,

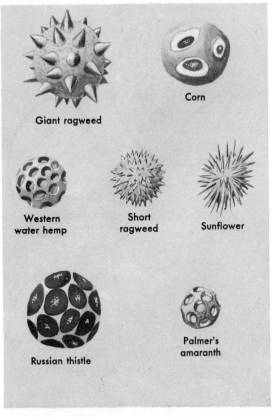

Giant ragweed

Corn

Western water hemp

Short ragweed

Sunflower

Russian thistle

Palmer's amaranth

Pollen grains (magnified).

and mussels. They may burrow into the wood to a depth of two feet, shell and all. In some countries many human deaths are caused by poisonous reptiles. This is true of India, where thousands of natives die annually of bites inflicted by the venomous cobra, which they will not kill. Coral reefs often make it impossible for a large ship to approach islands, so that communication with the large ship must be by means of smaller craft.

Some Plants Are Undesirable to Man. Plants too are sometimes pests. Many people are sensitive to the proteins found in the pollen grains of such plants as the ragweed, so that they suffer from "hay fever" during that part of the year when these plants are in blossom. Poison ivy and poison sumac cause

painful skin conditions, which sometimes become very serious if infection sets in. Other plants are obnoxious because they grow so vigorously that they crowd out cultivated crops. One of these, known as bindweed, or morning-glory, grows so rapidly and so luxuriantly that other plants have no chance against it. Because it is very hard to eradicate, it is sometimes a major pest. It can be completely killed only by digging it up with all its roots, which is no small task, since the roots are very numerous and grow deeply into the soil. Daisies will take permanent possession of a field if they are not constantly eliminated as rapidly as they appear. Hundreds of other plants grow wherever crops are cultivated, so that much of the farmer's time and energy is spent in cultivation to kill them and keep them in check. Some of these pests are so widespread that state laws have been passed making it compulsory to kill them when found on the premises.

Some plants, harmless enough in themselves, must be eradicated because they are hosts to plant diseases. Thus wheat stem rust cannot exist unless the fungus which causes it spends part of its life cycle on the common barberry. When the barberry is eliminated, the disease will cease to cause damage. The white-pine blister rust has done much damage to stands of the white pine. The microscopic plant which causes this disease must spend part of its life cycle on the leaves of the currant plant. To save the trees it has become necessary in some regions to eliminate completely the currants when they are near valuable stands of white pine. Much work of this kind is sponsored by the governmental agricultural agencies.

Microscopic plants cause much damage to man and may be classified as pests. Bacteria cause many diseases, such as tuberculosis, typhoid fever, and bacterial dysentery. Molds cause foods to spoil, while bacteria cause milk to sour and meat and other foods to decay and become unfit for human consumption. One of the mildews causes the potato disease known as late blight. Other mildews are the causes of diseases of grape and other plants, such as onions and cucumbers. Fungi attack such plants as peaches and plums. The brown rot of stone fruits is also a fungous disease.

As a result of the effect of plants and animals on man, we note that the struggle for existence affects the human species as much as any other. Man is as much a part of the struggle for existence as any other living thing; and not only does he affect other animals and plants adversely, but he is in turn affected adversely by them. He is learning that successful pest control depends upon a thorough study of the life cycle of the pest; where it lives at different stages in its life; its food and its natural predators. The same study should be made of the community of living things among which the pest lives and of the relationships existing there. Only then can man turn to measures of control without possible lasting damage to other members of the community. Pest controls force a consideration of complex human relationships as well, because the use of public money is often involved and the effects on people near and far must be carefully considered.

EXPERIENCE. *To study pests and the controls used.* Children should be helped to discover for themselves the kinds of animal and plant pests found in their own community. They may also be helped to learn ways in which man can control pests. Such a study might lead to active participation in a rat-extermination campaign, the killing of poison ivy in parks and play areas, and similar projects. In this work children might be helped to use authentic information found in books and to consult people in the community who are authorities in this field. Information might also be obtained from official government agencies. Any study of this kind should be made appropriate to the children's age and experience. Activities of this kind should be supervised by an adult.

Man Is Learning to Control Various Disease-producing Organisms. Many human ailments are caused by various plant and animal organisms. They have for centuries produced much suffering. It was not until the development of a definite science of medicine that human diseases were really understood. Many superstitions were held to explain sickness; everything from the devil to the weather was blamed. With Leeuwenhoek's discovery of bacteria during the latter part of the seventeenth century the door to the modern treatment of disease was opened, but nothing much was done until the time of Pasteur. Pasteur, a French chemist, is generally credited with the first important work on the nature of disease, and it was he who linked microorganisms to sickness. He was able to show conclusively that certain bacteria caused a disease in silkworms, and later he applied his theories to human diseases. At about the same time Robert Koch, who had been an obscure German physician in his earlier years, discovered the bacterium which causes tuberculosis. Sir Joseph Lister, an English surgeon, believed that the microorganisms discovered by Pasteur and Koch to cause diseases were probably also the cause of infections which occurred when open wounds were not properly disinfected. He set about developing means of controlling the infections which at that time invariably followed a surgical operation. His first antiseptic was a solution of carbolic acid, which to this day is used to some extent for disinfecting. Before his time hospitals had been so indescribably filthy that it is hard to imagine the conditions which were permitted to exist. The modern spotlessly clean hospital was unknown in Lister's day.

Today *immunization* against diseases is common in civilized countries, but its development has been recent. The idea of immunization is not a new one, for centuries ago people in Asiatic countries learned to inoculate themselves against smallpox. Their methods were crude, but the principle involved was correct. Smallpox vaccination was brought to the attention of European nations by the English physician Edward Jenner during the eighteenth century, who had noticed that milkmaids who suffered from cowpox never contracted smallpox. Cowpox is a disease in cattle similar to smallpox, but its effects on the human body are mild. Jenner set about vaccinating people with cowpox and found that those who were vaccinated did not contract smallpox. At first there was much public opinion against vaccination, but this has been gradually dispelled. Today smallpox is a comparatively rare disease because so large a percentage of our population has been given preventive treatment. No community is safe from an outbreak of this disease, however, until every member has been vaccinated.

Pasteur's work with sheep, dogs, and chickens made possible great advances in the control of disease organisms. He was able to prevent anthrax in sheep by inoculating healthy animals with the bacteria which cause this malady, thus enabling the sheep to build up an immunity against it. He also found that by injecting into the spinal cord of a rabbit a culture made from the nerve tissues of dogs which had rabies, he could cause the rabbit to contract the disease. Then by making a culture from the spinal cord of the rabbit and injecting it into human beings who had been bitten by rabid dogs, he found it possible to prevent the development of hydrophobia, which had been a scourge for centuries. His experimental work with hens showed him that cholera could be controlled. Pasteur was probably the greatest benefactor of mankind in all history. It has been said of him that his discoveries have saved more lives than were lost in all the Napoleonic wars.

Immunization, then, is an important step in disease control. Another important discovery was made when it was learned that some insects and other animals carry disease organisms and transmit them from one animal to another or to a human being. Development of this discovery was made by Theobald Smith, an American, who studied the Texas fever of cattle. This disease caused great losses to cattlemen in the Western states, but did not affect cattle in the Northern states. It was found that only those cattle which were parasitized by a certain tick (an arachnid) contracted the disease. This was followed by the discovery that the ticks themselves did not actually cause the disease. They carried the organisms which entered the blood of cattle when bitten by the ticks, and the organisms themselves were the direct cause. When the reasons for the disease were understood, control became an easy matter.

Many insects are the carriers of disease. Malaria and yellow fever are transmitted by mosquitoes, while African sleeping sickness is caused by a protozoan which is transmitted to human beings by the tsetse fly. Fleas may carry bubonic plague, the epidemic known in the Middle Ages as the black death. The common housefly is sometimes called the typhoid fly because of its importance in spreading typhoid fever. The list could be made much longer.

It is obvious that to control such diseases it is important to control the insects which transmit them. Malaria and yellow fever may be wiped out by making it impossible for mosquitoes to breed. This is done by draining ponds, ditches, and other places where water has a tendency to gather and become stagnant. Where drainage is impracticable, oil may be poured on the water every few days. The oil is light and consequently floats, making it impossible for the larval mosquitoes to breathe and thus exterminating them. Such measures must be carried on perpetually, especially in tropical and semitropical regions, in order that the mosquitoes may be kept permanently in check. A surface minnow, *Gambusia affinis,* has been used successfully in some parts of the world as another means of mosquito control. This minnow will feed on mosquito larvae and can live in small pools, stock-watering tanks, and cisterns, as well as lakes and rivers. Its native range is from New Jersey to Mexico. Many diseases may be avoided if flies are killed off as rapidly as they appear. Fly eradication may be made much simpler by proper garbage and sewage disposal; for this deprives the fly maggots of their food supply, so that they cannot develop to maturity. Eternal vigilance is the price of health.

Another cause of human diseases is a contaminated milk or water supply. Such diseases as typhoid fever and tuberculosis are often the direct results of using contaminated milk or water. Certain kinds of tuberculosis in human beings are caused by milk from cows which have had tuberculosis. When tuberculosis in cattle is eliminated, this type will disappear. Lack of cleanliness in the stable and in the dairy is conducive to the spread of many diseases on an epidemic scale. For this reason most of the milk sold today is pasteurized, for pasteurization kills most of the disease-producing bacteria and makes the product safe to use. Unpasteurized milk may be used when it is produced in very clean stables, is placed in sterilized containers, comes from tuberculin-tested cattle, and is handled only by men who are given periodical physical examinations to make sure that they are sufficiently healthy not to endanger the milk they are handling. Municipal, state, and federal and provincial agencies rigidly enforce sanitary and chemical standards insuring a supply of safe milk.

Another source of contamination of milk is strontium 90, which occurs as fallout from test explosions of nuclear bombs. It falls to Earth and is taken up by plants, which in turn are eaten by cows and people. The cows give milk that is widely consumed, and thus strontium 90 enters the human body. Strontium 90 is chemically similar to calcium, and like it becomes fixed in bones and teeth. In excess amounts it can cause health problems in the form of cancer and leukemia. Studies seem to indicate that the high calcium content of milk helps to cut down on the amount of strontium 90 that can be deposited in the bones and teeth. Scientists throughout the world are conducting studies of fallout and its effects, and are maintaining careful watch for signs of danger.

The purity of the water supply is far more important to the welfare of man, particularly in cities, than is generally realized. Cities like New York, Chicago, Los Angeles, Montreal, or Vancouver use so much water each day that it is difficult to conceive of the total volume. This water must be free of disease germs, for otherwise an epidemic of disease unprecedented in magnitude might break out. Every effort must be made to keep the water pure, and it must be tested in laboratories regularly for microorganisms which might cause diseases. In some cities it is customary to treat the water with chlorine in order to kill bacteria which might be present. Although the chlorine itself can sometimes be tasted in the water, it is not present in sufficient quantities to upset the normal functioning of the body (p. 168).

Man, as we have seen in this brief sketch of his activities, takes many precautions to remain in good health. He cannot relax his vigilance for even a short time, lest dire consequences follow. Life in crowded cities would be impossible unless these measures and others were taken.

EXPERIENCE. *To help children become aware of the importance of disease control.* A great many children are fully aware of all the "shots" they receive, but many may not fully understand why they receive them. They may have had little

A schematic drawing showing steps in a process commonly used in purifying water for towns and cities.

experience with disease and its results. Young children may be helped to an understanding that illness can be prevented in this way. Older children may wish to learn something of the history of immunization. In this connection, emphasize the fact that many organisms are too small to see with the naked eye and many are too small to see with a microscope. If possible they should look at a drop of pond water and a drop of tap water through a microscope. What do they see? Children may be interested to know that the diseases which attack cows, horses, and many other animals can be prevented by immunization when their cause is found.

Man Is Still Confronted by Many Health Problems. So much has been said and written about the control which man exercises

over disease-producing organisms that it becomes easy to lose sight of the fact that he is still confronted by many serious and unsolved problems. Medical science today finds itself face to face with many difficulties. There are many diseases which we do not know how to prevent. Tuberculosis, if diagnosed in its early stages, can be cured; but it cannot be prevented. Furthermore, this scourge is far more prevalent than is generally understood, and many people die of it each year. Some persons are still opposed to various health measures, little realizing that they are jeopardizing not only their own welfare but that of others.

Cancer is one of the diseases against which progress has been relatively slow until recently. There is considerable hope that great progress may be made in the treatment and eventual control of cancer in the near future. Radioactive isotopes, hormones, chemicals, and radiation are all useful in its treatment. Early detection is emphasized repeatedly, and surgery is often successful. There is much room for discussion about the causes and nature of this disease, and there is no certain method of treating it in its more serious phases. This is due to the fact that it is not caused by a microorganism, so far as is known. Heart diseases are receiving much attention, but there is much to be done before that particular problem can be said to be solved. Indeed, it may be said that medical science has just begun to meet the problems of health. Various types of mental disorders seem to be more frequent than ever and demand much investigation before more progress in their treatment can be made.

One of the greatest problems confronting mankind today is that of the so-called social, or venereal, diseases. Some authorities have estimated that 10 per cent of the population of the United States are suffering from diseases of this nature. Despite this fact, the general public has been apathetic. The two most prevalent veneral diseases are gonorrhea and syphilis, both of which are insidious in their effects on the human being, and both of which lead to a general breakdown of the individual. The seriousness of this problem cannot be overestimated; it calls for an educational program that must be well organized and nationwide in scope if it is to be effective. Many agencies are already at work, but much more needs to be done. If 10 per cent of the people suffered from diphtheria or whooping cough, drastic measures would be enforced. Syphilis and gonorrhea, if not properly treated, are far greater evils. Yet, despite this fact, they have not received the attention they merit.

Another means of controlling diseases which man has learned to use is the proper disposal of such wastes as rubbish, sewage, and garbage. In many of the large cities rubbish and

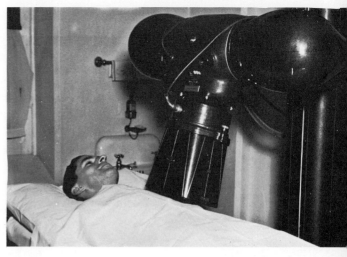

Many diseases are treated with X rays. (*H. Armstrong Roberts.*)

garbage are collected at the expense of the municipality and disposed of in huge incinerators. Sewage is often treated chemically, so that the bacteria and other living things in it are killed and can no longer be the cause of diseases. No city of any size could long escape an epidemic without proper waste disposal (pp. 168, 420).

In those cities and towns where rubbish and garbage are not properly disposed of, one frequently finds great numbers of rats, mice, cockroaches, and flies. A visit to the town dumping ground, if such exists, would be a worthwhile trip for boys and girls, and for their parents. Such places are usually heavily populated with rats, mice, cockroaches, and flies. The presence of these pests has a direct effect upon the town and its people. If one talks with the merchants and the housewives, he usually finds that they sustain a great economic loss due to the activities of such pests. Investigation may also show a high rate of typhus or typhoid fever in the community. In any place where man lives there is a high correlation between economic loss, certain diseases carried by rats, mice, cockroaches, and flies, and the methods of waste disposal. Proper waste-disposal methods can be put into practice for a fraction of the dollars lost over a period of years due to such pests, if the citizens of a town are willing to work together on the problem.

EXPERIENCE. *To help children to become aware that there is still much to be done to improve health and sanitation.* Children may notice that flies collect on a piece of garbage. Their attention may be called to the fact that the flies may then crawl over food, carrying to it the dirt collected on their feet from the garbage and elsewhere. They may be able to suggest ways that are used to keep flies from food. Can they think of better ways?

Older children may wish to discuss how their community might be made more healthful. In connection with sanitation, the children might like to learn how the water comes into their school and how the waste water is carried away. The custodian may be of some assistance here, for he will know the location and kind of pipes, where the water comes from, and where the waste water is deposited.

Man Develops New Types of Plants and Animals
Suited to His Purposes

Thousands of years ago, when culture and civilization were still in a rudimentary stage, man learned that he could not depend on wild plants and animals to furnish him with a constant source of food. When a tribal group settled for a time in a certain area, it remained until food was scarce and then migrated to new regions. Eventually, however, man learned to take with him the seeds of certain plants and to plant them at the proper season, so that he was more or less sure of some food under any circumstances. With the domestication of animals he found it easy to obtain meat whenever he wanted it, but the problem of feeding his animals during the winter season then arose. This led to an extension of his agricultural activities.

What progress man has made has been due to the fact that he has never been satisfied with his environment. He is constantly making efforts to improve everything about him which affects him to any degree. This tendency must have manifested itself early in the history of the species, and there has been constant improvement along every line of human endeavor. Both the plants and the animals which man has cultivated have come under the influence of this tendency.

Farmers Are Practicing Selective Breeding More and More. Agriculture today has reached a more efficient level than ever before because of the application of scientific principles. It has long been known that like produces like, but today we find the principle applied in the development of better plant and animal varieties. For example, the cattle of the Middle Ages were not like the cattle we find on farms today. There was no such thing as a dairy breed and a beef breed. Instead, the same herd of cattle was used as a source of meat and milk, and to do such work as plowing and other farm tasks. The animals were small and produced milk for only a short time after the birth of their calves.

Today we find that some varieties of cattle are designated as milk breeds, such as the Holstein, Jersey, and Ayrshire. By selecting only those cattle which conformed to a certain standard and which produced the greatest quantities of milk, these breeds were developed. When they were bred, care was exercised that only the better specimens should reproduce, so that their good characteristics were intensified. Other breeds, such as the Hereford and the Shorthorn, were developed specifically for the economic production of large quantities of meat. No particular attention was paid to the amount of milk they produced. By selecting those individuals which best represented ideal beef cattle, man has created a distinct variety which is unfit for commercial milk production but which yields a larger quantity of meat than ever before. Some varieties were bred for the distinct purpose of producing milk and yet retaining some of the qualities of beef cattle, so that their meat is of fine texture and quality. Such a breed is known as a dual-purpose breed. It must not be assumed that the meat of dairy cattle is unfit for human consumption. The dairy cow is a specialization for a given purpose.

Another example of selective breeding may be seen in the several types of horses which have been developed. Race horses have been developed from smaller, faster stock. By breeding mares of great speed with stallions whose records on the race track have been outstanding, the quality of speed is intensified in the variety. If the offspring should prove to be slow, it would not be used in breeding. Gradually a speedier breed would be developed.

Man has domesticated and trained many animals.

More than one hundred varieties of dogs have been developed by man, each of them along special lines. All dogs are members of the same species, but by selective breeding they have come to have a wide range of characteristics, as comparison of a Great Dane or a Saint Bernard with a Pekingese shows. Each variety was developed with a special function in mind; and since the function made necessary the development of certain characteristics, dogs with the desired features were used in breeding and others were eliminated.

Sheep, like cattle, horses, and dogs, have been bred for special purposes. Some varieties produce a fine grade of wool, while others are bred primarily for mutton. Hogs are differentiated into lard and bacon types. In each instance selective breeding has resulted in the achievement of some special quality which man deems desirable.

A similar development has occurred among cultivated plants. Plant-breeders are constantly on the alert for improvements which can be made by *selective breeding*. The farmer, by selecting his seed corn from vigorous, early-maturing, large-eared, and disease-free stalks improves the yield and resistance to disease of this important crop. When the white man first planted apple trees in North Dakota, most of them did not live. The winters were severe, and the young trees were not adapted to such conditions. Those that did live, generally produced fruit of an inferior quality. By planting many thousands of apple seeds each year, however, a tree was found that was adapted to conditions of that particular environment and at the same time produced a fine fruit. By grafting scions from this tree, it has become the parent of most of the apple trees in the state.

Similar selection has been practiced on other plants. In some cases it is desirable to select plants immune from diseases. With other plants, which take a long time to mature, the aim of selective breeding is to

Man has domesticated and improved many plants.

develop varieties that ripen quickly. A difference of ten days in the period needed for development is often important, sometimes making the difference between a successful crop and a failure. Still other plants are developed for certain qualities necessary to make them ship well. Strawberries, for instance, must not be too juicy, or they will spoil in shipment. Tomatoes which are firm and fleshy need to be grown if they are to be used in distant markets. These are only some of the reasons why selective breeding is used in the development of plants.

Varieties of Plants and Animals Are Sometimes Crossed to Produce New Forms. Sometimes two separate varieties of living things have characteristics which are desirable. Man in some instances is able to bring about a combination of these in the same individual, producing what is known as a *hybrid*. Hybrids are produced by breeding one variety with another. If a mare is bred to a jackass, the offspring is a hybrid, a mule. Hybrids generally are incapable of reproduction, although this is

not true of all of them. Mules, however, cannot be bred, so that to keep the supply of mules constant, the mare must always be bred to the jackass. Attempts have been made to cross cattle with the bison, and a few times such attempts have succeeded. The resultant offspring is called a *cattalo,* but it has not proved useful. Zebras have been mated with horses occasionally, and dogs have been known to mate with wolves. These are examples of cross breeding between *closely related species.*

Hybrids are often produced in plants. The process of breeding together two varieties has been used with great success in producing new kinds of wheat adapted for certain purposes. The Marquis wheat, grown extensively in western Canada, where the growing season is short, was produced by crossing a variety known as Red Fife with a wheat imported from India, the Hard Red Calcutta. The Red Fife wheat is grown in our Western states and is a spring wheat, which means that it is planted in the spring and produces a crop the same year. The Hard Red Calcutta ripens very early. By using the pollen of the Red Fife to pollinate the Red Calcutta, a new variety was produced which ripened before the frosts and yielded well. The development of this new (Marquis) wheat was an important factor in making possible the settlement of farmers from the province of Manitoba to Alberta. Today Canada produces millions of bushels of Marquis wheat. These are examples of cross breeding between *varieties within a species.*

EXPERIENCE. *To help children become aware that man is learning to develop characteristics in plants and animals that he wants.* Children all recognize that animals such as dogs and cats are of different sizes and colors; some dogs are strong and can run fast, and some dogs are naturally better watchdogs than others. Their attention may be called to differences in plants, too. If possible, children should be encouraged to visit a county fair or a plant and animal show where plants and animals are exhibited and judged. (The length of the visit should be appropriate to the age of the children.) Most of the plants and animals on exhibit will have been bred or developed with certain goals in mind. For instance, cows that give large quantities of milk, or cattle for beef; sheep whose wool is especially long; corn that will produce large, tender, even kernels, or wheat that will produce many seeds within a short time, so that it will produce a crop where the growing season is very short. These are only examples of the many goals set by plant and animal breeders.

New Varieties of Plants and Animals Sometimes Arise Spontaneously.

Occasionally, for reasons which are still obscure, an old and well-known plant or animal variety will give rise to an entirely new type. Such a new type is called a *mutation,* or a "sport." Mutations are not the result of experimentation by man, but he is often able to use them to his advantage. Plant-breeders have noticed in their fields that occasionally a plant which has grown from ordinary seed has characteristics markedly different from what is expected in that variety. If these characteristics are desirable, the seed is gathered from the mature plant, or cuttings are taken from it, so that it may be propagated further. Thus a new variety may be established. Mutations occur among animals also. A famous example is a short-legged variety of sheep, originating from a mutation which occurred in a flock of normal sheep.

Sometimes the mutations have undesirable characteristics, and the new variety is not perpetuated. Those plant mutations which are weak and cannot compete successfully with other plants are eliminated. If they are too slow in maturing, or if they produce fruit or seed inferior in quality, they are not useful. Mutations differ from hybrids in that they are generally capable of reproduction. They breed true to type; that is, the offspring resemble the parents in most characteristics. The hybrids which are capable of reproduction generally produce offspring that are worthless, for they do not transmit to their young enough of their own characteristics to make them worth keeping. Plant hybrids sometimes produce fruits with no seeds, so that the variety cannot be continued except by grafting.

EXPERIENCE. *To bring to the attention of older children that plants and animals having new characteristics may arise from an unusual plant or animal that appears.* This might best be brought to the attention of older children through a brief summary of Burbank's work with plants; or if there is a plant or animal breeder in the community he might be willing to tell the children of finding an unusual plant or animal and why its characteristics were unusual and desirable. Children who live on farms may have first-hand knowledge of new varieties of plants or animals and be willing to discuss them with the class.

Part IV

THE
ENERGY
OF THE
UNIVERSE

CHAPTER 22

Energy to Do the World's Work

There Is Energy Throughout the Universe

No matter in what direction man turns his studies, he finds bodies in motion. The stars, as we have seen, are in motion, traveling with tremendous speeds (Chapter 7). Earth and the other planets revolve about the sun, while the sun itself speeds onward through space, carrying them with it. The galaxy, the Milky Way, of which our solar system is a part, is in motion. In fact, it is motion which keeps the planets in their places, whirling about the sun like so many rocks at the ends of invisible strings of gravitation which tie them to the sun.

If we turn to Earth, we find that it, too, is in motion, turning about its own axis at the same time that it is moving about the sun. Wind and water move over the face of Earth, wearing away rocks and carrying the worn-away material to new locations, there to be changed by natural forces into new rocks. Even the apparently solid crust of Earth rises and sinks, forming new mountains and new shores in adjusting itself to the changing weight of the rocks.

Earth has been described as moving in a vast curve through space-time. As it moves, it encounters moving objects of many kinds. There are many meteors (p. 223) and other planetary fragments entering Earth's atmos-

phere. Most of these are small and do not reach the lower parts of the atmosphere. There are also ultra-high-frequency radio impulses from the radio stars, and light from the sun and stars. In addition, there are the high-energy particles known as cosmic rays.

Many scientists are attempting to find the source of cosmic rays. They have a number of ideas to explain where such rays come from, but at present there is much to learn. It appears that there may be great magnetic fields out in space which may help to generate the rays. One thing is clear, Earth receives these rays from all directions.

All of this reveals that space out beyond our atmosphere is not empty. There is evidence of matter and energy in space. In a real sense, energy seems to pervade the entire universe, in spite of its vastness.

After having looked at the universe for energy, we now turn to the atom. Here, too, we have evidence of movement and energy.

Studying the atom, once considered to be the smallest particle of matter, solid, hard, and indivisible, scientists have concluded that it, too, is a complex structure of parts in motion.

Later in this chapter we shall learn that heat is the result of the motion of molecules, the small particles of which a substance is composed (p. 722). From this we may see that heat is related to things in motion.

We ourselves, in common with the other animals, move. Even in the deepest sleep our hearts beat, our lungs expand and contract, our bodies remain warm. When we cease to move, we also cease to exist.

A body which is in motion is able to do *work*. For example, if we throw a stone and hit a target, the target may be moved, or it may be dented, or the stone may be broken. If we should miss the target, the stone may strike the ground and dig a little hole. In any case, work has been done. A body which is capable of doing work is said to possess energy. This statement does not tell what energy is, but it tells what energy does.

Inasmuch as motion seems to be one of the characteristics of the universe, it may be said that energy is distributed throughout space.

As geologists pursue their studies backward in time, they find evidences that many millions or even billions of years ago the same forces were at work on Earth as are at work on it to-day. Motion and energy were present, and work was being done in eroding and rebuilding. There was no point in time, so far as we know, at which energy was lacking.

From the time when man first appeared on Earth, he used the energy of his own muscles to do his work, just as other animals do. Until a comparatively recent date, his only additional source of energy was from the muscles of such animals as the horse, the ox, and the donkey, which he harnessed and forced to work for him. Work under such conditions was slow and laborious, and left the average man little time or inclination for creative activity. A very small group of people were freed for intellectual pursuits by the muscle labor of a great many slaves, who contributed only their muscular energy to society. As simple machines were invented, man was able to increase his output of work.

During about the last three centuries man has learned to make effective use of natural forces other than muscle power, such as wind, water, and fuels. This has made great amounts of energy available to do his work and has changed the course of civilization. During World War II, man found means of releasing the tremendous energy stored within the atom. By tapping the natural flow of energy and using it to do his work, man has made it possible in considerable measure to free himself from manual labor.

But mankind has not yet learned to use his discoveries for his greatest good. For example, modern warfare uses the latest machines, which depend on energy, for spreading death and destruction. It would seem to be of value to a democracy for children to learn something about this universal thing called energy in order to use it wisely and control its use democratically (p. 36).

Children and Energy. Energy is widespread throughout the universe, and therefore is a significant factor every moment of a child's life. Years before he even learns to use the word *energy* he has experiences with it (Chapter 1). He starts using energy before he enters the world; in the prenatal stage he is using his mother's energy. He is developing experientially with his own energy, as well as with that of other people and objects. For example, he may see that it requires energy to push a toy boat down under the surface of the water, and he may see that another form of energy keeps pushing it back up. In addition to having many experiences with energy, a child may observe it around him many times a day. While looking out of a window at home or at school, he may observe the energy of a storm, or the movements of an airplane, or listen to the sounds of other people. By the time children come to school for the first time, they bring with them considerable experiential knowledge of energy.

If one were asked to describe children, he would immediately think of the continuous drives of children from their moment of waking until they sink into sleep. A child is an energy system, and in all the universe we do not find its equal. Almost all the games that prove successful with children involve considerable activity.

The term *energy* has, through the years, become increasingly meaningful to younger children. We can say that it is almost a household word. This is undoubtedly a result of the fact that man, for the first time in history, has more energy available than he can use. The way in which man controls this energy may determine whether democracies can prevail.

It is one of the major tasks of the public schools to help children to be intelligent, responsible, and resourceful with energy. Every parent and teacher is aware of the tremendous drive of the energy within a child and of the importance of helping the child to direct his energy along lines that are constructive for himself and society.

Earth and the Stars Are in Motion. Not only is Earth moving about the sun, but the sun itself is also moving. This does not affect our life on Earth in the slightest (so far as we know), because, as the sun moves, it carries Earth and all the other planets with it. It is a little like a railroad train. As the engine moves, it pulls the cars after it; but the people inside the cars are free to walk about in normal fashion. If the track were very smooth, all the shades drawn, and the cars soundproof, people inside the cars would not know whether the train was in motion or standing still.

Just what caused the sun (or any other star) to start moving, no one knows. Some event or events possibly happened in the universe billions of years ago about which we can scarcely make a satisfactory explanation (p. 245).

Energy is required to start an object moving; but once it is moving, it will move on forever unless something stops it. Living on Earth, as we do, we have no example of this; for there is always something to stop a moving object—the friction of the air, if nothing else. In space, however, there is little to stop a moving object, so that once the stars were started moving they continued to move. There are no fixed objects in space.

EXPERIENCE. *To show centripetal force.* For this Experience provide plenty of room and a place where nothing can be injured. A ball or sponge swinging in different directions can be released to move toward ceiling, wall, or floor.

Securely fasten one end of a string 3 to 6 feet long to a tennis ball or sponge. (1) Let a child swing the ball around in a circle. (2) Then let him stand on the end of the string and roll or throw the ball away from him. When the string draws tight, the ball will go in a circle. The string pulls inward on the ball. It acts as a central or centripetal force, keeping the ball at a fixed distance from the center. Children can feel this force on the hand holding the string. (3) Now have the child holding the string swing the ball around and then let go. The ball will fly off in a straight line again, not outward from the one holding the string, but in the direction it was moving at the moment the string was released. It moves along a line that is *tangent* to the circle.

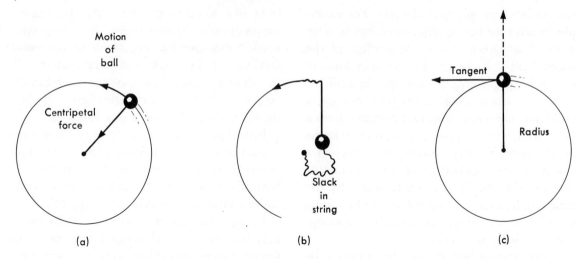

(a) *The string represents the centripetal force that compels the ball to move in a circle.* (b) *The ball when thrown moves in a straight line until it has taken up the slack, then it moves in a circle.* (c) *If the string is released, the ball flies off along a tangent to the circle.*

Experience. *To show tangent motion.* (Experience, p. 238).

Centripetal and Centrifugal Force. The Experiences above show that an object tends to move in a straight line unless it is pulled aside by a force. The string exerts a *centripetal* (center-seeking) force that pulls the ball toward the center of the circle. The ball is thought of as exerting an equal force directly away from the center. This force is called *centrifugal* (center-fleeing) force.

Although it is often said that centrifugal force pulls the ball away, it is more correct to say that the ball flies off at a tangent because of the failure of the centripetal force to keep it in a circular path (p. 237).

Athletes, when throwing the hammer (a round weight on the end of a chain), whirl and then release it, and in so doing make use of centrifugal force. Possibly the children have seen or read of such contests.

Whirl a pail partly full of water around your head, as shown. The water, instead of spilling, will be kept in the pail by centrifugal force.

The Particles of Which the Universe Is Composed Attract One Another. We have said that the sun exerts a force which tends to pull Earth toward it; in other words, the sun and Earth attract each other. It was one of New-

Centrifugal force keeps the water from spilling.

ton's great contributions when he developed the idea that every particle of matter in the universe attracts every other particle. Newton's *law of gravitation* tells us that the force of attraction between two particles or bodies is greater the larger their masses, and the nearer together the bodies are. Astronomers show how the planets revolve around the sun, and how the moons revolve around the planets, through the law of gravitation. The force of gravitation causes objects to fall on Earth, keeps the planets in their orbits, and causes tides. Even though the effects of gravity are felt in Earth and in the atmosphere, the effect upon the ocean is most evident. Tides rise as a result of the attraction of the moon and the sun. When both pull together in the same direction, the force is particularly marked.

That every particle of matter attracts every other particle is literally true. Your left hand attracts your right. You are attracted by the desk, the ceiling, the moon, and the stars. On the other hand Earth, being so much larger and heavier than any objects on its surface, has an attraction which is so great that these smaller attractions are not noticeable. Everything with which we are familiar is attracted by Earth. We express this truth when we say that things fall to Earth unless something prevents them from so doing. Water runs downhill because of Earth's gravitation. We can slide downhill on sleds or skis because of the same force. Of course it is obvious that nothing can fall down that has not first been lifted up, and work must be done to lift anything. We shall return to this point later.

Before the seventeenth century most people believed that heavy objects would fall faster than light ones. This was probably in part a result of the teachings of Aristotle. The words of this great Greek philosopher had come, in medieval times, to be regarded as authoritative on everything. In fact, an argument that was used against scientific truths as they were

discovered was that Aristotle did not mention them or that Aristotle had said otherwise. This acceptance, for two thousand years, of the words of one man as authoritative on everything may seem incomprehensible to us, but we shall not understand the working of the medieval mind or the great change which the methods of science have wrought in men's methods of thinking unless we attempt to understand such an attitude. Furthermore, we need to be careful to see that we have not simply transferred our allegiance from Aristotle to some other man whose words we may accept just as blindly.

The ancient Greeks, though great philosophers, did little experimenting. Aristotle apparently did not experiment to find out what really happened when weights fell; he merely thought about it. His conclusion seemed reasonable, but unfortunately it was wrong. If he had experimented, he would have probably discovered what Galileo discovered, eighteen hundred years later, by the celebrated experiment which tradition—perhaps mistakenly—says he performed from the leaning tower of Pisa. Galileo proved (about 1630–1638) that all objects fall with the same speed, regardless of weight, if we neglect the resistance of the air. Of course objects of large size and little weight (for example, a feather, a snowflake, a sheet of paper) have more difficulty in passing through the air. The air holds them back, and they fall more slowly. A feather and a coin will fall together in a tube from which the air has been removed.

Galileo's greatest contribution did not lie in the things he discovered about falling bodies or in proving Aristotle wrong. His greatest contribution was that he consciously and systematically experimented with a view to finding out information. He was among the first to make use of experimentation. He not only used logical reasoning and quiet thinking through of problems, but checked his results by experimentation, and accepted only those which were in accordance with experimental evidence.

Ever since Galileo, science has been based upon experimentation and observation rather than upon acceptance of dogmatic statements. After Galileo, ideas became subject to challenge at any time, for experimentation became an ongoing process (Chapters 3 and 5).

Obviously an object which is falling is able to do work. We have said that a body which is able to do work possesses energy. Therefore falling objects possess energy. This energy may appear to be traceable to gravity. But before we can use the energy of a falling object we must do work on the object to raise it to the height from which it falls. This work must be done against gravity. Therefore the energy which appears in a falling object is really the energy originally put into raising it. Gravity makes energy available. It is not a *source* of energy.

A ball which is thrown straight upward reaches the ground again with practically the same amount of energy which was used in throwing it. When a ball is thrown horizontally, it follows a path like the one shown in the illustration. It moves horizontally because of the energy given it by the thrower. At the same time it drops lower and lower, owing to the force of gravity. If two balls are thrown horizontally by two boys who are the same height above the ground, but one is thrown with twice as much velocity as the other, they will both strike the ground at the same time. They have equal distances to fall. One, however, will have gone twice as far away from the thrower as the other. This is an illustration of bodies under the influence of two forces acting at the same time.

If a ball is thrown upward at an angle, it will rise to a certain point before it begins to fall. Hence it will have farther to fall and therefore will have time to travel a greater distance from the thrower before striking the ground. In aiming a gun at a distant object, one must determine mathematically the angle

A fast bullet will travel straighter than a slow ball.

at which to aim it so that the shell will have time to reach the target before it hits the ground. A gun is never pointed directly at a target. On small guns, such as rifles, the sights are arranged so that when a person looks through them at the target, the gun is pointed a little above it.

A rocket derives its power from the force of hot gases expanding under tremendous pressure in a combustion chamber. The gases are allowed to escape freely at the rear, but continue to strike against the forward end of the combustion chamber, thus driving the rocket forward (p. 768). Children should feel free to discuss this subject in school. The older children can secure information from current events.

In order to be able to leave the surface of Earth, rocket motors must make available sufficient energy to overcome the major part of the force of Earth's gravitation. To do this a vehicle must attain a speed of about five miles per second. Even at this speed the vehicle can not leave the vicinity of Earth, but will proceed out into space until its outward movement is changed to a circular one by the force of Earth's gravitation drawing it back. In that case, the rocket might continue on around and around Earth forever, just as the moon does. In order to get away completely, a rocket would have to leave with a speed of about seven miles per second.

Once out in space, the next problem is that of getting back (p. 240).

Although scientists have been studying gravitation for a long time, they have not been able to explain what it is or what causes it. When a physicist drops his pencil, he has only a very hazy idea why it falls, although he can describe the fall in the most complicated terms. Yet gravitation is very common. It is useful to us every second of our lives. It is one of the first forces a child learns to utilize. (Chapter 1.) Suppose that gravitation ceased to work for only five seconds!

The plants and animals on Earth are adapted to the constant pull of gravity. Their organs and structures have evolved under that force throughout the long history of living things. For example, the roots of plants grow downward under this force, while the stems grow upward. The internal organs of the higher animals are supported against a constant downward pull.

EXPERIENCE. *Gravity affects all objects around us.* The following Experiences deal with gravity as such. Later we shall see that gravity plays a large part in man's activities on Earth. It is both a hindrance and a help. See particularly the section on friction and the description of water wheels (pp. 743, 771) and the section on the production of electricity from water power (p. 819). Note also the part played by the gravitational attraction of Earth for the atmosphere (p. 426).

EXPERIENCE. *Gravity pulls objects toward Earth.* Let the children suspend various objects on strings, and then cut the strings. Probably no curiosity will be aroused when the objects fall. Ask the children why they fall.

EXPERIENCE. *Force is required to overcome gravity.* To enable children to become acquainted with the force of gravity, let them try lifting heavy objects and note the amount of muscular force required to overcome gravity.

EXPERIENCE. *Objects which require more energy to lift have more energy when they fall.* Have the children lift a small pebble and a fairly large stone from the floor to a table. Then have them push these objects off, one at a time, and allow them to strike the flat side of a tin can, such as one in which varnish is sold. Note that the pebble dents the can little, if any, while the heavy stone puts a considerable dent in it. This experiment is very crude and has in it considerable opportunity for error; there-

Delicate balances.

fore two objects quite different in weight should be chosen.

EXPERIENCE. *Balance.* Children are interested in problems involving balance. An object is balanced when its center of gravity is at its lowest possible point. Any object acts as though all its weight were concentrated at one point, known as the *center of gravity*. Roughly speaking, the center of gravity is likely to be located in the region where most of the weight is. When this point is in such a position that any tipping of the object would raise the center of gravity, the object is *balanced*. In terms of energy, energy must be used to raise the center of gravity in overturning the object. For example, a box rests securely on its side, top, or bottom, because when we attempt to tip it over, we must raise it somewhat. Let the children experiment with tipping a box over and see for themselves.

When we roll a ball on a level surface, we neither raise nor lower the center of gravity. The center of gravity of a ball is at its geometrical center. As a result, a ball on a level surface remains in whatever position we place it. If we stick some modeling clay at any point on a smooth ball, the ball will tend to roll until the clay is as low as it can go.

There are a number of toys which illustrate the conditions necessary for balance. One of these is a doll with a rounded bottom. When the doll is upset, it immediately rights itself. By handling this doll in playing with it, children can easily feel that the bottom is weighted. Careful observation as the doll is tipped reveals that tipping raises the weight, which falls again when the doll is released. Another toy has a horse and rider, or some similar figure. Fastened under the horse by means of a curved rod is a weight, often a ball of wood. The horse can be set on his hind legs on the edge of a table with the weight below the table and remain perfectly balanced there. It can easily be seen that the weight hangs at its lowest possible point. When we rock in a rocking chair, we "shift our weight" (really our center of gravity) slightly, causing the chair to rock. Examination of any object which shows no tendency to tip over reveals that work must be done and weight raised in order to overturn it. The more work that must be done—that is, the more weight that must be raised and the farther it must be raised—the harder it is to tip over an object. It is harder to tip over an armchair than a high stool.

EXPERIENCE. *Gravity and young children.* Young children are interested in gravity. Help them to recognize the experiences with gravity in their lives. Gravity holds them to Earth. Rain falls to Earth. Water runs downhill.

A chair will rock as we shift our center of gravity.

When we let go of a pencil it falls. They have learned to look down for something that is lost. When they drink water it goes down their throats.

EXPERIENCE. *The air resists the movement of objects through it.* The effect of air resistance may well enter at this point. It may be shown by taking two similar pieces of ordinary writing paper and crumpling one of them into a ball. Drop the crumpled one at the same time as the flat one, and notice how much more slowly and erratically the flat one falls. Drop a piece of paper edgewise, and note that sometimes it falls very rapidly; but if it turns sidewise, it slows down in its fall. A feather is so constructed that it falls slowly, owing to the resistance of the air.

Scientists do not usually accept the results of one experiment only. Repeat the experiment several times and note whether the results are always the same. If not, discuss the reasons.

The Experiences can be observed with the experimenter standing on a chair or table in order to provide a little greater distance for the object to fall to the floor (or ground if done out of doors). Repeat with coins of different weights and sizes. Repeat with balls of different sizes and weights. Keep in mind that air resistance will slow up light objects more than heavy objects. All heavier objects like pebbles, coins, and so forth should fall in just about the same way.

EXPERIENCE. *A falling weight has energy.* Children may occasionally have opportunity to observe a drop-hammer type of pile-driver during building operations. In this type a heavy weight is raised by an engine and then dropped on the pile which is being driven into the ground. The energy for driving the piles comes from the falling weight, which in turn gets its energy from the engine which raises it. A pile-driver has the advantage that its operations can be easily seen from a considerable

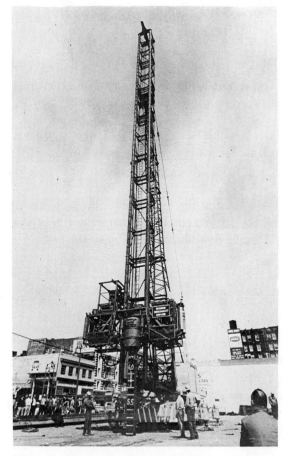

Instead of a heavy weight being used to hammer the pile into the ground, this machine uses energy to vibrate the pile—making the soil under its tip flow away and thus allowing the pile to quickly sink into the soil. This pile was sunk 52 feet into San Francisco soil in three minutes. (Wide World Photos.)

distance. Not all pile-drivers, however, are of this type.

EXPERIENCE. *Running water can do work.* Water in running downhill under the force of gravity is able to transport soil, small rocks, etc. During a rainstorm observe the many small streams of water running downhill and carrying sand and mud. If there is a creek or brook nearby, observe how the water cuts the banks away in some places and builds them up in others. Gullies are caused by running water.

Water pressure.

The source of the energy of running water is the agency which carried it to the top of the hill in the first place, namely the sun.

EXPERIENCE. *Water has energy which is due to its depth.* Punch about four small holes, one above the other in the side of a gallon can. If the can is filled with water, the stream from the lowest hole will have more force than those from the higher holes. The water at the bottom of the can is pressed by the weight of all the water above it.

EXPERIENCE. *Energy is required to push floating objects under water.* Young children playing with objects in a basin of water discover that some objects float while others sink. Energy is required to sink the floating objects and to hold them under water.

Energy for Earth

The energy which, perhaps, is most important to man is the energy which he uses here on Earth to do his work. In the following pages we shall learn something about how man harnesses energy, transforms it, and puts it to work.

The Forms of Energy. It has previously been said that a body which is able to do work possesses energy. Thus far in this book the energy which has been discussed has been in the form of something in motion. A moment's thought will show that this is not the only form in which energy can exist. Energy can exist in several forms: thermal or heat energy, sound energy, muscular and mechanical energy, electrical energy, chemical energy, nuclear energy, and radiant energy. Of these, light energy is the best-known form. A lump of coal, for example, if burned under a boiler, can make steam, which, in turn, can be used to set an engine in motion. Although the lump of coal is not itself in motion, it obviously possesses energy, since it is able to do work. Similarly a weight resting on a table had energy supplied to it when it was lifted to the table, and is able to do work if it is allowed to fall. The energy of actual motion is called *kinetic* (which means "moving") *energy,* while the other form, which exists as the potential ability to produce motion, because of its position, or the energy that is stored within, is called *potential energy.* Obviously one kind can be transformed into the other, as in the case of the lump of coal when burned or the weight when allowed to fall. These are examples of potential energy being changed into kinetic energy. An illustration of the latter would be the change which takes place when the burning of gasoline in the cylinder of an automobile engine is changed into kinetic energy which moves the pistons and, in turn, the automobile.

For the remainder of this discussion, the word *energy* will be used to mean either potential or kinetic energy. The foregoing explanation was introduced merely to show that an object does not need to be in actual motion in order to possess energy.

The classification which we shall henceforth use is based on the way energy appears rather than on whether something is moving or not.

Heat Energy. If we rub our hands together, they become warm. If we sandpaper wood, the sandpaper and the wood become warm. "Floor burns" result from sliding on gymnasium floors. A nail gets hot as it is drawn from wood. In fact, when any two substances are rubbed together, heat is produced. Experiments have been devised to show that the amount of heat produced in this way is exactly in proportion to the amount of work that is done in rubbing the two substances together. This indicates that the energy which is applied in rubbing is converted into heat. In addition to methods of producing heat energy that have already been discussed, such as utilizing mechanical, chemical, and electrical energy, there are other forms of energy, such as radiant and nuclear energy, that can be transferred into heat energy. Heat energy, likewise, may be transferred into other forms of energy.

Heat, then, is a form of energy. Heat was not always considered as a form of energy, however. It was once thought of as a separate substance called *caloric,* which was added to bodies when they became hot, and which was taken away when they became cool. The form of energy called heat energy is explained in the following paragraphs.

Every substance is composed of extremely small particles, called molecules, which in turn are composed of atoms and their still smaller parts. We have already had occasion to refer to these (pp. 375–377, 440–443). We shall refer to them again when we discuss magnetism. (In fact, an understanding of the principle that all substances are composed of molecules and atoms will be found to help a very great deal in understanding many phenomena.) In this explanation one may use either the word *atom* or the word *molecule.*

These molecules are believed to be in constant motion. In a solid they move more or less about one spot, while in a liquid they move about more freely. In a gas they move still more freely.

The hotter the molecules are, the faster they move. As the molecules in a solid move faster, the solid expands because more space is required for this movement. As the molecules move still faster, they lose their places and move about, and we say the solid has melted. Since heat is believed to be the cause of this motion of the molecules, we see that heat energy is really no different from the other forms of energy, which set bodies in motion, except that the bodies moved are smaller. There is heat energy involved in weather changes, in the growth of living things, in maintaining the body temperatures of birds and mammals (including man), in muscular power, and in using machines. Children have evidence of heat energy in themselves and in many events in their environment.

Heat, as we all know, may be produced by burning. The process of burning is a process in which fuel is chemically combined with oxygen. It is the need of a flame for oxygen which makes it possible to extinguish a fire by suffocating it. The heat energy from a fire is, then, a result of chemical change. The energy was originally locked up in some way in the fuel and the oxygen. (p. 373.)

Heat may also be produced by electricity. We make use of this fact in toasters, irons, heaters, broilers, and other appliances. Many of the experiments suggested in this chapter can be performed with electric stoves. The electric lamp, which is intended to give light, also gives off a good deal of heat. Lamps are often used to keep aquariums warm. The energy which appears as heat comes from the electricity used.

If we explain heat as the energy of motion of molecules, we can also explain other phenomena of heated bodies. For instance, we know from experience that if we put one end of a poker in the fire and hold the other end, the end in our hand soon gets warm and finally hot. The molecules in the end of the rod that is in the fire move faster and bump into the molecules next to them. The bumps start

Active play requires more space than quiet play.

these molecules moving, and they in turn set other molecules in motion. Eventually the molecules in the end of the rod that we are holding begin to move faster and faster, and we say that the heat has spread to that end. It is somewhat as though we had a number of marbles resting together on a level table, and we threw another marble into them. The energy of motion of the thrown marble would set the others in motion.

All substances expand when heated (with the exception of a few cases, such as water between 32° and 39°F.), some more than others. We can explain this by saying that molecules in rapid motion take up more room than molecules in slow motion. This is somewhat like a group of children who require more room when playing an active game than they do when sitting quietly.

Heat and the Thermometer. The thermometer does not measure the *amount* of heat. A spoonful of boiling water obviously has less energy and contains less heat than a barrel full of boiling water, yet a thermometer in one would read exactly the same as a thermometer in the other. A thermometer tells not how much heat is in a substance, but *how hot it is.* It does this by measuring the expansion of mercury when it is heated. In scientific language, a thermometer measures not the quantity of heat but its intensity.

The thermometer depends for its action on the fact that substances expand when heated,

some more than others. It consists of a thick-walled glass tube, with a very thin hole down its center, and a bulb at the lower end. The bulb is filled with mercury, colored alcohol, or possibly some other liquid. The air is then driven out of the tube by boiling the liquid, and the top of the tube sealed. When the liquid is heated, it "gets larger," as children say, and takes up more room. Some of it is forced out of the bulb and up the tube. Of course the glass gets larger, too, and allows more room for the liquid; but the liquid expands so much more than the glass that it needs much more room and so rises in the tube. In clinical (fever) thermometers there is a constriction in the column containing the liquid, near the bulb. The liquid in the column is separated from the liquid in the bulb upon cooling, leaving the column in a fixed position for easy reading.

A scale is attached to the thermometer, so that we can tell how high the liquid has risen. In high-grade thermometers the scale is marked directly on the glass. There are two scales commonly used. The Fahrenheit scale is in common use in English-speaking countries. On it the freezing point of pure water is 32° and the boiling point 212° above zero.[1] One account says that zero was the coldest temperature that Fahrenheit had ever experienced in winter and 100° on his scale the temperature of the human body. Another and more probable one is that he took the temperature of a certain mixture of ice and salt as zero and then marked the temperature of boiling water on his thermometer. Fahrenheit was a maker of astronomical instruments, and happened to have a machine which would divide the space between zero and the boiling point of water into exactly 212 parts. In any

[1] Notice the sign "°," meaning "degree" or "degrees." In reading the thermometer, one must always tell which scale one is using. The minus sign means below zero. Thus "134°F." means "134 degrees above zero Fahrenheit" and "−20°C." means "20 degrees below zero centigrade," and so on. The whole phrase should always be read.

case, Fahrenheit made good thermometers, and his scale came to be widely accepted.

The other common scale is the centigrade, or Celsius, scale. It was invented by Celsius about 1750. On it the freezing point of water is zero and the boiling point is 100°. The centigrade scale is used almost everywhere except in the English-speaking countries, and even there for most scientific work.

A third scale also used in scientific work is the *absolute*, or *Kelvin*, scale (p. 445).

EXPERIENCE. *To make a thermometer scale in terms of children's experiences.* Have children make a wall chart of a thermometer. Indicate on this thermometer activities and happenings at various temperatures: "Heavy-Coat Weather," "Water Freezes," "Ice Melts," "Summer Weather," etc. Perhaps they may wish to make pictures to represent the various temperatures. If there isn't room enough on the chart for such pictures, they can make them separately and run string or ribbons to the appropriate places on the chart.

Some thermometers do not contain a liquid, but instead consist of two strips of metal firmly fastened together. The two strips are of different kinds of metal—for example, brass and steel. Brass expands more when heated than steel does. Since the two strips are fastened together, one side of the combined strip thus formed expands more than the other, causing the whole strip to bend. The bending of the strip causes a pointer to move across a scale on the face of the instrument. Metallic thermometers are convenient and rugged, but less accurate.

The bending, when heated, of a bar or strip composed of two metals is also used in the thermostats which commonly control the temperature of schoolrooms and homes. The bending of the bar operates an electric switch which controls an electric motor which in turn shuts off or turns on the heat.

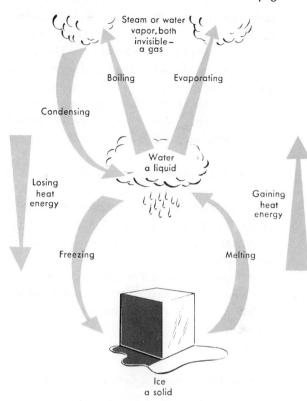

Energy and the three states of matter.

EXPERIENCE. *There are three states of matter.* Bring some ice or snow into the room. As the ice, which is a solid, melts, it becomes liquid water. Boil the water. It turns into an invisible gas. Hold a cold object over the boiling water. Drops of liquid will form on it. Many instances of the change of state of water will arise from day to day. It would be well for one to make certain that there has been good concept formation about the three states of matter, especially since adult language is frequently rather careless on some of the points. Frequently one hears the word *dissolve* used for the phenomenon of melting (p. 398).

Changes of state are common in the child's experience and in his reading. For instance, sugar and paraffin are solids at room temperature, but are easily melted on a stove. Alcohol and certain other liquids freeze at such low temperatures that they are used in automobile radiators to keep the water from freezing. Carbon dioxide is usually a gas, but it may be frozen at a very low temperature. Dry Ice is frozen carbon dioxide. Iron and many other metals must be heated very hot to melt, but they are melted in the processes used to secure them from their ores. Lead must be heated hot to melt, but not so hot as iron.

EXPERIENCE. *Make a list of solids, liquids, and gases.* Have children name some solids they know, such as chairs, desks, tables, and chalk. Write this list on a chart. Do the same for liquids and gases. Older children may recall some substance which they know may be in more than one state. For instance, gasoline is in the liquid form as it is poured into the tanks of cars at a filling station, but is a gas when it explodes in the cylinder of the automobile engine.

EXPERIENCE. *Heat is a form of energy.* Rub together as many things as you can. Note that the more work you do in rubbing, the hotter the substances get. See also the Experiences on pages 747–749.

EXPERIENCE. *Substances conduct heat.* Secure a rod of metal such as a knitting needle, and have someone hold one end of it with a potholder. A stand and clamp are desirable but not necessary for this purpose; or a wooden support may be made. Make several balls of cooking fat, candle wax, or paraffin—about

A metal rod conducts heat.

the size of small marbles. Stick these balls to the rod at equal intervals. Apply a flame to the lower end of the rod. As the heat is conducted along the rod, the balls melt and drop off. This gives a rather accurate means of telling when a certain temperature has been reached by different parts of the rod.

Time the dropping off of the balls. Note that the heat is conducted rapidly near the flame, but more and more slowly as it is carried farther and farther away. If the rod is long enough, a place will be reached where no more balls will drop off.

On a cold day notice the difference in temperature between an outside window pane and an inside pane, as in a hall door.

If there is a steam or hot-water radiator in the room, place a metal object in contact with the hot radiator and notice that after a time it is hot. Do the same for nonmetal objects. Which objects take the longer time to become hot?

Notice the difference in warmth of an outside wall and an inside wall or partition on a cold winter day. Do the same on a hot summer day.

EXPERIENCE. *Some substances conduct heat faster than others.* If rods of different metals are available, repeat the above experiment, using them. Note that some metals conduct heat faster than others.

Secure several rods, about six to eight inches long, of different metals. Have a child hold one of these by its end in his right hand, and another in his left. Thrust the two outer ends into a flame, holding them so that they are both heated about equally. Which one first becomes so hot that it must be dropped? In the lower grades two spoons made of different metals held in a cup of very hot water may be used to show the same principle.

Aluminum is often used for cooking utensils. One reason for this is that it conducts heat readily.

Secure (from a five-and-ten-cent store) an aluminum cup with an *aluminum* handle. Secure other cups with handles of other substances, such as enamel or china. Fill them all with boiling water. Which ones can be picked up comfortably? Why do utensils of aluminum usually have handles of some other material?

Put some hot water in each of two cups, one made of metal and the other of plastic or porcelain, and notice the difference in the outside temperature. Do the same with cold water.

Pack some ice in steel wool and some in excelsior or sawdust and notice the difference in melting time.

Notice the difference in the temperature of a glass window pane and the wooden frame around it on a cold day.

EXPERIENCE. *The use of the thermometer.*[2] If a suitable thermometer is available, the boiling temperature of water may easily be determined. Children can watch the column of mercury rise higher and higher until the water starts to boil. If the water is still further heated, the thermometer will not rise any higher than the boiling point. This is because the extra heat energy goes into changing the water from a liquid to a gas and not into raising its temperature.

Care should be taken to keep the water well stirred, and not to let the bulb of the thermometer touch the container in which the water is being boiled. In that case the thermometer would give the temperature of the container, not that of the water.

The boiling temperatures of other substances—for example, milk, cereal, candy, and salt solution—may also be determined. Do *not* attempt to boil inflammable liquids—for instance, alcohol—in the classroom.

If deep frying is done in the cookery class,

children will be interested to note that it is done at temperatures much above that of boiling water. That is why it is so much more painful to get a drop of hot fat on the skin than a drop of boiling water.

EXPERIENCE. *Providing experiences with the three states of matter.* In warmer regions children have few if any opportunities for experiences with ice or snow. However, in such regions children can have experiences with ice cubes from a refrigerator. Ice cubes can be used for instruction in the classroom and can be secured at any time of year. Young children can watch them melt. Also, the material which collects on the freezing unit in a refrigerator and which melts off when the refrigerator is defrosted, in many ways corresponds to snow.

If any of the children have had an experience with Dry Ice (solid carbon dioxide), ask them to tell about it.

The work with the three states of matter should be associated with experiences at home and school, especially for the young children.

If ice is available, children may find the freezing point of water. A glass containing some water may be set in a pan and a mixture of ice and salt packed around it. If the salt-and-ice mixture is kept packed tightly around the glass, the water will freeze after a time. Frequent readings of its temperature should be taken. If the thermometer is removed from the water after each reading, there will be no danger of its being damaged by the freezing water.

The freezing mixture of salt and ice in itself offers an interesting example of the exchange of heat energy. The salt causes the ice to melt. It takes heat to melt ice, or, in other words, the ice takes up heat when it melts. The ice gets its heat from the surroundings, in this case the glass of water. When the water has given up sufficient heat, it freezes.

Another example of the taking up of heat

---

[2] The use of the thermometer in regulating room temperature has been discussed in Chapter 12.

by ice when it melts is to be found in an old type ice refrigerator. Here the ice in melting takes heat from the food and other objects in the refrigerator. This type of refrigerator is very useful and is still used in some regions and for some purposes.

Many people in a misguided effort to save ice, wrap it in layers of newspaper. This effectively retards the taking up of heat by the ice; and since that is exactly what the ice is supposed to do, the practice defeats the purpose of the refrigerator. It is a bit surprising at first, but nevertheless true, that ice would not cool a refrigerator much if it did not melt. In an electric refrigerator the mechanism removes the heat as fast as it enters the refrigerator; so no melting takes place.

Perhaps the school doctor or nurse will demonstrate the way in which the clinical (fever) thermometer works. The children will enjoy having their temperatures taken. Notice that all the children have about the same temperature. Ask the doctor or nurse how much a person's temperature may vary without his becoming ill.

EXPERIENCE. *The thermometer does not tell the amount of heat.* Put about one inch of cold water in any cooking utensil. Put it on the stove and start to heat it. Use a watch to find exactly how long the water takes to boil. Stir it and take the temperature.

Now rinse the utensil in cold water and fill it nearly full. Heat it again and note the amount of time required to boil the water, and also the temperature. It requires more heating to boil a large amount of water than it does to boil a small amount, but the final temperature is the same.

EXPERIENCE. *Different substances hold different amounts of heat.* Place a piece of iron and a piece of wood of about the same size in boiling water. After a few minutes remove them. Notice which becomes cool enough to handle

first. Since they were in the same water, they must have been at the same temperature; but one cooled off much more rapidly than the other.

The same thing may often be noticed when you are eating hot foods. For instance, in many dishes meat and potatoes are cooked together. The meat cools off quickly, but the potatoes remain hot much longer.

EXPERIENCE. *Constructing a ribbon thermometer.* Draw the tube of a thermometer, with a bulb at the lower end, on a piece of cardboard. Draw the thermometer about ten inches long. Make a horizontal slit near the top of the tube and another one near the bulb. Obtain a piece of white ribbon twenty-two inches long, and as wide as the thermometer tube drawn. Dip eleven inches of the ribbon in red paint and allow it to dry. If paint is not available, color it red with red ink or a crayon. Color the bulb red. Insert the red end of the ribbon in the slit near the bulb and the other end near the top. Sew or tie the two ends together behind the thermometer. The red portion of the ribbon represents the column of mercury or alcohol in a thermometer. Draw the Fahrenheit scale on the cardboard, beginning with $-20°F.$ and going up to $230°F.$ The class can calculate with the teacher the best way to divide the degrees on the scale. The thermometer can be moved each day by pulling the ribbon up or down. A real thermometer, or weather reports from radio, television, or newspapers, may give the mean temperature each day.

EXPERIENCE. *Substances expand when heated.* Fill a bottle to the brim with colored water. Stopper it with a one-hole stopper through which a clear plastic tube or clear soda straw has been passed. (If a one-hole stopper cannot be secured, a substitute stopper can be made of modeling clay.) The lower end of the tube should not extend inside the bottle.

Place the bottle in a warm place, such as in hot water or in the sun. The liquid expands when heated.

The colored water will rise a certain distance in the tube. Mark the place to which it rises with a rubber band. Place the whole apparatus in various hot and cold places and notice if the liquid rises or falls. This makes a thermometer, although a very crude and inaccurate one.

EXPERIENCE. *To show that a wire grows longer when heated.* Tie one end of a piece of wire to a small rock. Suspend the rock from a stand so that the rock will swing back and forth but just clear the table top. Now heat the wire with a candle, moving the flame up and down along the wire. The wire should grow longer. If in the beginning the rock just cleared the table top when it was made to swing, the wire should now be so long that the rock cannot swing back and forth without striking the table.

EXPERIENCE. *To show other examples of heat expansion.* When a lid on a jar is tight, children may have seen their parents pour hot water on the lid so that it can be unscrewed. The hot water caused the metal lid to expand a little, making the process easier.

Railroad rails expand and contract in accordance with the temperature. The ends of the rails are not fitted closely together, but instead a space is allowed for expansion. Children occasionally have an opportunity to observe the difference in these spaces from winter to summer. Sometimes very long rails are made of Invar steel, which expands very little.

The wire grows longer when heated.

The joints that occur at regular intervals across some concrete highways are put there to allow the concrete to expand and contract.

Steel bridges must be designed so as to allow for expansion on hot days. In a long bridge the amount of expansion is considerable.

Telegraph and telephone wire must be strung in a way that will allow for expansion in the summer and contraction in the winter. When proper allowance for this has not been made, poles have been forced out of the ground by the contraction of wires in extremely cold weather. This happens more frequently in warmer climates of the middle latitudes than in cold regions, because cold weather is not so likely to be anticipated by people of warm regions.

Sound Energy. Sound is a form of energy. We know from experience that it is necessary to do work of some sort to produce sound. We must blow a trumpet or a whistle, strike a piano key or a drum, or draw a bow across the strings of a violin. Even in singing and speaking we must expel our breath, sometimes forcibly.

Sound is explained as a back-and-forth motion (vibration) of the molecules of the air, or of any other substance. This motion is much slower than the motion which we call heat, and is of a different type. The energy contained in ordinary sounds is not very great. We are more aware of the energy involved in producing loud sounds. For example, thunder may jar things off of shelves and shake the windows. Sounds from loud explosions may even break windows. Since sound is a movement of the air, it is a form of *kinetic*, or *"moving,"* energy.

More will be said about the nature of sound when it is discussed in relation to communication in Chapter 24.

EXPERIENCE. *Making a string telephone.* Get two cans of the size in which vegetables are sold. Remove the tops of both and punch a small hole in the bottom of each can. Take a piece of string about ten feet long. Insert one end of the string through the hole in the bot-

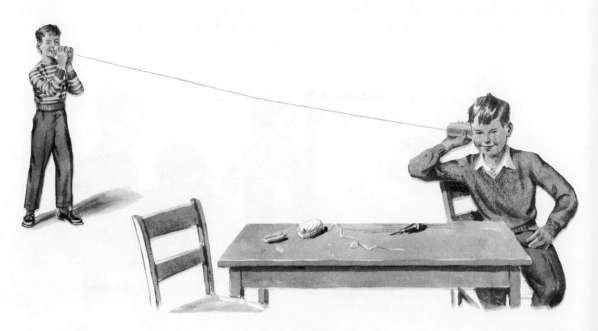

A string telephone.

tom of one can. Make a knot on the inside of the can so that the string cannot pull out. Repeat with the other can. Have two children each take one of the cans and stand ten feet apart, keeping the string taut. One person may talk into the can while the other can hear him by placing the can near his ear. Why must the string be taut?

EXPERIENCE. *To observe how sound is produced in musical instruments.* If any of the children have wind or stringed instruments, perhaps they could show in class how sounds are produced. For instance, what vibrates in a violin or cello, a trombone or trumpet, or in a drum, to produce sounds?

Muscular and Mechanical Energy. One of the most obvious forms in which energy is available is that of the muscles. For the greater part of the time that man has existed on Earth he has been forced to depend on his muscles to do all his work. He hunted his food and made his garments by the strength of his own muscles. As early civilizations rose to prominence, they did so on the basis of the energy provided by the muscles of slaves. The ancient Roman or Carthaginian galley was simply a large rowboat propelled by slaves. The pyramids of Egypt are monuments of what could be accomplished by human toil. It is believed that the great stones of the pyramids, some weighing fifty tons, were put into place by slave labor.

Men learned to harness animals and to use their muscular energy to help them to do work. Today in a great many places on Earth people have not advanced much beyond this stage. A good part of the world's pushing and pulling is still done by the muscles of men and domestic animals.

It takes about ten "manpower" to equal one horsepower. Thus an automobile engine developing 200 horsepower is equivalent to about 2000 men. Of course, even 2000 men could not give the car the speed that the engine does. A person driving a modern automobile, then, has the equivalent of 2000 slaves that he can call to service merely by "stepping on the gas."

We cannot rely upon machines alone, however. It is well that the human body is called upon to do work. Our muscles must have exercise. When men no longer need to perform labor in order to earn a living, we find them turning to golf, tennis, hiking, and gymnasium work to give their muscles sufficient work to do to keep them healthy. One is done from necessity; the other is done because the doing of it gives enjoyment.

The energy of muscles is of a type commonly known as mechanical energy. *Mechanical energy* is energy which takes the form of pushing, pulling, lifting, falling, turning, or forcing in some way.

Our muscles, like the rest of the body, get their energy in the first place from a nonmechanical source, but the muscles themselves turn this nonmechanical energy into the mechanical form in which it is used.

Muscular energy comes from the food we eat and the oxygen we breathe. The food is oxidized. (Chapter 11.) When things burn in a fire they, too, oxidize and, in a way, the oxidizing of food in our bodies may be thought of as a kind of burning. When food oxidizes, it is consumed so slowly that heat is liberated more slowly than in the case of an ordinary fire.

The majority of machines do work by means of energy in the mechanical form. They do not create the energy but simply turn it into a more useful form. For example, the gasoline engine takes the energy from the burning gasoline and turns it into the mechanical form. An engine may be thought of as a device for changing the potential (stored) energy of fuel into the kinetic energy of motion. A more complete description of the gasoline engine will be found on pages 767–768.

Many machines do not change the form of energy at all, but simply its *direction*. A back-and-forth motion or a steady push in one direction is sometimes not very useful. This sort of motion can be changed by machines into the more useful round-and-round (rotary) motion. A steady push on the handle of a lawn-mower causes a set of blades to whirl around and cut the grass. Other instances could be cited. Children should have the opportunity to examine and discuss various types of machines and see how they change the form or the direction of energy.

The Energy of Wind and of Falling Water. The energy of wind and of falling water is really a type of mechanical energy, but it is so important to us that it is here given a separate brief discussion.

Probably the first machines not driven by muscle power were driven by the wind. Some twenty-eight centuries before Christ the Egyptians used sails to help propel their boats. In the Middle Ages windmills were used for grinding grain, and their use probably helped to prepare the minds of men to accept the use of power-driven machinery. Sailing vessels and windmills are still in use, although their importance has declined greatly.

In most parts of the world the wind is much too irregular and unreliable to be used where a steady, dependable source of power is necessary, as in running factory machinery.

There is another and far more important aspect of wind energy. That is the fact that winds bring rain. It is the wind which distributes water over the surface of Earth to make crops and to replenish rivers and lakes. Without the energy of the wind to carry rain, Earth would speedily become a desert.

The energy of running water has been in use for about two thousand years. In all forms of water-power devices, a stream of water is made to push against paddles set on the rim of a wheel. In pushing against these the water does work and turns the wheel around. Mod-

Stored water is a useful source of energy. (Aluminium Ltd., Montreal.)

ern water turbines are simply complicated forms of the old-fashioned mill wheel, although they look very different.

The purpose of the dam which is part of most water-power developments is to pile water up and let it fall down. It also serves to store water for periods when the stream is low. If a suitable waterfall with a constant flow is available, a dam is not required.

As long as machinery had to be attached directly to a water wheel, factories had to be located on the stream. Since the development of electric generators, the water wheel may be used to turn a generator and produce electricity. Energy in the form of electricity may be sent many miles over wires to a city and used to run factories there. The development of electricity means that the energy of falling water need no longer be used in the place where it is developed. Industries can now be located at a distance from a power plant, since electrical energy is a form of energy which can travel over wires. As a result, industry is becoming less centralized.

Electrical Energy. Electricity can be made to do work. It can be converted into heat, as in flatirons and stoves; it can run motors, ring bells, and light lamps. Since it can do work, it is a form of energy. Other forms of energy can be converted into electrical energy. Thus electricity may be produced from the energy of falling water or burning coal, as in the great power-driven generators which supply our cities and towns. It may also be produced from the reaction of certain chemicals in batteries, either dry cells or storage batteries. An *electric current* is a movement of electrons through a wire or through some other conductor. An electron is a small packet of electrical energy.

Chapter 23 is devoted to magnetism and electricity; so an extensive discussion will not be attempted here. The principal fact to be noted is that other forms of energy can be changed into electricity, and vice versa.

Chemical Energy. It has already been stated that burning is a chemical change. As we well know, burning releases heat, which is a form of energy. Many other chemical changes also give off heat. On the other hand, heat must be supplied to bring about some chemical changes. In the first case, chemical energy is transformed into heat energy; in the second case, heat energy is transformed into chemical energy.

Chemical changes may also produce electrical energy, as in the case of batteries. In other cases—for example, in charging storage batteries—electrical energy may be transformed into chemical energy.

In general, it may be said that the energy which is released in chemical changes is energy which was stored in the chemicals at some previous time. The sun supplies the energy which is used by plants to build up their leaves, stems, and other structures. The plants may then be transformed into coal and burned several million years hence, or they may be burned immediately as wood. In either case, the energy is returned as heat and light.

In the same way the chemicals in the dry cell have had energy supplied to them, by natural or artificial means, in the course of their formation.

Chemical energy must not be confused with nuclear energy. Chemical energy is a result of the action of atoms on one another; nuclear energy is a result of the action of the parts within the atoms.

Nuclear Energy. (Pp. 196, 281, and 373.) Atoms, once thought to be the smallest possible particles of matter, are now thought to be composed of a large number of parts, held together by enormous forces. The nuclei of atoms of certain substances—for instance, radium—come apart "of their own accord," as it were. When they do so, energy is released, and part of the atom is shot forth violently. In the paint used on luminous watch dials these ejected particles are caught on substances mixed in the paint. When the particles, traveling at high speeds, strike these substances, their energy of motion is transformed into light, and we see a flash. A great many flashes are made each second, and so we see them as a continuous glow. If we were to look at the face of a luminous watch dial in a dark room, we would see these flashes. A magnifying glass helps us to see the flashes better.

This phenomenon, called *radioactivity,* was first discovered and studied toward the close of the nineteenth century, notably by Henri Becquerel, Pierre Curie, Marie Curie, and Lord Rutherford. The discovery gave a new impetus to the study of physics, for it had been hitherto thought impossible for a substance to go on giving up energy in this manner (p. 281).

It is the nuclei of atoms that contain the energy in which we are interested. Energy is released as a result of changes in these nuclei. Therefore, it seems more meaningful to refer to this energy as *nuclear energy* rather than *atomic energy*.

The atom has been compared to a very small solar system, where the nucleus represents the sun and is surrounded by electrons, which, like the planets, travel around the nucleus.

There are two methods whereby energy can be obtained from a nucleus. The nucleus of an atom of uranium is bombarded, causing the nucleus to split into two parts, with a tremendous release of energy. This process is called *fission*. The other method has to do with two nuclei uniting, with a resulting release of energy. This process is called *fusion,* and has been occurring on the sun continually for billions of years (p. 196).

Particle Accelerators. Known also as atom-smashers, particle accelerators send particles with increasingly enormous speeds from a source to a target element. The nuclei of the atoms of the target element are changed by this bombardment as particles are forced into them. The target element may become a new isotope of that particular element. Radioactive isotopes have many uses in medicine, industry, and research.

These machines are also used to produce nuclear fission or nuclear fusion. These reactions depend upon the kind of bombarding particle, the kind of target element, and the force or energy of the bombardment.

The most familiar particle accelerator is the cyclotron, in which the particle being accelerated starts at the center and spirals outward with increasing speed. In the synchrotron, the particle moves in a circle, and is given a push every time it passes a certain point. It is like a baseball on a string that whirls around a post, and a boy with a bat strikes it with force every time it goes by. In a linear accelerator the particle moves in a straight line as much as two miles long, and is given a series of pushes along. All of these machines operate on the same principle, but details differ due to the types of source and target materials and the amount of energy used. Accelerators capable of producing greater and greater amounts of energy are constantly being designed.

Engineers are utilizing nuclear energy as a source of power. Other peace-time uses of nuclear energy are in the fields of agriculture, medicine and industry (pp. 373, 418).

Light Energy. Light is a form of energy. It is familiar to children, for they have experiences with it almost every moment of their lives, except when they are sleeping. Light for children and adults is not confined to the daylight, for in but few cases does anyone experience total darkness, such as is found in the interior of some caves or a very dark closet.

Light is a form of *radiant energy* (that is, energy that radiates from a central point). Other forms of radiant energy are radio and television waves, ultraviolet rays, radioactivity, and X rays. The nature of light has long been a matter for investigation among scientists.

It was once believed that light was a stream of particles, shot out by a source of light, and that some of these particles entered the eye, causing the sensations of sight. Later some scientists found it necessary to develop an explanation of light as a wave motion. But to explain certain phenomena of light, it was necessary to return to the idea of particles called *photons*. Today many scientists find it necessary to use both ideas, for some phenomena can best be explained by reference to photons, and other phenomena by reference to waves; scientists, however, have had difficulty in combining the two explanations into one unified theory. It is interesting to find that scientists have difficulty in evolving a theory about, or making a single explanation for, something which is so much a part of our everyday life as light. We must recognize that light is not simple and that scientists need more time to study it.

Children are not disturbed by the fact that man has much to learn. In fact, they seem intrigued with the thought that there is much left to be discovered. For most instruction in science in the elementary school there would be little difficulty growing out of any discrepancies in these two theories. The information above is provided as background for teachers, should they need it.

If light is particles in motion, we know that such moving particles represent energy. If, on the other hand, it is waves, we know that energy is necessary to produce waves. In either case, light is a form of energy (p. 861).

Later we shall see that most, if not all, of the energy for Earth comes directly or indirectly from the sun. Most of the energy which Earth receives from the sun comes in the form of light.

Energy Changes. In the foregoing discussion of the forms in which energy occurs, it has often been mentioned that energy may be transformed, or changed, from one form to another. Thus we have seen chemical energy transformed into heat energy and mechanical energy into electrical energy. The total amount of energy resulting from an energy transformation is always the same as the amount available at the start. This important principle is known as *the law of the conservation of energy*. Briefly this law states that *energy cannot be created or destroyed, but only changed in form*. The fact that energy may be created from matter, as Einstein had predicted, does not disprove this principle. It is likely that energy and matter are different aspects of the same thing. Later it will be noted that energy may be created out of matter in the stars. The tremendous quantity of energy that results from nuclear reactions is due to matter being changed to energy.

This does not indicate by any means that all the energy which is transformed appears as useful energy. A good deal is lost, so far as useful work is concerned. This loss is very often in the form of heat. This heat may come from friction in the moving parts of a machine, or it may be generated as a by-product of the chemical action which makes the machine run, as when fuel is burned in a gasoline engine or in a steam boiler. The heat given up to the air by an automobile through its radiator is a total loss, as far as running the car is concerned. We must remember, however, that the car would not run at all if the engine did not get hot. As a matter of fact, we must always pay in loss of useful energy for every energy transformation.

The question naturally arises, "Why transform energy at all if we must lose some?" The answer is that we often transform energy from a form which cannot be used directly into one which can be used directly. For instance, the energy contained in a gallon of gasoline is of no value to us until it is transformed into the mechanical energy which moves a car.

The Source of Earth's Energy. You no doubt have noticed that the sources of the various forms of energy which have been discussed have always been other forms of energy. This is to be expected from the law of the conservation of energy, as stated. The question may have arisen, "What is the source of Earth's energy as a whole?"

The various types of energy used by man to do his work fall mostly into three great classes: energy from muscles, energy from burning fuels, and energy from wind and running water. Let us briefly trace the energy changes involved in each of these forms.

The muscular energy of man and other animals comes, as we have said, from chemical changes in the food they have eaten. This food is derived either from plants or from other animals. The animals used for food probably fed on plants. In either case the food used to supply muscular energy can be traced back in one or two steps to green plants. Green plants in turn make use of the energy of sunlight to build up their bodies. Thus the energy which we use to walk to school in the morning came from our food; and the energy of our food came in turn from the sun.

The common fuels are coal, oil, and wood. Coal, we know, was formed from plants which grew long ago. We are not sure of the exact process by which petroleum was formed, but we think that it came from plant and animal remains. The same source is true of natural gas, which accompanies petroleum in oil wells (pp. 177 and 391). Animals, as we have seen, depend on plants for their energy. Wood, of course, is part of a plant. Thus we see that coal, wood, and oil all come directly or indirectly from plants, and plants get their energy from sunlight.

We have already seen that winds depend on the unequal heating of Earth's surface by the sun; that rain depends on wind; and that running streams depend on rain.

Thus we see that each of the three principal sources of energy on Earth may be traced back, step by step, to the sun. The sun is the chief source of Earth's energy.

There remain certain minor but important sources of energy. One of these is the tides. The tides, as has been said, are caused by the movement of the moon around Earth and the movement of Earth around the sun, as well as by the attraction of these bodies for one another. The source of the tidal energy, then, is in the original energy which caused the solar system to be formed and set it in motion.

Another source of energy on Earth is radioactivity, or the breaking down of atoms. This energy comes directly from the atom itself. Its source is whatever built up the atom in the first place. This we do not know.

We know a few facts about the sun. We know that the sun is a ball of gases at a temperature of, in its interior, several million degrees. We know that it is sending out energy all the time at a tremendous rate. All the energy received by Earth equals only two billionths of that given off by the sun. There is the equivalent of one and one half horsepower developed on each square yard of the surface of Earth that gets light from the sun. Scientists tell us that there is evidence that the sun has been giving off energy at this rate for billions of years.

It was once thought that the sun was simply a ball of burning material like that of a great fire. When it became known that Earth is very old and that the sun has been shining for a long time, it was seen that the amount of any known kind of fuel equivalent to that in the sun would have burned away long ago.

Another theory was advanced. It is well known to scientists that squeezing a gas together, or compressing it, heats it. We also know that the gravitational attraction at the surface of the sun is tremendous. Perhaps the gases were being squeezed together by their own weight and so were becoming heated. Calculations, however, again showed that this source was insufficient to account for the sun's heat during the time that we know the sun has been giving off energy.

The latest theory seems to be that in the hot interior of the sun complex atoms may actually be built up out of simple ones, and energy may be given off in the process. For example, four hydrogen atoms unite to form one helium atom, involving a loss of matter and energy is evolved in the process. Thus matter itself may be convertible into energy (p. 197).

Any complete discussion of the source of the sun's energy would lead us far into the field of nuclear physics. Those who know most about nuclear physics admit that much remains for them to discover about the sun's energy and about nuclear energy.

Is the Energy Available on Earth near Exhaustion? The ultimate source of energy for Earth is the sun, and it gives no sign of exhaustion for many millions of years to come.

The principal sources of the energy which we use to run modern machines are the mineral fuels (coal, petroleum, and natural gas) and water power. It is obvious that there is a limit to the total amount of water power that can be developed in the world, and the fuel reserves, especially those of petroleum and natural gas, are limited. How long can they last? Must civilization collapse when they are gone?

In spite of the great increase in the amount of coal and oil used in recent years, new deposits have been discovered at an even faster rate. This has been done by scientific study of the way in which these deposits occur in Earth. Our present resources are probably sufficient to meet our needs for hundreds of years to come if we take care of them. Of course many of these resources are of low grade; but if we need energy badly enough, scientists will surely find ways to use low-grade material. For example, we know how to get oil from shale or from coal, but it is cheaper at present to get it from oil wells.

Is there enough water power available on Earth to supply our needs when the mineral fuels are gone? The development of water power has its limitations for various reasons. Frequently valuable valley farm land becomes covered with water and thus lost as agricultural land. Then, too, reservoirs back of dams become silted up and useless. Water power may help in many regions, but it will not furnish a final solution for the world's need for energy (Chapter 6). Much of this power would be extremely expensive to develop at present because of the inaccessibility of the power sites, distance from the place of use, or the extensive dams required. If, however, we ever feel the pinch of need sufficiently, we will utilize water power to the utmost.

But man is discovering new ways of utilizing the great stores of energy of Earth and universe. One of these is the use of nuclear energy (p. 733). An advantage of nuclear energy is that the fuel used does not take up much space and therefore can be easily transported to the place where it is to be used. Earth has vast deposits of ore which can be used to develop nuclear energy.

For years many scientists have been working to utilize directly the energy of the sun to do useful work (p. 414). Some have designed engines which run by sunlight. A battery has been made called a *solar energy battery* which changes the energy of the sun into electrical energy. Solar batteries are useful in furnishing power to operate the instruments in satellites. It is altogether possible that in a few years solar energy may be used for some of man's greatest achievements, such as changing ocean water into fresh water, or pumping water for irrigation, and so on.

A *solar furnace* concentrates the sun's rays by means of mirrors. The United States Army has such a furnace at Natick, Massachusetts. The sun shines upon a great square frame 36 feet high, composed of rows of plate-glass mirrors. The frame is geared so that it turns and faces the sun, thus collecting the maximum of radiation. The sun's rays (radiation) are directed to another large frame containing mirrors arranged in a parabola. These mirrors concentrate the energy of the sun's radiation collected in this way on a spot only four inches in diameter. An intense heat of nearly 5000°F. is produced at this spot. It is hot enough to melt a hole in a steel rail one fourth inch thick in one second.

A system of shutters is used to control the amount of the sun's rays falling upon the parabolic reflector. The principal use of many solar furnaces is to create high temperatures for experimental purposes. Small furnaces are used for household cooking.

From time to time children may be interested in discussing current developments in the use of solar and nuclear energy.

Scientists say that there is no reason to suppose that any catastrophe will occur to Earth for millions of years to come. There is nothing to make us believe that man will not be living on Earth ages hence. There is also nothing to indicate that civilization will collapse of itself, unless man through his own stupidity destroys it by war.

Let us suppose that all the water power is being used and that all the coal and oil are gone. Earth will still be receiving an immense daily income of energy from the sun. Long before our other energy resources are exhausted, scientists will have perfected the means of using energy directly from the sun. A start has already been made in a small way in this direction. When we reach this point, we shall cease using the fossilized bodies of plants and animals, supplementing them with running water. We need not fear the exhaustion of our energy resources.

The foregoing remarks should not be interpreted to mean that natural resources need not be conserved; indeed, their meaning is exactly the opposite. The avoidance of waste and the more efficient and more intelligent use of resources are the things which will prevent mankind from ever feeling the pinch of need. Engineers have helped by making power plants more efficient and by instructing in better furnace-firing methods. Yet many of our larger autos use about three times as much gasoline as is actually needed, due to oversized engines, and man still effectively wastes natural resources in wars.

Is the Universe Running Down?

We have seen that there is energy everywhere in the universe. The sun, like the other stars, is giving off energy at a tremendous rate. We have said that there is no probability that the sun will cease or perceptibly diminish its flow of energy for an immensely long time. But a long time is not forever. Can the sun and the stars keep up their output of energy forever? Scientists do not agree on this. One group thinks that just as energy may be created out of matter in the stars, so matter may be created out of energy somewhere in space.

Some scientists believe that hydrogen molecules are distributed all through space. As the sun moves along it attracts this gas to it. They believe that additional hydrogen may be formed from energy, to take the place of that which the sun "sweeps up." This would indicate that there may be an endless cycle from matter to energy and back again. It will be seen that at this point we have come a long way from the law of the conservation of energy. Perhaps we can formulate a new law and call it the law of the conservation of "mat-

(a)

(b)

ENERGY

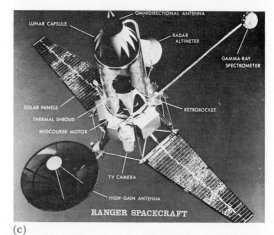

(c)

(a) *Solar energy is used to heat this house. (American Window Glass Co., and Engineering Experiment Station, University of Colorado.)*

(b) *The submarine* Nautilus. *An atomic reactor is used to produce steam for her engines. (U.S. Navy.)*

(c) *Solar panels make it possible to use energy from the sun to operate instruments in spacecraft. This is a scale model of the Ranger 4 spacecraft (April 19, 1962). (Three Lions, N.Y.C.)*

(d) *A cyclotron used for atomic research. (Radiation Laboratory, University of California, Berkeley.)*

(e) *Petroleum and natural gas are valuable sources of energy.*

(d)

(e)

(a)

(b)

(c)

(a) *Inertia. A downhill skier can neither stop nor turn easily because inertia keeps him going. (A. Devaney, Inc.)*

(b) *Friction. When the drill is spun rapidly and pressed against the fireboard, friction generates enough heat to start a fire in the dry tinder. (Ewing Galloway.)*

(c) *Lubrication. Skaters can move rapidly because a thin film of water lubricates the runners. (H. Armstrong Roberts.)*

(d) *Friction. The force needed to move an object can be measured by means of a spring balance. (Al Daigle.)*

(d)

ter-energy." These subjects are on the outer borders of knowledge.

Another group of scientists thinks that the sun and the stars must simply go on giving out energy until it is all converted into an unavailable form. The energy which passes into space, they feel, can never be returned.

In either case probably our sun will at last become cold, and Earth with it. But perhaps the universe as a whole will go on much the same forever. There may be other suns and other stars after the sun and stars we know are gone, with perhaps, by chance, other planets revolving around them.

Man Uses Energy to Move Things

Much of the energy which man employs is used to move something. The engines of boats, trains, and automobiles are used to move them. The engines or motors in factories are used to set machines in motion. Our muscular energy is used to turn egg-beaters, walk upstairs, or hoe the garden. In every case we are moving something.

We have said or implied in numerous places in this chapter that energy is the capacity to do work. Let us see just what we mean by doing work. When we do work, in the scientific meaning of the word, we are pushing or pulling or turning something and making the object move. So we see that *two things are involved in work—a push or pull* and *a movement of the thing pushed or pulled.* Scientists have agreed to call the push or pull *force,* and say that the amount of work done is equal to the force applied to an object multiplied by the distance the object is moved in the direction the force is moving. Thus, if we lift a two-pound weight one foot, we are doing twice as much work as we should do if we lifted a one-pound weight the same distance. Also, if we lift a one-pound weight two feet, we are doing twice as much work as we should do if we lifted the same one-pound weight only one foot. And if the weight is too heavy for us to lift at all, we do no work at all, even though we may get tired and out of breath trying.

Obviously some machines can do a given piece of work faster (that is, in a shorter time) than others. Suppose a truck is able to carry one hundred barrels of flour from a train to a warehouse in one hour and another truck is able to carry two hundred barrels over the same distance in the same time. The second truck does twice as much work as the first in the same time, and is said to be twice as powerful. Suppose a third truck is able to carry one hundred barrels but makes the trip in half an hour. This truck is also twice as powerful as the first. *Power,* then, is the *speed* of doing work. If two boys are shoveling snow, the more powerful one is able to shovel more snow each minute. A more powerful automobile engine is able either to drive a heavier car at the same speed as a less powerful engine or to drive the same car at a faster speed than a less powerful engine. Of course the more powerful car may be unable to move at a high speed on account of traffic. In this case, the more powerful car is not developing the power of which it is capable, and its owner is paying for something he is unable to use.

Energy and Inertia. Most of us have had the experience of being thrown forward on the seat when a car comes to a sudden stop or of having our heads jerked back when the car makes a sudden start. This is because, once our bodies are in motion, they tend to keep moving, and once at rest, they tend to remain motionless. This tendency of objects that are moving to keep moving and of those at rest to remain motionless is called *inertia*. This was stated by Sir Isaac Newton in his First Law of Motion (p. 237).

Inertia, like gravitation, is still poorly understood, but the two are closely related. One theory is that the inertia of a body is caused by the gravitational attraction of all the matter in the universe acting upon that body. As we learn more about the basic nature of the universe we shall probably come to have a better understanding of these forces that have such a great influence on our daily lives.

Out in space an object once started would keep on moving forever unless it ran into something, because there is almost nothing to stop it. No more energy need be supplied to it. On Earth energy must be exerted continually to overcome friction if objects are to be kept in motion, but the extra energy necessary to start an object would be needed even if there were no friction.

Since energy must be supplied to an object to set it in motion, it follows that an object in motion has energy. If the motion of the object is to be stopped, the object must lose this energy.

Now the law of the conservation of energy says that energy cannot be destroyed; so in order to stop a moving object its energy must be changed into some other form or transferred to some other object.

When it is desired to stop a moving train or automobile, the brakes are used. Brakes are nothing but devices for rapidly converting energy of motion into heat energy. They do this by rubbing against the wheels or against drums attached to the wheels. You remember that rubbing two objects together produces heat. When a train or automobile is stopped by the use of brakes, this heat energy is wasted, so far as useful work is concerned. If some automobile-drivers realized that they pay for gasoline to supply the energy which they

waste by the unnecessary use of the brakes, they would perhaps not approach traffic lights at high speed and jam on the brakes.

The energy of a moving object increases as the square of the speed with which the object is moving. This means that an automobile moving at 30 miles an hour has four times the energy of one moving at 15 miles an hour. A car moving at 60 miles an hour has sixteen times as much energy as one moving at 15 miles an hour. If the brakes are applied equally in each case, the fast car requires sixteen times as much distance to stop as the slow one. It is just as damaging for a car to run into something solid at 60 miles an hour as it is to fall off a twelve-story building. Most of us would not care to drive on the roof of a twelve-story building, for fear of falling off; but many of us take the same chance when we drive fast.

Many people are careless of the condition of the brakes of their cars. Others think it clever to brag about how fast they drive. Pedestrians often cross streets in front of oncoming cars. To do these things does not merely mean ignoring ordinances made by man; it indicates ignorance of the fundamental physical principles on which the universe is built. The policeman cannot see everywhere at once, but there is no evading the law of the conservation of energy. People need to be made more fully aware of these principles.

EXPERIENCE. *To discuss the use of brakes.* All children are interested in driving cars. They vicariously begin at an early age (Chapter 1). They have scooters, wagons, bicycles, and other vehicles with brakes. Frequently a child will drag his shoe on the sidewalk as a brake when playing with such vehicles.

This discussion can be made to fit a child's level of experience. How does a brake work? Get this in terms of a child's own ideas. Why does the use of a brake waste energy? Why does a brake wear out? To the last question children may have an answer in terms of their own experiences with homemade scooters and so on. Why does a good driver use his brake less than a poor driver?

The meaning involved in this section related to the study of energy, inertia, and friction can be useful in developing intelligent and responsible behavior. This is the goal of instruction in safety education. In a sense, this is content related to conservation; that is, conservation of human resources. This instruction should be started in the home, in preschool education. Read in Chapter 3 about learning to think through to consequences (p. 62) and growth in responsibleness (p. 68), and the contribution of science to intelligent planning (p. 74).

EXPERIENCE. *Energy must be used to start and stop objects.* Let the children push or pull a heavily loaded wagon on a level surface. Have them notice that it is harder to start the wagon than it is to keep it moving. The quicker they try to start it, the more force is needed. Now have them stop the wagon quickly when it is moving. The faster it is moving and the quicker the stop, the more force is needed.

Tie a rock with a strong piece of cord or rope, so that the rock can be pulled about by it. Take a spring balance[3] and fasten the hook into the cord. Now pull the rock along on a level surface, such as a floor or table. Note that the spring balance reads more while you are starting the rock to move than after it starts to move. This is explained as inertia. In starting the rock to move, one had to overcome the inertia of the rock at rest.

A good-sized steamship once got out of control and ran into a dock. Although it was

[3] Spring balances are useful in many experiences described for children in this chapter. They may be used by children to measure forces, weights, and so on. Spring balances of several different capacities should be obtained if possible. Local hardware stores may carry them in stock. Every elementary school should have a supply of spring balances of various capacities.

moving very slowly, it had so much inertia, owing to its great weight, that it broke the foot-square timbers of the dock like matches.

EXPERIENCE. *More force is needed to start an object quickly than to start it slowly.* Place a sheet of paper on a desk and place a book or two on it. By pulling the edge of the paper slowly it is possible to pull the books in any direction over the top of the desk. If, however, the paper is suddenly jerked, it will come out from under the books without disturbing them in the least. So much force was needed to move the books quickly that it was easier to move the paper from under the books than it was to move the books. Therefore the paper moved instead. Interesting variations may be made by using marbles, coins, or a tumbler of water.

EXPERIENCE. *Energy is needed to stop quickly.* Draw a line on the floor and have a child run up to it and try to stop suddenly. He will find that while he may be able to stop his feet, the upper part of his body continues to move forward.

Children often slide on their feet on ice or on a waxed floor. They also "coast" on a level surface on skates, bicycles, or sleds. It is inertia which enables them to coast and friction which finally stops them.

EXPERIENCE. *Objects at rest tend to remain at rest.* Place a card on a drinking glass so that it covers the top of the glass. Place a coin in the center of the card. Flick the card off the glass, horizontally. The coin does not move with the card but falls into the glass.

Friction—A Hindrance and a Help. We have made free use of the word *friction* in this chapter. Most people have a general idea of what friction is. Just as we have been forced to take friction into account in many places in this book, so we are forced to take it into account in our daily lives. There are very few things that we do which are not modified in one way or another by friction. It is both a hindrance and a help. Like gravity, it is an ever present factor to be reckoned with. It would seem to be worth while to examine the nature of friction a little.

Friction is the *resistance* encountered when one body slides or rolls over the surface of another. Even on the smoothest ice, no sled will slide for long unless we push it or unless we are sliding downhill. The sled stops because there is friction between its runners and the ice. In many instances there is a relatively small amount of friction when smooth surfaces rub together; the rougher the surfaces, the greater the friction. Even a surface which seems perfectly smooth to the touch will appear rough if examined under a microscope. It is impossible to make a surface which is absolutely smooth. The amount of friction is also dependent upon the pressure of one object on the other. The heavier the object, the greater the pressure and the greater the friction.

When two surfaces rub together, they both become warm—sometimes only a little warmer than they were before, sometimes very hot indeed. This heat represents the energy which we use to overcome the friction. It takes energy, for example, to push sandpaper over wood, and this energy makes the sandpaper and the wood warm, besides wearing away the sandpaper and the wood.

Substances rubbing against even the air encounter friction and develop heat. Pieces of material going at high speeds frequently enter our atmosphere from outer space. So great is the heat developed as they pass through the air that they become white-hot while still as much as one hundred and fifty miles above Earth, and most of them are entirely changed to dust and vapor before they can fall to the ground. Those that are seen in the air are called meteors (or incorrectly "shooting stars"), while those that strike the ground are called meteorites (p. 223).

Rockets and space vehicles passing through Earth's atmosphere may become red-hot from friction with the air. If they are to return safely to Earth they must be slowed down enough to prevent damage or total disintegration from heat.

For many centuries men have from time to time claimed to have made perpetual-motion machines. Such machines are supposed to run forever, after once being started, without having any additional energy supplied to them. We now realize that no such machine is possible, as there is bound to be friction in its parts. Even a very small amount of friction is enough to stop the machine eventually unless energy is supplied to it. Men who have an understanding of the above principles no longer waste time on perpetual-motion machines.

What Causes Friction? Friction is still poorly understood. Scientists formerly thought it was caused only by the mechanical intermeshing of small bumps and depressions, and was reduced by polishing the surfaces. This is partly true, but the problem proves to be more complicated. In some cases polishing *increases* friction. The reason for this is believed to be molecular attraction.

Two objects that appear smooth to the eye may look quite rough under a microscope. They touch only at the high spots, so that great pressure may exist at just a few points. At these points the molecules may be pressed close enough together to form molecular bonds, which are essentially electrical (p. 375). One object cannot slide across the other without breaking these bonds. If two pieces of metal, for example, are given a very high polish, *more* molecules come into contact than if the surfaces were separated by larger irregularities. This may be one reason why polishing sometimes increases friction.

It is easier to keep an object moving than to start it moving, because fewer bonds have to be broken. The surfaces skid along on their high spots, as a fast boat skips across the wave tops. A stationary object tends to slip into the material below, and must be moved "uphill" before it can move forward across the irregularities. Thus mechanical and molecular forces are both involved.

It is also likely that larger electrical charges contribute to friction. When some materials are rubbed together, they become strongly charged (pp. 806–811). Electrons are rubbed off one surface onto the other, so that one becomes positively charged and the other negative, and the surfaces are drawn together by the attraction of unlike charges. This static or frictional electricity may sometimes contribute toward the forces involved in friction.

Friction may be affected by a film of oxide on one of the surfaces, by the presence of a layer of air or gas between the surfaces, or by the generation of heat, which increases molecular activity. Frictional heat may cause a metal surface to melt slightly, thus lubricating the surface and reducing friction. Many factors are involved in friction, and we have much to learn about it.

Sliding and Rolling Friction. Children can readily observe two kinds of friction: *sliding friction* and *rolling friction.* When we push a box along the floor, we overcome sliding friction. When we push a wagon, we are working to overcome rolling friction. The rolling friction is less than the sliding friction. The wheel is therefore, when used in this manner, a method discovered by man for decreasing the friction he must work against. Although there is some sliding friction between the wheel and the axle, there is less than there would be between the wagon and the road if wheels were not used.

One can see why rolling may be less than sliding friction. In sliding friction two rough surfaces must rub over each other. In this case the bumps in one surface catch against the bumps in the other, causing friction. In rolling friction, both surfaces may be deformed depending on the hardness or softness of the surfaces. The wheel either rolls over the bumps on the road or pushes material ahead of it. In both sliding and rolling there may be varying amounts of molecular attraction.

We make use of this fact when we move a box with rollers under it. The rollers change the sliding friction to rolling friction. Ball and roller bearings make use of the same principle. In the ordinary wagon wheel there is rolling friction between the wheel and the ground, but sliding friction between the axle and the part of the wheel rubbing against the axle. In ball or roller bearings, balls or rollers are placed between the fixed axle and the moving wheel; thereby rolling friction is substituted for sliding friction. There is still a little sliding

Friction (resistance) occurs when objects in contact slide or roll past each other.

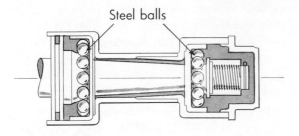

Ball bearings in a bicycle pedal substitute rolling friction for sliding friction.

friction where the balls or rollers rub together, but it is very slight.

A moving car is stopped by the friction of its brakes. As the speed decreases, friction increases, and the driver may have to let up on the brake to avoid stopping with a jerk. On icy roads it is important that the wheels keep a firm, unbroken contact with the road to take advantage of friction. If the wheels slide from too much braking, or spin from too much power, their grip on the road is reduced and the car is harder to control.

EXPERIENCE. *To show the principle of roller bearings.* Place some marbles (all the same size) on the floor in a group. Place a book on the marbles and then give the book a push. Note how far it goes and how easily. Can you send it halfway across the room? This could provide children with amusement on a rainy day. Be sure to have them responsible for picking up all the marbles before resuming other activities, since a serious fall can occur by slipping on a marble. Counting the marbles beforehand may be one way to determine whether all have been recovered.

Lubrication. Another way to help in overcoming friction is by the use of oil or grease or some other substance between the surfaces rubbing together. Substances used in this way are called *lubricants.* The exact action of a lubricant is not very well understood by scientists. The liquid appears to fill the low places in the rough surfaces. Also, a thin layer of liquid seems to form between the rubbing surfaces. Oil molecules cling to metal surfaces. In this way the surfaces themselves do not touch, and the motion takes place in this layer—actually, one film of oil rubs over another one. The friction of two solids sliding on each other is replaced by friction within a liquid. Friction within fluids, called viscosity, is a very different and much more complicated matter than friction between solids. *Fluid* friction is involved when a ship travels through water, and when automobiles and airplanes travel through air. We shall not go into it here except to say that most fluid friction is very much less than most solid friction. Under certain circumstances water or other liquids may act as lubricants.

The matter of lubrication is an extremely important one in the use of modern machinery. It is likely that we could never have developed our modern industry if there had not been a development of lubrication. In the modern automobile, for example, metal surfaces are moving past each other at extremely high speeds. The only thing that keeps them from rubbing on each other with destructive sliding friction is a thin layer of oil. This oil film is subjected to high temperatures and extreme pressures, yet it must stay in place.

Friction depends on the character of surfaces. The question might very properly arise, "Why is it that a sled will slide on ice, but not so well on glass, since glass is probably as smooth as ice?" The answer is that when anything presses on ice, some of the ice melts. The sled runner, pressing on the ice, melts it a little. A film of water forms under the runner. As soon as the runner passes, this film freezes again instantly; but while the runner is passing, it is lubricated by a film of water. The runner really does not touch the ice at all.

Friction and Gravity Work Together. Many of the effects of friction are made manifest by the combination of friction, gravity, and inertia acting together. When we are doing work, that is, pushing or pulling an object through a distance, we are working against inertia, friction, and gravity. A full box, for instance, is harder to drag across the floor than an empty one. The greater the weight, the greater the friction. If things had no weight, many of the effects of friction, both good and bad, would disappear.

Should We Be Better Off without Friction? Since a good part of our income is spent in buying energy in such forms as food, coal, and electricity, and much of our energy is used to overcome friction, causing us to lose power and money, the question may well be asked, "Would it not be a good thing if there were no such thing as friction?" A moment's thought would show that the answer must be "No."

When we walk, our feet push against the ground by means of friction. If it were not for friction, our feet would simply slip backward, and we should not be able to move forward at all. In the same way the wheels of a locomotive or automobile push against the track or the road, and so push the vehicle forward. When we wish to stop the train or car, we apply the brakes. Brakes are merely devices to increase the friction against which the energy moving the car or train must work. The friction of the brakes slows down the wheels, and these in turn, pressing against the road through friction, stop the car or train. Perhaps you have seen a car skidding on an icy road, or spinning its wheels in a vain effort to start. This is because there is not enough friction between the tires and the road. New tires with deep, sharp tread patterns have more friction than old tires that are worn smooth. That is why it is dangerous to drive an automobile with smooth tires. If it were

not for friction, we could not stop a train or an automobile unless we allowed it to hit something solid.

Friction aids us in other ways as well. For example, nails hold fast when driven into wood because of friction between the nails and the wood. Nuts remain on bolts because of friction. We hold our pencils by means of friction. Imagine a world where anything once started kept on moving until it hit something else!

We could not get along without friction; or rather, let us say, the plants and animals, the societies and the machines of the world have evolved in an environment which has always had to take friction into account, just as it has always had to take gravity into account. In short, for the kind of organization that Earth and its life have, *all* the physical forces are indispensable. Man is a part of this organization. Man can make the best use of the forces of nature for his own good only by the application of understanding and intelligence.

EXPERIENCE. *Friction develops heat.* Have the children rub their hands together vigorously. Let them examine the skin of their hands with a magnifying glass and see the rough places on them. The heat of friction may be effectively shown by rubbing wood with sandpaper. If, after the brakes of an automobile have been used a great deal, as, for example, in descending a steep hill, one feels the brake drums, they will be found to be hot. Primitive people sometimes made fire by rubbing pieces of wood together. A "Boy Scout Fire Drill Set" can be used for illustrating this. It can sometimes be bought in toy stores. The heat of friction ignites the inflammable material in the head of a match. Hot sparks fly from a grinding wheel in a machine shop. A nail drawn from wood is often warm. Sliding down a rope can burn one's hands and legs. Other examples may be named almost indefinitely.

EXPERIENCE. *Surfaces of different materials have different amounts of friction.* Pull a box along the sidewalk, the classroom floor, ice, or any other available surface. Notice the differences in the force required to pull it under different conditions.

EXPERIENCES. *Rolling friction is less than sliding friction.* Secure a wooden box and load it with something that is fairly heavy, such as blocks or books. Try to push it along the floor and note how hard it is to push. Have the children give each other "rides." Have several rollers at hand which have been cut from old broomsticks or other round wooden objects. These rollers should be somewhat longer than the box is wide. Place two or three rollers under the box. Load it as before and note how much easier it is to push. As the back end of the box leaves one roller, carry this roller to the front and proceed as before. In this way the box can be easily pushed across the room.

It is a nuisance to carry the rollers from back to front each time. It would be much simpler if the rollers were fastened in some way. Point out to the children the resemblance between a roller and a wheel. Probably the first wheels were disks cut from tree trunks which had been used as rollers.

Push a fairly heavy box along the floor or sidewalk; then transport the same box in a child's express wagon. Notice how much less the rolling friction of the wagon is as compared with the sliding friction of the box itself. If a spring balance is available, the actual force required in each case may be measured.

With thumbtacks fasten a strip of fine sandpaper to a table, rough side up. Roll a small wheel along the sandpaper. Now try to slide something along it.

If possible, let the children take apart a wheel containing ball or roller bearings. Such wheels may be found on bicycles, some velocipedes, and children's wheeled toys, and also in automobile junk yards. Study the construction carefully and decide where rolling friction has replaced sliding friction.

EXPERIENCE. *Friction is useful.* Take a smooth board and prop up one end high enough so that a toy wagon will roll down if placed on the board. Now place a small block of wood in front of each wheel. These blocks will prevent the wagon from rolling down if the board is not slanting too steeply. The blocks have sliding friction, which is greater than rolling friction.

Trucks often carry blocks which the drivers use in the same way when they wish to be perfectly sure that the truck will not roll downhill if left unattended.

Some children may by chance see an automobile spinning its wheels in an effort to start in mud or sand or on ice. Why do the wheels spin instead of pushing the car forward?

Locomotives and streetcars carry sand, which is sometimes sprinkled on the rails. Why is this done? Why are chains used on automobiles in snow, mud, or sand? Why do children wear rubber-soled shoes in the gymnasium? The answer to all these questions is the same: to increase friction.

Possibly a local garage man will be willing to show the children how a brake works. Notice especially the lining, which is used because it develops great friction when rubbed against the steel drums.

Children using rollers in moving a box.

EXPERIENCE. *Lubrication reduces friction.* Slide two blocks of wood over each other. Then rub the surface of each with soap or paraffin and notice how much more easily they slide. This illustrates lubrication. If a machine is not properly oiled and greased, the rubbing surfaces will eventually be worn down by the constant friction. A good engineer keeps his machine well oiled. Lubrication is needed, not only by large, impressive-looking machines, but by such common appliances as locks, hinges, pencil-sharpeners, and children's wheeled toys.

There are, however, places where lubrication is actually harmful. What would happen, for instance, if grease got on the friction surfaces of automobile brakes?

To show that water may act as a lubricant, rub the dry hands vigorously together, and then rub them together under water. In the second case they do not get hot. This is partly due to lubrication and partly to the fact that the water carries away some of the heat. Wash the hands with soap and water. There is less friction when hands are soaped than when water alone is on them.

EXPERIENCES. *Friction causes wear.* Examples of wear from friction may be found almost everywhere. When writing is done on the blackboard, bits of the chalk are worn off by friction and left on the rough board, making a mark. Chalk will not write on window glass, because the glass is so smooth that there is little friction. The "lead" (really graphite, a form of carbon) in a pencil wears off on the paper. Automobile tires wear by friction with the road. Parts of machines wear when poorly lubricated. They even wear somewhat when well lubricated, as some friction is always present. Stairs in public buildings are worn, sometimes dangerously, from the friction of many feet. Wood is worn by rubbing it with sandpaper. Metal may be worn by filing or grinding it. The heels and soles of shoes wear out through walking.

Show the children various worn objects, such as an old automobile tire, the wheel of an old roller skate, or tire chains which have been used for some time. Perhaps a friendly garage man will give or lend a few worn automobile parts.

Children have frequently expressed interest in where small, worn-out particles go. This is something to speculate about. One group of nine-year-olds decided quite rightly that a lot of the worn-out particles get into the air as dust. Have children examine a bit of dust with a hand lens.

Have children examine the steps or stairways in the school building. Perhaps stairways in a number of buildings and at home might be compared. In old buildings the constant wear by human feet has worn the steps down, and they may have been repaired.

Automobile parts, clothing, shoes, and rugs can be examined for wear. Here is an opportunity to develop values, a feeling for the care of materials. Perhaps an appreciation can be built for the service secured from an article, rather than an appreciation based upon its newness or vogue.

Machines

Man, through the use of machines, does his work more easily. It is difficult to think of a modern product which is not produced wholly or partly by machines. In many cases the work would have been impossible without the machine. In other instances the work could have been done without a machine or with very simple machines, but it would have required much more time, much more money, and many more men to perform it.

No one knows just when the first machine was used or what it was. Quite likely a prehistoric ancestor discovered accidentally that he could hit something harder if he used a branch of a tree than he could with his bare hands. Such a club is a machine. In moving a stone from the door of his cave he may have placed a stick under the stone to lift it and pry it away. This stick formed a machine which we know as a lever. Later on some cave man may have found out that a sharp stone would help him in cutting things. Stone Age men learned how to sharpen stones when they were unable to find sharp ones. Still later, men fastened handles to their sharp stones.

Other machines, which probably came into use somewhat later, are the pulley, which, before the Christian Era, was used to hoist things, the screw, which was used in presses, and the windlass.

Bow drills were first used to start fire and later for cutting gems and for carving stone in sculpturing. (Illustration p. 740.)

Water wheels were used for grinding grain in the fifth century A.D., and wind power in the twelfth century.

In the 1700's Newcomen invented the atmospheric engine, probably a forerunner of the steam engine, although it worked on a different principle. While endeavoring to improve the Newcomen engine a little later, James Watt invented the steam engine.

The development of man has not been a straight-line development for all mankind, nor without regard for time and place. There have been many civilizations. Some of these have been developed in comparative isolation from others. No one knows, for instance, whether the American Indians ever received any ideas from Asia, Europe, or Africa prior to Columbus's voyage. If not, the accomplishments in astronomical science, architecture, plant and animal breeding, and other fields were entirely independent developments.

The emphasis we wish to make here is that the inclined plane, lever, and club may have been invented *many times*. Likewise fire and its uses, magnetism, and static electricity may have been discovered independently by different peoples.

Different cultures passed through the "stone age" at different times. There are a few cultures left in the modern world that remain in the stone age. In most cases, however, such backward peoples have remained somewhat isolated from modern traffic routes.

It is difficult to conceive of the importance of some of the advances in civilization that re-

Man has used levers for many centuries.

sulted from certain inventions and discoveries. For instance, the club, fire, and the lever brought about revolutions for primitive man. Man was undoubtedly much more courageous after he discovered the club, for he could strike farther and faster with his arm than could most other animals. The club used as a lever helped him to do things he could not do otherwise. Fire brought with it the development of the family circle, the campfire, the telling of tales, the passing down of the tradition, table manners, the beginning of laws, and the council fire; and it extended the length of the day's activities, particularly the portion to be devoted to discussion, for now there was light at night. The fire also brought new friends —for the campfire attracted the ancestors of our modern dogs and at the same time frightened away more ferocious animals (p. 366).

What Are Machines? A *machine* has been defined as a combination of mechanical parts serving to transmit and modify force and motion so as to do work. While this definition accurately describes the machine from a strictly physical viewpoint, we may perhaps arrive at a better one from the standpoint of the elementary school if we consider what a machine does.

A jack, used for raising an automobile to repair a tire, enables a man to raise a heavy car with the use of comparatively little strength. A tractor makes it possible for one man, by pushing levers and pedals, to pull as much as many horses could. A power shovel enables the operator to fill a truck in a few minutes. A can-opener performs an operation which would require much strength without its aid. Examples might be multiplied indefinitely, but in each case it is seen that the machine enables a man to do work with less expenditure of muscular effort. In some cases the man merely controls the energy supplied by a motor or engine, while in others the man himself supplies the energy, but for a longer time

and with less force than would otherwise be possible.

Therefore we may define a machine as a device for enabling men to do work with the expenditure of less muscular force. It may also be considered as something that links a source of energy to the place where this energy can be utilized to do work. The main point, as far as human progress is concerned, is that one person, or a group of people working together, can do things with machines which could not be done before the machines were invented. Machines help to eliminate much of the back-breaking toil for mankind.

It is difficult to make a good short statement which will distinguish between a tool and a machine and which is not open to question. No attempt will be made to make such a statement here. Most people are able to make the distinction in their everyday speech.

For our present purposes, we shall consider that tools are machines.

Simple Machines. We shall see, later on, that every machine, no matter how complicated, is really a combination of a few simple types of machines. Thus an automobile, an egg-beater, or a clock is a combination of wheels, levers, inclined planes, and so on.

Writers of physics textbooks have for a long time distinguished between machines which are combinations of simple machines and the simple machines themselves. Machines which could not be analyzed into simpler machines were called simple machines. Unfortunately this distinction, easy to make in theory, presents difficulties in practice. As a result, different writers do not fully agree as to what the simple machines are. Physicists point out that, in a technical sense, machines never save work, since the work done on a machine is greater than the work done by the machine. Of course, this need not concern us, as we are willing to have this extra energy expended in order to get the work done.

Some simple machines.

It is felt in this book that the important thing for children in the elementary school is to realize that machines are often combinations of simpler types, rather than to become highly proficient in analyzing them to the last degree. For that reason, we shall use the phrase *simple machine* merely to mean a machine that is not complicated, instead of attempting to limit the term rigidly. Actually, there are two basic machines, the lever and the inclined plane. The other types are derivatives of these two. For example, the pulley, wheel and axle, and gears are forms of the lever, and the screw and wedge are forms of the inclined plane.

We shall see that with a machine man does not need to work as hard at any one moment as he would have to if he did not use a machine. However, with a machine man will have to work through a greater distance than if he did not use it. But since a man is limited in his strength, he can well afford to work over a greater distance. We shall see this principle in all the simple machines. Of course, modern man supplements his energy by using steam, electricity, the internal-combustion engine, and nuclear- and solar-energy generators; and so he has little to do but press buttons, shift gears, and steer. Of course, he also must take care of the machines and invent better ones as time goes on.

The Inclined Plane. One of the simplest of all machines is the so-called *inclined plane*. An inclined plane is merely a sloping surface. It is used to move an object to a higher level. Examples of the inclined plane may be seen almost every day. When new buildings are being built, workmen may often be seen pushing wheelbarrows full of concrete or other materials up slanting boards from the ground to a higher level. Many garages are built with the floor above the level of the ground. Inclined planes are used as approaches to these.

The gangplank leading to or from a ship is an inclined plane. A road winding up a mountainside is an example of a curved inclined plane. Stairs are really inclined planes with places to step on as we walk up or down. Workmen loading an object too heavy to lift directly upon a truck use a sloping board, or inclined plane, up which they push the object.

The inclined plane enables a man to do a piece of work gradually and raise an object more slowly but with less effort. Suppose, for instance, that a man wishes to load a 100-pound barrel of flour on a truck. If he lifts it directly, he must lift it five feet. If, however, he uses the inclined plane, which is ten feet long, he may roll the barrel over a larger distance with less effort. He has to push with a force of only about 50 pounds for ten feet. In the end he has accomplished the same thing; that is, he has lifted the flour from the ground to the truck; but he has done it by using less force. It makes no difference in the amount of work done whether he lifts the barrel directly or pushes it up the inclined plane. In one case he uses more force over a shorter distance, while in the other case he uses less force over a longer distance. The inclined plane is really a machine, because it enables the man to do work with the expenditure of less muscular force. This is spoken of as giving the man an *advantage*. It is a trade; the man trades distance for effort.

Measure the effort needed to pull the books up a short, steep inclined plane. Is there any difference in the effort?

EXPERIENCE. *To find the advantage in using an inclined plane.* Use a long board about eight or ten feet long as an inclined plane. Secure a rock weighing about ten pounds. Tie a rope securely around the rock so that it can be weighed. Weigh it by hanging it on a spring balance. This will show the weight of the rock, and what one would have to lift if doing so without a machine. By placing one end of the board on a box and the other end on the floor, one has an inclined plane. The height of the box can be measured. Now pull the same rock up the inclined plane with the rope, but fasten the spring balance to the rope so that you are pulling on the spring balance. Pull smoothly and read the spring balance. This should demonstrate that one does not have to pull as hard at any one time by using the inclined plane. However, the rock will travel farther up the inclined plane than the height of the box above the floor. To raise the rock a person works over a greater distance by using the inclined plane than if he lifted it up by "main strength and awkwardness."

The Wedge. The *wedge* is really two inclined planes back to back. As a wedge is forced between two objects (or into a substance), it pushes the objects apart. If it is forced in all the way, it pushes them apart a distance equal to the thickness of the thick edge of the wedge,

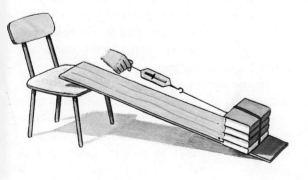

Measure the effort needed to pull the books up a long inclined plane.

but the force has been applied over a distance equal to the length of the wedge.

Knives and axes are really wedges. They force a substance apart. The point of a nail is a kind of wedge. Stakes to be driven into the ground are wedges. Pins, planes, and chisels are further examples of wedges.

EXPERIENCE. *To find the advantage in using a wedge.* Examine a wedge such as an ax. Note its thickness at some point. Measure this with the ruler and mark this point on the ax. Now measure the blade of the ax from the sharp edge. Note that to split a piece of wood apart to this point on the ax, it is necessary to drive the ax in the distance from the sharp edge to this point. So, again, one can split the wood with an ax, a task which would be very hard work without it, but one drives the ax the long distance across the blade. The same thing may be done with a kitchen knife.

The Screw. The *screw* is also an inclined plane. If you will examine a large screw closely, you will see that the thread really forms an inclined plane running round and round the screw. Many piano stools are built on the principle of a screw. The airplane propeller

An ax is a wedge, two inclined planes back to back.

and that of a boat are screws. A wood screw is a metal screw made to go into wood. Wood screws have pointed ends to enable them to pass into the wood more easily. They are really combinations of wedges and screws. Machine screws have blunt ends. They are used to hold together metal pieces in which holes have previously been drilled. Nuts, which are really pieces of metal with threads on the inside, may be used on machine screws, or one of the pieces of metal to be held together may have a thread on the inside of the hole. Bolts are similar to machine screws, but often have a coarser thread and are generally larger. A bolt always has a nut on one end, but a machine screw is sometimes without the nut. The distinction is unimportant except when buying screws.

EXPERIENCE. *To study the advantage of a screw.* Have children place a screw in some wood with a screwdriver. Note how many turns are made and that with each turn the screw goes into the wood the distance between the threads. Measure the length of the screw. Count the number of full turns necessary.

After the screw is firmly in the wood, it may be removed and examined by the children. Have them estimate the number of times the thread goes around the screw.

EXPERIENCE. *To examine a pencil sharpener and other familiar objects.* Have a group of children examine a pencil sharpener and report on how it works. Many pencil sharpeners are combinations of a wedge and a screw, and are termed spiral wedges.

Have children examine a meat-grinder at home, also a vise such as may be found at a workbench at home or in the industrial-arts shop. Note the screw used in a monkey wrench which helps to slide the jaws up and down.

Perhaps some children have been in a building such as a lighthouse, the Statue of Liberty, or the Washington Monument, where there is a circular stairway on the inside leading to the top. The stairway is an inclined plane and can be compared with a screw.

The Lever. The *lever* is a simple machine, and one of the commonest. The cave man who pried a stone loose with a stick was using a lever. Our arms are levers. The handles of hammers, baseball bats, and golf clubs are used as levers. Tools for prying, such as can-openers, nail-pullers, and crowbars, are levers. Many tools such as pliers, scissors, and nut-crackers, are levers. Wrenches are levers. In fact, it is rather difficult to name a common tool which does not include some form of lever in its construction.

A lever is simply a stiff bar, straight or bent, arranged so as to turn about some fixed point. The fixed point is called the *fulcrum.* The distance from the fulcrum to the weight which is to be moved is called the *weight arm,* and the distance from the fulcrum to the place where the force is applied is called the *force arm.* In teaching children about levers it was found that they tired of referring to the parts of the lever as "this place" and "that part" and asked if there were not names for the parts. As the need arose, they were given the names of the parts—force arm, weight arm, and fulcrum. The names should not be forced on children, neither should they be withheld when they are actually needed. The concept of a fulcrum comes easily for many children. This, in large part, is because children are good observers of mechanical work done by their parents or other adults in the community. Many children seem to have derived the idea of a fulcrum experientially.

There are three possible arrangements of the various parts of the lever. In the first type, the force and the weight are on opposite sides of the fulcrum, as in the case of the crow-bar (p. 750). We push down on the force arm to move the weight up. In the second type, the

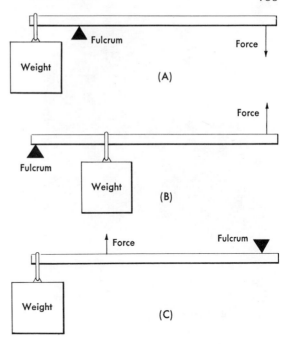

Three arrangements of the lever parts.

weight is between the fulcrum and the force, and we pull up to move the weight up, as in the case of the wheelbarrow (p. 756). In the third type, the force is between the fulcrum and the weight. In this case, a small movement of the force produces a large movement of the weight, as in the case of the elbow (p. 756).

Notice that in the first two arrangements of levers in the diagrams on this page the weight moves through a small distance, while the place where the force is applied moves through a large distance. A small force moving through a large distance is changed to a large force moving through a small distance.

Sometimes instead of transforming a small force into a large one, it is desirable to transform a small distance of movement into a large one. In this case, a lever of the first type may be used, with the fulcrum moved close to the force, or a lever of the third type.

Archimedes, an early scientist, was reported to have said that he could move the world

A lever of the second type and an inclined plane.

single-handed if he were given a lever long enough and a prop (fulcrum) strong enough.

EXPERIENCE. *To study the advantage of a lever.* There are frequent uses around school for a lever. Possibly a small playhouse has been built which may need to be moved to a new place. Or perhaps a box of blocks or garden tools needs to be relocated. If rollers (p. 748) are to be placed under the playhouse or box, a lever can be used to lift up one end in order to slip the rollers (perhaps broom or mop handles) under the structure to be moved.

Have children notice the long arm of the lever from the fulcrum to the place where they apply the energy (effort). Note the short distance from the fulcrum to the spot on the lever where the weight of the house or box is resting. Note the long distance the child or children working on the lever move in order to lift the structure an inch or so. Holding a yardstick still beside the hands of the children as they operate the lever will help to give a visual im-

pression. Place another yardstick beside the box or house to get a visual impression of the distance the weight is moved up.

The Wheel and Axle. Wheels have two different types of uses. One is simply as rollers to reduce friction. The other is to transform forces and motions. It is this latter aspect in which we are interested here. Very frequently the two uses are combined, as, for instance, in the rear wheels of an automobile.

If a wheel of any kind is fastened rigidly to a rod in such a way that turning the wheel turns the rod, the combination is called a *wheel and axle*. It is obvious that a small amount of force applied to turning the rim of the wheel will cause a large twisting force on the axle. Doorknobs, screwdrivers, automobile steering wheels, grindstones, and windlasses are all examples of wheels and axes.

The wheel and axle is a force-multiplying device. A large movement of the rim of the wheel produces a small movement of the axle.

The wheel and axle may be thought of as a development of the lever. If we consider each spoke of the wheel as a lever attached to the axle, we can easily see how this is so. Wheels which are solid may be considered to have many, many spokes.

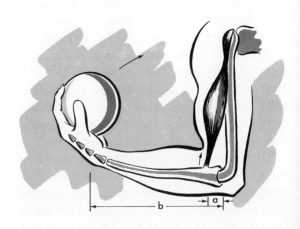

A lever of the third type.

EXPERIENCE. *To study the advantage of a wind-lass.* Show the illustration of the windlass on page 763 to some child who exhibits ability as a leader in this type of activity and encourage him to build one for class use. For more definite instruction concerning the construction of a windlass or hoisting machine, see the Experience on page 763. Find a weight, such as a stone, and fasten a rope around it so you can determine its weight by using the spring balance. Now fasten the free end of the rope to the roller or axis of the windlass. Next fasten the spring balance to the handle on the wheel and pull on the spring balance, to exert a pull on the rope. The spring balance will show how much one has to pull to lift the rock. Have children estimate the larger distance the person moves the rim of the wheel, as compared with the actual distance the weight is lifted.

Gear Wheels, or Cogwheels. *Gear wheels* (often called *cogwheels*) are simply further developments of the wheel and axle. Gears are used to increase speed at the expense of force, and vice versa. An automobile, for instance, moves forward more slowly but with much more force in low gear than in high gear.

If we arrange two sets of wheels and axles with the rims of the two wheels touching, and then turn the smaller axle by means of a motor or an engine, the friction between the touch-

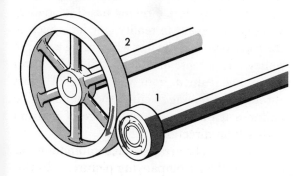

When wheel 1 turns, it turns wheel 2 by friction. Note direction of arrow in each wheel.

Gear wheels. Teeth are cut on the rims of wheels to prevent slipping. Note direction of arrow in each wheel.

ing rims of the wheels will cause the smaller wheel to turn the larger one. Suppose that it is five inches around the rim of wheel 1. Then when axle 1 turns once, a point on the rim of wheel 1 moves a distance of five inches. Suppose that it is thirty inches around wheel 2. Every time wheel 1 turns once it pulls wheel 2 five inches; and wheel 1 must turn six times in order to make wheel 2 go around once. Furthermore, wheel 2 goes around in the opposite direction from that of wheel 1. In this way speed can be reduced, since wheel 1 is turning more times than wheel 2.

If we were to reverse the process and have wheel 2 operated by some form of energy such as water power or electricity, we would find that wheel 1 would turn many times to one turn of wheel 2. We have, therefore, a device for transferring force and increasing speed.

In the foregoing case, the only thing which causes wheel 1 to turn wheel 2 is friction. If there is slipping between the wheels, some power is lost. To overcome this, teeth are cut on the rims of both wheels. These teeth mesh together and make slipping impossible.

More and more, in the interest of safety, the working parts of machines are covered in order to prevent accidents. This is a fine trend. However, it does mean that children do not have a view of how mechanical things operate. To remedy this, it might be well to have someone come in from some local industry to talk with the children. Perhaps an automobile dealer would talk to the children about how the gears and transmission work in a car.

If any children are interested, have them discuss how, in the car, we may increase force at the expense of speed, as when the car is in "low," or low speed (see diagram of gear wheels). They may also consider how speed may be increased at the expense of force, as when the car is in "high," or high speed. Finally, the children may consider how we can reverse the direction of rotation of the car's wheels without reversing the rotation of the drive shaft, as when the car is in "reverse."

In lifting a house, in operating canal locks and irrigation gates, and for many other uses a special gear called a worm gear is often used. There are many complicated-looking combinations of gears to be found, but they all may be reduced to the simple principles explained above.

Gear wheels may be directly connected with each other, or they may be some distance apart and work together by a chain, as in a bicycle. In the latter case, they are called sprocket wheels. The chain may be replaced by a round or flat belt, as in the foot-driven sewing machine. A shoe-cobbler's shop may be useful to show a running shaft and belts. The wheels are called pulley wheels; but they have a somewhat different function from that of the kind of pulleys which we shall discuss in the next section.

EXPERIENCE. *To examine a bicycle.* Have some child bring his bicycle to school. Have him explain how it works. How is the sprocket wheel used? How does this eliminate slipping? How does the large sprocket wheel affect the force acting upon the real wheel? What kind of care should the bicycle be given? How is the rider's effort (energy) transferred to the wheels on the road? Roller skates might also be examined.

A teacher need not be an authority, but she can insist that children give good, accurate reports.

Pulleys. The *pulley* is a machine which has been used for hoisting and pulling since early times. It is usually used to multiply force or to change the direction of pull. In its simplest form the pulley is merely a wheel over which a cord or rope is passed. If you examine a flagpole, you can easily see that if the free end of the rope is pulled down one foot, the flag is raised one foot. In this case the pulley does not change either the amount of force or the distance, but merely the direction of pull. Sometimes this is a distinct advantage, as in raising comparatively light weights quickly. This type of pulley is used with clotheslines and window-shade cords. Sometimes water is raised from a well by this means.

EXPERIENCE. *To use a simple pulley.* Frequently there are opportunities for small children to make use of a simple pulley in connection with their play, as with a play elevator, a toy derrick, or a play dumb waiter, or in raising a flag. Children can see that there is an advantage in using a simple pulley to raise a flag. They can watch the custodian raise the flag, and they can often participate in the ceremony. The advantage is one of *direction,* to pull *down* on the rope, thus sending the flag *up,* while one remains standing on the ground. This simple pulley has this one advantage alone, for, in reality, one lifts much of the rope as well as the flag when using a simple pulley. In a sense one might think of it as an advantage gained from the saving of effort through not having to climb the flagpole. To children it may be an advantage of position rather than direction.

Pulleys can be arranged in combinations, as shown in the accompanying pictures. In this arrangement a pulley with one or more wheels is attached to the load and another pulley is attached to some fixed point. Notice that if

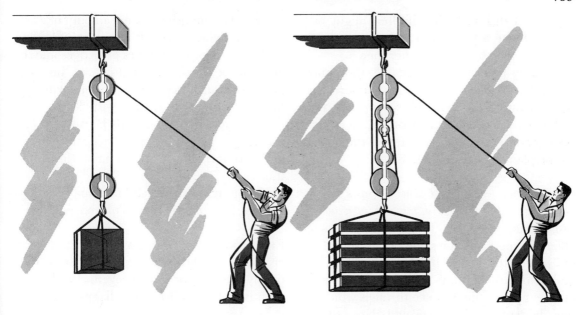

Pulleys. To lift a heavier weight requires more pulleys.

the weight is raised one foot, each of the ropes supporting it must be shortened one foot. Since the rope is one continuous piece, this means that the free end must be pulled as many times the distance the weight is raised as there are ropes supporting the weight. In the first picture the free end must be pulled two feet for every foot the weight is raised, and in the second picture the free end must be pulled five feet for every one-foot movement of the weight. A combination of pulleys, then, exchanges a small force moving a long distance for a greater force moving a shorter distance. The force applied is multiplied by the number of strands of rope holding the weight. The number of pulley wheels is not considered in computing this force. Of course friction in the pulleys causes some loss, as friction does in every machine.

Pulleys (called block and tackle) are extensively used in raising and handling the sails on sailing ships. They consist of a group of fixed and movable pulleys. They are also used in raising heavy weights, such as pianos, safes, machinery, in some kinds of elevators, and in construction work.

Additional Experiences with Simple Machines. In carrying out activities with simple machines, especially with young children, it is desirable, wherever possible, to work with materials which are of actual use to children.

EXPERIENCE. *Using the inclined plane.* Obtain a smooth board a yard or two long and support one end on a low box. Have the children try pushing something heavy up the inclined plane so formed and then let them try to lift the same heavy thing directly up on the box without using the plane. If the object is rather heavy for the children's strength, it will be obvious that the inclined plane helps them to do work with the expenditure of less force, but the force is exerted over a longer distance.

The inclined plane may be useful in aiding children to lift articles onto a child's express wagon in case it is necessary to transport them somewhere. In one class of young children working with boats the inclined plane was used to load "goods" on their toy boat. Sometimes tricycles, scooters, and toy vehicles of various kinds can be moved by children from one level to another by means of an inclined plane. In this case, the children might experiment with a long ramp and a short ramp by using a long board and a short one.

If spring balances are available, they may be used with older children to measure the forces required to lift the object directly and to lift it using the inclined plane. A roller skate may be used as a truck under the object on the plane to reduce friction.

EXPERIENCE. *An inclined plane decreases the effort at the expense of the distance through which anything must be pushed.* Try inclined planes of different lengths on the same box. Note that the longer the plane, the less the effort required to push anything to the top of the box, but the greater the distance through which it must be pushed. Use a spring balance to see that it takes much more force to pull a small wagon or car up the steep slope than it takes to go up the gentler slope.

EXPERIENCES. *Using wedges.* The commonest examples of wedges are probably knives. If a sharp and a dull knife are available, the usefulness of the wedge may be demonstrated by having the children cut with each of them and compare them. Knives are useful machines in the classroom. A sharp knife is a better wedge than a dull one. Children may be able to see the difference between a sharp knife and a dull one by using a magnifying glass.

It is easier to force a long gradual wedge into something than a short one, even though both are of equal thickness at the thick end. This is because less force is exerted over a longer dis-

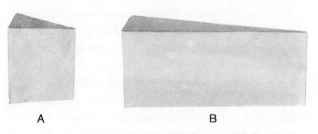

A   B

The longer wedge is easier to drive in.

tance to accomplish the same amount of work. In the drawing, wedge *B* is easier to use than wedge *A*. These two types of wedges may be cut out of wood and hammered into the ground in warm weather. The child will have more difficulty with *A* than with *B*.

A nail goes into wood easily because the end is a wedge. If possible grind or file the end of a nail until it is blunt. Such a nail is difficult to use.

In country districts children may see logs split for firewood by means of wedges.

EXPERIENCES. *The screw.* Fasten pieces of wood or metal together with screws. Notice how tightly they can be drawn together with comparatively little effort. (See diagram of screw, p. 869.)

Observe and examine common devices in which screws are used. Screw clamps and vises are to be found in the manual-training shop or on the custodian's workbench. Try squeezing a hard rubber ball or an old tennis ball in a vise. Have the children also try squeezing the ball with their hands. It can be squeezed more with the vise. A medium-sized steel vise can easily exert a pressure of about a ton.

If an automobile jack of the screw type is available, examine it to determine how it works. Screw jacks are combinations of screws, levers, and often gears as well.

In the home, screws are often used to clamp household devices in place. The food-chopper, for instance, is held to the table by a screw. Another screw forces the food through the cutters. One type of nutcracker employs pressure exerted by a screw to crack the nut.

Notice that many times (for example, in the vise and the food-chopper) screws are turned by means of levers. Compare the distance the end of a vise handle moves with the distance the jaw moves.

To show that the screw is really an inclined plane, cut a triangle out of paper. Have the

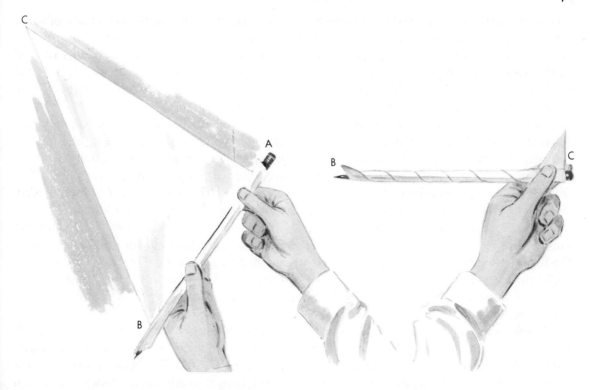

A paper triangle wound around a pencil forms a screwlike spiral. A screw is an inclined plane.

distance *AB* about the length of a pencil. Notice that *BC* is really an inclined plane seen from the side. Now, beginning with *AB*, roll the triangle about a pencil. Notice that *BC* now forms a screw.

Examine the propeller of a toy airplane or boat. Notice how it screws through the air or water. An electric fan is also a screw.

EXPERIENCES. *Using levers.* To show the usefulness of the lever obtain a block of wood or a small stout box and a stick or a narrow board. The block is to serve as the fulcrum and the board as the lever. If possible use the lever for some necessary work, such as lifting or moving a heavy box or furniture, or removing a rock from some land which the class is to use for a garden. The lever is used as illustrated. The point about which the stick turns is the fulcrum. Have the children try the lever with the fulcrum at different places on the stick.

The nearer the fulcrum is to the weight to be lifted, the easier it will be to lift it. In fact, if we multiply the weight to be lifted by the distance of the weight from the fulcrum, we shall get the same number that we get by multiplying the force which we must apply at the other end by the distance of our hands from the fulcrum. Obviously, if the fulcrum were placed exactly in the middle, it would be just as difficult to lift the weight by means of the lever as to lift it by hand. Place the fulcrum nearer to the hand than to the weight and have the children see that the weight is now much harder to lift than if the lever were not used at all, but the weight moves farther. Of course, in this part of the experiment, a light weight must be used.

The effect of the position of the fulcrum on the lever may also be shown if a seesaw is available. If the board is movable, place it so that it will be shorter on one side than on the other.

A heavier child must be placed on the shorter end to balance a lighter child on the longer end. If the seesaw is not adjustable, the heavier child must be placed nearer the fulcrum than the other child. The heavy child's weight multiplied by his distance from the fulcrum must be equal to the lighter child's weight multiplied by *his* distance.

A pair of scissors, a pair of tinsnips, and a pair of pliers form a group which will show clearly the effect of the position of the fulcrum. Ordinary scissors are designed to cut rapidly soft material, such as a cloth or paper. The handles are short, and the blades are long. The fulcrum—in this case the place where the two blades are joined—is near the place where the force is applied.

Tinsnips, or tinners' shears, are designed to cut sheet metal, such as tin, copper, or zinc. The handles are long, the blades are short, and the fulcrum is near the material to be cut.

Pliers are designed for squeezing, grasping, turning, or cutting hard substances. Their jaws are exceedingly short and their handles long. The fulcrum is nearest to the ends of the jaws and farthest from the handles. Of course special forms of pliers with long jaws are sometimes used to work in places which are hard to reach, but they have not so much strength as those with short jaws.

An ordinary nutcracker is really made of two levers. The fulcrums are at the end, then comes the nut, then the handles, where force is applied.

Examine tools designed for prying and pulling. Examples are crowbars, nail-pullers, box-openers, the claw ends of nail-hammers, etc. Notice where the weight is applied. The hammer is an example of a bent lever. Also, notice that a can-opener is a lever.

A knife handle is a lever. In cutting we often place the forefinger or thumb forward on the handle or along the blade. This acts as a fulcrum. The force is applied by the rest of the hand.

EXPERIENCES. *The lever is used in weighing.* A simple scales may be made from a good-quality yardstick. At the 18-inch mark drill a small hole through the yardstick. Through this hole pass a strong cord by which to hang up the scales. Make two scalepans from small tin pie plates, drilling three small holes at equal distances around their rims and tying cords in the holes. Drill two more holes in the yardstick at equal distances from the 18-inch

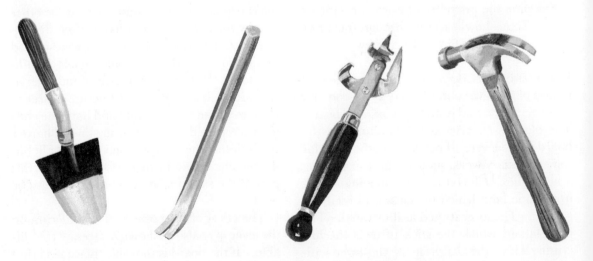

The position of the fulcrum varies according to the job to be done.

mark; the 6-inch and 30-inch marks are suggested. Tie the cords from the pie plates through these holes. Now hang up the scales from a support of some sort so that the pans do not touch anything. Balance the scales by wrapping wire around the light end of the yardstick. The substance to be weighed is placed in one pan, and known weights are placed in the other pan until they balance. Since the known and the unknown weights are at equal distances from the fulcrum, they are equal. Weights may be purchased from scientific supply houses, or made by weighing objects on a spring balance and marking their weights on them.

In another type of scales the unknown weight is hung close to the fulcrum, and the known weight is slid back and forth until the scales balance. In this case a small known weight can balance a large unknown weight. The known weight times its distance from the fulcrum is equal to the unknown weight times its distance.

If the school has a medical or gymnasium scales available for weighing the children, it is likely to be of a type which employs a lever. In this type a weight is moved back and forth until the scales balance. At a certain distance from the fulcrum, the sliding weight balances a certain weight on the platform. For a heavier child the sliding weight must be moved farther from the fulcrum.

EXPERIENCE. *The windlass.* The windlass is a simple hoisting machine. It is really midway between the lever and the wheel and axle. One may be made from a piece of broomstick or any wooden rod. Cut the broomstick about eighteen inches long. Through one end bore a hole large enough to take an iron rod or other stout metal rod. Prepare a base and two uprights, as shown, with holes in the uprights large enough for the broomstick to turn freely. The windlass is assembled as shown. A rope has its end fastened to the broomstick

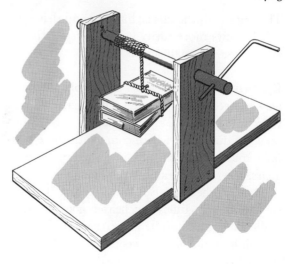

A windlass.

with a nail or a staple and is wrapped around the stick several turns. The metal rod is bent to form a crank and inserted in the hole in the end of the broomstick. The rod should fit tightly in the hole. The stick may be kept in place by small nails driven into it on each side of one upright. The windlass may be used for raising heavy weights.

EXPERIENCES. *The wheel and axle.* If a wheel is substituted for the crank in the windlass, a simple wheel-and-axle combination is formed. Notice that the handle of the crank as it is turned really traces the rim of a wheel in the air.

Screwdrivers, doorknobs, and the shutoff valves of many steam and hot-water radiators are illustrations of the wheel and axle. Have one child try to keep the shank of a screwdriver from turning while another child tries to turn the handle. The child at the handle always wins, no matter which child is the stronger. Drive a screw part way into a piece of wood and have a child try to remove it with his fingers. He will find this impossible to do, but he can easily do it with a screwdriver. Have children try using different sizes of screwdrivers.

The ones with the larger handles will drive or draw screws more easily. Small screwdrivers are for use on small screws.

EXPERIENCES. *Gear wheels.* Probably the best way to become acquainted with gearing is to work with a child's construction set. The books of directions which come with these sets offer many possibilities for learning about gears, wheels and axles, levers, etc.

Many eggbeaters also contain gears. Count the number of times the beater goes around while the crank handle is going around once.

Children may learn a good deal by taking a discarded clock apart. Before doing so, the teacher should be perfectly sure that the spring (*both* springs in an alarm clock) is completely run down. Avoid releasing the clock spring suddenly. Electric clocks have no springs.

What is the source of energy in a spring-driven clock?

EXPERIENCE. *Sprocket wheels.* Turn a bicycle upside down and spin the rear wheel by turning the pedals. Notice that the sprocket wheel which is attached to the pedals is larger and has more teeth than the one which is attached to the rear wheel. This causes the rear wheel

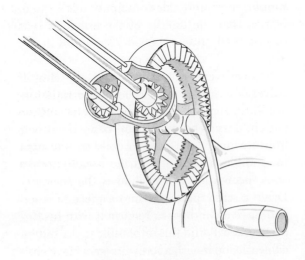

The gears of an eggbeater.

to turn faster than the pedal wheel. This means that the rider uses more force than he would use if the sprocket wheels were the same size, but he can go faster. Racing bicycles have extra large sprockets at the pedals and small ones at the rear wheels; ordinary bicycles do not. Why? Would you rather try to climb a hill on an ordinary bicycle or on a racing bicycle?

EXPERIENCES. *Using pulleys.* Young children need to become familiar with pulleys and their uses. Pulleys may be purchased from local hardware stores. Stretch a strong string with a small pulley on it across the room so that the pulley rides on the string. To the eye of the pulley tie another string long enough for the children to reach. A toy airplane or other toy may be tied part way up this string so that the children can pull it across the room.

Fasten a pulley at one side of the room near the floor. Through it pass a string or piece of clothesline long enough to reach across the room and back. A child may stand on the other side of the room and draw a toy cart *away* from him by pulling the end of the string *toward* him. This shows one use of a pulley— to change the direction of a pull.

To show that pulleys aid in lifting objects, fasten one to a long nail, board, or other support projecting from the wall of the room and use it as a device for hoisting. If two strands support the weight to be lifted, the child will have to pull only half as hard as if he were to lift the weight directly. If more pulleys are used with more strands, the pulling force needed becomes still less.

A spring balance at the weight and another in the pulling rope will enable children to measure the forces acting.

EXPERIENCE. *Recognizing simple machines.* The children can make a class list of all the simple machines that they can find in and near their homes and school.

Complex Machines. Gradually men have learned to combine the simple machines, forming more and more complex ones, until at present we have machines which can do things which a few years ago would have seemed impossible. Probably the first of such combinations was the use of a handle attached to the stone axes of the cave men. Such a tool is a combination of the lever and the wedge. Some of our modern machines involve so many of the simple machines that it is somewhat of a task to trace them all.

Steam Engine. The steam engine is perhaps the best type of complex machine to explain to children first, since it works on a very simple principle, although it has so many refinements that it looks complicated at first sight. Also, it is possible to obtain toy steam engines for classroom demonstration. Possibly a child in a class will have a toy steam engine that he is willing to bring to school. A cutaway model showing the inside is also useful.

The principle by which the steam engine operates was demonstrated more than two thousand years ago by the Greek mathematician Hero. His device consisted of a hollow base in which water was boiled. Steam was conducted to a globe and escaped through two bent tubes. This caused the globe to rotate just as water operates a rotating lawn sprinkler. This principle is the basis for jet propulsion, as will be seen later.

The largest part of a steam engine is the boiler, where the water is stored and heated to make steam. In real engines the water is usually heated by a coal or oil fire. In the toy engines it is heated by electricity or alcohol. In case the electrically heated type is used, make sure that the children do not become confused and think that it is an electric engine they are watching. As steam is continually being formed in the boiler, there will soon be too much of it for the boiler to hold, and it will push itself out into the pipe and thence into the cylinder. Here it keeps crowding in so fast that it pushes the piston to the other end of the cylinder. When the piston reaches the other end of the cylinder, a sliding valve in the steam chest next to the cylinder moves in such a way as to close the passage through which the steam has just been entering the cylinder and open another passage, so that now the steam enters the other end of the cylinder and pushes the piston back. The old steam is pushed out through the exhaust pipe. The back-and-forth motion of the piston causes this engine to be called a *reciprocating* engine.

The reason steam is able to push a heavy engine is that there is so much of it crowded in so small a space, making it possible for the steam to expand, thus creating power. A small amount of water makes a large amount of steam: 1750 times the original volume.

The rod which is attached to the piston is called the piston rod. The other end of the piston rod is fastened to the driving rod, which is in turn fastened to the flywheel, or driving wheel. This is often called the connecting rod instead of the driving rod. In some toy engines the driving rod and the piston rod are often combined into one rod. Notice that the driving rod is not attached to the center of the wheel. If it were not connected off center, the engine could not run. This is one way in which back-and-forth motion is transformed into rotary motion. It is the inertia of the heavy flywheel, or its tendency to keep spinning when once started, which carries it around past the "dead" point, where the piston is at the very end of the cylinder and for the moment is not being pushed by the steam.

Some toy engines have a throttle placed in the pipe which carries steam from the boiler to the engine. This has a handle on the outside. The handle turns a valve which blocks the steam pipe when it is closed but permits the steam to pass freely when it is open. When the steam is partly blocked, the engine runs slower.

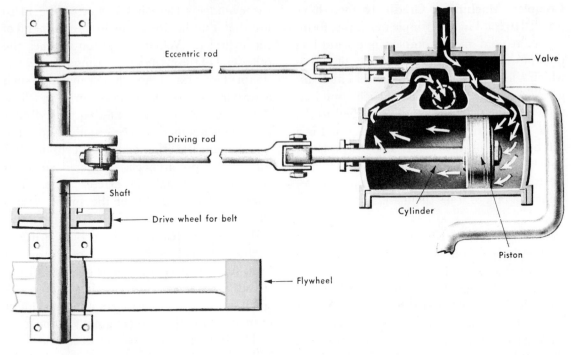

Eccentric rod

Valve

Driving rod

Shaft

Drive wheel for belt

Cylinder

Piston

Flywheel

Steam pushes the piston in a steam engine.

If the steam is not used in the engine fast enough, it keeps accumulating inside the boiler and the steam pressure keeps on increasing. The boiler would eventually burst if there were not some way for the steam to escape. In the early days of steam engines such boiler explosions were frequent and disastrous. To guard against explosions, all steam boilers, whether real or toy, are equipped with safety valves. In a toy engine the safety valve is usually kept shut by means of a spring. In real engines it is sometimes kept shut by a weight on a lever. In toy engines the safety valve is sometimes at the bottom of the "smokestack." Frequently it is located at the place where the boiler is filled with water. One should test the safety valve occasionally by pulling it open (cautiously!) while the engine is running.

In using a toy engine do not fill the boiler more than three-quarters full; otherwise there will not be sufficient room for enough steam to collect above the surface of the water. It is

very harmful to the boiler to heat it when there is no water in it, as this may melt the solder which holds the boiler together.

There are two main types of steam engines. We have discussed the reciprocating engine here. The other type, the steam turbine, will be discussed later (p. 772).

In the steam engine, fuel is burned outside the engine; this is an example of an *external-combustion* engine. The gasoline and diesel engines burn their fuel inside the engine, and are thus *internal-combustion* engines.

Boys and girls are living in a period in which the steam locomotive has been pushed into the background, and many may never see the great steam locomotives that raced across the continents with a great cloud of smoke following. Instead, they will know diesel engines.

However, it might be well to give them a feeling for the tremendous change that occurred in the world from 1830, as steam began to be applied to industry (p. 177). It is altogether possible there is a story of steam development in the immediate neighborhood. In many communities the first electric generators were run by steam engines, and even today many contend that steam plants are more efficient than water power. Edison used steam engines to run his generators in his development of electrical energy.

EXPERIENCE. *Watching water boil.* Help children place about 1 pint (2 cups) of water in a teakettle and put it on an electric plate. Let the water boil, but do not let the kettle go dry. This point can be determined when little or no steam comes from the spout. Note how slowly the water disappears, but how much steam seems to be leaving the spout. Water expands 1750 times; so 1 pint of water becomes 1750 pints of steam. We should recall that we cannot see the real steam. This may help to give children an appreciation of the power of steam.

Gasoline Engine. The gasoline engine is similar to the steam engine in that it has cylinders and pistons and utilizes a gas which is expanding. The gas which pushes the piston in the steam engine is water gas, that is, it is steam. In the gasoline engine, the piston is moved by the expansion of the exploding gasoline vapor instead of expanding steam.

Gasoline will not explode unless it is mixed as a gas with oxygen, or air which contains oxygen. In a gasoline engine this mixing takes place in the carburetor. The explosion always takes place at the same end of the cylinder, not at alternate ends, as in the steam engine. (Gasoline vaporizes easily. This is one reason that smoking is not permitted at filling stations or on the loading ramp at airports.)

The explosion is timed by the spark, when the piston has moved up and compressed the mixture. In this way the expansion of the exploding gas pushes the piston in a power

stroke. The burned gases are expelled in the exhaust stroke with the next upward movement of the piston. As the piston moves down again, a fresh mixture of gas and air is brought into the cylinder in what is appropriately called the intake stroke. This mixture of gas and air is compressed and ignited and so the cycle is repeated. Smooth running of the motor is the result of using several cylinders, thus assuring that one cylinder will always be delivering a power stroke.

In an automobile engine the cylinders are placed in a straight line, or else they stand out at an angle from either side of the crankshaft, as in a V-engine. The crankshaft is the main shaft, which is turned by means of the pistons. The piston rods may be attached as shown in the picture (p. 400). The illustration shows a method of changing back-and-forth motion into rotary motion.

Before the advent of jet propulsion, aircraft were driven by engines similar to those used in automobiles, but usually of the proportionally lighter, radial type with cylinders placed like the spokes of a wheel. Seven, nine, fourteen, or eighteen cylinders were used. However, the jet motor is rapidly replacing the piston engine in many types of aircraft and in some cars.

Since the explosions produce a great deal of heat in addition to the heat produced by the friction of the parts, means must be used to cool the engine to prevent damage. This is done by surrounding the cylinders with water. The water absorbs the excess heat from the cylinders. Of course the water would soon boil; so it in turn is cooled by being pumped through the radiator. Air is drawn through the radiator by means of a fan. The air absorbs the heat from the water.

Notice the train of events: The explosions produce heat. Some of this heat is transferred to the water. Heat is then transferred from the water to the air.

In most airplane engines the cylinders are

cooled by air blown directly against them. Some automobiles also have air-cooled motors.

Diesel Engine. Children will be very much aware of diesel engines. They might be taken on an excursion where they could see diesel engines pulling heavy trains. The diesel engine is very much like the gasoline engine except that it uses oil instead of gasoline as fuel, and the electric-spark ignition system is not used. In the four-stroke cycle diesel engine, the intake stroke admits only air. In order to make the oil-and-air mixture explode, the air is compressed to a high pressure in the cylinder before the oil is sprayed in. When it is sprayed in, the mixture immediately explodes. The reason for this is that the air becomes very hot when compressed, about 1000° F. so that no spark plug is necessary to ignite the oil. The cylinder must be made of much stronger metal than is necessary in a gasoline or steam engine in order to withstand such high pressure. The explosion forces the piston down in the power stroke, which is followed by the exhaust stroke.

The diesel engine is simpler than the gasoline engine. Since the air and oil are mixed after they are in the cylinder and the mixture is exploded by the heat of compression, the diesel engine needs neither carburetor nor spark plug.

Diesel engines were in the beginning heavy and rather slow. Their greatest use was for such services as driving ships and pumping water. More recently, however, diesels have been widely used in locomotives. Diesels use heavy and comparatively cheap fuel oil instead of highly refined gasoline; so their fuel costs are low. Since diesel fuel does not ignite easily in the open air, it is much safer to use than gasoline. Diesels are also giving highly satisfactory service in tractors, trucks, and busses. In many localities children will be accustomed to seeing trucks and tractors with diesel engines.

Some of the objections to diesel engines are overcome by the use of diesel-electric combinations, discussed on page 771.

Jet Propulsion. Children have often released balloons filled with air and have watched them shoot through the air. As the air escaped through the neck of the balloon, there was a push in the opposite direction that moved the balloon along. That is, the air rushed out in one direction and the balloon moved in the opposite direction. This is the same principle by which Hero's engine operated (p. 765). Sir Isaac Newton stated it thus: "For every action there is an equal and opposite reaction." The jet engine works in this manner. There are four parts to a jet engine,

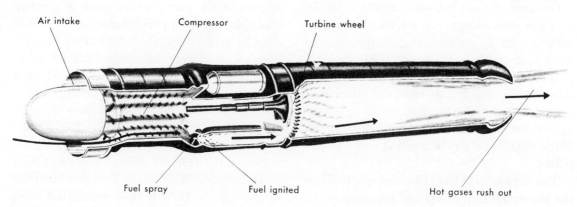

Air intake   Compressor   Turbine wheel

Fuel spray   Fuel ignited   Hot gases rush out

A jet motor. A plane is thrust forward by pressure from expanding gases escaping from the rear through the propelling nozzle.

namely, compressor, combustion chamber, turbine, and propelling nozzle. The jet engine takes in air from the surrounding atmosphere, compresses it, and delivers it to a combustion chamber. A kerosene-type fuel is injected into the same chamber and burns with the compressed air with almost explosive intensity, creating tremendous pressure. The forward thrust of the plane results from the pressure of the expanding hot gases. The pressure is exerted equally in all directions, and the gases escape through an opening in the rear, giving the plane a forward thrust at a tremendous speed. Jet speeds often exceed the speed of sound, which is about 760 miles per hour. Such speeds are referred to as *supersonic* speeds. Some research planes have gone faster than 4000 miles per hour, and speeds are continually increasing.

EXPERIENCE. *To study the action of jet propulsion.* Children can demonstrate jet propulsion by using toy balloons. Fill the balloons with air and then release them without tying the neck of the balloon. As the air escapes, the balloon will move in the opposite direction.

Rockets. As we go higher up in the atmosphere, the amount of oxygen decreases. Gasoline engines and jet engines rely upon oxygen for combustion, therefore their ascent is limited to about 13 miles unless means are found to supply them with oxygen. Rocket engines do not rely upon oxygen from the surrounding air for combustion. Instead, they carry their own fuel and also the materials to oxidize it, making it possible for them to function beyond Earth's atmosphere.

In rocket engines using solid fuels, the oxidizing material and the fuel are mixed together. They are stored and burned in the same place. Engines using solid fuels require no valves or pumps. They are safer than engines using liquid fuels, and can be prepared for launching ahead of time. However, it is hard to stop the burning of the fuel once it begins.

In liquid-fuel rockets, the fuel and the oxidizer are stored separately and are mixed in a combustion chamber by means of valves. There they are ignited. Gas is produced and escapes at the rear, as in jets, thus providing thrust. Liquid fuels have to be loaded at the latest possible time before launching, due to

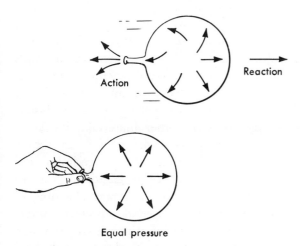

The balloon moves by jet-propulsion.

Action

Reaction

Equal pressure

When the balloon is filled with air there is outward pressure in all directions inside. When air escapes there is an action and a reaction.

View of the NASA Manned Spacecraft Center's Mercury-Atlas, carrying Astronaut John H. Glenn, Jr. Launch vehicles are designed for specific purposes. The Atlas-D used for the Mercury's Earth-orbital flights is a 1½ stage rocket providing 367,000 pounds of thrust. (Three Lions, N.Y.C.)

their chemical activity. Common liquid fuels are kerosene, alcohol, and liquid hydrogen. Oxidizers may be liquid oxygen, nitric acid, or nitrogen tetroxide.

A rocket may rise to a certain distance, then set off another rocket carried in its nose. This is called a two-stage rocket. Multi-stage rockets using a variety of fuels are used for launching satellites into orbit.

Plasma Jet Engines. These engines, sometimes called ion rocket engines, are of several different types. All are designed to generate a small amount of thrust, which presumably can be maintained for varying lengths of time;

in some, for months or even years. This makes some of them especially well suited to take over the propulsion of vehicles in space, after they have been launched by powerful chemical rocket engines. Their power is based on the use of superheated gases, such as nitrogen or cesium, whose atoms have been stripped, during the heating process, of some of their electrons. The gas is then an ionized gas, or *plasma,* a mixture of free electrons and positively charged ions. This plasma is capable of conducting an electrical current, and is subject to acceleration by magnetism from magnets built into the engine. These magnetic forces compress the ionized gas. It is then forced at high speed from an exhaust, as in a jet engine. This provides the small amount of thrust that may be needed to propel vehicles through space to other planets. The source of the energy to heat the gases may be a nuclear reactor, or the sun, through the use of a solar furnace or solar batteries.

Nuclear (Atomic) Reactors. A nuclear reactor is a means of obtaining energy from such fissionable elements as uranium or plutonium. When atoms divide in nuclear fission (p. 733), large quantities of energy are given off as heat and other forms of radiation. The heat may be used, as in any ordinary power plant, to generate steam, which in turn, will drive machines, such as electric generators or ship's turbines. In one type of reactor rods of uranium are permitted to disintegrate and give off heat, which is taken up by water, liquid sodium, or some other material. Blocks of graphite are placed where they can absorb some of the radiation. Rods of cadmium are moved into or out of the reactor in order to control the reaction. A heavy shielding of concrete or metal is needed to protect workers from harmful radiation, and this adds so much weight that it is not practical to use such reactors in small vehicles. Large vehicles, however, such as aircraft carriers, merchant ships, or nuclear submarines, can steam for many months or even years without needing to re-fuel. It requires only a few pounds of uranium fuel per year, whereas formerly hundreds of tons of petroleum fuels had to be provided to do the same job.

Electric Motor. Electric motors do not make use of gasoline or any other fuel. Their parts move when they are furnished with a current of electricity. The current flowing through a coil in a magnetic field causes the coil to move. (p. 841.)

Electric Generator or Dynamo. The electric gen-erator is exactly opposite in its purpose to a motor. The motor uses electricity to drive something; the generator is driven by some form of energy (see below) and the rotation of a coil in a magnetic field will produce elec-tricity. The motor converts electrical energy into mechanical energy; the generator con-verts mechanical energy into electrical energy (Chapter 23).

The generator may be driven by a steam, gasoline, or diesel engine, by a water wheel or turbine, or by any other source of motive power. (p. 841.)

Diesel-Electric Combination. In diesel locomo-tives the diesel engine, the electric generator, and the electric motor are combined. The diesel engine runs an electric generator. The electricity from the generator is used to run electric motors, which in turn drive the loco-motive. This roundabout combination gives a smooth, steady flow of power, and eliminates the need of a friction clutch to start the train. Rail-diesel cars use a fluid coupling, similar to that in the automatic transmission of some automobiles, instead of the electric drive.

In many steamships and naval vessels a turboelectric combination is used for very similar reasons. A steam turbine is used in these instead of a diesel engine.

The windmill is a source of power.

Windmills. Energy from the wind was uti-lized by the Egyptians over 5000 years ago to sail ships. As early as the twelfth century, windmills were used to grind grain and to pump water. Windmills are used in many areas today for pumping water and in some cases to drive generators.

Water Wheels. Many of us have stopped along the countryside and admired some picturesque water wheel which may have long since ceased to be useful. Possibly we have seen one which is still doing duty. The use of the water wheel as a means of grinding in a mill is not new. Various types have been used for many cen-turies. The *undershot* water wheel was one of the early types. This type is adapted to parts of a stream which are somewhat re-moved from falls. Where the mill can be lo-cated near a small waterfall, the *overshot* type of wheel is much more efficient. The overshot wheel is revolved partly by the force of the water moving in the direction of the stream and partly because the water falls to the lower part of the stream as the result of gravity. Water strikes the wheel at the top, and much of the energy of the falling water is changed

Note the design of the wheels and where the water strikes each wheel. The first wheel is an undershot water wheel; the second, is an overshot wheel.

to useful work. Gravity plays no part in operating the undershot wheel, except indirectly, in that it is responsible for the swift motion of the stream. Sometimes a *breast* type of water wheel is used where the falls are such that the overshot type cannot be conveniently placed. The water strikes the wheel at mid-point. Hence, this wheel combines some of the advantages of both types.

The purpose of a dam is to create an artificial waterfall where none exists naturally.

The Water Turbine. The water turbine is frequently used in the generation of electricity, where the fall of water is less than a few hundred feet. The distance the water falls is called the *head*. Where the head is over seven hundred feet, the Pelton wheel is generally used. Turbines in the hydroelectric plants are placed at the bottom of a waterfall. These turbines may be arranged so that the wheel is horizontal rather than vertical. Water is led to the wheels by means of large pipes called penstocks.

Each of these turbines is connected to a ver-

tical shaft. As the turbine wheel revolves, the shaft revolves. The upper end of the shaft operates electric generators.

Of course the turbines have numerous refinements and are really more complicated than the description above would indicate. The important principle for the elementary school is that the mechanical (moving) energy of water may be *converted* into electrical energy which is very useful.

Steam Turbine. Not only can a wheel containing blades be rotated by means of running water, but steam can also do the work. A jet of steam is directed against blades set in the rim of a wheel, at very high speeds. This jet of steam simply pushes the blades, causing the wheel to rotate. In commercial turbines there are a great many blades, and the moving steam is passed from one set to another until all the energy possible has been used to move the wheel.

Notice that the water wheel, the water turbine, the windmill, and the steam turbine have much in common. In all a *moving*

An electric power plant. Three steam turbines (left) *drive the electric generator* (right). *Each unit is covered for safety and efficiency.* (*Boston Edison Company.*)

stream of something is made to push against blades, eventually turning a shaft.

A toy steam turbine may be secured at a toy store. In the activities accompanying this section there are directions for making a toy turbine. The special advantage of the turbine is that it converts the energy of the steam directly into rotary motion without any intervening rods and cranks and without vibration. The turbine has no back-and-forth-moving parts. It is compact and clean. The steam turbine is a much more efficient machine for converting heat energy into mechanical energy than the reciprocating steam engine.

In localities where water power is not readily available, steam turbines are commonly used to run electric generators. Turbines are also extensively used on steamships. The principal disadvantages of the turbine are that it must run at extremely high speed and it cannot be reversed. In steamships the speed is reduced by gears before being used to turn the propeller.

Mercury vapor, instead of steam, has been used in some plants to operate turbines.

Jackhammer. If you live in an urban locality, you may have seen workmen engaged in tearing up the paved road or sidewalk by means of a machine which they hold in their hands and which seems to jump up and down, making a terrific noise. This is known as a *jackhammer.* It works in much the same way as the steam

Breaking up pavement with jackhammers.

engine, except that the piston is pushed back and forth not by steam but by compressed air. A machine on wheels which can always be seen near the jackhammer compresses the air which is to be used. A hose carries the compressed air from the compressing machine to the jackhammer. The rod at the bottom of the jackhammer, which jumps up and down when the machine is running, corresponds to the piston rod of a steam engine. The jackhammer is a simpler machine than the steam engine in that the back-and-forth motion of the piston rod is used directly and does not have to be transformed into rotary motion.

The machine which hammers rivets after they are in place is really a jackhammer, although it has a different name. It is called a *riveting machine*. Children might think of other machines using compressed air in the community, such as air brakes on trucks and pumps for the inflation of tires.

Water Pumps. Lift pumps are still used in some rural districts to raise water from shallow wells. These pumps do not directly lift water, but depend upon atmospheric pressure for their operation.

The column of water in the pipe is supported by air pressure, just as is the column of mercury in the barometer. Water is lighter than mercury, and instead of supporting a column only thirty inches high, as in the barometer, the pressure of the air will support a column of water thirty-four feet high. This means that under ideal conditions a lift pump cannot possibly work if the water in the well is more than thirty-four feet below the pump, since the air will not be able to push the water high enough to reach the plunger. In actual practice, water is generally not lifted above 28 feet by the lift pump.

Sometimes it is necessary to force water to a considerable height through long pipes. The *force* pump is a pump that can raise water to greater heights than a lift pump by lifting it part way and then pushing or forcing it still higher.

Force pumps were used in old-time fire engines for throwing a strong stream of water. They were also used for pumping the water supplies of villages and towns. Such large pumps were driven by steam or by other engines. At present force pumps are largely replaced by centrifugal pumps.

The Centrifugal Pump. The centrifugal pump depends for its operation on centrifugal force. In the centrifugal pump there is a kind of wheel with blades, called the *impeller*. The impeller looks somewhat like a fan. It is enclosed in a steel casing. There is an inlet pipe for water at the center of the casing and an outlet pipe at the rim. The impeller is whirled at high speed by an electric motor or some other source of motive power.

In operation, water is admitted at the center of the casing, opposite the hub of the impeller. This water is caught by the blades and whirled rapidly around. As the water is carried past the outlet opening, some of it flies out by inertia. This leaves a partial vacuum inside the pump, and more water is forced in by air pressure.

Like the turbine, which it resembles, the centrifugal pump has no parts moving back and forth. To run it, rotary motion does not have to be transformed into back-and-forth motion. This is always an advantage. Furthermore, the centrifugal pump has no valves to give trouble. Large-sized centrifugal pumps can handle enormous volumes of water in a short time.

Centrifugal pumps are used in many towns and cities to furnish the water supply. Modern fire engines also have centrifugal pumps. The cooling water in automobiles is circulated by pumps of this type.

Centrifugal pumps have made it possible for communities to utilize vast quantities of underground water. As a result, in many

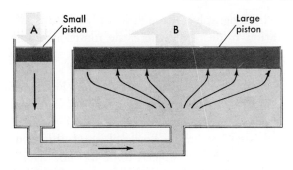

A hydraulic press. A force of one pound on the small piston can lift a weight of twenty-five pounds on the large one, because its area is twenty-five times as great.

localities the underground water supply is becoming exhausted. One of the great problems of the present period is to fill these reservoirs again.

A modification of the centrifugal pump is sometimes used to blow air in ventilating systems. Such pumps are called blowers.

Hydraulic Press. The French scientist Pascal showed that pressure applied to a confined fluid (liquid or gas) is transmitted equally in all directions. We can obtain a great force with the exertion of a comparatively small one. The hydraulic press consists of two cylinders, each filled with liquid. A piston fits into each cylinder. One cylinder has a much greater diameter than the other one. Pressure on the small piston is transmitted through the liquid and forces the large piston upward. This principle is made use of in lifting heavy objects, for compressing objects or in brakes.

EXPERIENCE. *Making a model water wheel.* Obtain a large spool and several pieces of sheet copper, or tin from a can. The pieces of metal should be about as wide as the spool is long and of uniform length. Bend the ends of the pieces at right angles, and tack each piece to the spool, forming a sort of fan or bladed wheel. Use small tacks so as not to split the spool. Prepare a base and two uprights of wood. The axle may be a pencil or a piece of

glass tubing. Hold the wheel under a faucet so that the water strikes the blades. This represents a water wheel or very crude water turbine.

In one class a water wheel was made of a spool on which electric wire had come. Six blades were made of sheet copper, each about three inches long.

EXPERIENCE. *Examining steam engines.* Children should have an opportunity to examine toy or model engines. A cutaway model of a steam engine will also prove useful. Be sure the children realize that they are looking at a cutaway model, not an engine which can work.

EXPERIENCE. *To observe a pin wheel.* Make a paper pin wheel. Blow against the vanes. Place it near a radiator or ventilator. Hold it in the breeze. Move it rapidly through the air. In what ways is it like a windmill or a turbine?

EXPERIENCE. *Devices to change back-and-forth motion into rotary motion are useful.* Children should observe devices which are used to

A homemade water wheel.

change straight motion into rotary motion or vice versa. The steam engine is one example. The crank is another. Children can no doubt suggest other examples.

EXPERIENCE. *Observing machines at work.* Visits may be made to the local water works, to an electric generating plant, to road and building construction, to a farm where agricultural machinery is in operation, to a factory, and to observe bulldozers and tractors.

Notice the workmen you may see. Are they merely contributing muscle labor, as in digging, lifting, etc.? Are they performing the same motions over and over again (as in machine tending)? Are they actually building, developing, or originating something? Do the workmen you see need to have good judgment? Which ones?

What is the immediate source of the energy used by the machines? Can you trace the energy back of this "source"? Tracing the energy to its source can be recorded by chainlike expressions, such as gasoline⟶petroleum ⟶plants and animals of long ago⟶sun's energy of long ago.

Observations of work in the community can be done at all levels of the elementary school with different purposes in mind. Young children can gain some understanding of the use of energy and the value of machines, while older children, particularly those in upper years, begin to show interest in the nature of vocations and their own individual plans.

These observations can lead to a study of vocations. For those with special abilities in science, trips can be conducted to the laboratories of some of the industries. Visit the laboratory at the local water-supply plant. Most industries are happy to co-operate with teachers.

These trips can be combined with art work through the development of murals and records; with history, through a study of how man has done some of this work in the past; and with geography, through a study of transportation routes and where the materials came from that are used.

EXPERIENCE. *Working with levers.* (For older children.) Make working models of the three types of levers (p. 755). You will need three yardsticks or similar pieces of wood, three fulcrums, and three objects to be moved. Demonstrate the various positions of the fulcrums, the objects, and the forces applied.

Make a working model of the forearm raising an object. This is an example of a third type of lever.

Performance of Machines. In ordinary conversation, the word *power* is used in a way which is not strictly accurate from a scientific point of view, for it is used as a synonym for the word energy. Power is the rate at which a machine does work. Therefore, in considering power, the time it takes to do a bit of work is necessary information.

Power is expressed in terms of *horsepower* and *watts*. If we express the power of a machine we may use the term horsepower; if we are speaking of electricity, we use the terms watts and kilowatts.

It was only natural, with the coming of steam and the industrial revolution, that power should have been expressed in terms of what up to that time was considered the most powerful "engine," the horse.

If a machine can lift 100 pounds to a height of 5 feet in 1 second, the machine does 500 foot-pounds of work per second. Horsepower was estimated on the basis that a horse does work at the rate of 550 foot-pounds per second. Some automobile engines can operate with the power equivalent to 300 horses, or 300 horsepower.

The power of rocket and jet motors is usually expressed in terms of *thrust*. Some rocket motors develop a thrust of more than a million pounds, and constantly increasing sizes are being designed. Several such motors may be combined in a cluster to give greatly increased power for launching an ever-growing array of satellites.

All machines develop some friction. The energy which is used in overcoming this friction is lost, so far as useful work is concerned. Often energy is lost in other ways. For instance, the parts of most machines move in the air. The entire machine, in the case of a train, an automobile, or an airplane, must move through the air. Some energy is used merely on pushing the air aside.

On account of these and other losses, we are never able to get out of a machine as much energy to do useful work as we put into it. If the losses are small in comparison with the useful work, we say the *efficiency* of the machine is high; but if the losses are large, we say the efficiency is low.

Efficiency is usually expressed as the useful work done by the machine divided by the work put in. This fraction is usually expressed as a per cent. Thus, if we have a simple pulley, and it takes a downward pull of 100 pounds to raise a 90-pound weight, the machine is $\frac{90}{100} = .9 = 90$ per cent efficient.

Many of our most common machines are surprisingly inefficient. The very best steam engines are not more than 22 per cent efficient. Gasoline engines are from 20 per cent to 30 per cent efficient. The efficiency of some diesel engines is nearly 50 per cent. The reason for the low efficiency of these machines is very complicated; but it is inherent in their nature, and in some types little can be done to improve it (see below).

One method of making vehicles more efficient at high speeds is to *streamline* them. (p. 743.) Air resistance is negligible at low speeds; but above forty miles per hour it becomes important, and its importance increases rapidly as the speed is increased. Streamlining the body permits the air to slip by it easily instead of pushing against it so much. It is surprising to realize just how important streamlining is for fast travel. At high speeds the old-fashioned nonstreamlined vehicle may actually use more fuel in overcoming air resistance than it does in making the wheels go around. Streamlining is even more important in the case of airplanes. Once an airplane is in the air, the only resistance it encounters is that occasioned by pushing itself through the air.

The fact that the efficiency of certain types of engines is not likely to be much improved does not mean that machines as a whole cannot have their efficiency raised. One of the directions in which development is likely to take place is along the line of improved

Higher airplane speeds require better streamlining.

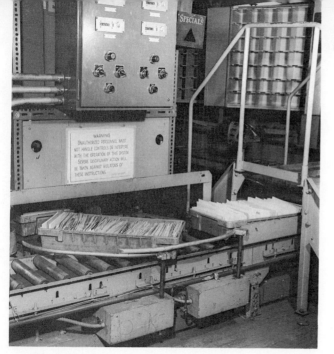

Control panel shunting mail into aisle for separation. (Three Lions, N.Y.C.)

efficiency. Engines of new types may be invented. There is no reason to suppose that man has invented all possible types of engines.

Man may increase the efficiency of the use of energy after it has been made available by engines. To do so will aid in the conservation of our fuel resources.

Automation. Automation is thought of as machinery that moves materials and performs certain necessary operations without human help, as in a bottling factory; or as controls or devices that will maintain or regulate machinery so that it works properly, such as in a thermostat; or as machinery that manipulates or works with information, such as computers of various kinds and degrees of complexity.

Degrees of automation or mechanization are recognized as extending from the use of simple hand tools to the machines that solve problems, that make corrections in work while operating, or that anticipate a certain kind of performance. Others combine production machinery with the machines that handle information. Some machines are even adjusted to lubricate and repair themselves.

Developments in the field of *microelectronics,* making possible the use of extremely small parts that will switch, amplify, and change electric currents make possible more compact and more complex machines, such as computers. These small parts may also increase the efficiency with which the energy is used that makes the machine run.

Computers can be built to do a great many jobs. They are essentially machines that will pick up information by means of electronic devices; manipulate it as directed and then give the result, changing the electronic signals into information that has meaning. Some are built that will "store" information.

Automation has become increasingly important through the years. Some industries, such as oil refineries, are so complex that it is impossible to operate them without automation. Farmers have had to rely upon primitive tools and their own muscle power to handle tons and tons of materials. Automatic and multiple-use machinery now enables them to produce more and better food in a fraction of the time it did take. Automatic road machinery promotes rapid transportation. Automation does things that men cannot do as well; and it frees men for more creative tasks and eliminates much drudgery.

EXPERIENCE. *To discuss experiences with automation.* Children may be interested in relating any experiences they have had with automation. Where did they find it? At home, at school, or elsewhere? What is the source of the energy that runs the machines? How could the work be done by people if they did not have the machines? How much time would it take? Could satellites or man be put into orbit without automation? Children have many experiences with different degrees of automation. The cold drink, sandwich, candy, and stamp machines are all common examples of machines with a limited amount of automation.

Man and Machines in the Future

In this chapter we have tried to explain how man puts to his use some of the energy which comes to Earth from the sun. To avail himself of this energy, man uses his knowledge of physical principles and builds machines in accordance with these principles. These machines enable him to get his work done with the use of less of his own muscular energy.

New inventions create new wants, which in turn call forth still other inventions. A century ago, for example, only a few visionaries could have foreseen that many people would want automobiles. The automobile, in turn, called forth many machines to produce it and to supply and service it. Presumably in the future we may look for other wants still undreamed of.

Viewing the future in the light of the past, he would be a rash person indeed who would venture to make more than a general guess as to the machines of the future.

EXPERIENCE. *To see that there are many kinds of vocations.* Have children study the classified telephone directory of a large city. Note all the kinds of work. Can they guess what each of the vocations listed is? Use the dictionary and find out about a few. Through science man makes new lines of work.

Sheer muscular labor will gradually be reduced or eliminated. Many kinds of work now done almost wholly by hand, such as housebuilding, will be done by machinery.

Energy will probably become more plentiful with the development of nuclear and solar sources. As a result, energy will become cheaper to produce and hence will be used more freely in the home. At the same time, articles requiring a great deal of energy to make will become cheaper.

New knowledge about the behavior of atoms and their parts, heat and cold, magnetism and other forces sometimes called "space-age principles," will be applied increasingly to the making of new products and the improvement of old, giving rise to many new lines of work.

We have seen that man has available what seems like an inexhaustible source of energy—the sun—and he is learning how to make use of it. It is probable that as the demand for energy increases, man will depend more and more upon the direct use of the sun's energy.

Magnetism and Electricity

Magnetism

Magnetism is a popular topic with children in the elementary school. It is a subject which lends itself well to learning through experimentation and is appropriate to all levels of the elementary school, beginning with the kindergarten. It has advantages in that it is an almost inexhaustible subject, permitting activities and learnings at later levels.

The division between magnetism and electricity is a purely arbitrary one, mostly for convenience. In nature such a hard-and-fast division does not exist.

A lodestone is a natural magnet. (Ward's Natural Science Establishment.)

Magnetism Is an Old Study. Magnetism is a very old subject. As early as 585 B.C. philosophers noted some of the properties of the lodestone.[1] The credit for discovering that a freely suspended, or floated, lodestone comes to rest in an approximate north-and-south position, therefore acting as a compass needle, is claimed for many peoples—the Greeks, Phoenicians, Chinese, and Arabs.

An early European reference to the mariner's compass occurs in the works of Alexander Neckam (1157–1217), one of the English schoolmen. He writes as follows in his book *De Utensilibus:*

If, then, one wishes a ship well provided with all things, one must have also a needle mounted on a dart. The needle will be oscillated and turn until the point of the needle directs itself to the north, thus making known to the sailors the route which they should hold while the Little Bear is concealed from them by the vicissitudes of the atmosphere.

Although natural magnets and magnetic compasses have been used for centuries, there

[1] Often spelled *loadstone.*

is much that remains to be discovered by man about magnetism. In recent years, many important discoveries have been made about magnets, but there is still much that is not known about the great force called magnetism. It is well for children to know that the magnets which seem to be mere toys are a great challenge to scientists.

Kinds of Magnets. There are several kinds of magnets—the natural magnet, bar magnet, horseshoe magnet, U magnet, and electromagnet. These may be divided into two types—*permanent* magnets and *temporary* magnets. All the foregoing types may be classified as permanent magnets except the electromagnet, which is temporary.

Natural magnets, or lodestones, were known as early as 585 B.C. They are made of an iron ore called magnetite and when suspended assume a north-and-south line. The word *lodestone* means "leading stone." These lodestones are found at different places on Earth's surface. They are called *natural* magnets because they are made by natural processes rather than by artificial means. They probably secure their magnetism from Earth (p. (788–790).

It is probable that the first magnetic objects known in Greece came from an iron-smelting district in northeastern Greece, called Magnesia, whence the name magnet. Bar, horseshoe, and U magnets are essentially the same except for shape; that is, the horseshoe and U magnets may be thought of as bent bar magnets. Children frequently bring horseshoe magnets as well as bar magnets of the toy type to school, and in some regions they may have U magnets.

These magnets, including the lodestones, are called permanent magnets. It is true that these magnets can lose much of their magnetism, particularly if they are not treated with proper care. However, they are permanent in the sense that the magnetism can

Magnets are made in many different shapes.

not be turned on and off. These magnets can retain their magnetism for years, perhaps even decades. The Experience on page 783, entitled "Keeping magnets in storage," if followed, will keep magnets in good condition.

However, the subject of magnetism, with its tremendous contribution to the new developments of energy, should not be left to the chance that children may possess magnets. Every school should have available for use a sufficient supply of magnets of all these types so that children can have a background of experience with magnetism. To do many of the Experiences listed in this chapter, not less than a pair of each kind should be made available.

They can usually be purchased in local stores, or in school or scientific supply houses. It is recommended that a school purchase some of the magnets made of the alloy called "alnico" and described later (below), because they provide such satisfactory results in the Experiences described in this chapter.

The electromagnet is a soft-iron rod surrounded by a coil of wire through which electricity is made to flow. This is temporary in that the rod is magnetic only as long as the electricity flows through the coil (p. 796).

Magnets Attract. *What Kinds of Substances Will a Magnet Attract?* Secure different kinds of substances, such as paper clips, pins, needles, a tin cup, paper, rubber bands, chalk, pieces of wood, and coins of various denominations. Bring a magnet near them. What objects are attracted by it?

Objects made of iron and steel are attracted by the magnet. Iron and steel are therefore called *magnetic materials.* Cobalt, nickel, and certain alloys are magnetic; but generally children will not have opportunity to observe their magnetic qualities.

A tin can will be attracted by the magnet, since it is made of iron coated with tin. It is the iron that is attracted by the magnet and not the tin. Not all pins are attracted by the magnet, since some are made of brass or other substances.

Nickel to many people is associated with some of the pieces of money used in various countries, and particularly the five-cent piece used in the United States. However, this coin is an alloy of various metals and is not attracted to a magnet. Some coins, such as pennies, and some coins of various nations made during World War II when there was a shortage of critical materials, used iron as one of the elements of the alloy. As a result, many pennies and other coins of small denomination are attracted to magnets.

The alloy called *alnico,* containing alumi-num, nickel, cobalt, and iron, is used in making magnets. Magnets made of alnico are very good permanent magnets. It is interesting to note that many magnetic toys now on the market use alnico magnets. These toy magnets are usually quite small, and are frequently concealed to contribute an element of magic to the top (p. 416).

EXPERIENCE. *Magnetism may affect a watch.* In working with any kind of magnet, be careful not to bring it near a valuable watch. The steel parts of the watch may become magnetized, and it will be necessary to have a jeweler remove the magnetism.

The question may be raised, "Why does magnetism harm some watches?" In every watch there is a tiny balance wheel which revolves back and forth regularly and thus keeps time. The spokes of this wheel are made of steel. If they become magnetized, they tend to assume a north-south position like a compass. This tendency interferes with the regular motion of the wheel and spoils the timekeeping of the watch. Other steel parts of the watch are also affected in much the same way.

Some watches are constructed with an iron case in such a way as to protect the works from any effect of a nearby magnet. The case may be thought of as a protective cage. Such watches may be called by various names, such as magnetic proof, antimagnetic, and so on. Some children's watches are magnetic proof. Many people find it necessary to carry watches that are protected in this way because their work takes them into places where there are strong magnets. Such watches may still become magnetized if exposed to very strong magnets.

Examine a cheap watch or alarm clock to see the little balance wheel mentioned above. It is not wise to touch the mechanism.

Where Is the Strongest Attraction on a Magnet? Hold the middle of a magnet near different iron objects. Repeat with the end of the magnet. Is there any difference?

Dip the magnet into a package of small iron tacks, thumbtacks, or iron filings.[2] To what part of the magnet do they tend to cling?

The magnetic force of attraction seems to be concentrated near the ends of a magnet. These ends are called *poles*. In a horseshoe magnet the bar has been bent and the poles are close together. This brings the strong parts of the magnet together, thus increasing its lifting power.

Ordinary magnets have one north and one south pole. A lodestone may have several poles, but always as many north as south poles. There is no such thing as an *isolated* pole.

EXPERIENCE. *Locating the poles of a lodestone.*[3] If you have a lodestone, or natural magnet, you can find the poles by determining where the magnetic force of attraction is concentrated. Dip the lodestone into some tacks, small paper clips, or iron filings. They will cling in bunches at the poles. Bring the lodestone close to a compass. The needle of the compass will point to a pole of the lodestone. Lodestones can be secured from school or scientific supply houses, or they may be found in deposits of magnetite, an ore containing iron.

EXPERIENCE. *Making a magnet.* To magnetize a piece of steel, such as a knife, scissors, or needle, rub one end of a magnet, such as the north pole (and always the same end), along the object, always in the same direction. Press gently and rub slowly. When you come back for another stroke, lift the magnet a distance up in the air and come back above the

Magnetizing an iron nail. Some are more easily magnetized than others.

blade. Repeat for at least twenty strokes. Let the children magnetize various steel objects that they use. (See illustration above.)

EXPERIENCE. *Keeping magnets in storage.* In order to keep magnets in good condition they should be wiped before storing with a little oil to keep them from rusting. They should be put away in a dry place. Lay a piece of soft iron across the poles of a horseshoe or **U** magnet. Store bar magnets by twos so that the north pole of one magnet is beside the south pole of the other. Place a piece of soft iron across the ends of the magnets. Soft-iron nails may be used. Soft-iron pieces used in this way are called *keepers,* because they help to keep magnets strong.

Magnetic Transparency. All substances allow magnetism to pass through them. In this they may be considered as *transparent* to magnetism, just as glass is transparent to light, for light can pass right through the glass. But not all substances are equally transparent to magnetism. By performing the following Experience, children can see that a piece of

---

[2] In some regions, magnetite sand or iron filings in small quantities have been secured by pushing a magnet through sand. Iron filings can also be secured by cutting up steel wool. They can also be purchased at school and scientific supply houses. Some children with special aptitude for this field have filed nails and collected the particles.

[3] Lodestones are very challenging to children, and it would be advisable for every school to have a number of them for study.

iron is not nearly so transparent to magnetism as are other substances. In fact, soft iron will, for the most part, protect an area from magnetism. The amount of iron necessary depends upon the amount or strength of the magnetism.

EXPERIENCE. *Magnetism acts through most substances.* Place a piece of cardboard over a handful of tacks. Then place over the cardboard a pole of a magnet. The tacks will cling to the cardboard on the side away from the magnet if the magnet is a strong one. Repeat the experiment with other available materials, such as glass, copper, or lead in place of the cardboard. Notice that the magnetic attraction passes through all these substances. Children sometimes do this as a trick by placing paper clips or other iron objects on top of tables and moving a magnet beneath the table, making the iron objects move about as if by a mysterious force. If an iron plate (a stainless-steel pie plate) is used instead of the cardboard, little or no attraction is exerted; in other words, an iron plate will partially or entirely screen the region beyond it from magnetic attraction.

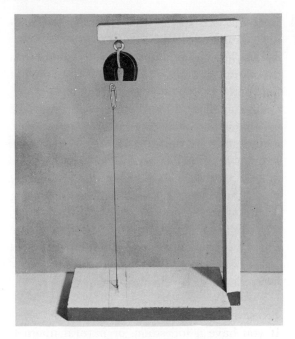

The magnet attracts the paper clip.

This helps to explain how watches are made magnetic proof (p. 782). A suitable piece of iron may be cut from a "tin" (really tin-coated) can.

EXPERIENCE. *To test substances to determine whether magnetism can pass through them.* Fasten a paper clip to the bottom of a stand by a fine thread as shown in the illustration. The paper clip should be suspended in mid-air so that it does not quite reach one of the poles of the magnet. Now pass thin strips of various kinds of material through the gap between the paper clip and the magnet, such as paper, cloth, wood, iron, coins, and so on. What happens?

This Experience develops the same meanings developed by the simpler method. However, it will provide children who have special abilities with an opportunity for leadership in constructing the stand and setting up the Experience for all.

Magnetic Poles Which Are Unlike Attract Each Other. Take two bar magnets; bring them to-

Magnets attract iron through most substances.

gether so that the two unlike poles, north and south magnetic poles (usually indicated by "N" and "S" marked on the magnet), touch each other. Pull them away from each other. Notice that there is a tendency for them to cling together; in fact, you can pull one magnet about with the other one. Now bring them together so that two like poles (north and north or south and south) touch each other. Notice that there is no tendency for them to cling to each other. In fact, the two magnets tend to push each other away.

Children like to dip the north pole of the magnets in bright paint. In this way they can tell at a distance the polarity of an end of a magnet. Of course, whatever color they adopt for a pole should be applied consistently on all magnets. Blue is frequently adopted as the color for the north polarity. Red could then be used for south polarity.

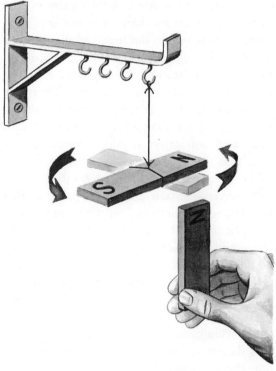

Like poles repel.

EXPERIENCE. *Unlike magnetic poles attract each other; like poles repel each other.* Hang up one bar magnet by a piece of cord or thread as in the illustrations here, so that it can swing about freely. Bring near one of its ends, first the north pole and then the south pole of another magnet. Notice what happens when unlike poles are brought together; when like poles come together. The north pole of the suspended magnet should be attracted by the south pole, and the south pole should be attracted by the north pole. On the other hand, the south repels the south, and the north repels the north. This illustrates a law of magnetism, namely, unlike magnetic poles attract, like magnetic poles repel.

EXPERIENCE. *Magnets in magnetic toys have magnetic poles.* There are small bar magnets in many of the toy magnets sold at toy shops. Frequently these magnets are of good quality.

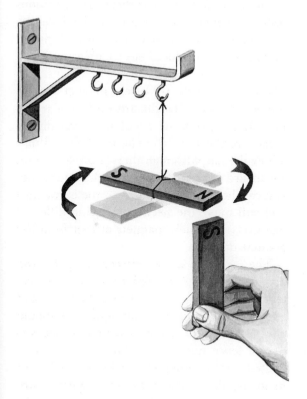

Unlike poles attract.

Sometimes there are animal figures on the bars, such as an elephant or a donkey. On some of these, when the heads of the animals are brought together they repel each other, but when the head of one is placed near the tail of the other, there is attraction. There are other variations of attraction and repulsion. It is easy to see that when heads repel and head and tail attract it is a variation of the idea that unlike magnetic poles attract each other, while like poles repel each other.

There is a certain amount of jingle to this first law of magnetism. Since the same general principle will be applied to like and unlike charges of electricity, it might be a good idea to allow the children the pleasure of making a jingle out of it if they desire, although as a general principle memorizing as such is scarcely to be condoned.

Have children bring to school any magnetic toys they may have. See if they can explain how the toys work.

EXPERIENCE. *Making* U *and horseshoe magnets attract and repel each other.* Children can bring the poles of two U magnets or two horseshoe magnets together. In one position the magnets attract each other; in fact, sometimes one magnet can be held up against the force of Earth's gravitation by the magnetic force of the other magnet. As one tries to bring these magnets together, one may feel the force of the attraction; one magnet may almost seem to jump out of one's hands. Now reverse the poles that are in contact. Note that they repel each other. It is difficult to push the magnets together. If one tries to push them together, a strong force of repulsion can be felt. Perhaps two children can work at this attempt to place two magnets together in spite of the repulsion.

This force that can be felt but not seen is interesting to children. Every child in the group should have an opportunity at leisure to manipulate magnets and to feel the force. These Experiences can be useful in developing concepts of a magnetic field.

Borrowed (Induced) Magnetism. A piece of iron that touches or is even brought near a magnet becomes magnetized temporarily. Hold a large soft-iron nail against a magnet. Then dip the nail, which is clinging to the magnet, into a handful of small tacks so that the nail touches some of the tacks. The nail attracts the tacks as if it were a magnet. Pull the big nail away from the magnet. What happens to the tacks? The nail was made of soft iron. Soft iron is magnetized only so long as it is in contact with or near a magnet; therefore the nail becomes a temporary magnet. This is called *borrowed,* or *induced,* magnetism. Because soft iron behaves as a magnet only temporarily, it is used extensively in commercial work. (pp. 796, 797.) A very small amount of magnetism, called *residual* magnetism, usually remains for a time in the soft iron. The residual magnetism may cause a few tacks to continue to cling to the nail.

Later we shall see that there are conditions under which electrical charges are induced on substances. So we not only have induced magnetism but induced electricity as well.

Magnets Have Fields. Move a magnet around under a paper or cardboard on top of which have been laid some needles or iron filings. What are the results? The needles or filings follow the bar, although there is air space and cardboard between them. See how far away you can hold the magnet from the cardboard and still move the needles. Trying different magnets, see which magnets attract from the greatest distance.

The region or space between the poles and about the poles of a magnet is called the *magnetic field,* for it is in this region that iron and steel are attracted by the magnet. It should not be thought of as a field with an exact border or fence about it. It has been demonstrated that a magnetic field is filled with magnetic force which causes magnetic substances to be attracted by the magnet. The direction of the force in a magnetic field is

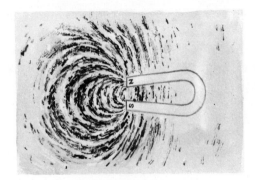 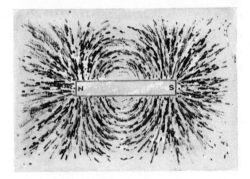

Iron filings can be used to indicate the magnetic field.

represented by *imaginary* lines called *lines of force*. They begin near the N pole and loop around toward a region near the S pole. They are nearer together at the poles where the attraction of the magnet is strongest and they may be thought of as continuous loops passing through the magnet. We live in a magnetic field, that of Earth. The needle of the compass points to the magnetic north and south because it is in Earth's magnetic field.

There are magnetic fields in the sun in the form of sunspots (p. 802), and there is evidence of magnetic fields out in space.

The concept of *field* is one that may grow in importance in the years to come. Already education and other fields of science are borrowing from physics for their basic ideas in the field of dynamic psychology.

A field is an area or space in which a force or forces operate. The young child who feels the magnet attract or repel feels the effects of a force but he cannot see the force, so he is securing an elementary but basic concept of a magnetic field. (The term *field* should be introduced when the children are ready for it or have a need for it.)

The fact that a force cannot be seen but can be felt is interesting to children. They never see magnetism, gravitation, or electricity, but they can have experiences with each of these forces.

The development of the concept of a magnetic field of force has many rich opportunities for experiences, such as the manipulation of magnets, the feel of the force, trying to hold a magnet still while another is brought near to it, and so on. Here are lifeless materials exhibiting forces to be used by man. These experiences can be used to develop constructive emotions needed in a world of new sources of energy.

A magnetic field is not the only kind of field of force. We have already described children and adults as being in the gravitational field of Earth (p. 720). The sun has a gravitational field and takes Earth and the other planets and their moons along through space. We shall see later that there are also electrostatic fields of force, and discuss electromagnetic energy.

EXPERIENCE. *To find a region through which a magnet works (operates).* Much of this can be sheer play. Note with toys how the opposite magnet can respond at a distance. How great a distance is this? Can you make tacks jump to the magnet?

Place a magnet on the table. Bring another magnet near. Holding the magnet so that the poles that are unlike are near each other may cause the one magnet to roll or slide toward the other. Or reversing the magnet so that the poles that are alike are near each other will cause the one magnet to slide away. This operation of a force through what seems to be mere space with air in it can give a child a feeling for a field of force.

EXPERIENCE. *Examine the shape of the iron filings clinging to a magnetic pole.* Roll a magnet in bits of iron, such as iron filings, small tacks, or particles of steel wool. Note how they hang about one of the poles. Now bring another magnet near. Try first a pole of the same polarity and then a pole of the opposite polarity. Note the probable effect on the field. Note how the iron particles cling to the magnet in tufts.

EXPERIENCE. *Demonstrating a magnetic field.* Secure some iron filings and place in a saltshaker. (Various types of cans may be used for this purpose. A tin can with holes punched in it or a sugar-shaker will do.) Place a piece of glass (or a piece of cardboard or stiff paper) over a bar magnet. Sprinkle iron filings over the glass. Tap the glass gently and see what pattern the filings take. The pattern seems to be built about lines, most of which are curved and tend to connect the poles of the magnet. These lines have been called lines of magnetic force, since they are in a field of magnetic force.

EXPERIENCE. *Making permanent diagrams of a magnetic field.* Use blueprint paper in place of the cardboard. Expose the blueprint paper to strong sunlight as soon as the iron filings have arranged themselves along the lines of force. Expose paper for two or three minutes, or more if necessary. Develop it by washing in clear water for several minutes; then hang it up to dry.

Another way to make the designs permanent is the use of shellac. Cut a piece of clean smooth paper. Coat the paper with shellac and let it dry thoroughly. Then make the design. Carry this carefully to a warm place, such as a sunny spot or a radiator, and hold it there until the heat has melted the shellac. This will cause the filings to stick to the paper; and when the paper has dried, the diagram of the field will be preserved.

Still a third way is to use a piece of very heavily waxed paper. You may make your own waxed paper by dipping wrapping paper in melted paraffin. The waxed paper is used in exactly the same manner as the shellacked paper.

EXPERIENCE. *Other magnetic fields.* Lay two thin books or two pads of paper on the table about three inches apart. Place a piece of stiff paper, cardboard, or glass over the books. Place in the space between the books two bar magnets so that two unlike poles are about an inch apart. Sprinkle iron filings or very small tacks over the cardboard or glass just above the poles. Tap the cardboard or glass a little. The filings will arrange themselves in lines running between the unlike poles. Repeat with two like poles near each other. Notice the difference. The lines from the different poles seem to repel each other. Repeat with a horseshoe magnet. Since the poles of a horseshoe magnet are unlike, the lines attract each other.

Earth Is a Magnet. *Earth's Magnetic Field.* For centuries man has been guided about over Earth's surface by means of magnetic compasses. Frequently one reads the story of how disturbed the sailors were who sailed with Columbus when he discovered America, when they found the compass was no longer pointing exactly north. It is likely, however, that they were aware of the fact that the compass which pointed east of north in the Mediterranean Sea was now pointing west of north. As Columbus sailed westward, the sailors found the difference increasing; and they felt that their compass had become unreliable. They thought it was bewitched. They almost mutinied, for it seemed to them that they were entering a strange region with new physical principles. We know now that the magnetic needle points in a general north-south direction over most of the Earth's surface but it does not point *exactly* in the direction of either the

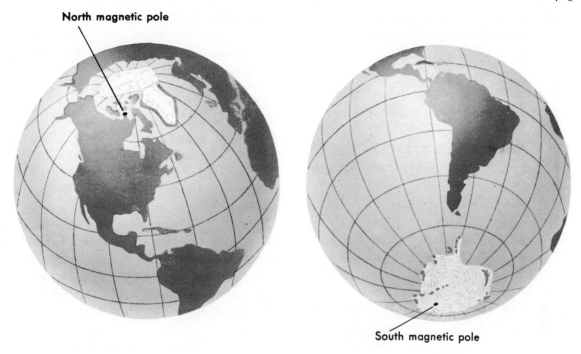

The magnetic poles of Earth slowly shift.

geographic or magnetic poles. The north magnetic pole was located by J. C. Ross in 1831 in the extreme north of North America. The south magnetic pole is in Antarctica and was discovered by the Shackleton expedition in 1909. The magnetic poles are not definite points but *regions* in which a dipping needle— that is, a kind of magnetic compass so constructed that the needle can swing up and down—points straight down. The magnetic poles are not fixed; they move about slowly but constantly. Mariners have books which give the differences between magnetic north and true north in all parts of the world, and these books are revised from time to time in order that they may provide correct information (p. 803).

EXPERIENCE. *To make and use a dipping needle.* The materials needed are a steel knitting needle, a cork or some modeling clay, two drinking glasses (the same size), and two darning needles. Assemble and use as shown in the diagrams on the next page. Follow directions carefully.

Recall that the north pole of the magnetized knitting needle will repel the north pole of the compass needle. To show how much the magnetic field of Earth dips where you live, place the darning needles on the glasses so that the north pole of the magnetized knitting needle points north. This end will dip toward Earth.

Man is rapidly learning more about the magnetic field that surrounds Earth. The Experience "Demonstrating a magnetic field" (p. 788) will give some idea of what this field is like. Scientists think of Earth as surrounded by similar lines of force. They are like invisible loops extending many thousands of miles out from Earth. Due to their direction in the polar regions, those places are often called "windows" for observing phenomena in space.

A lightning flash in the northern hemi-

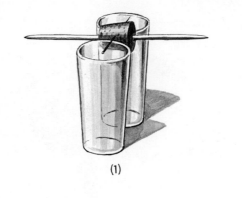

(1)

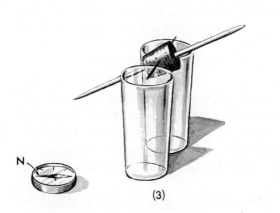

(2)

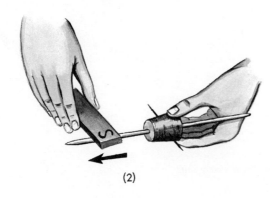

(3)

Making a dipping needle. (1) Assemble tumblers, cork, steel knitting needle, and two darning needles. (2) Magnetize the knitting needle by stroking in one direction only with the south pole of a bar magnet. (3) Test to find the north pole of the knitting needle with a compass. Then turn the needle and glasses so the north pole of the needle points north. It should then dip downward.

sphere appears to send radio signals along the nearest loop to its other end in the southern hemisphere, producing "whistlers," which make whistling sounds heard only on suitable receivers. These are sometimes reflected back and forth along the same line of force. Radar signals apparently do the same thing. This was an important discovery not only because it helps to locate Earth's lines of force but also because it helps man to learn something more about the behavior of the electrically charged particles along the lines of force.

The Van Allen belts are an important part of this pattern. They are concentrations of charged particles that lie in two zones within Earth's magnetic field at a distance between 400 and 28,000 to 44,000 miles. They must be considered in manned space exploration (p. 244).

Although Earth's magnetic field is considered weak, yet its total energy is high. A better understanding of the magnetic field and especially of the changes that go on in it will give a better understanding of the interior of Earth and how Earth's magnetism is generated.

Why Does the "North Pole" of the Magnet Point North? People are often confused when they learn that opposite poles attract, and then notice that the end of the bar magnet marked "N" points to the north magnetic pole. The reason for this is historical rather than scientific. When men first learned that one end of a magnet always points north, they knew little about the laws of magnetism and about Earth, but they were learning. They named the north-pointing end the north pole of the magnet. We may be fairly certain that the end of the needle that points north has a different kind of pole (polarity). So if we say that the end of the needle pointing north is a north pole, then we must decide that at the magnetic pole of Earth in northern Canada Earth has a magnetic pole with south polarity, while in the Antarctic continent Earth has a magnetic pole with north polarity.

In a sense, here is a place where children can argue and take their choice for an explanation and not be forced to agree.

It is awkward to say that the end of the needle pointing north is a south magnetic pole. Some scientists have proposed calling the end pointing north, a *north-seeking* pole and the end pointing south, a *south-seeking* pole. Many prefer to think of Earth as having a huge magnetic field with a pole of south polarity called the north magnetic pole in the Arctic, and a pole of north polarity in the Antarctic called the south magnetic pole.

EXPERIENCE. *Using Earth's magnetic field to magnetize iron.* Take a piece of iron, such as an iron rod (a long nail will do), and hold it so that it is pointing north and south, with the north end (if you live in the Northern Hemisphere) lowered toward the pole. (The farther north one lives, the more nearly vertical one should hold the piece of iron. Children may need to experiment to find the proper position. This latter study is something that the children with special aptitudes for science may take as a special project.) Strike it with a hammer a few times. The iron rod should indicate some magnetism—by repelling a compass needle, attracting iron filings, etc. (The attraction of a compass needle is not a reliable test of magnetism unless the other end of the needle is repelled, as any iron or steel will attract the compass needle. Why? p. 782.)

EXPERIENCE. *To test materials to find if they are magnets.* If *both* poles of a magnet or a compass are attracted by a piece of material, the material is not a magnet. It is without magnetic poles. If it had poles, it would attract one pole of the magnet or compass and repel the other.

Since iron is attracted to a magnet, we usually think of iron as clinging to the magnet as iron tacks might. However, when one holds a piece of iron so that it cannot move, as in this Experience, the compass needle, which is a magnet, must do the swinging. So if the piece of iron does not repel, at one of its ends, one pole of the compass needle, then one can assume the iron has become magnetized. (See next to last Experience p. 785.)

After the piece of iron has been made into a magnet, it can be demagnetized; that is, its magnetism can be removed by pounding it while holding it in an east-and-west position. Or one can throw the nail down a number of times on the ground or floor, so that it falls in an east-west position. Test it out. It should no longer have a north and a south pole, but respond as a piece of iron.

EXPERIENCE. *Iron objects in Earth's magnetic field become magnetized.* Frequently one can find iron objects which are magnetized. Sometimes these objects have become magnetic because of being in Earth's magnetic field. The top of an iron object frequently will attract one end of a compass needle, and the bottom of the object will attract the other end. Test out a radiator in this manner. See if different poles of the needle are not attracted by the top and the bottom of the radiator. Also try the tops and bottoms of tin cans, filing cabinets, and such things.

Difficulty has been experienced in using compasses on iron ships. Soft-iron bars are placed near such compasses so that magnetism induced in them will in every position of the ship just balance that induced by Earth's magnetism in the ship. Permanent steel magnets are sometimes used to compensate the permanent magnetism of the ship.

EXPERIENCE. *How Earth's magnetism affects a bar magnet.* Suspend a bar magnet so that it can swing about freely; a fine silk thread makes the best suspension. Allow it to stop swinging. Try to avoid interference from air currents. In what direction does it come to rest? The bar magnet should come to rest approximately in a north-and-south direction, following the lines of Earth's magnetic field. The magnet should point approximately to the magnetic north and south poles.

NOTE. A variety of suspension devices can be utilized. Some can be prepared for temporary use; others can be permanently mounted. The same suspension devices can be used for a variety of purposes, as for instance, the suspension of balloons in the Experiences with static electricity on page 809. A stick about two feet long fastened at right angles to the wall or blackboard will prove a useful addition to the classroom, as it can be used in this and many other experiments. Several small hooks screwed into the stick will be useful as places from which to hang things. Notches or holes can be made in the wood to serve the same purpose.

A homemade wooden stand for suspending objects.

A simple stand like that shown in the illustration on this page can be made by some of the older children. Strips of wood are nailed together and a hook screwed into the top strip. See also the illustrations on pages 784 and 810.

Magnetic Compasses Are Used to Tell Direction. When the bar magnet was suspended in the preceding Experience, it pointed nearly north and south. It acted in this position as a compass. In fact, a magnetic compass[4] such as the children bring to school is nothing more than a bar magnet arranged so as to swing about freely. In some compasses the entire dial, or face, swings about. In this case the same principle is involved, since beneath the dial, which is usually made of cardboard, is attached a magnet. The cardboard is pulled about with the magnet. Earth's magnetic field causes the magnet to turn toward the magnetic north and south. The magnet in a compass is called the needle.

The Compass Does Not Point True North at All Places on Earth's Surface. Since the magnetic poles do not coincide with the geographic poles, the compass does not, in general, point to the geographic north and south. On the Atlantic coast of the United States the needle points west of true north, while on the Pacific coast the needle points east of true north. At the magnetic poles the compass needle will tend to assume a vertical position, pointing straight up and down. Much of Earth's surface has been studied to determine the variation that the compass needle makes from the geographic north and south. It has been found that these variations change from time to time; nevertheless the maps of the variations are reliable enough to assist navigators

[4] Every elementary school should have a number of magnetic compasses for children's use. The usual Boy Scout or Girl Scout compass is quite satisfactory. It would be a good plan to use compasses frequently on excursions and for general orientation to directions in activities at school or in the community.

and surveyors. Observations of position from the stars are, of course, more accurate, but the stars are not always visible.

EXPERIENCE. *To show that the needle of a magnetic compass is a magnet.* Hold the north pole of a bar magnet near a compass. What happens? Try the south pole.

If the compass needle were a nonmagnetic piece of steel, either end of it would be attracted toward either end of the magnet. The fact that one end of the needle is attracted by the south pole and the other by the north pole of the magnet shows that the compass needle has a north and south pole itself, and hence it is a magnet.

EXPERIENCE. *Principle of the compass.* Magnetize a long needle, such as a steel knitting needle (p. 790). Unwind a piece of silk thread so as to obtain one of the small cords that compose it. Tie this small cord to the middle of

A magnetized needle floating in a glass dish of water makes a compass.

the needle and suspend it so that it is free to turn. It should point north and south. The end that points north can be marked by dipping it in paint or by attaching a piece of tape to it.

Magnetize a darning needle, thrust it through two small corks, and float it in a glass, plastic, or porcelain saucer. This is the type of compass used by the Genoese mariners. Why will this experiment not work if an iron dish or one made of enamel over iron is used?

EXPERIENCE. *How the compass needle points at different places.* Have a child locate the magnetic north pole and the true north pole on a globe. Selecting some point on Earth's surface (for example, San Francisco, Vancouver, Halifax); trace a line to the true north and another to the magnetic north. (Strings may be used to avoid marking the globe.) Notice that the angle between the lines is not the same at different points on Earth. Select a point *between* the magnetic north pole and the true north pole. How does the compass point in this region? Can you find a place on the globe at which you think the compass needle will point true north? Locate this place on the globe where you live. A small lump of modeling clay can be used to mark the locality. A pin with a small flag can then be stuck into the clay. Does the needle in your locality point to the geographic north?

NOTE. This experiment is not entirely accurate, as the *magnetic declination* (the angle between true north and magnetic north) is subject to rather irregular variations.

EXPERIENCE. *To check a compass needle for its reading.* A compass needle may be influenced by a nearby magnet or iron object, and as a result not point to the magnetic north. When studying magnetism there may be a number of magnets present. Some of the modern magnets may influence the needle of a compass or a suspended bar magnet several feet away. Frequently there is iron used in constructing school buildings. This iron may not be visible, since it may be concealed by other building materials, but at times it will influence the needle of a compass.

To determine whether a needle is influenced by iron or by a magnet, the children may use a compass in many different places— in the classroom, in hallways, or in another part of the building. In each case, get a good, clear idea of the way the needle is pointing. Try to line up the north-south line in reference to distant objects, if possible. When this involves considering points that cannot be seen from the schoolroom because of the walls, children can visualize distant points by going outside. Then try the compass outside at a distance from any structures made of iron, including automobiles, machines, and pumps. Do the directions indicated outside, away from all magnets or iron objects, agree with the directions indicated by the compass in the classroom? Perhaps some children may have opportunity to try a compass inside an automobile. Perhaps some children have observed their parents install a car compass inside an automobile. Such a compass is arranged so that it may be compensated (adjusted) to neutralize the iron and the magnetism of the automobile frame and engine. It will then respond to Earth's magnetic field.

Scientists Have Attempted to Explain Magnetism. Magnetism, like light (p. 859), gravitation (p. 719), and other phenomena, has not been explained in any final sense. It is much easier to describe what magnetism does than to state what makes it work or what it is. Scientists have developed theories of magnetism; but as time goes on and new discoveries are made, theories need revision. It should be kept in mind that a theory, even though it may be considered by scientists to be the best possible at the time, may not be the final explanation.

In recent years it has been necessary to revise the theories because of modern developments in physics. We shall see later (p. 859) how important some of the revisions of earlier theories have been. Any theory of magnetism, to be satisfactory, must be one that will explain the things that happen. The following Experience is one that helped scientists for a number of years to explain some things about magnets.

EXPERIENCE. *When a magnet is broken, each piece has a north pole and a south pole.* Small, thin, toy horseshoe magnets that are very brittle can be purchased at stores selling cheap toys. These magnets are very thin, and usually can be broken by a little pressure with a pair of pliers.

Test the ends of each of these pieces with the compass or with iron filings or small tacks. Notice that you have two magnets instead of one, since one end of each piece is a north magnetic pole, while the other end is a south magnetic pole. Cut both of these and notice that you have four magnets instead of two. This Experience indicates that a magnet may be subdivided into small parts and yet that each small part exhibits polarity (each end being a magnetic pole). No matter into how many small bits we may break the magnet, each piece is still a magnet.

As a result of Experiences such as the one above it has been assumed for a number of years that a piece of iron or steel is composed of tiny particles called molecules, each one of which is a little magnet. Before the steel is magnetized, it is thought that these particles are so turned as to form closed groups in which the south pole of one particle is turned toward the north poles of near-by particles. These groups neutralize one another, so that no magnetism is exerted at the ends of the piece. If, now, we bring one pole (the north pole, let us say) of a magnet near the piece of iron or steel, the south poles of many of the molecules will be attracted toward it. If we pass the magnet

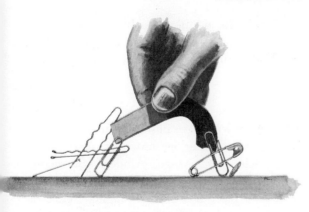

If we break a magnet, each part is a complete magnet.

from one end to the other of our piece of iron or steel, these south poles will tend to be turned so that most of them point toward one end. The end, then, toward which most of the south poles are pointing will become the south pole of the piece of iron or steel, and the other end will become the north pole.

This theory explains why a magnet cannot be cut up so that it will have only one pole; for in every case, if the molecules are lined up, there will be two poles. Each molecule will still have a north and a south pole.

The theory also explains why we must stroke a needle in one direction to magnetize it. If we stroke it back and forth, the molecules are not drawn into orderly lines, but left almost as helter-skelter as before.

This theory also makes it possible to explain why hard steel can be permanently magnetized, while soft iron cannot. Once the molecules are lined up in hard steel, they are not readily able to move out of their orderly arrangement. In soft iron, on the other hand, they are somewhat free to move, and keep their arrangement only when held by an outside force, such as a permanent magnet or a current of electricity (p. 796). Knives, needles, and scissors are hard steel; nails, bolts, and screws may be fairly soft iron.

When we heat a substance, the molecules move more freely. If a permanent magnet is heated to redness, the molecules are set free

enough to lose their orderly arrangement; and thus the magnet loses its magnetism. If a magnet is pounded violently, the molecules are jarred out of their arrangement; and the magnet loses some of its magnetism. The magnets in the classroom should not be pounded together or dropped on the floor.

Many magnetic phenomena can be explained on the basis that molecules of magnetic substances act as magnets. It should be noted, however, that this theory does *not explain why* the atoms or molecules behave as magnets. Scientists do not consider the molecular theory to be satisfactory. This theory does, however, help to clarify and explain some of the actions of magnets. It says that they act *as if* molecules of iron have poles and can be arranged.

To explain the atomic theory of magnetism, it is necessary to learn a few things about electricity. After we have done this, we shall consider atoms in relation to the production of both magnetism and electricity.

An Electric Current Has a Magnetic Effect. Oersted, a Danish physicist, in 1819 or 1820, while experimenting with batteries, discovered that a compass needle is affected by a wire carrying a current of electricity, and concluded that such a wire carrying a current is surrounded by a magnetic field. You can duplicate his historical experiment in this way.

EXPERIENCE. *A compass needle is affected by a wire carrying a current of electricity.* Arrange a compass, a dry cell, and a piece of insulated wire as shown in the illustration (top p. 796). Arrange the wire so that it points in the same direction as the compass (north and south). Now attach the other end of the wire to the dry cell.[5] Close the switch only a few seconds,

---

[5] Dry cells and insulated copper bell wire may be purchased at a hardware store. It is a good idea to ask the dealer to test the cells at the time they are purchased. For work with younger children, it is well to make certain that the wire is flexible enough to be readily handled by them.

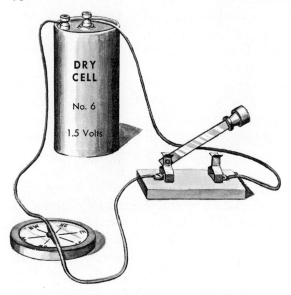

When the knife switch is closed the compass needle will swing in one direction. Open the switch. Then remove the wire attached to the center post, attach it to the outer post, and move the wire attached to the outer post to the center post. Close the switch. The needle will then swing in the opposite direction.

so as not to wear out the dry cell, for in this Experience the dry cell is being short-circuited (p. 826). The needle should move instantly.

Now reverse the current by changing the wires on the dry cell. The needle should swing in the opposite direction. This indicates that there is a magnetic field surrounding an electric current. One might say that magnetism goes along with electricity in this experiment.

It should be noted that this kind of a magnet is temporary rather than permanent, like the bar, the horseshoe, and the lodestone. One might think that something that is temporary would not have lasting value for mankind. But the fact that here was something which could be made a magnet one moment and lose its magnetism the next, was a discovery of great importance. It had almost as much influence on history as did the steam engine. In fact, it has outlived the steam

engine in its usefulness. If for any reason electromagnets should cease to operate, our modern society would be completely paralyzed.

Electromagnets. Soon after Oersted discovered that a wire with current flowing in it has magnetic properties, as we have just discovered, other scientists (Arago, Ampère, Sturgeon) found that if the wire is wound in a coil around a piece of iron, the magnetic effect is greatly increased. Such a device is called an *electromagnet*. Here is a way to make one.

EXPERIENCE. *Making an electromagnet.* Take a piece of soft iron, such as a big nail or spike, and around it wind some doorbell wire, which can be bought at any hardware store. It is best to wind on it two or three layers of wire. Fasten the two ends of the wire to the terminals (the two screws at the top) of a dry cell. See that the insulation is torn off the part of the wire that is fastened to the posts of the dry cell. Test the nail (now an electromagnet) for magnetism by picking up small objects, such as thumbtacks, paper clips, and nails. Unfasten one of the wires. Most of the objects should drop off. Those that cling can be easily shaken off. Try to pick up the objects with the wire still unfastened from the dry cell. The soft iron, which is called the core, will not attract the objects.

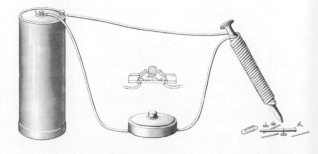

An electromagnet. When the button is pressed the nail becomes magnetized. Note the cross section of the push button.

Again connect the electromagnet and note that it again attracts the iron objects. Test your magnet with a compass to find which end of the nail is the north pole and which the south. Now connect to the center terminal of the cell the wire which was connected to the outside terminal, and attach the other wire to the outside terminal. Test again to see which end is north and which south. Do the poles of the electromagnet depend on the way the wires are connected? Such a magnet is called *temporary*, since it is magnetic only when electricity flows through the wires. While the electricity flows, it behaves exactly like any other magnet.

In the Experience above, a switch, such as an ordinary push button (which can be secured at a local hardware store), can be used to turn the current on and off and will be more convenient than it would be to fasten or unfasten the wires.

EXPERIENCE. *An electromagnet can be made stronger.* Repeat the foregoing Experience, using more dry cells. See if the electromagnet is stronger.

Repeat the Experience, using one dry cell but twice as many turns of wire. The strength of an electromagnet seems to depend on the number of dry cells and the number of turns of wire.

EXPERIENCE. *To discuss the importance of electromagnets.* Encourage children to discuss the value of the electromagnet. Place a permanent magnet and an electromagnet side by side. Compare them. What can be done with electromagnets that cannot be done with permanent magnets? More about this should come out in a consideration of the telegraph and telephone.

It should be obvious that a magnet which can be controlled has many commercial uses. The lifting magnet illustrates one such use. This device consists of a very powerful electromagnet attached to a crane. It is used to move iron about, particularly scrap iron, which is very difficult for men to handle. In use the lifting magnet is simply lowered onto the iron to be moved, and the current is turned on. The magnet, together with the iron it is holding, is then lifted and moved to the place where the iron is wanted; the current is then turned off from the magnet, and the iron is dropped. This is an example of a machine performing a task which is difficult, dangerous, and laborious for men to do.

Closing a switch at one place and causing a magnet to move something at another place may be used to transmit signals, as in the telegraph. It is also extensively used for controlling machinery from a distance.

Since the telegraph and other adaptations of the electromagnet involve an electric circuit, they will be explained more fully in the section on current electricity.

Steel Is Used in Making Permanent Magnets. Make an electromagnet with a core of hard steel. This may be done by wrapping wire around a knife blade, a knitting needle, or a pair of scissors. Pass a current of electricity through the wire for one or two minutes.

Children may experiment with simple electromagnets.

Turn the current off and test the steel for magnetism. It should become permanently magnetized, whereas the soft iron was only temporarily magnetized. Soft iron may be easily magnetized, but *it will not hold its magnetism.* Why is soft iron used in making electromagnets?

New Ideas about What Magnetism Is. A number of the important developments of science in modern times have come out of the studies that scientists have made into the peculiar relationship between magnetism and electricity. The discoveries in this field have contributed to the increase in electrical energy from power plants, more efficient telephone and radio service, the invention of television, the development of nuclear energy, and many of the convenient appliances we have at home, at school, and in other parts of our community. In fact, it would be difficult to list all the ways in which our life has been affected by the discoveries that have been made about the relationships of magnetism and electricity. There can be little doubt that the children in our schools today will live in a time when there will be many new discoveries in these two fields. Some of these children will be participants in tomorrow's developments. But whether a child is to be a discoverer in this field or not, he will need some acquaintance with it, if he is to develop the intelligent and resourceful behavior necessary to a people making up a democracy. It is important that the people of tomorrow have the ability to use electromagnetism in building their own world.

It is possible for children to build up an experiential background for the concept that magnetism surrounds an electric current. The Experiences listed on page 797 are designed to assist children to this background. It would be well for the materials of these Experiences to be left on a table for several weeks, so that every child in a class making this study will have free opportunity to manipulate these materials. In this way, he can learn through a number of sensory gateways such as sight, touch, sound, and the kinesthetic sense.

From such Experiences as the children will be doing, scientists have concluded that wherever there is an electrical current there is a magnetic effect. Thus, magnetism goes along with movement of electrical particles.

It has been developed in this book on page 375 that scientists regard all substances or matter as made up of atoms composed of particles of electricity. So matter, everything about us, and we ourselves are composed of these particles.

In the study of static electricity (p. 806) we shall find Experiences that demonstrate that there are two kinds of electrical charges. These were called positive and negative charges by Benjamin Franklin, who made a considerable study of electricity.

For our purposes here, we need to recall that those particles in an atom called electrons, each carrying a negative charge of electricity, rotate or spin and at the same time revolve around the positively charged nucleus or center. Usually scientists prefer the word *spin* when speaking of the rotation of an electron. However, the word used should be one that is meaningful to children. Later we shall see that an electric current is produced by these spinning electrons. The movements of electrons about the nucleus of an atom can be thought of as a kind of electric circuit. It has been demonstrated that a magnetic effect accompanies an electrical current (p. 796).

Since scientists are inclined to think all matter is magnetic to some extent we might wonder then, why, of all the substances, we find only a few, such as iron, nickel, cobalt, and a few others, commonly used as magnets. Such metals are described as being ferromagnetic.

All others respond feebly and either repel a magnet (diamagnetic) or are weakly magnetic (paramagnetic).

A spinning electron has a north and south pole like a magnet. Electrons tend to spin in pairs that have opposite spin, held together like two magnets by the attraction of unlike poles.

It is now known that magnetism is produced by the movements of electrons within atoms. As each electron spins and revolves within an atom, it generates a small amount of magnetism.

In the atoms of most elements the electrons spin in pairs and in opposite directions. Each spinning electron has a north and a south pole, and when they spin in pairs they are held together by the attraction of unlike poles, just as if two bar magnets were placed side by side, with the north pole of one placed beside the south pole of the other. Due to this, the magnetic effects of these electrons cancel each other.

However, the atoms of some elements, such as iron, nickel, and cobalt, contain one or more *unpaired* electrons. If these unpaired electrons are lined up and spin in the same direction, the atom as a whole will act as a small magnet. Briefly, an atom will act as a small magnet when more of its electrons spin in one direction than in the other.

Atoms may line up in groups known as *domains,* each of which is a magnetic unit, and under the influence of a strong magnetic field many of these units may be turned and lined up parallel to each other and to the magnetic field (p. 782). Thus the particles pull together in the same direction. When this occurs in a bar of iron, we say that the iron is magnetized. This explains why, of all the substances in the universe, some make better magnets than others.

This explanation of *why* atoms behave as magnets goes further and refines the molecular theory of magnetism. It should be recalled that molecules are made up of atoms (Chapter 11).

Magnetic materials have been developed that will meet the demands of space technology.

Why the movements of particles should produce magnetism is something that remains to be explained by scientists. If a teacher or children are perplexed, they should take comfort from the fact that in these matters scientists recognize that they have much to discover. Magnetism, like light, gravity, and other phenomena of daily life are not completely understood, yet we get along with them and use them while we are learning more about them.

For practical purposes in our daily life, the fact that all matter is magnetic has little significance. However, scientists have found this is important information which has helped them to some very important discoveries in recent years.

It might be well to keep in mind that magnetism is not matter. We cannot pick up a bit of it and say that here is a bit of magnetism, and there is nothing in it except magnetism. We cannot pour magnetism into a cup as we would water, and have nothing in the cup but

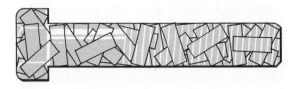

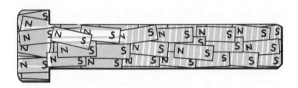

Domains in an iron bolt before and after magnetizing.

magnetism. Rather, we must think of magne-tism as a force, or as a characteristic of some things, or as scientists would say, "It is a prop-erty of matter." Magnetism is invisible, but we can experience its force as attracting or re-pelling objects. It is a property or character-istic of things, just as wetness is a characteristic of liquid water.

Why Is Earth a Magnet? The concept that Earth is a magnet is one that can have a basis in real experience for children. Young chil-dren, for instance, can see that the needle of a compass always points the same way, regard-less of where they may go with it, around the room or around the block. This constancy is true, provided the compass is not brought close to iron or a magnet. Later they may use the compass to learn directions or to make a map of the area around the school, or to guide them on instructional and recreational excur-sions. Still later they may use Earth's mag-netic field to magnetize and demagnetize a piece of iron (Experience, p. 791). They can also discover for themselves whether certain objects at home and school have become mag-netized by Earth's field.

Children should acquire the feeling of the continuous nature of Earth's magnetic field. It is operating every second. They were born in it, and they will live their entire lives in it. It operates both day and night, and in all sea-sons and weather and climates. Earth's mag-netism never stops operating. It has been in operation for a very long time.

Human beings have ears which hear sounds and eyes which see light, but they do not have organs in their bodies which detect magnetism. Man has had to develop instruments and knowledge to help him experience magnetism.

Earth's magnetism has been of great value to man. It has helped him to explore and to travel about on Earth. Man was much more courageous in making explorations far from home after he learned to use the compass.

This instrument has also been used in survey-ing the land and water areas of Earth. But in recent years man has discovered that Earth's magnetism may be related to a number of phenomena that happen on Earth, in the outer part of the atmosphere (p. 448), and on the sun (p. 200).

Although Earth has a magnetic field which seems huge to us, at any one spot its field is comparatively weak. This is shown in the fol-lowing Experience, in which children and teachers can participate.

EXPERIENCE. *To compare the strength of Earth as a magnet at any one spot with the strength of a magnet at school or at home.* (Essentially the ac-tivities in this Experience have been described in some of the previous Experiences, but the meanings to be developed are enlargements of earlier concepts. It frequently happens that Experiences can be repeated for new concepts in science. In this case we are concerned with a comparison of Earth's magnetic field with the field of a bar or horseshoe magnet.)

Place a compass on a table away from any large objects of iron or other magnets. (A sus-pended bar magnet as illustrated on page 785 could be used for a compass in this Experi-ence.) Note the reading of the needle.

It should be clear to everyone making the observation that the needle is responding to Earth as a magnet. One child can use his arm or a pointer to indicate the direction of the needle.

Someone can then bring a bar or horseshoe magnet toward the compass very slowly. Ob-serve what happens. The needle which pointed toward Earth's magnetic poles, or in other words, responded to Earth's magnetic force, now swings so that one end of the needle is pointing to a pole of the magnet. Note how far away the magnet is before the needle be-gins to change. This distance can be meas-ured. Try this out with a number of magnets and compare the distances.

Of course, Earth is a larger magnet than any magnet we might possess. Its poles are far away from the schoolroom, as we can see by examining a map or globe of Earth. One of our toy magnets exerts more magnetic force close to its poles than Earth does at any spot where the magnet happens to be. The needle of a compass is controlled by the nearby magnet when this needle comes within the field of the magnet. Of course, this does not mean that the magnet we work with is a stronger magnet than Earth. It might be well for children to realize that even our strongest magnets at school or at home exert a magnetic field in only a small space.

Earth's magnetic field causes large objects to become magnetized, such as radiators and automobiles, and even larger objects, such as the steel structure in skyscrapers and steel ships, and deposits of iron ore (p. 787). These bodies, once magnetized, seem to remain so for decades, and in the case of iron deposits, for centuries. All of this probably is due to the size and continuous nature of Earth's magnetic field.

Many scientists have been interested in attempting to explain the causes for Earth having a magnetic field. They have not found it an easy matter to find a single explanation.

In fact, there seem to be many possible explanations.

As men learn about the magnetism of Earth, they find many new problems. For instance, there is some evidence that Earth has two magnetic fields, or possibly we might say, one field with two parts, or as some scientists would prefer to say, two component fields.

One of these fields seems to be associated with Earth's rotation on its axis. This magnetic field seems to be lined up in a constant fashion with Earth's axis. We might call it the main magnetic field of Earth. It is Earth's *general field*.

But this main field is modified by a *secondary field* in Earth. This field varies irregularly over Earth, but in general it has been moving westward. Its motion has been compared to a formation of moving clouds. The causes of these two fields are not completely understood at the present time. A compass at any one point is affected by the field which has the greater force, or in some cases may be influenced by both. For this reason, for all practical purposes we can treat Earth's magnetic field as a single *unified field*.

Rotation and Magnetism of Earth. The rotation of Earth has been advanced by many scientists as a cause of magnetism. Attention has been called to the fact that the solar system seems to resemble a big atom. The sun has been compared to the nucleus of the atom and the planets moving about the sun resemble electrons. It has been proposed that these planets in their movements of revolution and rotation produce magnetism, just as electrons do by their movements within the atom. Such an explanation would apply to the main, or general, field of Earth.

Another explanation related to the rotation of Earth has to do with the rates at which various parts of Earth rotate. Some have thought there was evidence at times that the inner part or core of Earth may be rotating faster than the outer parts. This, they contend, could be compared to a kind of electrical generator or dynamo. As it generates electricity it exerts a magnetic effect upon Earth.

There is little doubt about Earth being charged with electricity (p. 812). There is also much evidence that there are electrical currents within Earth and these currents could produce magnetism in the core of Earth. Some students have contended for a long time that the core of Earth contains a large amount of iron and nickel. Earth, if these ideas are accepted, could be compared somewhat to an electromagnet.

There are quantities of electrical energy stored in the atmosphere. Later, in connection with lightning (p. 811) and thunderstorms (p. 469), atmospheric and ground electrical charges will be discussed.

The Sun and Magnetism. It is only natural that man should look to the sun for some of the causes of magnetism. It is well to keep in mind that the sun is a vast broadcasting center. It, like other stars, is bombarding space around it with various kinds of energy. In addition to light, there are invisible radiations, such as infrared, ultraviolet, X rays, and radio waves. All of these are electromagnetic in nature. Some of this radiation tends to electrify the atmosphere, especially the outer parts. This outer part of the atmosphere is called the ionosphere (p. 448) or electric sphere. It is likely that children will hear much about the ionosphere throughout their lives, for what occurs in these outer layers is of great importance to us.

Since there is a magnetic effect wherever electrical particles are moving, as indicated in the Experiences on page 796, we might well anticipate that Earth secures some magnetic effect from the movement of the electrical particles that come to it from the sun.

Sunspots are magnetic storms in the sun, often with north and south magnetic poles (p. 199). In addition to the sunspots, some authorities see much evidence pointing to the fact that the sun has a large main, or general, magnetic field. The sunspots, although very large as compared to Earth, are much smaller than the sun's main magnetic field.

At times of sunspot activity there are magnetic storms on Earth. During such a storm many things can happen. Communication service, such as teletype machines, wire-photo networks, and short-wave radio may be affected. Sometimes communication between continents may be disrupted for hours. Power companies frequently have difficulty with interruptions along their transmission lines, which may disrupt electrical service. There are magnetic stations scattered over the surface of Earth for the purpose of measuring Earth's magnetism. During magnetic storms the needles on the measuring compasses behave wildly.

Keep in mind that a magnetic storm is not a weather storm, such as a thunderstorm, a tornado, or a hurricane. The weather can be fair and pleasant throughout a magnetic storm. Children may learn about it because of difficulties with reception over radio and television, and the storm may be reported as a news item in newspapers and magazines.

EXPERIENCE. *To discuss what happens when electrical power is stopped.* In case of power interruptions children may have a number of experiences to discuss. Perhaps electric clocks, refrigerators, lights, and other household appliances ceased to operate. Candles, flashlights, and kerosene lamps may have been brought into use. Both in the city and on the farm, the usual pattern of living was changed greatly. In some cases serious problems of an economic nature as well as those of personal and community safety arise quickly. While children need not be alarmed, it is well for them to gain an appreciation of the need for a dependable source of energy. Since electricity is important in our modern life, it is important that children learn early about the importance of electrical energy being well managed.

Some Effects of Particles from the Sun. Exploration is greatly increasing man's knowledge concerning the universe and what is happening there. Interrelationships are being found that may help him to better understand his own planet. Magnetic fields are found to exist on and around Earth, on and around the sun, and in space. The sun, a vast body of gases erupting in prominences, flares, and sunspots, and with a corona extending far into space, may have a greater impact on Earth than suspected.

At times of heavy sunspot activity, electrically charged particles, such as protons and electrons from hydrogen, are poured out from the sun and may reach Earth's magnetic field. Here they are held and move with Earth through space. Traveling at terrific speed, they may reach Earth's atmosphere within a day or so (it takes sunlight eight minutes to do this).

Such particles are turned downward toward the poles by way of the lines of force in Earth's magnetic field. The particles excite the atoms in the atmosphere as they collide; energy is given off, producing luminescence and giving raise to the northern lights, or aurora borealis, and the southern lights, or aurora australis. The auroras seem to occur in both hemispheres at the same time, and are most brilliant a day or so after the sunspots have crossed the center of that portion of the sun that is turned toward Earth, thus giving time for the corpuscles to reach Earth.

Many adults and children may be familiar with magnetic storms on Earth, when power and communication lines are disrupted. These events occur at times of unusual solar activity (pp. 200, 448).

Electrically charged particles also influence the Van Allen belts, and they seem to shield Earth from the full impact of cosmic rays, high-energy particles from the sun and regions beyond our galaxy (p. 200).

The sun's corona is found to stream far outward into space. It has been called the solar "atmosphere," or wind, although *wind* is said to be too strong a word for this movement of charged particles. These reach Earth and beyond, and some scientists believe they distort Earth's magnetic lines of force, compressing them on one side and lengthening them on the opposite side. These affect the course of satellites, and may have an effect on the auroras and other electrical phenomena in Earth's atmosphere.

Changes in Earth's Magnetic Field. As has already been indicated, Earth's magnetic field changes from time to time. In order to know the latest changes in the magnetism, stations are located at various parts of Earth where the magnetism of Earth may be measured. It has been found that the compass needle changes a trifle during the day. It swings slightly to the east as the sun rises and to the west as the sun sets. This might not be too surprising when we realize that sunlight is electromagnetic radiation. But there are greater changes than these that occur over longer periods.

There is evidence that the magnetic compasses do not give the same reading today in the Mediterranean Sea and in western Europe that they did in the days of Columbus. In fact, some scientists think they have proof that the magnetic poles of Earth have moved in the past and are slowly moving today.

Some even contend that Earth may have reversed its polarity (its poles) several times in its long history. They base this on the study of rock layers. They find beds of iron ore in many regions which do not have their magnetic lines in accord with the present magnetic field of Earth. In fact, in the same region where rocks have been formed at different times, iron particles present may be lined up in different directions, and often are completely reversed with respect to the present magnetic field of Earth. In some cases, layers of rock close together may have their iron particles lined up in opposite ways, so that the north pole of one rock layer may lie in the opposite direction from the north pole of other rock layers. Rocks having iron in them secure their polarity at the time they are formed. It is not likely that a rock layer would ever change its poles once it was formed. Therefore, these students think that this is evidence that Earth changed its polarity at different times in its long history. Some students, however, think this has been brought about by causes that were quite independent of Earth's magnetic field.

Electricity

Electricity, which but a few score years ago was a mysterious and awe-inspiring force, causing lightning and giving peculiar shocks at unexpected moments, has become our slave, doing a multitude of arduous tasks—cleaning our homes and our clothes, lighting our streets and homes at night, carrying our messages, bringing entertainment from distant places, and running great factories where our clothing and other necessities are manufactured. Electricity has undoubtedly become a most important factor in the social and economic life of the world. The use man has made of electricity distinguishes the present century from all previous ones of man's sojourn on Earth. The recent developments of nuclear energy have come about in large part as a result of the study of electricity as a form of energy.

Electricity is a subject which deserves greater consideration in the education of children. Its importance in modern thought is increasing rapidly. Some of the profound concepts of electricity rival the thought-provoking concepts of time and space derived from the fields of astronomy and geology. Too frequently in considering this subject in the curriculum we stress the practical aspects of electricity with respect to man's convenience and comfort and fail to develop the revolutionary concepts concerning the nature of electricity and matter. Since electrons and other electrical particles make up matter and energy, it is obvious that there is no physical, chemical, mechanical, electrical, or other phenomenon that is not in some manner influenced by these particles of electricity. Much of the biology of life and even the physiology and psychology of man are becoming more understandable as a result of developments in the study of the electrical nature of life.

The material which follows is designed for the purpose of helping children to develop responsible and resourceful behavior for democratic living.

Electricity Was Known Long Ago. Electricity, like magnetism, has been known for a long time. Thales, a Greek mathematician,

The study of electricity has brought about new concepts of matter and energy that have transformed our civilization. (H. Armstrong Roberts.)

astronomer, and philosopher—three occupations closely related in ancient days—called attention about 600 B.C. to the fact that amber (which the Greeks called *elektron*), when rubbed, had the property of attracting bits of straw, feathers, and leaves. The words *electricity* and *electron* are derived from the old Greek word for amber.

This property of amber remained little more than a curiosity until the reign of Queen Elizabeth I. Then William Gilbert, a physician at her court, made extensive investigations of both electricity and magnetism. Since Gilbert's time there has been almost continuous investigation of electrical and magnetic phenomena.

Although men have known electricity so long, it is only recently that they have understood much about its nature or about how to make use of it. This has been brought about by careful scientific study on the part of many men over a long period of time.

Important discoveries about electricity have been made by many different scientists in many countries. Some of the great names in this field are Von Guericke, Galvani, Volta, Franklin, Oersted, Henry, Faraday, Ampère, Ohm, Maxwell, and Edison. Each scientist, no matter where he happened to live, used the work of scientists who had studied electricity at other times and in other countries.

What Is Electricity? The teacher will find it useful from time to time, in answering the children's questions concerning electrical phenomena, to know about the nature of electricity. All of the information given on pages 805–829, and under this heading is not intended as something which need necessarily be taught to children, but rather as professional background for the teacher.

Scientists may not have a final answer to the question "What is electricity?" They can, however, explain many of the things that happen in electrical phenomena, whether it concerns the display of lightning, the ringing of doorbells, or the operation of vacuum tubes in our radios. The teacher will find a simple explanation of electricity that has been advanced by scientists very helpful as background content, whether she teaches in the kindergarten or in the sixth grade. The explanation of electricity is completely entwined with our understanding of matter, that is, the material out of which all substances are made.

In the section which follows, on static electricity, the present theory of the electrical nature of matter is developed in connection with a simple experiment.

Electricity May Be Produced by Rubbing. Probably every child has had the experience of getting a spark or shock from a metal object after he has walked on the carpet, or of hearing a crackle and seeing hairs follow the comb about as he combed his hair, or of picking up tiny bits of paper with a fountain pen which was rubbed on woolen cloth or a piece of fur. All these happenings were due to electricity called *static,* or motionless, electricity.

Static electricity jumps from the boy's finger to the key.

Static electricity is of interest to the child because of his experiences; it provides the basis of numerous amusing activities; it is also of historical interest and has many practical applications, such as the collection of dust from flues and the determination of the quality of coal. It is also used in certain printing processes and in the painting and insecticide industries. If that were all, its value in the elementary school might be doubtful; but the study of static electricity does more than amuse children. It helps them to understand the more useful current electricity, and it helps, in developing an understanding of the nature of matter. Even in regions such as humid parts of the tropics where experiences with electrical shocks are rare it would be well for children to learn that such a phenomenon does exist. If materials are well dried, some of these experiences may be performed in humid regions.

EXPERIENCE. *Electric charges attract and repel light objects.* A simple experiment may be performed which may be used to illustrate the theory underlying much of the scientist's concept of matter. Although experiences with static electricity are common in some places, it would be difficult to study electricity if we were not able to get a small quantity of it in a place where we could experiment with it. It is easier to explain electricity if we make use of a small piece of light material which is free to move. By a silk thread about eight inches long suspend freely a ball made of the pith from a cornstalk (material may be purchased from a scientific or school supply house). A grain of "puffed wheat" or a ball of balsa wood (used in model airplanes) will do. The ball should be about a quarter of an inch in diameter.[6]

[6] Teachers will find described on pages 784, 785, and 792 some devices for suspension that are suitable for use in any of the experiences with static electricity described in this section that require objects to be suspended.

With a piece of fur or woolen cloth vigorously rub a large stick of sealing wax or an article of hard rubber such as a comb. Bring the sealing wax or hard-rubber comb near to the pith ball. At first, the ball is strongly attracted to the wax. However, shortly after the ball touches the wax, it jumps away, and the wax now strongly *repels* the ball. How can we explain this action?

Like magnetism, electricity is involved with the structure and behavior of atoms and their parts. Recall again that atoms are composed of particles carrying positive and negative charges of electricity; that the electrons (negatively charged particles) spin and revolve around the nucleus at various energy levels; that atoms are neutral electrically, due to the balance between the protons of the nucleus and the electrons circulating around it, unless something occurs to disturb the balance by removing electrons or by an atom taking on electrons (Chapter 11).

To illustrate, suppose an election district has an equal number of people in two political parties. If every member of a party voted a straight party ticket, neither political party would win. But if someone moved out of the election district, the party to which he did not belong would have the most votes.

Electrons are light and may be rubbed off things rather easily. We probably go around all day rubbing electrons off of the things we touch, but on many days we do not notice it, for reasons that we shall learn about later. This may even happen when violent winds occurring in thunderstorms rub electrons off raindrops (p. 472).

So when we rub a comb or wax rod, which was neutral at the beginning, with the wool or fur, which was also neutral, we rub some electrons *off* the fur and *onto* the rod. The rod now has an *excess* of electrons (negative particles), while the fur lacks some electrons. As a result, the rod is *negatively* charged, and the fur is *positively* charged.

Now when we approach the neutral pith ball with the negative rod, many electrons in the ball are repelled by the excess of electrons on the rod because like charges repel each other. Being somewhat free to move, many electrons move to the far side of the ball. This leaves the near side of the ball positive (induced charge). Unlike charges attract each other; therefore the ball is attracted to the rod.

As soon as the ball touches the rod, some electrons begin to run off the rod and upon the ball. In a few seconds the ball has also acquired an excess of electrons, which makes it negative, too. Since like charges repel each other, the ball is now repelled by the rod and flies away.

If instead of rubbing a rubber or sealing-wax rod with wool or fur, we rub a glass rod with silk, electrons are rubbed off the rod and onto the silk, leaving the rod with a deficiency of electrons and making it *positive*. This positive rod will attract the pith ball after we have made the ball negative, as in the foregoing Experience.

In all these Experiences in which two substances are rubbed together, it is important to note that both substances receive charges; one substance receives a negative charge and the other a positive charge. When we begin to study the nature of lightning, we shall need to keep this in mind, for we must look for both positive and negative charges.

Children will notice that Experiences with static electricity do not occur when there is much moisture in the air. This is because each particle of water in the air acts just as our pith ball did, and is attracted to a charged substance, there to give up or receive some electrons. When there is much moisture in the air, this process goes on so rapidly that it is difficult or impossible to keep any substance charged long enough to experiment with it. We might say the charge is carried away by the moisture as rapidly as it is made. Children should be encouraged to try some static-electricity experiments on damp days so as to observe the difference. If some expected results are not obtained, this in itself can frequently serve as a most desirable learning experience.

In some of the dry regions of Earth, such as parts of southwestern United States or northern Mexico, charges of static electricity can be secured at different times during the year because of the lack of moisture. On the other hand, children living in humid regions would have had little or no experience with it. In many regions, such as northern United States and most of Canada, more experiences with static electricity are secured in cold periods when there is usually less moisture in the atmosphere.

Electrons are much more *free* to move about in some substances than in others. Substances in which electrons are quite free to move are called *conductors,* while substances in which electrons are held rather firmly are called *nonconductors,* or *insulators.* The metals form one large class of conductors, while nonconductors include such substances as glass, silk, wool, wood, paper, hard or soft rubber, sealing wax, and many other substances. It will be noted that experiments with static electricity are all done with nonconductors; for if we used conductors, the electrons could easily run off through our bodies. That is

why this electricity is called *static,* for it is held relatively static, or motionless, on nonconductors. For a way to test substances to see if they are conductors or nonconductors, see the Experience on page 813.

We shall see later that when electricity *moves* (or, in other words, when electrons move), it is able to do useful things. We call electrons in motion *current electricity.*

It will be noted from the discussion above that a body can be charged by either adding or removing electrons—adding electrons giving a negative charge, removing electrons giving a positive charge.

EXPERIENCE. *Experimenting with static electricity: static charges with paper.* Make a small pile of tiny bits of paper. Have one of the children comb his hair with his own rubber or plastic comb, then hold the comb near the pile of paper.

The Experience could be varied by rubbing a fountain pen on wool or fur and then holding it near the bits of paper. Add to this pile of paper bits, bits of various light materials, such as thin tin foil, tissue paper, or feathers. Notice that some of the paper is attracted to the pen. On a dry day some of the paper may later jump away. If the material is not attracted, cut it up into still smaller pieces and warm the fur and the bits in order to get them

quite dry. Repeat this experiment on a rainy day, a cool, dry day, or a cold, sunny day, if you have this variety of weather in your climate. If not, use as much variety as you have. If you are in a moist climate and have experienced cold weather in some other region, describe your experiences with shocks of static electricity. The children will enjoy hearing how people are frequently surprised when they feel a charge of electricity.

EXPERIENCE. *Static charges from combing hair.* Have children use their combs to comb their hair. On a dry day does the hair stand up as it is attracted to the comb? Now hold the comb to the bits of light material used in the last experiment. What happens?

EXPERIENCE. *Developing static electricity on glass.* Put two thin books on a table so that they are a few inches apart. In the space between them place some tiny bits of paper or short clippings of hair. Over the books and covering the space between them place a piece of glass. Now rub the glass *vigorously* with a piece of silk or nylon and note what happens to the paper or hair. The glass will be charged with positive electricity. Note that the bits of paper were charged through the glass. (This charge, however, was induced; p. 807.)

EXPERIENCE. *Charging balloons with static electricity.* On a dry day inflate two toy rubber balloons and hang them on a piece of thread so that they are free to swing about and yet touch each other. Now rub the balloons with wool. They will often follow your arms about as you rub. If two children each rub a balloon at the same time, they can often get the balloons to repel each other if the day is dry. If another child will rub a comb or fountain pen with wool or fur and push it forward toward the balloons, the balloons should be repelled by the electrified comb or fountain pen.

Charged balloons.

EXPERIENCE. *Fastening things to a wall by static charges.* Heat a piece of Manila drawing paper in order to dry it thoroughly. Rub it with wool. If you are wearing a woolen suit, you can hold the paper under your arm and rub it by pulling it. Place the paper against the wall or blackboard. It will cling to the board firmly and remain for several minutes, owing to the electric charge given it by rubbing. The paper has a charge, but the wall is neutral. As we saw in a preceding section, a charged body attracts a neutral one. Rub an inflated balloon with wool, fur, or hair. Then place it on the wall. It should hang for a while.

EXPERIENCE. *To produce charges on sand particles.* Place a little dry sand or soil in a flat saucer or on a sheet of paper. Now rub a rubber balloon with wool or fur. Hold the balloon an inch or two above the sand. Listen. Be very quiet and you will hear the sand striking the balloon. The sand sounds like a very gentle rain. Many of these grains of sand after clinging to the balloon are repelled and fall back into the saucer or paper, but perhaps later will be attracted again by the balloon's charge.

Bending a very fine stream of water with a charge of electricity.

The sand is first attracted to the balloon because there is an excess of electrons (or negative electricity) on the balloon. These electrons cause many of the electrons on the near side of a grain of sand to flow around to the opposite side. This leaves the side toward the balloon positive, and the sand is attracted to the balloon. Once on the balloon, the entire grain becomes saturated with electrons. Thus it has the same charge as the balloon and is repelled. Gravity helps to return it to the paper or the saucer.

EXPERIENCE. *Bending a stream of water.* Turn on the water faucet in such a way as to get a *very* fine stream of water. Rub a rod of sealing wax or hard rubber comb with wool or fur and hold it near the stream of water. The stream should bend toward the rod. The charged rod attracts the neutral stream. If the comb or fur becomes moistened during the experiment, it may be impossible to secure results if there is an attempt to repeat the events. In that case, dry the comb and fur again, or take another comb or piece of fur for the repetition.

EXPERIENCE. *Should we clean clothes with gasoline?* When rubbing rods or combing our hair we can often notice crackling sounds. These sounds are caused by tiny electric sparks. We occasionally get a shock and see a spark when we touch metal after walking across the carpet. Now we can see why it is very dangerous to clean clothes with gasoline or benzine. The vapor of these fluids is extremely inflammable, and a tiny spark of electricity produced by rubbing the clothes would cause a fire in which a person might be seriously injured. It is much better to use a fireproof cleaning fluid or to send our clothes to the cleaner.

Substances with Like Charges Repel Each Other. Using any of the same materials as in the Experience on page 806, a number of interesting variations will serve to *focus attention* on the fact that substances with "like charges repel; unlike charges attract each other." If pith balls are used they should have a diameter of a quarter to half an inch.[7] Fasten a pith ball to

[7] This experiment will work faster if the pith balls are painted with bronze or aluminum paint and then allowed to dry thoroughly. The metal paint allows electrons to move freely about the surface of the balls. They are prevented from escaping by the silk thread. Bits of carbon from a burned match may also be used in place of pith balls.

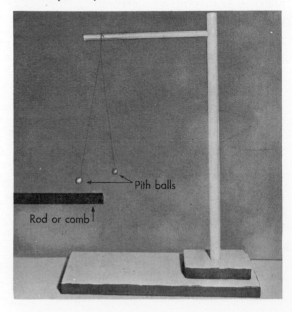

each end of a silk thread about twelve inches long, by sewing them with a needle or using a little glue. Hang them from a support (p. 810). Now bring near to the balls a rubber comb or sealing-wax rod which has been rubbed with fur or wool. Such a rod or comb is charged negatively; that is, it has an excess of electrons. Note that the balls are first attracted to the rod, and then after a little while they are repelled. Sometimes it is necessary to allow the balls to roll along the rod and to rub the rod several times. Soon both the balls secure the same charge as the rod, and they are repelled by the rod and by each other. You can chase them about with the rod. This shows that *substances charged in the same way repel each other.* Next bring near the balls a glass or plastic rod which has been rubbed with silk. The rod is charged positively; that is, it has a deficiency of electrons. It attracts the pith balls, which were repelled by the rubber rod, showing that *unlike charges attract each other.* After a time the moisture in the air allows the charge on the balls to leak away, and they become neutral again. The more moisture there is in the air, the faster the charge will leak away.

Suspend a hard-rubber object such as a pocket comb (or pen, or sealing-wax rod) so that it is free to swing horizontally, as shown in the diagram below. Rub the comb with fur or wool. Bring near to it another rubber

object or sealing-wax rod which has been rubbed with fur. The comb should be repelled. Bring a glass rod rubbed with silk near the swinging comb. The comb should be attracted. Like charges repel; unlike charges attract.

EXPERIENCE. *To compare the action between magnetic poles with that of electrical charges.* The children may have learned in their study of magnetism that "like poles repel; unlike poles attract." Now they learn "like charges repel; unlike charges attract." They are always interested in the similarity of wording.

What Is Lightning? Franklin did his famous experiment with the kite to find out whether the display of lightning during a thunderstorm was similar to the sparks he secured in his electrical experiments. Franklin caused some of the electricity in a thundercloud to be drawn off by means of a pointed wire attached to the top of a kite. He found that the "electric fire," as he called it, from the clouds could be used in doing the same experiments that he performed with frictional electricity; and thereby he demonstrated that lightning is a discharge, or spark, of electricity.

When the kite string became wet by the rain, it became a conductor of electricity, and allowed the electric current to pass from the wire at the top to a key tied to the lower end of the string. He held the key by means of a silk ribbon, which is a good insulator. During the thunderstorm he obtained a large spark from the key.

Franklin's experiment was a very dangerous one, and no one is advised to repeat it. He might easily have received a fatal shock.

As indicated in the discussion of thunderstorms, there are violent updrafts and downdrafts (p. 472). These are violent currents in which air, raindrops, raindroplets, and sometimes ice crystals and snow are buffeted against each other. This action produces friction, and

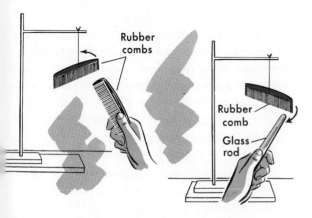

Rubber combs

Rubber comb

Glass rod

Like charges repel.   Unlike charges attract.

(Washington Post Photo.)

from the Experiences listed in this chapter we know that friction can produce static electrical charges.

The outermost surface of drops is composed to a considerable extent of electrons. It is thought that in the great drafts of air some of the electrons can be carried off by the air currents, leaving the drop with a positive charge. In some of the updrafts the drops may become quite shattered. So a thunderstorm cloud may have portions that have a positive charge and other portions that are negative.

That friction in the air can produce static electricity is indicated by studies in which it was found that ice crystals sliding along the metallic wings of an airplane will create charges. In these studies the airplane accumulated a negative charge and the ice crystals a positive charge. It has been found also that

snow blowing along the ground may acquire an electrical charge.

On page 472 there is a discussion of the discharge which produces the huge spark we know as lightning. Positive and negative electrical charges become separated in a thunderstorm and build up until the electrical attraction between becomes so great there is a surge toward each other. This generates heat, light, and sound and the radio waves heard over radios as static. In addition, a lightning flash makes nitrogen in the air available for plant growth. It then falls with the rain.

A lightning flash is so rapid and so much happens in a wink of the eye that it is difficult for an observer to know what goes on. Photography has been helpful in studying the flashes. A charge breaks out through a series of leader strokes. Each leader thrusts farther than the last. Finally a leader may reach the opposite charge, which may be in another cloud, or portion of the same cloud, or on the ground. What is not usually realized is that there are one or more upward strokes across the same path over which it has come. This path or channel is already electrified (ionized). As a leader approaches the ground, charges there may rapidly assemble and stream upward.

In spite of the fact that air is a fairly good insulator, it has been found that Earth loses to the air its fair-weather negative charge. Scientists have been puzzled about the fact that Earth has continued to be negative in spite of this leakage. Some have proposed carefully developed ideas that Earth becomes replenished with negative charges through thunderstorms. It has been shown by studies that 87 per cent of all lightning shocks carry negative electricity to the ground.

According to this hypothesis, thunderstorms may help to keep an electrical balance between Earth and the atmosphere. This seems possible when one realizes that statistics on the occurrence of thunderstorms indicate that

Materials vary widely in their ability to conduct electricity.

40,000 to 50,000 such storms occur every day! Several thousand thunderstorms are in progress at any one moment.

Current Electricity. Thus far we have been working with electricity at rest, that is, *static electricity.* If man did not know something about electricity in motion, he could do little to make electricity his servant. Let us now turn our attention to some of the elementary phases of electricity in motion, which we shall call *current electricity.* Until now we have been dealing with the way in which electricity behaves with nonconductors, or insulators. We shall now observe how it behaves with conductors.

Conductors and Nonconductors. We know that conductors allow electrons to move rather freely (p. 808), while in nonconductors the electrons do not move so freely. All metals conduct electricity, some better than others. Carbon and some kinds of solutions are also conductors. When we want electricity to move along over a path called a *circuit,* we use conductors. Copper wire is frequently used

for this purpose. Glass, rubber, sealing wax, porcelain, paper, and other substances do not conduct electricity and are therefore examples of nonconductors. Another word for nonconductor is *insulator.* Nonconductors, or insulators, are used to keep electricity from going where it is not wanted. Copper wire is generally insulated with material which is a nonconductor, to keep the electricity traveling along in the circuit in the wire. Glass or porcelain is frequently used as an insulator on the poles carrying electric-power lines to prevent the electricity from escaping.

The matter of insulation is an important one in working with electricity, whether it be in the simple wiring done by the children in wiring electric bells or a doll house or in complicated work done by electrical engineers about powerhouses or with high-power transmission lines. The fundamental principles are the same, regardless of the complexity of the tasks. Most of us use electricity every day, turning it on and off with little thought; yet the electric apparatus must be so installed that it does us no personal injury and does not set our buildings on fire.

Even the simplest electric apparatus, such as a lamp socket, would not work if we did not have the means of keeping electricity where it is wanted. By looking about us we can gain a little appreciation of the magnitude of the problems of electrical engineering and how the solution of these problems has given us many comforts and conveniences.

In a conductor like a copper wire, each copper atom has a single loosely held electron in its outer shell (p. 378). In a copper wire these relatively free electrons tend to drift about at random. If the two ends of the wire are connected to the poles of a battery, excess electrons from the negative pole of the battery will move along the wire, displacing the free electrons in a steady stream. This stream of electrons returns to the battery at the positive pole, forming a complete circuit. When electrons move in such a circuit, they constitute an electric current.

As such a current flashes along the wire it is thought that electrons push other electrons ahead of them. When electrons are supplied at one end of a wire, they tend to crowd off other electrons at the other end of the wire. Although any one electron may move only a very short distance at a time, there are such large numbers of them that a continuous movement of electrons results. Electrons collide with copper atoms along the way. This slows down the current somewhat, and produces heat as the electrons transfer their energy to the atoms. We say that the copper wire offers *resistance* to the current. The wires of an electric toaster are made of material that offers high resistance to the current, thus producing a great deal of heat (p. 838).

Copper offers little resistance to a current, and is therefore said to be a good conductor of electricity. For this reason, and because it is a relatively plentiful element, copper is widely used in electrical work. Silver is a better conductor, but is more expensive.

It has been found that some materials under

certain conditions offer *no* resistance to an electric current. Such materials are called *superconductors*. The rare element technetium, formed in atomic reactors, is one of these. A closed circuit can be made of this material and cooled by liquid helium to a temperature of 11° above absolute zero (p. 445). If a current is started in this circuit by a battery and the battery is then disconnected, the current will continue to flow indefinitely without losing energy. One explanation for this depends upon the fact that the atoms of any substance at ordinary room temperature are in a state of constant motion known as *thermal vibration*. As the substance is cooled, this vibration is reduced, and at a temperature close to absolute zero it virtually disappears. Since the atoms remain practically motionless, collisions with electrons are greatly reduced. It is thought that pairing of electrons may also help to eliminate resistance.

Some materials, such as glass, rubber, sealing wax, porcelain, and paper, do not have loosely held outer electrons. All their electrons are held tightly bound within the atoms. Such materials will not carry an electric current, or at least they will carry only an infinitesimally small one. This is why these materials are called nonconductors, or *insulators*.

EXPERIENCE. *Testing substances to see if they are conductors.* When a scientist wishes to find out the truth, he tries out his ideas to see what happens. Probably many children will ask, "How can we tell which substances are conductors and which are not?" The following experiment will offer some suggestions.

Connect a dry cell and bulb[8] as shown. Leave two bare ends of copper wire. Of course the circuit is broken at this point. Put the two bare ends together to determine if the circuit is working properly, and disconnect them

[8] Dry cells, doorbells, bell wire, miniature sockets, and miniature light bulbs such as are used in flashlights may be purchased at hardware stores.

A simple hookup that can be used to test whether substances can conduct electricity.

again. Do you see that if anything conducts electricity across this break, the light will come on? Touch the bare ends of the wire to two points on various objects. If they are conductors, the light will burn. (The brightness of the light may give a rough indication of how well the substance conducts.)

Test in this way the following substances and as many more as you can obtain: a blackboard eraser, a pencil eraser, the handle of a screwdriver, the blade of the screwdriver, a tin can, a rubber ball, an aluminum pan, a glass dish, a silver fork or spoon, painted and bare metal objects, paper clips, paper, porcelain, glass, chalk, wood, slate, silk, wool, sealing wax, rubber, paraffin, carbon from an old dry cell (p. 817) or what is called lead but is carbon from a pencil, pure water in a clean glass, (*relatively pure* water can be obtained by melting the ice that forms on a freezing unit of a refrigerator), pure water with a handful of table salt added, pure water in a clean glass with some sugar added.[9]

Test other solutions—for example, lemon juice, vinegar, or any other mild, household acid in water, baking or washing soda or Epsom salts in water.

[9] In testing solutions it may be necessary to use three or four dry cells. See page 826 for a method of wiring more than one cell.

In general, the metals and some solutions are good conductors. The nonmetals (except carbon) and other solutions are poor conductors; they are insulators. The solutions which conduct are those made with salts, acids, or alkalies. Other solutions are nonconductors (p. 848).

EXPERIENCE. *To make a record of results.* Make a list of substances found to be good conductors and a list of substances found to be nonconductors. If the children have already studied static electricity, perhaps they will be interested to find out whether the substances they used in developing charges are conductors or not. They should find that all such materials are poor or nonconductors.

EXPERIENCE. *Placing a charge on a nonconductor.* A conductor can hold a static charge if the conductor is insulated. For instance, in a dry atmosphere one could charge a piece of aluminum provided that the aluminum piece was located on a nonconductor such as glass. In this case the charge could be put on the aluminum by rubbing something charged over it.

One could place a charge on a fork hung up by a string. This could be done by charging a piece of hard rubber or plastic and then rubbing the object over the fork in order to allow some of the excess electrons to pass over to the fork.

EXPERIENCE. *Joining wires.* Children will frequently need to know how to join two pieces of wire when they wish to make a longer one, or when they wish to connect another device to a circuit.

The rubber, cloth, or thread which covers the wire is an insulator. It is put there to keep the electric current in the wire, where it is wanted, and to prevent it from going astray if another conductor happens to touch the wire.

If we wish to join two wires, then, we must remove the insulation (by scraping or cutting

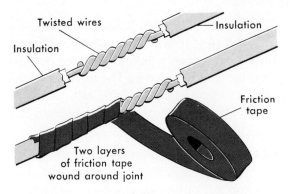

Wires that have been joined should be carefully taped.

it off) so as to expose the bare metal ends which are to be joined. These bare ends are then joined by twisting them around each other.

This procedure brings the copper-wire ends into contact and provides the necessary metal path for the electricity but leaves the bare copper without its covering of insulation. It is now necessary to cover the joint with insulating material. Black sticky tape, commonly called *friction tape,* is used by electricians for this purpose, and is the most satisfactory material. It is applied by wrapping a layer or two around the joint in such a way as to cover all the bare copper thoroughly.

EXPERIENCE. *Developing responsible behavior in reference to electricity.* It is well to impress upon the children that while dry cells are harmless, the current which flows in ordinary house wiring can be dangerous. This is especially true when the hands are wet, for wet skin is a very much better conductor of electricity than dry skin. Every year people are killed by turning electric fixtures on or off while their bodies are in contact with the water in a bathtub or washbowl. The fixture or the pull chain becomes "alive," due to some defect in its insulation, and current flows from the fixture through the person's wet hand and body and thence through the water pipe to the ground. This is one reason why bathroom fixtures often have

a cord or string of nonconducting material instead of a pull chain.

The following safety hints will prove useful, not only to children in the schoolroom, but to every individual at all times:

a. Never touch a bare wire which *may* be connected to the house current or to some other source of high voltage. Never under any circumstances touch wires which you may find dangling from poles after a storm. A discussion might assist children to learn what agencies in the community repair damages to circuits as a result of storms.

b. Never put the fingers or any metal object inside an electric socket, or outlet.

c. Never turn lights on or off or touch the fixtures while the body is in contact with water in the bathtub or washbowl. Even linen or cotton cord is likely to be a conductor if it is wet.

d. Never attempt to repair extension cords or household electric apparatus unless you know exactly what you are doing. If not, consult someone who does.

Electricity May Be Made by Chemical Action. It is not surprising to learn that electricity can be obtained in many different ways when one realizes that electricity seems to be a constituent of all matter. We have already discussed how electricity can be produced by detaching electrons from atoms by rubbing certain substances together.

A second method of obtaining electricity is by chemical means. Volta, in 1799, found that by placing copper and zinc in a solution of dilute sulfuric acid, he could secure an electric current through a wire connected to the two metals. We need not go into the rather complicated chemistry of this cell, which was named the voltaic cell after Volta. The acid, in attacking and combining with the zinc, sets free electrons which run off the zinc and through the wire to the copper. The essential feature of the voltaic cell is that it changes energy which was in the chemicals (zinc and acid) into electrical energy.

The voltaic cell has been introduced in this discussion because of its historical significance. There is no need for constructing one in the elementary school. One reason for this is that sulfuric acid is not a safe acid for children to use. A second reason is that the cell is quite unsatisfactory for the Experiences suggested in this chapter. The modern dry cell can serve for all the Experiences involving electrical circuits.

His discovery was of great importance to mankind and ushered in a new period of electricity, that of *current electricity*. Many types of cells have been devised since the original voltaic cell. The modern dry cells are a development of this early cell.

The Dry Cell. Everyone is familiar with dry cells. They are found inside our flashlights. They are sometimes used to ring our doorbells. They are sometimes used in radios. In the early days of automobiles they were used to ignite the gas in the cylinders. Many kinds of apparatus which at one time utilized electricity generated by dry cells are now operated by electricity secured from other sources. Storage batteries have supplanted dry cells in

many places, especially in automobiles, while in many homes a transformer is used to change the house current so that it is suitable to ring bells, thereby replacing dry cells in that use.

One advantage of dry cells as compared with voltaic, or wet, cells is that they have no harmful acids. Teachers need have no fear in using dry cells in the classroom, either because of the materials in them or because of the current produced. With the ordinary apparatus in the classroom, it is almost impossible to secure enough current from a dry cell of about 1½ volts even to feel an electric shock.

EXPERIENCE. *What is inside a dry cell?* Have the children open a dry cell. It can be opened with a screwdriver, a chisel and a hammer, or an ordinary can-opener. First take off the paper cover. Notice that a zinc cup is now exposed with a tar, sealing-wax, or metal top. Cut through the zinc. It will be well to do this work on a big piece of paper, such as a newspaper, in order to keep the black powder from getting on the table, as it is rather dirty. Notice that inside the cup there is a black powder which in fresh dry cells is moistened into a paste (in old cells it may be quite dry). This powder is a mixture of ammonium chloride, manganese dioxide, zinc chloride, coke, and

Zinc can   Carbon rod   Chemical mixture   Paper lining

Parts of a dry cell.

graphite. (With children no great importance need be attached to the names of these substances.) Lining the zinc inside the cell is a heavy pasteboard, like blotting paper, which absorbs moisture and helps to keep the paste moist for a longer time.

In the center of the dry cell is a carbon rod. Attached to the carbon rod and to the zinc are places to fasten wires. These are called *binding posts.* The carbon rod is called the *positive* (+) *pole,* and the zinc cup forms the *negative* (−) *pole.* With young children it may be important to show that there are two places on dry cells to which wires may be fastened. The top of the dry cell is covered with sealing wax or metal to prevent the paste drying out. A dry cell is dry only on the outside. If the inside becomes dry the cell is "dead."

In examining the interior of a dry cell it is important for children to learn that electricity is *not stored* in a dry cell but rather that there are chemicals inside which produce electricity when the two posts are connected with a conductor, as is the case in ringing a doorbell. In this case, energy which was stored in the chemicals is converted into electrical energy which we can use to light lamps or ring bells. It is important for children to appreciate the significance in modern society of the principle that energy may be transformed from one form to another (Chapter 22). We shall see later that the energy we use has undergone many transformations.

When a circuit is made (closed), a dry cell acts as a pump or pusher for the movement of electrons. In a chemical reaction, zinc atoms from the zinc cup give up electrons that are then *free* to move from the negative pole through the conducting wire into the positive pole in the center. At that point, the electrons are taken on by chemicals within the dry cell. The usuable parts of the zinc cup and the paste may be gradually used up.

EXPERIENCE. *Reviving a "dead" dry cell.* Many times a dry cell goes "dead" because it has dried out. It may be partially revived for a time by moistening the paste inside it.

With a nail and a hammer, punch a number of holes in the bottom of a "dead" dry cell and set it in a pan of water. In about ten minutes test the cell with a bell or lamp. Usually the cell will be found to be partially revived. The addition of some ammonium chloride (sal ammoniac) or some vinegar to the water will improve the process.

EXPERIENCE. *To make an electric cell from a lemon.* Cut two slits in a lemon. Place in one slit a narrow strip of copper and in the other a strip of zinc. Touch the two ends of the strips to the tongue. The taste buds in the tongue should be stimulated slightly by the electric current, giving a characteristic "electric taste."

The Storage Battery. Where regular service is needed, as in an automobile, storage batteries are used.

The ordinary automobile storage battery consists of two sets of lead plates in a solution of sulfuric acid. One set of plates is connected to a binding post, the negative terminal (anode). The other set is spaced alternately between the plates of the first set, without any of the plates touching, and is connected to the positive terminal (cathode). The sulfuric acid, H_2SO_4, or hydrogen sulfate, forms two sets of ions: hydrogen ions, H^+, and sulfate ions, SO_4^{--} (p. 379). The minus signs show that the sulfate ions carry excess electrons. These electrons are released at the negative terminal, and pass along a cable to operate the starter or lights of a car. After they have done their work they return by another cable to the positive terminal, where they spread out on the second set of plates and help to form a deposit of lead sulfate. In the process, the sulfuric acid is used up and water is formed. The battery thus acts as a pump that sends electrons around a circuit and receives them back. The sulfate ion is the "ferry" that carries electrons across the liquid part of the circuit.

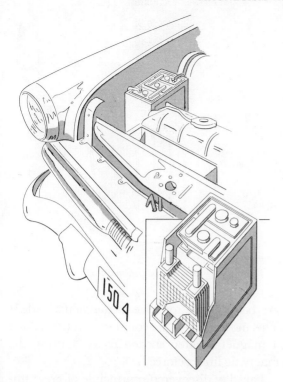

The storage battery in a car has to operate starter, lights, ignition, and numerous accessories.

The battery can be recharged by passing an electric current through it in the opposite direction. In this case the lead sulfate and water are converted back to sulfuric acid, and the sulfate ions are ready to go to work again.

It is the migration of ions through the solution that helps to carry the electrons in the desired direction and thus either build up or release the charge of the battery.

Strictly speaking, this kind of "double set" of plates in its container forms a cell. Two or more cells connected in series constitute a battery. However, the term *battery* is often used loosely for cell. A lead-sulfuric acid cell produces 2 volts. Cars usually have 12-volt batteries, composed of 6 cells.

The battery is charged by means of a generator run by the car motor. The generator looks like an ordinary electric motor, and in fact it is built the same way. When the armature is rotated, the generator pumps electrons into the battery, or directly to the lights or radio if they are turned on. The rate of charging is controlled by a voltage regulator. Battery chargers are available at repair garages and also for home use. They use ordinary 110-volt house current.

The storage battery is something like a bank into which we can put money when we have a surplus, and on which we may draw in time of need. There is, however, this important point to be noted: no electricity is stored *as such* in the storage battery; *energy* is stored there in the form of potential chemical change.

It would be useless to try to recharge dry cells with a generator, for in them the chemical change is of a kind that can proceed in only one direction. Storage batteries last much longer than dry cells because they can be recharged. They are not very satisfactory for the classroom, because they contain a strong acid and because they can produce a current strong enough to be somewhat dangerous.

EXPERIENCE. *Excursion to learn more about storage batteries.* Take children to a garage where storage batteries are being charged. Ask the mechanic to show the children a battery, a generator, and a battery charger. Perhaps he will show the children an old battery which he has torn apart.

Generating Electricity by Mechanical Means: Electrical Generators, Dynamos, and Magnetos.[10] It is obvious that storage batteries and dry cells could not be used to operate modern electrical appliances on the huge scale on which they are used today, although very large storage batteries may be used to supply emergency power in power plants and telephone exchanges. Most of the electricity

[10] There is frequently confusion over the terms *dynamo, generator,* and *magneto. Dynamo* is the older term, and usually means the same thing as *generator,* though it can also apply to any rotating electric machinery, such as motors or magnetos. A magneto, as explained in this section, uses permanent magnets.

that we use in our daily lives comes from large power-driven machines called *generators,* which can produce great quantities of electricity and send it to distant places to be used. Few inventions have done more to revolutionize modern life than the generator.

EXPERIENCE. *Excursion to an electric power plant.* Take the children to see a power plant. Caution the children against touching anything and direct them to stay where the guide tells them to. Observe the large generators. Note that there are moving parts. These parts must be moved by some kind of power. Sometimes they are moved by a steam engine which is operated by coal. Sometimes they are run by water which turns a wheel. Ask the guide for information. Perhaps he will show you the steam boiler or how the water power is used. Perhaps a power plant utilizing nuclear energy has been introduced into your community.

See how the electricity is sent out to the community. Possibly the wires may be traced back to the school. Find out if these wires are underground or above.

While the explanation of many of the principles involved in the generator should be left for the later education of children, it is well for the teacher to bear in mind that the electric current is secured by mechanical means.

Farm and country homes that are beyond the power lines may have a gasoline-driven generator and storage batteries. Sometimes direct current is needed for a special purpose. In such a case an alternating-current motor may be used to drive a generator that produces direct current. Such a combination is called a *motor-generator* set.

Michael Faraday, an English scientist and experimenter, was the first to discover that if a conductor which is part of a closed circuit is moved in the field of a magnet, a current will flow in the conductor. The whirling parts of the generator have in them conductors which

A hand-powered magneto.

are being made to move in magnetic fields.[11] This movement of the conductor in the field of a magnet is often spoken of as "cutting the magnetic lines of force."

Faraday discovered a principle of great importance to modern civilization. His life is an interesting story and one well worth reading. It should be noted that his discoveries, like most of the advances of science, were based on the discoveries of other scientists before him. He utilized what was known and developed it a little further.

The Magneto. The magneto is much like the generator except that the lines of force (or field) are produced by permanent magnets, whereas in the generator the lines of force are produced by electromagnets.

Perhaps you have observed a magneto that has an electric lamp attached to it. When the crank is turned, the magneto generates electricity, which lights the lamp. The energy which you use to turn the crank comes from the food you eat, which in turn comes directly from plants or from animals which have eaten

[11] A full explanation of the generator involves a number of concepts not yet considered; so it will be deferred to a later place in this book (p. 841–843).

plants. The energy which these plants have stored came from the sunlight in which they grew (Chapter 22).

How Steam Engines Light Electric Lights. The Energy Which We Use Came Originally from the Sun. Some toy engines operate a generator or magneto which in turn lights an electric light. It will help to build up the children's concept of the change of energy from one form to another if they trace the energy changes which take place in such a toy.

In one model, water in a boiler is heated by an electric heating coil. Electrical energy comes over wires to an outlet in the room. Passing through the heating coil, the electrical energy is changed to heat energy. This heat boils the water in the boiler. Steam is produced. The heat energy has now become energy stored up as steam pressure. The steam passes through a pipe to the engine, and in the engine the energy stored in the steam pressure is converted into the energy of motion; in other words, the engine runs. The engine turns the generator. In turning, the generator converts the energy of motion into electrical energy. This electrical energy is sent through wires to a small lamp. In the lamp the electrical energy is converted into light and heat.

The question may be asked at this point why the lamp which the toy generator lights is not so bright as the lamps in the schoolroom, since the energy of both may be traced back to the same source, namely, the house wiring. The answer, while simple, involves an important concept. Every time the energy was transformed, some of it was lost to other forms of energy which could not be used. Some was lost in the form of heat from the boiler and engine, some was used up in friction, and so on. For every transformation of energy we must pay a price in the form of a loss. A good deal of the lost energy is in the form of heat.

In some power plants the heat beneath the boiler is supplied by burning coal. This coal was made from vegetation which grew in the sunlight long ago. If the children have studied the formation of coal, it would be instructive to have them trace the growth of plants under the influence of the sun, their conversion into coal, the burning of the coal to get heat, the heating of water to make steam, the use of steam power to turn the generator, and finally the use of the electricity to give us light or power.

In other power plants the generators are driven by water wheels or turbines which are turned by the energy of falling water, on the same principle as an old-fashioned millwheel. In this case, the energy came from the sun also. The sun's heat evaporates water. The water condenses in the form of a cloud and falls as rain. The rain, running downhill in the rivers, turns water wheels. The water wheels drive generators.

In either case, the energy which we now use as electricity came originally from the sun.

a. Sunlight ⟶ ancient plants ⟶ coal ⟶ heat ⟶ steam ⟶ mechanical motion ⟶

electricity ⟶ { light / heat / power

b. Sunlight ⟶ water vapor ⟶ clouds and rain ⟶ running water ⟶ mechanical motion ⟶ electricity ⟶ { light / heat / power

Electricity Can Flow Only in a Closed Circuit. *Wiring a Simple Circuit.* Children can learn to wire electric bells in the primary grades.

A good beginning is to wire the bell with one dry cell without a push button. Take two pieces of electric wire. Scrape off the insulation for about three quarters of an inch at the ends of the wires. Fasten one end of one wire to a binding post (the place for fastening a

A bell circuit.

wire) of the dry cell and the other end to a binding post of the bell. (See illustration above.) Take the other wire and fasten it in a similar way between the other posts of the dry cell and bell. You now have wires attached to both posts of the bell and both posts of the cell. The bell should ring. If it does not, see that the wire is securely fastened beneath the posts. Make sure that only bare wire is under all posts. The metal of the wire should touch the metal of the post in a good firm contact. This provides an opportunity to utilize the learning concerning the difference between insulators and conductors. A little difficulty may be a good thing from the point of view of learning. It might be well to let the children solve their own problems.

You now have a *closed circuit*. Electricity can pass from the dry cell, through the wire to the bell, through the bell, and back through the other wire to the dry cell. When you disconnect a wire, you open the circuit. Have the children draw a diagram on the board or on paper if it will help them to understand more clearly the idea of a closed path, or circuit.

Now that the children know what a closed circuit is, can they see the reason for the development of responsible behavior in reference to electricity? (p. 816.) If you touched a live fixture and at the same time a waterpipe or other pipe which goes into the ground, you would close a circuit which would pass through your body. The electricity which would flow through this circuit might be dangerous or even fatal.

The principles involved in wiring an electric bell are the same as those involved in a simple circuit. The children can wire toy motors and miniature electric lights in the same way, by substituting a lamp or motor for the bell.

Be sure of the following points in wiring: (1) that the insulation is cleaned off the parts of the wire that are attached to the posts; (2) that all connections are securely made. Twist the wire completely around the post.

Trace all the circuits you use in this section. To trace the circuits, start at one post of the dry cell and carefully follow the path of the electricity, seeing that it goes through the devices it is supposed to operate and gets back to the other post of the cell. Where branch circuits occur, some of the electricity goes one way, some the other. If you begin by tracing the simplest circuit, you should have no trouble with the more complicated ones. Diagrams may be drawn on the board, and the path of the electricity may be shown by arrows. This tracing of circuits is just what electricians and radio and television men must do in their work.

Switches in a Circuit. Children will readily recognize the difficulties of having to connect the wires to the battery every time they desire to ring the bell. It is all right for a while but not convenient if they wish to use the bell for real service in the classroom—for instance, as a signal or in connection with dramatic plays. Such a need may be presented and used as a means of introducing the use of switches in electric circuits.

We have learned (p. 821) that electricity can flow only in a closed circuit, that is, in a continuous metallic path from the dry cell or other source of power through the device to be operated and back to the dry cell again. If we provide a means for breaking the circuit, we can cause the current to start or stop at will.

A switch which is used for turning electric devices on and off is simply a means of closing or opening a circuit. If one of the wires in the simple bell circuit above is cut in two, the circuit is broken, or opened, and electricity no longer flows. The bell stops ringing. If the cut ends of the wire are again joined, the path is again completed, and the bell rings. This use of the cut ends of a wire to close a circuit and thus cause the bell to ring will serve to introduce and to develop the concept of an electrical switch. Young children might think of these two ends as a rudimentary switch.

A knife switch is a simple type of switch (p. 827). When it is closed—that is, when the movable part, or *blade,* is touching the fixed part, or *jaws*—there is a continuous path through the switch. When it is opened, the path is broken. The action of a switch is like that of putting together the two cut ends of the wire.

To insert a switch in a circuit, we need only cut one of the wires. We then scrape the insulation from the cut ends and fasten them under the binding posts, or screws, of the switch, one wire to each screw. Of course we can use two separate pieces of wire instead of cutting one in two.

A switch may be inserted in any part of a circuit because, so long as the circuit is broken, it does not matter where the break is made.

An ordinary push button is a kind of switch. It frequently contains a flat coil-like spring which flies back and breaks the circuit, or con-

A cross section of a push button.

nection, as soon as one removes one's finger. It is inserted in a circuit in the same manner as any other switch. It is sometimes necessary to unscrew and lift off the cover to find the two screws to which wires are to be attached. Sometimes these screws are on the bottom of the push button.

A knife switch is convenient for teaching purposes, since it shows clearly how the circuit is broken. The porcelain forming the base of the switch is insulating material.

The switch may be inserted in any part of the circuit. Take off one of the wires leading to a battery and attach it to the switch or push button. Attach another wire from the switch to the battery. Be sure that insulation is removed from the ends of the wires.

EXPERIENCE. *Working with electric circuits.* Have the children wire a simple bell circuit, using only a bell, two wires, and a dry cell. Follow the directions given in the section on simple electric circuits (p. 821).

Children will probably see the need of some means of turning the bell on and off. Show them knife switches and push buttons and allow them to put these devices in the circuit. Lead them to see that a switch is a means for breaking a circuit.

Let children take a push button apart and explain how it opens and closes the circuit. Note how quickly they will come to an understanding of it, once they have had an opportunity to examine and manipulate it.

This kind of activity will provide opportunity for the development of leadership in science. The children having special ability in this work can help others in learning about the simple circuit. The material used may be placed on a table where all children may have experience in wiring a bell or a light or some other electrical device which can be operated with a dry cell at free times or activity periods. Every child should have an opportunity to do the wiring, to dismantle the circuit and re-wire it again and again. Make certain that the girls have this experience, for they, as much as boys, need to establish an acquaintance with simple circuits and a constructive attitude toward energy. This kind of activity could be carried out with a minimum of supervision on the part of the teacher.

Constructing a simple switch is not essential to this work. However, there will probably be many children at the older levels who can make such a switch by following the illustration showing the parts.

EXPERIENCE. *Making a switch or push button.* A simple switch or push button is easy to make. Cut out and bend a metal strip about two inches long, as shown. Sheet copper or aluminum or even a piece of a "tin" can will do. Punch a hole in one end with a nail and a hammer, and bend as shown. Take a piece of

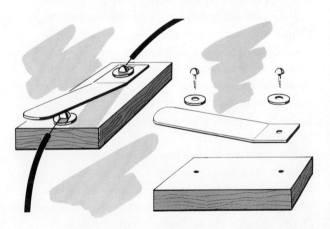

A switch made from a block of wood, screws, washers, and a strip of metal.

wood about three inches long. Near one end drive in a roundheaded wood screw. Before driving it in all the way, wrap around it a piece of wire with the insulation removed from the end; then drive in the screw firmly. Secure the end of the metal strip with a screw driven through the hole into the wood. Before you finish driving the screw, wrap a wire around it, as before. Small washers under the head of each screw may be used to hold the wires more securely. Attach the wires in the circuit just as you would the wires of a push button.

EXPERIENCE. *An electric-circuit explanation.* We have seen the electric current explained in terms of a flow of electrons along a conductor (p. 813). The switch is a contrivance which makes a gap in the conductor, so that the electrons can no longer move throughout the circuit.

You can play a game which is a kind of role-playing with children that may help the children to understand how electricity passes along wires. First secure a supply of sheets of paper of the usual tablet size. If possible have the paper of more than one color. Have the children write "electron" on each sheet of paper. Each boy or girl will represent an atom. Let each child have two sheets of paper, except for one child, who receives but one sheet, or you can get in the circle yourself with but the one sheet. The boys and girls form a circle. Each child should be close enough to the next one to be able to reach him easily. The sheets of paper represent electrons, and an electron is a tiny charge of electricity. It should also be kept in mind that the children could have more than just two pieces of paper, just as atoms of many substances have each a number of electrons.

For the purpose of our play we might think that each child (atom) is well balanced as to positive and negative charges of electricity (p. 375) when the child has two pieces of paper. The child who was given but one piece of paper (electron) has a positive surplus (charge), or we could say he is no longer balanced, and as a result attracts any electron (negative charges) which get too close. This child is temporarily a sort of generator who starts the action. He pulls a sheet of paper from a child standing to one side. We could think of these papers (electrons) as revolving about each child (atom) with a piece of paper belonging to one child getting too close to another child (atom) who needs more paper (electrons). This in turn causes the next child to need a piece of paper and he secures one from the next child, and so on, until pieces of paper are passing along the circuit.

The same piece should not be circulated all the way around the circle. To show this, having paper of different colors is useful. A child may receive a yellow piece of paper, but the child next in the circuit pulls a white one from him. In other words, the same electrons need not pass along the entire circuit. An electron may pass on to another atom and become quite permanent, while other electrons in the atom may become quite loose and easily lost by the atom. One can use any number of sheets desired, so long as one child holds less than the others. The teacher, if she wishes, can start this movement of electrons by entering the circle with fewer sheets of paper than any of the children have.

Somewhat as these sheets of paper are passed from one child to another, so electrons in a wire are passed from one atom to the next atom, and so around the circuit. In this way little charges of electricity are carried from one atom to the next. This causes a flow of electricity. The children will see that it is not necessary to stand in a circle, so long as each child is standing near enough to receive and pass on a sheet of paper.

No demonstration of an electrical current such as this can be perfect. For instance, it may occur to the children in repeating this play demonstration to move the paper in the opposite direction. It makes no difference which way the paper circulates around the group. However, in a real electrical current, there would be some source of electricity such as a dry cell (p. 817) or electrical generator (p. 819), and the electrons would flow in only one direction. In this case the dry cell or generator could be thought of somewhat as a pump which pumps electrons.

Now let one boy or girl be the electric switch. The boy or girl can stop or start the electric current by stepping out of the play circuit. When he gets out, the sheets of paper can no longer move about the circuit. We say he has opened the circuit. When he steps in, he closes it, and the sheets of paper can again move about. A switch opens and closes the circuit. Push buttons and chains that we use to turn electric lights on and off operate switches. They close and open electric circuits. When we press a button to turn on electric lights, we close the circuit, so that electrons flow from one atom to another.

A Short Circuit. Sometimes you may hear someone speak of a *short circuit*. Electricity always tends to take the *easiest path* back to the place where it started. If it is able to get back without going through the lamp, bell, or other device which it is supposed to operate, it will do so. This easy path is called a *short circuit*. When it occurs, the lamp or bell does not operate. If it occurs on a device connected to the house current, a fuse will blow. You will learn more about fuses on page 840.

The illustrations show two kinds of short circuits. Trace the paths of the electricity in its journey from one post of the dry cell to the other. What will happen in each case? Try it.

EXPERIENCE. *To give a play explanation of a short circuit.* Use children to represent atoms and paper electrons as in the Experience "An electric circuit explanation" on page 824. Ask

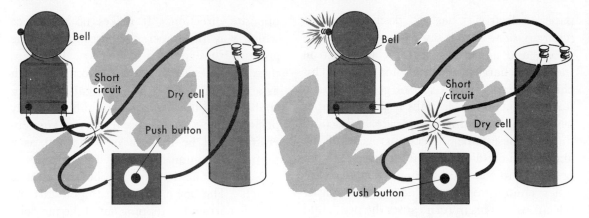

Two kinds of short circuits.   What will happen in each case?

children to demonstrate a short circuit.   This can be done by having children within the circuit pass paper from one to another without going the full length of the circuit.   The word *easiest* used two paragraphs above is an important one.   In this play, children can arrange themselves so that the paper can circulate over a short path more easily than complete the total path.

EXPERIENCE.   *To learn about short circuits.*   In connection with this work children are likely to encounter a short circuit.   The cause of the short circuit can be located.   They can note the heating of the wire, or perhaps the continued ringing of the bell.   The advantage of the dry cells is that the amount of electrical energy is small and as a result children will not be frightened or injured.

With the older children the matter of the short circuit can be actively associated with the probelms of the home (pp. 838–841).   However, children should *not* be encouraged to experiment with the home circuit.

EXPERIENCE.   *To discuss experiences at home with short circuits.*   Children like to discuss home experiences.   Have they known times when a fuse was blown?   What did father or mother do?   Did they find the cause?   Perhaps some-

one can bring an electrical cord to school.   Examine it.   Perhaps an old discarded extension wire can be found.   Why might this latter cause a short circuit if used?   Have the children discuss the importance of having cords for electrical appliances at home in good condition.   This discussion can be related to the fuse box (p. 838).

Wiring with Two or More Cells.   In many experiences more than one cell will be needed.   It is likely that in some of the experiences already described one cell may not provide enough electrical energy for the best results.   Children can work out the wiring of two or more cells into a circuit.   They will notice how much more loudly the bell will ring.

EXPERIENCE.   *To use more than one dry cell in a circuit.*   Frequently two or more dry cells are needed for greater power.   They are wired with the center, or positive, post of one cell connected to the negative (outside) post of the other cell.   Connect a third cell in a similar way by connecting the center post of the second cell to the outside post of the third cell.   Otherwise the wiring of the circuit is the same as in the case of one cell.   There will always be two free posts to which to fasten wires to the appliances.   Older children will be interested in the fact that this wiring is a *series* wiring, since it is a series of negative-positive-negative-positive connections.

Some important elementary meanings can be developed through wiring simple electric devices. The following are examples:

1. The bell, battery, and push buttons each have two places to which wires can be attached. Two places are provided so that electricity can flow into the device and out of it. Young children are quite thrilled by the fact that there are always two such places. They repeat, "Two, two, two." This can be compared to a yard with a front gate and a back gate.

2. Electricity must have an opportunity to flow back to the place from which it started. This gives an opportunity to teach the idea of a circuit. Children will see that one wire attached to one post of a dry cell does not make a circuit.

Methods of Wiring for Classroom Activities. There are, in general, two methods of wiring: the *series method* and the *parallel method.* The word *multiple* is sometimes substituted for *parallel.*

Series Circuits. In a series circuit the electricity must pass through a series of devices, one after the other. Thus, in the picture showing this, the current leaving the dry cell passes in turn

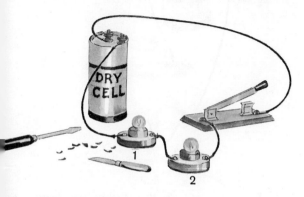

Two lamps connected in series. Note the knife switch.

through the two lamps, the switch, and back to the dry cell.

The concept of series is that of a repetition or succession of events or objects, such as the World Series, or a series of books. This same concept applies to series wiring. It is possible to connect a series of lamps so that electricity will pass through first one lamp, then another. Many Christmas-tree lighting outfits are connected in this way. We shall have more to say about this type of circuit presently.

EXPERIENCE. *To secure flashlight bulbs for miniature sockets.* Children manifesting special ability in this field may be interested in using different kinds of bulbs. Usually one can buy flashlight bulbs of different voltages (volts, p. 847). This voltage will usually be marked on the box in which the bulbs come, or marked on the base of the bulb. (In some cases a reading glass is necessary to read these numbers.) The number indicates the number of volts at which the lamp operates at its best. Each dry cell can furnish an electromotive force of about 1½ volts. For series wiring you add the numbers. That is, two dry cells would run about 3 volts. If one uses a bulb which is designed for more volts, one will not have a good light. On the other hand, if one buys a bulb that is of too low voltage, it may burn out quickly. With three dry cells one could have a voltage of three times one dry cell, or about 4½ volts. Bulbs designed for this voltage should be used.

For children with great interest in this field, different bulbs can be tried out with a different number of cells. Do not feel chagrined if these children are superior to you in their manipulation of these materials.

EXPERIENCE. *To trace an electric circuit in a flashlight.* Older children will be interested in examining a flashlight. Some of them might like to bring a flashlight to school. Have them take it apart and reassemble it. Have them see if they can explain how the circuit is com-

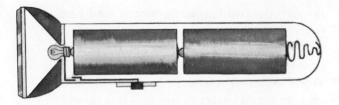

A flashlight is a series circuit.

pleted. The wiring of a flashlight is a series wiring. The diagram could be made as a chart by the children with arrows to indicate the current.

Parallel Circuits. In a parallel circuit the electricity, in going from the source through a circuit and back to its source again, has several different independent paths which it may take. Some of the electricity goes one way, some another. Let us examine the circuit shown below. Here we see that the electricity comes from the dry cell and proceeds along the wire until it comes to the place where the first lamp is connected. Here it divides. Some of it goes through the first lamp and then back to the dry cell; some of it keeps on to the second lamp and through it back to the dry cell. The lamps are said to be in *parallel.* A series circuit has been defined as one in which there is only one path for the current; a parallel circuit, as one in which there are two or more paths. Of course the mere fact that the wires happen to lie side by side does not make any circuit a parallel one. Furthermore, it is possible to have two or more dry cells *in series* supplying two or more lamps in *parallel.* Such a circuit is very common, and is very useful for wiring in the primary classroom. It may be used for play houses, stores, or communities. Sometimes older children will assist the primary children in making wirings.

How Series and Parallel Circuits Work. If children wire a dry cell and two (or more) lamps, first in series and then in parallel, they will notice at once that the lamps burn much dimmer when in series than when in parallel. The question immediately arises, "Why is this?" The answer involves some very important concepts. Let us follow the course of the electricity through the circuits. In the diagram of lamps in series the electricity leaves the dry cell, passes through lamp 1, then through lamp 2 and back to the dry cell. The same electricity must pass through both lamps. The more lamps, the more the resistance which the electricity meets, and the less the current which flows. Since the brightness of the lamps depends on the current flowing in them, the lamps will be dim.

Likewise, in the series connection of dry cells, electricity flowing from one cell is aided by the force (voltage) of the next, so that the total voltage of a group of dry cells in series is the sum of their individual voltages.

In the parallel circuit (below) the electricity flowing through lamp 1 is entirely separate from that flowing through lamp 2, and normally one lamp is not affected by the other. An exception would occur if the wires close to a lamp touched each other, forming a short circuit. Practically all the current would flow

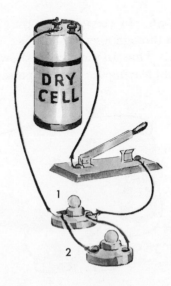

Two lamps connected in parallel. Note the knife switch.

through the short circuit, and there would not be enough left to light the other lamps.

Note that in the parallel circuit, if one lamp is removed or burns out, there is still a complete circuit through each of the remaining lamps. In a series circuit, however, if one lamp is removed, the circuit through *all* the lamps is broken. In a series circuit we must have all the lamps connected, or no current will flow.

When one light burns out on a string of Christmas-tree lights wired in a series wiring, all the lights go out because the circuit is broken. This accounts for the fact that Christmas-tree lights are now frequently wired in a parallel circuit. Any light can burn out in a parallel wiring without interfering with the other lights.

Children may ask why the lamps burn brightly in a series Christmas-tree lighting outfit. The answer is that they are connected, not to a 2-volt or 3-volt source, such as dry cells, but to a 110-volt or 120-volt source—the house current. The bulbs for such a circuit are so designed that if eight of them are connected in series, each will receive the proper amount of current. This illustrates again that electrical equipment is carefully designed to give the service expected of it, and we should not expect such equipment to do what it was not designed to do.

Working with Electricity in the Primary Grades. Children in primary grades have been taught to wire doorbells and miniature lights. Each one should be given an opportunity to work at the problem. This can be done by placing the materials on a table and allowing the children to work individually or in groups. Be sure to encourage the girls from the very beginning. Unless they have been discouraged, girls show as much interest in electricity as boys, sometimes even more. Give every child a chance. Break down any fear of shocks from the dry cells from the very start.

The house current can, of course, inflict serious injury, and children should not work with it except under the supervision of someone who understands the proper precautions.

There is frequently a need for wiring small lights in the primary grades. It may be desired to wire the street of a village which the children have constructed, or a dollhouse which they have built, or a dark corner which they plan to use as a museum. In any case, the principles involved are similar. Teachers of lower grades may find children in the upper elementary-school grades who will be glad to come in and help the younger children. This represents a fine type of cooperation in a school where older children can give of their knowledge and skill to younger grade groups. Encourage it as much as possible. Sometimes the older children are very successful in presenting concepts, skills, and facts.

The principal idea in wiring a playhouse is the same as in the wiring of the homes in which the children live. It is the principle of parallel wiring. There are two insulated wires which run from the battery throughout the house or street to be wired. These wires remain completely insulated from each other except at places where electric attachments, such as lights, are fastened.

If a cross street or another floor is to be wired, or a branch run off for any purpose, the principle is the same. Simply attach a wire securely to each of the original ones. If the children desire to have each light turned off separately, they will have to place a push button or switch in the circuit with the light concerned. Tape may be wrapped around each place to which wires are attached.

Pendant miniature sockets can sometimes be secured at local electrical stores or can be obtained by cutting up a Christmas-tree lighting outfit. Ordinary porcelain-base miniature sockets may also be used. Flashlight bulbs will do for most purposes in the primary grades.

The study of reflection of light may be introduced in connection with a wiring activity. In some schools this study has resulted in the children's constructing reflectors out of tin for each lamp.

EXPERIENCE. *To recognize electricity.* There are many experiences in the kindergarten, nursery school, and early primary work which will help children to recognize electricity in their world. Children may have experiences with shocks from static electricity in some seasons. To know that this is an experience with electricity is a learning. They can also see electrical power lines, and wires in pipes (conduits) in the building and at home which carry (conduct) electricity. In all this the adult, whether teacher or parent, should avoid building up fear, and cultivate a feeling that electricity is very useful.

EXPERIENCE. *Working with electricity with young children.* Some children expressed a desire for an electric bell in one of their playhouses. The children and teacher assembled some bell wire, a push button, a pair of wire-cutters, a pair of scissors, a dry cell, and an electric doorbell. The first objective was to introduce the children to the doorbell circuit. Small tables were pushed together to make a long table about which all the children might gather with the teacher. The objects were placed on the table.[12]

Several small pieces of wire were cut from the coil by some of the children under the teacher's supervision. These pieces were passed around to the group and examined with interest. The children noticed the insulation about the wire, which they called cot-

ton. It was explained by the children, with the teacher's assistance, that this covering kept the electricity from escaping and so forced the electricity to move through the wire. Some of the children thought the wire was made of iron. It was explained that it was copper. The children connected the battery and the bell under the teacher's supervision. This operation required considerable time. The bell rang.

While this was going on, some of the children were at work with the wire and a switch which was near by. Some were attaching wires to dry cells. In each case, they were attaching but one wire to each. Each was held up to the class. It was noted that electricity does not flow unless it can get back to the place from which it started. The children were asked to see how many places there were on the dry cells to which wires could be attached. They said, "Two." They were asked how many on the push button. They said, "Two." The same question was asked about the door bell. They said, "Two." This two, two, two, amused them, and they examined carefully the push button, dry cell, and doorbell.

One of the girls was anxious to place a push button in the circuit. She had been busy attaching wires to it. The children now, with the teacher's help, wired the bell with the dry cell, placing a push button in the circuit. Several electric bells, push buttons, dry cells, wire-cutters, pieces of wire, and screwdrivers were left on a table in the room. Whenever the children had time they worked most earnestly with these materials.

A miniature pendant lamp socket with a small flashlight bulb in it was also placed on the table. At a later time, this pendant socket was wired to a dry cell and was being used as a light inside the house. This gave an opportunity for some instruction. The children wanted the light placed over the door. The concern was how they might wire the light and leave the dry cell on the floor. They proposed

[12] In this type of activity, reading of authoritative material prepared for children is most important. Such material can relieve the teaching load of a teacher, since the children can share much of the responsibility with the guidance of books. Reading can be utilized to provide readiness for the subject of wiring and the actual manipulation. Books may be utilized to help in answering questions and solving the problems of children.

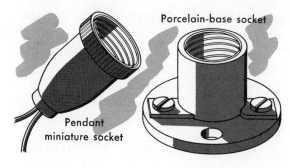

Porcelain-base socket

Pendant miniature socket

A pendant socket and a porcelain-base socket.

that wires be added to the light. The teacher showed them how to splice the wire. While this was being done, the bare parts of two wires rubbed together, and there was a short circuit. The light went out. One boy proposed the term *short circuit* when asked why the light went out. The children were shown that electricity could return through the short circuit and not go through the light. Their attention was called to the fact that the wires became hot and began to smoke. Some insulating, or electrician's, tape (secured at a local store) was

The bulb will not light if there is a short circuit.

offered to the children. Some of the girls cut off strips of tape and covered the bare places. The children said electricity could not flow through the tape. They were still challenged by the problem of placing the light over the door and wiring it to the dry cell.

At a later time the light was in place. There was also a push button at the door, which was attached to a bell inside the playhouse; the bell worked.

The children now wanted more lights in the playhouse. They were shown how the lights might be attached wherever needed by scraping off insulation on two parallel wires—the same wires which ran to the light outside the door. A pendant socket was attached to the wires from which the insulation was scraped.

Ordinarily a unit as extensive as this does not occur before the third or the fourth grade. In this particular group the children did most of their own experimentation. The teacher gave a little help at moments when they needed it. This experience probably supports the desirability of having materials readily available in the classroom.

It was explained to the children early in the work that short-circuiting the cell would soon ruin it. They were shown that they should cause the electricity to flow through something, such as a bell, a light, or a motor, and should not place a wire directly across the cell from one post to the other.

Some children asked if they could get a shock from a dry cell. The teacher said, "You will not get a shock from a dry cell. You can get one from other sources of electricity. Would you like to try to get one with a dry cell?" They tried by grasping the wires attached to the dry cell. They did not get one, and all fear of shocks from dry cells was gone.

The teacher should take care at such a point to discriminate between the current which can be obtained from a few dry cells and that from the school or home lighting system, which can be dangerous (p. 825).

EXPERIENCE. *Working with electricity with ten-year-olds.* Some instruction which grew out of a classroom situation in the fourth grade of an elementary school gave the children firsthand experience with electricity and a considerable body of information that proved useful and challenging to them. The children wished to utilize some shelves in a corner for museum purposes. The corner proved to be too dark, and some of the children suggested that the shelves should be wired for electricity. At a class conference the question of the wiring and of attaching the wire to the regular school lighting circuit was discussed.

During the discussion a desire was expressed to see where the electricity used in the room was generated. An excursion was made to see the generators, and the children gained an elementary idea of the transformation of energy from green plants growing in the sunlight long ages ago in the region now known as Pennsylvania to the electricity which flowed through the wires in their room. The wires were traced from the power plant to their own classroom, and the children were given an opportunity to see some of the devices used to prevent fires and promote safety. The engineer at the power plant co-operated by answering many of the questions.

At the close of this trip the children decided not to use the school current in wiring the shelves and raised the question as to whether dry cells could be used. They were interested to know what was in a dry cell and enthusiastically opened a "dead" cell. Not finding electricity inside, they desired an explanation as to how electricity was generated by a dry cell.

The question of wiring the lights on the shelves created a need for studying wiring in general. Many toys were brought from home, and the children wired them and learned much about closed, short, and open circuits, conductors and insulators, and the function of switches. The children worked out the various circuits under the supervision of the classroom teacher.

The children expressed a desire to turn their attention to the more complicated wiring of the shelves. It was proposed to call in a local electrician to give some estimates on the kind of wire and lights that should be used. The electrician came into the classroom and gave the information needed.

Certain children who had exhibited proficiency in electricity took the leadership in wiring the shelves. Many problems occurred in the course of their tasks, which called for a use of the principles of circuits and conduction which they had already learned.

Occasionally the lights did not burn. This called for utilization of their previous learnings in order to locate the cause. A question arose as to the best color to be used on the walls behind the lights. This created a need for the study of color and reflection of light.

EXPERIENCE. *The energy of the dry cell.* Strictly speaking, the dry cell contains chemicals. When the dry cell is placed in a circuit, these chemicals become active and develop chemical energy. This chemical energy is converted into electrical energy, so that electricity passes over the wires.

Some children were very much interested in seeing the electricity in a dry cell. They described what they thought electricity would look like. They thought it would be blue-white and bright, like the electrical spark. Then they tore the dry cell apart. The teacher had given them an old, worn-out dry cell. They noted that some of the chemicals had seeped outside. They tested this to see if it was electricity.

Somewhat disappointed to discover no electricity in the dry cell, these children pointed out that they had torn apart a worn-out dry cell. They asked for a new one. They found this to contain a paste, whereas the worn-out cell had contained dry chemicals. Since the chemicals in the form of a paste were tied up in a package, they could raise or lower the chemicals, and when the cell was connected to a bell, could thus change the loudness of the bell.

Now they revised what they had said. They now said there was electricity in the wire when they pressed the switch closing the circuit; there was no electricity anywhere in the wires or dry cell when the switch was open.

EXPERIENCE. *Why the light stopped burning.* A group of ten-year-olds had constructed a parallel lighting system for some shelves. One day the lights were not burning. The children had a long discussion. They decided that the failure might be caused by any of three difficulties: (1) the dry cells might be worn out; (2) the wiring might be defective; or (3) the lights might have burned out.

By trying out new dry cells and new light bulbs they were able to reinstall their lighting.

A Wire Carrying an Electric Current Is Surrounded by a Magnetic Field. You may recall that the Experience on page 795 demonstrates that an electric wire is surrounded by a magnetic field. This principle is utilized in the electromagnet, where the wire is coiled about a soft-iron core, which concentrates the magnetic field in the small area inside the coil, in which the iron core is placed. If the iron core were not present, the coil of wire would still be a magnet; but the iron makes it a stronger magnet.

EXPERIENCE. *Making an instrument to detect a small electrical current.* A simple instrument can be made to detect a very small electric current. It depends for its operation on the fact that a wire carrying an electric current is surrounded by a magnetic field.

Wind a number of turns of fine wire around a pocket compass, as shown. Connect the two ends of the wire to a dry cell. The compass

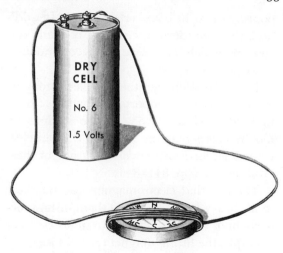

A galvanoscope is a very sensitive instrument useful in detecting an electrical current.

needle should move, showing that current is flowing in the coil. Reverse the connections to the cell. The compass will deflect in the opposite direction. It will therefore be seen that the direction in which the needle is deflected depends on the direction in which the current is flowing in the wire.

This instrument is called a *galvanoscope.* It is useful in *detecting* an electrical current. Since a magnetic field always surrounds a current of electricity, a compass can be used to detect the electrical current. In this experiment place the galvanoscope so that, when no current is flowing, the coil will be parallel to the compass needle at rest. That is, the coil should pass directly over and under the compass needle as it points north and south.

Uses of Electromagnets. Electromagnets may be used to perform most of the experiments which are described for permanent magnets. In addition, numerous experiments may be devised to illustrate the property which electromagnets have of losing their magnetism as soon as the current is turned off. They may be extensively used in classroom situations in the elementary school which involve picking up nails, tacks, pins, and iron filings and depositing them in boxes or drawers. In addition, they may form the subject of many discussions which may lead to a continuously enlarging concept.

It may be safely said that the electromagnet is one of the most important devices we have in modern civilization. In the sections on motors and generators we learn that an electromagnet forms a part of every one of these vital devices (pp. 841–845).

The fact that electromagnets can be made to lift heavy loads and drop them instantaneously finds wide application in industry. For example, the lifting magnet (p. 797) is extensively used in mills and factories where much iron has to be moved.

The telegraph also depends on electromagnets. Essentially the telegraph receiving instrument (called the sounder) is nothing but a piece of iron held by springs near an electromagnet. When the circuit is closed, the iron is attracted and makes a click. When the circuit is opened, the iron is released; and the spring pulls it back, making another click. If the circuit is closed for only a short time, the clicks are close together. The operator calls the two sounds close together a "dot." If the circuit is closed a longer time, the sounds are farther apart. This combination is called a "dash." The telegraph code is made up of combinations of dots and dashes.

The circuit is opened and closed by a device called a key. Although this device does not look like a push button, it works very much like one, since a push button really is a kind of switch.

EXPERIENCE. *Making a telegraph set.* To make a simple telegraph set, drive two fairly large nails or screws into a board so that most of their length remains exposed. Wind on these nails as many turns of wire as they will hold, first winding one full, and then going on without breaking the wire to the other. Wind the two nails in opposite directions; that is, if you wind the wire around one nail from left to right, wind it around the other nail from right to left. Leave two generous ends of wire. Bend a piece of "tin" (really iron coated with tin) cut from a coffee can, as shown, so that it is about a quarter of an inch from the heads of the nails. Bend another piece of tin so as to form a stop for the first piece to hit as it comes up. A bent nail may be used for the stop.

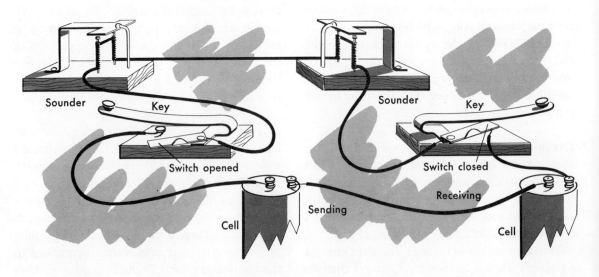

A telegraph set made with simple materials.

The key is made by fastening a strip of tin to another board and bending it. A stopper from an ink bottle forms a knob, and a tack with a wire fastened under the head makes a lower contact. The set is wired according to the accompanying diagram. If two sets are used for communication between rooms, the key on the receiving end must be held down while receiving a message. To avoid this, switches may be placed as shown in the diagram.

In setting up a telegraph line, realistic poles may be made from wooden sticks with wooden crossarms, and glass pushpins (five-and-ten-cent stores or stationers) may be used to resemble glass insulators. The activities involved in constructing the telegraph set may be undertaken by the children who wish to push on a little faster than others in this area. However, all children should take some part in operating the set.

EXPERIENCE. *Explanation of how the telegraph works.* Provide children with an opportunity to explain the operation of the telegraph. Children with special ability may have an opportunity here to develop leadership based on real democratic principles. It would be well for them to develop leadership without demonstration of superiority, so that their fellow classmates feel free to turn to them for assistance.

EXPERIENCE. *Relating the telegraph to the westward movement of people in North America.* The place of the telegraph in the history of the people of the Western Hemisphere is an important one.

The importance of the telegraph in the national development of communication may form a subject for discussion or investigation in the social-studies class. Before the invention of the telegraph, people living beyond the Appalachian Mountains felt remote and cut off from the center of the federal government at Washington. After its invention the people of the Western states were brought into much closer touch with all events at the national capital.

The telegraph likewise played an important part in the development of relationships between the provinces in Canada. In similar fashion, the people of other countries in the world were brought into much closer touch with their neighbors. No longer did it require weeks for news to travel from one part of the world to another. No longer did the people of one country need to feel remote and separate from those of another.

The completion of the laying of the first submarine cable across the Atlantic by Cyrus Field on August 16, 1858, was an event which in reality helped to unite the world. Since that time, anything which happens on one side of the Atlantic can be speedily known by the people on the other side. A number of cables now span the Atlantic Ocean.

Instruments used to send messages by cable work much like ordinary telegraph instruments, although they do not look much like them.

Children may be interested in reading the story of Samuel F. B. Morse and how he invented the telegraph. Making a telegraph set seems to us a simple matter, and we are likely to wonder why it took Morse so long to develop it. We must remember that Morse did not have the materials we have today to work with. He had no insulated wire and no reliable dry cells. He had to make his own materials as he went along. The materials that we use now were developed *after* the inventions were made that called them forth.

Still more important than the matter of materials was the matter of ideas. It is easy to follow someone else's ideas or even to improve upon them, but the first man to think of an invention has no one to show him the way. Children in the elementary school today know a great deal more about electricity than the foremost scientist knew a century ago.

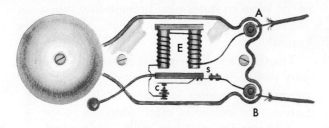

Inside an electric bell.

The Electric Bell. The electric bell is another useful and interesting device which utilizes an electromagnet. If you remove the cover from an electric bell, you will see two spools wound with wire. These are electromagnets. In some bells there is only one spool. Close to the end of each spool there is a piece of iron called an armature, held away from the spool by a spring. Fastened to the iron is another small flat spring carrying a contact point. Also fastened to the iron is a clapper, which strikes the bell. There is also a fixed contact point, fastened to the base of the bell, but insulated from it.

The circuit in the bell is as follows: The current enters at the binding post (*A* in the drawing). The current then flows to and through the wires of the electromagnets (*E*). From the electromagnets the current flows to the fixed contact point (*c*), then to the other contact point which is fastened to the armature, through the spring (*s*), thence to the other binding post (*B*). Bells often differ in the details of their wiring, but the principle is the same as in the one here described.

The operation of the bell is as follows:

1. When current is flowing through the wires of the electromagnets, they become magnetic and attract the soft-iron armature.

2. The armature is pulled toward the electromagnets. The clapper hits the bell.

3. The contact point which is fastened to the armature is also pulled away from the fixed contact point.

4. The circuit is broken when the contact points separate, and current no longer flows through the electromagnets.

5. The electromagnets no longer attract the armature, and it flies back, drawn by the spring which supports it.

6. The contact points again touch, the circuit is completed, and current again flows through the electromagnets.

7. The armature is again drawn toward the electromagnets, and the whole cycle of operations is repeated. This continues rapidly as long as the button is pushed.

EXPERIENCE. *Explanations of how the electric bell works.* Have some of the children give explanations of how the electric bell operates. Perhaps they can make an enlarged diagram for purposes of explanation.

EXPERIENCE. *Electromagnets are useful to us in many ways.* Children may list all the devices they can think of which use electromagnets. Such a list may include the following and perhaps many more:

1. Electric bell.
2. Electric buzzer.
3. Telegraph.
4. Motor.
5. Generator.
6. Telephone.
7. Lifting magnets.
8. Surgical magnets (used to remove pieces of iron from the eye, for instance).
9. Door-openers.
10. Spark coils (used in gasoline engines).
11. Transformers.

The Telephone. The explanation of the operation of the telephone involves so many of the concepts of electricity that it makes an excellent culminating activity. The various steps may also be performed as separate activities. The activities which follow can be used with children who are specially interested. The children can use the diagrams found on these

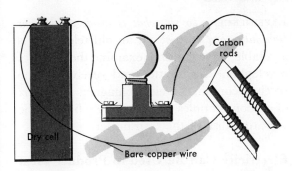

The more tightly the pieces of carbon are pressed together, the more brightly the lamp burns.

pages. They can explain their work to their classmates from time to time.

STEP 1. *Carbon is a variable conductor.* Remove the carbon rod from the center of a worn-out dry cell. Break this rod in two with a hammer. Wrap some bare copper wire around each part, twisting it tightly to ensure a good connection. Connect these wires in a circuit with a lamp and dry cell, as shown. When the two pieces of carbon are brought together, it is obvious that if carbon is a conductor, current will flow and the lamp will light. Touch the two pieces of carbon together *very lightly.* The lamp should light dimly. Now press the carbon pieces together tightly. The lamp should get much brighter. With a little practice, you can control the brightness of the lamp easily. This shows that more current can flow between pieces of carbon when they are pressed tightly together than when they are loose.

STEP 2. *The strength of an electromagnet depends on the amount of current flowing through its winding.* Connect an electromagnet (p. 796) to one dry cell and see how many nails it will pick up. Now connect it to two dry cells and again see how many nails it will pick up. With two cells it should pick up more nails than with one. The more current there is flowing through the winding of an electromagnet, the stronger the magnet is.

STEP 3. *The telephone circuit.* A simple one-way telephone circuit may be constructed. Current flows from the batteries, through the

transmitter, through one wire to the receiver, through the receiver, and through the other wire back to the batteries.

Inside the transmitter (the part into which we speak) there is a thin disk of iron called the diaphragm. Fastened to this disk is a little cup containing pieces of carbon. When we speak against the diaphragm of the transmitter, the sound waves cause the diaphragm to vibrate, or move back and forth (p. 873). When the high-pressure part of the sound wave strikes the diaphragm, it is forced in a little; and when the low-pressure part strikes, the diaphragm springs out a little. When the diaphragm is pushed in, the carbon grains in the cup are squeezed together tightly. When the diaphragm springs out, the carbon grains are pressed together loosely. As the carbon granules are pressed together tightly or loosely, more or less current flows in the circuit.

In the receiver there is a diaphragm much like that in the transmitter. Instead of a cup and carbon granules there is an electromagnet wound with very fine wire. This electromagnet is fastened just behind the diaphragm. When more current flows through the electromagnet, it becomes stronger and pulls the diaphragm inward. When less current flows, the diaphragm is somewhat released.

There is also a permanent magnet in the receiver, which pulls the diaphragm constantly. This constant pull enables the diaphragm to reproduce sounds more distinctly. The explanation of this is rather complicated, and is not necessary to a general explanation of the telephone.

Let us follow the cycle of operations in the telephone:

1. Sound waves strike the diaphragm of the transmitter and cause it to bend in and out, or vibrate.

2. As the diaphragm of the transmitter bends in, the carbon granules in the cup are pressed together, and more current flows in the circuit.

3. More current flowing in the circuit makes the electromagnet in the receiver stronger.

4. The electromagnet, being stronger, pulls in the diaphragm of the receiver. The net result, then, of bending in the diaphragm of the transmitter is to bend in the diaphragm of the receiver.

5. As the receiver diaphragm is bent in and out, it sets the air next to it into vibration. This vibration reaches the ear as a sound wave like the one which originally moved the transmitter diaphragm. If the transmitter were in Halifax, for example, and the receiver in San Francisco, a person listening in San Francisco would hear a reproduction of the voice of the person in Halifax.

Note that the sound waves do not pass over the wires. Sound waves are used to vary an electric current at the transmitter, and at the receiver the varying electric current is used to produce sound waves.

In a real telephone system there are many complicated pieces of apparatus, but the principle of operation is essentially the same as with a laboratory set.

EXPERIENCE. *To compare a regular telephone with the string telephone.* Many of the children in your classroom may have used a string telephone at home or at school at some time or other, as well as the regular telephone. One thing to notice is that, in the string telephone, sound waves or waves travel all the way from the speaker to the listener. In the regular telephone, the sound waves travel only from the mouth to the transmitter in the mouthpiece, a matter of only a few inches, and again from the receiver to the ear, again a matter of a few inches, and usually less than one inch. The great distance from person to person in a regular telephone conversation is covered by electrical waves.

EXPERIENCE. *To see what is inside a telephone transmitter and receiver.* If an old telephone is available, have children examine the inside of a telephone transmitter and receiver. The receiver contains an electromagnet. The box of carbon granules is immediately behind the vibrating disk of the transmitter.

Electricity Can Be Used to Produce Heat and Light. It might be well for a teacher to show children how to do this before they try to do it. Place a *thin* wire, such as a single strand of picture wire, between the two posts of a dry cell. The wire should be just long enough to reach across the distance and to fasten under the posts. The wire should get red-hot immediately. It may stay hot only a short time, owing to the fact that you have short-circuited the battery. Remove the wire with pliers in order to avoid burning yourself. After a while repeat the experiment.

Repeat, using wires of different sizes. Notice that fine wire gets hot faster than coarse wire. The fine wire offers more resistance to the flow of the current. Why must electricians be careful to use large enough wires in houses?

Every substance resists the flow of electricity somewhat. Some substances are much more resistant than others, but all conduct electricity to some extent. Those which conduct very poorly are those which we have referred to as nonconductors, or insulators; those which conduct fairly well are the conductors. There is no perfect insulator or perfect conductor (p. 813).

When electricity flows through a substance, some of its energy is used up to overcome the resistance. (Resistance may be compared tentatively for the sake of concept-formation to a football game where the opposing team resists your team attempting to carry the ball down the field.) This energy is transformed into heat, and the substance gets hot. The more resistant a substance is, the more energy is

Types of heaters. When an electric current passes through resistance wire, heat is generated.

used up and the hotter it gets. In devices the object of which is to produce heat (for example, toasters) wire of fairly high resistance is used. For wiring houses, where we do not wish to waste much energy, copper wire is used. Silver wire would be even better, but it would, of course, be too expensive. Silver and copper are among the very best conductors of electricity.

EXPERIENCE. *Heat from electricity is useful.* What inventions has man made which produce heat and light by passing electricity through certain substances?

EXPERIENCE. *Electrical energy can be transformed into heat energy.* Secure an electric heater, iron, or toaster. Turn the electricity on in the appliance. Observe the reddening of the wires and the heating effect. Note that the wires get hot when the electricity is turned on. How have such inventions helped man? Where has the energy come from? Trace the energy back to the coal or to water power. In either case, the sun is the *real source of heat.* It helped the plants to grow from which coal was formed. It also heated Earth, causing the water to evaporate from oceans, lakes, and rivers in order that it could come down again through

rivers to be used as water power by man. The sun is the source of energy (p. 736).

EXPERIENCE. *Electrical energy can be transformed into light energy.* Examine an ordinary electric light bulb. See the wires which become white-hot. The children may wish to study the life of Edison and how he invented the electric light.

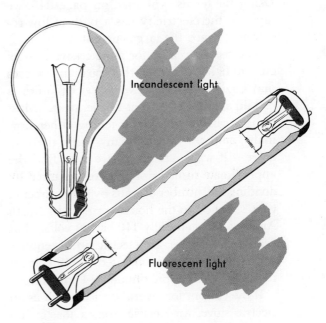

Incandescent light

Fluorescent light

An ordinary light bulb and a fluorescent lighting tube.

Examine a fluorescent light, but do not break it. Electric current flows through a gas inside the tube. Electrified particles strike the walls of the tube, which are coated with a substance that glows when struck by the particles.

Fuses. We have seen in the previous section that passing a current of electricity through a wire may heat it. The more current that passes, the hotter the wire gets. If we should pass large amounts of current through the wires in our houses, they might get red-hot and start a fire.

There are two general reasons for an excessive flow of current in house wires. Ordinarily electricity is passed through some device, such as a lamp, a toaster, or a television set, which it operates. If the insulation becomes worn or broken on the wires carrying current to the device, the two wires may touch each other in the bare places. In this case, the electricity can get back to the place from which it started very easily (p. 825). If this happens, a very large current of electricity will flow. Using the terms explained on page 849, we say that the electricity has a path of low resistance; hence the large current.

The second reason for an excessive flow of current in house wires is that too many devices may be used at once. Every device requires a certain amount of current to operate it. Most devices carry name plates telling either how many amperes or how many watts they require. If watts are given, we may find the approximate number of amperes required by dividing the number of watts by the number of volts supplied to the house wiring. In North America this is usually 110 or 120 volts. For example, suppose an electric iron requires 1500 watts. If this is operated at 110 volts, it requires $\frac{1500}{110}$, or approximately 14 amperes.

If the current for several devices, such as an electric stove, an electric iron, a toaster, an electric heater or air conditioner, and a dish washer, must be supplied by one pair of wires,

it may be that the combined current required by all of them is more than the wires can safely carry.

To safeguard the house wires in case of a short circuit or overload, fuses are provided. A *fuse* is essentially a short piece of wire which melts at a low temperature. It is inserted in the circuit in such a way that the current must pass through it on its way to the devices to be operated. When too much current flows, this wire becomes hot and melts before the house wires become dangerously hot. This breaks the circuit and stops the flow of electricity.

A blown fuse is a danger signal that something is wrong. Usually there is a defective wire, or else too many devices are being used. In any case, the fault should be found and corrected before a new fuse is inserted.

Additional fuses should always be kept on hand in case they are needed. When a fuse blows, only a good fuse should be inserted in its place. Sometimes people insert a penny in the socket to replace a blown fuse. Although this will complete the circuit and permit the lights to go on, it is a *very* dangerous practice. The current no longer goes through the fuse, but instead passes through the penny. Of course the penny can carry a great deal of current—much more than the house wires can. The house wires may become red-hot before the penny melts. Insurance companies say that placing pennies behind fuses is a common cause of fires.

Fuses are marked on the base or on the rim with a number which tells how many amperes of current they can safely carry. One should never substitute a fuse of a higher capacity for one of a lower capacity, except upon the advice of a skilled electrician, because the house wiring may not be able to carry so much current as the fuse can. In such a case, the house wires may get red-hot before the fuse melts.

Fustats are a variation of the common household fuse that allow for a momentary overload such as starting a motor.

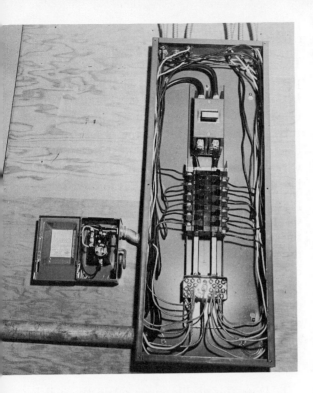

One kind of fully installed circuit breaker board and box. (Three Lions, N. Y. C.)

Circuit-breakers. Many newer houses are equipped with circuit-breakers instead of fuses. One type of circuit-breaker contains an electromagnet that opens a switch when the circuit is overloaded. The handle of the switch shows the fact plainly by moving to the "tripped" position. After the trouble has been corrected, the handle is easily pushed back to the "on" position. One advantage of the circuit-breaker is that it eliminates the possibility of anyone inserting a fuse of the wrong size.

In recent years there have been many new electrical appliances invented for use in the home. But many of the older houses were wired for purposes of lighting the house only. When many of these new appliances are operated at the same time, the wires become overloaded. Overloaded wires can become heated and houses can be set on fire in this way. If for any reason the fuses do not operate, there may be the loss of a home. Unfortunately, too many modern builders are not wiring new

homes for this increased modern load. It might be well for children to realize that there may be many more new inventions to be placed in the homes of the future. The demand for electricity will increase, not decrease.

EXPERIENCE. *To locate fuse boxes at school and at home.* Older children and the teacher can go on an excursion with the custodian and some member of the central administrative staff to see the fuse box. Perhaps someone of authority will locate the fuses that control the lights in their schoolroom. Perhaps their fathers will show them the fuse box at home.

There should be a discussion of precautions to be taken in changing fuses. It is well to use but one hand to unscrew old fuses and screw in new ones. Also, it is well to avoid touching any pipes. If the basement is damp, it would be well to call the service company or an electrician.

Motors, Generators, and Transformers. This section is included not so much with the idea that the teacher will teach it as to provide her with information which she may find useful for her own background. Frequently a child brings in a toy generator, transformer, or motor and wants to know something about it. We will try here to provide a reasonably simple explanation.

In 1819 Oersted discovered that an electric current would produce a magnetic field (p. 795).

Michael Faraday reasoned that if a magnetic field could be produced by an electric current, then an electric current could be produced by a magnetic field. In 1831, after years of unsuccessful experimentation, he found that when a wire is moved in a magnetic field, or when a magnetic field is moved about a wire, a current of electricity is generated in the wire.

One of his experiments was performed with an apparatus something like that in the pic-

A magnet moving inside a coil of wire produces a current in the wire.

EXPERIENCE. *To generate an electric current.* Prepare an open coil of wire, as shown. This may be made by winding up to one hundred turns of wire around a mailing tube. Remove the tube and tie the coil with string, or wrap it with electrician's tape. Connect the two ends of the wire by twisting them together tightly. Now lay the loose loop of wire thus formed over a pocket compass. Pass the coil quickly over one pole of a powerful magnet. The needle of the compass should move momentarily. Note the direction in which it moves. Remove the coil quickly. The needle should deflect in the opposite direction. The loop of wire to the compass should be long enough so that the attraction of the magnet itself does not greatly affect the compass needle, and move the coil instead of the magnet, for the same reason.

1. Does the needle move when the coil is not moving?
2. Does it move in the same direction when the coil is moving toward the magnet as it does when the coil is moving away from the magnet?
3. Does the needle move *farther* when we move the coil faster?

In the magneto the coil is moved mechanically. The generator is the same as the magneto except that an electromagnet is used in place of the permanent magnet (p. 796).

4. Does the needle move when the magnet is moved through the coil while the coil is held still?

It is impossible to overestimate the importance of the discovery that a current of electricity is generated when a wire is moved in a magnetic field. It laid the foundation for our modern electrical development. The great generators in our powerhouses are nothing but devices for moving a great many coils of wire in very strong magnetic fields.

Older children can learn what form of energy is used to do the moving of these coils.

ture. When the magnet is moved into the coil, a momentary current is indicated by the *galvanometer,* which is an instrument to indicate an electric current. This current stops as soon as the magnet comes to rest, and starts in the opposite direction when the magnet is removed. A story has been told that Gladstone, Great Britain's Prime Minister, watched Faraday demonstrate this principle of electricity. It is said that Gladstone remarked that it was interesting, but inquired of what importance it could possibly be. Tradition has it that Faraday replied, "Mr. Prime Minister, the time will come when the British Empire will tax the results of this demonstration." And so it has come to pass, for out of Faraday's work has grown the modern generator and a revolution in man's way of living.

Generating Electricity by Movements of a Coil in a Magnetic Field. Among the older children in the elementary school there may be some who would be interested in demonstrating for the others the principle utilized in the modern generator. This is the principle by which man has been supplied with great quantities of energy. These children can give this demonstration, as indicated in the next Experience.

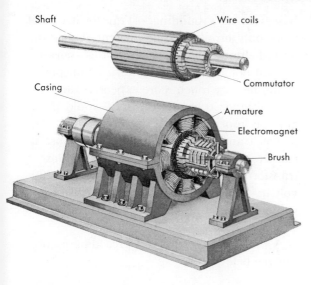

Shaft

Wire coils

Commutator

Casing

Armature

Electromagnet

Brush

The parts of a generator.

It will be apparent to them that it would not pay to have this done by man power. It will be water power in some communities. In others it may be steam, using the energy obtained from burning coal.

Now if a current is generated when a wire moves in a magnetic field, it does not matter whether the wire moves or the field moves. The field around a current-carrying wire can be made to move by merely varying the current flowing in it. If another wire is in this moving field, it in turn will have a current made to flow in it.

Faraday also arranged a coil of wire carrying a current, and close to it placed another coil, insulated from the first and connected to a galvanometer. When the circuit through the first coil was suddenly broken, and the current ceased to flow, the magnetic field around it collapsed, and a current (called an *induced current*) was generated in the second coil. When the circuit was again closed and current flowed, the magnetic field again expanded, and the current again flowed in the second coil, in the opposite direction.

Faraday's discovery may be summed up thus: Whenever a conductor cuts lines of force, or lines of force cut a conductor, a current flows if the conductor is part of a closed circuit. Lines of force at rest with respect to a conductor induce no current.

Transformers. It was also found that if the coils were wound on an iron ring or on two sides of an iron square, a much greater effect was produced. Note that there is no electrical connection between the two coils of wire. This device is called a *transformer.*

Note that when the current in the first, or primary, coil is made to vary, the current in the secondary coil varies correspondingly. It increases from zero to a maximum in one direction, falls to zero and increases to a maximum in the other direction, and then falls again to zero. A current varying in this manner is called an *alternating current.* In most house wiring in the United States this cycle of operations takes place sixty times every second. On the other hand, *direct current* flows steadily in one direction. The circuits in which dry cells are utilized (for instance, the ones described for children in this chapter) as a source of energy are using direct current.

Alternating house current surges rapidly back and forth sixty times every second, thereby making lamps supplied by alternating current "go out" 120 times each second; but this flicker is much more rapid than the human eye can detect, and the lamps look as if they were burning steadily. If a toy transformer

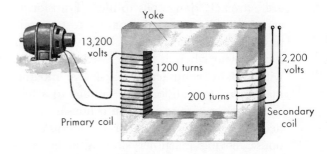

Yoke

13,200 volts

1200 turns

200 turns

2,200 volts

Primary coil

Secondary coil

A transformer may be used to raise or lower the voltage of an alternating current.

Step-down transformers are used on power lines to provide voltages suitable for cooking or lighting.

basement of a building. Transformers will work only on alternating current; hence the overwhelming popularity of this current. Were it not for these useful devices, our power would be very much more expensive, and our long-distance transmission lines would probably be impracticable if not impossible.

Toy transformers, such as children use to run trains, are miniature copies of larger transformers. They take the 110-volt to 120-volt house current and transform it to a low voltage (about 6 to 12 volts), which is safe for children to play with.

A brief summary of the preceding section is given below:

1. OERSTED. Discovered that a wire carrying a current is surrounded by a magnetic field. *Use.* For electromagnet.

2. FARADAY. *a.* Discovered that a current is generated when a wire moves in a magnetic field. *Use.* For generator.

b. Discovered that a moving magnetic field may be provided by varying the current passing through another conductor. *Use.* For transformer.

is held close to the ear while the current is on, a low hum may often be heard. This is caused by a slight vibration of the iron parts as they are rapidly magnetized and demagnetized by the alternating current.

Many believe that the transformer stands second only to the generator in importance in the life of today. Its use explains largely why most house current is alternating and why very little direct current is now in use. The question will be asked, "Why is this?"

Where power is to be transmitted very far, it is very much cheaper to do so at high voltages than at low voltages, but high voltages are extremely dangerous to life. Transformers enable the power companies to transmit power at these economical high voltages to a point near where it is to be used, and there, without any complicated expensive moving machinery, to transform the voltage to a low one which is safe to bring into houses. It is necessary to provide elaborate buildings to house moving machinery and attendants to care for it, whereas a transformer can be put on a pole, in a manhole in a street, or in the

A transformer is used to operate an electric train.

Do you see how each of these discoveries grew out of the previous one?

The Electric Motor. The electric motor is based on two principles which you have already learned:

1. Like magnetic poles repel; unlike attract.
2. The location of the poles of an electromagnet depends on the direction in which the current is flowing in the coil.

Suppose we have an electromagnet pivoted between the poles of a U-shaped magnet. Suppose that with the current, which may be supplied by a dry cell, flowing in a certain direction, the poles of the electromagnet are as shown. Since like poles repel, the poles of the electromagnet will be pushed away from the poles of the permanent magnet, and the electromagnet will rotate one half-turn, taking the position shown in the second picture.

Now suppose the direction of current flow

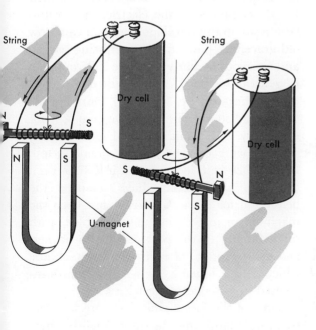

The principle of the electric motor.

to be reversed in the electromagnet, by interchanging the wires on the dry cell. The N and S poles of the electromagnet will also be interchanged. Conditions will again become as they were at first, and the electromagnet will again rotate.

It would be extremely inconvenient—in fact, impossible—to shift the wires on a dry cell at every half-turn of a motor. In order to reverse the direction of current flow, mechanical means are adopted. A reversing switch is mounted on the same shaft with the electromagnet and turns with it. This automatically reverses the direction of the current at exactly the right time to keep the motor running continuously. The following are the names of the parts of a motor:

1. The permanent magnet is called the *field* magnet. In commercial motors it is not a permanent magnet but an electromagnet.
2. The rotating electromagnet is called the *armature*. In commercial motors the armature may have many poles, just as an automobile may have many cylinders.
3. The moving part of the reversing switch is called the *commutator*.
4. The stationary parts of the reversing switch are called the *brushes*.

Motors and generators are very much alike in construction. The generator has in general the same parts as the motor, but the energy change is different. In the generator mechanical energy is changed into electrical energy. In the motor electrical energy is changed into mechanical energy.

Perhaps some of the older children with a special interest in electricity will be interested in examining a simple toy dry-cell motor. Perhaps they can point out to their classmates the field magnet, armature, commutator, and brushes. Perhaps they can explain the toy motor in terms of magnetic attraction and repulsion.

Electricity in the Education of Children.
It is well for teachers and parents to view electricity in the education of children from the developmental point of view. As such, electricity should be seen in its large role in our modern life. It should also be recognized that electricity is a very significant factor in the early experiences of our modern children (pp. 2, 806). Electricity has become so much the basis of the energy in our modern life that children are forming attitudes and behavior patterns toward it before they have words to express their meanings (Chapter 3). We may have every reason to believe that the behavior patterns and emotional attitudes of children toward energy will play an important role in the destiny of mankind. Early basic patterns and emotional feelings frequently become fixed in the individual during childhood and remain with little change throughout life. It is the task of education to assist children to develop a feeling of responsibility and resourcefulness in reference to the wise development and utilization of this form of energy. In a democracy it is well for the people to know how to manage the energy resources for the welfare of all.

From the developmental point of view, electricity should be viewed by teachers and parents as more than merely an area of physics. Electricity has emerged as basic to an understanding of both matter and energy, and who knows but that in time it may contribute to the understanding of life itself. This indicates that as an important aspect of the environment it has all the qualities necessary to an area of child development. That is, it can provide new meanings for the growth of the individual from the cradle through old age, regardless of whether the individual specializes in electricity or not.

Electricity is universal in character. Far out in the remote galaxies are evidences of electrical charges. The universe is composed of positive and negative charges of electricity.

The material of the stars, the rocks of Earth, and the structure of living things, including human beings, are in a real sense electrical in character. Normally, the positive and negative charges are balanced. The usual atom, or normal atom, is neutral (electrically) p. 375), since there is an equilibrium between the positive and negative charges. It is altogether possible that the future will reveal that electricity may account for the cohesiveness of the universe. For some time scientists have been attempting to develop a general field theory that would integrate gravitation, magnetism, and electricity. Today, the chemist finds that an explanation of the electrical charges in atoms is useful in understanding chemical changes (Chapter 11).

If there were no forces to upset the balance in the atom, there would be probably very little energy in the universe, and the universe would run down. But there are forces at work which make for the production of energy. Man is learning to utilize this energy for the accomplishment of his work. He has multiplied manyfold his available energy through the development of the electrical generator. As a result of this development, man can grow old gracefully now, rather than being broken and worn out by hard toil while still young, as in generations past. As a result of the electrical generator (pp. 841–843), man can use the energy stored in coal or water power for the heavy and menial work of life. Man is rapidly being relieved of back-breaking toil. It should be kept in mind that it has not been machines alone which have removed the heavy toil for man. Rather it has been the machines invented by man coupled with man's ability in the past century to harness enormous supplies of energy to his machines. Much of this latter is the result of man's increased knowledge of electricity.

Some of the forces which operate for electrical unbalance may be quite small in character, and can be observed by children, either by design or as a matter of usual experience, as when they develop electrical charges as a result of walking on a thick carpet, stroking a cat's back, or combing their own hair. Forces of unbalance on a larger scale are operating in the thunderstorm. The lightning is a result of the tendency for unlike charges to attract each other, establishing an electrical balance, at least on a temporary basis.

But on the other hand, there are forces in the universe which make for unbalance of the positive and negative charges which are titanic in character. These forces, such as those in the sun and other stars, do not stop at a mere removing of electrons from the outer part of the atom, but result in a coming apart of the very nucleus of some atoms. The nuclei of other atoms combine. As a result vast quantities of energy, invisible and visible, in the form of electromagnetic energy, are received on Earth. This form of energy has been used for ages by green plants in making food, and animals have secured this energy by eating the food which the plants manufacture. In the future, man is likely to harness this energy from the sun directly for power. So the new sources of energy from the sun are and will continue to be electromagnetic in character. Our children will live in a world of vast new developments of solar energy. The new advances in the solar battery and in nuclear energy will furnish our children with lavish amounts of energy (p. 196).

EXPERIENCE. *To show that the sunlight is energy.* If you can secure a light meter, show it to the children. Use it in different places, such as in bright light and in shadows. Have them note the readings. The light striking the meter is turned into an electric current in the meter.

The basic nature of electricity still remains largely unknown to man. In fact, to study electricity man must study its effects, such as the heating effect, the magnetic effect, and the chemical effect. However, scientists have been able to develop new hypotheses which have been very useful in explaining electricity. It seems that charged particles of matter are not at rest, as they may seem to be when we look at the objects around us, but are rather in continual motion. If an atom loses one or more of its electrons, according to atomic theory, it becomes positively charged (electrified). If an atom gains one or more electrons, so that there is an excess of electrons, it becomes negatively charged. Such particles are called ions (p. 379).

In substances which are good conductors of electricity, such as metals, it is thought that the outer electrons leave the "parent" atom rather easily and wander about.

In substances which are nonconductors or insulators, the electrons do not leave the parent atom easily. It is thought they are more or less held to the atom, and as a result there is not so much wandering about in an insulator.

Although in a conductor the electrons may wander about, they are influenced by almost anything that comes into their sphere, such as other electrons, other parent atoms, and magnetic fields. Now if a force is added which causes this wandering to become a drift in a definite direction in the conductor, we have an electrical current. A dry cell, a storage battery, or a generator will create such a force. We call this kind of force an *electromotive force*. This force is measured in *volts*. Almost everyone uses the word *volt* at one time or another. Older children ask about this term. We have learned that the electromotive force in homes and schools in North America is usually 110 volts. The letter *v* is usually the symbol for volt. Dry cells usually have a voltage of 1½ volts. The storage battery in an automobile may be 6v, 12v, or even (experimentally) 18v.

Direction of Current. The difficulty in describing current as positive or negative arises from the fact that the behavior of electricity had been studied for many centuries before its nature was well understood.

All of the early workers in the field of electricity, such as Ampère, Faraday, and Franklin, thought the positive particles were the ones that flowed. But within recent decades scientists have determined that electrons, the negative and lighter particles, were the ones which moved. Yet long years of tradition, with emphasis on the movement of the positive charge, have caused some to cling to the older idea. This is not so confusing as it might at first seem to be. If one will watch the children passing the paper sheets in the electrical-circuit play explanation (p. 824), one will notice that while the paper is going in one direction, *the loss of the paper* is moving in the *opposite* direction. If the paper represents a negative particle, the child atom becomes positively charged as it gives up the electron. But, of course, a child atom soon has another sheet from his classmate at his side, and becomes neutralized immediately.

For some purposes it is unimportant which way the current moves. Scientists, in general, prefer to regard the movement of electrons as the true current. In a storage battery, for example (p. 818), electrons are concentrated at the negative pole and move outward from that pole when power is needed.

In the circuit the same electrons do not go all the way around. An electron may move to another atom, while other electrons from other atoms are moving on. In the play explanation it was suggested that children have more than one sheet of paper to indicate that the same sheet need not go all the way around. A given child may pull a yellow sheet from the child on one side, while the next child may pull a white or blue sheet. The disturbance continues around the circuit, even though a given sheet remains with a given child throughout the demonstration.

It is interesting, however, to see how many times some older idea remains in a society. For instance, we still say the sun rises and sets, when in reality Earth rotates. We say on a cloudy day that the sun is not shining, when in reality far up above the clouds the sun is shining. It has become a custom to speak of the sun as not shining when we cannot see it, though in reality we know it shines all the time.

The modern electrical generator is a device for developing electromotive force. In this case mechanical movement maintains a continuous electrical potential difference, and the electricity will flow through the wires into our schools and homes and operate the many electrical devices on its way back to the source. However, the actual current we use in school or at home may only go as far as the nearby transformer box (p. 844).

Something similar may occur when a dry cell is placed in a circuit. There is a chemical action within a dry cell when the switch is closed. The carbon rod acquires a positive charge or potential, and the zinc cup with an excess of electrons has a negative charge or potential. In a dry cell which is not attached to a circuit, there is not much electrical activity because the chemical action retards the passage of the electrons through the paste of the dry cell. But when the circuit is closed, the electrons can flow around through the circuit to the carbon rod. The zinc is at a "higher level" as to electrons than the carbon; that is, we say that there is a difference chemically and electrically between the zinc and the carbon. The electrons drift through the wire from the zinc to the carbon, much as water or air would flow from a high place to a lower level. This difference of level in electricity is called *potential difference*. Potential means stored energy. In the dry cell the zinc is the fuel which is used in operating the electrical circuit.

If a child walks on a heavy carpet or rubs a cat's fur on a dry day, he may accumulate a surplus of electrons. He may then have an electrical potential difference with respect to something else he may happen to touch, such as a doorknob. His body is at a "higher level" (electrically) than the knob, and some of the surplus electrons may flow off to the knob. After they have flowed off he is again balanced electrically, and will remain so until he does something to gain or lose electrons.

In a circuit, free electrons will shift in whatever direction they are urged. In a dry cell the chemical action causes electrons to be removed from the carbon rod and to be added to the zinc cup. Consequently, the carbon rod has a positive charge and the zinc cup a negative charge. This creates a difference in potential. That is, there is a difference in level electrically, which can create a flowing of electrons. Usually scientists prefer to use the words electromotive force or potential difference to identify the *motive* (moving) force back of a current.

In a way, electromotive force can be explained as the tendency of electric charges to reach equilibrium or to balance each other. Unlike charges attract, like charges repel. The attraction can bring positive and negative together and so restore the balance. It almost seems as if our world were held together by these electromotive forces, and we secure energy from the universe when these forces are not balanced and there is more strength in one place than there is in another. Physicists prefer the word *potential* rather than strength. Potential has been a term long used with energy, meaning "stored energy." Electricity is a form of energy; therefore it is quite appropriate to use the term potential in connection with electricity.

In addition to electromotive force, two other characteristics associated with electricity as it flows through a circuit should be mentioned: the amount of electricity being transmitted each second or each minute, and the resistance offered to the flow of electricity. The rate of flow of electricity, called the *current,* is measured in *amperes,* and the *resistance* of the circuit is measured in *ohms.* The names of these electrical units are taken from the names of scientists who helped to discover the facts about electricity: Volta (an Italian), Ampère (a Frenchman), and Ohm (a German).

One can see that in any circuit if the difference in potential (volts) is increased, more electricity (amperes) will be transmitted through the circuit each second; and if we decrease the resistance (ohms), more electricity (amperes) will flow. If the potential difference is doubled or the resistance is cut by half, the current will be doubled. This is expressed in a famous mathematical formula, known as Ohm's law. It is as follows:

$$\text{Current (amperes)} = \frac{\text{potential difference (volts)}}{\text{resistance (ohms)}}$$

or

Current in amperes multiplied by resistance in ohms = the potential difference in volts.

This law may be said to be one of the more fundamental laws of electricity, for it enables us to calculate any one of the values if we know the other two.

Electricity plays many roles in our lives. There is the obvious one, of which we are constantly aware, of operating the numerous devices we have at home, at school, in a store, in an office, and so on. We are especially aware of this whenever there is a failure of power and we resort to candles, and our electric clocks and refrigerators do not operate. If the stoppage lasts long enough, the area is called a disaster area, the community is placed under martial law, and assistance is sought from the government and the Red Cross.

EXPERIENCE. *To see how dependent we are on electricity.* Children at all ages enjoy describing vivid experiences. Perhaps they have experienced a power stoppage. Ask them to describe the events. How were they and their families affected? Relating the events at home will help to make electricity more real.

But electricity means even more than this. We, too, are made up of positive and negative charges of electricity. Most of the time these charges are balanced and we do not notice our electrical structure. The electrical currents in our bodies are only partially understood.

Electricity can operate in our mouths. Dentists have learned that some materials used for fillings may actually operate as a kind of battery in the human saliva and an electrical current can be set up which will aid the corrosion of the fillings. Of course, no one gets a shock from this action, and it may be months or years before the filling is greatly affected.

Many times there are electrical circuits set up in the ground because of the nature of materials used underground (p. 816). Electrochemical action in moist soil can cause pipes and walls in the ground to be weakened and corroded in time. Engineers must take this into consideration when constructing buildings, underground conduits, and the like.

Sometimes the structure of the ground is such as to cause the chemical generation of electric currents, much as in a great dry cell. There are other times when these currents flow through the ground and cause a movement of particles which have become electrified (ions). This latter process is an electrochemical action called *electrolysis*. It has been an important agent in building soils. It should be remembered that such a process in the ground may seem quite feeble to us, but when it goes on continuously year after year, it can be quite effective in disintegrating rocks.

There is no need for a teacher to learn all the ideas that have been presented in this section. The content presented in this chapter may be considered as source material to be utilized as needed. It would be well, however, to recognize that the material of the universe is electrical in nature. Also that there is a tendency toward equilibrium of charges in the universe, just as there is a tendency toward equilibrium in the atmosphere, in living things, and in practically all phenomena we observe. We can be glad, however, that there are vast forces which prevent complete equilibrium and make for the unbalancing of nature's charges. If this latter were not true there would be no energy, no life, and the universe would be a static, dead affair. It is likely that the very process of learning in human beings themselves grows out of the tendency of an individual to gain balance, poise, and adjustment in new situations and new experiences.

CHAPTER 24

How Man Finds Out about Things around Him

Everyone has two great means of finding out about the universe around him. One of these is observation of objects and the events that take place in the environment. He sees the stars; he hears sounds around him; he tastes, feels, smells, and otherwise senses things. He often uses instruments to supplement his own senses. He uses the telescope, for instance, to learn about the stars, and the radio to hear things from a distance.

The second of these means is learning about things from others. We read a book written by an author who lives today. We receive news by word of mouth or by radio. We write letters to our friends. One of the things which distinguishes man from other animals is the

ability to pass much information from one individual to another. Civilized man has learned to leave permanent records so that those who live after him may build on the knowledge which has been accumulated before. Higher civilizations are distinguished from lower ones partly by the greater mass of knowledge which is available to the individual. This knowledge, passed down from generation to generation, constitutes a great resource, perhaps the greatest resource of any people.

While a child's own learning from his own experiences is important in building his own concepts, he should recognize that the social heritage has been the result of the learning of many people over many generations (see Chapter 3). Science itself is the result of carefully recorded experiences and logical thinking, and therefore it is constantly subject to revision.

It is a worthy educational enterprise to enlarge a child's understanding of how man learns about the universe around him and how he has learned to pass this information to others who may be remote from him in time and space.

Light and Sound Help Man to Learn about the Universe

Of all the various means that man has of learning about the universe, probably light and sound are the most important. We see by means of light and we hear by means of sound. While some exceptional individuals, deprived of both the sense of sight and the sense of hearing (Helen Keller, for example), have been able to lead full and useful lives, such individuals are not common. Those people have succeeded in using other senses in place of those which have been lost. They read by feeling raised letters in Braille type; they "hear" by feeling the vibrations of sounding objects or by having someone move his fingers so as to make signs for letters and words.

In this chapter we shall devote our attention to the way in which man learns about the universe by means of light and sound. It was said in a previous chapter that light and sound are forms of energy. We have seen how man has learned to do most of his work by making available and using large amounts of energy. In this chapter we shall see how he gathers and distributes information by the exact control of extremely small amounts of energy.

Light and Communication

For uncounted centuries man has used light for communicating with others. The first man who beckoned or nodded or made some other gesture to convey information to another used light. Probably signs came before spoken language.

No elaborate explanation is necessary to convince us that gestures and signs involve light. We recognize the fact when we light a lamp "to see by." If a person sat across from us in a perfectly dark room, the most elaborate sign language would convey nothing to us, because without light we could not see him.

Other ways of communication which depend upon light are also quite commonly used. Boy Scouts and Girl Scouts are familiar with flag signaling, or wigwagging. Two flags, one in each hand, are used, their positions standing for letters of the alphabet. An observer stationed at a distant point reads the letters by watching the flags. Sometimes a single flag is used in another code. Wigwagging and the blinking of lights are extensively used by the navies of various nations for signaling between ships when the ships are not too far apart.

American Indians used a method of signaling which depended on puffs of smoke. A smoking fire was made, and the column of smoke was interrupted by cutting it off with a blanket. In clear air smoke signals can be seen for a long distance.

We use light in reading. Light comes from the sun or from your reading lamp and strikes a page printed with symbols. Some of the light is reflected from the page. This reflected light enters your eyes. In the eyes it is converted into nerve impulses which are carried to your brain. In your brain something happens, and you "see" the printed symbols. If, in addition, you are able to read the language in which the book is printed, the symbols convey to you a whole group of ideas.

Many other means by which light is used for communication will occur to the reader.

Light, Communication, and Safety. Many safety precautions and warning signals depend upon light for their proper functioning.

Streets, highways, and tunnels are illuminated by a complicated system of electric lights. Vehicles are equipped with lighting facilities in order to provide the light necessary for safe driving. Traffic lights facilitate the movement of traffic and provide opportunities for pedestrians to travel with greater safety. What would otherwise be dark areas in homes, schools, and other buildings are illuminated in order that people may see better. Many household appliances, such as stoves, toasters, and coffee-makers, have signal lights.

For hundreds of years illumination from stars has helped navigators determine their position. A periscope works when a submarine is submerged because light can be reflected by a series of mirrors and prisms. A lighthouse beacon warns ships of treacherous areas, and indicates the location of land which might not ordinarily be seen.

Airports and airplane runways are illuminated, and signal towers are provided to give directions to pilots. High buildings are equipped with electric lights which warn pilots of the impending danger.

Controlled light provides for greater safety everywhere.

Some Obects Reflect Light and Others Give Off Light. There are in general two ways by which we see an object. In the first, the object itself *gives off* light. The sun, the stars, electric-light bulbs, and flames are examples of this. We see these objects by their own light. As a matter of fact, any substance, if it can be heated enough without undergoing a chemical change, will give off light. We have only to heat a nail or other piece of metal in the fire to prove this. When the object first begins to give off visible light, the light is red; then, as it becomes hotter, the light becomes yellowish; finally, if the fire is hot enough, the object becomes glowing white, and gives off a great deal of light as long as it is kept hot. A white-hot object is *incandescent*. In an electric-light bulb there is a fine wire which is heated white-hot when an electric current passes through it. This white-hot wire gives off the light. That is why electric-light bulbs are sometimes called incandescent lamps. The sun and other stars are incandescent.

We may also see an object which *reflects* light. The object itself does not give off any light, but light falling upon it is reflected from the object to the eye of the observer. Most of the objects around us are seen by reflected light. Light which enters the eye after it has been reflected from an object is different in

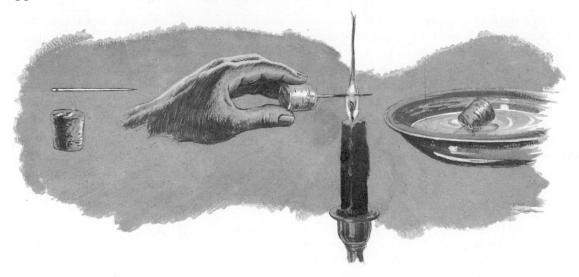

If the needle is heated sufficiently it will give off light.

quality and quantity from light which reaches the eye directly from the source.

Light Affects the Eye. We have seen above that the process of seeing really takes place when light enters the eye and affects it so as to send a message to the brain. The eye is sensitive to the radiant energy which we call light; however, no two individuals perceive this light exactly the same; no person can know how this light is "seen" by another person's brain.

The eye is an exceedingly complicated organ. It consists essentially of a system of *lenses* which bend the rays of light which enter the eye from an object so as to form an image of the object on the posterior two thirds of the eye. This posterior region is called the *retina*. It is made up of individual nerve cells. These nerve cells are highly differentiated, and are arranged in ten layers. Light passes through most of the cells of the retina before it reaches the *rod-and-cone layer*. There is little doubt that it is the rods and cones which are the light-sensitive receptors of the eye, and it is in the rod-and-cone layer that the light is converted by some unexplained process into nerve impulses which are transmitted by other cells through the optic nerve to the brain.

EXPERIENCE. *To study incandescent lamps.* Observe the wires of incandescent lamps when they are disconnected from the current. A clear bulb is easy to use for this purpose. Note what wire becomes incandescent. One should not look directly at a lighted incandescent lamp (p. 839).

EXPERIENCE. *How light helps us to see.* Have children look around the room. What do they see? Which of these things are seen by reflected light? Which are seen because they are sources of light? Usually the only sources would be the sun, electric lights, and once in a while a candle flame or a fire in the fireplace. We see each other and objects about us by reflected light.

EXPERIENCE. *Changing the direction in which light travels.* By studying how light comes into dark hallways at home or school, one can see that light travels in straight lines. However, light reflected from the walls at one end of a long hall may be seen by others at the other end. Light from one room may be reflected into another room which is otherwise quite dark. Light can also be reflected by mirrors and in this way its direction of travel changed. Chil-

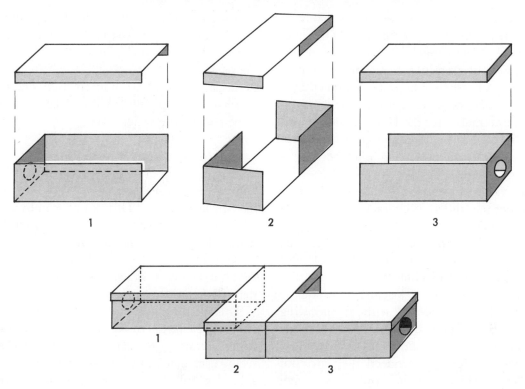

Assemble shoe boxes as shown. Shine a flashlight in one hole and look in the other. Then reverse the light and observation point. Are the rooms in the boxes well lighted? Is any light reflected?

dren can experiment with pocket mirrors in this way.

That light travels in a straight line can be shown by using three shoe boxes cut and put together to correspond to the design of the rooms on page 865. Cut a round hole in one end of two of the boxes so that a flashlight can be inserted. Assemble and tape together. Shine the flashlight in one hole and look into the other. How well are the rooms lighted? Note the reflected light. Try it the other way around.

EXPERIENCE. *Light travels in a straight line.* Cut a hole in the center of each of two or three pieces of cardboard. Light a candle and place it on a table in a darkened room. Have children move the cardboards so that the holes are in the same straight line, centered on the flame. When they are, one can see the candle flame and the beam of light it sends through the holes in the cardboard. Try it out with other objects such as a bright metal object, to demonstrate that reflected light travels in straight lines, too (p. 862).

EXPERIENCE. *Do animals have the same kind of vision we do?* Many times fictional stories about animals give the impression that animals have much the same kind of vision we have. Dogs and horses are often so described.

The kind of vision animals have is the kind that has helped their ancestors to survive. A close study of dogs and horses will reveal that their vision is not the same as ours. It is not accurate to state that they get the same impression of a scene. In addition, animals may use a combination of their senses, just as we do; the dog may rely on his sense of smell to supplement his vision. We are more likely to supplement our vision by our sense of hearing, and sometimes by touching. Animals are frequently highly sensitive to the movement of objects. A horse may become frightened by a harmless piece of paper blown by the wind.

Most animals have the kind of vision that is essential to securing food and gives them protection, although protection may be only a matter of flight.

The vision of insects with compound eyes is of an entirely different character. This kind of vision aids the housefly to escape.

It suits the purpose of fiction writers to ascribe to other animals the same kind of emotions, vision, and psychological reactions that people have. However, we can appreciate the fine qualities of animals without endowing them with human qualities. This is not to say that horses, dogs, elephants, and other animals are not intelligent, for indeed they are, but they are intelligent in their own way. Man alone stands at the pinnacle of intelligence among all the animals.

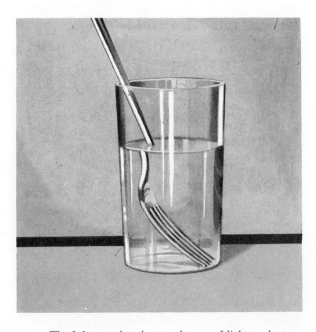

The fork seems bent because the rays of light are bent.

EXPERIENCE. *Bending light rays.* Place a pencil in a tumbler of water so that part of the pencil is in the air and part in the water. Note that the pencil seems to be bent at the water level. Perhaps children have noticed that oars used on rowboats or paddles used with canoes seem to be bent at the water level.

Light is bent when it passes through two or more substances of *different densities.* It is also bent when it passes through one substance that has *varying densities.* This can be seen by looking over the top of a warm radiator or electric stove. Objects beyond the heat source seem to be shimmering. The air being heated over the warm object is expanding and has less density than the air nearby.

This bending helps to give the shimmering effect of a *mirage.* In Arizona there is a ranch called Phantom Ranch. A cowboy reported seeing a strange monster moving about on the side of a hill. Later, prehistoric bones were found at the surface of the ground. The heated air in expanding gave a shimmering effect as the cowboy looked through air of different densities, and the bones seemed to be moving. Mirages produce strange optical illusions!

Children might be encouraged to tell of some of the strange things they have seen in mirages.

The bending of light rays is called *refraction.* We make use of refraction in eyeglasses or spectacles, hand lenses, projection lanterns, cameras, and microscopes. All of these utilize lenses in order to refract the light in the way that is wanted. Probably the first use of refraction by man was in the development of the lens within his own eye.

Notice that the actual seeing is done in the brain, not in the eye.

The cones are concentrated in the central retina. It is generally accepted that it is the cones which are primarily concerned with daylight vision and color reception. The rods,

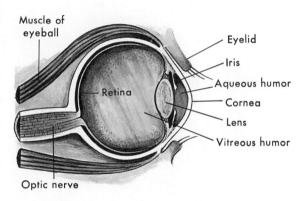

Muscle of
eyeball

Eyelid

Iris

Aqueous humor

Retina

Cornea

Lens

Vitreous humor

Optic nerve

Light entering the eye passes through the transparent parts and strikes the retina. The transparent parts act as a system of lenses and each bends the light somewhat.

EXPERIENCE. *The size of the opening in the eye depends on the light falling on it.* Have the children separate into groups of two. Let one child close his eyes for a minute or two and then open them. Have the other child watch his partner's eyes closely. He can readily see the iris grow smaller. Have a child go from a dark part of the room to a window while his partner watches him. Note the change in the iris.

EXPERIENCE. *Care of the eyes.* Often the school doctor or nurse will be glad to give a talk on the proper care of the eyes. He will probably stress rest, sufficient and proper light, and regular eye examinations.

located in greater numbers in the more outlying regions of the retina, enable us to determine brightness.

Referring to the illustration on this page, the reader can see that light entering the eye passes through the cornea, aqueous humor, crystalline lens, and vitreous humor. These substances are all transparent, and each of them bends the light somewhat. They thus act as a system of lenses. For present purposes, one may consider the whole system as acting like one lens.

The eye is equipped with muscles which can change the shape of the crystalline lens slightly, thus focusing the eye on objects near by or far away.

The eyes are pointed toward objects by a complicated system of muscles which turn the eyeballs.

Located between two parts of the lens system is the *iris,* which is a sort of partition with a hole in it. The size of the hole is regulated by a set of muscles in such a way as to control the amount of light that reaches the interior of the eye. In bright light the hole is small, while in dim light it becomes larger. It is the iris which controls the amount of light that enters the eye and enables us to see, not only in bright sunshine but also in quite dark places.

Glasses and Eye Defects. Our eyes are admirably adapted to primitive life, where they seldom need to focus on small objects for long periods. With the stress which modern life places on reading and study, many eyes have been found to need artificial aid.

A great deal could probably be said about the social significance of eyeglasses, for without their aid a great deal of study leading to increased understanding would have been more difficult, if not impossible, for many people. Most eye defects fall into a few rather simple forms. In *nearsightedness* the eyeball is too long (front to back) or the lens is curved too much, so that rays of light are focused before they fall on the retina. A nearsighted person can see clearly only those objects which are close to his eyes. This defect is corrected by using a lens which bends the rays of light apart. Such a lens is called a *concave,* or *diverging, lens* and is thicker at the edges than in the center.

In true *farsightedness* the eyeball is too short, and the rays of light cannot be focused soon enough to form an image on the retina. This defect is corrected by a *convex,* or *converging, lens.* This lens is thicker at the center than at the edges, and helps the lenses of the eye to focus the light sooner.

The lens of the eye must be slightly more curved to focus clearly on nearby objects than it needs to be when the objects are far away. This change in the curvature, called *accommodation,* is brought about by muscles which control the shape of the lens. As a person grows older, the lens hardens somewhat, so that the muscles can no longer focus it properly on nearby objects. This type of farsightedness is really caused by lack of accommodation. It is remedied by having bifocal glasses so arranged that when looking through the bottom part of the glasses we look through lenses with a different curvature than when we look through the top part.

Many people have the mistaken idea that the need of bifocal glasses is necessarily a sign of old age. This is not so, for the lens hardens much earlier in some people than in others.

Another very common type of eye defect is that in which the lens is curved too much or too little in just one direction. For example, it may be curved too much in a vertical direction but be all right in a horizontal direction. When one or both eyes are unequally curved in this way, the person is said to have *astigmatism.* Astigmatism is easily corrected by using an eyeglass lens that is unequally curved to compensate for the unequal curvature of the lens of the eye.

A great many children have astigmatism. Many do not discover this until they get beyond the elementary school, as the eye muscles are able to correct the defect, although it strains them to do so. It is when a child reaches the point when he must do a good deal of reading that trouble becomes evident. The strained muscles often give rise to painful headaches. Of course more severe cases may be discovered when the child is younger.

Care of the Eyes. The foregoing description of the eye should imply a few suggestions for its care. Although the eye is capable of seeing with little light, it should not be

Faces often indicate inadequate lighting.

strained by forcing it to function in a dim light. More light is necessary to see fine work, such as reading or sewing, than to see coarse work. A sufficient amount of illumination, shaded so as to prevent glare either directly from the lamp itself or reflected from the page, should be provided for anyone who is reading. A shadow across the page is distinctly harmful. The practice of reading with a single bright light on the page and the rest of the room in darkness is not good, for the contrast between the brightly lighted book and the shadows beyond tends to cause eyestrain. Since the eyes are not well adapted to fine or close work, all such work straining the eyes to some extent, it is a good plan to raise the eyes from the work at frequent intervals and look for a few moments at some large distant object.

Eyestrain is an insidious thing and frequently affects the entire nervous system, possibly causing a person to become irritable or affecting the appetite or digestion.

Teachers should be alert to find out if any children have trouble seeing the blackboard or the printed page. Many a child has been considered dull when he was really unable to see the board clearly. Eyes which are in need of glasses should not be strained by our trying to get along without them. It is well to have the children's eyes tested at regular intervals by a nurse or physician who is competent to do so. The ordinary eye-card tests, as performed by untrained persons, are useful only to show certain kinds of gross defects, such as nearsightedness. A child may have a serious eyestrain and yet be able to make a good score on these tests.

In many schoolrooms some seats may be distinctly better than others in their illumination. It is a good plan to change the children's seating arrangements occasionally.

Light Comes to Us from the Sun

Earth receives light from two sources— *directly* from the sun and the other stars and *indirectly* from the moon and the planets. The direct light from the sun is, of course, the more important. Most of the energy which comes to Earth from the sun comes in the form of visible light. Man's attempts to provide artificial illumination are feeble in comparison with the illumination provided by the sun.

Light Energy from the Sun. Our greatest source of light energy is the sun. We know that only a small amount of the light energy which the sun radiates reaches Earth. We also realize that this limited amount of the sun's light provides the entire Earth with energy. From where does this tremendous amount of energy come? How is it produced?

We now know that electrons revolve around the center of each atom. Under certain conditions the electrons acquire increased energy. This increased amount of electron energy is released as light. The electrons of some atoms give off light energy when heated to a high temperature.

Most of the sun is composed of hydrogen in gaseous form. When four atoms of hydrogen gas combine, they form one atom of a new gas called helium, and tremendous amounts of energy are released. It is believed that the released energy heats other atoms in the sun.

This is repeated over and over, and very high temperatures are obtained. When some of these materials are heated to these very high temperatures, the electrons of their atoms give off light energy. The light energy passes through space, and some of it reaches Earth (p. 196).

The Nature of Light. Scientists are continually learning more and more about light, but there are still many questions unsettled. Many explanations have been proposed as to the nature of light, but not all scientists agree as to its exact nature.

At one time it was believed that light consisted of small particles called corpuscles which were shot out of a luminous body. According to the *corpuscular theory,* it is only natural for light to travel in a straight line, because anything will travel in a straight line if it is free from any outside forces. Thus, when light is reflected, it is like a completely elastic ball bouncing off a smooth and solid surface. Further study indicated that this theory could not be used to explain all of the phenomena of light (Chapter 22).

Not all scientists could support the corpuscular theory of light. In 1678, even before Newton had developed his theory of the "corporeity of light," Huyghens stated that light was really some form of motion, and proposed a wave hypothesis to explain the nature of light. This theory is known as the *wave theory*.

It is very difficult to imagine a wave without something to be waved, yet we know that light can travel through a vacuum. Therefore, in order to explain how waves get from the sun to Earth, scientists imagined a substance filling all space and able to transmit waves. This substance they called the ether. The word *ether* comes from the Latin word *aether,* which means "heavenly gas." It is not the kind of ether used in hospitals.

Careful experiments were carried on by the American physicists Michelson and Morley and by other scientists for the purpose of determining if the ether really exists, but they failed to find evidence of it. Space and ether are now considered as coextensive, that is, they have equal extent. Actually it is difficult, if not impossible to think of one apart from the other. At one time it was believed that the ether was at absolute rest in space; however, with the acceptance of the theory of relativity this no longer has any meaning. Today those properties which once specifically characterized the ether are now considered properties of space.

Light comes to us from the sun and stars through space. It is interesting to note that the space between the sun and Earth is probably very dark. If one traveled out beyond Earth's atmosphere, the blue sky would give place to dark night with a blazing sun. Astronauts cruising at high altitudes have difficulty reading their instruments because of the lack of the scattered daylight to which we are accustomed.

At present no one appears to have explained completely how light travels through space.

Further experiments by other investigators indicated that light was not continuous, as would be required by assuming that it was wave motion alone. A more recent theory accepted by many is the theory of radiation, known as the *quantum theory*. It is supported by a great deal of experimentation. This theory is different from the electromagnetic theory, which assumed that emission and absorption of radiation were continuous processes. The quantum theory states that light is emitted and absorbed in small bundles, packets, or units called *quanta*. According to this theory, radiation is not emitted and absorbed continuously in arbitrary amounts. It is always emitted and absorbed in discrete quantities called quanta. Each quantum of light is referred to as a *photon*. Photons have properties which we attribute to both particles and to waves, although these characteristics are not always apparent. If light is not continuously emitted and absorbed, why is it that we assume that the light energy which enters our eyes is continuous? This is because we receive very large numbers of quanta, and each quantum has very little energy. At the present time we do not possess instruments which are capable of detecting a single quantum when the frequency is low, since this energy is very small. X ray frequencies support the quantum theory, and a single quantum at this frequency can be detected (Chapter 22).

The Photon. We can get some idea of the nature of a photon by considering an atom of carbon. We have seen that an atom that has its electron or energy shells filled will have 2 electrons in its first shell, 8 in its second shell, and so on (p. 378). A carbon atom contains a total of 6 electrons, 2 of which are in the first shell and 4 in the second shell. Thus the second shell has 4 vacancies.

Suppose we heat a carbon rod until it is red-hot. The heat energy we have supplied is absorbed by the atoms and "excites" them to vibrate more rapidly. Consider a single carbon atom. Electron *a* in the first shell absorbs enough extra energy to enable it to jump outward, away from the nucleus, into one of the vacancies in the second shell. Electron *b*, attracted by the nucleus, jumps into the space

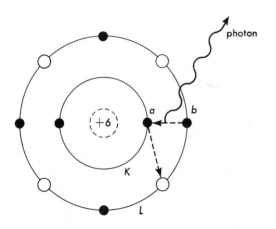

A simple diagram showing ejection of photon from heated carbon atom. Electron a absorbs heat energy, jumps to vacant space (circle) in higher orbit (shell L). Electron b takes its place. In falling to lower orbit (shell K), it gives off excess energy as a photon. (After T. C. Ridout.)

left vacant by *a*. Since less energy is required for an electron to exist in the first shell, the excess energy is given off as a *photon*. In this case the photon has the wave length of red light. Large numbers given off in this manner produce a red glow. They form *light*. They strike the retina of the eye, where they are converted into electrical impulses, which are then transmitted over the optic nerve to the brain, and we "see" that the rod is "red-hot."

Photons occur in different frequencies and wave lengths. They form beams of light or of X rays. We say that the photon is a *basic unit*, or quantum, of electromagnetic energy.

We may think of streams of photons combining to form a light wave, somewhat as molecules of water move in a regular pattern to form water waves. Thus matter has different forms, according to what aspect of it we are studying.

Amplifying with Atoms. Using the principles just described, it is possible to amplify or generate electromagnetic waves from certain substances. Certain gases and solid substances, such as synthetic rubies, are used for this pur-

pose, although the crystals of other substances may be found useful, too. A ruby is made of aluminum, oxygen, and chromium; it is the arrangement of electrons in the chromium atoms that make amplification possible.

In one device called a maser (from *micro-wave amplification by stimulated emission of radiation*), a ruby is subjected to a magnetic field. Amplification of microwaves takes place and are given off. Masers are useful in picking up faint radio signals and are used wherever an extremely sensitive receiver is required, as in radio astronomy.

In a *laser,* an optical or an infrared maser, light is applied to a ruby crystal, which in turn gives off a highly concentrated beam of light as the excited atoms return to their usual states (see "The Photon"). It is expected that such beams of light will transmit radio, television, and telephone messages around Earth and into space. These devices hold great promise for communication.

Light Is Energy. We have already considered light as energy in the discussion of energy from the sun on page 734. Although most of our light energy is derived from the sun, light can be obtained from many sources. Thermal, electrical, chemical, and fluorescent excitations are some of the familiar sources of light.

We know that at all times objects are absorbing or giving off radiant energy. Some of this radiant energy can be detected by instruments or by touch, but it is not visible until the emitted radiation is from an object at a temperature greater than 500°C. (932°F.). Objects do not become "white hot" until they reach temperatures of 1200°C. (2192°F.) and above. This radiant energy that the eye is capable of seeing is called light.

On page 853 we described how light is produced by heating certain materials. There are ways other than thermal excitation by which light can be emitted. In the neon light

Light travels in a straight line.

it is the electrical excitation which causes light. Sometimes light is produced with neither a rise in temperature nor an electrical discharge. Phosphorescent substances, such as decaying wood, sometimes produce light by means of a transformation of a chemical nature. It is believed that the cold light produced by fireflies results from an electrical as well as a chemical change.

Light travels with a perfectly measurable speed of about 186,000 miles per second, or more than 660 million miles an hour. This extremely rapid speed has been measured very accurately by Michelson. It takes light about eight minutes to reach Earth from the sun and about four and a third years to reach it from the next nearest star. Some stars are so far away that it takes thousands and even millions of years for their light to reach Earth. Light energy travels in straight lines in a uniform medium. Even when light energy changes its direction, the light continues to travel in straight lines. There are times when light waves do bend; however, this is difficult to detect because the wave lengths of light are very short. Shadows are formed because rays of light travel in straight lines.

Light Can Be Reflected. When energy in the form of light strikes a surface, three things usually happen. Some of the light energy is absorbed and converted into heat, the proportion absorbed depending on the nature and color of the surface. Some of the light may penetrate the substance. Substances which light penetrates easily are said to be *transparent* those which light does not penetrate easily are *opaque.* Window glass is transparent; bricks are opaque. The light which is neither absorbed nor transmitted is turned back, or *reflected,* at or near the surface.

EXPERIENCE. *The moon shines by reflected light.* In a darkened room have a child hold up a black ball representing the moon. The children can see the ball only dimly if at all. Turn a flashlight on the "moon." It can now be seen clearly (Chapter 7).

A rough surface will reflect light in many directions and scatter, or diffuse, it. A smooth surface will reflect light in a definite direction. The direction in which light is reflected from a smooth surface depends on the direction in which it falls upon that surface. Such a smooth surface forms a mirror.

Moonlight is reflected sunlight.

EXPERIENCE. *Smooth surfaces act as mirrors.* Use the bottom of a shiny tin can as a mirror. Polish it with metal polish. The children can probably see themselves in it quite clearly. Now roughen it with coarse sandpaper. The mirror effect will be destroyed.

The reason why we can see ourselves in a mirror is that the light from each part of our bodies is reflected to the eye in a manner which forms an image rather than being reflected in a scattered or haphazard way.

The smooth surface of glass or of highly polished metal forms an excellent mirror. We can observe that glass is a reflector when we see our reflections in the plate-glass show window of a store. Most common mirrors found in the home do not depend on the reflection from the glass, but from a film of metal, usually silver, on the back of the glass. If we hold a pencil in front of a thick mirror, we can often see a faint reflection just outside the principal one. This is the reflection from the surface of the glass, while the principal reflection is from the polished metal behind it.

EXPERIENCE. *Mirrors are made of glass coated with metal.* Examine an inexpensive mirror. Notice the coating on the back. This is usually silver with a protective coating of some sort of paint or varnish. Scrape some of the coating away.

Probably because ancient people thought that there was some sort of supernatural connection between a person and his reflection in a mirror, a superstition has grown up that it brings all sorts of evils to break one of these pieces of glass and metal. A child who understands something about mirrors ought to be freed from this superstition.

Some mirrors are not flat but curved. One type is curved inward. Such an inwardly curved mirror is called a *concave* mirror. If concave mirrors are curved in a proper way, a beam of light coming to them is almost all reflected to one small place called the *focus* of the mirror. Concave mirrors are used in some astronomical telescopes. The object of such telescopes is to collect as much light as

A mirror is a good reflector.

possible from a distant star and throw it into the eye of an observer. Concave mirrors achieve this by concentrating the light into a small space.

They are also used in the opposite way (p. 203). Light which originates at the focus and strikes the mirror is reflected as a beam. In automobile headlights, flashlights, and searchlights a source of light, usually an electric-light bulb, is placed at the focus. Most of the light from the bulb is projected as a beam instead of being scattered in all directions. The exact description of the action of a concave mirror under all conditions is complicated, and will not be attempted here.

EXPERIENCE. *Studying curved mirrors.* Examine the curved mirror which reflects the light of an automobile headlight. Do not touch the reflecting surface; some reflectors are silver and are very easily scratched. Many mirrors used while shaving or for applying cosmetics are curved.

Reflected Light Is Useful. Probably of more importance to man than light reflected from polished surfaces is light reflected from rough surfaces. As we have said, this is the condition under which we see most objects. The

world would indeed present a different appearance if we could see only things which are either sources of light or polished surfaces.

The moon and the planets give off no light of their own (Chapter 7). Instead we see them by the sun's light reflected from their surfaces. On a moonlight night it would not be incorrect to say that Earth is really lighted by sunlight.

The particles of dust in the air also reflect light. They reflect some light even into places on which the sun is not shining directly—for example, in the shade of a building. It is this dust which enables us to see objects which are not in the direct rays of the sun (p. 435).

When sunlight is reflected from a colored object, it is changed in some manner, as will be explained on page 868.

EXPERIENCE. *To observe the planets and the moon.* Children sometimes have opportunities to observe the sky at night. Ask them to determine whether they can locate any planets. Frequently there may be items in newspapers or in children's periodicals about what planets are visible in the sky and at what hour. What do they notice about the difference in appearance of stars and planets? Do they detect any color? (Chapter 7.)

Also have them observe the moon. Have them note that the moon is sometimes visible during the day. If binoculars of any kind are available, suggest that they use them.

Much of this kind of work can be done by children at home. In some cases, the children may live near enough together to go on a field excursion to observe the stars. In looking at the stars, have them recall that the stars are suns, making their own light. Consider how far away they must be to seem no larger than they do.

EXPERIENCE. *To observe a prism.* Secure a prism and place it in different parts of the room at different times during the day.

Some light is reflected by the walls.

Watch for the spectrum colors. If there is a rainbow at any time of the day, take time out for its observation. Do you see a secondary bow?

EXPERIENCE. *Describe experiences in a hall of mirrors.* Perhaps some children have been to an amusement park where there have been different kinds of mirrors which made people look very thin, very fat, very tall, very short, or distorted in other ways. Perhaps children have been in rooms that were made to appear much larger than they really were by means of mirrors. Have they ever almost walked into a mirror? Have they seen show windows where they couldn't locate the glass?

Light and Shadow. For many years shadows have been of interest to children and adults of all ages. Most children can remember when a harmless image was interpreted as a men-

acing threat. Shadows are also a source of entertainment.

Ancient Chinese performers made extensive use of the shadow play as they went from place to place. Many schoolchildren enjoy making shadow puppets. Teachers may encourage children to experiment by making their own shadows on a wall, large sheet, or screen.

Children frequently play games involving shadows. They step on the shadows of others or try to make their own shadows disappear. Kindergarten children often stand in the larger shadows of trees or buildings in order that their own shadows will not be visible. Thus through play they acquire knowledge of the relationships of the real objects to their shadows.

When children are encouraged to look around, what can they learn about shadows? What shadows can they see indoors and what shadows can they see out of doors? What

Shadow pictures.

shadows can they move? When do shadows disappear? Do shadows vary under certain conditions?

If boys and girls look at their own shadows on the ground, they will observe that the shadow of their feet is distinct, whereas the shadow of their head is not as sharp. When a five-year-old child observed that his shadow became increasingly hazy toward his head he told his friend that he was "dissolving like a lump of sugar."

Without light there can be no shadow.

Over the course of a year children will notice that the position of shadows within their classroom or home at a specific time of the day varies, depending upon the time of year. If a long object is placed in a vertical position, one can observe that the length and position of the shadow that the sun's light casts will vary, depending upon the sun's position in relation to Earth. When the sun is at its highest position, shadows will be found to be shortest, whereas at sunrise and sunset shadows are longer.

Contrary to popular belief, ordinary shadows are colored. They are not completely black. They are colored because there is light from some source. Most of our light is the brilliant yellow from the sun, and these rays predominate over light from other sources, such as the sky. Thus the light in the shadow cast by the sun is the blue or gray from the sky. Therefore, by contrast with their surroundings, shadows are usually more blue in appearance. On cloudy days when shadows cast by the sun are no longer apparent, there are still areas that have shadows.

EXPERIENCE. *To discover that light is needed in order to cause an object to cast a shadow.* Young children in play chase a shadow, or think of their shadows as chasing them. When the children run into the shade of a tree or other large object, they lose their own shadow. Sometimes they go into the sunshine to find their shadow.

EXPERIENCE. *At night we are in the shadow of Earth.* Children can discuss this subject (Chapter 7). Use a globe and a light. Children of seven and eight, and even younger children, are interested in the fact that the sun is always shining on Earth.

Sunlight and Color. Almost everyone is familiar with the array of brilliant colors produced when sunlight strikes glass in a certain

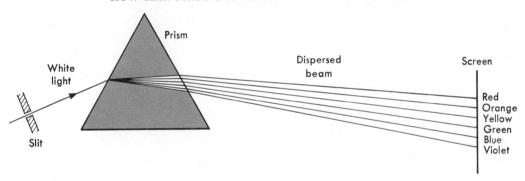

Sunlight may be broken up by a glass prism, showing the colors of the spectrum. (*Adapted from* Physics, *4th edition, 1957, by Erich Hausmann and Edgar P. Slack, D. Van Nostrand, Princeton, N. J.*)

way. The beveled edge of a mirror, a cut-glass bowl, glass tanks in an aquarium, or a piece of crystal jewelry will often show this effect. This band of colors is called the sun's spectrum. If sunlight is passed through a triangular piece of glass, called a prism, an especially fine spectrum may be produced.[1]

Sir Isaac Newton, who must be credited with many other important contributions to science, was the first to study this band of colors intensively. His book *Opticks* was published in 1704. Newton made a small hole in a dark window shade and allowed the beam of bright sunlight which came through the hole to pass through a prism. On the wall opposite the window he saw a brilliant band of colors. The colors always appeared in a certain order—red, orange, yellow, green, blue, and violet. There was no sharp dividing line between the colors, but one blended gradually into the next.

From experiments such as this it has been concluded that white light, such as sunlight, is composed not of a single color but of all colors. Whenever light passes at an oblique angle from one substance into another of different optical density, it is *bent;* that is, its direction is changed. The different colors are

bent differently, the violet being bent most and the red least. Hence, when the light comes out of the prism, the different colors are bent differently, the violet most and the red least; moreover, the different colors are traveling in somewhat different directions, and they do not strike the screen in the same place.

EXPERIENCE. *White light is made up of many colors.* Secure a prism and use it to split the sun's light into colors. The light from a projection lantern may be used instead of the sun. A little practice will be needed to throw a good spectrum on the wall or ceiling. Let the children do the practicing. Let them tell about or demonstrate other ways in which they have seen a spectrum made.

When white lights falls on a white object, all the different colors are reflected equally to our eyes, and we see the object as white.

When light is colored, some of the components of white light are missing. We can produce red light, for instance, by passing white light through red glass or red cellophane. The red glass lets red through, but holds back all the other colors. If red light only falls on a white surface, there is nothing for the white to reflect except red. White objects appear red in red light. Many objects appear colored when seen in white light. Some substances do not reflect all colors, but absorb some and

---

[1] Prisms can usually be secured from local department stores. If not, they can be ordered from a school supply house. Every elementary school should have a small supply of prisms.

reflect others. When an object appears red, it absorbs all the colors except red, and reflects only the red to the eye (p. 888).

EXPERIENCE. *How objects look in colored light.* Secure some pieces of colored cellophane or colored glass. Place them in the projection lantern in place of slides so as to produce colored light. To make this easier, it is recommended that several thicknesses of colored cellophane be bound between two clear lantern-slide glasses. Darken the room and throw the colored light on objects of various colors.

EXPERIENCE. *Colored slides let through light of one color only.* Look through colored slides at objects of various colors and tell how they look. Expected results may not be obtained unless the colors are "pure." For instance, a bright-blue dress may not appear black through red cellophane unless the red cellophane is unusually good. It might let some blue light through.

When we mix two colors of paints, we sometimes get a third color. For example, blue and yellow paints when mixed often give green. This is because some kinds of coloring materials, called pigments, reflect two colors. They reflect more of one of the colors than they do of the other. The yellow pigment reflects mostly yellow and some green; the blue, mostly blue and some green; yellow absorbs blue and violet, while blue absorbs red and yellow. When mixed together, green is the only color which neither will absorb, and hence it is the color reflected.

Black objects absorb nearly all the light falling on them and reflect very little of it.

If light of one color falls on an object capable of reflecting only another color, the object will reflect no light at all and will appear to be black. A blue dress seen in pure red light looks black.

The principles of color are sometimes used with startling effects in stage lighting. Some materials do no reflect just one color, but a combination of several colors. Such objects are likely to appear to be of different colors in different lights. Striking stage effects are secured by changing the color of the lighting.

Color, then, is a characteristic of the light which falls on the retina; it is not a characteristic of the object which appears colored in our minds. However, although color exists as a sensation within our bodies, we most frequently consider it as characteristic of that which we see in our environment. An object really does not have any specific color of its own. Its color is dependent upon the color contained in the radiant energy.

Rainbows. Prisms do not need to be made of glass, nor must they be triangular in shape. A droplet of water under certain circumstances may also act to bend and reflect light. In some cases this gives rise to a rainbow.

Rainbows are most frequently seen after a shower either early or late in the day. Some-

Raindrops act as prisms to produce a rainbow.

times more than one rainbow is seen. The rainbows are on the opposite side of the sky from the sun.

When white light is bent, each of the colors of which it is composed is bent differently. It is this different bending which creates the rainbow colors.

EXPERIENCE. *Making rainbows.* Children can easily make "artificial" rainbows if they have a chance to experiment with a hose or lawn-sprinkler which can be made to throw a fine spray. Have them put on old clothes or bathing suits and do this outside on a warm day.

Complementary Colors. If a disk of paper painted with certain combinations of two colors in the right proportions is whirled rapidly, the blurring of the two colors as seen by the eye seems to give white. This is due, not to the fact that we have produced white light, but to the construction of the eye. Colors which when mixed together in this way give the effect of white are called complementary colors. Examples are blue and yellow, red and green.

The mechanism of color vision is not at all well understood by scientists, but the general theory is this: Parts of the retina are sensitive chiefly to red, others to blue, and still others to green. Other colors are seen because they stimulate more than one of the three sensitive areas. White light stimulates them all. If by means of a color wheel we can stimulate all areas in the right proportions, we get the sensation of white. Note that we have not made white light; we have only caused the eye and brain to act as if white light were seen.

EXPERIENCE. *To study the use of color in art work.* The study of color in science can be integrated with art work. Note the various colors in the environment; the colors of soil and the many shades of green. Note the colors after a long drought and then a few days after a rain.

Have children watch for the colors in the sky, especially at sunrise and at sunset.

Lenses. A lens is a piece of glass or other transparent substance curved on one or both sides. The purpose of a lens is to bend light.

We have observed that when a ray of light passes at an angle from one substance to another—for example, from air to glass or from glass to air—it is bent. We call this bending, *refraction.*

There are two general types of lenses—diverging, which bend the rays of light apart, and converging, which bend them together. A converging lens is thicker in the middle than at the edges. An ordinary hand lens, or magnifying glass, is such a lens as this.

In the accompanying picture is shown a simplified diagram of how a magnifying glass works. It may serve to illustrate the general principle on which all lenses work.

Rays from the object to be viewed—for instance, the object *AB*—enter the lens and are bent together. They enter the eye at a wider angle than they would without the lens, and we see the object as if it were the larger one located at *CD*, from which the light seems to come.

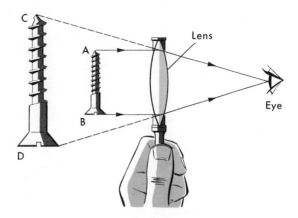

A magnifying glass. The ray from A passes through the lens and is bent toward the eye, so that it appears to come from C.

Magnifying glasses are often used by children to concentrate the rays of the sun so as to set fire to paper. In this case, the rays of the sun enter in the same way as the rays from *AB* and are concentrated on paper placed where the eye is in the diagram.

Compound microscopes, telescopes, cameras, field glasses, and projection lanterns all contain lenses the object of which is to bend light.

EXPERIENCE. *Objects give off light when heated.* If there is an opportunity to heat a nail in a flame, you can demonstrate that a nail can give off light if heated hot enough. Perhaps the gas stove can be used in the kitchen of the cafeteria. Tongs or pincers or pliers can be used to hold the nail. Hold the nail after heating in as dark a place as is available near to the stove.

Children having fireplaces, coal or wood stoves, or furnaces at home may have observed a poker becoming so hot it glowed. Ask them to tell about it.

The light given off by a candle is due to hot particles of carbon in the flame. Hold a cold pan in a candle flame for a few minutes and notice the carbon (soot) which is deposited on the pan.

EXPERIENCE. *Various colors are produced by mixing paints.* Experiment to learn how paints can be mixed to produce various colors. Perhaps the simplest mixture is blue and yellow water colors to produce green.

EXPERIENCE. *Experiments with curved mirrors and lenses. Light can be reflected and bent in various useful ways.* While the full explanation of the action of curved mirrors and lenses is a subject in their later education, children can easily see light being reflected or bent and ought to have the opportunity. In a darkened room—the darker, the better—let the children pass the light from a projection lantern or a good flashlight onto mirrors and through lenses. The beam of light may be made visible by clapping blackboard erasers near it. The path of the light is shown as it is reflected from the chalk dust.

Radiation Seems to Be Everywhere. Radiation (energy) in its many forms, heat, light, X rays, ultraviolet, and others are mentioned many times throughout this book. Children and adults alike will continue to hear about, use, and work with radiation in some of its many forms.

Radiant energy is generated and given

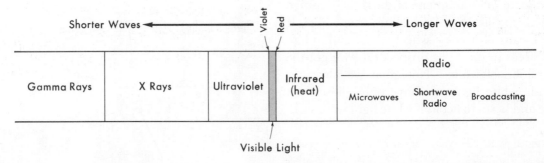

A remarkable feature of the electromagnetic spectrum is that it includes so many things that appear to be so different. Radio waves, heat, light, ultraviolet, X rays, and gamma rays are all part of one continuous spectrum or range of waves. They differ only in wave length and frequency. There is no sharp dividing line between the various kinds of waves; they merge or overlap. The diagram is not drawn to scale. Inasmuch as matter and energy are both regarded as composed of waves, it is evident that the study of electromagnetism goes to the very heart of our existence.

forth by the sun and the stars, and probably spreads throughout space. Every electron in an atom, by its motion, generates a very small electrical current with an equally small magnetic field. Each atom is electrical and magnetic in nature, and radiation is a result of these properties. Radiation consists of electromagnetic waves that travel at the speed of light, about 186,000 miles per second, but each kind of wave is distinguished from the others by having a different wave length and frequency. Consequently, each kind of electromagnetic wave has different properties. In general, the shorter the wave, the greater power it has for penetrating materials. Man has learned to produce and use the same kind of electromagnetic waves. They are all oscillating electrical charges.

An opposite process may take place. Radiant energy may strike atoms and change them. Certain kinds of radiation cause atoms to combine, forming molecules and systems of molecules of great complexity.

Children are familiar with the colors they see in a rainbow, a bubble, or a prism. This range or spectrum of colors is only the very small part of the whole spectrum of radiation having wave lengths and frequencies that we are able to see. There is radiation with shorter and radiation with longer wave lengths and frequencies. Each color is slightly different in that respect from the others.

Everyone is familiar with the tanning of the skin and sometimes the sunburn produced by invisible waves. These are the ultraviolet waves and are shorter than the visible light waves. Man also produces these and uses them to purify air and water; in refrigerators; in the treatment of rickets; and in a great many other ways. They are unable to penetrate glass for the most part.

Beyond the ultraviolet are the X rays, with still shorter wave lengths and frequencies. X rays have the property of producing a chem-

ical reaction on a photographic plate. This property is used by dentists and doctors, in industry, and in research. Unlike visible light, they can penetrate most materials, and it takes thick layers of a metal such as lead to stop them. They are used with great care.

The gamma rays are still shorter than the X rays and have greater frequencies. Some scientists think of them as exceedingly short X rays. They were discovered while studies were being made of radioactivity, in the way the nuclei of atoms break up. They are very penetrating, and man produces and sometimes uses them in nuclear reactions and in the treatment of certain diseases.

As the sun warms Earth during the day, heat is felt. Radiation is given off by every warm object. Each atom vibrates more rapidly as the temperature goes up and at the same time radiates energy. If a piece of iron is held in a hot flame long enough, it will become red-hot, giving off not only red light waves but also the longer but invisible infrared waves, felt as heat. If the iron finally becomes white-hot, it will give off a still greater range or spectrum of light waves. Infrared waves are longer than visible light waves and are often called heat waves. They are widely used in medicine, industry, the graphic arts, and other areas.

A whole series of longer wave lengths and frequencies called wireless or radio waves lie beyond the infrared waves. These waves can pass through moisture in Earth's atmosphere. Man produces these also and uses them in radio, television, and radar sending and receiving.

There is a great difference in the length of electromagnetic waves. The longest are several miles long and have correspondingly low frequencies. The shortest are about one million-millionth of a centimeter in length, and these have exceedingly high frequencies. Because some waves are so very short, the word *angstrom* (Å) is often used to express their length. It takes 100 million angstroms to make one centimeter. Otherwise the length of electromagnetic waves is measured in meters. The frequency is measured in cycles.

EXPERIENCE. *To assist children in gaining a conception of wave length and frequency.* A long jumping rope may be used. A child might lay it on the floor and, holding one end, wave it back and forth slowly. Then he might wave it quickly. Compare the size of the waves and their number or frequency.

A stone tossed into a quiet pond will also provide waves of various lengths and frequencies.

Sound and Communication

The second great gateway by which individuals learn about the experiences of other individuals and about the events of the physical world is by means of sound. From early childhood every person born with normal hearing has been receiving and interpreting messages brought by means of sound. If we hear a sound in the next room, we know immediately by some quality in the sound itself whether a china cup or a tin pieplate was dropped or whether the door slammed. We recognize the voice of a friend even when we cannot see him. We attach meanings to certain spoken sounds, so that we can receive or transmit ideas by means of speech. Words spoken in an unfamiliar language have little meaning for us beyond our recognizing that words are being spoken. Almost everyone has noticed that children learn a great deal through sounds. They seem to enjoy sounds, and spend a great deal of their time making sounds. The sounds they make may be vocal, or may be caused by their striking objects on different materials. The enjoyment of sounds is often in evidence. An eighteen-month-old child was observed to be delighted while he was plucking strings on a guitar. Children enjoy repeating sounds, and frequently vary the sound. In this way they learn more about loudness, pitch, and echoes through repetition (Chapter 1).

Children learn to speak through the use of sounds and through their imitation of the speech of others. Many deaf people who do not use hearing aids seem to speak peculiarly because they do not hear themselves speak. Other animals sometimes act as if certain sounds have certain meanings to them, but we cannot have any actual knowledge of this, since we cannot know what goes on in the animals' brains. We can only observe how they act.

EXPERIENCE. *Chickens can make many kinds of sounds.* If there is an opportunity to observe chickens over a period of time, a catalogue of their sounds may be made. Perhaps some children on a farm can tell about them. There are the crowing of the rooster, the cackling of the hens after an egg has been laid, the protective sounds of a mother hen, the calling of the young chickens by the mother hen when she is scratching on the ground for food, the peeping of the little chickens under the hen, the sounds of alarm at sight of a hawk, and many others.

Perhaps children can describe the different kinds of sounds that other animals make, such as a pet dog or cat.

Probably spoken language began with the grunts of our early ancestors. As man evolved and came to have a culture, certain sounds came to have certain meanings attached to them. This, of course, is pure speculation, since no record of sounds could be left. Certainly a spoken language is one of man's most distinctive attributes.

Throughout the history of civilization until recently the distance over which spoken communication could be carried on was limited by the range of the human voice. Within comparatively recent times, however, man has learned to control electrical energy by means of his voice. This means that spoken language can be transmitted for long distances by the telephone or radio, or can be greatly amplified to address huge gatherings of people.

The social significance of this can scarcely be overestimated. It means that by radio broadcasting it might be possible for one man to speak to every person on Earth at once. It means that an event anywhere in the world can become news for the entire world in a few minutes. We can use television and radio to prevent many catastrophes resulting from such things as hurricanes, floods, fires, volcanic eruptions, and other events of like nature.

EXPERIENCE. *How various languages got started.* In the past the peoples of our Earth were separated in their living by natural barriers such as rivers, mountains, and oceans. On every continent, people on one side of a mountain range might use a different language from those on the other side. Today with television, radio, and rapid transportation there is less of a trend to develop different languages. The countries of the Western Hemisphere and Australia, developed only shortly before the introduction of rapid transportation, are much less inclined to the development of new languages than Europe, Asia, and Africa were for centuries in the past. So except for Indian dialects, of which there are many, the languages of Europe have been transplanted to the Western Hemisphere. These languages hold sway except over those regions where bilingualism has been

accepted. The languages of the Western Hemisphere are Spanish, English, Portuguese, and French.

It is likely that radio and television and rapid transportation will have profound influence in producing a uniform inflection and accent.

EXPERIENCE. *To detect the causes of sounds that we hear.* We grow so accustomed to certain noises that we hardly, if ever, hear them. People living near airports seldom notice the sound of the planes unless they fly exceptionally low, and those living near a railroad may sleep while a fast express passes within a few feet of them. On the other hand, noises may be heard at night that are disregarded during the day.

The teacher and children might be motionless for a short period. (This experience might be used sometimes at rest period.) What noises do you hear? What caused them? How far away were the noises? Were they manmade?

All might close their eyes to concentrate on listening. Do this at different times of the year—in the spring when windows are open, in the fall and in the winter, at different times of day. Do you hear birds or insects? Do you hear wind or rain? Farm noises or city noises? Encourage the children to discuss the sounds they hear. Records could be kept by the older children for comparison. Such an experience might help to make children conscious of the world of sound. What noises do they like? What noises in the community should be eliminated? Can we help to eliminate unpleasant sounds?

Sound Is Caused by Vibrating Objects. If a child holds his fingers lightly against a piano or violin which is being played, he can feel that it is vibrating, or moving very rapidly back and forth. He can tell this by the slight tingling sensation in his fingers. If he taps a bell to

The vibrating strings of the piano produce musical tones.

start it ringing and then touches his fingers lightly to the rim, he can feel vibrations. If he touches his throat while he is speaking or singing, he feels vibrations there too. If he strikes a table fork sharply on the table and quickly brings it close to his ear, he can hear a high-pitched note. (A light cardboard, such as the kind found on a pad of paper, placed on the table at the place to be struck with the fork will protect the table top without interfering with the vibration of the fork and the sounds.) At the same time he can feel the fork vibrating in his hand. A large serving fork works particularly well. In short, wherever a sound is being made, something is vibrating.

Experience. *To make a tone with a fork.* Set a table fork in vibration by the method suggested above. Note the faint tone. Strike the fork again, but lower the handle so that the base of the handle touches the table top. The sound should be reinforced for a second or two as the table top vibrates with the fork.

To say that a thing is vibrating means that it is moving back and forth or up and down. A bedspring moves up and down when a child jumps on it. A springboard vibrates just after a diver has left it.

Experience. *To see a drum vibrate when it is beaten.* A child may beat a drum and put his fingers on it in order to feel the drum moving. There can be a visual experience if he puts some sand on the drum and strikes it. The sand will bounce up and down.

How does the fact that an object is vibrating cause us to hear something? To answer this question we must use an idea which we have frequently used before, namely, that all matter is made up of molecules. Let us take as an example of a vibrating object a table fork or, better still, a tuning fork[2] which has been struck sharply on a table. Each of the prongs of the fork is set into vibration. For simplicity we will study what happens to only one prong.

When this prong moves one way, it pushes away some of the air molecules, crowding them closer together. When the prong moves the other way, it leaves a space with too few

[2] Tuning forks can be secured from a local music shop or from a school supply store or scientific supply house.

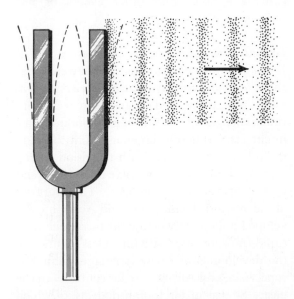

The prongs of a vibrating tuning fork alternately push together and then make less dense the air surrounding them. Waves in the air are produced which can be heard. (After General Physics, 3rd Edition, 1963, O. H. Blackwood, W. C. Kelly, and R. M. Bell, John Wiley and Sons, N. Y.)

molecules in it. The molecules in the crowded space then rush back to the partly empty space. As a result, the air molecules near a vibrating object are themselves moving back and forth, or vibrating.

As the molecules of air near the object move, they bump into other molecules near them, and set them in motion. Consequently the vibrations are communicated through the air. The molecules of air which are bumped are not always knocked straight ahead; so the sound waves are spread in every direction, and a sound can be heard from any point on the circumference of a circle that surrounds the sounding object, which is the point of origin. This is similar to the ever increasing circles caused by a pebble dropped into a pool of water.

It would naturally be expected that, since something is set in motion, energy is required. This is, in fact, the case. We did work and supplied energy to the fork when we struck it. Therefore sound waves are a form of energy.

The foregoing explanation may help to show that sound can be transmitted through anything made of molecules,—in other words, every substance,—but not through a vacuum, where there are very few molecules.

EXPERIENCE. *To study water waves.* In a tub of water or wading pool have someone disturb the water by tossing something into it. Children may watch the waves set up. If near a water transportation route, watch the disturbance set up by passing vessels, or even by rowboats. In a recreation area see the small waves set up by bathers in the swimming pool and see how far the waves seem to travel.

Sound Affects the Ear. So far we have been describing sound as though it were simply the waves mentioned above. Nevertheless the most important property of sound is that it does something to us so that we hear it.

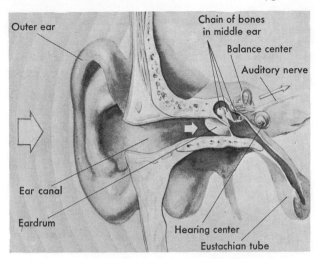

The ear changes sound waves to nerve impulses.

Just as we have special organs—the eyes and their associated nervous system—which are affected by light, so we have other special organs which are affected by sound. The ears are our sound-receiving instruments. The part of the ear we see is called the *outer ear*. It serves to collect sound waves and direct them into the central opening. The outside ear opens into a short, usually crooked tube. The inner end of this tube is closed with a membrane somewhat like the head of a drum, called the *eardrum*.

When sound waves strike the eardrum, they cause it to move back and forth, or vibrate. Behind the eardrum there is a chain of three little bones called, from their shapes, the *hammer,* the *anvil,* and the *stirrup.* The vibrations of the eardrum move this little chain, and the chain in turn moves some little tubes containing liquid. Inside the liquid are the ends of nerves leading to the brain. In some way not well understood the shaking of the liquid causes impulses to be sent over the nerves. When these impulses reach the brain, we hear. If the sounds we hear are familiar to us, we understand.

Normal ears are sensitive to extremely weak sounds, that is, to sound waves carrying an exceedingly small quantity of energy. A person whose ears are not sensitive to such weak sounds is said to be deaf. The extent of deafness varies from a person who is "slightly hard of hearing" to one who can hear no sound at all.

Deafness may result from several causes. Of course injury to an eardrum would result in partial or total deafness in that ear. For this reason, one should never poke into the ear with anything. Also, one should be careful not to put any hard or solid object of any sort into the ear, as there is always danger of its getting stuck there. In case some object gets stuck in the ear, do not attempt to remove it, but go at once to a nurse or a doctor.

Much deafness results from infections inside the ear. Many of these infections are a consequence of various so-called children's diseases. A great deal of deafness could be prevented by early and proper medical attention to such diseases.

Electric devices are available for the relief of partially deaf persons. These function somewhat like a telephone. In some types the receiver is placed just behind the ear and serves to transfer vibrations directly to the bones of the skull.

Teachers ought to be alert to note if any child seems unable to hear clearly, as poor hearing is as much a handicap as poor eyesight. They should also try to impress upon parents the danger of neglecting "minor" diseases. Children who are noticeably hard of hearing should have the advice of a physician.

Direction of Sound. It is usually easy for a person to tell from what direction a sound comes. We are enabled to ascertain the direction of the source of a sound by the relative loudness produced in each ear. A sound is slightly louder in the ear nearer the source of the sound. Had we but one ear instead of two, we should have difficulty in doing this. If we should arrange a tube on each ear ex-

If we "swap ears" we misjudge the direction of sounds.

tending around the head to the opposite side, as shown, so that sound from the right would be directed into the funnel and through the tube to the left ear, and sound from the left would go into the right ear, we should judge sounds from the left as having come from the right and vice versa. Of course, after a little practice, the brain would become accustomed to interpreting the sounds as coming from the correct directions.

EXPERIENCE. *Can we locate a sound when only one ear is used?* Have one group of children cover their eyes and hold one ear tightly closed. Have other children and yourself make noises —one noise at a time—in different parts of the room. Can the blindfolded people listening with but one ear locate the noises successfully? Then have them use both ears while remaining blindfolded. Are they more successful?

EXPERIENCE. *To study the way that animals use their ears.* Animals can be observed by children to see how animals learn about things about them. Did they ever steal up on a pet and surprise it? Did any of the children ever drive cows in from the pasture? Did any ever try to catch a horse? Does their pet dog know them? What senses do the animals use? Do they move their ears? Did the children ever observe a wild rabbit on the alert for danger? Did they ever see a cat stalking a mouse?

Have they seen a mother animal protecting its young?

Note that an animal's senses work with complete integration; to the children, this can mean that they work together.

Animals which hunt other animals for prey, such as wolves and wild dogs and cats, usually have their eyes at the front of the head. The animals which are hunted, such as horses, deer, and others, have their eyes somewhat to the side. These latter animals are more likely to see an approaching predator. Anyone attempting to walk up on a horse unwilling to be caught in a pasture knows how well a horse can see an approaching person, although the animal seems to be busy grazing.

What animals can move their outer ears to catch sound waves better? How does the sense of smell help some animals to know a predator is approaching?

The Speed of Sound. Since sound waves travel because of molecules bumping into one another, it seems reasonable to suppose that the process takes time. As a matter of fact, sound waves travel rather slowly in comparison with some other waves, such as light waves.

It has been found by experiment that sound travels in air at a speed of about 1100 feet per second, or about 5 seconds to travel a mile. Strictly speaking, this is true only near a temperature of 45° F, or a little more than 7° C in still air. The hotter the temperature of the medium in which sound is traveling, the faster the sound travels. The speed of sound increases at the rate of one foot per second per degree Fahrenheit, or two feet per second per degree centigrade. Therefore, sound travels faster in summer than in winter.

During a thunderstorm you can determine the distance away from the storm. Thunder and lightning occur simultaneously. Since the speed of light is so rapid, you may assume that you see the flash the instant it occurs.

Time the interval that elapses between seeing the flash and hearing the thunder. Sound travels about 1100 feet per second; therefore multiply the number of seconds you waited by 1100. Sound needs some medium through which to travel. Therefore, sound will not travel through a vacuum.

Sound travels in some substances much faster than it does in others. In water it goes more than four times as fast as it does in air. In some metals it travels about sixteen times as fast as in air.

Supersonic Speed. Speeds of fast airplanes are often given in terms of *Mach number,* which is based on the speed of sound. A plane traveling at the speed of sound, about 760 miles per hour, is said to have a speed of Mach 1; at twice the speed of sound, Mach 2; and so on. Speeds greater than Mach 1 are referred to as *supersonic.* Speeds greater than Mach 5 are sometimes called *hypersonic.* Aircraft maneuvering at supersonic speeds form shock waves in the air, which often produce explosive sounds and sometimes break the windows of houses. These are known as *sonic booms.* The aircraft is said to have broken the sound barrier.

Sound Can Be Reflected. Most of us have had experience with echoes. Some echoes are so perfect that they will repeat whole words after us. Occasionally children may have heard the peculiar sound of their voices in a vacant auditorium or other large vacant room. The unusual sound effects one may obtain by singing in a bathroom are proverbial. Some children may have tried speaking or singing into an empty barrel. All these effects are the result of the reflection of sound.

Sound waves, like light waves, are reflected, or turned back, when they strike a solid object. Like light, also, they are reflected best by a smooth flat surface. In much the same way as a rubber ball bounces best from a smooth hard sidewalk, so sound "bounces" best from a smooth hard surface.

Substances through which sound travels are *sound conductors*. Other substances conduct sound poorly. Examples of these are porous materials, such as cork, draperies, curtains, etc. These materials absorb sound. *Acoustics,* which is the science of sound, utilizes this knowledge in reducing the echoes in a room. Materials that absorb sound are hung in a room to reduce the bouncing of sound waves off the ceiling and walls into a person's ears.

In the case of a vacant auditorium, the sound is reflected from the walls and other objects. Such reflected sound is called an *echo*. Since it takes time for sound to travel from the speaker to the walls and back again, we hear the reflected sound a little later than the original sound. The echo so formed can be very annoying if we are trying to understand the speaker. When an audience is present, bodies and clothing do not reflect the sound very well, but absorb some of it and help to break up the echo. Curtains or pictures which hang away from the wall also help. Sometimes the walls or ceiling must be covered with a special porous material which does not reflect much sound and so serves to stop troublesome echoes.

It is most important that buildings be constructed in such a way as to reduce reflection of sounds and echoes. Any teacher knows that cafeterias and classrooms poorly constructed so that sounds are reflected a great deal can produce unnecessary fatigue for both teachers and children. Some cafeterias are so well constructed that hundreds of children can be fed in a quiet atmosphere. Good acoustics can do a great deal to develop good human relationships.

Some schools have committees of children responsible for selecting and playing good musical recordings at lunch period, thus encouraging a quiet atmosphere. It is good for the children to assume responsibility for the

Echoes are produced by reflected sound waves.

elimination of unnecessary noises. One of the problems they will face in their future will be the democratic control of sounds.

Out of doors, sound is often reflected from a mountain, hill, or rocky cliff. The farther away the reflecting surface is, the more time will elapse between the time we speak and the time we hear the echo. Sometimes there are several such reflecting surfaces, and sound is reflected from one to another. In this way a sharp sound, such as the blow of an ax or the report of a gun, will be reflected to our ears over and over again, gradually dying away.

People standing under bridges will frequently be able to hear very loud echoes; these echoes are due to the reflection of sound from the bridge overhead and from the piers which support the bridge at each end. Anyone who has walked through a tunnel with children remembers how the youngsters thrilled to the loud echo of their voices.

Pitch, Loudness, and Quality of Sounds. The three principal characteristics of most sounds are pitch, loudness, and quality.

Sounds Are High or Low (Pitch). *Pitch* is often thought of as the place of a sound on the musical scale. Thus the E above middle C on the piano is higher in pitch than middle C.

When any object is vibrating regularly, it makes a certain definite number of vibrations each second; therefore a certain number of sound waves leave the vibrating object each second. The more vibrations that strike our ears each second, the higher the pitch of the sound we hear. The higher the sound, the greater the rate at which our eardrums vibrate. In other words, the more frequent the vibrations, the higher the pitch. The number of vibrations per second is called the *frequency*. A shrill sound has many vibrations per second, or has a high frequency. *Pitch*, therefore, depends upon frequency.

The normal human ear is capable of hearing sounds with a range of frequency from a little below twenty to about twenty thousand vibrations per second. Sounds having fewer or more than this number of vibrations per second cannot be heard by most people. Sounds that are beyond our range of hearing are called *ultrasonic*. They are produced by electronic generators built for that purpose. The study of ultrasonics was put to use in World War II for detecting the presence of submarines. The navy utilized sonar (the word *sonar* stands for *sound-navigation-ranging*). Sonar sends out sound waves. If they strike an object, they bounce back, just as in the case of echoes (p. 877). Sonar equipment is also used to detect schools of fish or sunken ships, and in charting the bottom of such bodies of water as seas and oceans. Another important use of high-frequency sound (ultrasonics) is for detecting imperfections in metals.

There is reason to believe that some mammals and some insects may hear sounds of more than twenty thousand vibrations per second. Whistles that cannot be heard by human ears are sold for calling dogs. Children, as a rule, can hear a higher pitch than adults can.

These high-frequency waves have low energy or power and are used for measuring, detecting, and controlling.

Ultrasonic waves of high energy or power (produced by using vibrating quartz crystals) are used in changing substances. Hence, they are useful for fast, perfect, and cheap cleaning of ball bearings, sewing-machine parts, and metal parts of many kinds, and are especially valuable for cleaning parts that are small or almost impossible to clean otherwise. Other uses are in making emulsions, destroying bacteria, as in the preservation of food, and so on. Many other practical applications of ultrasonics may yet be made.

Doppler Effect. Everyone has noticed the change in pitch of an automobile horn or a train whistle when it is approaching and after it has passed. Children ask about it. This change in pitch is called the *Doppler effect.*

The reason is that when a source of sound draws closer, the ear picks up more sound waves per second than are given out by the object. The waves become shortened and closer together, and therefore higher in pitch. As the source moves away, the sound waves are lengthened and become lower in pitch. The ear receives fewer vibrations per second. The true pitch of the sound is between the two extremes (p. 897).

The sound from the whistle of a fast-moving train seems normal in pitch to an observer at 3 and 4, higher to an observer at 1, and lower to an observer at 2. (After Harvey E. White, Modern College Physics, *4th edition, 1962, D. Van Nostrand, Princeton, N. J.)*

Sounds Are Loud or Soft (Intensity of Sound). The *loudness* (or *intensity*) of a sound depends partly on the energy with which the sounding body is vibrating and partly on the pitch of the sound. The human ear does not respond equally well to all pitches, so that it takes more energy to make us hear a sound of very low or very high pitch than one near the middle of our range of hearing. The louder the sound, the greater the distance back and forth our eardrums move. A loud sound has more mechanical energy than a soft sound, and causes the eardrums to vibrate through a greater distance than a soft sound.

If we strike a key on the piano very gently, we get a soft sound; if we strike the same key firmly, that is, if we put more energy into the blow, we get the same pitch as before, but the sound is louder. If we blow a whistle first gently, then vigorously, we get the same result. The more energy we put into making a sound, the louder sound wc gct.

As we move away from a source of sound, the sound gradually grows fainter and fainter because energy is being used up in moving, or vibrating, more and more air.

Sounds May Be Pleasant or Unpleasant (Quality of Sound). So far we have been considering sound as if a vibrating object sent out sound waves of just one frequency. As a matter of fact, most vibrating objects do not send out such simple sound waves. Instead they vibrate in several ways at once, and, as a consequence, send out waves of several frequencies at the same time. These other sound waves are called *overtones*.

We all know that a piano does not sound like a violin or a trumpet, even though all three are playing a note at the same pitch. The sounds of different musical instruments are distinguished from one another by their qualities. The *quality* of a sound depends on the number and strength of the various overtones present. This is determined partly by

the shape and material of the instrument and partly by the skill of the player.

Distinction between a Musical Tone and Noise. In the case of the sounds we call *noise*, there is no regular relation between the sounds at all. Noise is a mixture of vibrations of all sorts and all degrees of loudness; on the other hand, the vibrations producing *musical tones* remain regular or steady, even while the musical tone fades or dies out. Of course the decision as to whether a given sound is noise or music often rests largely on the judgment of the individual, and it is sometimes hard to agree where to draw the line.

EXPERIENCE. *To develop pleasant sounds.* Children can develop an appreciation for good sounds. It is well to have times each day when children can hear good music. It can be arranged to have music during an activities period. An appreciation for good voice tone can be developed. Almost anyone can develop a pleasant voice. Harshness or raspiness in voice should be avoided. A teacher or parent can set a good example.

The program for the development of a good voice should be positive rather than negative. Nothing can be more disconcerting in the development and expression of thought than to be asked to correct an expression that has been creative, in order to change the tone or grammar. Approval for good voice tone is more constructive than criticism of a harsh voice tone.

In some cases children may need the assistance of a voice specialist. For many people a good voice is necessary, particularly if they have important functions in the development of human relations, which is true of almost everyone in our modern democracy.

Frequently a good voice will flow out of good human relationships and a proper understanding of one's own place in a group, whether a class at school or in a community.

The voice tones of a human being are inter-related with his human relationships.

Musical Instruments. Musical instruments depend for their functioning on the principles of science which apply to sound. They are, in general, devices for producing and controlling sounds of definite pitch and loudness and pleasing qualities.

Stringed Instruments. In the case of stringed instruments such as those of the violin family, the piano, and the banjo, mandolin, and guitar group, the vibrations are produced in stretched strings or wires. Three factors determine the pitch of a string: length, weight, and tension. A stretched string vibrates more rapidly the more tightly it is stretched or the shorter it is. We tune stringed instruments by making the strings tighter or looser to cause them to sound the proper pitch. In playing, the desired pitch is obtained by shortening the string by pressing it with the finger.

Wind Instruments. The vibrating object need not be solid. It can be a column of air contained in a pipe or tube. Instruments using air as the vibrating object are usually blown by the player's breath. The air within the tube is set in motion or vibration in different ways. One way is by the vibration of the player's lips which are held against a bell-shaped mouthpiece. This group includes the trumpet, trombone, tuba, and French horn.

The shorter a column of air, the more rapidly it vibrates. Therefore we may secure dif-

Instruments in an orchestra may sound the same pitch, but each has its characteristic tone quality.

ferent pitches by shortening or lengthening the column. This may be done by valves which cut out different amounts of tubing, as in the trumpet, or by sliding one tube inside another, as in the trombone. It is possible for a column of air to vibrate at several different frequencies. For this reason a trumpet may be made to play several different notes at the same position of the valves, depending on how the player holds his lips.

Reed Instruments. Another way in which air within a tube is set in vibration is by the vibration of a reed or tongue, usually made of wood and held in the player's mouth. This group includes the clarinet, saxophone, English horn, and oboe.

One type of instrument uses the vibration of a sheet of air directed against a sharp edge. Examples of this type of instrument are an ordinary whistle, a flute, and a pipe organ.

The Human Voice. Possibly the most important sound-producing mechanism is that connected with the human voice. Without speech our cultural development would certainly have been vastly different. The voice is one of our principal means of communication with others. The voice box or *larynx* is located at the top of the windpipe or trachea. Over the top of the voice box are stretched two bands of tissues called the *vocal cords.* Sounds are produced when air from the lungs is blown through a narrow slit (glottis) between these two bands. These vocal cords are set in vibration by the moving air. By means of muscles the vocal cords may be stretched or relaxed, and thus the pitch of the voice is regulated.

The vibration of the vocal cords causes the air column contained in the mouth, nose, and upper part of the throat to vibrate, somewhat as the vibrating lips of a trumpet-player cause the air column within the instrument to vibrate. The quality of the resulting sound is

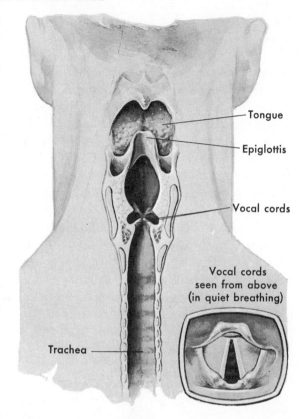

The human voice is produced by the vibrations of the vocal cords.

varied by changing the positions of the lips, teeth, and tongue as one does in speaking.

In singing, the sound is produced more smoothly and continuously than in speaking. The pitch, intensity, and quality of the voice depends to a great extent on control of the breath, the degree of tension of the vocal cords, the length of the cords, and the air passing over them. The vocal cords of men are thicker and longer than those of women, accounting for the lower pitch of men. A young boy's voice is high-pitched. As his vocal cords grow thicker and longer, the pitch of his voice gets lower. By practice we may improve the quality of our voices and make them more pleasing, even though we cannot all be great singers. Straining the vocal cords by loud or shrill talking impairs the quality of the voice. Obstructions in the nose also affect the quality, so that we say a person is "talking through his nose," which really means that he is *not* talking through his nose (p. 884).

EXPERIENCE. *Sound is produced by the vibration of something.* Have the children feel the piano and any other available musical instrument while they are being played. Notice the tingling sensation in the fingers. Do the same thing on the throat. Speak into an empty hatbox or cereal box while touching the bottom lightly with the fingers.

Strike a table fork and hold it near the ear. Notice the sound.

Tuning forks are useful in the elementary school. They may be purchased from scientific supply houses. Strike a tuning fork lightly and dip a prong into water. Notice how the vibrating fork splashes the water.

Secure a small sewing needle to one prong of a tuning fork, using a bit of sealing wax. Smoke a piece of glass in a candle flame. Strike the fork lightly, and quickly draw it across the glass in such a way that the needle draws a wavy line in the smoke. This experiment requires considerable practice in order to get the right motion of the tuning fork.

To prove that a fork which is not sounding is not vibrating, repeat the experiments of the two last paragraphs without striking the fork.

EXPERIENCE. *Sound travels.* Children are often able to observe for themselves that sound travels rather slowly. When a wood-chopper is some distance away, they see the ax fall before they hear the sound of the blow. They see the puff of "steam" from a locomotive or steamboat whistle before they hear the blast.

An experiment may be performed to show the speed of sound. Divide the class into two groups and station them about five hundred feet apart. Have one group provided with a good whistle similar to a police whistle. Have the other group provided with a flag. The group with the whistle blows a vigorous blast. The group with the flag signals as soon as it hears the whistle. The whistle group thus observes that it takes some time for the sound of its whistle to reach the other group. Interchange whistle and flag and repeat the experiment.

EXPERIENCE. *Having two ears enables us to tell from what direction sound comes.* Have children perform the experiment in directing sound to the opposite ear, suggested on page 876.

Other senses than that of hearing also contribute to our perception of direction. In the dark in strange surroundings our sense of sound direction is apt to be very faulty. Let a child be well blindfolded. Using a "beetle" (a toy which makes a clicking sound) make noises in front of, behind, to right and left of, and over the head of the blindfolded child. Let him see if he can tell from what direction the sound came. He will often make highly erroneous responses.

EXPERIENCE. *Sound can be reflected.* If possible take the children, a few at a time, into a large, bare, vacant room. Notice how the sound is reflected so as to modify the sound of their voices. Notice the difference between speaking from the stage into an empty auditorium and one that is filled.

Take the children to a bridge over any small stream. Have them throw rocks into the water away from the bridge and under it. Notice the difference in the sounds. Take them under the bridge, if possible, to hear the echo.

EXPERIENCE. *Sounds differ from one another in pitch, loudness, and quality.* In studying sound, musical instruments will be found to be of great value. In some cases toy instruments may be effectively used. In others, children who play instruments may be encouraged to bring them to school and demonstrate to the class the way in which they are played.

Look inside of a piano to see the strings and the hammers which strike them. The bass strings are longer and heavier than the treble strings.

Have a child who plays a violin, banjo, ukulele, or other stringed instrument show how he tunes the instrument by tightening or loosening the strings and how he changes the pitch while playing by shortening the strings. He shortens the strings by pressing on them with his fingers.

Someone who plays a wind instrument may show how he lengthens or shortens the air column inside the instrument. If possible, examine both a wood-wind, or reed, instrument, such as a clarinet or saxophone, and a "brass" instrument, such as a trumpet or trombone. In the reed instrument the length of the air column being used at any moment is the distance from the mouthpiece to the first *open* hole.

Have a child play his instrument first softly, then loudly, on the same note. Notice that he must work harder to play loudly, but the pitch remains the same.

Compare the different tone qualities of several instruments.

EXPERIENCE. *The quality of our voices is partly controlled by the position of our tongues, lips, and teeth.* Have the children sing, on some convenient pitch, the syllables *ah, aw, oh, oo.* Note the changing position of the mouth as they pass from one syllable to another.

EXPERIENCE. *Obstructions in the nose affect our speech.* Have a child carefully say the sentence "Spring is coming." Now let him close his nose by pinching it lightly between thumb and forefinger, and repeat the sentence. Note the difference. Why is it hard to speak clearly when we have a cold?

EXPERIENCE. *To make a tumbler "piano."* Arrange several glasses in a row and pour a different amount of water in each. Strike the

The tumblers are tuned by adjusting the amount of water in each.

glasses with a spoon and you will hear different notes of the scale. Try to play a tune on these glasses.

EXPERIENCE. *Making a string telephone* (p. 730).

EXPERIENCE. *Sound travels through wood.* Place a clock on top of a wooden desk or table. Place your ear on the table top near the clock. Keep moving away until you can barely hear the clock ticking. At this point, have someone hold the clock in the air. Since sound travels better in wood than in air, you will no longer hear the clock tick.

EXPERIENCE. *Vibration from speech.* Hold a sheet of paper several inches away from your mouth. Talk loudly, and you will be able to feel the paper vibrating.

EXPERIENCE. *Effect of a gap on sound.* Hold two rulers end to end. Hold one end to your ear. Have someone scratch the other end. Listen to the volume of the sound you hear. Now separate the two rulers, leaving about a one-inch air gap between them. Again have someone scratch the free end. The volume of the sound is lower than before.

The solid material of the stick carries sound waves even better than does air.

A spoon on a string produces a pleasing musical tone.

EXPERIENCE. *Listening through a stick.* Listen to the ticking of an alarm clock. Hold one end of a yardstick to your ear and the other end on the clock. Now listen to the ticking. The sound is louder through the stick than through the air.

EXPERIENCE. *Producing a musical tone with a spoon.* Have a piece of string about a yard long. Tie the center of the string around the handle of a large spoon. Hold each end of the string and swing the spoon against a table; listen to the sound. Now hold one finger in each ear. Have someone swing the spoon again and listen. It is amazing how beautiful the sounds secured from this experience will be.

EXPERIENCE. *Making a rubber-band harp.* Make a rubber-band harp by stretching several rubber bands of varying lengths and thicknesses across a frame. When plucked, you can produce the different notes of the scale. Try to play a tune on these rubber bands.

EXPERIENCE. *Producing a sympathetic vibration.* Place two tuning forks having the same pitch near each other. Tap one of them hard enough to set it vibrating. Soon the other fork will be vibrating. This occurs without its being in physical contact with the first tuning fork. (When one object causes another to vibrate, they are in *resonance*.)

Some Instruments by Which Light and Sound Aid Man to Understand the Universe about Him

Man has discovered how to construct a number of instruments which utilize the principles of light and sound to enable him to make new discoveries and to record facts and ideas and transmit them from one individual to another. From the many instruments which are used a few have been chosen which seem to be of greater importance than the others. These will be discussed very briefly.

Instruments for Discovering. *Magnifying Lens.* The magnifying lens has been discussed earlier (p. 869). Its purpose is to bend light in such a way as to make an object appear larger than it really is.

Compound microscopes, telescopes, cameras, field glasses, and projection lanterns all contain lenses the object of which is to bend light.

The Telescope. By means of the telescope astronomers have learned a great deal about the stars and other bodies in space. Pluto was discovered in 1930 by examining photographs of the portion of the sky in which its location was predicted mathematically. Many of the most thought-provoking concepts of science concerning the nature of the physical universe are derived from the field of astronomy. Most of these have been discovered by the use of telescopes and other instruments in connection with them. It is not too much to say that the discoveries which have been made with the telescope have changed man's whole philosophy.

Hans Lippershey, a Dutch optician, is credited with having observed that convex lenses placed between a distant object and the eye cause the object to appear nearer than it actually is. One year later, in 1610, Galileo developed this idea into an instrument used to investigate astronomical bodies.

The purpose of a telescope is to concentrate as much light as possible from a distant object, such as a star, and bring this light together at a point in front of the eyepiece of the telescope, that magnifies the image of the star. The eyepiece is similar in principle to an ordinary reading glass. This makes it possible to see many stars too dim to be seen with the naked eye.

The light can be brought together in two

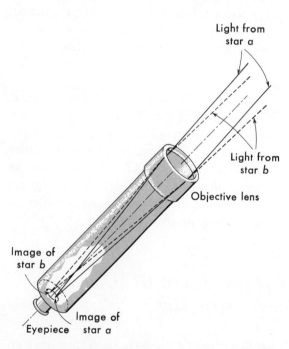

A simple diagram of a refracting telescope. A refracting telescope makes use of lenses to concentrate light at a point in front of the eyepiece from which it may be observed. (After Planets, Stars, and Galaxies, *1961, Stuart J. Inglis, John Wiley and Sons, N. Y.)*

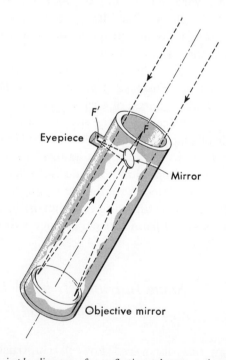

A simple diagram of a reflecting telescope. A reflecting telescope makes use of mirrors to concentrate light and reflect it to an observer at the eyepiece. (After Planets, Stars, and Galaxies, *1961, Stuart J. Inglis, John Wiley and Sons, N. Y.)*

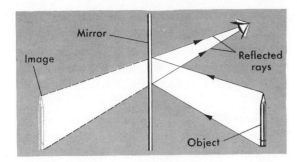

Although the object is at the right of the mirror, it appears to be at the left.

ways—by using a lens or by using a curved mirror (pp. 805, 869). Telescopes that use lenses to collect light are called *refracting* telescopes; those that use mirrors are called *reflecting* telescopes. The larger the lens or mirror, the more light will be concentrated, and the fainter the star that can be seen.

The tube of the telescope is connected to gears, so that after it has been pointed to a field of stars it will follow the same group of stars for many hours. The astronomer may then take his station at the eyepiece and make careful observations without the necessity of constantly adjusting the instrument to compensate for the rotation of Earth. As Earth rotates to the east, the telescope will swing to the west.

When one is interested in observing details of fairly near objects, a refracting telescope is best suited. The reflecting telescope is used for observing more distant bodies. Telescopes produce magnifications that may range from three to several thousand.

It is very difficult to get a large block of glass sufficiently free from defects to make a very large lens. The largest telescopes of this type are at Yerkes Observatory in Wisconsin, with a lens 40 inches across, producing a magnification of 4000 and the 36-inch lens at the Lick Observatory in northern California.

It is much easier to make a large mirror than a large lens. Since the light is reflected from the surface of a coating of metal placed on the glass, defects within the glass itself are of little importance. Furthermore, the rays of light can be brought together in a shorter distance; therefore the telescope does not need to be so long.

Mirrors used for telescopes are not coated with metal on the back, as are ordinary mirrors, but are coated on the front. The metal used was formerly silver, but it has recently been found that polished aluminum not only lasts longer but reflects better than silver the kind of light which affects a photographic film.

Very large telescopes of the mirror type do not have tubes at all. The mirror is supported in a framework of girders.

Since we must always look through our atmosphere, any dust or haze in the air cuts down on the value of a telescope. Therefore, the largest telescopes are generally located in remote places where the air is clearest.

A 72-inch reflecting telescope. (Dominion Astrophysical Observatory, Victoria, Canada.)

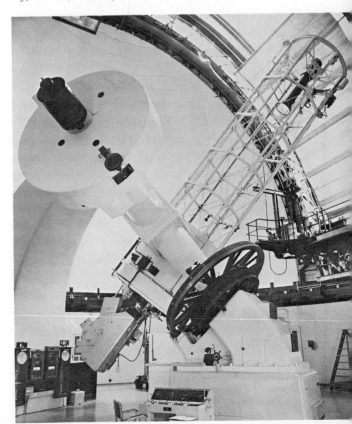

The reflecting telescope at Mount Palomar Observatory, in southern California, has a mirror that is 200 inches across. This instrument collects about 1 million times as much light as the eye can, and with it stars that are about 1 billion light-years away can be seen. The David Dunlap Observatory in Ontario and the Dominion Astrophysical Observatory in British Columbia also have large telescopes of this type. Telescopes do not greatly magnify the apparent size of a star. They are used to make stars appear very much brighter and somewhat larger.

Photography is another way by which stars and other objects in space can be studied. Instead of the eye, a photographic plate or film can be placed at the eyepiece or focus of the telescope. It is then a combination telescope and camera. If the photographic plate is exposed to the same field of stars for an hour or two, the plate will register many stars that were too faint for the eye to detect. Even very feeble rays striking one point on the photographic emulsion will have a cumulative effect, and will finally form a picture. Thus many faint stars are discovered that would otherwise be unknown.

An important type of photographic instrument is known as the Schmidt telescope. It has an advantage in being able to take in a much wider view than some others, so that large areas of the sky can be photographed.

A *photoelectric cell* placed at the focus instead of a photographic plate is being used for some kinds of work. With it the astronomer can make very precise measurements of the color and brightness of stars, and thus calculate their distances.

The range and efficiency of telescopes is being extended with new devices and attachments.

Opera Glass. The opera glass and the field glass (very useful for study of birds and other animals, the moon, airplanes, and clouds),

consist of two telescopes mounted together. More expensive glasses use prisms inside the tubes which act as mirrors. The incoming light ray strikes a prism, is reflected to a second one, and is reflected by it to the eyepiece.

The Spectroscope. The spectroscope is another kind of instrument that helps man to learn not only more about Earth but also more about the sun and other objects in space. Its tremendous value lies in the information it gives us about the composition, heat, and motion of far distant galaxies as well as objects nearer to us.

We are all familiar with the band of colors produced when sunlight passes through a prism. Newton studied this band of colored lights and concluded that white light is a mixture of all the colors of the rainbow. A simple spectroscope is a convenient instrument with which to study this spectrum, or band of colors. In this instrument a prism is placed on a platform and the light passes through it from a slit. The band of colors thus formed is thrown on a screen or photographed, and the positions of the different colors can be studied and identified (p. 867).

Each chemical element, such as iron, copper, hydrogen, or sodium, emits its own characteristic lines at definite positions in the spectrum. These can be observed by heating the element or by passing an electric discharge through it. Where there is a mixture of elements, each gives its own characteristic line, unaffected by the other ones.

If a prism is inserted in a Schmidt telescope, the light from each star will be spread out into a band of colors. Every star will record its own particular spectrum on the photographic plate. By studying the bright and dark lines of the spectrum the astrophysicist can learn a great deal about the elements present in the star and what condition they are in.

The spectroscope probably deserves to rank with the telescope as a changer of human thought patterns, for it has shown us that the same substances we know on Earth are probably to be found throughout the universe.

Radio Telescopes. Radio waves come from many sources, and radio telescopes are used to study them. Stars not only give off visible light but some of them radiate energy in the longer wave lengths, as radio waves. Regions in the sky where no stars can be seen also send out radio waves. Clouds of hydrogen in space radiate on a 21.1-centimeter frequency. The sun's atmosphere steadily gives off radio waves, increasing at times of sunspots or flares. Even the moon and planets emit these electromagnetic waves. Their study is important to everyone.

One type of radio telescope uses a metal dish shaped like a parabola (p. 201). It works like a reflector of an optical telescope, collecting radiations and concentrating them at a focus. A radio telescope receiver registers these incoming signals on a meter or records them on a chart. By steering the antenna across the sky and tuning the receiver to different wave lengths the astronomer can make a "radio map" of the sky.

The Microscope. When we consider the important role which infectious diseases and their control have played in the development of man's cultures, and the fact that much of our knowledge of the cause and prevention of these diseases has been gained by the use of the microscope, we will readily grant it a place of importance equal to that of the telescope and the spectroscope. Nor is it only in the study of diseases that the microscope assumes importance. The microscope has also been used to tell us much about the principles on which life goes on and about the structure and functions of living things, both helpful and harmful.

Man has used the microscope to learn not only about living things but about nonliving things as well. Much knowledge about minerals and metals has been gained by looking at them through specially constructed microscopes. Microscopes are built to fill specific needs. The instrument was invented by Zacharias Janssen in 1590, and also by Galileo in 1610.

The microscope consists essentially of two sets of lenses. The first set, at the lower end of the tube, bends the rays of light in such a way as to form an enlarged image of the object. This image is inside the tube. You then look at this image with a magnifying glass. The set of lenses at the upper end of the tube really forms a magnifying glass.

The magnification is expressed in diameters. If an object has been magnified ten times, the magnification is said to be ten diameters, 10X. Each set of lenses magnifies the object, and the total magnification is computed by multiplying the magnification of the lower set by the magnification of the upper set. Microscopes of up to 2000X are used.

The sets themselves are not simple lenses, but are combinations of several lenses arranged so as to secure great magnification of the object without distortion. It is the fact that these lenses are complex and must be very accurately made, and that the mechanism for controlling them must also be accurate, which makes microscopes so expensive.

The *electron microscope* has extremely high magnification power. It uses a stream of electrons controlled by electric or magnetic fields instead of rays of light. The magnified image may be formed on a fluorescent screen, or it may be photographed.

EXPERIENCE. *The telescope, spectroscope, and microscope.* If there are in the community persons owning these instruments, they may be willing to show the children how they are used and let them look through them. The actual operation of all three is a matter which almost demands personal instruction. Telescopes can be homemade, but they require considerable time and skill for construction.

Instruments for Recording.

Not only does man make use of light and sound for discovering facts about the universe, but he also uses them for recording what he has discovered. Some of our ways of making records more or less permanent are writing, printing, making pictures and recording sounds on motion-picture films, phonograph records, and wire and tape recorders.

Writing and Printing. Writing and printing depend on light. We see written or printed words because the pencil or ink marks reflect light differently from the rest of the paper. If they did not do so, the writing would be invisible. Chemical methods of secret writing use a colorless ink which does not show against the background of the paper. When properly treated, the writing is made visible because the color of the ink is changed. Ink eradicators work in the opposite way, bleaching the ink to make it colorless.

There are a number of machines for printing, ranging from the great rotary presses which print our newspapers to a child's rubber-stamp printing set. Among these are the typewriter, the mimeograph, and the multigraph. The result of the work of these machines is much the same; that is, colored ink marks are made on paper of a different color.

EXPERIENCE. *We see writing because of its contrast with the paper.* If children write with different-colored inks on different-colored paper, they will notice that the darker inks are easier to see on paper of light color, and the lighter inks on dark paper.

EXPERIENCE. *Invisible ink.* There are a number of substances used for invisible ink. A simple one is lemon juice, which is nearly invisible on paper but becomes brown when the paper is heated.

EXPERIENCE. *Various ways of printing.* There is a typewriter somewhere in most schools, and many schools have mimeograph or multigraph machines. Children should have an opportunity to examine these. Notice especially how the ink is put on the paper.

If there is an opportunity, children may wish to visit a printing press. They should see the type from which the letters are printed. In a newspaper plant they ought to see a linotype working. The linotype, as its name indicates, casts a line of newspaper type from molten metal as the operator strikes keys somewhat like typewriter keys.

Pictures also depend on our ability to see one color against a background of another color. Pictures are of two general sorts: drawings made in pencil, ink, or colored paints by an artist, and photographs.

Photography. Photography depends on the fact that chemical changes take place when light falls on certain substances (p. 409). We have already had an illustration of how light can promote chemical change in the fact that plants make food only in the presence of light. In photography, light causes the chemicals on the film to turn black.

In the camera there is a film of celluloid or a plate of glass coated with chemicals which change when light falls on them. Rays of light from an object are bent by a lens so as to form an image of the object on the film or plate. The white or light-colored parts of the object reflect much light and cause considerable chemical change, while the black or dark-colored parts reflect little or no light and cause little or no chemical change.

The chemical change on the film or plate takes place very quickly; therefore light must be permitted to enter the camera for only a very short time. For this reason a shutter which opens only a fraction of a second is used.

After the film has been exposed to the light, developing is necessary to bring out the picture. Since the light parts of the object photographed caused the most chemical change, they come out darkest on the developed film or plate. Because light parts of the object are dark and dark parts light, this film or plate is called a negative. In order to obtain a picture with the light and dark parts the same as in the original object, the photograph must be printed.

Printing consists of placing the negative over a piece of paper which is also coated with chemicals sensitive to light. The paper and negative are then exposed to light. The transparent sections of the negative let a great deal of light reach the sensitive paper and darken it. The darker sections keep away some of the light, and the paper under them remains lighter. The prints must be developed in somewhat the same way as the negative.

It is also possible to take pictures in natural color. There are two types of color film available. One type, commonly used with 35-millimeter cameras is processed by first developing the negative and then converting it into a transparent positive. This picture can be seen by using an eye or table viewer, or by casting an enlarged picture in color upon a screen. Another type of color film is available for most ordinary camera sizes. The film is developed and a negative made which shows a reversal of light and shade, and colors complementary to those in the subject photographed. From this negative, color prints can be made. Color prints can also be made from the transparencies mentioned above.

Cameras. A simple camera consists of a light-tight box with a convex lens at one end, and a light-sensitive film at the other. More complex cameras employ a shutter, a device for focusing, a diaphragm that controls the size of the lens opening, and a view finder. The joint purpose of all these parts is to focus a sharp image of an object on the film for the exact amount of time required. This exposure produces an inverted image on the film

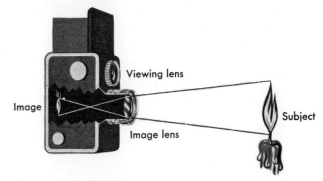

The camera focuses light on a sensitive film.

which is made visible upon subsequent chemical processing. This image becomes a negative, as mentioned above.

In dim light the shutter must remain open longer than in bright light. The larger the lens, the less bright is the light necessary to take a picture. Therefore cameras with large lenses can take pictures in dimmer light than cameras with small lenses.

The lens in a fine camera is not a single piece of glass, but a complicated combination of several accurately made lenses. Shutters whose speed can be accurately controlled are delicate mechanisms. The high prices of cameras are due to the cost of making the lenses and shutters.

EXPERIENCE. *A pinhole camera* (p. 892). Cut a square opening three inches on a side out of the bottom of a rolled-oats box. Over this hole paste some very thin paper. Tissue paper or onionskin paper will do. Cut another square hole about the size of a postage stamp in the exact center of the top of the box. Cover this hole with tin foil, taking care that there are no holes in the tin foil. In the center of the tin foil punch a very small hole with a needle.

Hold the box about two feet from a lighted candle in a dark room. Point the pinhole at the flame and look at the tissue paper. If the pinhole is directly opposite the flame, you should see an image of the candle flame on the

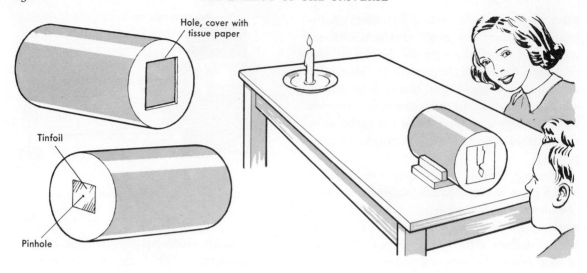

A pinhole camera. If the pinhole is small, the image is clear.

tissue paper. Notice that the image is upside down. When everyone has looked, enlarge the hole and notice that the image is destroyed.

EXPERIENCE. *How a camera works.* In a real camera, a lens is used instead of a pinhole to form an image of an object. If a folding camera from which the back may be removed is available, remove the back and hold a piece of tissue paper over the place where the film normally goes. Set the shutter on "time" and open the shutter. Point the camera at a nearby tree or building and notice the image on the tissue paper.

Projector. Semitransparent slides or films (still or motion pictures) may be projected upon a screen. A source of light passes through condensing lenses which spread the illumination uniformly on the slide or film. This light falls on the projection lens, which puts the image on the screen. It is necessary to invert the slide or film in the projector in order to obtain an upright image on the screen.

Motion Pictures. You remember that on page 854 we said that light falling on the retina of the eye produces certain changes, probably chemical, which enable us to see. These changes persist for a little while after the light which causes them is no longer falling on the retina. Thus we see an object for a little while after we are no longer receiving light from it. This phenomenon is called *persistence of vision.* It is persistence of vision which causes us to see rapidly moving objects as a blur, for we continue to see them in one position at the same time that we see them in another.

If a disk one half of which is red and the other half blue is rotated rapidly, the entire disk appears purple. This is because we see the red at one place and a fraction of a second later we see it at another. The sensation of red still persists when we see the blue half, so that we think we see both colors all over the disk all the time. The mixture of red sensations and blue sensations gives us the sensation of purple.

Motion pictures make use of the persistence of vision by showing a succession of pictures on a screen. Each picture is slightly different from the preceding one. The light from the machine is cut off by a shutter while the pictures are being changed, leaving the screen completely dark. The successive pictures are shown so rapidly that we continue to see one while the next is being shown. As a result, the pictures seem to blend into one another, and we get the effect of seeing pictures in motion. Modern motion-picture machines in theaters show twenty-four pictures every second.

If pictures are taken slowly, so that a great deal of motion takes place between successive pictures, and the film is then run at normal speed, we get the effect of very rapid motion. If, on the other hand, pictures are taken very rapidly, so that only a small amount of motion takes place between successive pictures, we get "slow motion" when the film is run at normal speed.

Pictures may be taken of real actors and scenes or of drawings. In the latter case, the drawings must show things in successive positions. Such pictures are called *animated cartoons*.

EXPERIENCE. *Motion pictures.* Most schools now have motion-picture machines. In some schools some of the older children assume responsibility for these machines. Many people also take "home movies." Children should have an opportunity to see and examine a motion-picture projector.

EXPERIENCE. *The eye continues to see things when they are actually no longer there.* Cut out a disk of cardboard about four inches in diameter. Divide it into halves and color one half red and the other half blue. Pass a thumbtack through the center of the disk and into the rubber eraser on a lead pencil. Spin the pencil between your hands and watch the disk change color.

Make a drawing of a cage on one side of a card and an animal on the other side, in approximately the same position. Cut a slit in

the eraser of a pencil and insert the bottom of the card in the opening made. Spin the pencil between your hands, and the animal appears to be in the cage.

Make a series of drawings where each differs slightly from the preceding one. For example, show a child raising and lowering his hand. Hold the cards at the bottom, and riffle the top end. The child should appear to be waving.

Sound Motion Pictures. In talking pictures the sound is recorded directly on the film. This is done in the following manner: Sound is converted into a varying electric current, in much the same manner as in the telephone. This varying current is then used to make a special kind of electric lamp brighter or dimmer. Another means of changing sound waves into light waves involves the use of mirrors that vibrate when sound waves strike them. The moving mirrors reflect a beam of light whose strength depends upon the sound. Light from the lamp is allowed to fall on the edge of the film, and becomes the sound track. When the light is bright, it makes a dark spot on the film; and when it is dim, the film is affected only a little. When the film is shown, light from a lamp is passed through the strip on the edge of the film where the light marks are. After passing through the sound track, the light falls on a photoelectric cell. A photoelectric cell is a device for converting light into electricity. The beam of light of varying strength is converted into a varying current of electricity which in turn affects a loud-speaker, thus reproducing the original sound. The loud-speaker is somewhat like a telephone receiver.

Of course the actual apparatus is very much more complicated than this simplified account might lead one to believe. Different manufacturers of apparatus also use somewhat different systems of sound-recording.

The social possibilities of talking pictures as

a means of recording are great. Imagine the advantages of having talking pictures of Aristotle or George Washington or Sir Isaac Newton.

EXPERIENCE. *Sound track.* Obtain a portion of sound motion-picture film from a school film library or from a neighborhood theater. Examine the sound track.

The Phonograph. In the phonograph sound is recorded by means of a wavy groove cut in a wax disk. In the simplest arrangement sound is directed against a thin disk, or diaphragm. This is somewhat like the diaphragm in a telephone mouthpiece. The sound waves cause the diaphragm to vibrate. A needle is connected to the diaphragm in such a way that, as the diaphragm moves back and forth, the needle moves, too. Under the needle is a moving disk of wax. The vibrating needle is made to cut a wavy track around and around the wax disk, making a record.

When the record is played, another needle follows the wavy line. This line moves the second needle in exactly the same way that the first needle moved in making the record. This second needle is also connected to a diaphragm, which vibrates and gives out the same kind of sound waves as those originally recorded.

Many phonographs make use of electric devices to aid in recording and playing; but the essential principle is the same, that of having one needle cut a wavy line and having another needle follow the line and reproduce the sound.

The normal revolving speed for a phonograph record used to be 78 revolutions per minute. Slower recording speeds enable more sound to be placed on a record. Speeds of $16\frac{2}{3}$, $33\frac{1}{3}$ and 45 rpm (revolutions per minute) as well as 78 rpm are in common use today. Other improvements that make listening to records more pleasant are automatic record changers, which when used with low-speed

records can give many hours of uninterrupted music, and durable phonograph needles that last several years.

The records we buy are not made of wax, but of a hard, tough compound. They are copies made in an ingenious way from the original record.

High-Fidelity and Stereophonic Reproduction. Technical improvements in the recording and reproduction of sound have eliminated distortion and made it possible to reproduce music and other sounds with high fidelity to the original. By using two microphones in the recording process and two speakers in a room it is possible to suggest the position of individual musicians, as in a symphony orchestra, and give the effect of "three-dimensional" sound. Hence, the term *stereophonic* sound, from a Greek word meaning "solid," or "having three dimensions."

EXPERIENCE. *The phonograph.* Examine a phonograph record with a hand lens in good light.

Fasten a sewing needle with sealing wax to a piece of cardboard about two by three inches in size. Put a discarded record on the phonograph turntable and start it revolving. Hold the needle in the grooves on the record. You can probably hear the phonograph play and feel the vibration in your fingers.

Tape Recording. A spool of plastic tape coated with magnetic iron oxide is threaded through an electromagnetic system. A person speaks into a microphone and sound vibrations are recorded on the tape. The magnetic pattern placed on the tape produces an electric current when played back. The current is amplified and sound is produced. When no longer needed, the recording may be magnetically erased and the tape used again.

Tapes are used in some very complex operations. They may carry questions that are fed into a computer, as well as the answer received from the computer. Satellites are directed by small computers built into them, receiving instructions from larger computers at ground stations. Scientific data are tape-recorded by satellites in orbit, played back on command, recorded at the ground station, and relayed from there to scientists for study. The entire operation of an automatic oil refinery or other industrial process may be programed on tapes and controlled by computers.

Computers. (See p. 778.)

Instruments for Rapid Communication. In the category of rapid communication may be included those means of communication which might be called instantaneous. Thus, for example, air mail is a far more rapid means of communication than was a courier on a horse; yet it is slow indeed compared with the telephone or radio.

Of course the first means of rapid communication that come to mind are those based on light and sound directly, such as ordinary speech and signaling with lights and flags. These methods of communication, however, can be carried on only over relatively short distances. Powerful lights for communication are to be found in lighthouses. These have a maximum range of about twenty-five miles, owing to the curvature of Earth.

Electrical means of communication include, among other things, telegraph, telephone, radio, radar, and television.

Telegraph and Telephone. (See p. 833–838.)

Lasers. (See p. 861.)

Radio. Radio, or wireless, is a method of transmitting messages without the use of a wire to connect the sender and the receiver.

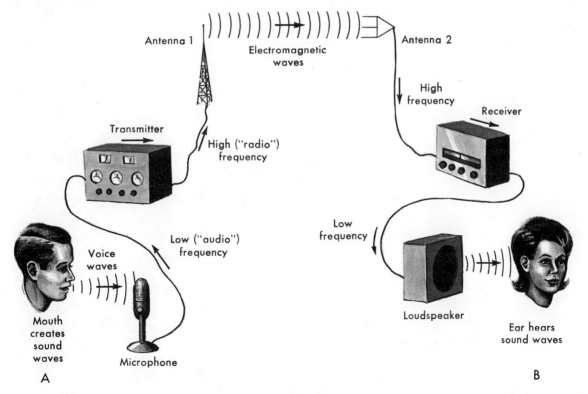

A simple diagram showing the steps in sending and receiving sound waves by radio. (After T. C. Ridout.)

Radio waves are among the so-called electro-magnetic waves, which have the same nature as light waves. They can travel through space without a wire, just as light does. A broadcasting, or transmitting, station sends out what is known as a carrier wave. This carrier wave corresponds to the current which continuously moves in a telephone circuit as soon as it is connected. In the telephone the sound waves are modified in such a way that they cause the strength of the current to vary. In a radio the sound waves may cause a change in the amplitude of the carrier wave. This type of broadcasting is called *amplitude modulation* (AM). A second type causes a change in the frequency of the carrier wave, and is called *frequency modulation* (FM).

Some radio microphones work like a telephone transmitter (p. 837). After the sound has been transformed into a changing current, the current is used to modulate, that is, to vary, the carrier wave. The carrier wave is sent out from the broadcasting antenna and picked up by a receiving antenna. When radio waves reach the antenna, they are transformed back into a varying electric current. This current is subsequently transformed into sound vibrations by the radio receiving set. When there is a pause in a station's broadcasting program, we hear a faint noise over the radio. Some of this may be due to the carrier wave, which keeps on coming, though it is not modulated.

FM reception has two advantages over AM reception. It has truer reproduction of tone, and static is eliminated. One disadvantage of FM is that it does not work well when obstructions exist between the transmitting station and the receiver. FM waves are not ordinarily reflected back by the ionosphere, hence their range is normally limited to the horizon, or "line of sight" transmission.

In the wireless telegraph, signals are made in code by starting and stopping the carrier wave, just as, in an ordinary wire telegraph, they are made by starting and stopping an electric current.

Radar. Radar is an abbreviated way of saying "*r*adio *d*etection *a*nd *r*anging." Its purpose is to locate an object's direction, speed, and distance. Originally used to reveal ships and airplanes, it is now used in addition to locate

The radar antenna sends out impulses which are reflected back by the airplane. The operator, by looking at the scope, can "see" the plane.

storm centers and to check the speed of automobiles. Radar sends out very short waves. If an object is struck by these waves, the waves are deflected back to the receiver, and are observed as specks of light upon a screen. The velocity of the radar wave is known, and the time required for the wave to complete the round trip is recorded. This information gives the location of the object.

Radar is two-dimensional. It does not show a third dimension. In the case of a plane, the third dimension would be its altitude when seen from a control tower at an airfield. Three-dimensional radar, or *3-D radar,* as it is called, uses various devices to receive signals indicating altitude.

Doppler Radar. Safety on dangerous parts of a highway is promoted by the use of Doppler radar. These places are marked SPEED CONTROLLED BY RADAR. This is a system that detects differences in the frequency of waves reflected by moving objects. It is related to the Doppler effect (p. 879).

Cars with radar equipment may be stationed by the roadside and send radio signals down the road. These are reflected by every car and are taken in by the receiver. The faster a car is traveling, the greater the number of pulses it reflects. These may be picked up and registered on a dial, and the passing car may even be photographed.

Infrared Tracking. Tracking by means of infrared radiation is of use when an object is obscured by smoke or dust or when too many echoes are given off. The detector, sensitive to infrared radiation, registers electronically the position of the object giving off the radiation. Radio waves and infrared waves are the same except for the length of the waves.

Television. Television works in a manner like radio, except that light, instead of sound, is transformed into electromagnetic waves. In general, the principle of television is to allow light from an object—say, a person's face—to fall on a photoelectric cell. This cell, as we have stated, converts light into an electric current. The varying electric current is used to modify a radio carrier wave.

At the receiving station these electromagnetic waves are converted into a varying electric current again. This current is converted into light of varying intensity by a special lamp. The transmitting and receiving apparatus must be so arranged that light from a given small section of the object at the transmitter is directed to the corresponding section of the final picture at the receiver. The picture is broadcast by AM, or ordinary radio waves. The sound is transmitted and received in the same way for television as for FM radio. The whole process is controlled by means of vacuum tubes or transistors.

Energy and Man in the Future

Man's progress through the long centuries of his history has been described by Arthur H. Compton in the following statement: "To visualize how our gradually growing knowledge has from the beginning stimulated Man's growth, let us imagine the last million years of his history to be compressed into the lifetime of a middle-aged man of fifty. Let us suppose that he is reading this article on a Saturday evening. It was then as a child that he learned the use of certain odd-shaped sticks and stones as tools. The meaning of sounds became definite as he learned to talk, and as his vocabulary increased, so likewise did the clarity of his thought. By the time he was forty, he had developed the art of skillfully shaping stones to fit his needs. Last year he became an artist, and a few months ago he learned to use simplified pictures as symbolic writing. Less than two months ago the Phoenicians introduced to him the alphabet, and after a fortnight came the brilliant art and science of Ancient Greece. Five weeks ago was the dawn of Christianity and the start of the Roman empire, and he recalls how a week later Rome fell, hiding for some weeks the values of civilized life. Last Sunday morning, so the report has it, Galileo dropped the heavy and light cannon balls from the Leaning Tower of Pisa, refuting a proposition of Aristotle and starting the period of modern science. By Wednesday afternoon this had led to building the first practical steam engine, and it was at about this time that the United States came into being. On Thursday the major laws of electromagnetism were being discovered which by last evening had given us the telegraph, the telephone, and incandescent electric lights. Only last night X rays were discovered, followed quickly by radium and wireless telegraphy. It was this morning that automobiles came into general use. Air mail began to be carried only at noon today. Popular short-wave broadcasts, practical color photography, and fluorescent lighting were unknown until this afternoon. . . ."[3]

This was written in 1941. To bring this statement up to date, the reader can add much from his own knowledge and experience. In reading this one gains the impression there have been great changes in the way man has used the materials and energy of the universe in the last century. This is true, but without the ancient basic developments of mankind, the modern discoveries and inventions would have been impossible. Man has a record of great achievement, and children have a right to develop a feeling of pride in belonging to the human race.

In this book the extreme importance of energy in the universe has been stressed. Wherever there is movement, whether of the largest stars or the smallest molecules or of the particles within molecules, energy is present.

On Earth, as elsewhere in the universe, nothing may move without energy. The movement of materials by geological forces and the transportation of goods by man alike require energy. Without energy the world would indeed be lifeless; more than that, the molecules themselves perhaps could not exist.

All living things require energy to carry on life, although in the dormant stage the energy supply may be very minute. Every living thing which is active requires a continuous supply of energy.

There are apparently great quantities of energy available for our generation and for many generations to come. Some of this energy has been received from the sun in past ages and stored on Earth, while an additional supply is being received daily from the sun. Mankind has learned to use the stored energy, but so far has been unable to make use of the daily income of energy to any great extent.

Modern civilization rests very largely upon man's wise use of energy. If civilization is to continue to improve, if men are to lead happier and richer lives, they must learn to use energy in a progressively more intelligent manner.

Today's problems call for co-operation between people, not only as citizens of a nation but also as inhabitants of Earth.

[3] Arthur H. Compton, *Sigma Xi Quarterly,* Vol. 29, No. 1 (April 1, 1941), pp. 39–48.

Part V

SCOPE, CONTINUITY, AND EVALUATION OF SCIENCE IN THE EDUCATION OF CHILDREN

Scope and Continuity

The following material is offered to the classroom teacher as illustrative of possibilities that are derived from modern science in the education of children. The meanings listed here have been secured from two types of studies: (1) analysis of science for meanings of value in the education of young children, and (2) study of children's patterns of growth toward the development of behavior consistent with the preservation and improvement of democracy. The basis for the selection of the meanings is described in Part One in the discussion of a dynamic psychology of science education, the nature of science and its contribution to the education of children in a democracy, and the place of content and procedure in teaching and learning science in the elementary school.

In a sense these meanings might be considered as statements of possible interpretations of the environment in which the child, the teacher, and the environment all interact. It is hoped that the teacher may participate in directing the instruction the more adequately because of the guidance secured from this suggested sequence based on available knowledge of the growth of children. These statements are intended as a portion of the professional background of the teacher rather than as statements of facts to be memorized by the child. They indicate the kind of interpretation used in the solution of problems.

Learning occurs in connection with a situation. A situation involves a problem, a challenge, the unknown. Learning involves meaning, and meaning makes content essential. The meanings considered as interpretations of natural phenomena in a dynamic universe are applicable and essential to many situations in life. There is no intention, therefore, in this sequence of dictating a classroom situation in which these fundamental meanings will be needed, nor the order of the learning, because both of these must vary with place and time.

It is not necessary, and probably, in most cases, it is undesirable, for the teacher to start with the children at the beginning of the numbered learning elements and follow through. Rather, one would start with a situation (or problem) and with the children's own ideas, regardless of the imperfections and inaccuracies involved, since growth must start where the children are (p. 12). However, the suggested continuity is derived from the experience and research of many elementary-school workers concerning the problem of the patterns of growth made by the children in their development toward a fuller understanding of the conceptions of science. It is hoped that this suggested continuity will give the teacher a vision of some of these possible patterns of growth and therefore of possible steps and procedures by which children may grow toward intelligent adjustment through scientific interpretations of natural events (p. 79). The meanings are cross-referenced to other sections in the book which will give the teacher a background of needed content and procedure.

The meanings are not provincial in character; rather they are universal. For the most part, they are intrinsic to the interpretation of phenomena in any region of the world; in the woods, mountains, marsh, seashore, and prairie; in the city, village, and country. They are therefore basic to the understanding of many of man's social problems. The teacher should strive to secure a vision of the place of such meanings in the social scene and the adjustment of the individual to life.

It will also be noted that much experience

and the content derived from experience are necessary before the ideas involved in the meanings set forth below become acceptable and meaningful to the child in any real sense. These meanings should not be treated as mere facts but rather as interpretations of new worlds of deeper understanding.

An attempt has been made in this sequence to consider the environment of the child in terms of its entire scope—that is, to include everything to which he may react. This may extend from the charges within an atom or the life within a drop of water to the stellar systems beyond our Milky Way.

The suggested continuity, for the convenience of teachers, is divided into the eight levels of the elementary school.

It is scarcely necessary to suggest to teachers that such a classification is only an approximate one, and that teachers at one level may find guidance from essential meanings suggested at other levels, depending on many factors, such as the intelligence, the previous experience, and the social background of children. Maturity levels in science do not correspond with age levels. Two children of the

same chronological age may not be at the same place in their development or their ability to grow toward an understanding of the basic working conceptions of science presented in this volume. Native ability and environment vary among children. The amount of travel, the employment in small tasks on a farm, the accessibility to an environment of the out of doors, a library of scientific books, or a previous study of science in school may all be factors in growth, producing change in maturity levels in science.

Many teachers will find members of their class in borderline situations and therefore will need to consult two or more of these levels for guidance.

Finally it is hoped that teachers will not use this suggested continuity until they have at least browsed through the first six chapters and have become familiar with the values of science in elementary education as presented in this volume. It would be well for the teacher to turn back to these chapters from time to time during the school year, in order that she may construct for herself an understanding of the role of science in the education of children in our modern era.

Grade One[1]

Air (pp. 424–458). Children's experiences with air are everyday occurrences to them. Sometimes they see no evidence of moving air; however, air is constantly in motion. Numerous phenomena involve air and can be explained as one learns about some underlying principles. Therefore, it is important that young children begin to gain some background for making interpretations about this vast ocean of air that surrounds them at all times. Innumerable situations can be created

for leading children to question, observe, and explore new ideas as to where air is, what it can move, how it can be found in many places, how air can be used, and ways it might cause destruction.

We can make air move.
We can feel air move.
We can see what air does when it moves.
Wind is air that moves fast.
Air pushes.

Changes in Weather (pp. 463–490). Everywhere on Earth there are changes in weather. Children see, feel, and become aware of dif-

[1] This material is based on Gerald S. Craig and Bernice C. Bryan, *Science for You, Book One.* Boston: Ginn and Company, 1965; and on the accompanying Teachers' Edition, 1965.

ferences in weather conditions throughout the day or night as temperature changes, wind stops blowing, degree of cloudiness varies, visibility decreases, a rainbow appears, or lightning and thunder occur. Young children are curious about these changes. They try to make interpretations about the various phenomena and adjust to changing conditions.

Temperature of the air changes.

Sometimes it rains.

Sometimes the wind blows.

Sometimes there is rain or fog.

Snow falls in some places.

The weather changes in all places.

There are many kinds of weather.

How You Can Change Foods (pp. 397–399). Numerous changes can be observed as foods are prepared. Children need opportunities to become aware of these changes by actually preparing foods at school as well as at home. Changes brought about by heating, cooling, and adding sugar are usually taken for granted by young children. They need guidance to help them focus on the way heating and cooling can change the state of ingredients and sometimes even the color. Also if experimentation is encouraged, a child may gain certain concepts relative to how taste is altered by using varying amounts of sugar.

Some foods are changed by heating.

Some foods are changed by cooling.

Sometimes heat changes the color of foods.

Sugar changes the taste of foods.

How Your Body Grows (pp. 686–693). Six-year-olds are confronted with various changes in body growth. They are exhilarated by some of these changes because it means "growing up" to them. By interesting children in their change in growth, teachers and parents can help them develop an appreciation of their bodies, see the need for proper food to take care of their teeth as well as care for themselves in general.

Your body grows.

Your body changes.

Your body needs food to grow.

Bones give shape to the body.

Bones help support the body.

Children get new teeth.

You need to care for your teeth.

You need to care for your body.

Where Animals Live (pp. 532–543). Many animals live in wooded areas, meadows, or on the desert, whereas various others are found around the habitations of people. Some animals live in cold places and others in hot climates. Also, there is an infinite variety of animals having adaptations for living in water or for staying in air part of the time.

Three of the large basic patterns—variety, interrelationship, and adaptation—give perspective relative to the science meanings given below. As children make observations of animals and the places where they live, there will be many opportunities to gather data and gradually come to see that there is great variation in these animals and where they live as well as many interrelationships. Also, children may gradually find out that there are likenesses and differences among animals and, because of their adaptations, that it is possible for them to live and survive in the particular place for which each is more or less suited.

Animals live in many places.

Some animals make homes.

We can make a home for some animals.

Animals need food and water.

We need to protect some animals.

There are many kinds of animals.

How Animals Move (pp. 518–523). As children observe many different animals, they will gradually develop concepts pertaining to the variation in ways animals move. By watching an animal jump, fly, or crawl, children may gain ideas about its structure or its adaptations for moving in certain ways.

Animals move in different ways.
Many animals move by swimming.
Many kinds of animals move by flying.
Animals use their wings to fly.
Some animals crawl.
Some animals use their legs to run.
Some animals use their legs to jump or hop.
Some animals do not have legs or wings.

Falling Down (pp. 187–189). By focusing attention on falling objects young children can be led to become curious about the force of gravity. With guidance as they encounter many experiences, the beginnings of ideas about gravity may be developed. They can find out that the force of gravity pulls down on everything though nothing may be falling.

Gravity makes things fall.
Gravity pulls down on everything.
It is hard to go uphill.
It is easy to go downhill.
Sometimes gravity is useful.
Sometimes gravity is not useful.

Floating and Sinking (pp. 716–722). Water play holds much interest for young children. Through body muscles and visual perceptions as a child manipulates objects in water, he gathers impressions, raises questions, makes interpretations, and draws generalizations relative to the way certain things float or sink and the feel of the force of buoyancy.

Many things float in water.
Many things sink in water.
Gravity pulls down on things.
It is hard to push floating things down.

Different Sounds (pp. 872–885). Sound is a form of energy, and it is produced by changes known as sound waves or energy waves. There are various opportunities for boys and girls to find out that sounds occur when something moves very fast or vibrates. Through experimentation a child may develop the beginnings of ideas concerning this form of energy. Emphasis also needs to be given to sounds made by animals as well as those associated with particular places.

There are many different sounds.
Sounds are made when something vibrates.
When something moves fast it vibrates.
High sounds are made when something short vibrates.
Low sounds are made when something long vibrates.

Water around You (pp. 475–479). Children everywhere have experiences with evaporation. In humid weather they may feel uncomfortable because the perspiration on their bodies does not evaporate readily.

Water goes into the air.
Water evaporates around you.
Heat can make water evaporate fast.
Moving air can make water evaporate fast.

Earth (pp. 250–263). The atmosphere as well as land and water make up the planet Earth. There is much variation in different places on our Earth. The elevation of the land varies greatly, as do the depth of the oceans and the changing conditions in the atmosphere. As children make observations from high or low places, see hills in some places and valleys in others, view a river or a wash, notice an outcropping along a highway, and make comparisons between places nearby with those far away, they may gradually begin to see many variations in land forms as well as places where there is water.

The land is part of Earth.
Water is part of Earth.
Air is part of Earth.
The land is not the same in all places.
Our Earth has many kinds of land.

Far from Earth (pp. 185–231). Young children are curious about the moon, sun, stars, and about Earth being in space. The extensive work being done during the last few years to learn about outer space and especially about the moon has heightened this interest of boys and girls.

The moon is far away from Earth.

The sun is far away from Earth.

The sun is far away from the moon.

The sun is very big.

Large things look small when they are far away.

The moon is not as big as Earth.

Stars are far from Earth.

Stars are far from the sun.

Some stars are very large but they look small.

Stars look small because they are far away.

People want to find out about space far away.

People want to find out about the sun, moon, and stars.

Spacecraft help people find out about the moon and space far away.

Care of Garden Plants (pp. 586–589). Developing a school garden can be a very rewarding experience for children. By working with soil, planting seeds, and caring for the young plants, a child may develop the beginnings of ideas about the ways plants are adapted to certain growing conditions. As records are kept, the data will reveal variations in the time it takes for different plants to germinate and grow to maturity. By caring for the garden, children will have many opportunities to find out about interrelationships relative to plants, sunlight, water, need for appropriate soil, and insects that may affect growth in the garden. If a school garden is not available, plant boxes may be used in the classroom.

Many garden plants grow from seeds.

Some seeds make new plants.

Seeds have food for new plants.

Some seeds may not grow.

Some plants grow fast.

Some plants grow slowly.

Garden plants need much care.

Our Soil (pp. 151–162). Soil is one of our most important natural resources. Therefore, young children living in urban centers as well as rural areas need to develop some understanding and appreciation of it as well as find out about conditions that affect it. In some school yards where there is erosion, it may be possible for six-year-olds to participate in making some contribution that will eliminate the loss of soil. Such a focus can do much to extend children's learnings about soil.

Water can move soil.

Wind can move soil.

Roots of plants hold soil.

Some roots hold much soil.

Rocks hold soil.

People need to care for soil.

People need to stop soil from moving away.

Magnets and You (pp. 780–786). A study of magnetism has significance for young children as well as for adults. Many of their toys operate because of magnetism. A child also uses magnets in the home and sees various places where they are in use. By handling magnets he can begin to build meanings and gain a feeling for energy as he experiences the push or pull of a strong magnet. He needs many opportunities to manipulate, experiment, and work with magnets in order to try out his own ideas and make discoveries about magnetism for himself.

Magnets attract some things.

Magnets do not attract many things.

Magnets attract things that have iron.

The magnetism of a magnet attracts iron things.

Magnets may be of different shapes, sizes, and colors.

All magnets have magnetism.

Electricity (pp. 829–833). Electricity is one of the greatest sources of energy. It plays a significant part in the lives of children as well as adults. Therefore, guidance needs to be given in developing an awareness of how it is used in numerous places at school, at home, and in the community.   Also as young children use electricity it is possible for them to develop various concepts concerning this form of energy.

Electric wires are put between walls in a building.

Electricity can go through wires.

Sometimes electricity cannot go through wires.

Electricity can make a light.

Electricity can make a bell ring.

Electricity can be turned on and off.

Use of Wheels (pp. 749–759).   Young children have worked with and gained some con-trol over forces in nature, such as momentum, balance, friction, and gravity, while manipulating the simplest of wheeled objects as well as some of the more complex machines having wheels.   With guidance, a child can extend his learnings relative to where wheels are used and also how wheels can make work easier for him.

Wheels make it easy to move things.

Some wheels are very big.

Wheels go around in pulleys.

Pulleys are used in many places.

Pulleys can be used to lift heavy loads.

Pulleys make it possible to lift a load by pulling down.

Pulleys make it easy to move things.

Grade Two[2]

Our Earth (pp. 245–273).   Mass communication helps young children to interpret vast distances and spatial relationships.   Children in today's world can be helped with many interpretations of science happenings or physical phenomena on planet Earth, on which they live.

You live on Earth.

Earth is many times larger than where you live.

All of ground, water, and air belong to Earth.

You live on a body in space called Earth.

Earth Moves in Space (pp. 185–244).   Children spin around.   They can spin as they move in space, too.   They spin a globe around as well as move it in the space of a room.   They can discover many objects that spin and move in space.   With imagination and curiosity, they seek interpretations about Earth and other bodies that spin and move in space.

Earth is moving all the time.

Earth spins as it moves.   Many objects spin.

It takes one day and night for Earth to make one spin.

There is space wherever Earth moves.

Gravity of Earth (pp. 187–189).   Children observe and experience many happenings dealing with the force of gravity of Earth.   With help they can interpret the phenomena of falling objects, weight, and gravity as a force you cannot see, but you can see what it does.

Gravity is a force that holds Earth together.

Gravity pulls everything toward Earth.

"Up" is away from the center of Earth. "Down" is toward the center of Earth.

You can measure the pull of gravity.

Air of Earth (pp. 424–450).   Air around children and Earth is a common everyday phe-

[2] This material is based on Gerald S. Craig and Etheleen Daniel, *Science for You, Book Two*. Boston: Ginn and Company, 1965; and on the accompanying Teachers' Edition, 1965.

nomenon. But they need guidance in giving their explanations and in making hypotheses. They can discover through sensory experiences much about air around and above them and Earth.

Air is all around you and Earth.

Air can be thought of as the outside of Earth.

Air goes up many miles above you.

Air is in the way of falling things.

Air presses on you and objects. Using a siphon.

Heat and Water (pp. 445–486). Heat and water give young children many clues to science happenings around them. They do not discover these phenomena for mankind, but through many first-hand experiences they can inquire into and make some self-discoveries about thermometers as instruments, the three states of matter, evaporation, condensation, and heat energy.

Thermometers are instruments. They tell how hot or cold things are.

Ice is solid water. Ice melts when it turns into liquid water.

Liquid water changes into a gas.

Steam must lose much heat to become liquid water. Water condenses.

When water turns into ice it loses heat. Heat is a kind of energy.

Water goes into the air.

Water comes out of the air. Loss of heat energy.

From Seeds to Plants (pp. 586–589). Children may have some difficulty deciding, upon observing seeds and pebbles, whether both are alive. Through experimentation, however, they can discover that seeds sprout under certain conditions and have materials and energy that come from the parent plant, and in time seeds grow into parent plants.

Seeds need materials and energy to sprout.

Seeds need certain conditions to sprout and grow.

Seeds grow into parent plants. They grow into plants like the ones they come from.

A good place for one kind of plant may not be good for another.

Seeds Are Moved About (pp. 568–573). As young children grow in their power to observe and interpret happenings or physical phenomena, changes in behavior become more evident. They can see that seeds are moved by animals, wind, and water; and that the moving of seeds causes plants to grow in new places.

Seeds are moved about in many ways.

Some seeds are moved to new places by the wind. They float in the air.

Some seeds float on water to new places.

Many plants cannot grow well in one place.

Electricity by Rubbing (pp. 804–813). Children frequently experience electricity by rubbing, but are at a loss to interpret such phenomena. Behavior observed may be fear or irritation. Through experiences with common materials they may gain a better understanding of attraction and repulsion, and electrical charges.

Sometimes electricity (charges) is produced by rubbing.

Sometimes materials are pulled toward each other. Sometimes they are pushed away.

Scientists think that there are bits of electricity in materials.

You break up some of the electricity that makes up the wool when you rub off particles of electricity. It breaks into electrical charges.

There are plus and minus charges of electricity. (These can be called positive and negative charges.)

You can use this sign $(-)$ for a minus charge. Use this sign $(+)$ for plus charges.

You can use electricity to move tiny bits of material from one place to another.

You can put a charge on a piece of paper. It is difficult to make electrical charges on wet days.

Like charges may repel each other.

Space around a Magnet (pp. 780–794). The force of magnetism may be an expansion of the seven-year-old's interpretation. He may have had experiences with magnets in toys, tools, or in his home. Now he can find out more about the space around a magnet or field of magnetism and polarity. Wise use and care of magnets in order to keep the force of magnetism strong is important, too.

There is a force around a magnet.

A magnet has a north and a south pole.

The space around a magnet is a field of magnetism.

Magnets can help you do work.

Magnets must be used wisely. Keeping the field of magnetism strong.

Our Sun in Space (pp. 185–244). Children of today's world are growing more sensitive to our sun and other bodies in space because of space travel and explorations. They need guidance in interpreting the size of our sun, distances in space beyond Earth, energy from our sun, sources of light and reflected light, and light and color.

The sun is very different from Earth.

Our sun seems small because it is far away in space.

Light from our sun travels quickly to Earth.

Earth gets just a little of the heat and light energy from our sun.

Many of the stars you see are suns, too.

There are two sources of light. Some objects shine by their own light, and others reflect light.

When light does not go through objects they make a shadow.

When sunlight is broken up you see many colors. Some materials break up light into the rainbow colors.

Water of Earth (pp. 167–172). Evaporation of water from the surface of Earth is a major world problem. Indeed, children, our youngest citizens, need to become oriented to this problem early. They can be of help to make more adequate interpretations of science happenings: water goes into air; water is stored above and below the ground; plants, animals, and people need much water; and ways of getting more water for more people.

Water comes out of the air. It goes into streams, rivers, lakes, and oceans. Water goes back into the air.

Much water is stored in the ground in many places.

Water is stored above the ground.

If there is much water there can be many plants. If there are many plants there can be many animals.

If there is little water there are few plants. If there are few plants there are few animals.

How people get water to dry places.

How water becomes muddy sometimes.

Some materials go into water. They dissolve.

People use water in many ways. They need clean water.

Some people have been studying ways salt can be taken out of ocean water.

Science Happenings (pp. 3–102). As young children observe and inquire about the common everyday happenings, they will investigate some scientific phenomena around them appropriate to their own maturity. If children are helped to view science as inquiry, they will naturally strive to interpret happenings or scientific phenomena.

Many things happen everywhere on Earth. Some are science happenings.

We try to explain science happenings.

You grow and change.

Scientists study happenings, too.

There are materials and energy in science happenings.

Grade Three[3]

Finding Out What Is around You (pp. 851–898). Since birth, a child has learned through the use of his senses. A study of the functioning of the senses and related meanings regarding light and sound energy can aid a child in more effective interpretations of his world. Resourceful behavior is encouraged as a child has experiences in observing and in keeping records of observations. An eight-year-old can learn about the importance of the use of instruments in making more accurate observations. A child can also discover that cursory observations may yield inaccurate ideas.

Observing is paying close attention and thinking about what you notice.

The eyes, ears, nose, tongue, and skin are special parts of your body that you use for observation.

Messages are sent to your brain from different parts of your body. With your brain you are able to understand what is happening.

Seeing, hearing, feeling, smelling, and tasting are called senses. They help you to find out about your world.

There must be light in order to see. Light shines on an object and then is reflected to your eyes.

The eye has different parts. Each part has a special function.

There must be sound in order to hear. Sound is made when something vibrates.

Vibrations of an object cause the air to vibrate. The vibrations of air move out in all directions and reach your ears.

The ear is the special part of your body made so that you can receive sound.

There are different parts of the ear, each of which has a special function.

Feeling, smelling, and tasting are other senses that you have.

The nose and tongue are made so you can smell and taste. The senses of smelling and tasting usually work together.

You can sense the pull of gravity. You have a sense of balance. You can sense when time has passed.

You usually use several senses at the same time when you observe. Your senses work together in many ways.

Some instruments help man make better observations with his eyes; others can be used to give more exact information than the body alone can give; some can be used to keep records of observations.

Ideas gained from observation need to be checked.

Seasons in Many Places (pp. 645–683). Some seasonal changes take place nearly everywhere on Earth. The types of seasonal changes vary from place to place. A study of seasonal changes can lead children to an awareness of the changes taking place out of doors in the region where they live. Children may observe the activities of animals and the appearance of plants as the seasons change.

There are many kinds of weather on Earth.

In some places there are many weather changes during a year. In other regions, the weather may be very much the same all year long.

The weather changes as the seasons change, in some places.

Some seasonal changes take place nearly everywhere on Earth.

[3] This material is based on Gerald S. Craig, Anne B. Hopman, and Marguerite W. Lambach, *Science for You, Book Three*. Boston: Ginn and Company, 1965; and on the accompanying Teachers' Edition, 1965.

Living things often change as the seasons change.

The weather in a region from season to season, year after year, is its climate.

Earth has many different climates.

Many living things are adapted to the climates in which they live.

The climate is warm all year in many places near the equator.

Some warm regions are also wet regions.

Climates near the north and south poles are usually very cold the year around.

Antarctic plants are usually very small.

People do not make their homes in the Antarctic.

Many plants grow and bloom during Arctic summers.

In both the Arctic and Antarctic most of the soil remains frozen year after year.

Many kinds of animals live in the Arctic during the summer season.

Some people make their homes in the Arctic.

There is great variety in seasonal changes throughout Earth.

Paths for Electricity (pp. 813–833). As children observe the use of electricity in home and school and as they make complete circuits with simple equipment, science meanings related to certain phenomena about electricity can be developed. Third-grade children can use electricity with greater understanding and safety after having these kinds of experiences.

Electricity can be put to use because it can move along wires.

Electricity needs a round-trip path if it is to be put to use. This round-trip path is called a complete circuit.

A simple circuit can be made by connecting wires to the posts of a dry cell and to a bell or to a socket containing a light bulb.

More complicated circuits can be made by adding dry cells and more lights to a simple circuit.

Using more than one dry cell in a circuit causes a light or lights to be brighter and the sound of a bell to be stronger.

There are two ways of adding more lights to a simple circuit.

A break in an electrical circuit stops the flow of electricity.

The use of a switch in a circuit provides a convenient way to control the flow of electricity.

Some materials make good connections for electricity. Electricity moves easily along these materials, which are called conductors.

Some materials do not make good connections for electricity. Electricity does not move easily along these materials, which are called nonconductors or insulators.

Living through Many Changes (pp. 645–683). This study points up the variety of ways in which living things are adapted to survive as conditions around them change. Through activities providing opportunities for observing, discussing, hypothesizing, and recording, children may gain a better understanding of plant and animal adaptations.

Plants and animals need warmth, sunlight, food, air, and water in order to live.

The place in which a plant or animal lives is its habitat. They live in a variety of habitats.

Habitats vary greatly in the amount of heat, water, sunlight, food, and air available to plants and animals.

The special ways in which plants and animals get along in their habitats are called adaptations.

Changes in seasons and weather often cause changes in a habitat.

Living things must change with the changes in their habitats or die.

Plants and animals are adapted to different habitats in a variety of ways.

The body temperature of some animals changes with temperature changes in their habitats. These animals are known as cold-blooded animals.

Some animals have body temperatures that remain nearly the same, regardless of temperature changes in their habitats. These animals are known as warm-blooded animals.

Estivating, hibernating, and migrating are three ways in which animals are adapted to living through changes in their habitats.

Hibernating and estivating for animals are very different from the resting or sleeping that people do.

Most plants are adapted to live through changes in their habitats.

Some kinds of plants die when the weather becomes cold. These kinds of plants live only one year. Most one-year plants make many seeds.

The loss of leaves, the growth of buds, and large numbers of seeds are three ways in which plants are adapted to living through cold.

Air and You (pp. 424–436). Air is essential to the life of human beings and many other living organisms, both plant and animal. Because of our dependence upon air, the quality of the air we breathe is important. This study develops some science meanings to help children better understand the ocean of air in which they live, and its relationship to their lives; to find out more about some of the constituents of air; to determine some ways in which air may become dirty; and to explore some ways in which air may be made cleaner and more desirable to breathe.

You need air in order to live.

The atmosphere is made of gases.

The gases of the atmosphere are invisible.

You need oxygen in order to live.

Carbon dioxide and water vapor are two of the gases in the air.

Dust and smoke can make the air hazy.

Dust is moving in and out of the air nearly all the time.

Dust goes into the air from many different places.

Smoke goes into the air when some materials are burned.

Some smoke goes into the air from factory chimneys and the exhaust pipes of automobiles.

Smoke in the air often makes people feel uncomfortable. It is difficult to breathe in smoky air.

People who live where there is smog must often breathe dirty air.

More and more people want cleaner air to breathe.

People are finding ways to keep dirt out of the air.

The Moving Sun and Earth (pp. 185–283). By introducing some meanings dealing with astronomical principles, children can be helped to project their thinking beyond what appears to be true. They will come to understand some of the limitations of observation and will learn to turn to reliable sources of information in order to check their first-hand experiences. Learning about the sun's movement in space and Earth's revolution and rotation clarifies concepts about gravity, daytime and nighttime, and the appearance of the sun in different places in the daytime sky.

Earth is the name of the planet we live on.

Earth is in space. Everything on Earth goes with Earth as it is moving in space.

Space goes on and on and on.

The sun moves in space all the time.

There is nothing in space to stop the sun from moving on and on.

The sun has gravity that reaches far out in space. The sun's gravity pulls on Earth, and Earth moves along in space with the sun.

The sun's gravity pulls Earth in a path around the sun. This path of Earth is called an orbit.

Earth's movement around the sun is called revolving. It takes one year, or 12 months, for Earth to make one complete revolution around the sun.

The sun appears to be small in the sky, but it is really very, very large. The sun seems to move across the sky from east to west.

Observation is only one way of learning. Ideas from observation may not always be correct. If observation is to be a useful way of learning, observations must be checked.

Earth spins as it revolves around the sun. This spinning movement is called rotating. It takes 24 hours for Earth to rotate one time. This 24 hours is called a day.

Earth receives light from the sun. Only one side of Earth has light at any one time. The rest of Earth is in Earth's shadow, or darkness.

The part of the day that is light is called daytime. The part of the day that is dark is called nighttime.

When objects spin in one direction, things observed from the spinning object seem to move in the opposite direction. Earth rotates from west to east. From Earth the sun appears to be moving from east to west.

We are traveling with Earth as it revolves, rotates, and moves in space with the sun. But we cannot see, hear, or feel Earth move.

The Changing Land of Earth (pp. 284–371). Children are confronted with the forces of gravity, moving water, and wind every day of their lives. Directed experiences of observation and experimentation can point up significant science learnings in relation to the small and slow changes in the land that continually take place. This study also develops some basic concepts that will encourage children to be sensitive to some problems of conservation.

The land of Earth looks different in different places.

The land of Earth may seem to stay the same, but changes to land are continually taking place.

Gravity pulls everything on Earth toward the center of Earth. Rain falls, water flows downward, loose rocks and soil move downward, and things carried by wind fall because of gravity.

Gravity is a force. A force is something that can push or pull and can cause things to move.

A raindrop has a force. The force of many raindrops can wear down soil and splash soil to other places.

Water can soak into soil and into rocks that have cracks and holes. When this water freezes, it expands, and the force can loosen soil and crack rocks.

The greater the slope of the land, the more swiftly streams flow.

Swiftly flowing water can usually move more materials than slowly flowing water.

Moving water in streams can wear away or build up the land.

Wind has a force and can cause things to move.

Soil and sand carried by wind can strike against surfaces and cut, scratch, and polish these surfaces.

Changes to land have happened in the past. Changes are taking place all the time.

Changes can happen slowly, or changes can happen quickly.

Changes may be small, or changes may be large. Small, slow changes over a long, long time may become large changes.

The Force of Magnetism (pp. 780–804). This unit is designed to build upon a child's earlier experiences with magnetism and to explore additional magnetic phenomena. Through activities and experiments a child has many opportunities for first-hand experiences with the force of magnetism. He is encouraged to make hypotheses; to predict outcomes; to record information; and to check results again and again before drawing conclusions.

There is force in a magnet. This force is magnetism.

You may feel what the force of magnetism can do.

Materials attracted by a magnet are known as magnetic materials.

There are many uses for magnets.

There are always poles on a magnet, no matter what its size or shape.

Earth has north and south geographic poles. It also has north and south magnetic poles.

Two unlike poles attract each other; two poles that are alike repel each other.

The force of magnetism acts in the space around a magnet. This magnetized space is called a magnetic field.

The force in a magnetic field follows lines of magnetic force from one pole to the other.

Lines of force are close together where the force in a magnetic field is stronger.

There is a very, very large magnetic field all about Earth. You live within Earth's magnetic field.

Magnetic materials may be attracted by the force in Earth's magnetic field.

Free-moving magnets can be attracted by the force in Earth's magnetic field.

They often turn toward the regions of Earth's north and south magnetic poles.

A compass needle is a free-moving magnet.

Plentiful Times for Living Things (pp. 568–684). Among living things, times of plenty are often accompanied by times of increased activity and an increase in numbers. Children may observe this time of activity and rapid changes out of doors wherever they live. As they compare plant and animal activities in plentiful times with their activities during times of great changes, children may become more conscious of conditions necessary to life and the interdependence of living things. They may also gain a further understanding of the relationship of plants and animals to the physical forces in their environments.

Spring and summer are often plentiful times in regions with four seasons.

Plants make many changes when warmth, food, and moisture are plentiful.

Plant buds open in warmer weather.

The young leaves and flowers of some plants are found in buds.

Some plants grow from seeds.

Some plants send up shoots from plant parts that have lived through the cold seasons.

The underground parts of some plants live throughout the year.

Spring is often a time of many changes for plants.

Many hibernating animals come forth as the sun warms the air and soil.

Toads and frogs lay many, many eggs as the weather becomes warmer.

A tadpole's way of breathing changes as it grows.

Many birds migrate as the weather becomes warmer.

The eggs of many insects hatch in spring.

Moths and butterflies come out of their special coverings in warm weather.

Many kinds of animals are very active in plentiful times.

Living Things Change the Land (pp. 284–331). The larger and more rapid changes, such as weather changes and changes from daylight to darkness, can be noticed immediately by children. Other changes, such as the growth of a tree or the formation of soil, are not so easily observed. These are usually slow changes or small changes. In this study, a child's attention is directed to changes in his environment resulting from the life processes of animals and plants. He should have an opportunity to make observations; recall experiences; keep records; and make predictions concerning changes caused by living things.

Plants and animals can change the land.

The changes animals make are the results of the ways in which they live.

Moles make ridges as they tunnel through soil.

Insects may change the land by eating plants.

Beavers change the land as they get food and build homes and dams.

A beaver dam holds back the water in a stream to form a pond.

Plant roots often help to hold soil in place. They may also loosen soil as they grow.

Some underground changes made by growing plants may go on for a long time before they may be seen.

Growing plants may push their roots into cracks in rocks and break the rocks apart.

Growing plants may change the land around them, even when the land is covered with other materials.

Some plants grow in water.

Water hyacinths change the waters in which they grow. The roots and leaves spread out in the water and cover the surface.

People often change the land around them.

Some changes made by people are small. Other changes affect the land over miles and miles.

Satellites of Earth (pp. 185–244). This study of Earth's satellites has to do with both our natural satellite, the moon, and man-made objects that revolve around Earth. From children's experiences with these topics, they will come to accept attitudes and behaviors of open-mindedness, such as realizing that there is much yet to learn as man continues to raise new questions and to seek new answers.

Astronomy is the study of space and the objects in space. Astronomers use telescopes, cameras, and other instruments in their study.

Satellites are used to carry instruments that send information about space back to man on Earth.

Rockets push satellites fast enough and far enough in space so that they are not pulled back immediately to Earth by gravity. The gravity of Earth has a pull on a satellite and causes it to revolve around Earth in an orbit.

A satellite is a smaller object that revolves around a larger object.

Satellites made by man and put into space with rockets are artificial satellites.

Man can travel in some satellites.

The moon is a natural satellite of Earth. It has been in space for as long as man knows.

Because of Earth's gravity, the moon revolves in an orbit around Earth. It takes about four weeks, or one month, for the moon to revolve around Earth one time.

Only one side of the moon can be seen from Earth; therefore, we know that the moon rotates.

It takes about four weeks, or a month, for the moon to rotate one time. This is about the same length of time for a complete revolution of the moon around Earth.

The sun shines on the moon. As the moon rotates, different parts of the moon turn into light and into darkness.

The sun's light on the moon is reflected to Earth. This reflected light is called moonlight.

Sometimes the moon looks round in the sky, and other times it seems to have other shapes. The round shape of the moon stays the same, but from Earth only some of the lighted part of the moon is seen at different times.

Grade Four[4]

Molecules in the Universe (pp. 372–499). By the time children reach Fourth Grade, they have had numerous experiences with matter in its gaseous, liquid, and solid forms. They are now ready to investigate the nature of matter in a more mature manner. They will learn that matter is composed of tiny particles that scientists have called molecules, and that molecules are composed of one or more atoms. They will investigate the molecular theory and learn how this theory helped scientists to explain many common phenomena that they observed on almost every hand.

Matter is composed of tiny particles called molecules.

Molecules are composed of smaller particles called atoms.

Molecules and their atoms are in constant motion.

Matter may exist in one of three forms—solid, liquid, or gaseous.

Matter may be changed from one form to another.

Molecules of substances move more rapidly when heated and less rapidly when cooled.

Heating and cooling of substances causes them to change form.

Most substances expand when heated and contract when cooled.

Solids tend to keep their shape.

Liquids take the shape of the container they are in.

Gases spread out to fill whatever space is available.

An hypothesis is a statement made as a possible explanation of a phenomenon.

[4] This material is based on Gerald S. Craig and Beatrice Davis Hurley, *Science for You, Book Four*. Boston: Ginn and Company, 1965; and on the accompanying Teachers' Edition, 1965.

Present scientific knowledge is tentative in nature.

Newer knowledge supplants much that was once considered to be true.

The Planet, Earth (pp. 185–283). Children will have had many direct experiences with the planet upon which they live. This unit seeks to add to the store of concepts the children are building about Earth, strengthening the concepts through providing additional experiences carefully directed to develop understanding of the larger environment—the whole Earth.

Earth is composed of three parts: a solid sphere, a liquid sphere, and a gaseous sphere.

The three spheres of Earth are held together by gravity.

Gravity pulls everything toward the center of Earth's solid part.

Weight is the measure of the force with which gravity pulls on an object.

The lithosphere is all one huge piece, even though roughly three fourths of its surface is covered with water.

Gases, liquids, and solids mix together.

A theory is a statement of an explanation of some phenomenon that remains yet to be validated.

Careful gathering of evidence in support of or to refute a theory is needed.

Careful gathering of evidence is a science behavior.

The Atmosphere (pp. 424–499). A great many phenomena are explained through greater understanding of the atmosphere. Space probes extending far away from Earth are yielding new information about the atmosphere. Children are interested in these probes and the information gained from them.

The atmosphere is made up of gases and other materials.

The atmosphere completely surrounds Earth's solid and liquid, moving with them as they move around and with the sun.

Change is a characteristic of the atmosphere.

The troposphere is the region of greatest change.

Gravity causes the air to have pressure. This pressure may be measured with a barometer.

Heating of the land and water surfaces of Earth by the sun causes the air to be unevenly heated.

Air extends out into space, becoming thinner with height. Changes in the troposphere produce weather.

There is much that remains to be learned about the atmosphere.

Scientists continue to study it in search of more information.

New knowledge of the atmosphere will greatly assist men in exploring weather changes, making long-range weather predictions, and enlarging possibilities for further safe exploration of regions beyond Earth.

Men can use what they learn about the weather to help them plan their daily lives.

Animals and How They Are Protected (pp. 568–585). Almost every child has had numerous direct experiences with animals of many kinds. Some will have had the responsibility of caring for pets. Others will have observed animals carrying on their normal functions of living.

As children make further observations of animals, they will become aware of the infinite variation the animal kingdom exhibits. Especially will they become alert to the ways animals are protected. These protective adaptations for survival have evolved as ani-

mals continued to live in certain environments found on Earth.

There is infinite variety in the animal kingdom.

Animals need food in order to keep alive and to continue the species.

The struggle to survive is a sharp one among living things.

Some animals prey upon other animals and use them for food.

Some animals are preyed upon by other animals, yet the species survives.

Each animal has certain adaptations that aid in its survival.

The adaptations of each animal are usually suited to that animal and are not necessarily good for other animals.

These adaptations help the animal to be suited to its particular niche in the environment.

Some animals protect their young by giving them care.

Making Things Move (pp. 713–799). The unifying themes in this study are energy and motion. As children pursue their study of moving things, they will become increasingly aware of the fact that, as far as is known, everything in the universe is in motion and that energy is needed to move things. They will observe men using their muscles to get some moving jobs done. They will observe the energy stored in wind, water, steam, and electricity as it is employed in getting work done. Their own pushing, lifting, pulling, rolling, sliding, and swinging activities will reveal to the children their own use of energy in daily living.

Each child will bring to this unit, as he does to any other area of learning, a unique background of experience. For this reason children's understanding of energy and motion will vary.

Everything in the universe is in motion.

Energy is needed to move things.

Objects at rest tend to resist starting.

Objects in motion tend to resist stopping.

The tendency of objects at rest and in motion to resist starting and stopping is called inertia.

Friction is resistance to movement encountered when two objects rub against each other.

Friction is useful.

Friction causes wear.

Men have found ways to reduce friction.

Men have found ways to increase friction.

Men have made progress in using energy partly because they have been able to use tools and invent machines.

Machines help to make available sources of energy that assist men in their work. Men use energy to greater advantage with a machine. Complex machines may be analyzed into one or more types of simple machines.

The six simple machines are the lever, wheel and axle, wedge, inclined plane, screw, and pulley.

Our Solar System (pp. 185–244). Man's continuous search for more knowledge about the universe has served only to increase his wonder and spur his desire to learn more. Children, too, are challenged by the antiquity and vastness of the universe as they pursue their study of the solar system and regions beyond it. The study of space and its exploration furnishes the teacher with many opportunities to help children enlarge their concepts of space, time, and variety.

Everything in the solar system is moving with the sun as it moves in space.

The sun is a medium-sized star.

The sun is the largest body in the solar system.

The heat and light from the sun warm and light the bodies in the solar system.

Some of the sun's heat and light reaches beyond our solar system to other bodies in the universe.

There are nine known planets in our solar system.

There are moons of planets, planetoids, comets, and meteors in our solar system. All these bodies revolve around the sun.

Planets have days and years as Earth does, but each are of different lengths. The reasons for having years and days are the same.

Life upon Earth has evolved as it is because of the conditions that exist on this planet.

If there is life upon other planets it might differ from life upon Earth, because conditions on each planet differ.

Man uses instruments to advance his knowledge of our solar system and regions beyond.

Data gathered from advanced and precise instruments are carefully recorded and studied.

Much remains to be found out about the solar system.

Spacecraft carry instruments for exploring far from Earth.

Plants and How They Are Protected (pp. 503–604). This study will provide many direct experiences with plants. It will help children become aware of plants that grow in the immediate community and to extend awareness of plants growing in distant communities. This unit furthers an understanding of variation, interrelationships, and adaptation. As children pursue their study of this unit, it is hoped that they will become conscious of the economic and aesthetic value of plants and will make wiser use of them.

Plants are living things.

Plant life upon Earth is abundant.

The abundance of plant life is a kind of protection.

There is great variety in kinds of plants living on Earth.

Plants are adapted to living where they live.

Plants have developed certain adaptations that serve as a protection.

Tough stems and bark are a protection.

Spines, thorns, and stings are a protection.

Production of many seeds and spores is a protection.

Dispersal of seeds is a protection.

Roots are a protection to plants.

Leaves may be a protection to some plants.

Man protects some plants.

Plant and Animal Communities (pp. 532–567). Every kind of plant and animal grows better in some places than in others. Fish live in water. Horned toads live in deserts. It is hoped that children will become increasingly observant of the adaptations of living things to the conditions under which they live. In addition, children will also become aware that plants and animals live together in characteristic communities and that these communities of plants and animals are closely interrelated to one another and to the physical environment around them.

Many kinds of plants and animals live together in communities.

Life in a plant and animal community is interrelated.

Living things in a community have become adapted to living there.

Left undisturbed, a community of living things tends to stabilize itself.

Man makes changes in the natural community of living things.

Man should study the interrelationships within a living community before making changes in the environment.

Communities of living things keep changing.

All living things within a community depend upon green plants for food.

Our behavior tells much concerning the way we think and feel about our environment.

We should learn to study and enjoy living things in their natural surroundings.

Magnetic and Electrical Forces (pp. 780–850). This unit builds upon earlier experiences and attempts to move children ahead in their interpretations of magnetic and electrical forces. It introduces the domain theory as a possible explanation of magnetic phenomena. It is recommended that children have many

direct experiences to help them build certain concepts and behaviors through actually working with materials. Among these are the following: learning to be careful observers of phenomena, learning to gather evidence pertinent to an investigation, learning to draw conclusions supported by evidence gathered, and learning to test the validity of conclusions drawn. Children develop a greater understanding of the use of such explanations as theories and hypotheses.

Magnetism and electricity are forces.

Materials attracted by magnets are called magnetic materials.

The repulsion test may be used to determine whether a piece of iron is a magnet.

Lodestones are natural magnets.

A compass needle is a magnet.

Earth, itself, is a huge magnet.

Electromagnets can be made by passing an electric current through a wire coiled around an iron core.

Electricity produces heat and light.

The use of electricity has greatly changed man's way of life.

Safety devices such as circuit breakers and fuses are used in buildings using electricity.

Much remains to be learned about magnetic and electrical forces.

Present theories concerning these forces are useful.

How Animals Live Together (pp. 605–644). Children may already be aware that certain animals live together in communities often called colonies or societies. These animals, such as honeybees and ants, are called social animals. However their cooperation within a society is far different from the social life man lives. Life within an anthill or a bee hive is almost wholly based upon the instinctive behavior of its members. Life in a human society is largely based upon reason and planning. This study should highlight these basic differences. It also develops an understanding of other ways animals live. Some animals are social at times and solitary at other times. Here again, there is opportunity to help children develop an understanding of the infinite variety in the universe, of the interrelationships and adaptation living things exhibit throughout their life span.

Many animals live together in a social organization.

Some animals live together all their lives.

Some animals live together part of the time and alone part of the time.

A few animals live alone all, or most, of the time.

The social organization of some animals is highly complex.

Man is a social being.

Many acts of man result from rational thought.

Social animals, such as honeybees and ants, behave by instinct.

Man's social life and that of bees, ants, beavers, and other social animals, differ markedly.

There are advantages and disadvantages in social living.

Exploring the World of Sound (pp. 851–898). Sound is a form of energy. It is produced whenever anything vibrates. This unit seeks to enlarge children's awareness of the tremendous significance of sound as an element in modern communication, to give them direct experiences in producing it, and to present information of how it travels from place to place. The large patterns of energy, interrelationships, and variety are dealt with in this unit.

Sound is a form of energy.

Sound is caused by something vibrating.

Sound waves are set in motion when something vibrates.

Sound waves travel out in all directions from their source.

Sound waves travel through many kinds of materials.

Sound waves can be produced in different ways.

The vocal cords in human beings produce sound waves.

The ear is the organ through which sound waves come to us.

Sounds may differ in pitch.

Sounds may differ in intensity.

Sound may differ in quality.

Echoes are reflected sounds.

Sound makes communication around the world possible.

Grade Five[5]

Plant Life on Earth (pp. 503–661). Plants, whether green or nongreen, make use of nonliving substances in the form of liquids, solids, and gases as they grow and change. Ten- and eleven-year-old boys and girls may move toward a fuller understanding of green and nongreen plants, their parts, and the role of these parts in a plant's growth.

The root systems of plants vary in shape and size.

Water and substances dissolved in water are absorbed by roots.

Molecules are in constant motion inside the roots, stems, and other parts of plants.

Molecules move out of plants.

Green plants use nonliving substances and light energy to produce food by a process known as photosynthesis.

Green plants, nongreen plants, and all animals are dependent upon the food produced in cells containing chlorophyll.

Plants differ as to size, method of reproduction, and length of lifetime.

[5] This material is based on Gerald S. Craig and Katherine E. Hill, *Science for You, Book Five*. Boston: Ginn and Company, 1965; and on the accompanying Teachers' Edition, 1965.

Forces and Earth Changes (pp. 245–331). The dynamic processes operating on the outside and the inside of the solid part of Earth may be clarified by focusing attention on day-to-day changes in the environment and on changes that have taken place over eons of time. This concerns gravity and pressure as it is involved in the slow movements of large portions of Earth's crust as well as the more rapid and sudden movements of the crust.

Earth's gravity field is believed to extend far out in space.

Everything above, on, and beneath Earth's solid surface is in its gravity field.

The inner portion of Earth's solid part is the core; around this is the mantle; and around the mantle is the crust.

Earth's solid portion does not seem to be of uniform density.

Wind and water cause changes on the surface of Earth's crust.

Pressure in the solid part of Earth is due to Earth's gravity.

Changes in pressure in parts of Earth's crust appear to be due to the effects of the movement of soil, rocks, water, and other things.

Pressure in the crust of Earth appears to have much effect on the heating of rocks.

The shifting of materials from place to place seems to result in changes in balance in Earth's crust.

Moon, Earth, and Sun (pp. 185–283). Earth, its moon, and the sun form a system in constant motion. The mutual gravitation of these bodies holds the system together. The relationships existing between the moon, Earth, and sun are responsible for Earth's tides.

The cycle, called phases of the moon, is regular and is repeated every 29 $\frac{1}{2}$ days approximately.

Half of the moon is lighted by the sun at all times except during an eclipse of the moon.

The moon goes through phases as seen from Earth because a different amount of its sunlit surface is seen each night.

On any one night, the phase of the moon seen from any place on Earth is the same.

An eclipse of the moon occurs when it enters Earth's shadow; an eclipse of the sun occurs when the moon is directly between Earth and the sun.

The movements of the moon-Earth-sun system in space seem to be due largely to the effects of mutual gravitation and inertia.

Mutual moon-Earth-sun gravitation accounts for tides in the bodies of water on Earth.

The times and heights of tides are due to the relative positions of the moon, Earth, and the sun and to the effects of shorelines.

Unmanned and manned vehicles are being used for exploration in the moon-Earth-sun system.

The effects of gravitation and inertia on satellites and other space vehicles must be considered in planning their flights.

Because conditions on the moon are quite different from those on Earth, man must make special preparations for exploration there.

Inside Atoms (pp. 372–423). Since 1913, theories concerning the structure of atoms have been under constant revision. Atoms differ from one another with regard to the number of protons in a nucleus and the corresponding number of electrons revolving around the nucleus. A "normal" atom is balanced electrically. When an electron is lost or gained by an atom, the atom becomes unbalanced. Children may gain some understanding of the structure and nature of atoms.

Atoms are everywhere on Earth.

Any single atom is far too small to be seen with the unaided eye.

Scientists have revised their ideas about the structure of atoms many times on the basis of evidence concerning their behavior.

Atoms seem to be mostly space.

Each atom is believed to have a nucleus, made up of one or more protons as well as other particles, around which one or more electrons revolve.

There seems to be much motion inside atoms.

Atoms appear to be held together by powerful forces.

Usually atoms seem to be balanced, having the same number of electrons as protons, but they also may become unbalanced by gaining or losing electrons.

There are more than 100 different kinds of atoms, and each of these kinds is an element.

Each element has been assigned an atomic number that indicates the number of protons believed to be in its nucleus.

Scientists are not the only people who revise ideas; each of us revises his ideas from time to time.

Theories about Electricity and Magnetism (pp. 713–850). Boys and girls may observe some of the effects of magnetism and electricity and will be challenged to consider reasonable explanations of such effects. Imbalance may occur within atoms, thus producing electrical and magnetic phenomena.

Electricity produced by rubbing some things together is known as frictional electricity.

It is thought that an object becomes positively charged when the atoms of which it is made lose electrons.

It is thought that an object becomes negatively charged when the atoms of which it is made gain electrons.

An object may be discharged when electrons move away from it.

Another name for frictional electricity is static electricity.

Objects that have the same kind of electrical charge repel one another, and those that have unlike electrical charges attract one another.

An electrical charge may sometimes be produced on a neutral object just by bringing an electrically charged object near it.

Lightning is considered to be a discharge of static electricity.

A wire in which an electric current is moving is surrounded by a magnetic field.

The spinning motion of an electron seems to produce an electric current, which in turn produces a magnetic field.

Electromagnets are used in electric bells and buzzers.

When an object becomes magnetized, it may be because more electrons are spinning in one direction than in another.

Unbalanced directions of spin of the electrons in an atom may be thought of as resulting in magnetic effects.

Above Earth's Land and Water Surfaces (pp. 424–499). The atmosphere is as real a part of Earth as the lithosphere and hydrosphere. Boys and girls may build upon their concepts concerning the atmosphere and learn more about the characteristics of the various layers. Equilibrium and balance appear to operate in Earth's atmosphere and serve to interpret many of the phenomena occurring in it.

Earth's atmosphere is one of the three major parts of Earth.

Earth's atmosphere extends far out from Earth in all directions. How far is not known.

In the troposphere, the layer of the atmosphere nearest land and water, there is much turbulence.

Above the troposphere are these layers: stratosphere, mesosphere, thermosphere, and exosphere.

There are some layers in the atmosphere where the temperature is above the boiling point of water and some layers where it is exceedingly cold.

Among the electrical effects in the atmosphere are lightning and the Northern and Southern Lights.

The instruments carried by rockets and man-made satellites have gathered much information about Earth's atmosphere.

Water is in the atmosphere in the following forms: invisible water vapor, clouds or condensed water vapor, rain, snow, sleet, and hail.

The relative humidity and pressure of the atmosphere may be determined by the use of instruments.

Places in the atmosphere where there are large high- and low-pressure areas are called highs and lows.

High- and low-pressure areas often follow one another around Earth in the regions of the westerlies.

Results of observations of the weather made at stations all over Earth are sent to central collection stations, where they are recorded to produce weather maps.

Hurricanes, tornadoes, and typhoons are areas of extremely low air pressure.

Much has been learned about the layers of Earth's atmosphere, but much remains to be learned.

Light in the Universe (pp. 851–898). Light is a form of energy that man uses but does not yet understand fully, although he attempts to learn more about it. Boys and girls may add to their understanding of light—its characteristics and origin.

Light is given off by some things and enables us to see.

Light seems to be made up of tiny pieces of something, called photons, which appear to travel through the universe in wavelike paths.

It may be that photons are activated when excitation, which perhaps is a special kind of motion, occurs within atoms.

Light travels in straight lines on Earth.

Light travels long distances on Earth and throughout the universe.

Light travels at the tremendous speed of 186,282 miles per second.

Light travels through transparent and translucent substances but not through opaque substances.

Light may be reflected.

Light may be bent, or refracted, by water, lenses, prisms, and other objects.

Lenses are used to enlarge and reduce the sizes of objects.

The lens in an eye is very important for proper vision.

We use our knowledge of light in many ways.

Living Things and Changing Climates (pp. 332–371). It is likely that the first living things on Earth were one-celled green plants that lived in warm salt water. Considering the probable length of time Earth has been in existence, the living things of today appeared a very short time ago. Many forms of life have become extinct. Land forms and climates have changed during Earth's long history.

Some plants and animals once living in North America long ago no longer live there.

Among the animals that have become extinct are dinosaurs.

Fossils—traces of ancient plants and animals—are useful evidence in determining the living things in a particular place at some time in the past.

There are different kinds of fossils.

The horses, mammoths, and other ancient animals that once roamed North America are extinct now.

Climates of Earth have changed through the years.

Theories have been developed to explain why climates of Earth have changed.

Some plants survived great changes in climate, probably because of certain adaptations.

Some warm-blooded animals seem to have survived climate changes because of certain adaptations, among which are hibernation and migration.

Some cold-blooded animals seem to have survived climate changes because of certain adaptations, among which are hibernation, migration, and metamorphosis.

Perhaps the extinction of dinosaurs, horses, mammoths, and other ancient animals in North America was due to changes in climate.

Chemical Changes and Atoms (pp. 372–423).   Chemical reactions are among the naturally occurring phenomena in any environment.   They are also among the daily phenomena resulting from man's ceaseless use of materials he finds around him.   Theories concerning atomic and molecular structures and reactions may serve to interpret chemical phenomena in the natural environment.

Chemical changes go on around us all the time, some occurring naturally and some with man's help.

When two or more atoms combine, a chemical change occurs that produces a molecule.

When two or more different atoms combine, a molecule of a compound is formed.

From the more than 100 elements that are known, hundreds of thousands of compounds can be made.

Oxidation is a chemical process.

When mixtures are made, no chemical change takes place.

A solution is a mixture made by dissolving a solid in a liquid.

Many mixtures may be separated rather easily, but this is not true of compounds.

Countless chemical changes go on in our bodies all the time.

Animal Life on Earth (pp. 503–709).   The bodies of each kind of animal are organized in a manner unique to that kind of animal, and it is possible to use one's knowledge of these organizational patterns in interpreting some of the actions of animals.   Animals may be grouped for study in many different ways.

Animals depend upon green plants for food, and they also need air and water.

Atoms pass into animals and some remain to become a part of the animal whereas others pass out of the animal.

Some animals are made of only one cell; others are made of many cells.

There is a constant movement of materials into and out of the cells that form an animal's body.

A group of similar cells form a tissue, and different kinds of tissues are organized into systems; such as a muscular system, a nervous system, a circulatory system, a respiratory system, a digestive system, and a skeletal system.

Each system in an animal seems to have a special function.

Animal growth is a process of forming cells from materials that enter the bodies of animals.

Our bodies have cells, tissues, and systems.

There is a constant exchange of atoms and molecules among living and nonliving things on Earth.

Earth's Water Resources (pp. 145–331).   The water supply must be understood as a renewable, natural resource dependent upon man's wise utilization of his increasing knowledge and skill in making water available when and where it is needed.   Living things are dependent upon a certain amount of water.

Earth's water, or hydrologic, cycle is automatic.

Water is found in solid, liquid, and gaseous forms on Earth.

Water is found in living things, in bodies of water, in the atmosphere, and in the solid part of Earth.

Some living things are surrounded by water, and others are surrounded by air that varies in water content.

Water molecules are in motion everywhere.

The land over which water drains into a stream or a river or a lake is called a watershed.

Gravity pulls water downward in Earth's crust until it reaches a rock layer through which it cannot pass.

Water collects underground into large reservoirs, or aquifers.

People need a great deal of water each day, but there seems to be enough on Earth if the hydrologic cycle can be controlled properly.

Many problems must be solved as man tries to control the hydrologic cycle to some extent.

Systems in Space (pp. 185–283). Although man knows there are innumerable bodies in space and though he understands something of the relationships among these bodies, much remains to be learned concerning the nature of and the relationships among stellar bodies. Boys and girls may focus their attention in a realistic manner on the tremendous number of star systems, the enormous size of each, and the vast distances between them. More realistic appraisals of the possibilities of exploration outside our solar system may be possible.

Our solar system has enough organization so that we depend upon the bodies forming it to move in certain ways.

The organization in our solar system seems to be due largely to mutual gravitation and inertia.

Our solar system would look different from various positions in space.

Our system of stars, the Milky Way Galaxy, is composed of billions of stars, one of which is the sun.

Our solar system is a very small part of the Milky Way Galaxy.

Stars move within our galaxy, and the entire galaxy is moving in space.

There are billions of other galaxies moving in space.

Galaxies are natural systems of stars held together by natural forces, but constellations are groups of stars related to one another only because they form imaginary pictures in the sky.

People have revised their ideas about systems in space many times as new evidence is discovered.

Grade Six[6]

Ways of Thinking and Behaving (pp. 3–144). There are as many ways of thinking and behaving as there are people. Each individual is unique in his background as an individual and in his experiences. Yet certain ways of thinking and kinds of behavior have emerged as being useful and desirable.

There is wide variation in what people think.

The behavior of people is often as varied as their thinking is.

With different problems we seek help from

different specialists by reading or listening.

The use of more than one source of information is desirable.

The same event may be interpreted differently by different people.

Observation is one of several ways to gain information.

Some people are skilled in one kind of observation only.

There is variation in the way scientists work, depending on the problem.

Reading, studying, and exploring may necessarily precede a statement of a problem.

Checking an hypothesis may require more reading, experimentation, or other testing.

---

[6] This material is based on Gerald S. Craig and Mary E. Sheckles, *Science for You, Book Six*. Boston: Ginn and Company, 1966; and on the accompanying Teachers' Edition, 1966.

This may result in a new hypothesis or in a tentative conclusion.

Finding out is a thinking process.

Information becomes useful as it becomes a part of behavior.

Consideration of new evidence is open-mindedness.

Critical examination of new evidence involves knowing the source, testing and checking with previously acquired authoritative information, and perhaps seeking additional information.

Being resourceful involves observation and critical thinking, and the use of information previously learned in new and different situations.

Learning to understand the natural sequence of events may contribute to responsible behavior.

The act of doing his best thinking or his best quality of work by an individual is responsible behavior.

Behavior demonstrates the thinking and attitudes of an individual toward his environment.

Plants and Animals of Earth Are Different (pp. 503–531). Great differences exist between living and nonliving things on Earth. Differences also exist between living plants and animals.

Living things may be grouped in three large divisions: the Plant Kingdom, the Animal Kingdom, or the Protists Kingdom.

. There are no characteristics which will distinguish all plants from all animals.

Green plants make food for themselves and other living things; they are called producers.

Those forms of life that use food produced by green plants are called consumers. A series of producers and consumers constitutes a food chain.

Nongreen plants and animals cannot make their own food.

Many animals can move from place to place; most plants are attached to a given place for life.

The cells of plants differ from those of animals in shape, size, and kind.

The liquids in animal bodies are saltier than are those in plants.

Entomologists have studied and named over 850,000 kinds of insects. For purposes of study, they have been placed into different groups, or orders.

All adult insects have six legs and three parts to their body. They differ as to antennae, the number of wings, and size.

Many insects are harmful to man because they feed on or carry diseases to plants or animals useful to man and even to man himself.

Many insects are useful because they feed on plants and animals that are harmful to man; they may pollinate many plants useful to man.

Plants are divided into groups; the two largest groups are the green and nongreen plants.

Seed plants vary in size, shape of leaves, and produce different kinds of seeds.

Human beings vary. All individuals have certain likenesses, but in many ways each is different from another.

It is normal for an individual to be different from others.

The Nature of Soil (pp. 284–331). Regardless of where man lives, city or country, he is dependent for life on the quality of soils. The proper conservation and management of soils involves knowing something of their origin and characteristics.

The process of soil formation has been going on continuously for millions of years.

The kind of bedrock, climate, slope of land, time, plants, and animals determines the kind of soil.

Good mineral soils are composed of minerals with 6 to 20 per cent of organic material—dead or living organisms, air, and water.

Mineral materials come from bedrock broken by the mechanical and chemical processes of weathering.

The kind of bedrock determines the kind of minerals released by weathering.

The kinds of minerals in a soil determine its suitability for growing plants.

Mechanical weathering involves such things as changes of temperature, wind, water, plants, and animals.

Chemical weathering involves such things as water with carbon dioxide as a solvent, other acids, oxidation, plants, and animals.

Soil profiles show a record of a soil's formation.

Organic soils contain an abundance of organic material, sometimes as much as 20 to 95 per cent.

Depending on the kinds of plants forming organic soils, they may be grouped as sedimentary, fibrous, or woody peat or as muck soil in which plant parts can no longer be recognized.

The solid part of the soil furnishes support for green plants and 12 of the 16 chemical elements needed for growth; gases mostly come from the air and from water.

Good management of soil includes the testing of soil and addition of plant nutrients, called fertilizers, in the required amounts.

Magnetism Everywhere (pp. 780–850). Much has been learned about magnetism in materials, the relationship of magnetism and electricity, and about Earth's magnetism, but man's interest in magnetism goes beyond Earth. Vehicles carrying instruments into the upper atmosphere and beyond are used to obtain further understandings.

Magnets, wires carrying an electrical current, and Earth have magnetic fields.

Electricity is produced in each atom by the spinning of each electron on its axis and by its movement around the nucleus. Magnetic fields are produced in this way.

Each kind of atom has a specific number of electrons.

Electrons exist in shells around the nucleus.

Each shell can contain only a certain number of electrons.

If a shell contains all of the electrons possible, it is said to be complete. Half of its electrons spin in one direction; half in the opposite direction. A neutral reaction occurs, and there is no magnetic effect.

If a shell contains fewer electrons than its maximum number, it is said to be incomplete. Such a shell may or may not be magnetically neutral.

An iron atom has four unpaired electrons in its third shell, which are responsible for the magnetic field of the atom.

In iron, groups of atoms spontaneously come together. These groups are called domains.

In iron that is not magnetized, the unpaired electrons in the domains are thought not to be spinning in the same direction. When iron is placed in a magnetic field, the unpaired spinning electrons in the domains tend to spin in the same direction.

Magnetic fields are so small as to be of little or no practical importance in some materials called paramagnetic and diamagnetic materials.

Evidences of Earth's magnetic field are as follows: the compass that can be observed in the lower atmosphere; the Van Allen belts, auroras, and cosmic rays, which are all phenomena of the upper atmosphere. The auroras are visible from some parts of Earth.

Instruments in vehicles used in space exploration may record data on Earth's magnetic field.

The position of Earth's magnetic polar areas gradually changes. This is thought to have occurred in the distant past as well.

Earth's magnetism may arise from electric currents created by the movements of the interior of Earth.

The sun has general and local magnetic fields.

There are magnetic fields beyond the solar system.

Good Health (pp. 685–779). The need for an adequate supply of food is commonly recognized. That it should be grown on good soil; that it should receive careful washing and cooking is less commonly thought about. Personal and environmental cleanliness are also necessary in preserving and attaining good health.

Food is the source of energy for living things.

Foods containing carbohydrates, fats, and proteins are necessary for repair and growth of the body. They will also contain vitamins, minerals, and roughage.

Water is essential to the proper functioning of the body.

Soils containing all the necessary plant nutrients can supply good plant and animal food.

Fruits, vegetables, and meat may become contaminated by dust, chemicals, or living organisms.

The health of plants and animals used for human food is essential.

Proper washing and cooking to preserve nutrients and make food safe for human consumption are necessary.

Careful government inspection and handling of meat are necessary.

Clean bodies are essential from both the health and esthetic viewpoints.

Parasites may gain entrance to the body. Steps should be taken at once to relieve the condition and prevent their spread.

Some parasites are more prevalent than others in some parts of Earth.

Cleanliness, proper cooking of food, or the wearing of shoes may be adequate in avoiding the entrance of parasites into the body.

Clean air to breathe, clean water to drink, and soil that is not contaminated by waste are necessary to maintain good health.

Motion in the Universe (pp. 185–244). Everything that scientists have studied in our universe has movement of some kind, beginning with the atoms of which all matter is composed. As far as we know, we and the objects around us will never again be in the same place in space.

Movements of air are due to heat and loss of heat (cold).

When heated, air molecules move rapidly. Air may move with great speed and force.

When air is heated in a closed container, it expands, and pressure on the walls of the container builds up.

When air is cooled in a closed container, it contracts, and pressure decreases.

Cold air is heavier than hot air and moves downward.

Hot air is lighter than cold air and moves upward.

When water is heated, its molecules speed up and they may move into the atmosphere (evaporate). Upon cooling they may return to the solid and liquid parts of Earth.

The rapid movements of molecules in solids due to heat cause solids to expand.

The slowed movements of molecules in solids due to loss of heat (cold) cause solids to contract.

There is movement within the cells of plants and animals.

There is movement of air in and out of one's body.

The movement of blood, lymph, digestive juices, and materials given off by glands to parts where needed takes place automatically.

The movements of many parts of the body are conscious.

Auxin causes plant stems and leaves to turn toward light—something in the environment.

Surface movement of soil takes place due to animals, plants, wind, and running and freezing water.

Earthquakes and volcanoes and geysers

show that materials beneath the surface are moving.

All parts of the solar system are moving; parts move in different ways and rates of speed.

Earth's axis is tilted $23\frac{1}{2}°$ from the perpendicular to the ecliptic at all times.

The change of seasons is due to the tilt of Earth's axis as Earth moves around the sun.

The length of day and night is not the same all over Earth.

Adaptation of Living Things (pp. 586–709). Changes in plants and animals over a long period of time may or may not make it possible for them to exist well in a certain environment. No purpose or design is involved in adaptation. Many kinds of plants and animals have become extinct; many kinds have lived on over long periods of time.

Adaptations may be of three kinds: the changes that take place in living things that are inherited; changes that the body makes that are not inherited; changes in the body resulting from conscious effort, not inherited and true only for human beings.

The physical environment determines in part the kinds and numbers of plants and aimals living there.

Other species of living things also help to determine the kinds and numbers of plants and animals living in an environment.

When only one species of animal predominates in an environment, individuals within the species may be affected by competition for food and for finding a mate.

Plants of the same species may compete for space, water, nutrients, and sunlight (for green plants).

Organisms need to be able to make bodily adjustments to temporary changes in the environment.

Adaptations permit plants and animals to live and prosper in a wide variety of environments.

Man's body makes temporary adjustments to the environment; vaccination and immuni-

zation helps the body build defenses against disease.

Man must take his environment with him if he leaves Earth for space exploration.

Earth's Changing Atmosphere (pp. 429–499). Changes in the atmosphere of Earth results in the phenomenon called weather. Heat, pressure, moisture, and winds contribute to changes in the atmosphere.

Heat energy is important in determining our weather.

The sun is the only significant source of heat for Earth.

Rays from the sun come through space as radiant energy.

Radiant energy travels through space in the form of electromagnetic waves.

Ultraviolet and infrared waves are invisible; sunlight is the visible part of solar radiation.

Only 19 per cent of the incoming solar radiation is absorbed directly into the atmosphere; only 47 per cent may be absorbed by the solid and liquid parts of Earth.

Absorbed radiant energy is changed into heat energy which is then reradiated from the solid and liquid parts of Earth. This accounts for much of the heating of Earth's atmosphere.

The solid and liquid parts of Earth lose heat to the air by radiation, conduction, and convection.

Heat energy from the sun that reaches water is absorbed at the surface.

Weather is influenced by the differences in the way land and water areas are heated.

The pressure of air differs with altitude. At sea level, air pressure is about 15 pounds per square inch.

Air currents (vertical movements) and winds (horizontal movements) are due to the unequal heating of land and water surfaces of Earth.

The rotation of Earth causes winds in the Northern Hemisphere to be deflected toward the right; in the Southern Hemisphere, toward the left.

The rotation of Earth constantly shifts the area being heated by the sun.

Friction between air molecules and soil molecules and surface irregularities affect the direction and speed of the wind.

The air over large areas of land or of water takes on some of the characteristics of the land or water areas—that is, temperature and moisture.

In general, the movement of air masses is from west to east.

When air masses with noticeably different temperatures or moisture content come together, they produce a front, which may be either warm or cold.

Explaining Electricity (pp. 780–850). Materials are made up of molecules composed of different combinations of atoms of certain chemical elements. The structure of atoms and the behavior of electrons are useful in explaining electricity.

The nucleus of an atom exerts a force of attraction on the electrons surrounding it.

The force of attraction acts most strongly on the nearest electrons. They are sometimes called bound electrons.

The force of attraction is least between the nucleus and the electrons in the outer shell. These may escape from the atom more easily than the others, and when they do, they are called free electrons.

The loss of an electron creates a lack of balance in an atom and a tendency to attract or capture a free electron—it acquires an electrical charge.

A free electron has a tendency to move toward an atom that has lost an electron.

Rubbing materials together frees some bound electrons nearest the surface. These may be transferred to one of the materials, providing an electrical charge to both materials.

Electrons on the surface of an object, and are no longer a part of an atom, are called static charges of electricity.

Static charges of electricity do not move; they act only on other static charges.

Moving charges of electricity involves the freeing of electrons and their movement.

The direction of movement of individual electrons varies, but the general movement is in one direction.

A force is needed to set electrons in motion. Friction, chemical action, magnetism, photoelectric cells, thermocouples, and pressure on crystals of certain minerals are five sources of such a force.

In a dry cell the zinc combines with oxygen from the manganese dioxide. The energy produced from this chemical reaction is electrical energy.

When a wire connects the two terminals of a dry cell, a circuit is formed.

The zinc sends electrons into the wire; the carbon rod attracts them from the wire.

The force from the dry cell that causes electrons to travel through the wire in a current may be called electromotive force, or emf. Because it is measured in volts, it is also called voltage.

Increasing the force increases the number of electrons traveling in a circuit.

The speed of electron movement as well as their number determines the strength of the current. The speed is measured in amperes.

Length, cross-sectional area, temperature, and the material of which a conductor is made influence the resistance to the flow of current.

In making use of resistance, materials are used that will become sufficiently hot but will not melt.

Guiding the flow of electrons may be done by connecting dry cells in various ways.

In a series circuit, dry cells and lamps are connected one after another; there is only one path for the current.

In a parallel circuit, the connections are made in such a way that the current has two or more paths.

Different combinations of these ways of wiring may be made.

Interrelationships in the Environment (pp. 532–709). The existence and welfare of an individual or species, either plant or animal, depends not only upon other living things but also upon nonliving things as well. The total environment is not restricted to the region of immediate contact.

Both plants and animals are prolific.

The necessities of life include food, water, light, air, heat, and space to grow.

The need for the necessities varies in different species.

A deficiency in food, water, light, heat, or space to grow may act as a natural check on the numbers of living things.

Other living things and physical events may act as a check on the numbers of living things.

Plant parts and plant seeds may be spread by wind, water, and animals.

Plants may be spread by means of parts growing underground or on the surface.

Due to their ability to move, animals may migrate.

Connections between land masses, past and present, permit migration of land forms of life.

Connections between bodies of water, past and present, permit migration of water forms of life.

Man moves plants and animals wherever he goes.

By moving plants and animals, man may introduce species that will upset the balance existing in the region to which they are moved.

Disease-carrying organisms may be introduced.

Pests, both plant and animal, may be introduced.

There may be no natural controls for the organisms introduced.

Man sets up quarantine laws at some state and international borders to prevent the importation of certain unwanted plants or animals.

If an invasion of unwanted plants or animals does occur, steps may need to be taken to control them by using such things as chemicals, by confining them to a small region, by using such biological controls as an organism that will use them as food or by competition.

When no longer able to cope with the environment, species may become extinct.

Many species are now extinct.

Some species are in danger of extinction today partly due to man's interference.

Moving into Space (pp. 185–244). Man has had to devise ways to leave the ground on which he lives. He has had to learn about the atmosphere, about gravitation, and about inertia. This has led to studies of sources of energy and their application to his needs. Man's concepts of space have changed from time to time.

A source of energy is necessary to lift any vehicle off the ground against the pull of gravity.

The amount of energy needed depends on the weight of the vehicle and on its destination.

Energy is needed to keep the vehicle moving while in the atmosphere.

When flying airplanes, man makes use of the atmosphere.

The design of an airplane may either help or hinder its progress through the atmosphere.

When going beyond Earth's atmosphere, man must use energy to push vehicles through it to the space beyond.

The amount of gravity varies with distance from Earth or other bodies in space.

The amount of atmosphere varies with distance from Earth.

The amount of speed (velocity) with which a vehicle is launched into space determines its orbit.

A return to Earth is accomplished by reducing the speed.

Space vehicles may carry instruments designed to record and transmit data about special projects.

Command signals from tracking stations on Earth turn on transmitters in unmanned vehicles, which send data back to special receivers on Earth.

A special network of tracking stations can follow and receive data from unmanned vehicles.

Another special network of tracking stations can follow manned satellites in their orbits and communicate with the astronauts.

Rotation of Earth makes the orbital paths of some satellites pass over different parts of Earth.

The development of weather, communication, and navigation satellites is of immediate value.

Information is being secured about the nature of the bodies in the solar system and of the space between them. Much remains to be discovered.

Grade Seven[7]

Using Machines To Do Work (pp. 713–779). Much of the work in everyday life is done by using machines. Machines are used to transfer energy for doing work from one place to another. A machine is a link between the source of energy and the place where the energy is to be used to do work.

Work is done when something with weight is moved (pushed or pulled).

Force is the push or pull used in doing work.

Energy is used in applying force to a machine in doing work.

An object that has weight and opposes a force is called a resistance.

Work is measured in foot-pounds: the force (in pounds) multiplied by the distance (in feet) the resistance is moved.

Machines are used to transfer forces. For example, the pedal of a bicycle is pushed to move the wheel of the bicycle.

Direction of force may be changed by a machine, such as a pulley or lever.

Force may be increased by a machine, such as a lever, wheel and axle, or pulley.

Machines may be used to increase speed; gears are an example.

Some simple machines, such as the lever, wheel and axle, pulley, inclined plane, wedge and screw, may be combined in complex machines.

Mechanical advantage expresses how much easier it is to do work with a machine than without a machine.

To determine mechanical advantage, the resistance (in pounds) is divided by the force applied (in pounds).

Increasing the distance through which the force acts gives more mechanical advantage.

Some machines increase force and speed to such an extent that they are very dangerous. Safety precautions should be used in working with machines.

How Is Your Body Organized for Life? (pp. 503–709). Boys and girls want to know more about themselves. As they learn about their body systems, they begin to understand how these systems work together. They also learn about keeping their bodies working well and in good health. This study presents protoplasm as the basis of all life on Earth. Protoplasm makes up the cells that are organized into tissues, organs, and systems of the body.

Living protoplasm uses the energy of sunlight obtained through foods.

Carbon, hydrogen, oxygen, and nitrogen

[7] This material is based on Gerald S. Craig and Elizabeth Burger Jackson, *Science for You, Book Seven*. Boston: Ginn and Company.

are the chief elements forming compounds making up protoplasm.

Protoplasm takes in and gives off water and other materials.

Skeletal and muscular systems provide for support, protection, and movement in your body.

Your vertebrate skeleton is composed of more than two hundred bones.

Bones are made of living cells that are capable of growth and self-repair.

Muscles across joints bring about movement of skeletal bones.

Special organs of the body are protected by bones, and muscles protect bones.

Food provides energy for your body.

Digestion occurs before food enters the blood stream and is carried to the cells.

Energy from food is not released until oxygen combines with the food in the cells.

Respiration includes an exchange of gases by the cells. When oxygen is taken up, carbon dioxide is given off.

Breathing is only the mechanical process of admitting air to the lungs and releasing carbon dioxide from the lungs.

Blood is the medium for transfer of food and oxygen to the cells as well as waste materials from the cells.

The heart pumps blood through the body; heart beat may be observed easily as pulsations in arteries of the wrist or throat.

Our Stars and Planets (pp. 185–244). The sky affords an area of study that is readily available to boys and girls and of great interest to them. However, it is not easy for them to interpret correctly what they see in the sky. Knowledge gathered by astronomers over many years helps people interpret their observations of stars and planets more accurately.

Stars are all around Earth both day and night.

Reference lines on sky maps are used to lo-

cate stars and planets. These are similar to longitude and latitude lines for Earth.

Certain stars are circumpolar for observers in a particular location and are visible through the year.

Stars appear to form patterns known as constellations.

Different constellations may be observed during the year as Earth revolves.

Stars are not actually of the same brightness as they appear to be.

Planets are located by their positions with certain background constellations.

Planets are always located within the ecliptic, which is the apparent path of the sun.

Meteors, flashing across the sky in a few seconds, may be observed any clear night.

Comets, remaining visible for at least several nights, are much rarer than meteors.

Artificial satellites are only visible when the observer is in Earth's shadow and the satellite is receiving light from the sun.

As Earth rotates, the night sky seems to shift from east to west.

Light telescopes collect light from distances and magnify the light.

Radio telescopes are more powerful than light telescopes; they pick up invisible radio waves.

Spectroscopes have made it possible to determine composition of stars.

Scientists are developing new ways of studying celestial objects; for example, rockets carry telescopes into space.

Producing and Using Electricity (pp. 780–850). Electricity is a very important form of energy for most boys and girls. They see the use of electricity at home, at school, in factories, and other places. They learn that electricity can be carried from place to place and changed to other forms of energy.

Electricity is produced from other forms of energy.

When electrons are rubbed from atoms of one material to atoms of another material, static electricity is produced.

Electroscopes show whether an object is charged with static electricity.

Galvanoscopes show the flow of electrical current.

Voltaic cells change chemical energy to electrical energy.

Difference in potential between poles of a chemical cell determines voltage.

Storage batteries store chemical energy, which is converted to electrical current.

Light produces a weak electrical current in a photoelectric cell.

Heat energy may be changed to electricity by a thermocouple.

Generators use energy of motion and effects of magnetism to produce electricity.

Alternating current is produced by generators; chemical cells produce direct current.

Electrical energy is changed to the energy of motion when it runs electric motors and does work.

Materials that resist the flow of electricity produce heat.

Electricity may produce enough heat to give light.

Payments for electricity are based upon the rate of flow (amperes) and the strength of the current (volts).

Plants and Animals Live in Communities (pp. 532–567). Every living thing belongs to a community. Communities differ as conditions for life in the community vary. It is important for boys and girls to understand the relationship between kinds of communities and conditions affecting the communities. They should learn about their own community and also develop an appreciation of other communities.

Wherever you find a community, energy is being used; this energy comes from the sun.

The first step in using sun's energy is through the work of green plants.

Within every community the requirements of life, food, water, and heat, must be provided.

There are many kinds of natural communities, such as a pond, arctic ice, forests, or anthills.

Artificial communities are maintained for space explorers.

Characteristic plants and animals of a community depend to a large extent upon climate.

Length of growing season for plants is directly related to amount of sunlight. It increases with the region's nearness to the equator.

Limitations on plant life of a community decreases the number and variety of animal life.

Communities may be very extensive, such as those of polar regions, middle-latitude forests, rain forests, grasslands, deserts.

Plants and animals show unusual adaptations for life in different communities.

Communities vary with local conditions of altitude.

Changes in communities may occur rapidly as conditions change. Forest fires, floods, and volcanoes produce many changes in a community.

Any change of conditions may bring about other changes affecting both plant and animal life of the community.

Sound and Light Energy (pp. 851–898). You learn about your environment chiefly through sound and light energy. Hearing and seeing are two of your most important senses. Sound is very helpful, but light is essential to living things. Many ways of producing and controlling sound and light have been discovered.

Sound is energy due to vibrations of molecules.

Sound vibrations travel in longitudinal waves through solids, liquids, and gases.

The speed of sound varies as it passes

through different materials, and at different temperatures and pressures.

Sound travels through air at an average speed of about 1,100 feet per second.

Pitch, loudness, and quality are characteristics of sound.

Musical instruments change the characteristics of sound.

Voice is produced by vibrations of air passing the vocal cords.

Sounds may be reproduced by record players, sound film, and tape recorders.

Hearing results when sound vibrations stimulate the auditory nerve and brain.

Scientists have learned much more about what light waves can do than what they are.

Both the quantum and wave theories of light are being used to explain the way light behaves.

Visible light is a form of radiant energy bounded by infrared and ultraviolet waves.

Different wave lengths of light cause the eye to see different colors.

Some objects produce light, and others reflect light.

Light energy produces changes in plants and animals, in photographic film, and in pigments and dyes.

Lenses and mirrors may be used to control reflection and refraction of light.

Pigments and dyes are used to control absorption and reflection of light, producing colors.

Adequate lighting is important to proper eye care. The type of work being done sets the standard for adequate lighting.

Our Earth's Lithosphere (pp. 245–371). Numerous changes are continuously taking place on Earth. Materials are changed from one form to another and carried from place to place. Many physical and chemical forces operate in bringing about these changes. Boys and girls will be learning how to work more advantageously with these forces. They will also learn how to use wisely the valuable resources of our Earth's lithosphere.

Earth's surface is covered by broken rock and soil.

Rocks on Earth have been formed in many different ways.

Most rocks are mixtures of minerals and do not have a definite chemical composition.

Minerals are one element or compounds of elements and have a definite chemical composition.

Natural processes on Earth have concentrated many minerals.

Soil may be formed from decomposed rock. Organic materials improve soil.

Study of earthquake waves is one method geologists used to study Earth's interior.

There are many evidences of heat within Earth.

Many changes on Earth are brought about by gravity.

Gradual movements of Earth may cause folding and form folded mountains.

Eathquakes are the result of rapid Earth movements due to slippages known as faulting.

Weathering and erosion are constantly changing Earth. Agents of weathering may be grouped as mechanical and chemical.

Weathering loosens and softens rock and aids in erosion.

Good soil is our heritage and responsibility.

Soil deposited in one place has been removed from another.

Man has done things to increase the rate of erosion in some places.

Practices that reduce loss of soil by erosion have saved much good soil.

Interpreting Motions in Our Solar System (pp. 185–244). Boys and girls have a natural interest in learning about celestial bodies. Everywhere they look in our solar system they find motion. They will learn that many celestial phenomena can be explained on the basis of motions in our solar system.

Stars, planets, natural satellites, and artificial satellites rotate.

Sun's rotation is evidenced by sunspot studies and by findings with the spectroscope.

Foucault's pendulum experiment showed that Earth rotates.

Time progresses one hour for each 15° longitude from east to west as Earth rotates.

Movements of celestial bodies are not of sufficient regularity to give most accurate time; atomic clocks provide most accurate time.

Precession of Earth's axis causes a gradual shift in the zodiac of constellations.

Astrology is a false study that attempts to relate a person's fortune to the zodiac of constellations.

Earth's revolution causes the appearance of different constellations during the year.

Many scientists contributed to our present ideas about our solar system.

Kepler's laws of motion gives the formula for determining orbital distances for artificial satellites.

Revolutions of our planets are explained by using Newton's Laws.

Forces of gravitation between sun and planets and forces of motion of planets oppose each other.

Artificial satellites are pulled toward Earth but are moving ahead so rapidly that they fall into an orbit around Earth.

Because our moon rotates and revolves at the same speed, only one side is visible from Earth.

Revolution of our moon affects the tides on Earth.

Our Earth moves in the Milky Way Galaxy and with this galaxy.

Air and Water for Your Community (pp. 145–181). Air and water are important to everyone. Boys and girls learn that air and water are important because living things depend to a great extent upon a sufficiency of good air and water. Air and water are so important to us that the best methods of procuring and maintaining them must be found by scientists and engineers. Boys and girls need to understand and practice ways in which they can help in the problems of maintaining good air and water.

Water is found in air, and air also contains water.

Living things are made up chiefly of water, and body processes of living things require water.

Respiration of plants and animals uses oxygen found in air and water.

Contamination of air and water may be unpleasant, unhealthful, or bring death to living things.

Air and water receive many wastes from homes and industrial plants.

Rise in population strains the capacity of air and water for scattering man-made wastes.

Concentration of people and industry in cities has caused increased contamination of air and water.

Products of burning fuels and use of fuels in diesel and gasoline engines add seriously to wastes in air.

Pollution of air and water by wastes has brought about huge economic loss.

A study of the water cycle provides an understanding of sources of water for Earth and shows relationships between air and water.

It is difficult to balance demand and supply of water; dams and reservoirs have been built for this purpose.

Increased use of water often requires increased facilities for waste disposal.

Careful planning is necessary to insure good air and adequate water supply for the future.

Our Oceans (pp. 245–331). Since early days the vast oceans have challenged man. Oceans, once a barrier to travel, were later a means for trade and transport. Challenges of oceans today go far beyond their use for transportation. Recently, the very broad science of oceans developed. Oceanographers are scientists studying the biology, physics, chemistry, and geology of oceans. Boys and girls will want to learn about the findings of these scientists who explore oceans from surface to depths. The challenge today and for the future is how we can obtain and use wisely resources of the oceans.

More than three fourths of Earth's surface is covered by oceans.

Boundaries of oceans have changed in the past and are changing today.

Sodium and chlorine are the most abundant elements in sea water; over fifty other elements have been found in sea water.

Depth of water affects amount of light and kind of living things.

Oceans are great factors in climate.

Oceans stabilize temperature and moisture.

Heat from the sun brings about some of the circulation of sea water.

Tides can be predicted because of their relationship to the sun and moon.

Winds produce waves, with their breakers and undertow.

Many occurences on land, such as earthquakes and volcanoes, take place under water.

Oceans support a great variety and abundance of life.

Living things are found in environmental zones in the sea.

Many food chains occur in the sea, usually beginning with minute plankton.

Sea life is formed from materials in the sea; these materials return to the sea when the organism dies.

Vast food sources of the seas are being used to supply increasing populations.

Fossil fuels are obtained from the sea.

Sea water may become an important source of fresh water.

Our Forests and Wildlife (pp. 145–181). Boys and girls enjoy wildlife areas every time they walk in the fields, the forests, along

streams, swamps, beaches, or on mountains. These are all natural wildlife environments. Wildlife and forest resources are closely related to the soil, water, and vegetation of their environments. When any part of their environment is changed, far-reaching and unforeseen results may occur. People have often caused natural environments to change. Many times these changes have been unfavorable for plants and animals.

Every citizen should develop a feeling of personal responsibility for our natural resources. The care and wise use of natural renources is a trust handed down to every boy and girl.

Our forests and wildlife are useful and enjoyable to mankind in many ways.

As man has progressed in transportation, industry, and building of cities, forests and wildlife have suffered.

Clearing forests, plowing grasslands, draining swamps, and building dams have changed wildlife habitats.

Wildlife requires an environment suited to its needs for food, shelter, and protection.

Different kinds of animals have varied needs.

Forests are our greatest renewable resource.

Kinds of forests vary with different regions of soil, moisture, and temperature.

Good practices of planting and thinning and control of fires, insects, and diseases are important in conservation.

Many steps have been taken to restore and protect forests and wildlife. You can help by observing regulations of fires and hunting and by restocking wildlife and planting trees.

Weather in Our Troposphere (pp. 424–499). The part of the atmosphere we live in is called troposphere. Changes in the troposphere make up our weather. Many physical forces acting together bring about changes in our weather. Learning more about our troposphere and its weather helps boys and girls to understand weather changes and to plan their activities in relation to weather.

Weather is the result of a dynamic energy cycle.

The sun is the most important source of heat for Earth's atmosphere.

The atmosphere shows many effects of gravitational pull.

Air is a mixture of several gases, chiefly nitrogen and oxygen.

Atmospheric pressure is due to the weight of molecules of air.

Scientific instruments indicate conditions of the atmosphere used in weather forecasting.

Changes in water vapor give us our several forms of precipitation.

Condensation occurs when warm, moist air is cooled.

Man has attempted to modify weather by producing rain and changing temperatures.

Weather changes in North America have been traced to movements of large air masses.

The zone of contact between a warm air mass and a cold air mass is called a polar front.

Cyclones develop along polar fronts; rising air produces a low-pressure area called a cyclone.

Forces operating in changing Earth's weather are world-wide.

Major wind belts of Earth are convection currents.

Differences in temperature produce convection currents in the atmosphere.

Satellites are being used to collect information for prediction of weather changes and warning for storms.

Grade Eight[8]

This Changing Planet (pp. 245–371). Earth has not always appeared the same as it does now. Its long history is one characterized by changes in climate, in land forms, and in kinds of living things.

The surface of Earth has been changing for many millions of years.

The age of Earth has been estimated in different ways. It is now believed to be more than 3 billion years old.

Much of the past history of Earth can be deduced from a study of sedimentary rock layers.

Sedimentary rocks are usually found in horizontal layers, but they may be tilted into anticlines and synclines by mountain-forming processes.

Deposits of such minerals as salt and gypsum

are the result of the evaporation of ancient seas in which they were dissolved.

Geological processes such as weathering, erosion, sedimentation, volcanism, and mountain formation began in Precambrian times.

During the Paleozoic era much of North America was uplifted and submerged several times.

The Appalachian Mountains arose at the end of the Paleozoic era.

The Rocky Mountains, Black Hills, and Big Horn Mountains arose at the end of the Mesozoic era.

The present era is the Cenozoic; it began about 60 million years ago.

Four great glacial periods have occurred on Earth in the last million years.

Glaciated regions may be recognized by knob and kettle topography, scratches in rock surfaces, erratics, ponds and lakes, drumlins, eskers, gravel deposits, and unassorted till.

[8] This material is based on Gerald S. Craig and John Urban, *Science For You, Book Eight*. Boston: Ginn and Company.

Much information about past life on Earth can be gained from a study of fossils.

Fossils are of several kinds: entire preserved organisms, molds, casts, petrified objects, footprints, and coal deposits.

Fossil coral reefs are evidence the place where found was once covered by warm, shallow, ancient seas.

There is little evidence that life existed during early Precambrian times. Simple plants and animals are known to have existed during the latter part of Precambrian times.

A large variety of plants and animals inhabited Earth during the Paleozoic era.

Large land plants and numerous species of dinosaurs characterized life in the Mesozoic era. The first mammals appeared during this era.

Mammals are the dominant animals during the present (Cenozoic) era.

Many species of mammals that arose during this era are already extinct.

There is fossil evidence to indicate that the climates of Earth have changed from warm to cold to warm again, several times.

Sun, Stars, and Space (pp. 185–244). A study of the sun reveals its characteristics and the reasons for its influence on Earth and other bodies in the solar system. Such study also reveals the place of the solar system in a universe containing billions of stars.

The sun, nearest star to Earth, is huge and massive but less dense than Earth.

The sun is composed of elements also present in Earth.

Solar radiation is the result of nuclear reactions in the sun.

The surface of the sun has disturbances called sunspots.

Temperatures in the sun's corona, which extends millions of miles from its surface, are very high.

The sun rotates on an axis and revolves on an orbit.

The Milky Way Galaxy, in which the solar system is located, is made up of about 100 billion stars.

Distances between stars may be measured in units called light years.

Stars vary greatly in their diameters, mass, density, temperature, color, and magnitude.

Like the sun, all stars are in motion.

Some stars vary periodically in brightness, a few having been known to flare up into great brilliance.

Some stars occur as visual pairs; others, as eclipsing pairs. Multiple stars are three or more stars that revolve around a common center of gravity.

Space between stars in our galaxy contains gases and dust particles.

Some stars in the Milky Way are found in globular clusters; others, in open clusters.

Beyond the Milky Way there are many other galaxies of stars.

Instruments such as radio telescopes enable us to obtain new information about the stars.

The possibility that there may be intelligent life in some distant part of the galaxy is being studied.

Artificial satellites will carry instruments that will enable man to gain a better understanding of the stars and our galaxy.

Space Science (pp. 185–244). Man's progress has been marked by numerous important advances in his understanding of his environment and of his adaptation to it. Among these advances, sometimes called breakthroughs, were such things as the discovery of fire, the wheel, the electric generator and motor, the internal combustion engine, and the use of nuclear energy. Space exploration is another advance.

Space exploration is a scientific and technological breakthrough.

A spacecraft launching is based upon the principle that to every action there is an equal and opposite reaction.

In a spacecraft the potential energy in the rocket fuel is changed to the kinetic energy of motion.

Rocket engines must develop a thrust that is greater than the weight of the spacecraft being launched.

Satellites in orbit close to Earth must have a greater velocity than those revolving farther from Earth.

The first manned orbital flight demonstrated that people can make such trips safely.

Many problems of long space flights, such as to the moon and Mars, present problems new to human experience.

Tiros and other weather satellites are providing much world-wide weather information.

Communication satellites are making possible world-wide television and microwave radio transmission.

Close-up pictures of the moon's surface have been made.

Satellite exploration of Mars began in 1964–1965.

Special devices are being developed to find out if there are living things on other planets.

Earth and Its Life (pp. 503–709). Evidence shows that Earth may be about 5 billion years old. The many events through which it has passed make it difficult to recognize traces of early life whose first forms may have appeared a billion years ago. There has been an abundance of life on Earth for about a half billion years.

Gravity is an environmental force important to living things because it is related to the distance between Earth and the sun; it holds Earth's atmosphere to the planet, and is involved in weather changes.

Plant stems react negatively to gravity; roots respond positively.

Seeds of many plants have adaptations for resisting gravity, thus causing them to become widely scattered.

Many species of animals have adaptations for overcoming gravity.

Plant life cycles are related to the number of hours of daylight.

Adaptations to long days prevent northern plants from spreading to the low latitudes, where days and nights are about equal in length the year round.

The activities and behaviors of animals are affected significantly by the daily number of hours of light.

Daily variations in light intensity, from dawn to night, change rates of photosynthesis, the opening of blossoms and leaves, and other plant reactions.

Temperature affects the rate of metabolism in both plants and animals.

Temperature changes in bodies of water are both slower and smaller than in terrestrial environments.

Altitude, latitude, and direction of slope are related to the temperature in a given place.

In North America the spring season progresses northwards, eastwards, and upwards.

Ultraviolet radiation can be harmful to living things, but it also has beneficial effects.

Oxygen, nitrogen, water, carbon dioxide, and various minerals are essential to life.

Soils are a reservoir of many elements needed by living things.

The kind of life found in a region is related to the chemical and physical characteristics of the soil in that region.

Reproduction, Heredity, and Change (pp. 503–531). Every organism alive today has a long line of ancestors. Each generation resembles its parents in many important ways; yet each individual differs from all others in some ways. Man has made use of his knowledge of heredity and has developed many new varieties of plants and animals.

Many species of plants, and some species of animals, reproduce asexually by cell division, budding, or by vegetative parts.

Plants can be propagated from underground stems, fleshy roots, from leaves, or from stolons.

Sexual reproduction involves the unit of special cells called gametes, two of which must unite to form a zygote.

Male gametes are called sperms; female gametes are called ova.

Many species of plants, including the flowering plants, reproduce by alternation of a sexual with an asexual generation. Most species of animals reproduce sexually; a few species reproduce by alternation of generations.

The eggs of fish and amphibians are fertilized by sperms discharged by male animals into the water.

The animal zygote develops in a definite pattern.

Organs and systems of the higher animals develop from three embryonic cell layers.

Food for the developing embryo is in the egg in many species of animals.

Mammalian embryos are nourished by means of a special organ, the placenta.

The period of mammalian development from fertilization to birth is its period of gestation, which varies from species to species.

In the human species multiple birth may result from the fertilization of two eggs by two sperms, or from the division of a single zygote into two or more embryos.

Hereditary traits are transmitted from one generation to the next by means of chromosomes in cell nuclei.

Chromosomes are composed of genes; genes control the specific hereditary characteristics.

The sex of human offspring is determined at the time of fertilization by the X and Y chromosomes.

Mutations are spontaneous changes in hereditary characteristics.

Mutations are known to occur naturally in all species; they can be induced artificially by X rays and in other ways.

Some mutations are detrimental to the organism; others are favorable because they improve the species' chances of survival.

The occurrence of many mutations over a long period of time eventually results in a new species.

Fossils offer evidence that species change as time goes on.

Man has developed many new varieties of plants and animals.

Understanding Heat Energy (pp. 713–779). Energy can be converted from one kind to another, but it cannot be destroyed. Heat energy is used to do many kinds of work.

Heat is a form of radiant energy; it is also associated with molecular motion in matter.

Temperature is related to molecular velocity.

Heat can be measured quantitatively in such units as calories, kilocalories, and BTU's.

Heat causes substances to expand in length and other dimensions; each substance has its own coefficient of expansion.

When gases are heated, their molecular velocity is increased, which results in an increase in volume, or an increase in pressure if the gas is in a rigid container.

The boiling point of water is related to atmospheric pressure.

Heat may be transferred by radiation, conduction, or convection. Some materials are better heat conductors than are others.

Each substance has a specific heat, which is the quantity of heat needed to raise the temperature of a given quantity of it by 1°.

The high specific heat of water is of importance for its effects on climate and living things.

Heat of fusion is the quantity of heat required to change a solid at its melting temperature to a liquid.

Heat of vaporization is the quantity of heat required to change a boiling liquid to the gaseous state.

Some substances change directly from the solid to the gaseous state.

The sun is the original source of the heat energy stored in conventional fuels.

Burning is a chemical reaction involving a fuel and oxygen that results in the release of heat.

Electrical energy may be transformed into heat energy.

Nuclear reactions result in the release of vast quantities of heat energy.

Turbines, internal combustion engines, diesel engines, jets, and rockets are all heat engines.

Using Resources Wisely (pp. 145–181).

Each year there are more people to feed, house, clothe, educate, and amuse. Man is completely dependent upon the planet he inhabits to produce the things he needs. Wise utilization of resources is indicated.

Man is completely dependent upon Earth for everything he needs.

Soil is a complex material composed of many components.

Soil composition changes from the surface downward, with the most fertile layer usually at the top.

Gravity is the basic cause of soil erosion.

Erosion is a natural process that can only be slowed down by such practices as contour plowing and cultivation, damming gulleys, strip cropping, mulching, and maintaining soil fertility.

Land may be classified according to the uses to which it may best be put.

Wind erosion may be reduced by strip cropping, using a vegetation cover on the soil, and tree planting.

Water conservation is now more important than ever, due to increasing demands.

Ground water sources are being seriously depleted in many places.

The amount of surface water available for use is being seriously reduced by pollution.

Water conservation includes control of pollution, returning used water to the ground for reuse, storing run-off water, controlling floods, and in other ways.

Fossil fuels are the source of most heat energy today; the demand for them is increasing rapidly.

Conservation of coal and other fuels involves such practices as more efficient procurement, more efficient combustion, and better heat insulation.

Petroleum and natural gas are increasing in use; hence conservation practices should be applied to their use.

Metals used in industry are classified as (1) iron and steel; (2) ferrous alloys; (3) nonferrous metals.

Nonferrous metals are in particularly short supply.

If properly handled, metals are reusable resources.

The Study of Matter (pp. 372–423).

Bodies in the universe are composed of matter. It exists in great variety, yet cannot be created or destroyed. However, it may undergo physical or chemical change.

All matter is composed of atoms.

Atoms of each element have a specific number of protons and neutrons in their nuclei, and a specific number of electrons in orbit around the nucleus.

Eight elements make up about 99 per cent of Earth's crust.

Elements may be classified according to their properties into metals, nonmetals, and metalloids.

Organic compounds are those the molecules of which contain carbon atoms.

Inorganic compounds are composed of molecules that have no carbon atoms.

Mixtures are aggregates of different compounds that may occur in any proportion.

Suspensions, solutions, and colloids are different kinds of dispersions.

Solutions may consist of gases dissolved in gases, gases dissolved in liquids, liquids in liquids, and other such dispersions.

Inorganic compounds are classified as acids, bases, or salts.

Changes of state in matter are physical changes.

Chemical changes result in the formation of compounds different from the original ones involved in the reaction.

Chemical changes may be combination reactions, decomposition reactions, or replacement reactions.

In some reactions molecules dissociate into positive and negative ions.

Whole molecules of some compounds can be made to join together to form larger, more complex molecules.

Energy changes are involved in chemical reactions.

Nitrogen, potassium, and phosphorus compounds are the most needed fertilizers to improve soil.

Chemicals are being used increasingly in the control of weeds and insect pests.

Chemistry of the Human Body (pp. 503–531). Living organisms are composed of atoms and molecules forming compounds in a constant state of chemical activity. Complex molecules are broken into simpler ones; simpler ones build into complex molecules continuously.

Protoplasm is composed of organic compounds, inorganic compounds, and water.

Protoplasm is living material that carries on chemical reactions synthesizing more of the compounds of which it is composed.

Sugar, starch, and fat molecules are composed of different proportions of carbon, hydrogen, and oxygen atoms.

Protein molecules always contain nitrogen atoms; they may also contain atoms of sulfur, iron, and other elements.

Foods contain chemical compounds that the body uses as a source of energy, for replacing wornout cells, and for synthesis of additional protoplasm.

Overweight is usually the result of eating more than is needed for health and growth.

Vitamins are food compounds essential to normal growth and good health.

Digestion is a process by which complex food molecules are broken down into simpler molecules that the body can use.

Some food materials are indigestible; they cannot be broken down into molecules that the body can use.

Molecules of digested foods pass into the bloodstream and are distributed to the cells where they are needed.

Oxygen, which is an active element, combines with food molecules in the cells, as a result of which energy is liberated.

The quantity of food and oxygen needed is related to the body activities that affect the rate of metabolism.

Chemical reactions in the cells result in the formation of waste compounds that must be excreted.

Hormones are chemical compounds that act as regulators of many body processes.

Hormones are produced by special glands, and pass from the glands directly into the bloodstream.

Human Health (pp. 685–709). Contagious diseases are still a world-wide health problem, and organic diseases require further investigation. Scientific research has already greatly improved human health.

Contagious diseases are caused by bacteria, protozoa, or viruses; a few diseases are caused by worm parasites.

Contagious diseases may be spread by droplet infection, contaminated foods, impure water, insects, and in other ways.

Each contagious disease has certain symptoms.

The body produces chemical substances

that aid in recovery from contagious diseases.

Protection against some contagious diseases may be developed by techniques of immunization.

Chemical compounds are being used effectively in the treatment of some of the contagious diseases; antibiotics are useful in disease treatment.

Good health can be promoted by such measures as proper sewage, garbage, and rubbish disposal, providing safe water, food sanitation, and other similar measures.

The chances of developing a heart disease can be reduced in several ways.

The blood itself is subject to diseases called anemia.

Cancer is a serious health problem affecting persons of all ages.

There are several kinds of cancers, each of which has certain recognizable symptoms with which everyone should be familiar.

Allergies are common diseases; there are many kinds, and they have many causes.

Mental health is being recognized as a serious problem.

Mental illnesses have definite symptoms, such as phobias, compulsions, depression, and extremes in behavior.

The use of narcotic drugs is basically a mental health problem.

Alcohol is an organic compound, the use of which may lead to alcoholism—a serious health problem.

Tobacco, especially in the form of cigarettes, is a serious health hazard.

Overexposure to X rays and radioactive substances may imperil one's health.

Evaluation of Learning in Science and the Study of Children

Is my teaching of science good? How effective is it? Am I securing the results that I should secure? Such questions as these involving evaluation of the work in science in the classroom are frequently asked by teachers.

Evaluation as an Integral Part of Teaching. Evaluation should be thought of as an integral part of teaching, rather than as something set aside to do at a special time, such as a test at the end of a period of instruction. As a teacher works, she can study the children to determine the effect of the learning upon them. This study of the children guides the teacher moment by moment, as she proceeds with the instruction. She must continuously consider whether or not the children in her classroom are developing satisfactorily toward worthy long-range purposes for the education of children. Such questions as the following may come to her mind. What kinds of boys and girls are being developed in my classroom? Do the children maintain a natural interest in the study? Do they employ good thinking in the work? Is their quality of thinking improving? Do they report matters accurately? Do they utilize previously learned knowledge spontaneously? Do they see value in their learning? Are they developing worthwhile ideas and attitudes? Are they making progress toward good citizenship? Are they moving toward improved use of democratic methods? Are they developing responsibleness and resourcefulness? ("Studying Children while Teaching Science," pp. 24–33 for additional ideas about evaluation.)

Consideration of evaluation as an integral part of teaching conforms to the point of view of dynamic psychology (pp. 3–24). According to this psychology, a child is an active organism affected continuously by forces within and without his being. In his struggle to maintain equilibrium and adjustment to the environment he makes interpretations, and therefore undergoes continuous change. Sometimes the changes are such as to develop improvements in his behavior. At other times the changes in his behavior may be undesirable. A teacher in planning her instruction is concerned with assisting children to make those changes that will secure the maximum of good for themselves and those that will cause children to develop intelligent responsibility.

Using a Variety of Behaviors in Evaluation.
Many forms of behavior can be utilized in evaluation. One of the most important is children's oral expression of ideas. Teachers should assist children to improve their ability to express their ideas about science as they proceed through the elementary school. Frequently forms of oral reporting on observations should be utilized. It should be kept in mind that some children will be superior to others in oral expression in science.

Written work may be used as a means of evaluating children. However, teachers should be on the alert to avoid destroying interest in science by excessive use of notebooks and other forms of written work.

Perhaps the goal in reference to written work is that children learn to make records. Keeping this goal in mind will prevent excessive use of such forms of work. Records in which a number of children participate are feasible. There are also needs for reporting observations and other records in which children may share responsibility.

There are times when ideas can best be expressed through art work such as small drawings or larger murals. Sometimes a teacher can discover children's true ideas, including

their misconceptions, more easily from their art work than by any other means.

In using materials from the environment, the importance of developing the behavior patterns of responsibleness and of conservation should be considered.

The Classroom Teacher in Her Role as a Guide. "Scope and Continuity" (pp. 901–945) will assist a teacher in evaluating children's growth. Are the children developing an understanding of the meanings listed for the particular level involved? Do they find the meanings real? Do they find them interesting? Do they spontaneously recall these meanings? Do they utilize the meanings in new situations? Do they find the meanings challenging? Are they ready for new learning?

Evaluation is not an end in itself, for the study of children can provide a teacher with guidance for her instruction. Viewing evaluation in this manner is evidence of the desirability of planning instruction so that it is flexible in character (see pp. 135–144). Teachers should plan their instruction, but at the same time be prepared to modify their plans to meet the needs of the children (see "Instruction through Interaction," pp. 104–108).

With evaluation in mind, the total behavior of the teacher is important. A spontaneous smile, a cheerful note, or a laugh may be significant at times to the child in improving his feeling for science as well as his status and his outlook on life. A teacher's acknowledgment of an error on her part, or a willingness to listen, or an indication of personal interest in a child, may be as important in the development of children as the more formal class instruction.

In considering evaluation teachers must recognize that there are many educational agencies—the home, television, movies, comic books, playmates, and so on. Sometimes these agencies have desirable effects and sometimes not. The classroom teacher, as the official representative of democracy in the education of the children in her classroom, must make certain that the total or aggregate influence on the lives of children is beneficial. This is a large and important task. It is difficult to think of any service of greater value to the children of a nation and of the world than this. The teacher and the parents must make certain that children in free countries recognize the heritage of science, democracy, and religious freedom.

It should be kept in mind that the human hand has played an important role in the development of man's cultures of the past and present. Children should be encouraged to follow out their natural interest in building simple mechanical appliances or wiring simple electrical equipment such as electromagnets. In some cases parents may assist in this work, and the teacher should feel gratified if some of the children outstrip her in certain lines of creativity with equipment (see p. 143). One of the best guarantees that democracies can have for survival is the development of responsibility and creative resourcefulness on the part of our children in the classroom.

Evaluation in This Publication. In keeping with the point of view that evaluation is an integral part of teaching, this book has been designed so that teachers may secure assistance and guidance in evaluating instruction in every chapter.

In Chapters 1–3 the purposes of science instruction are discussed. These purposes may be utilized by teachers and other elementary school personnel in the evaluation of the growth of children (see Chapter 5).

In Chapter 4 the content of science is considered in its place in education. Important and vital as content may be, it does not constitute the final purpose of education (see pp. 43–181). However, large patterns of the universe are presented as guide lines for instruction and the use of content.

In Parts II, III, and IV, and in Chapter 6, the professional background of content and procedures for teachers is presented in keeping with the large patterns of the universe and the development of intelligent and responsible behavior in children. A study of this professional content will provide teachers with a wealth of ideas for evaluation.

The chart on the following page may assist in planning and integrating evaluation with instruction.

PLANNING OF INSTRUCTION AND EVALUATION

Experiences of Children →	Meanings Derived from the Experiences →	Educational Values of Meanings →	The Long-Range Purposes of Science in the Education of Children to Which the Educational Values Contribute
These are the experiences of children in life situations and those resulting from teacher-children planning. They may involve discussions, play, excursions, reading, recording, imagination, creative developments, proposals of ideas (hypotheses), or manipulations of objects.	These meanings may be expressed by the children in discussion, oral reports, art work, and writing.	These values are in the mind of the teacher. She is concerned that children move toward these values.	Are these children developing in directions which indicate that they can participate in the world of the present and the future with intelligence and resourcefulness?
What kind of experiences are the children having in and out of school?	The meanings children secure are learnings from the experiences. These are best evaluated in terms of what children may express or do spontaneously, such as ideas, problems, challenges, remarks, or activities.	What value do the meanings have in the development of children?	Are they developing toward an appreciation of their heritage in science and democracy?
What is the quality of these experiences?	What do they carry over as learning from one topic or project to another study or to a later year?	Do the meanings contribute to growth in open-mindedness, critical-mindedness, responsibleness, and resourcefulness?	Are they developing patterns of the wise utilization of their resources?
The total experiencing of children should be considered, including use of muscles, senses, kinesthetic sense, emotions, and mind.	What meanings do they offer in new situations?	Are there signs of the development of desirable emotions?	Are they developing toward responsibleness for the use of science in a democracy?
How can the experiences of children be improved to provide the long-range purposes you hold for science in the education of children?	The most reliable meanings are those secured from authoritative books; thoughtful reading is essential to the formation of meanings.	Are the children improving in planning for safety?	Are the children learning to become intelligent and democratic leaders and followers?
See the experiences for children described in the various parts of this publication.	Are the children developing meanings consistent with the long-range purposes of science in the education of children?	Do they use materials with conservation in mind?	See Chapters 2 and 3.
		Do they think of the welfare of others?	
		Are they improving in their democratic and scientific attitudes?	
		How do these educational values contribute to the long-range purposes of science in the education of children?	
		See Part I.	

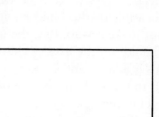

Awareness of the Long-Range Purposes of Science in the Education of Children Will Assist a Teacher in Providing Richer Experiences and Meanings for Children.

INDEX